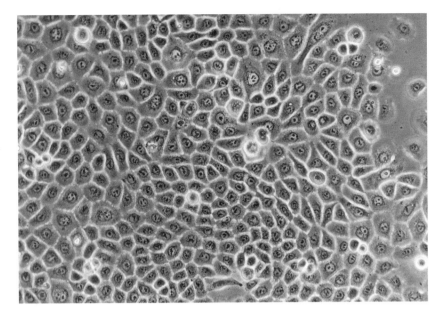

COLOR PLATE 1 Colony of normal human primary keratinocytes grown as a suspension of cells for 7 days (×15). (See "Growth of Human Keratinocytes in Serum-Free Medium" by John P. Daley and Jean M. Donovan.)

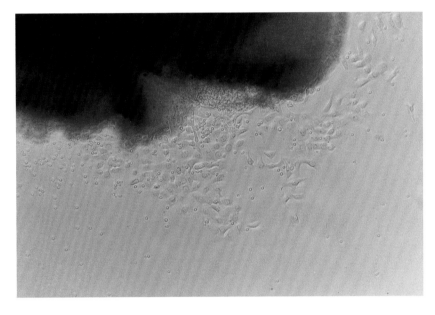

COLOR PLATE 2 Human primary keratinocytes migrating from an explant of neonatal foreskin after 2 days in culture (×7.5). (See "Growth of Human Keratinocytes in Serum-Free Medium" by John P. Daley and Jean M. Donovan.)

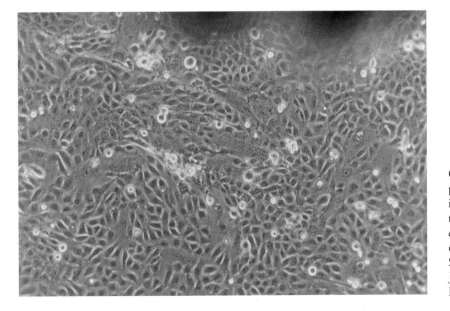

D1418485

COLOR PLATE 3 Human primary keratinocytes migrating from an explant of neonatal foreskin after 11 days in culture (×7.5). (See "Growth of Human Keratinocytes in Serum-Free Medium" by John P. Daley and Jean M. Donovan.)

COLOR PLATE 4   (a) JE-6B elutriation rotor with a standard separation chamber (left) and a bypass chamber (right). (b) Standard separation chamber (left) and bypass chamber (right) installed in the JE-6B elutriation rotor. (See "Isolation and Culture of Oval Cells from Carcinogen-Treated Rats" by Pablo Steinberg.)

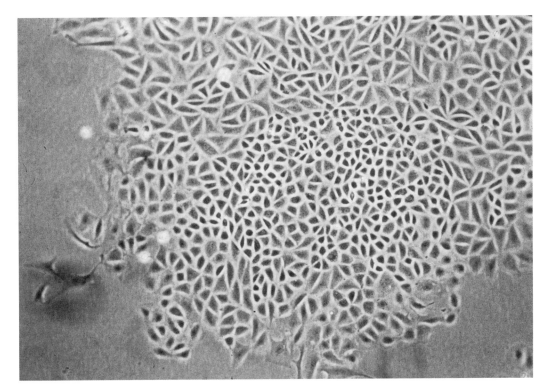

COLOR PLATE 5   Oval cells in culture (passage 22) that had been isolated from the liver of a rat fed a choline-deficient/DL-ethionine-supplemented diet for 6 weeks (×95). (See "Isolation and Culture of Oval Cells from Carcinogen-Treated Rats" by Pablo Steinberg.)

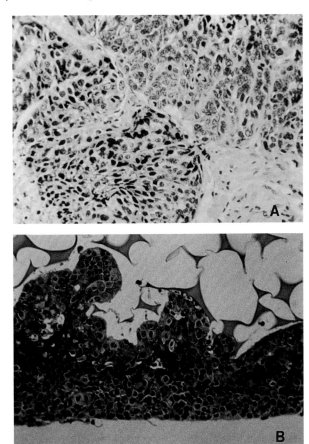

COLOR PLATE 6   Sponge-gel matrix histoculture of a stomach tumor (B) versus the original tumor (A). The tumor was histocultured for approximately one week. Note the similarity of the tissue architecture between the original and histocultured tumors. Thus histoculture maintains tumor architecture. (See "Three-Dimensional Sponge-Gel Matrix Histoculture: Methods and Applications" by Robert M. Hoffman.)

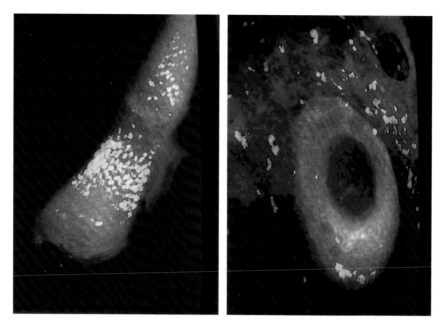

COLOR PLATE 7   Viability of hair follicles in 8-day gelatin-sponge histoculture of intact human scalp skin, as assessed by confocal laser scanning microscopy of vital-dye double-stained histocultures [BCECF-AM (green), live cells; propidium iodide (red), dead cells]. Vast majority of follicle cells appear green and are therefore alive (×337.5). (See "Three-Dimensional Sponge-Gel Matrix Histoculture: Methods and Applications" by Robert M. Hoffman.)

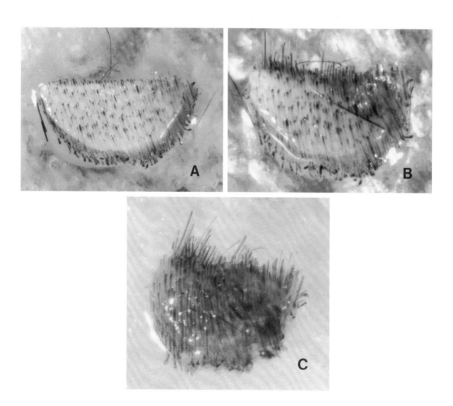

COLOR PLATE 8   Hair growth with progressing pigment production from 14-day anagen-induced C57 B1-6 mouse skin after histoculture at 0 (A), 7 (B), and 14 (C) days of histoculture. Note the large number of hair shafts growing out and their increased length with color change from grey to dark over time. (See "Three-Dimensional Sponge-Gel Matrix Histoculture: Methods and Applications" by Robert M. Hoffman.)

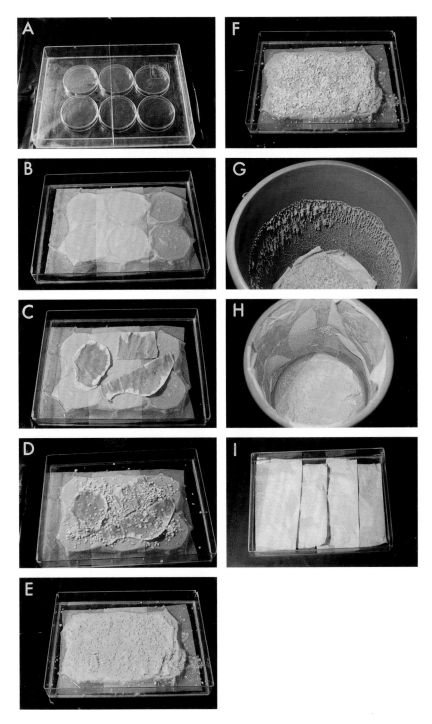

COLOR PLATE 9   Surface culture of *Physarum* plasmodia. (A) Six dishes are placed in a box (See Section IIIA, Step 1). (B) The plates are covered with paper towels after the box is partially filled with tap water (See Section IIIA, Step 3). (C) Sclerotia are placed on the towels (See Section IIIA, Step 4). (D) Rolled oats are scattered on the towels (See Section IIIA, Step 5). (E) Oats are covered with proliferating plasmodia (See Section IIIA, Step 6). (F) More rolled oats are placed on the plasmodia (See Section IIIA, Step 7). (G) Plasmodia climb up the wall of a bucket. The plasmodia climbing up the sides of the bucket, not those on the bottom of the bucket, are harvested. (H) Plasmodia are grown on paper towels to prepare sclerotia (see Section IIIB, Step 3.) (I) The paper towels on which plasmodia have grown are transferred to a dry plastic box (see Section IIIB, Step 4.) The plasmodia are dried in a dark room to become sclerotia. (See "Large-Scale Culture of Physarum: A Simple Method for Growing Several Hundred Grams of Plasmodia" by Kazuhiro Kohama, Ryoki Ishikawa, and Mitsuo Ishigami.)

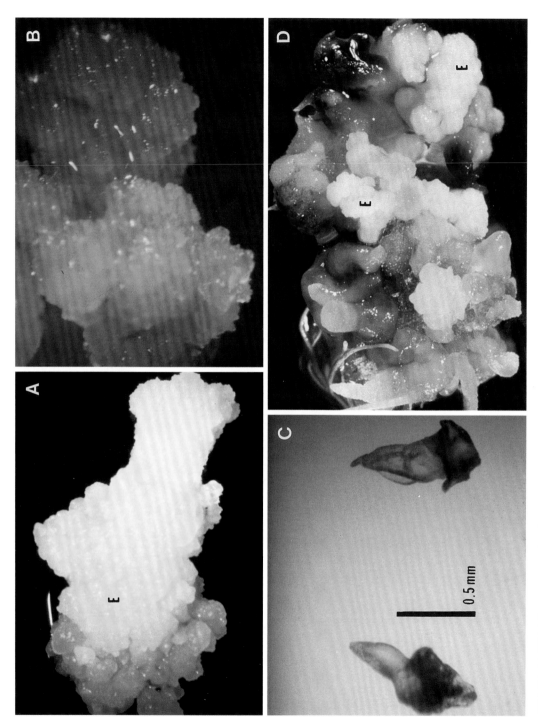

COLOR PLATE 10   (A) Smooth white, embryonic rice callus. Embryonic rice callus is knobby in appearance. (B) Yellow-to-translucent, wet, crystalline-appearing nonembryogenic rice callus. (C) Sorghum shoot tips from 2- to 3-day-old seedlings. (D). Embryogenic rice callus is milky white and knobby in appearance (E, embryogenic callus). (See "Induction of Regeneration-Competent Monocot Callus" by Roberta H. Smith and Shyamala Bhaskaran.)

COLOR PLATE 11   Isolation and culture of mesophyll protoplasts from tobacco shoot cultures. (See "Isolation, Culture, and Plant Regeneration from Protoplasts" by German Spangenberg and Ingo Potrykus.)

COLOR PLATE 12   Plant regeneration from protoplast-derived colonies in tobacco. (See "Isolation, Culture, and Plant Regeneration from Protoplasts" by German Spangenberg and Ingo Potrykus.)

CELL BIOLOGY

A LABORATORY HANDBOOK

VOLUME 1

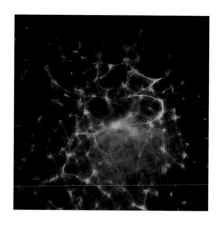

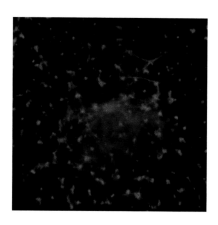

ACADEMIC PRESS

San Diego   New York   Boston
London   Sydney   Tokyo   Toronto

CELL BIOLOGY

A LABORATORY HANDBOOK

Edited by

JULIO E. CELIS

Danish Centre for Human Genome Research
Aarhus, Denmark

VOLUME 1

Cover Photograph for Volume 1: TC7 cells treated with Cytochalasin B stained with a broad specificity keratin antibody. Courtesy of J. E. Celis.

This book is printed on acid-free paper. ∞

Academic Press, Inc.
A Division of Harcourt Brace & Company
525 B Street, Suite 1900, San Diego, California 92101-4495

United Kingdom Edition published by
Academic Press Limited
24-28 Oval Road, London NW1 7DX

Library of Congress Cataloging-in-Publication Data

Celis, J. E. (Julio E.)
     Cell biology / Julio E. Celis.
          p.   cm.
     Includes indexes.
          ISBN 0-12-164714-5 (set). -- ISBN 0-12-164715-3 (v. 1). -- ISBN
     0-12-164716-1 (v. 2). -- ISBN 0-12-164717-X (v. 3)
          1. Cytology-Laboratory Manuals.   I. Title.
     QH583.2.C45   1994
     574.87' 078--dc20   94-27690
                                                CIP

PRINTED IN THE UNITED STATES OF AMERICA
94 95 96 97 98 99 DO 9 8 7 6 5 4 3 2 1

CONTENTS OF VOLUME 1

Contents of Other Volumes   xv
Contributors to Volume 1   xxv
Preface   xxxv

PART 1
TISSUE CULTURE AND ASSOCIATED TECHNIQUES

Section A
General Techniques   3

General Procedures for Tissue Culture   5
Ariana Celis and Julio E. Celis

Development of Serum-Free Media and Methods
for Optimization of Nutrient Composition   18
David W. Jayme and Dale F. Gruber

Testing Cell Cultures for Microbial and Viral Contaminants   25
Robert J. Hay

Section B
Primary Cultures from Embryonic Tissues   43

Primary and Extended Culture of Embryonic Mouse Cells:
Establishment of a Novel Cell Culture Model of Apoptosis
and Neural Differentiation   45
Deryk T. Loo and Carl W. Cotman

Tissue Culture of Embryonic Stem Cells   54
Martin Evans

Isolation and Culture of Germ Cells from the Mouse Embryo   68
Massimo De Felici

**Section C
Cultures of Specific Cell Types**   **81**

Epithelial Cells

Cultivation of Human Epidermal Keratinocytes with a 3T3
Feeder Layer   83
Fiona M. Watt

Growth of Human Keratinocytes in Serum-Free Medium   90
John P. Daley and Jean M. Donovan

Isolation of Hepatocytes   96
Per O. Seglen

Isolation and Culture of Oval Cells from
Carcinogen-Treated Rats   103
Pablo Steinberg

In Vitro Culture of Mouse Fetal Choroid Plexus Epithelial Cells   109
Elizabeth Stadler, Tim Thomas, and Marie Dziadek

Isolation and Culture of Type II Pulmonary Epithelial Cells   116
Stephen R. Rannels and D. Eugene Rannels

Mesenchymal Cells

Maintenance of Human Diploid Fibroblast-like Cells in Culture   124
Robert T. Dell'Orco

Isolation of Osteoclasts and Osteoclast Plasma Membranes   128
*Miep Helfrich, Takuya Sato, Ken-ichi Tezuka, Masayoshi Kumegawa,
Stephen Nesbitt, Michael Horton, and Patricia Collin-Osdoby*

Culturing of Human Umbilical Vein and Dermal
Microvascular Endothelial Cells   142
Eyðfinnur Olsen

Neuroectodermal Cells

Isolation and Proliferation of Adult Mammalian Central
Nervous System Stem Cells   148
Brent A. Reynolds, Catherine Leonard, and Samuel Weiss

Hemopoietic Cells

Clonal Cultures *in Vitro* for Hemopoietic Cells Using Semisolid
Agar Medium   153
Gregory R. Johnson

Gonads

Properties of Isolated Sertoli Cells   159
Pierre S. Tung and Irving B. Fritz

Culture of Ovarian Granulosa Cells: Calcium Imaging
at the Single-Cell Level   170
Jorge A. Flores and Johannes D. Veldhuis

Section D
Cell Separation Techniques   177

Isolation of Peripheral Blood Mononuclear Cells and
Identification of Human Lymphocyte Subpopulations
by Multiparameter Flow Cytometry   179
Marianne Hokland, Hanne Jørgensen, and Peter Hokland

Purification of Functionally Active Epidermal Langerhans Cells
Using Immunomagnetic Beads   185
Jenny Morris and Anthony Chu

Section E
Model Systems to Study Differentiation   191

Nonterminal and Terminal Adipocyte Differentiation of
Murine 3T3 T Mesenchymal Stem Cells   193
Hanlin Wang, Dawn B. Sturtevant, and Robert E. Scott

Cell Systems for *ex Vivo* Studies of Myogenesis: A Protocol for
the Isolation of Stable Muscle Cell Populations from Newborn
to Adult Mice   199
Christian Pinset and Didier Montarras

Induction of Cell Differentiation in Human HL-60
Promyelocytic Leukemia Cells: Quantitation of a Myeloid
Specific Antigen, MRP-8/MRP-14 Protein Complex   207
Shinichi Murao, Mamoru Nakanishi, Seiya Matsumoto, Norifumi Ueda,
and Eliezer Huberman

Differentiation of Murine Erythroleukemia Cells (Friend Cells)   213
Victoria M. Richon, Richard A. Rifkind, and Paul A. Marks

Cultured PC12 Cells: A Model for Neuronal Function and
Differentiation   218
Kenneth K. Teng and Lloyd A. Greene

Growing Madin-Darby Canine Kidney Cells for Studying
Epithelial Cell Biology   225
Kai Simons and Hilkka Virta

In Vitro Studies of Epithelium-to-Mesenchyme Transitions   232
Ana Maria Vallés, Jean Paul Thiery, and Brigitte Boyer

**Section F
Immortalization of Cells**   **243**

Inducible Immortalization of Cells from Transgenic Mice
Expressing Simian Virus 40 under *lac* Operon Control   245
Ruth Epstein-Baak

Immortalization of Rat Ventral Prostate Epithelial Cells Using
Simian Virus 40 T Antigen   251
Debra A. Gordon and Roger L. Miesfeld

**Section G
Cell Cycle Analysis**   **259**

Cell Cycle Analysis by Flow Cytometry   261
Zbigniew Darzynkiewicz

Preparation of Synchronous Populations of Mammalian Cells
in Specific Phases of the Cell Cycle by Centrifugal Elutriation   272
R. Curtis Bird, Shiawhwa Su, and Gin Wu

Synchronization of Normal Diploid and Transformed
Mammalian Cells   282
Gary S. Stein, Janet L. Stein, Jane B. Lian, Thomas J. Last, Thomas Owen,
and Laura McCabe

Synchronization of Transformed Human Amnion Cells by
Mitotic Detachment   288
Julio E. Celis and Peder Madsen

Stimulation of DNA Synthesis in Quiescent 3T3 Cells   294
Theresa Higgins and Enrique Rozengurt

Section H
Cytotoxic Assays   **303**

Quantitative Determination of Compound Cytotoxicity
in Proliferating Cells: Monitoring DNA Synthesis by
[^{3}H]Thymidine Incorporation   305
Kathy May

Section I
Senescence, Programmed Cell Death, and Others   **311**

Serial Propagation of Human Fibroblasts for the Study of
Aging at the Cellular Level   313
Vincent J. Cristofalo, Roberta Charpentier, and Paul D. Phillips

Morphological Criteria for Identifying Apoptosis   319
John F. R. Kerr, Clay M. Winterford, and Brian V. Harmon

Use of the Terminal Transferase DNA Labeling Reaction for
the Biochemical and *in Situ* Analysis of Apoptosis   330
Jonathan L. Tilly

Growth and Induction of Metastasis of Mammary
Epithelial Cells   338
Barry R. Davies and Philip S. Rudland

Measurement of Cell–Cell and Cell–Extracellular Matrix
Interactions: A Quantitative Cell Attachment Assay   345
Thomas E. Lallier

Section J
Electrophysiological Methods   **353**

Patch-Clamp Recording   355
James L. Rae and Richard A. Levis

Section K
Histocultures   **365**

Three-Dimensional Sponge-Gel Matrix Histoculture: Methods
and Applications   367
Robert M. Hoffman

Section L
Other Cell Types   **381**

Anthropoda

Primary Culture of *Drosophila* Embryo Cells   383
Paul M. Salvaterra and Izumi Hayashi

Caenorhabditis elegans

Laboratory Cultivation of *Caenorhabditis elegans* and Other
Free-Living Nematodes   389
Ian M. Caldicott, Pamela L. Larsen, and Donald L. Riddle

Protozoa

Cultivation of *Tetrahymena Cells*   398
Yoshio Watanabe, Osamu Numata, Yasuhiro Kurasawa, and Mariko Katoh

Acanthamoeba castellanii: A Model System for Correlative
Biochemical and Cell Biological Studies   405
Ivan C. Baines and Edward D. Korn

Fungi

Cell Biological, Molecular Genetic, and Biochemical Methods
to Examine *Dictyostelium*   412
*Sandra K. O. Mann, Peter N. Devreotes, Susannah Eliott, Keith Jermyn,
Adam Kuspa, Marcus Fechheimer, Ruth Furukawa, Carole A. Parent,
Jeffrey Segall, Gad Shaulsky, Philip H. Vardy, Jeffrey Williams,
Keith L. Williams, and Richard A. Firtel*

Large-Scale Culture of *Physarum:* A Simple Method for
Growing Several Hundred Grams of Plasmodia   452
Kazuhiro Kohama, Ryoki Ishikawa, and Mitsuo Ishigami

Plants

Induction of Regeneration-Competent Monocot Callus   456
Roberta H. Smith and Shyamala Bhaskaran

Isolation, Culture, and Plant Regeneration from Protoplasts   462
German Spangenberg and Ingo Potrykus

PART 2
VIRUSES

Propagation and Purification of Polyoma and Simian Virus 40   471
Roland Sahli and Peter Beard

Construction and Propagation of Human Adenovirus Vectors   479
Mary Hitt, Andrew J. Bett, Ludvik Prevec, and Frank L. Graham

Tissue Culture Techniques for the Study of Human
Papillomaviruses in Stratified Epithelia   491
Craig Meyers, Mark G. Frattini, and Laimonis A. Laimins

Growth and Purification of Murine Leukemia Virus   500
Jette Lovmand, Anders H. Lund, and Finn Skou Pedersen

PART 3
ORGANELLES, CELLULAR STRUCTURES,
MACROMOLECULES, AND FUNCTIONAL ASSAYS

Purification of Rat Liver Golgi Stacks   509
Paul Slusarewicz, Norman Hui, and Graham Warren

Preparation and Purification of Post-Golgi Transport Vesicles
from Perforated Madin-Darby Canine Kidney Cells   517
Lukas A. Huber and Kai Simons

Purification of Clathrin-Coated Vesicles from Bovine Brain,
Liver, and Adrenal Gland   525
Robert Lindner

Functional Identification of Membranes Derived from the
Rough Endoplasmic Reticulum of Yeast   531
Christopher M. Sanderson and David I. Meyer

Isolation of Yeast Mitochondria and Study of Mitochondrial
Protein Translation   538
*Johannes M. Herrmann, Heike Fölsch, Walter Neupert,
and Rosemary A. Stuart*

Inclusion of Proteins into Isolated Mitochondrial Outer
Membrane Vesicles   545
Andreas Mayer, Arnold Driessen, Walter Neupert, and Roland Lill

Isolation of Peroxisomes   550
Alfred Völkl and H. Dariush Fahimi

Purification of Secretory Granules from PC12 Cells   557
Jane C. Stinchcombe and Wieland B. Huttner

Preparation of Synaptic Vesicles from Mammalian Brain   567
Johannes W. Hell and Reinhard Jahn

Purification and Reconstitution of the Ca^{2+}-ATPase of Red
Blood Cells   575
Paolo Gazzotti and Ernesto Carafoli

Isolation of Focal Adhesions from Cultured Cells   584
Markus Niederreiter and Mario Gimona

Isolation of Laminins from Tumor Sources and from
Normal Tissues   589
Mats Paulsson and Anders Lindblom

Isolation of Centrosomes from Cultured Animal Cells   595
Mohammed Moudjou and Michel Bornens

Preparation of Yeast Spindle Pole Bodies   605
Michael P. Rout and John V. Kilmartin

Preparation of Nuclei and Nuclear Envelopes: Identification
of an Integral Membrane Protein Unique to the
Nuclear Envelope   613
Einar Hallberg

Preparation of Cytoplasts and Karyoplasts from HeLa Cell
Monolayers   619
Julio E. Celis and Ariana Celis

Isolation and Visualization of the Nuclear Matrix, the
Nonchromatin Structure of the Nucleus   622
Jeffrey A. Nickerson, Gabriela Krockmalnic, and Sheldon Penman

Preparation of U Small Nuclear Ribonucleoprotein Particles   628
Sven-Erik Behrens, Berthold Kastner, and Reinhard Lührmann

Rapid Preparation of hnRNP Core Proteins and Stepwise
Assembly of hnRNP Particles *in Vitro*   641
Mei Huang and Wallace M. LeStourgeon

Preparation of Ribosomes and Ribosomal Proteins from
Cultured Cells   657
Jean-Jacques Madjar

Preparation of Proteasomes   662
Keiji Tanaka and Akira Ichihara

Small-Scale Preparation of Nuclear Extracts from
Mammalian Cells   668
Kevin A. W. Lee, Kenn Zerivitz, and Göran Akusjärvi

Purification of DNA Using Guanidine Thiocyanate and
Isobutyl Alcohol Fractionation   674
James E. Nelson, Mohamed Khidhir, and Stephen A. Krawetz

Single-Step Method of Total RNA Isolation by Acid
Guanidine–Phenol Extraction   680
Piotr Chomczynski

CONTENTS OF OTHER VOLUMES

VOLUME 2

PART 4: MICROSCOPY TECHNIQUES

Section A: Light Microscopy

Phase-Contrast, Nomarski (Differential-Interference) Contrast, and Dark-Field Microscopy: Black and White and Color Photomicrography   5
Dieter Brocksch

Reflection Interference Microscopy   15
Jürgen Bereiter-Hahn and Pavel Vesely

Using Interference Microscopy to Study Cell Behavior   25
Graham A. Dunn and Daniel Zicha

Section B: Fluorescence Microscopy

Fluorescence Imaging in Living Cells   37
Michael Whitaker

Practical Laser-Scanning Confocal Light Microscopy: Obtaining Optimal Performance from Your Instrument   44
James B. Pawley and Victoria E. Centonze

Caged Fluorescent Probes for Monitoring Cytoskeleton Dynamics   65
Timothy J. Mitchison, Kenneth E. Sawin, and Julie A. Theriot

Section C: Video Microscopy

Video-Enhanced Contrast Microscopy   77
Dieter G. Weiss

Section D: Confocal Microscopy

Confocal Microscopy of Polarized MDCK Epithelial Cells   89
Sigrid Reinsch and Ernst H. K. Stelzer

Real-Time Confocal Microscopy and Cell Biology   96
Alan Boyde, Colin Gray, and Sheila Jones

Section E: Electron Microscopy

Fixation of Cells and Tissues for Transmission Electron Microscopy   105
Arvid B. Maunsbach

Embedding of Cells and Tissues for Ultrastructural and
Immunocytochemical Analysis   117
Arvid B. Maunsbach

Negative Staining   126
Andreas Bremer and Ueli Aebi

Whole-Mount Electron Microscopy of the Cytoskeleton: Negative
Staining Methods   135
J. Victor Small and Monika Herzog

Glycerol Spraying/Low-Angle Rotary Metal Shadowing   140
Andreas Bremer, Markus Häner, and Ueli Aebi

Rapid Freezing of Biological Specimens for Freeze-Fracture
and Deep Etching   148
Nicholas J. Severs and David M. Shotton

Freeze Fracture and Freeze Etching   157
David M. Shotton

Use of Ultrathin Cryo- and Plastic Sections for
Immunoelectron Microscopy   168
Norbert Roos and Gareth Griffiths

Cryo-Transmission Electron Microscopy of Thin Vitrified Sections   177
Nathalie Sartori and Laurée Salamin Michel

Preparation Methods for Quantitative X-Ray Microanalysis of
Intracellular Elements in Ultrathin Sections for Transmission Electron
Microscopy: The Freeze-Dry, Resin-Embed Route   186
Hugh Y. Elder and Stuart M. Wilson

High-Resolution Scanning Electron Microscopy in Cell Biology   193
Terence D. Allen and Martin W. Goldberg

PART 5: MICRODISSECTION TECHNIQUES

Microdissection-Based Techniques for the Determination of Cell
Proliferation in Gastrointestinal Epithelium: Application to Animal and
Human Studies   205
Robert A. Goodlad

Micromanipulation of Chromosomes Using Laser Microsurgery (Optical
Scissors) and Laser-Induced Optical Forces (Optical Tweezers)   217
Michael W. Berns, Hong Liang, Gregory J. Sonek, and Yagang Liu

Microdissection of Chromosomes and Microcloning 228
Uwe Claussen and Bernhard Horsthemke

PART 6: HISTOCHEMISTRY

Mayer's Hematoxylin–Eosin: An Example of a Common Histological
Staining Method 239
Hans Lyon

Selected Enzyme Staining in Histochemistry 245
Joseph Chayen and Lucille Bitensky

PART 7: ANTIBODIES

Section A: Production of Antibodies

Production of Polyclonal Antibodies in Rabbits 257
Christian Huet

Production of Mouse Monoclonal Antibodies 269
Ariana Celis, Kurt Dejgaard, and Julio E. Celis

Production of Human Monoclonal Antibodies via Fusion of
Epstein–Barr Virus-Transformed Lymphocytes with Heteromyeloma 276
Miroslaw K. Gorny

Rapid Production of Antibodies in Chicken and Isolation from Eggs 282
Harri Kokko, Ilpo Kuronen, and Sirpa Kärenlampi

Section B: Purification and Labeling of Immunoglobulins

Purification of Immunoglobulins 291
Christian Huet

Conjugation of Fluorescent Dyes to Antibodies 297
Benjamin Geiger and Tova Volberg

Section C: Antibody Specificity

Determination of Antibody Specificity by Western Blotting and
Immunoprecipitation 305
Julio E. Celis, Jette B. Lauridsen, and Bodil Basse

Western Blotting and Ligand Blotting Using Enhanced
Chemiluminescence and Radioiodine Detection 314
Amandio Vieira, Robert G. Elkin, and Karl Kuchler

Enzyme-Linked Immunosorbent Assay 322
Hedvig Perlmann and Peter Perlmann

A Simple Solid-Phase Mutual Inhibition Assay Using Biotinylated
Antigen for Analyzing the Epitope Specificities of
Monoclonal Antibodies 329
Masahide Kuroki

DNA Immunoprecipitation: Application to Characterization of Target
Sequences for a Human Centromere DNA-binding Protein (CENP-B) 335
Kenji Sugimoto

PART 8: IMMUNOCYTOCHEMISTRY AND VITAL STAINING OF CELLS

Immunofluorescence Microscopy of Cultured Cells 347
Mary Osborn

Immunofluorescence Microscopy of the Cytoskeleton: Double and
Triple Immunofluorescence 355
Monika Herzog, Annette Draeger, Elisabeth Ehler, and J. Victor Small

Immunocytochemistry of Frozen and of Paraffin Tissue Sections 361
Mary Osborn and Susanne Isenberg

Fluorescent Labeling of Nascent RNA in the Cell Nucleus Using
5-Bromouridine 5'-Triphosphate 368
Derick G. Wansink, Alison M. Motley, Roel van Driel, and Luitzen de Jong

Labeling of Endocytic Vesicles Using Fluorescent Probes for
Fluid-Phase Endocytosis 375
Esther L. Racoosin and Joel A. Swanson

Labeling of the Endoplasmic Reticulum with $DiOC_6$ (3) 381
Mark Terasaki

Use of Fluorescent Analogs of Ceramide to Study the Golgi Apparatus
of Animal Cells 387
Richard E. Pagano and Ona C. Martin

Vital Staining of Mitochondria with Rhodamine 123 and of Acidic
Organelles with Acridine Orange 394
Julio E. Celis and Kurt Dejgaard

PART 9: INTRACELLULAR MEASUREMENTS

Measuring Membrane Potential in Single Cells with
Confocal Microscopy 399
Leslie M. Loew

Measurement of Cytosolic pH in Single Cells by Dual-Excitation
Fluorescence Spectrometry: Simultaneous Visualization Using Hoffman
Modulation Contrast Optics 404
Robert Romanek, Ori D. Rotstein, and Sergio Grinstein

PART 10: CYTOGENETICS AND *IN SITU* HYBRIDIZATION

Basic Cytogenetic Techniques: Culturing, Slide Making, and G-Banding 415
Chih-Lin Hsieh

Production of Viable Hybrids between Adherent Cells 422
Doris Cassio

Microcell-Mediated Chromosome Transfer: Selective Transfer
and Retention of Single Human Chromosomes into Recipient
Cells of Choice 428
Michael J. Anderson and Eric J. Stanbridge

Microcell Transfer of Chromosomes from Mitotic Cells 435
Elton Stubblefield and Mark Pershouse

Chromosome Painting Using Degenerate Oligonucleotide-Primed
Polymerase Chain Reaction-Amplified, Flow-Sorted
Human Chromosomes   442
Nigel P. Carter

Fluorescence *in Situ* Hybridization of Human and Mouse DNA Probes
to Determine the Chromosomal Contents of Cell Lines and Tumors   450
*James D. Tucker, John W. Breneman, Denise A. Lee, Marilyn J. Ramsey,
and Roy R. Swiger*

In Situ Hybridization Applicable to Abundantly Expressed mRNA Species   459
Roeland W. Dirks, Frans M. van de Rijke, and Anton K. Raap

In Situ Hybridization of Frozen Sections Using ³⁵S-Riboprobes   466
Daniel Carrasco and Rodrigo Bravo

In Situ Detection of Human Papillomavirus DNA after Polymerase Chain
Reaction Amplification   477
Gerard J. Nuovo

Accurate Quantitation of mRNA Species by Polymerase Chain Reaction
and Solid-Phase Minisequencing   488
Ann-Christine Syvänen and Leena Peltonen

VOLUME 3

PART 11: TRANSFER OF MACROMOLECULES AND SMALL MOLECULES

Microinjection of RNA and DNA into Somatic Cells   3
Monika Graessmann and Adolf Graessmann

Microinjection of Proteins into Somatic Cells: Needle Microinjection
and Scrape Loading   16
Yu-Li Wang

Computer-Automated Capillary Microinjection of Macromolecules
into Living Cells   22
Rainer Pepperkok, Rainer Saffrich, and Wilhelm Ansorge

Syringe Loading: A Method for Inserting Macromolecules into Cells
in Suspension   30
Mark S. F. Clarke and Paul L. McNeil

Electroporation of Cells   37
*Stefan Herr, Rainer Pepperkok, Rainer Saffrich, Stefan Wiemann,
and Wilhelm Ansorge*

Electroporation of Antibodies into Mammalian Cells   44
Ratna Chakrabarti and Sheldon M. Schuster

Virus (Sendai Virus Envelopes)-Mediated Gene Transfer   50
Yasufumi Kaneda

Liposomes in Drug Targeting   58
Gregory Gregoriadis

Electroporation-Mediated DNA Transfer to Tobacco Protoplasts for
Transient Gene Expression Assays   67
Geert Angenon, Willy Dillen, and Marc Van Montagu

Electroporation-Mediated DNA Delivery to Embryos of
Leguminous Species   72
Willy Dillen, Marc Van Montagu, and Geert Angenon

Permeabilization by α-Toxin and Streptolysin O   77
Gudrun Ahnert-Hilger

Introduction of Small Molecules into Cells Using a Transient Cell
Permeabilization System   83
Curtis J. Henrich

Microinjection of RNAs into *Xenopus* Oocytes   88
Glenn Matthews

PART 12: CLONING OF EMBRYOS, TRANSGENICS, AND GENE TARGETING

Cloning Rabbit Embryos by Nuclear Transplantation   99
Philippe Collas

Production of Transgenic Mice by Pronuclear Microinjection   106
Jon W. Gordon

Gene Targeting by Homologous Recombination in Embryonic
Stem Cells   112
Miguel Torres and Ahmed Mansouri

Transgenic Plants: *Agrobacterium*-Mediated Transformation of the
Diploid Legume *Lotus japonicus*   119
Kurt Handberg, Jiri Stiller, Thomas Thykjær, and Jens Stougaard

PART 13: CELL-FREE EXTRACTS, PERMEABILIZED CELL SYSTEMS, AND EXPRESSION SYSTEMS

Preparation and Use of Translocating Cell-Free Translation Extracts
from *Xenopus* Eggs   131
Glenn Matthews

A Permeabilized Cell System to Study Peroxisomal Protein Import   140
Martin Wendland

Baculovirus Expression Vector System: Production and Isolation of
Recombinant Viruses   148
Linda A. King, Susan G. Mann, Alison M. Lawrie, and Robert D. Possee

Expression of Recombinant Proteins in the Vaccinia Virus
Expression System   155
Henrik Leffers

PART 14: PROTEINS

Section A: Protein Determination

Protein Determination   169
Martin Guttenberger

Section B: Preparation of Tagged Proteins and Others

Controlled Radioiodination of Proteins   181
Michael J. Rudick

Cell Surface Biotinylation Techniques   185
Chiara Zurzolo, André Le Bivic, and Enrique Rodriguez-Boulan

Assays for Cellular Protein Binding and Ligand Internalization   193
Kim Vettenranta, Guojun Bu, and Alan L. Schwartz

Identification of Cell Surface Binding Proteins via Covalent
Crosslinking   199
Guojun Bu and Alan L. Schwartz

Section C: Gel Electrophoresis

One-Dimensional Sodium Dodecyl Sulfate–Polyacrylamide

Gel Electrophoresis   207
Julio E. Celis and Eyðfinnur Olsen

Nondenaturing Polyacrylamide Gel Electrophoresis (NPAGE) as a
Method for Studying Protein Interactions   218
Daniel Safer

High Resolution Two-Dimensional Gel Electrophoresis of Proteins:
Isoelectric Focusing and Nonequilibrium pH Gradient
Electrophoresis (NEPHGE)   222
Julio E. Celis, Gitte Ratz, Bodil Basse, Jette B. Lauridsen, and Ariana Celis

High-Resolution Two-Dimensional Electrophoresis of Proteins Using
Immobilized pH Gradients   231
Angelika Görg

Mini Two-Dimensional Gel Electrophoresis   243
Mario Gimona, Barbara Galazkiewicz, and Markus Niederreiter

Two-Dimensional Gel Analysis of Posttranslational Modifications   249
Scott D. Patterson and James I. Garrels

Detection of Protein Kinase Activity after Renaturation of Proteins
Transferred from Sodium Dodecyl Sulfate-Polyacrylamide Gels
to Membranes   258
Deborah A. Shackelford, Richard Y. Yeh, and Justin A. Zivin

Zymography of Proteases   264
Christian Paech and Teresa Christianson

Electroelution of Proteins from Two-Dimensional Gels   272
Julio E. Celis, Gitte Ratz, and Bodil Basse

Monitoring Sodium Dodecyl Sulfate Contamination   276
Michael Arand, Thomas Friedberg, and Franz Oesch

Section D: Staining

Ultrasensitive Silver-Based Stains for Protein Detection   281
Carl R. Merril, Janet E. Joy, and G. Joseph Creed

Detection of Subpicogram Quantities of Protein in
Polyacrylamide Gels   288
Andrew Wallace and Hans Peter Saluz

Section E: Overlay Techniques and Others

Blot Overlay Assay: A Method to Detect Protein–Protein Interactions   301
Aaron W. Crawford and Mary C. Beckerle

Calcium Overlay Assay   309
Hans Jürgen Hoffmann and Julio E. Celis

Blot Overlay Assay for the Identification of GTP-Binding Proteins   313
Pavel S. Gromov and Julio E. Celis

Two-Dimensional Gel-Based Mapping of *in Situ* Crosslinked
GTP-Binding Proteins   317
Marcus E. Peter and Lukas A. Huber

Protein-Blot Analysis of Glycoproteins and Lectin Overlays   323
Shoshana Bar-Nun and Jonathan M. Gershoni

Purification of Lectins and Determination of Their Carbohydrate
Specificity   332
Halina Lis, David Belenky, Aaron Rabinkov, and Nathan Sharon

Two-Dimensional Northwestern Blotting   339
Kurt Dejgaard and Julio E. Celis

In Vivo Genomic Footprinting with Dimethyl Sulfate   345
Jean-Pierre Jost and Hans Peter Saluz

Section F: Microsequencing and Other Techniques

Internal Amino Acid Sequencing of Proteins Recovered from
One- or Two-Dimensional Gels   359
Joël Vandekerckhove and Hanne H. Rasmussen

Amino-Terminal Protein Sequence Analysis   369
Heinz Nika and Ruedi Aebersold

Sequencing Peptides Derived from the Class II Major
Histocompatibility Complex by Tandem Mass Spectrometry   380
*John R. Yates, III, Ashley L. McCormack, James B. Hayden,
and Michael P. Davey*

Mass Spectrometry: Detection and Characterization of
Posttranslational Modifications   389
Beth L. Gillece-Castro

Plasma Desorption Mass Spectrometry of Peptides and Proteins   399
Peter Roepstorff

Methods Optimization for the Analysis of Peptides Using
Capillary Electrophoresis   405
Michael Albin and John E. Wiktorowicz

Section G: Amino Acid Analysis

Amino Acid Analysis on Microscale from Electroblotted Proteins   417
Friedrich Lottspeich, Cristoph Eckerskorn, and Rudolf Grimm

Phosphopeptide Mapping and Phosphoamino Acid Analysis on
Cellulose Thin-Layer Plates   422
Peter van der Geer, Kunxin Luo, Bartholomew M. Sefton, and Tony Hunter

PART 15: APPENDICES

Cell and Tissue Culture Media: History and Terminology   451
Dale F. Gruber and David W. Jayme

Representative Cultured Cell Lines and Their Characteristics   459
Robert J. Hay

Working Safely with Radioactivity   471
Richard W. Davies

Suppliers List   479
Index   499

CONTRIBUTORS TO VOLUME 1

GÖRAN AKUSJÄRVI (668), Department of Cell and Molecular Biology, Medical Nobel Institute, Karolinska Institutet, Stockholm, Sweden

IVAN C. BAINES (405), Laboratory of Cell Biology, NHLBI, NIH, Bethesda, Maryland 20892

PETER BEARD (471), Swiss Institute for Experimental Cancer Research, 1066 Epalinges, Switzerland

SVEN-ERIK BEHRENS (628), Istituto di Ricerche di Biologia Molecolare (IRBM), 00040 Pomezia (Roma), Italy

ANDREW J. BETT (479), Departments of Biology and Pathology, McMaster University, Hamilton, Ontario, Canada L8S 4K1

SHYAMALA BHASKARAN (456), Department of Soil and Crop Sciences, Texas A&M University, College Station, Texas 77843

R. CURTIS BIRD (272), Department of Pathobiology, Auburn University, Auburn, Alabama 36849

MICHEL BORNENS (595), Centre de Génétique Moléculaire, Centre National de la Recherche Scientifique, 91198 Gif-sur-Yvette, France

BRIGITTE BOYER (232), Laboratoire de Physiopathologie du Développement, URA CNRS 1337, Ecole Normale Supérieure, F-75230 Paris Cedex 05, France

IAN M. CALDICOTT (389), Division of Biological Sciences, University of Missouri, Columbia, Missouri 65211

ERNESTO CARAFOLI (575), Department of Biochemistry III, Swiss Federal Institute of Technology (ETH), CH-8092 Zürich, Switzerland

ARIANA CELIS (5, 619), Institute of Medical Biochemistry and Danish Centre for Human Genome Research, Aarhus University, DK-8000 Aarhus C, Denmark

JULIO E. CELIS (5, 288, 619), Institute of Medical Biochemistry and, Danish Centre for Human Genome Research, Aarhus University, DK-8000 Aarhus C, Denmark

ROBERTA CHARPENTIER (313), The Center for Gerontological Research, Medical College of Pennsylvania, Philadelphia, Pennsylvania 19129

PIOTR CHOMCZYNSKI (680), Division of Endocrinology and Metabolism, College of Medicine, University of Cincinnati, Cincinnati, Ohio 45267

ANTHONY CHU (185), Unit of Dermatology, Department of Medicine, Hammersmith Hospital, London W12 0NN, United Kingdom

PATRICIA COLLIN-OSDOBY (128), Department of Biology, Washington University, St. Louis, Missouri 63130

CARL W. COTMAN (45), Irvine Research Unit in Brain Aging and Departments of Psychobiology and Neurology, University of California, Irvine, California 92717

VINCENT J. CRISTOFALO (313), The Center for Gerontological Research, Medical College of Pennsylvania, Philadelphia, Pennsylvania 19129

JOHN P. DALEY (90), Biomedical Applications Group, Life Technologies Inc., Grand Island, New York 14072

ZBIGNIEW DARZYNKIEWICZ (261), The Cancer Research Institute, New York Medical College, Valhalla, New York 10595

BARRY R. DAVIES (338), Scion Health Limited, University of Cambridge, Cambridge CB3 OJQ, United Kingdom

MASSIMO DE FELICI (68), Dipartimento di Sanita Pubblica e Biologia Cellulare, Sezione di Istologia e Embriologia, Universitá de Roma, I-00173 Roma, Italy

ROBERT T. DELL'ORCO (124), Noble Center for Biomedical Research, Oklahoma Medical Research Foundation, Oklahoma City, Oklahoma 73104

PETER N. DEVREOTES (412), Department of Biological Chemistry, Johns Hopkins University, School of Medicine, Baltimore, Maryland 21205

JEAN M. DONOVAN (90), Biomedical Applications Group, Life Technologies Inc., Grand Island, New York 14072

ARNOLD DRIESSEN (545), Department of Microbiology, Biologisch Centrum, University of Groningen, 9750 AA Haren, The Netherlands

MARIE DZIADEK (109), Institute of Reproduction and Development, Monash Medical Centre, Clayton, Victoria 3168, Australia

SUSANNAH ELIOTT (412), School of Biological Sciences, Macquarie University, Sydney NSW, Australia 2109

RUTH EPSTEIN-BAAK (245), Medical Biology Institute, La Jolla, California 92037

MARTIN EVANS (54), Wellcome Trust, Cancer Research Campaign, Institute of Developmental Biology and Cancer, and Department of Genetics, University of Cambridge, Cambridge, CB2 3EH, United Kingdom

H. DARIUSH FAHIMI (550), Department of Anatomy and Cell Biology (II), University of Heidelberg, D-69120 Heidelberg, Germany

MARCUS FECHHEIMER (412), Department of Zoology, University of Georgia, Athens, Georgia 30602

RICHARD A. FIRTEL (412), Department of Biology, Center for Molecular Genetics, University of California, San Diego, La Jolla, California 92093

JORGE A. FLORES (170), Division of Endocrinology and Metabolism, Department of Internal Medicine, University of Virginia, Charlottesville, Virginia 22908

HEIKE FÖLSCH (538), Institut für Physiologische Chemie der Universität München, 80336 München, Germany

MARK G. FRATTINI (491), Departments of Biochemistry and Molecular Biology, University of Chicago, Chicago, Illinois 60637

IRVING B. FRITZ (159), Department of Molecular and Cellular Physiology, AFRC Institute of Animal Physiology and Genetics Research, Cambridge CB2 4AT, United Kingdom

RUTH FURUKAWA (412), Department of Zoology, University of Georgia, Athens, Georgia 30602

PAOLO GAZZOTTI (575), Department of Biochemistry III, Swiss Federal Institute of Technology (ETH), CH-8092 Zürich, Switzerland

MARIO GIMONA (584), Institute of Molecular Biology, Austrian Academy of Sciences, A-5020 Salzburg, Austria

DEBRA A. GORDON (251), Department of Biochemistry and Arizona Cancer Center, University of Arizona, Tucson, Arizona 85724

FRANK L. GRAHAM (479), Departments of Biology and Pathology, McMaster University, Hamilton, Ontario, Canada L8S 4K1

LLOYD A. GREENE (218), Department of Pathology and Center for Neurobiology and Behavior, Columbia University, College of Physicians and Surgeons, New York, New York 10032

DALE F. GRUBER (18), Departments of Cell Culture Research and Development and Technical Services, GIBCO-BRL, Life Technologies Inc., Grand Island, New York 14072

EINAR HALLBERG (613), Department of Biochemistry, Arrhenius Laboratory, Stockholm University, S-106 91 Stockholm, Sweden

BRIAN V. HARMON (319), School of Life Science, Queensland University of Technology, Brisbane, Queensland 4000, Australia

ROBERT J. HAY (25), Cell Culture Department, American Type Culture Collection, Rockville, Maryland 20852

IZUMI HAYASHI (383), Department of Molecular Genetics, Beckman Research Institute of the City of Hope, Duarte, California 91010

MIEP HELFRICH (128), Department of Medicine and Therapeutics, University of Aberdeen Medical School, Foresterhill, Aberdeen AB9 2ZD, Scotland, United Kingdom

JOHANNES W. HELL (567), Department of Pharmacology, School of Medicine, University of Washington, Seattle, Washington 98195

JOHANNES M. HERRMANN (538), Institut für Physiologische Chemie der Universität München, 80336 München, Germany

THERESA HIGGINS (294), Imperial Cancer Research Fund, GB-London WC2A 3PX, United Kingdom

MARY HITT (479), Departments of Biology and Pathology, McMaster University, Hamilton, Ontario, Canada L8S 4K1

ROBERT M. HOFFMAN (367), Laboratory for Cancer Biology, University of California, San Diego, La Jolla, California 92093

MARIANNE HOKLAND (179), Institute of Medical Microbiology, Aarhus University, DK-8000 Aarhus C, Denmark

PETER HOKLAND (179), Department of Medicine and Hematology, Aarhus University, DK-8000 Aarhus C, Denmark

MICHAEL HORTON (128), Imperial Cancer Research Fund, Haemopoiesis Research Group, St. Bartholomew's Hosptial, Dominion House, London EC1A 7BE, United Kingdom

MEI HUANG (641), Department of Molecular Biology, Vanderbilt University, Nashville, Tennessee 37235

LUKAS A. HUBER (517), Department of Biochemistry, University of Geneva, CH-1211 Geneva, Switzerland

ELIEZER HUBERMAN (207), Center for Mechanistic Biology and Biotechnology, Argonne National Laboratory, Argonne, Illinois 60439

NORMAN HUI (509), Cell Biology Laboratory, Imperial Cancer Reseach Fund, London WC2A 3PX, United Kingdom

WIELAND B. HUTTNER (557), Institute for Neurobiology, University of Heidelberg, D-69120 Heidelberg, Germany

AKIRA ICHIHARA (662), Institute for Enzyme Research, The University of Tokushima, Tokushima 770, Japan

MITSUO ISHIGAMI (452), Department of Biology, Faculty of Education, Shiga University, Otsu 520, Japan

RYOKI ISHIKAWA (452), Department of Pharmacology, Gunma University School of Medicine, Gunma 371, Japan

REINHARD JAHN (567), Howard Hughes Medical Institute, Boyer Center for Molecular Medicine, Yale University School of Medicine, New Haven, Connecticut 06536

DAVID W. JAYME (18), Departments of Cell Culture Research and Development and Technical Services, GIBCO-BRL, Life Technologies Inc., Grand Island, New York 14072

KEITH JERMYN (412), The Imperial Cancer Research Fund, Clare Hall Laboratories, South Mimms, Herts EN6 3LD, United Kingdom

GREGORY R. JOHNSON (153), Leukaemia Foundation of Queensland Daikyo Research Unit, Queensland Institute of Medical Research, Brisbane, 4029, Queensland, Australia

HANNE JØRGENSEN (179), Institute of Medical Microbiology, Aarhus University, DK-8000 Aarhus C, Denmark

BERTHOLD KASTNER (628), Institut für Molekularbiologie und Tumorforschung, 35037 Marburg an der Lahn, Germany

MARIKO KATOH (398), Institute of Biological Sciences, The University of Tsukuba, Tsukuba, Ibaraki 305, Japan

JOHN F. R. KERR (319), Department of Pathology, University of Queensland Medical School, Herston, Queensland 4006, Australia

MOHAMED KHIDHIR (674), Department of Molecular Biology and Genetics, Wayne State University School of Medicine, Detroit, Michigan 48201

JOHN V. KILMARTIN (605), MRC, Laboratory of Molecular Biology, Cambridge, CB2 2QH, United Kingdom

KAZUHIRO KOHAMA (452), Department of Pharmacology, Gunma University School of Medicine, Gunma 371, Japan

EDWARD D. KORN (405), Laboratory of Cell Biology, NHLBI, NIH, Bethesda, Maryland 20892

STEPHEN A. KRAWETZ (674), Department of Molecular Biology and Genetics, Wayne State University School of Medicine, Detroit, Michigan 48201

GABRIELA KROCKMALNIC (622), Department of Biology, Massachusetts Institute of Technology, Cambridge, Massachusetts 02139

MASAYOSHI KUMEGAWA (128), Department of Oral Anatomy, Meikai University School of Dentistry, Sakado 350–02, Japan

YASUHIRO KURASAWA (398), Institute of Biological Sciences, The University of Tsukuba, Tsukuba, Ibaraki 305, Japan

ADAM KUSPA (412), Department of Biology, Center for Molecular Genetics, University of California, San Diego, La Jolla, California 92093

LAIMONIS A. LAIMINS (491), Departments of Molecular Genetics and Cell Biology, Howard Hughes Medical Institute, University of Chicago, Chicago, Illinois 60637

THOMAS E. LALLIER (345), Department of Anatomy and Cell Biology, University of Virginia, Charlottesville, Virginia 22901

PAMELA L. LARSEN (389), Division of Biological Sciences, University of Missouri, Columbia, Missouri 65211

THOMAS J. LAST (282), Department of Cell Biology, University Massachusetts Medical Center, Worcester, Massachusetts 01655

WALLACE M. LESTOURGEON (641), Department of Molecular Biology, Vanderbilt University, Nashville, Tennessee 37235

KEVIN A. W. LEE (668), Imperial Cancer Research Fund, Clare Hall Labs, S. Mimms, EN6 LD Herts, United Kingdom

CATHERINE LEONARD (148), Neuroscience Research Group, Departments of Anatomy and Pharmacology and Therapeutics and Graduate Department of Neuroscience, University of Calgary, Calgary, Alberta, Canada T2N 4N1

RICHARD A. LEVIS (355), Department of Physiology, Rush Medical College, Chicago, Illinois 60612

JANE B. LIAN (282), Department of Cell Biology, University Massachusetts Medical Center, Worcester, Massachusetts 01655

ROLAND LILL (545), Institut für Physiologische Chemie, Physikalische Biochemie und Zellbiologie, der Universität München, 80336 München, Germany

ANDERS LINDBLOM (589), M. E. Müller-Institut für Biomechanik, Universität Bern, CH-3010 Bern, Switzerland

ROBERT LINDNER (525), Department of Pathology, Washington University School of Medicine, St. Louis, Missouri 63110

DERYK T. LOO (45), Irvine Research Unit in Brain Aging and Departments of Psychobiology and Neurology, University of California, Irvine, California 92717

JETTE LOVMAND (500), Department of Molecular Biology, Aarhus University, DK-8000 Aarhus C, Denmark

REINHARD LÜHRMANN (628), Institut für Molekularbiologie und Tumorforschung, 35037 Marburg an der Lahn, Germany

ANDERS H. LUND (500), Department of Molecular Biology, Aarhus University, DK-8000 Aarhus C, Denmark

JEAN-JACQUES MADJAR (657), Immuno-Virologie Moléculaire et Cellulaire, Faculté de Médecine, Université Claude Bernard Lyon-I, CNRS UMR 30, F-69372 Lyon Cedex 08, France

PEDER MADSEN (288), Institute of Medical Biochemistry and Danish Centre for Human Genome Research, Aarhus University, DK-8000 Aarhus C, Denmark

SANDRA K. O. MANN (412), Department of Biology, Center for Molecular Genetics, University of California, San Diego, La Jolla, California 92093

PAUL A. MARKS (213), DeWitt Wallace Research Laboratory, Memorial Sloan Kettering Cancer Center and the Sloan Kettering Division of the Graduate School of Medicine Sciences, Cornell University, New York, New York 10021

SEIYA MATSUMOTO (207), Department of Pathology, Ehime University School of Medicine, Ehime 791–02, Japan

KATHY MAY (305), SmithKline Beecham Pharmaceuticals Research Division, Betchworth, Surrey RH3 7AJ, United Kingdom

ANDREAS MAYER (545), Institut für Physiologische Chemie, Physikalische Biochemie und Zellbiologie der Universität München, 80336 München, Germany

LAURA McCABE (282), Department of Cell Biology, University Massachusetts Medical Center, Worcester, Massachusetts 01655

DAVID I. MEYER (531), Department of Biological Chemistry, School of Medicine and Molecular Biology Institute, University of California, Los Angeles, California 90024

CRAIG MEYERS (491), Departments of Molecular Genetics and Cell Biology, Howard Hughes Medical Institute, University of Chicago, Chicago, Illinois 60637

ROGER L. MIESFELD (251), Department of Biochemistry and Arizona Cancer Center, University of Arizona, Tucson, Arizona 85724

DIDIER MONTARRAS (199), Unité de Biochimie, Département de Biologie Molécu-laire, Institut Pasteur, F-75015 Paris, France

JENNY MORRIS (185), Unit of Dermatology, Department of Medicine, Hammer-smith Hospital, London W12 ONN, United Kingdom

MOHAMMED MOUDJOU (207, 595), Centre de Génétique Moléculaire, Centre National de la Recherche Scientifique, 91198 Gif-sur-Yvette, France

SHINICHI MURAO (207), Department of Pathology, Ehime University School of Medicine, Ehime 791–02, Japan

MAMORU NAKANISHI (207), Department of Pathology, Ehime University School of Medicine, Ehime 791–02, Japan

JAMES E. NELSON (674), Department of Molecular Biology and Genetics, Wayne State University School of Medicine, Detroit, Michigan 48201

STEPHEN NESBITT (128), Imperial Cancer Research Fund, Haemopoiesis Research Group, St. Bartholomew's Hosptial, Dominion House, London EC1A 7BE, United Kingdom

WALTER NEUPERT (538, 545), Institut für Physiologische Chemie, Physikalische Biochemie und Zellbiologie, der Universität München, 80336 München, Germany

JEFFREY A. NICKERSON (622), Department of Biology, Massachusetts Institute of Technology, Cambridge, Massachusetts 02139

MARKUS NIEDERREITER (584), Institute of Molecular Biology of the Austrian Academy of Sciences, A-5020 Salzburg, Austria

OSAMU NUMATA (398), Institute of Biological Sciences, The University of Tsu-kuba, Tsukuba, Ibaraki 305, Japan

EYðFINNUR OLSEN (142), Institute of Medical Biochemistry and Danish Centre for Human Genome Research, Aarhus University, DK-8000 Aarhus C, Denmark

THOMAS OWEN (282), Department of Cell Biology, University Massachusetts Medical Center, Worcester, MA 01655

CAROL A. PARENT (412), Department of Biological Chemistry, Johns Hopkins University, School of Medicine, Baltimore, Maryland 21205

MATS PAULSSON (589), M. E. Müller-Institute für Biomechanik, Universität Bern, CH-3010 Bern, Switzerland

FINN SKOU PEDERSEN (500), Department of Molecular Biology, Aarhus Univer-sity, DK-8000 Aarhus C, Denmark

SHELDON PENMAN (622), Department of Biology, Massachusetts Institute of Technology, Cambridge, Massachusetts 02139

PAUL D. PHILLIPS (313), The Center for Gerontological Research, Medical College of Pennsylvania, Philadelphia, Pennsylvania 19129

CHRISTIAN PINSET (199), Unité de Biochimie, Département de Biologie Molécu-laire, Institut Pasteur, F-75015 Paris, France

INGO POTRYKUS (462), Institute for Plant Sciences, Swiss Federal Institute of Tech-nology, CH-8092 Zürich, Switzerland

LUDVIK PREVEC (479), Departments of Biology and Pathology, McMaster Univer-sity, Hamilton, Ontario, Canada L8S 4K1

JAMES L. RAE (355), Department of Physiology and Biophysics and Ophthalmol-ogy, Mayo Foundation, Rochester, Minnesota 55905

D. EUGENE RANNELS (116), Department of Anesthesia, The Pennsylvania State University College of Medicine, Hershey, Pennsylvania 17033

STEPHEN R. RANNELS (116), Department of Cellular and Molecular Physiology, The Pennsylvania State University College of Medicine, Hershey, Pennsylvania 17033

BRENT A. REYNOLDS (148), Neuroscience Research Group, Departments of Anatomy and Pharmacology and Therapeutics, and Graduate Department of Neuroscience, University of Calgary, Calgary, Alberta, Canada T2N 4N1

VICTORIA M. RICHON (213), DeWitt Wallace Research Laboratory, Memorial Sloan Kettering Cancer Center and the Sloan Kettering Division of the Graduate School of Medicine Sciences, Cornell University, New York, New York 10021

DONALD L. RIDDLE (389), Division of Biological Sciences, University of Missouri, Columbia, Missouri 65211

RICHARD A. RIFKIND (213), DeWitt Wallace Research Laboratory, Memorial Sloan Kettering Cancer Center and the Sloan Kettering Division of the Graduate School of Medicine Sciences, Cornell University, New York, New York 10021

MICHAEL P. ROUT (605), HHMI, The Rockefeller University, New York, New York 10021

ENRIQUE ROZENGURT (294), Imperial Cancer Research Fund, GB-London WC2A 3PX, United Kingdom

PHILIP S. RUDLAND (338), Department of Biochemistry, University of Liverpool, Liverpool L69 3BX, United Kingdom

ROLAND SAHLI (471), Institute of Microbiology, Centre Hospitalier Universitaire Vaudois, 1011 Lausanne, Switzerland

PAUL M. SALVATERRA (383), Division of Neurosciences, Beckman Research Institute of the City of Hope, Duarte, California 91010

CHRISTOPHER M. SANDERSON (531), Department of Microbiology and Immunology, UCLA School of Medicine, Los Angeles, California 90024

TAKUYA SATO (128), Department of Oral Anatomy, Meikai University School of Dentistry, Sakado 350–02, Japan

ROBERT E. SCOTT (193), Department of Pathology, The University of Tennessee College of Medicine, Memphis, Tennessee 38163

JEFFREY SEGALL (412), Department of Anatomy and Structural Biology, Albert Einstein College of Medicine, Bronx, New York 10461

PER O. SEGLEN (96), Department of Tissue Culture, Institute for Cancer Research, The Norwegian Radium Hospital, Montebello, 0310 Oslo 3, Norway

GAD SHAULSKY (412), Department of Biology, Center for Molecular Genetics, University of California, San Diego, La Jolla, California 92093

KAI SIMONS (225, 517), European Molecular Biology Laboratory, Cell Biology Program, D-69124 Heidelberg, Germany

PAUL SLUSAREWICZ (509), Cell Biology Laboratory, Imperial Cancer Reseach Fund, London WC2A 3PX, United Kingdom

ROBERTA H. SMITH (456), Department of Soil and Crop Sciences, Texas A&M University, College Station, Texas 77843

GERMAN SPANGENBERG (462), Institute for Plant Sciences, Swiss Federal Institute of Technology, CH-8092 Zürich, Switzerland

ELIZABETH STADLER (109), Institute of Reproduction and Development, Monash Medical Centre, Clayton, Victoria 3168, Australia

GARY S. STEIN (282), Department of Cell Biology, University Massachusetts Medical Center, Worcester, Massachusetts 01655

JANET L. STEIN (282), Department of Cell Biology, University Massachusetts Medical Center, Worcester, Massachusetts 01655

PABLO STEINBERG (103), Institute of Toxicology, University of Mainz, D-55131 Mainz, Germany

JANE C. STINCHCOMBE (557), MRC Laboratory for Molecular Cell Biology, University College London, London WC1E 6BT, United Kingdom

ROSEMARY A. STUART (538), Institut für Physiologische Chemie der Universität München, 80336 München, Germany

DAWN B. STURTEVANT (193), Department of Pathology, The University of Tennessee College of Medicine, Memphis, Tennessee 38163

SHIAWHWA SU (272), Department of Pathobiology, Auburn University, Auburn, Alabama 36849

KEIJI TANAKA (662), Institute for Enzyme Research, The University of Tokushima, Tokushima 770, Japan

KENNETH K. TENG (218), Department of Pathology and Center for Neurobiology and Behavior, Columbia University, College of Physicians and Surgeons, New York, New York 10032

KEN-ICHI TEZUKA (128), Department of Oral Anatomy, Meikai University School of Dentistry, Sakado 350–02, Japan

JEAN PAUL THIERY (232), Laboratoire de Physiopathologie du Développement, URA CNRS 1337, Ecole Normale Supérieure, F-75230 Paris Cedex 05, France

TIM THOMAS (109), Institute of Reproduction and Development, Monash Medical Centre, Clayton, Victoria 3168, Australia

JONATHAN L. TILLY (330), Division of Reproductive Biology, Department of Population Dynamics, Johns Hopkins University, Baltimore, Maryland 21205

PIERRE S. TUNG (159), Banting and Best Department of Medical Research, University of Toronto, Toronto, Canada M5G 1L6

NORIFUMI UEDA (207), Department of Pathology, Ehime University School of Medicine, Ehime 791–02, Japan

ANA MARIA VALLÉS (232), Laboratoire de Physiopathologie du Développement, URA CNRS 1337, Ecole Normale Supérieure, F-75230 Paris Cedex 05, France

PHILIP H. VARDY (412), Department of Biological Sciences, University of Western Sydney-Nepean, Westmead, NSW Australia 2145

JOHANNES D. VELDHUIS (170), Division of Endocrinology and Metabolism, Department of Internal Medicine, University of Virginia, Charlottesville, Virginia 22908

HILKKA VIRTA (225), European Molecular Biology Laboratory, Cell Biology Program, D-69012 Heidelberg, Germany

ALFRED VÖLKL (550), Department of Anatomy and Cell Biology (II), University of Heidelberg, D-69120 Heidelberg, Germany

HANLIN WANG (193), Department of Pathology, The University of Tennessee College of Medicine, Memphis, Tennessee 38163

GRAHAM WARREN (509), Cell Biology Laboratory, Imperial Cancer Research Fund, London WC2A 3PX, United Kingdom

YOSHIO WATANABE (398), Institute of Biological Sciences, The University of Tsukuba, Tsukuba, Ibaraki 305, Japan

FIONA M. WATT (83), Keratinocyte Laboratory, Imperial Cancer Research Fund, London WC2A 3PX, United Kingdom

SAMUEL WEISS (148), Neuroscience Research Group, Departments of Anatomy and Pharmacology and Therapeutics and Graduate Department of Neuroscience, University of Calgary, Calgary, Alberta, Canada T2N 4N1

JEFFREY WILLIAMS (412), The Imperial Cancer Research Fund, Clare Hall Laboratories, South Mimms, Herts EN6 3LD, United Kindgom

KEITH L. WILLIAMS (412), School of Biological Sciences, Macquarie University, Sydney, NSW Australia 2109

CLAY M. WINTERFORD (319), Department of Pathology, University of Queensland Medical School, Herston, Queensland 4006, Australia

GIN WU (272), Transgenic Technologies Inc., Freemont, California 94538

KENN ZERIVITZ (668), Gladstone Institute of Virology and Immunology, University of California, San Francisco, California 94141

PREFACE

The source for this laboratory manual can be traced back to 1968 when I was introduced to international laboratory courses by Professors Jorge and Catherine Allende, who established a tradition in South America of teaching state-of-the-art technology in the biological sciences. In 1978, I began to teach similar courses in Denmark, and more recently, thanks to the continuous support from the Federation of European Biochemical Societies (FEBS), we have been able to establish an international practical course for Basic and Specialized Techniques in Cell Biology that is taught annually in Aarhus. As a result, we had gathered a small number of protocols, but it was not until late 1992—when I was approached by Dr. Phyllis B. Moses, Senior Acquisitions Editor at Academic Press—that the opportunity to prepare a comprehensive laboratory manual in cell biology finally arose. The task seemed overwhelming at that time, but the prospects for starting a long-term project that contemplated regular, although well-spaced, updates were far reaching.

To determine content, I consulted several hundred scientists worldwide, with the aim of identifying areas and techniques that would appeal to a wide audience. I take this opportunity to thank all of those who took the time to provide me with valuable advice and suggestions. Once the framework was established, a handful of colleagues helped me to organize the sections, identify additional techniques, and pinpoint potential authors. In particular, David Shotton, Kai Simons, and J. Victor Small were instrumental at this stage of the project, and I am indebted to them. My colleagues Kurt Dejgaard and Hans-Jürgen Hoffmann carried out numerous literature searches, and the whole project relied on the administrative skills of our secretary Lene Svith. Needless to say, without Lene's dedication and love for computers this project could not have been completed.

The text has been divided into 15 sections. These contain about 190 protocols, flowing from cells to proteins. Volume 1 deals with tissue culture and associated techniques, viruses, organelles, cellular structures, macromolecules, and functional assays. Volume 2 covers microscopy, microdissection techniques, histochemistry, antibodies, immunocytochemistry and vital staining of cells, intracellular measurements, cytogenetics, as well as *in situ* hybridization. Volume 3 completes the three-volume set with transfer of macromolecules and small molecules; cloning of embryos, transgenics, and gene targeting; cell-free extracts, permeabilized cell systems, and expression systems; and proteins. The appendices include information on media, common cell lines, and safety procedures for handling radioactivity.

The protocols are written in an explicit, friendly, "recipe style". They should be easy to reproduce, as the contributors have included the catalog numbers and sources of key reagents, materials, and instruments as well as selected references for further reading. To facilitate execution, the protocols spell out the preparation of solutions and illustrate important steps. Since we plan to update the manual regularly we would very much appreciate suggestions to improve the techniques, or corrections of possible mistakes in *Cell Biology: A Laboratory Handbook.*

Obviously, any laboratory manual covering such a vast area of biology cannot be expected to be complete. This book is no exception and I apologize for any omissions. With time, we plan to fill in the gaps. In this context I am pleased to announce that Nigel Carter, Tony Hunter, David Shotton, Kai Simons, and J. Victor Small have agreed to participate as Associate Editors for future publications. Collection of new material and planning for the first update, in 1997, including CD-ROM, has already begun.

In addition to the authors, who went out of their way to keep the deadlines, there are several other people who contributed to the making of *Cell Biology: A Laboratory Handbook.* Among them, I would like to name Inge Detlefsen, Lone Romar, Frede Nielsen, Eyðfinnur Olsen, Hanne Holm Rasmussen, Peder Madsen, Bent Honoré, Henrik Leffers, and Poul Gromov. My wife and children provided me with much support at hectic times, and in particular, my son Juan Pablo spent many weekends in the laboratory preparing the artwork for some articles. My deepest gratitude goes to all of them.

Finally, while things developed in Aarhus, Phyllis B. Moses of Academic Press, San Diego, provided a dynamic and dedicated presence to this project, that in part, is rightly hers. My thanks to her and all the staff in Editorial, Production, and Marketing Departments at Academic Press for having produced these three handsome volumes on schedule.

Julio E. Celis

PART 1

TISSUE CULTURE AND ASSOCIATED TECHNIQUES

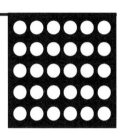

SECTION **A**

General Techniques

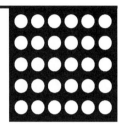

General Procedures for Tissue Culture

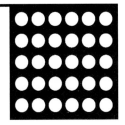

Ariana Celis and Julio E. Celis

I. Introduction

Tissue culture has become a widespread technique as cultured cells are being used in a spectrum of disciplines ranging from biochemistry to molecular and cell biology. In general, tissue culture procedures are simple but require extreme care to avoid contamination. Here, we describe general procedures to subculture continuous cell lines grown in monolayers [transformed human amnion (AMA) cells] and in suspension (Molt-4 leukemia cells) cultures. Procedures for subculturing other continuous cell lines as well as for preparing and propagating primary cultures are given in various articles in this volume. For a detailed, and more comprehensive treatment of the subject, the reader is referred to books by Paul (1975), Freshney (1987, 1992), Jakoby and Pastan (1987), Adams (1990) and Baserga (1990). See also articles by Dale F. Gruber and David W. Jayme; David W. Jayme and Dale F. Gruber and by Robert J. Hay.

II. Materials and Instrumentation

Dulbecco's modified Eagle's medium (Cat. No. F0435), glutamine (Cat. No. K0282), penicillin/streptomycin (Cat. No. A2213), and $NaHCO_3$ (L1713) were purchased from Biochrom KG. Fetal calf serum (Cat. No. 04-001-1A) was obtained from Biological Industries, trypsin (Cat. No. 25090-028) from Gibco BRL, Hoechst 33258 (Cat. No. 33217) from Riedel-de Haën, glycerol (Cat. No. 4094) from Merck, 0.4% trypan blue (Cat. No. T8154) from Sigma and Diversol BX from Diversey A/S, and 7X PF detergent (Cat. No. 7667121) from ICN.

The 25-cm^2 (Cat. No. 690160) and 75-cm^2 (Cat. No. 658170) tissue culture flasks and 1-ml (Cat. No. 604181), 10-ml (Cat. No. 607180), and 25-ml (Cat. No. 760180) pipettes were purchased from Greiner. Ten-milliliter plastic conical centrifuge tubes (Cat. No. 347759), 1.8-ml cryotubes (Cat. No. 377267), and tissue culture dishes (40 mm, Cat. No. 153066; 58 mm, Cat. No. 150288; 92 mm, Cat. No. 150350) were from Nunc and Pasteur pipettes from Denley Instruments Autoclave bags (600 × 780 mm, Cat. No. 861200) were from Sarsted, Dumont No. 5 forceps from Neo Lab, and the hemocytometer (Neubauer improved chamber) from Rudolf Brand. Round glass coverslips (Cat. No. LDR 012) and object glass (Cat. No. O 41206) were purchased from Menzel. Disposable sterile forceps were obtained from UNO Plast, the steriband (Cat. No. 12130) from Gen Pack, the sterile disposable scalpels (Paragon No. 11) from Paragon, the cryoboxes from Nalgene, the tape for sterilization from St. Paul 3M Center, and the automatic pipette (pipet plus, Product No. 152000) from Tecnomara.

The laminar flow cabinet (Dan Laf) was purchased from Claus Damm and the

CO_2 incubator from ASSAB (T 305 GF). We have also used laminar flow cabinets from Heto Holten and ASSAB and CO_2 incubators from Forma Scientific and Queue. The oven (Memmert UL50) was from Memmert, the pump (S1.5) from Leybold Heraus, the pedal from Bernstein, the autoclave (type AWA 50) from ALA, the liquid nitrogen freezer (Locator 4) from Barnstead Thermolyne, and the washing machine (Miele GA33) from Miele. The UV lamp (T UV 30W E30 T8) was obtained from Philips. The inverted microscope (Telaval 31) equipped with a 20× phase-contrast objective and a 10× eyepiece was from Zeiss. For immunofluorescence we used an upright Zeiss fluorescence microscope (Axioplan).

III. Procedures

A. THE TISSUE CULTURE LABORATORY

1. The Laminar Airflow Cabinet

The laminar air flow cabinets (preferably vertical airflow) (Fig. 1A) should be equipped with a gas line and a Bunsen burner (Fig. 1A, a), an automatic pipette aid (Fig. 1A, b), and a vacuum line to aspirate the medium (Fig. 1B). The vacuum line should be interrupted by a trap consisting of two flasks, one of which contains disinfectant (4% Diversol or other disinfectant; Fig. 1B, a). The second flask (Fig. 1B, b), which is connected directly to a small vacuum pump (Fig. 1B, c), is empty and protects the vacuum line from overflow. The whole device is operated by a pedal (Fig. 1B, d) that turns the pump on and off. In addition, the flow cabinet should contain a bottle with 4% Diversol to rinse pipettes before disposal (Fig. 1A, c), a plastic squeeze bottle with 4% Diversol to clean the working area (Fig. 1A, d) and a small container with 70% ethanol (Fig. 1A, e) to sterilize forceps. Also, there should be a stand to keep Pasteur pipettes and regular sterile pipettes (Fig. 1A, f).

Outside the laminar flow cabinet should be containers to dispose plasticware (Fig. 1C, a) and pipettes (Fig. 1C, b) as well as a paper basket. A humidified CO_2 incubator (Fig. 1D), an inverted microscope equipped with phase-contrast optics (Fig. 1E, a), and a small clinical-type bench centrifuge (Fig. 1E, b) should also be located close by.

Other apparatus required include standard storage equipment such as refrigerators, $-20°C$ and $-80°C$ freezers, and a liquid nitrogen freezer. A low-pressure mercury vapor lamp is recommended to sterilize the air in the room. The lamp can also be placed inside the laminar flow cabinet.

2. Plasticware and Materials

A large variety of disposable sterile plasticware are available for tissue culture, including tissue culture flasks (Fig. 2A, a), dishes (Fig. 2A, b), multiwell dishes (Fig. 2A, c), cryotubes (Fig. 2B, a), containers (Fig. 2B, b), centrifuge tubes (Fig. 2B, c), tweezers (Fig. 2B, d), pipettes (Fig. 2C, a and b), syringes (Fig. 3D), and sterile filters of various diameters (Fig. 3D).

3. Sterilization

Solutions, glassware, and other items can be sterilized by moist heat in an autoclave (Fig. 2E). Sterilize for 30 min at a pressure of 15 lb/in^2. Empty bottles should have the cap loosely screwed, whereas partly filled bottles should have their caps tightly screwed on. The cap should be covered with a piece of aluminum foil and a strip of indicator tape placed (Fig. 2E, a). When sterilization is complete, the pressure should be lowered gradually to avoid boiling of the liquid.

FIGURE 1 The tissue culture laboratory. (A) Laminar flow cabinet with accessories: (a) Bunsen burner, (b) automatic pipette aid, (c) bottle with Diversol, (d) squeeze bottle with Diversol, (e) container with ethanol, (f) stand for Pasteur and regular pipettes. (B) Trap to collect medium: (a) flask containing Diversol, (b) empty flask connected to a small vacuum pump, (c) pedal to operate the pump. (C) Containers to dispose (a) plasticware and (b) pipettes. (D) CO_2 incubator. (E) (a) Inverted microscope equipped with phase-contrast optics and (b) small bench centrifuge.

Pasteur pipettes placed in glass cylinders covered with aluminum foil (Fig. 2C, b), other glassware (glass coverslips placed in glass Petri dishes), as well as small items wrapped in aluminum foil (gauze, surgical instruments, etc.) can be sterilized

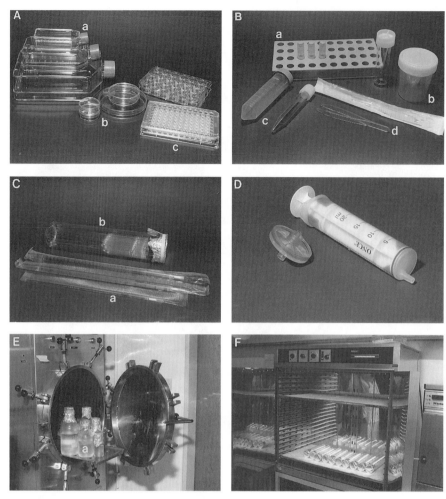

FIGURE 2 Materials and additional equipment required for tissue culture. (A) Sterile plastic culture vessels: (a) flasks, (b) dishes and (c) multiwell plates. (B) Sterile plastic containers and tweezers: (a) cryotubes, (b) containers, (c) centrifuge tubes, and (d) plastic tweezers. (C) (a) Sterile plastic pipettes and (b) sterile Pasteur pipettes. (D) Syringe and sterile filter. (E) Autoclave with bottles (a). (F) Oven.

by dry heat in an oven (Fig. 2F). Sterilization is for 90 min at 160°C. Indicator tape is used to assess sterility.

Plasticware (open dishes) can be sterilized by exposure to an ultraviolet light (UV) germicidal lamp.

4. Disposal

a. Media
Aspirate into disinfectant trap (Fig. 1B, a) and autoclave when filled. Autoclave for 60 min at 15 lb/in².

b. Plasticware
Place all disposable plastics (flasks, dishes, etc.) in a stainless-steel container lined with an autoclave bag (Fig. 1C, a). Autoclave as above.

c. Pasteur pipettes and regular disposable plastic pipettes
Place in autoclave bags (Fig. 1C, b) and autoclave as above.

d. Contaminated dishes
Do not open them. Seal in plastic bags and place in autoclave bags for autoclaving. Autoclave as above.

e. Blades, needles, and scalpels
Place these items in an appropriate plastic container. When full, wrap the container in an autoclave bag and dispose in accordance with the safety regulations enforced in your laboratory.

5. Glassware Washing

a. Regular glassware
Prerinse the glassware with demineralized water after use and immerse for 2 to 3 hr in a 1% solution of a mild detergent such as 7× PF. Scrub using soft brushes. 7× PF can be reused several times. After detergent treatment, the glassware is washed once in warm tap water, twice in distilled water, and once in double-distilled water. Thereafter, the glassware is dried in an oven at 160°C for 2 hr. Clean glassware should wet uniformly when exposed to a thin stream of distilled water. For larger-scale washing we use an automatic Miele washing machine and 7× O-matic (ICN Flow, Catalog No. 76-675-21) at a concentration of 0.25%.

b. Glassware that has been in contact with biological material
Add a 5% solution of 7× detergent and autoclave. Thereafter wash as described above.

c. Glass coverslips
Place the glass coverslips in a solution containing 60 ml of alcohol and 40 ml of HCl. Leave for at least 30 min at room temperature. Afterward, rinse several times with distilled water. Dry each coverslip with tissue paper, place in a 100-mm glass culture dish, and sterilize in an oven (see above).

NOTE

Use protective clothing and safety glasses when preparing the solution. After mixing let the solution stand for 30 min at room temperature. The solution can be reused several times.

6. Safety

1. Do not eat, drink, or smoke in the tissue culture laboratory.

2. Use a laboratory coat and wear gloves. Wash your hands thoroughly after tissue culture work.

3. Use automatic pipette aids. Do not pipette by mouth.

4. Make sure that samples of human origin have been screened for human immunodeficiency virus type 1 (HIV-1) and hepatitis virus. Samples should be handled as if they were contaminated even after screening, for a few possible sources of contamination.

5. To avoid injuries from frostbite or ruptured vials, wear safety glasses and insulated gloves when handling samples frozen in liquid nitrogen.

B. SUBCULTURING OF CONTINUOUS CELL LINES GROWN IN MONOLAYERS

The procedure is illustrated with the subculturing of transformed human amnion cells (AMA), a cell line that can be propagated indefinitely.

Media and Solutions

1. *Dulbecco's modified Eagle's medium containing bicarbonate (DMEM):* Keep at 4°C.

2. *100× glutamine stock (200 mM):* Aliquot in sterile 5-ml portions and keep at −20°C.

3. *100× penicillin/streptomycin (10.000 U, 10.000 μg/ml):* Aliquot in sterile 5-ml portions and keep at −20°C.

4. *Fetal calf serum (FCS):* Keep at −20°C in 100-ml portions.

5. *Complete Dulbecco's modified Eagle's medium (DMEM):* DMEM medium containing antibiotics (penicillin, 100 U/ml; streptomycin, 100 μg/ml), glutamine (2 mM), and 10% fetal calf serum (FCS): To make 500 ml, mix 440 ml of DMEM medium, 5 ml of 10× stock penicillin/streptomycin, 5 ml of 10× stock of glutamine, and 50 ml of FCS. Keep at 4°C.

6. *Hanks' buffered saline solution (HBSS) without Ca^{2+} and Mg^{2+}:* 10× stock solution. To make 1 liter, weigh 4 g of KCl, 0.6 g of KH_2PO_4, 80 g of NaCl, and 0.621 g of $Na_2HPO_4 \cdot 2H_2O$. Complete to 1 liter with distilled water.

7. *1× HBSS without Ca^{2+} and Mg^{2+}:* To make 1 liter of 1× solution take 100 ml of the 10× stock HBSS and complete to 1 liter with distilled water. Autoclave 30 min at 15 lb/in² and keep at 4°C.

8. *Trypsin stock (2.5%):* Keep at −20°C.

9. *0.25% trypsin:* Dilute stock trypsin solution (2.5%) 10 times in sterile HBSS. Filter-sterilize (0.20-μm filter) and dispense in 8-ml aliquots. Keep at −20°C.

10. *4% Diversol:* To make 1 liter, weigh 40 g of Diversol and complete with demineralized water.

11. *70% Ethanol.*

Steps

1. Take a 25-cm² tissue culture flask containing exponentially growing AMA cells from the 37°C humidified 5% CO_2 incubator. Observe in an inverted microscope under phase-contrast optics (Fig. 3A).

2. Wipe the surface of the working area with Diversol. Flame the top of the flask (Fig. 3B) and aspirate the medium with the aid of a Pasteur pipette connected to a vacuum line leading to a Diversol trap (Fig. 3C). Rinse the pipette with Diversol before disconnecting from the vacuum line. Place the Pasteur pipette directly in autoclave bags (Fig. 1C, b) for autoclaving and disposal. When withdrawing a Pasteur pipette from the glass cylinder, try not to touch other pipettes. If in doubt, discard.

3. Add sufficient 0.25% trypsin (2 ml for a 25-cm² flask and 3–4 ml for a 75-cm² flask) to cover the monolayer of cells (Fig. 3D). Use an automatic pipette aid.

4. Leave the flask for 1 min at room temperature and aspirate the excess solution (Fig. 3C). Incubate the flask at room temperature or at 37°C in the CO_2

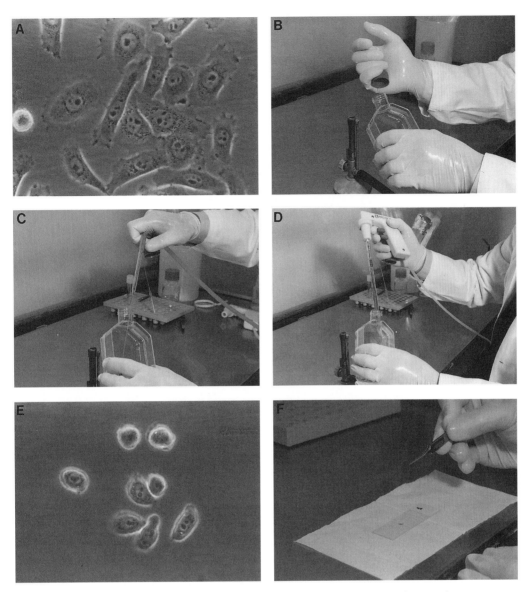

FIGURE 3 (A) Phase-contrast micrograph of AMA cell monolayers. (B) Flaming the top of a flask. (C) Aspirating the medium with a Pasteur pipette connected to a vacuum line. (D) Pipetting medium with an automatic pipette aid. (E) AMA cells treated with trypsin. (F) Mounting a glass coverslip.

incubator until the cells start rounding up (Fig. 3E). These steps take from 2 to 4 min. Tap the flask gently against the palm of the hand a couple of times and observe against the light or in an inverted microscope. Usually one can see the monolayer running down when the cells are ready to be resuspended. For some cell types it is necessary to use 0.25% trypsin containing 0.02% EDTA (also longer incubation time).

5. Resuspend the cells in 5 ml of complete DMEM (kept at 37°C). Pipette up and down a couple of times and plate at a split ratio of 1:5; that is, add 1 ml of the cell suspension to a new 25-cm² tissue culture flask containing 7 ml of complete DMEM. Loosen the cap and place the flask in a 37°C humidified 5% CO_2 incubator. Rinse the pipette with Diversol before discarding. Place the original culture flask in a stainless-steel container for autoclaving (Fig. 1C, a). If the time of trypsinization was too long and the cells detached, add 6 ml of

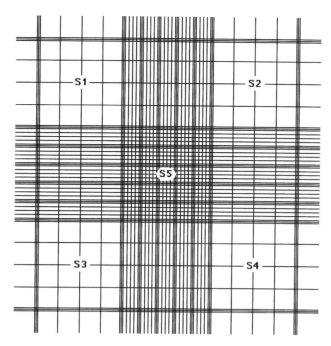

FIGURE 4   Diagram of hemocytometer's chambers.

complete medium and centrifuge at 300–400 *g* for a couple of minutes in a
bench centrifuge. Aspirate the supernatant and start from step 5. Record the
passage number, split ratio, and date.

6. Observe the cultures regularly and replace the complete DMEM medium if
required. This is usually indicated by increased acidity (the medium becomes
yellow). Make sure that the cap of the flask is loose at all times.

7. If the cells are to be used for immunofluorescence or autoradiography, plate
them in 40- or 58-mm tissue culture dishes containing several 12-mm round
sterile glass coverslips. Use sterile Dumont No. 5 forceps (dip in alcohol and
flame) to handle the coverslips (Fig. 3F). For [^{35}S]methionine labeling, cells can be
plated in 96-well plates or 40-mm tissue culture dishes (see also articles by Julio
E. Celis, Jette B. Lauridsen, and Bodil Basse and by S. D. Patterson and J. I.
Garrels).

8. Wipe down the working surface with Diversol or 70% ethanol when you
finish. Dispose of the waste if necessary.

C. PROCEDURE FOR COUNTING CELLS USING THE DYE-EXCLUSION HEMOCYTOMETER PROCEDURE

The method consists of microscopically counting the number of cells in a very
small volume of cell suspension. The hemocytometer is a microscope slide with grids
on it to give nine large squares divided by triple lines (Fig. 4). Each large square
has an area of 1 mm^2. The depth of fluid in the slide chamber is 0.1 mm, and
therefore the total volume of fluid over each large square is

$$1 \times 1 \times 0.1 = 0.1 \text{ mm}^3 = 0.0001 \text{ cm}^3 = 0.0001 \text{ ml or } 10^{-4} \text{ ml}$$

Cells can also be counted in an electronic cell counter such as the Coulter counter
Model ZM.

Solutions

1. 0.4% *Trypan blue in HBSS*: Store at 4°C.

Steps

1. Cover the Neubauer chamber with a precision ground coverslip and press gently until Newton rings are visible. Place a drop of the cell suspension (usually diluted 1:5; 0.2 ml of cells plus 0.3 ml of HBSS and 0.5 ml of 0.4% Trypan blue) at the edge of the coverslip.

2. Place the chamber on the stage of an inverted microscope and count all the cells that exclude trypan blue in the four large squares in each corner of the central area (S_1–S_4) and in the square in the central area (S_5). Count cells touching the right and upper lines but not those touching the left and bottom lines. Nonviable cells absorb the dye and appear blue.

$$\text{Total number of viable cells/ml} = \frac{\text{cells in the five large squares}}{5} \times \text{dilution} \times 10^4$$

D. SUBCULTURING OF CONTINUOUS CELL LINES IN SUSPENSION

Cultured cells that grow continuously in suspension are subcultured by dilution. Here we illustrate the procedure using Molt-4 human leukemic cells, a continuous cell line that can be propagated indefinitely in suspension.

Solutions

Solutions are as described in Protocol B.

Steps

1. Remove a tissue culture flask with Molt-4 cells from the 37°C humidified 5% CO_2 incubator. Close the cap and stir gently. Flame the top of the flask and take a small aliquot in a plastic conical tube. Dilute if necessary and count in a hemocytometer (see Protocol C).

2. Take an aliquot from the original flask and dilute to appropriate cell concentration (5×10^4 to 1×10^5 cells/ml) with complete DMEM. Loosen the cap and place the flask standing up in the CO_2 incubator. Observe regularly. Shake gently and add additional medium if necessary.

E. FLUORESCENT PROCEDURE FOR DETECTING MYCOPLASMA

Solutions

1. *Acetic acid/methanol*: To make 900 ml, mix 300 ml of acetic acid with 600 ml of methanol.

2. *Hoechst 33258 stock (1 mg/ml)*: To make 10 ml, weigh 10 mg of Hoechst 33258 and add 10 ml of HBSS. Store at 4°C in the dark.

3. *Hoechst 33258 working solution (100 ng/ml in HBSS)*: To make 500 ml, take 50 μl of the Hoechst 33258 stock solution and add 500 ml of HBSS.

4. *Mounting medium (Gelvatol)*: Prepare as described in the article by Monika Herzog *et al.*

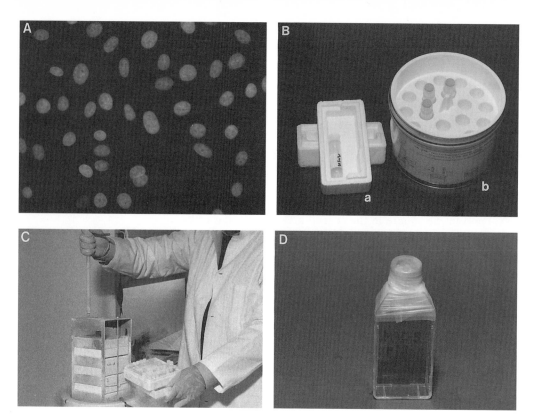

FIGURE 5 (A) Hoechst 33258 staining of AMA cells. (B) Expanded polystyrene container (a) and cryo freezing box (b) used for freezing cells. (C) Liquid nitrogen freezer to store frozen cells. (D) Tissue culture flask containing a monolayer of MRC-5 fibroblasts ready to be shipped.

Steps

1. Plate AMA cells on 12-mm glass coverslips placed in a 58-mm tissue culture dish containing 8 ml of complete DMEM. Wait until the cells reach about 65% confluence.

2. Rinse twice with HBSS.

3. Add HBSS diluted 1:1 with acetic acid/methanol (1:3). Rock the tissue culture dish and discard the solution.

4. Add acetic acid/methanol. Rock the tissue culture dish and discard the solution.

5. Add acetic acid/methanol. Leave for 10 min at room temperature.

6. Discard the acetic acid/methanol and wash twice with HBSS.

7. Add the Hoechst solution (100 ng/ml in HBSS) and leave for 10 min at room temperature. The solution should be disposed in accordance with the safety regulations enforced in your laboratory.

8. Rinse three times with HBSS. Pick up the coverslip with Dumont No. 5 forceps and place it cell side down on a glass slide containing a drop of mounting medium (Fig. 3F). Leave for 1 hr at 37°C or overnight at room temperature and observe in a fluorescence microscope using an appropriate filter. Hoechst 33258 excites at 360 nm and emits at 490–500 nm. Cells free of mycoplasms should stain only in the nucleus (Fig. 5A). Contaminated cells exhibit bright, punctated staining in the cytoplasm (not shown).

1. Cryopreservation

Solutions

1. *Fetal calf serum containing 10% glycerol:* To make 10 ml, mix 9 ml of fetal calf serum (FCS) and 1 ml of glycerol. Mix and filter-sterilize (0.2-μm filter). Dispense 3 ml of the mixture in sterile plastic tubes. Keep at $-20°C$.

Steps

1. Select a 75-cm^2 flask with cells (AMA or Molt-4 leukemic cells) in the logarithmic phase of growth and just approaching confluency. It may be necessary to renew the culture medium 24 hr before harvesting the cells.

2. Trypsinize and/or centrifuge the cells as described in Protocol B or D. Suspend the cells (pipette up and down) in complete DMEM at a concentration of 2×10^6 cells/ml. Check the cells for mycoplasm (see Protocol E).

3. Centrifuge to pellet the cells and resuspend at $5-6 \times 10^6$ cells/ml in FCS containing 10% glycerol.

4. Dispense the cell suspension in 1-ml aliquots into sterile cryoampoules. Tighten the screw cap and place in expanded polystyrene (Fig. 5B, a) or a cryo freezing container from Nalgene (Cat. No. 5100-001) (Fig. 5B, b). Follow the instructions from the manufacturer as to how to use the Nalgene cryo freezing container.

5. Place the expanded polystyrene container or the cryo freezing box with the ampoules at $-80°C$ for 24 hr. Ideally the temperature should decrease 1°C per minute.

6. Place the frozen ampoules in a labeled Nalgene cryobox and transfer to a vapor-phase liquid nitrogen freezer (Fig. 5C). Cells can be stored for many years. A temperature of $-80°C$ is not adequate for storing cell lines except for very short periods. It is important to keep many ampoules in reserve.

NOTE

Avoid injuries from frostbite or ruptured vials by wearing safety glasses and insulated gloves.

---

2. Thawing

Steps

1. Remove the ampoule from the liquid nitrogen freezer, loosen the cap, and immediately plunge the ampoule into water at 37°C until the liquid starts melting. Make sure that the cap does not touch the water.

2. Clean the ampoule all around with a tissue paper soaked with 70% ethanol.

3. Add the contents of the ampoule (still with ice) to 5 ml of complete DMEM medium kept at 4°C. Centrifuge in a bench centrifuge for 1–2 min at 300–400 *g* and resuspend the cells with 8 ml of complete DMEM at 37°C. Plate all the cells in a 25-cm^2 flask and place it in the 37°C humidified 5% CO_2 incubator. Change the medium after 2 hr, when most of the cells have attached.

4. Change the medium after 24 hr.

G. SENDING AND RECEIVING CULTURED CELLS

1. Frozen Ampoules

Frozen cryoampoules are sent in dry ice. Tighten the cap and place in a sealed plastic bag. On receipt, follow the procedure described under Protocol F.2.

2. Tissue Culture Flasks

Select tissue culture flasks containing sparse growing cells (monolayers or suspension cultures) and fill them to the top with fresh medium. Tighten the cap, flame, and wrap firmly with Parafilm (Fig. 5D). Place in a plastic bag and seal. Flasks should be well protected when shipping. You can use a latex glove as extra security. Place the sealed plastic bag with the flask into the glove and tie the cuff. On arrival place in a CO_2 incubator for 24 hr without removing the medium. If possible, place the cells in an incubator reserved for this purpose. After 24 hr remove the medium and replace with fresh medium.

IV. Comments

The simple procedures described here are applicable to many continuous cell lines. Detailed protocols for specialized cell types that require special conditions (media, matrix coated plates, growth factors, etc.) can be found in other articles in this volume.

A few basic procedures have not been included in this article because they are covered in other articles. These include cell cloning (see article by Barry R. Davies and Philip S. Rudland), growth in semisolid medium to assess anchorage independence (see article by G. R. Johnson), and autoradiography with [³H]thymidine (see article by Theresa Higgins and Enrique Rozengurt).

V. Pitfalls

1. If the cells do not grow, check the quality of the water and/or use a different batch of fetal calf serum.

2. If you share the laminar flow cabinet with other colleagues, make sure you have a strict procedure on how to leave the hood when finished.

3. To avoid contamination, remove all waste at the end of the day. Do not leave windows or doors open.

4. Clean the CO_2 incubator regularly. Check for any spills and wipe with

Diversol. Clean the water container and change the water at least once a week.

5. Check cultures periodically for mycoplasma.

REFERENCES

Adams, R. L. P. (1990) "Cell Culture for Biochemists. Laboratory Techniques in Biochemistry and Molecular Biology," 2nd rev. ed. Elsevier, Amsterdam.

Baserga, R. (1990) "Cell Growth and Division: A Practical Approach." IRL Press, Oxford.

Freshney, I. R. (1987) "Culture of Animal Cells: A Manual of Basic Technique," 2nd ed. A.R. Liss, New York.

Freshney, R. I. (1992) "Animal Cell Culture: A Practical Approach," 2nd ed. IRL Press, Oxford.

Jakoby, S., and Pastan, I. (eds.) (1979) "Methods in Enzymology," Vol. 58. Academic Press, New York.

Paul, J. (1975) "Cell and Tissue Culture," 5th ed. Livingston, Edinburgh.

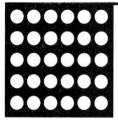

Development of Serum-Free Media and Methods for Optimization of Nutrient Composition

David W. Jayme and Dale F. Gruber

I. Introduction

The advantages of cultivating cells and tissues in completely defined nutrient medium were recognized more than 80 years ago. Realization of this objective, particularly for fastidious cell types, required development of more complex nutritional formulations and the discovery of the various growth and attachment factors required by cells in culture (Waymouth, 1984; Ham and McKeehan, 1979).

A curious paradox emerges from the use of serum as a culture additive. Animal sera, particularly fetal bovine serum, represent the most universal growth supplement for cell culture, yet no cell types actually grow in serum. Rather, most cultured cells grow in a highly specialized microenvironment which may be mimicked *in vitro* by diluting or eliminating serum and replacing it with a mixture of metabolic precursors, macromolecules, and biophysical elements (Ham, 1982; Bottenstein *et al.*, 1979). Recognition of the broad serum functions in cell culture is a fundamental prerequisite to the decision to eliminate serum. Failures frequently are traceable to inadvertent omission of medium constituents that substitute for serum functions. A review of serum functions is outside of the scope of this article, but has been provided elsewhere (Freshney, 1987; Jayme and Blackman, 1985).

There are, in fact, at least three general means for arriving at a serum-free culture environment: (1) replacing whole serum with serum or other humoral fluid fractions or with serum processed to remove certain undesirable constituents; (2) adapting or genetically modifying parental cells to reduce or eliminate their requirement for targeted serum factors; or (3) supplementing a basal serum-free formulation with cytokines, nutrients, and transport and adhesion factors required for the targeted cell function.

A useful exercise at the outset of developing a serum-free medium is analysis of your primary motivation (Jayme and Greenwold, 1991). Is it because serum is ill-defined and variable from lot-to-lot, so that you are uncertain of all factors that impact your culture environment? Are you concerned with cost and availability of serum additives that "work" in your system? Is your cell type unable to grow with serum supplementation because of overgrowth by contaminating fibroblasts or inhibitory or differentiation factors present in serum? Does serum contain elements that mask or inhibit a normal biological function you desire to study? Are you concerned with potential adventitious contaminants or degradative enzymes? Is your project exclusively a laboratory study or will its results ultimately be transferred to pilot or production-scale environments for diagnostic or biopharmaceutical applications? Results from this analysis lead the investigator along different paths toward development and optimization of serum-free culture medium (Jayme, 1991).

II. Materials and Instrumentation

The basic laboratory materials, equipment, and instrumentation for cell culture have been described elsewhere (Freshney, 1987). Several key issues critical to serum-free medium development are emphasized below.

A. BASAL MEDIUM

Efforts to design and validate an effective serum-free formulation are often thwarted by improper selection of the basal medium. In such situations, supplementation by serum and other variable factors provides an expensive alternative to using a nutritionally fortified basal medium. Basal formulations commonly employed for serum-free medium development, because of their ability to support both clonal growth and high-density culture, include Dulbecco's modified Eagle's medium (DMEM)/Ham's nutrient mixture F-12 (F-12) (1/1); Iscove's modified Dulbecco's medium (IMDM); and RDF medium (RPMI-1640/DMEM/F-12) (1/1/1).

B. BUFFERING REQUIREMENTS

Classical media were derived primarily from Earle's buffered salt solution, which contains sodium bicarbonate and relies on regulated $p\text{CO}_2$ to maintain constant pH. Alternative formulations use inorganic phosphate and the intrinsic buffering capacity of certain nutrients for pH buffering in the absence of supplemental atmospheric CO_2. Sulfonic acid esters and organophosphates with physiological pK values have been used in serum-free media, although their cytotoxicity and effect on cellular physiology may be amplified in the absence of serum.

C. WATER PURITY AND CONSISTENCY

Often underemphasized, water is the principal constituent of cell culture medium. Water source, treatment, and storage can critically affect serum-free cultures, by contributing trace metals, organic materials, and bacterial endotoxin. As these contaminants have different effects on various cultured cell types, useful guidelines are to follow recommendations for producing injectable-grade water, to produce water consistently using validated procedures, to confirm quality by periodic testing, and to use water within a few hours of processing. Even experts at medium formulation have been frustrated by variability in serum-free medium performance on relocation to a new facility using a different water source.

D. CHOICE OF CULTIVATION SYSTEM

A discussion of the variety and complexity of cell culture bioreactors, feeding strategies, and attachment matrices (if required) is beyond the scope of this work. A valuable consideration is to begin (or at least, refine) development of serum-free culture conditions with the end in mind. For example, if the ultimate objective is to cultivate an adherent cell line in a specialized, three-dimensional matrix, then nutrient requirements obtained from monolayer cultivation on a polystyrene dish may be erroneous. Similarly, if the goal is to maintain cells at high density to study biological function or harvest a biological product, then the serum-free medium developed based on growth from low-density inocula may be flawed. The cultivation system used for medium development should approximate the eventual test environment as closely as is practical.

III. Experimental Procedures

A. CULTURE ADAPTATION TO SERUM-FREE MEDIUM

Adaptation to serum-free medium may occur by at least three temporally independent phases: (1) synthesized or transported nutrients are used to produce metabolic energy and cellular regulatory factors; (2) regulated transport and metabolic pathways adjust activities to respond to the altered external environment; and (3) altered conditions select for or against preexisting mutant subpopulations with altered phenotype. It is critically important to screen the resultant cell population to ensure that the selection events do not result in loss of target cell function. There are key factors to observe in adapting established cells from serum-supplemented culture or adapting primary cells obtained by tissue dissociation.

Growth state of cellular inoculum
Cells to be adapted to serum-free medium should be harvested from cultures in exponential growth phase, preferably cells that were subcultured at a relatively low split ratio within the past 24–48 hr. Cell viability as determined by trypan blue exclusion must be at least 95% for best recovery results. Processes used to produce a monodisperse cell suspension from primary tissues, suspension aggregates, or monolayer cultures should be gentle to minimize cell disruption or degradation of externally oriented cell proteins.

Cellular inoculation density
To maximize paracrine feeding of cell-secreted factors that may have been omitted from your serum-free formulation or that are short-lived *in vitro*, it is advisable to inoculate cells at 2- to 10-fold higher densities than would be normally used for passage of an adapted culture.

Subcultivation techniques
The timing and method of subcultivation are critical to facilitate culture transition through adaptive crisis. Population doublings rather than elapsed time should dictate the appropriate time for medium replenishment, with optimal subculturing occurring in midlog phase. Use a procedure that minimizes mechanical stress, such as decanting spent medium and replenishing with fresh medium. Centrifugation, if required, should be at gentle speeds, minimizing the period of cell anoxia during pelleting. Cell suspension should be accomplished by gentle swirling in a mixture of conditioned and fresh culture media. If possible, adherent cells should be dislodged using divalent cation chelates (e.g., EDTA) rather than enzyme treatment or mechanical scraping.

Biophysical factors
Recognize that cells undergoing adaptation to a novel exogenous environment are more fragile and susceptible to mechanical disruption and environmental fluctuations. Ensure that pH and medium osmolality are carefully controlled throughout cultivation. Avoid exposure to light to minimize free radical generation and lipid peroxidation. Maximize gas diffusion in open atmospheric vessels by increasing the

surface:volume ratio. Culture adaptation in mobile bioreactors, such as stir tank and airlift fermenters, is not recommended due to mechanical agitation.

B. NUTRIENT OPTIMIZATION FOR CELLS ABLE TO GROW IN SERUM

General considerations in serum-free medium development are described else-where (Ham, 1982; Waymouth, 1984; Jayme and Blackman, 1985). Depending on your objectives, total serum elimination may not be required or even desirable. The guidelines described below may also be followed for serum reduction or for evalua-tion of alternate mammalian sera as substitutes for fetal bovine serum. Key steps toward development of a serum-free formulation for the desired cell type include the following:

1. Review published literature, scan commercial catalogs, and contact colleagues working with similar cell types to determine whether a suitable formulation may already exist.

2. Establish *in vitro* growth of the target cell type by any available means, including use of serum, organ extracts, etc., to serve as a reference control.

3. Subclone (where appropriate) using limiting dilution technique to ensure that medium development is performed on a stable, homogeneous cell population. Screen subclones for viability, target function(s), and absence of contaminants. Cryopreserve an adequate master seed stock for subsequent comparison.

4. Identify a minimal level of serum or other undefined additive supplementation that supports cell survival or slow proliferation for several (3–6) days in culture.

5. Using the minimal additive concentrations determined in step 4, determine the lowest cell inoculum that sustains culture survival or proliferation. For example, into duplicate 60-mm culture dishes containing 4 ml of supplemented medium, inoculate 10^3, 5×10^3, 10^4, 2.5×10^4, 5×10^4, 10^5, and 2×10^5 cells into each dish, incubate cultures for several days, and determine cell count. Reference performance relative to control plates containing the normal additive levels and cells inoculated at the normal seeding concentration.

6. Determine the qualitative elements of the basic serum-free medium, either using external suggestions obtained in step 1 or by assuming that many cells require insulin, transferrin, and an additional growth factor in serum-free culture. Two sets of control plates are required, one containing the reference additives and the other serum free, and all plates are inoculated at the optimal (minimum) cell count determined in the previous step. In addition to controls, plates should contain various combinations of insulin and transferrin with other common additives (suggested initial concentrations are given in parentheses), such as insulin (5 μg/ml), transferrin (5 μg/ml), epidermal growth factor (EGF, 10 ng/ml), fibroblast growth factor (FGF, 50 ng/ml), hydrocortisone (10^{-8} M), progesterone (10^{-8} M), triiodothyronine (10^{-11} M), sodium selenite (2×10^{-8} M), putrescine (100 ng/ml), and trace element mixtures (recommended dilution). After culture incubation for 4–5 days, quantitate test cultures relative to controls and determine the combination of factors supporting optimal growth stimulation.

7. Refine the qualitative serum-free formulation derived from step 6 by determining a dose–response relationship for each factor over several logs of additive supplementation.

8. Examine the proposed optimized serum-free formulation by passaging target

---

cells for multiple generations to ascertain persistent growth rate and to evaluate target biological functions in cells maintained in serum-free culture. If cells are proliferating at near-normal (or perhaps, superior) rates relative to controls and if biological function is acceptable, cryopreserve an adequate working bank of cells adapted to serum-free cultivation conditions by addition of 9–10% (v/v) DMSO to monodisperse suspensions of log-phase cultures.

IV. Comments

A. NUTRIENT OPTIMIZATION FACILITATED BY SPENT MEDIUM ANALYSIS

Nutrient clearance by high-density cultures used for biological production and cellular therapy applications may differ both quantitatively and qualitatively from nutritional requirements of comparable cultures maintained at low density. Determination of component exhaustion kinetics by quantitative analysis of spent medium can yield valuable information regarding metabolite reduction or enrichment to optimize culture productivity. Nutrient modifications derived from iterative analysis, resulting in either formulation adjustment or addition of concentrated nutrient supplements, have resulted in enhanced bioreactor longevity and specific productivity (Jayme, 1991).

B. ALTERATIONS REQUIRED TO OPTIMIZE MEDIUM FOR ADHERENT CELLS

Various attachment matrices are commercially available that vary with respect to charge density, curvature radius, surface coating, cost, scalability, etc. Many adherent cell types can deposit complex extracellular matrices, using exogenous attachment factors and synthesized glycosaminoglycans. Some attachment-promoting factors may be included in culture medium, although they pose solubility and stability challenges and tend to adsorb to container surfaces. Other factors may be cytotoxic and require aseptic precoating procedures prior to cell inoculation. Many attachment factors are contributed to the culture environment by serum: cell cultivation in the total absence of serum requires approaches similar to those described above in developing serum-free medium, using available attachment factors individually and in combination to determine the optimal mixture for the target cell type and proposed substratum. For circumstances permitting limited serum addition, precoating of substratum surfaces with serum, reduced serum supplementation in conjunction with a fortified medium, or serum addition during cellular attachment with nutrient-replenishing, serum-free feeds may be beneficial options.

C. MISCELLANEOUS COMMENTS

To develop the ideal nutrient formulation, it is necessary to identify an endpoint assay, such as cell growth or product biosynthesis, for comparative purposes. It is important, however, to differentiate between "optimization" and "maximization," as the nutrient combination that stimulates most rapid proliferation may not necessarily sustain normal cellular function or maximize product yield. The optimal nutrient mixture may actually support slightly diminished proliferation while sustaining superior overall cellular functionality.

Similarities often exist between the nutritional requirements of established cell lines and primary cells obtained from similar source material. However, significant quantitative variation in exogenous medium requirements may be observed in cells derived from analogous tissues of dissimilar species. Major qualitative differences in serum-free medium composition exist among cells derived from different organs or tissues obtained from the identical species or even the same donor.

V. Pitfalls

Serum supplementation provides a broad nutritional umbrella, allowing nearly universal support of cell proliferation. Serum-free media provide significant advantages for many culture systems, but require some sacrifice in breadth of use, component stability, and culture system durability.

A. MEDIUM

Stability of medium components
Unlike classical media, which have validated a shelf-life of 1–3 years, serum-free media typically contain labile constituents prone to inactivation with prolonged storage. A formulation supporting "optimal" cell function that requires daily preparation from frozen or lyophilized stock solutions may be useful at the laboratory scale, but would be unacceptable for bioindustrial applications. Certain key components may be removed from solution through nonspecific adsorption to sterilizing filters or to vessel walls. Low protein and lipid-binding filters and plastic containers with minimally required surface area are recommended.

Cost
The cost per liter of culture medium is a factor of variable weight, depending on the primary motivation for eliminating serum. Total elimination of serum generally requires supplementation of basal medium with expensive raw materials, frequently resulting in a more costly nutrient solution. The additional cost may be justified based on reduced regulatory concerns, elimination of serum-associated artifacts, or improved downstream product recovery. In other circumstances, however, considerable cost savings may be realized by partial reduction in serum supplementation permitted by growth factor addition to the basal formulation.

Definition/standardization of raw materials
Unlike the constituents of classical medium formulations which have compendial specifications for pharmaceutical use, many growth and attachment additives frequently used as components of serum-free media remain unstandardized. Some factors are quantitated based on protein content, whereas others provide units of activity based on bioassay performance. Although the percentage purity is often reported, there may be substantial variation among suppliers regarding impurities. Some so-called serum-free media contain substantial quantities of ill-defined serum fractions or organ extracts, which exhibit lot-to-lot variability in biochemical composition and biological performance.

B. CULTURE SYSTEM

Sensitivity to environmental changes
Cells cultivated in serum-free medium are exquisitely sensitive to fluctuations in the exogenous environment which may be mitigated in serum-supplemented medium. Drifts in extracellular pH and medium osmolality due to generation of metabolic acids and other by-products can irreversibly damage serum-free cultures. Pro-

phylactic antibiotic supplements may need recalibration to avoid cytotoxicity. Termination of enzymatic dissociation of cell monolayers by addition of specific inhibitors may be required to prevent excessive damage to cell surface proteins under serum-free culture conditions.

Deterioration of cellular function with passaging

Cultures converted from serum-supplemented conditions may appear adapted to serum-free medium during initial cultivation; however, proliferative rate or biological function may deteriorate with multiple passages. Adsorbed serum factors carried over during subculturing despite buffer washes and secretion of endogenously synthesized cytokines may still support proliferation for the initial culture period. After sequential culture amplification and dilution of carryover effects from the previous culture environment, nutritional deficiencies in the serum-free medium become apparent and the culture becomes unable to thrive without further supplementation.

REFERENCES

Bottenstein, J., Hayashi, I., Hutchings, S., Masui, H., Mather, J., McClure, D. B., Ohasa, S., Rizzino, A., Sato, G., Serrero, G., Wolfe, R., and Wu, R. (1979) The growth of cells in serum-free hormone-supplemented media. In "Methods in Enzymology" W. B. Jakoby and I. H. Pastan, eds.), Vol. 58, pp. 94–109. Academic Press, New York.

Freshney, R. I. (1987) "Culture of Animal Cells: A Manual of Basic Technique," 2nd ed. Alan R. Liss, New York.

Ham, R. G. (1982) Importance of the basal nutrient medium in the design of hormonally defined media. In "Growth of Cells in Hormonally Defined Media" (G. H. Sato, A. B. Pardee, and D. A. Sirbasku, eds.), pp. 39–60. Cold Spring Harbor Laboratory, Cold Spring Harbor, NY.

Ham, R. G., and McKeehan, W. L. (1979) Media and growth requirements. In "Methods in Enzymology" (W. B. Jakoby and I. H. Pastan, eds.), Vol. 58, pp. 44–93. Academic Press, New York.

Jayme, D. W. (1991) Nutrient optimization for high density biological production applications. Cytotechnology 5, 15–30.

Jayme, D. W., and Blackman, K. E. (1985) Review of culture media for propagation of mammalian cells, viruses and other biologicals. In "Advances in Biotechnological Processes" (A. Mizrahi and A. L. van Wezel, eds.), Vol. 5, pp. 1–30. Alan R. Liss, New York.

Jayme, D. W., and Greenwold, D. J. (1991) Media selection and design: Wise choices and common mistakes. Bio/Technology 9, 716–721.

Waymouth, C. (1984) Preparation and use of serum-free culture media. In "Methods for Preparation of Media, Supplements, and Substrata for Serum-Free Animal Cell Culture," Chap. 2, pp. 23–68. Alan R. Liss, New York.

Testing Cell Cultures for Microbial and Viral Contaminants

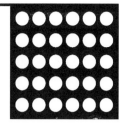

Robert J. Hay

I. Introduction

The presence of microbial contaminants—bacteria, fungi, mycoplasma, or protozoa—in cell cultures seriously compromises virtually all research or production work involving culture technology. Although many contamination events are overt and readily apparent to the responsible investigator, others are insidious and more difficult to detect. Similarly, viral infection may be obvious if cytopathogenesis is effected, but many viruses do not induce such drastic alteration in host cells and some are present in latent forms.

This article provides representative test protocols suitable for detecting most microbes and many viruses that might be expected in cell culture systems. The perspective is that of staff operating a national cell culture repository.

II. Materials

The following media and reagents were obtained from Difco: Bacto Sabouraud dextrose-broth, dehydrated (Catalog No. 0382-1); Bacto fluid thioglycollate medium, dehydrated (Catalog No. 0256-01); beef extract (Catalog No. 0131); brain–heart infusion broth (Catalog No. 0037-01-6); neopeptone (Catalog No. B119); proteose peptone (Catalog No. 3); YM broth (Catalog No. 0711-01); nutrient broth (Catalog No. 003-01); Bacto yeast extract (Catalog No. 0127-01); trypsin, 1:250 Difco certified (Catalog No. 0152-15); blood agar base (Catalog No. 0045-01). Trypticase soy broth powder (Catalog No. 01-162) and trypticase (Catalog No. B11770) were obtained from Becton Dickinson Microbiology Systems (formerly BBL). Fresh defibrinated rabbit blood (Catalog No. 82-8614) and sheep blood were obtained from Editek, and North American Biologicals provided Diamond's TP-S-1 broth base powder (Catalog No. 73-9502) and Diamond's TP-S-1 vitamin solution (40×, Catalog No. 72-2315). Cell culture media (various) and sera were obtained from Sigma, Gibco, BRL, or Hyclone.

Template-primers poly(rA)·poly(dT)$_{12-18}$ (Catalog No. 7878) and poly(dA)·poly(dT)$_{12-18}$ (Catalog No. 7868) were obtained from P-L Biochemicals, and [methyl-^{3}H]thymidine triphosphate ([^{3}H]TTP, carrier-free, specific activity 50–60 Ci/mmole, 1.0 mCi/ml, Catalog No. NET 221-X) was from Dupont New England Nuclear. Scintillation counter fluid (Betafluor, Catalog No. LS-151) was purchased from National Diagnostics.

Sigma, VWR, Fisher, or Thomas supplied general laboratory chemicals and solvents plus such items as instruments and bacteriological or cell culture glass- and plasticware.

The following specialty items were required: Leighton tubes (Catalog No. 3393) from CoStar; cellulose filters, 0.45 and 0.22 μm (Catalog Nos. HATF 14250 and GSTF 14250, respectively) from Millipore; GasPak anaerobic systems (Catalog No. 60465) from Becton Dickinson Microbiology Systems; embryonated chicken eggs from SPAFAS; egg candlers (Catalog No. C6372N-50001) from Nasco; egg drills, cutters, and moto tool (Catalog No. 9826-00) from Cole–Parmer; stainless-steel sterilizing pans (Catalog No. 2065-5) from Orem; adjustable microliter pipets, Pipetman (Catalog No. P-20 D/P-200D) from Rainin. Reference microbes, cell lines, and viruses were obtained from the American Type Culture Collection (ATCC): *Pseudomonas aeruginosa* (e.g., ATCC 14502), *Micrococcus salivarious* (e.g., ATCC 14344), *Escherichia coli* (e.g., ATCC 4157), *Bacteroides distasonis* (e.g., ATCC 8503), *Penicillium notatum* (e.g., ATCC 8537), *Aspergillus niger* (e.g., ATCC 34467), *Candida albicans* (e.g., ATCC 10231), influenza virus (e.g., (ATCC VR-95 or VR-810), Newcastle disease virus (e.g., ATCC VR-108 or VR-109), Rous sarcoma virus (e.g., ATCC VR-140 or VR-724).

III. Procedures

A. BACTERIA AND FUNGI

Tests for sterility are performed routinely at ATCC on all culture media used, on cultures submitted from the community, on cultures at various stages during the accessioning process, and on all seed and distribution freezes. *Pseudomonas* species, micrococci, and *E. coli* are common bacterial isolates, whereas *Penicillium, Aspergillus,* and *Candida* species are common fungal contaminants.

1. Preparation of Media

Solutions

1. *Sabouraud dextrose broth:* Dissolve 30 g dehydrated powder in 1000 ml distilled water and dispense 10-ml aliquots into each of one hundred 16 × 150-mm test tubes. Cap each tube loosely and sterilize in an autoclave for 15 min at 15 lb pressure (121°C) on slow exhaust. After removing the tubes from the autoclave, press down caps securely and store at room temperature until used.

2. *Nutrient broth with 2% yeast extract:* Dissolve 8 g of nutrient broth powder plus 20 g of Bacto yeast extract in 1000 ml distilled water and dispense 10-ml aliquots into each of one hundred 16 × 150-mm test tubes. Cap each tube loosely, sterilize, and store as described for solution 1.

3. *Thioglycollate medium:* Suspend 29.8 g dehydrated powder in 1000 ml distilled water in a 3-liter flask and heat to boiling to dissolve the powder completely. Dispense 10-ml aliquots of the thioglycollate medium into each of one hundred 16 × 150-mm test tubes; cap each tube loosely. Sterilize in the autoclave as described for solution 1. After removing the tubes from the autoclave, press down caps securely and store in the dark at room temperature. This medium changes color in processing. As it dissolves it turns red or gold depending on the amount of dissolved oxygen. After autoclaving it is clear and gold in color, like nutrient broth. After cooling, the top layer of medium oxidizes and the indicator in the upper portion of the tube turns pink or red. The fluid should not be used if the indicator has changed to a red color in the lower third of the tube.

4. *Trypticase soy broth:* Suspend 30 g powder in 1000 ml distilled water and mix thoroughly and warm gently until solution is complete. Dispense 10-ml aliquots of the trypticase soy broth into each of one hundred 16 × 150-mm test tubes; cap each tube loosely and sterilize and store as described for solution 1.

5. *Brain–heart infusion (BHI) broth:* Suspend 37 g powder in 1000 ml of distilled water, dissolve completely, and dispense 10-ml aliquots of BHI into 16 × 150-mm test tubes. Cap each tube loosely. Sterilize in the autoclave for 15 min at 15 lb pressure on slow exhaust. After autoclaving, press down caps securely, cool, and store at 4°C.

6. *YM broth:* Dissolve 21 g powder in 1000 ml distilled water and dispense 10-ml aliquots of the broth into each of one hundred 16 × 150-mm test tubes; cap each tube loosely. Sterilize and store as described for solution 1.

7. *Blood agar plates:* Suspend 40 g blood agar base in 950 ml cold distilled water and heat to boiling to dissolve the powder completely. Sterilize in the autoclave for 15 min at 15 lb pressure on slow exhaust. When the sterile blood agar base is cooled to 50°C, add 5% (50 ml) of pretested, fresh, defibrinated rabbit blood and mix by swirling. Dispense aseptically to 9-cm plates and store at 4°C. The rabbit blood is pretested for sterility by inoculating 0.5-ml aliquots into BHI broth and YM broth and onto blood agar base plates with subsequent incubation at 25 and 37°C. Negative results in 48 to 72 hr are usually sufficient to permit use of the tested fluid.

2. Examination

Steps

1. Using an inverted microscope, equipped with phase-contrast optics if possible, examine cell culture vessels individually. Scrutiny should be especially vigorous in cases in which large-scale production is involved.

2. Check each culture first using low power. After moving the cultures to a suitable isolated area, remove aliquots of fluid from cultures that are suspect; retain these for further examination. Alternatively, autoclave and discard all such cultures.

3. Prepare wet mounts using drops of the test fluids and observe under high power.

4. Prepare smears, heat-fix, and stain by any conventional method using filtered solutions.

5. Examine under oil immersion for microbial contaminants.

6. Consult Fogh (1973) for further details.

3. Inoculation and Incubation of Test Samples

Steps

1. After cryopreserving stocks of cells (Hay, 1992), retrieve and thaw about 5% of the ampoules from liquid nitrogen or vapor storage. Pool and mix the contents of the ampoules from each cryopreserved lot using a sterile 1-ml disposable pipette. It is recommended that antibiotics not be included in media used to prepare stocks of cells for preservation. If antibiotics are used, the pooled suspension (step 3 above) should be centrifuged at 2000 *g* for 20 min and the pellet should be resuspended in antibiotic-free medium. A series of three such washes with antibiotic-free medium prior to testing eliminate traces of antibiotics that would obscure contamination in some cases.

TABLE I Suggested Regimen for Detecting Bacterial or Fungal Contamination

Test Medium	Temperature (°C)	Gas phase	Observation time (days)
Blood agar with fresh defibrinated rabbit blood (5%)	37	Aerobic	14
	37	Anaerobic	14
Thioglycollate broth	37	Aerobic	14
	26		
Trypticase soy broth	37	Aerobic	14
	26		
Brain–heart infusion broth	37	Aerobic	14
	26		
Sabouraud broth	37	Aerobic	21
	26		
YM broth	37	Aerobic	21
	26		
Nutrient broth with 2% yeast extract	37	Aerobic	21

2. From each pool, inoculate each of the following with a minimum of 0.3 ml of the test cell suspension: (a) two blood agar plates, (b) two tubes of thioglycollate broth, (c) two tubes of trypticase soy broth, (d) two tubes of BHI broth, (e) two tubes of Sabouraud broth, (f) two tubes of YM broth, (g) two tubes of nutrient broth with 2% yeast extract.

3. Incubate test plates and broths as follows: (a) Prepare blood agar plates— one at 37°C under aerobic conditions and one at 37°C anaerobically (a BBL Gaspak anaerobic system is convenient for the latter). (b) Prepare tubes of thioglycollate broth, trypticase soy broth, BHI broth, Sabouraud broth, YM broth, and nutrient broth with yeast extract—one at 37°C and one at 26°C under aerobic conditions. (c) Incubate and examine periodically for 14 days the tubes of thioglycollate, trypticase soy broth, BHI broth, and blood agar plates. (d) Observe the tubes of Sabouraud broth, YM broth, and nutrient broth with yeast extract for 21 days before concluding that the test is negative. Contamination is indicated if colonies appear on solid media or if any of the liquid media become turbid.

4. Repeat any components of the test series that are positive initially to confirm the presence of a contaminant.

5. Autoclave and discard any contaminated cultures or ampule lots.

Comments

Of the seven media employed, trypticase soy, BHI, blood agar, and thioglycollate are suitable for detecting a wide range of bacterial contaminants. Sabouraud broth, YM broth, and nutrient broth with yeast extract will support growth of fungal contaminants. Stock media and incubation conditions used can be tested with the following ATCC control strains: *Pseudomonas aeruginosa, Micrococcus salivarius, Escherichia coli, Bacteroides distasonis, Penicillium notatum, Aspergillus niger, Candida albicans*. Table I summarizes this recommended test regimen.

Pitfalls

Although this test regimen permits detection of most common bacterial and fungal organisms that grow in cell cultures, we have noted at least one very fastidious bacterial strain that initially escaped observation. This was present in nine different cultures from a single clinical laboratory in the United States submitted for testing and expansion under a government contract. The organism grew extremely slowly but could be detected after 3 weeks of incubation with cell cultures that had no antibiotics and had no fluid changes. Samples so developed were inoculated into sheep blood agar plates and New York City broth (ATCC medium 1685). The organism could be observed during a subsequent 6-week incubation period at 37°C.

The Bacteriology Department at ATCC determined the appropriate culture conditions for this microorganism and tentatively identified it as a *Corynebacterium*. Antibiotic sensitivity tests revealed bacteriostasis with some compounds but no bactericidal antibiotics have yet been found.

This incident emphasizes the critical importance of diligent testing of cell cultures for contaminant microorganisms. By combining protocols such as those described here with procedures discussed elsewhere (e.g., fluorescent or nucleic acid probes for mycoplasma and viruses) one can be more certain that clean cell cultures are available for experimentation.

B. MYCOPLASMA

Mycoplasmal contamination of cell cultures has been established as a common occurrence that is capable of altering normal cell structure and function. Mycoplasmas have been shown to inhibit cell metabolism and growth, alter nucleic acid synthesis, affect cell antigenicity, induce chromosomal alterations, interfere with virus replication, and mimic viral actions. Basically, the growth of mycoplasma in cell cultures can be detected either by a direct microbiological agar culture procedure or by indirect procedures using staining, biochemical methods, or nucleic acid hybridization techniques (Hay *et al.*, 1989). The excellent Hoechst staining method is described in the article by Ariana Celis and Julio E. Celis.

Duplicate screening techniques such as Hoechst staining plus direct culture trials are generally recommended for rigorous cell line testing. Alternative methods include nucleic acid hybridization and a new technique involving the polymerase chain reaction. Details are available elsewhere (Hay, 1992; Hay *et al.*, 1989, 1992; Harasawa *et al.*, 1993).

C. PROTOZOA

The overall frequency of infection of cell cultures with protozoans is low but the incidence may be higher if one is working with tissues such as human clinical material and monkey kidney or colon. The small limax amoebae belonging to the *Acanthamoeba* (or *Hartmanella*) genus are ubiquitous in nature, and have been isolated from cells and tissues in culture in a significant number of laboratories. Jahnes *et al.* (1957) first reported spontaneous contamination of monkey kidney cells in culture by such free-living amoebae. The organisms also have been detected as occasional contaminants in such diverse cell lines as dog lymphosarcoma (LS30), HeLa, chick embryo fibroblast-like, and Chang liver cells (Holmgren, 1973). In some cases protozoans are demonstrably cytopathic in cell culture (Willaert *et al.*, 1978).

Observation, cytological examination, and attempts at isolation are required in the detection of protozoan contaminants. These techniques are suitable for detection of many of the most common flagellates and amoeboid protozoans including species of the genera *Acanthamoeba*, *Giardia*, *Leishmania*, *Naegleria*, and *Trypanosoma*. (See Dilworth *et al.*, 1979, and Hay *et al.*, 1992, for more detail.)

---

1. Preparation of Solutions and Protozoan Media

Steps

1. *Trypsin–EDTA:* Combine 2.5 g trypsin (1:250 Difco certified), 0.3 g EDTA, 0.4 g KCl, 8.0 g NaCl, 1.0 g glucose, 0.58 g NaHCO$_3$, and 0.01 g phenol red in 1 liter double-distilled water, sterilize by filtration (0.22-μm Millipore filter), and store at $-40°$C.

2. *Hanks' balanced salt solution without divalent cations:* Combine 8.0 g NaCl, 0.4 g KCl, 0.05 g Na$_2$HPO$_4$, 0.06 g KH$_2$PO$_4$, and 0.02 g phenol red in 50 ml double-distilled water to dissolve chemicals; then bring volume to 100 ml. Autoclave on slow exhaust for 15 min, adjust pH to 7.2 to 7.4 with sterile 0.4 N NaOH, and store at 4°C.

3. *Giemsa stock solution:* For stock solution of stain, combine 40 ml glycerol, 65 ml absolute methanol, and 1.0 g Giemsa powder. Filter two or three times and store at 4°C.

4. *Price's buffer (10$\times$):* Combine 6.0 g Na$_2$HPO$_4$, 5.0 g KH$_2$PO$_4$, and 1.0 liter distilled water. Before use dilute buffer with distilled water to 1$\times$.

5. *Price's Giemsa stain:* Dilute Giemsa stain stock 3:97 with 1$\times$ buffer. After staining, discard unused portion.

6. *ATCC medium No. 400, Diamond's TP-S-1 medium for axenic cultivation of Entamoeba (ATCC medium No. 400):* Dissolve one packet of Diamond's TP-S-1 broth base powder in 875 ml distilled water, adjust pH to 7.0 with 0.4 N NaOH, and filter through Whatman No. 1 paper. Sterilize at 120°C for 15 min. Aseptically add 100 ml inactivated (56°C for 30 min) bovine serum and 25 ml Diamond's TP-S-1 vitamin solution (40$\times$, North American Biologicals), and aseptically dispense 13 ml per sterile test tube. Some commercial lots of Diamond's TP-S-1 medium have been shown to be toxic to *Entamoeba*. To test for toxicity, subculture a culture of *Entamoeba* through three to five passages.

7. *Locke's solution:* Combine 8.0 g NaCl, 0.2 g NaCl, 0.2 CaCl$_2$, 0.3 g KH$_2$PO$_4$, 2.5 glucose, and 1.0 liter distilled water, and autoclave the solution for 20 min at 121°C.

8. *Diphasic blood agar medium (ATCC medium No. 1011):* Infuse 25.0 g beef extract in 250 ml distilled water by bringing to a rapid boil for 2 to 3 min while stirring constantly. Filter through Whatman No. 2 filter paper and add 10.0 g Difco neopeptone, 2.5 g NaCl, and 10.0 g agar. Heat to boiling and filter through Whatman No. 2 paper, make up volume to 500 ml with distilled water, and adjust pH to 7.2 to 7.4. Autoclave for 20 min at 121°C, cool mixture to 50°C, aseptically add 30% sterile, defibrinated rabbit blood (Editek) to whole mixture, and dispense in sterile tubes and slant. After the slants have set, cover with 3.0 ml sterile Locke's solution.

9. *PYb medium (ATCC medium No. 711):* Combine 1.0 g Difco proteose peptone, 1.0 g yeast extract, 20.0 g agar, and 900.0 ml distilled water. Prepare and sterilize separately each of the following stock solutions, and add to the basal medium as indicated below to avoid precipitation: CaCl$_2$ (0.05 M), 4.0 ml; MgSO$_4$·7H$_2$O (0.4 M), 2.5 ml; Na$_2$HPO$_4$ (0.25 M), 8.0 ml; KH$_2$PO$_4$ (0.25 M), 32 ml. Make the volume to 1 liter, check that the pH is at 6.5, and sterilize by autoclaving for 25 min at 120°C. Pour into petri dishes and allow to solidify.

10. *Brain–heart infusion blood agar (ATCC medium No. 807):* For the agar component, dissolve 37.0 g Difco BHI broth and 18.0 g agar in 1 liter boiling water. Dispense 5.0 ml solution per tube (16 $\times$ 125 mm) and sterilize for 25 min at 121°C. Cool to 48°C. Add 0.5 ml per tube of sterile, defibrinated rabbit blood and slant. After slants have set, cover with 0.5 ml BHI broth (1.0 liter distilled

water and 37.0 g BHI broth with sterilization by autoclave at 121°C for 25 minutes.

11. *Leishmania medium (ATCC medium No. 811):* Combine 1.2 g sodium citrate, 1.0 g NaCl, and 90.0 ml distilled water. Dispense 1.0 ml per tube, autoclave 25 min at 121°C, and cool. Add 1.0 ml defibrinated, lysed rabbit blood solution (prepare by mixing equal parts of whole rabbit blood and sterile distilled water and freezing and thawing twice).

12. *NTYG medium (ATCC medium No. 935):* Combine 5.0 g trypticase, 5.0 g yeast extract, 10.0 g glucose, and 1.0 liter distilled water. Dispense 10.0 ml per test tube and sterilize. Just before use, add 0.2 ml dialyzed, heat-activated bovine serum and 0.1 ml defibrinated sheep blood. Protozoan growth media retain stability for at least 3 months if maintained at 4°C, with the exception of ATCC medium 400 which maintains stability for 2 to 4 weeks.

2. Preparation of Cell Culture Samples for Inoculation into Protozoan Media

Steps

1. Rapidly thaw a frozen ampoule of the sample in a water bath at 37°C.

2. Aseptically open the ampoule. Continue to use sterile techniques.

3. Transfer 0.8 ml of the concentrated cell suspension from the ampoule into a T-25 flask. Save 0.2 ml of the suspension for Giemsa staining (below).

4. Add 7 ml of the appropriate cell culture medium to maintain the culture.

5. Incubate at 37°C until the monolayer becomes confluent (3 to 5 days depending on the cell line). Examine the culture microscopically during this incubation period for the presence of (a) movement (i.e., motile cells), (b) intracellular contaminants, and (c) cytopathology.

6. Transfer the supernate from the confluent test cell culture to a sterile 15-ml plastic centrifuge tube and retain at room temperature for use in step 12.

7. Rinse the cell monolayer (T-25 flask, step 1d) with 5 ml Ca^{2+}- and Mg^{2+}-free Hanks' saline and discard saline solution.

8. Add 2 ml 0.25% trypsin–EDTA solution to the T-25 flask and incubate at 37°C for 10 min.

9. Add 7 ml of cell culture medium to the T-25 flask and aspirate gently to obtain a single-cell suspension.

10. Dispense aliquots (0.5 ml) of the trypsinized single-cell suspension to the following ATCC protozoan growth media: (a) ATCC medium No. 400 (for *Entamoeba,* Giardia); (b) ATCC medium No. 711 with *Enterobacter aerogenes* (for *Acanthamoeba*) [use a wire loop to streak medium No. 711 with *Enterobacter aerogenes* (ATCC 15038) 48 hr before use]; (c) ATCC medium Nos. 807, 811, and 1011 (for trypanosomatids); (d) ATCC medium No. 935 (for *Naegleria*).

11. Incubate samples for 7 to 10 days at 35°C and examine microscopically for the presence of flagellate, cyst, and trophozoite forms of protozoa.

12. Prepare five wet mounts for each test cell monolayer using the supernate collected in step 6. Examine microscopically with phase contrast for the presence of motile and nonmotile protozoans.

3. Preparation of Culture Cells for Giemsa Staining

Steps

1. Aseptically add 1.5 ml of the appropriate culture medium to a sterile Leighton tube containing a coverslip.

2. Dispense 0.2 ml of the original cell suspension (sample preparation above) into the Leighton tube and incubate at 37°C until the culture is confluent.

3. Remove the coverslip from the Leighton tube, fix with absolute methanol for 1 min, and air-dry.

4. Stain for 10 min with Price's Giemsa, rinse with tap water, and mount the coverslip to a glass slide using Aquamount.

5. Examine the slide; use low power (20×) for scanning and high power (100×) for close examination.

Controls

It is recommended that positive controls be included. For example, if cultured cells of the upper respiratory tract are being used, *Acanthamoeba castellanii* (ATCC 30010) or *Naegleria lovaniensis* (ATCC 30569) can be used as positive controls. *A. castellanii* was isolated from human clinical material (Willaert *et al.*, 1978). *N. lovaniensis* strain TS, another nonpathogenic strain of amoebae, was isolated from a Vero cell culture at passage 120. *Entamoeba histolytica* (ATCC 30042), the common pathogen causing amoebic dysentery, or the nonpathogenic *Entamoeba invadens* (ATCC 30020) can be used for positive controls if cells are being isolated from the intestinal tract. *E. histolytica* is a human isolate, and *E. invadens* strain PZ is a snake isolate (Dilworth *et al.*, 1979).

Comments

The methods described are suitable for the detection of most common protozoan genera (i.e., limax amoebae) that could survive in association with cells in culture. Because cysts and trophozoites closely resemble damaged tissue cells, their presence as occasional contaminants can remain unnoticed. On the other hand, cells in cultures productively infected with amoebae of the genus *Acanthamoeba* frequently become granular and gradually progress to complete disintegration. The time elapsed depends on the inoculum size and whether cysts or the motile trophozoites predominate in the inoculum. The cytopathic effect of amoebic contaminants has been reported, and in some cases the responsible agent has been mistakenly identified s viral in origin (Willaert *et al.*, 1978). Therefore, frequent observation of the cell culture is particularly stressed when examining for parasitic protozoan contaminants.

The possible presence of other genera (i.e., *Entamoeba* or trypanosomatids) should be considered not only in experimental studies involving primary tissues but also with work requiring development or utilization of cell lines. The only known case of an isolation other then an amoeboid protozoan occurred in the isolation of a trypanosomatid from liver tissue (R. B. McGhee, personal communication).

The particular animal and tissue employed provide valuable clues as to the type of protozoan contaminant and determine the specific media and staining procedures required.

D. VIRUSES

Of the various tests applied for detection of adventitious agents associated with cultured cells, those for endogenous and contaminant viruses are the most problem-

TABLE II Representative Viruses of Special Concern
in Cell Production Work

Human	Other
Human immunodeficiency viruses	Hantavirus
Human T-cell leukemia viruses	Lymphocytic choriomeningitis virus
Other endogenous retroviruses	Ectromelia virus
Hepatitis viruses	Murine hepatitis
Human herpesvirus 6	Simian viruses
Cytomegalovirus	Sendai virus
Human papillomavirus	Avian leukosis virus
Epstein–Barr virus	Bovine viral diarrhea virus

atical. Table II lists representative problem viruses. Development of an overt and characteristic cytopathogenic effect (CPE) will certainly provide an early indication of viral contamination; however, the absence of a CPE definitely does not indicate that the culture is virus free. In fact, persistent or latent infections may exist in cell lines and remain undetected until the appropriate immunological, cytological, ultrastructural, and/or biochemical tests are applied (Docherty and Chopan, 1974; Friedman and Ramseur, 1979; Temin, 1974). Unfortunately, separate tests are necessary for each class of virus and for specific viruses. Additional host systems or manipulations, for example, treatment with halogenated nucleosides, may be required for virus activation and isolation (Aaronson et al., 1971). Common screening methods or tests for specific virus classes are listed in Table III.

Without such screens, latent viruses and viruses that do not produce an overt CPE or hemadsorption will escape detection. Some of these could be potentially dangerous for the cell culture technician. For example, Hantaan virus, the causative agent of Korean hemorrhagic fever, replicates in tumor and other cell lines. Outbreaks of the disease in individuals exposed to infected colonies of laboratory rats have been reported separately in five countries. An incident of transmission during passage of a cell line was confirmed in Belgium. As a result of these findings, cell lines expanded in this laboratory were screened using an indirect immunofluorescent antibody assay (LeDuc et al., 1985) and were found to be negative.

Substantial concern over laboratory transmission of the human immunodeficiency viruses is also evident. Cases of probable infection during processing in U.S. laboratories have been described; one, for example, was presumed due to parenteral exposure and another to work with highly concentrated preparations (Weiss et al., 1988). In the latter circumstance, strict adherence to Biosafety Level 3 containment and practices is essential. More detailed discussion of safety precautions for work with cell lines in general is provided elsewhere (Caputo, 1988).

ATCC cell lines from selected groups have been screened for HIV-1 using polymerase chain reaction (PCR) amplification followed by a slot-blot test for envelope and GAG sequences (Ou et al., 1988). The oligonucleotide primer pairs SK 38/39 and SK 68/69 plus SK 19 or SK 70 probes were used. Human cell lines of T-cell, monocyte–macrophage, brain and nervous system, B-cell, and gastrointestinal origin plus an array of other primate lines have been examined to date. Only those known to be infected with HIV-1 have been positive. Additional viruses that could present a substantial health hazard to cell culture technicians include, for example, hepatitis and cytomegalovirus. Rapid PCR-based tests for these have been described (e.g., Ulrich et al., 1989, and Cassol et al., 1989, respectively).

Other viruses that may present problems generally in cell culture work include

TABLE III Common Methods for Detection of Viruses
in Cell Line Stocks[a]

Cytopathogenic effect observation	Reverse transcriptase assays
Chorioallantoic membrane inoculation	Nucleic acid hybridization
Hemagglutination	Fluorescent antibody staining
Hemadsorption	Electron microscopic fine structure
Cocultivation	Animal inoculation

See IABS (1989) and Coriell (1973) for more detail.

ectromelia virus, the causative agent of bovine viral diarrhea, and Epstein–Barr virus (EBV). (See also Bolin *et al.*, 1994; Harasawa *et al.*, 1994; and Hay *et al.*, 1992, for testing methodology and further discussion.)

It should be emphasized at the outset that the protocols provided below represent an expedient compromise established at ATCC to monitor for readily detectable viruses associated with cell lines. Egg inoculations plus select cocultivations and hemadsorption tests are included in addition to routine examinations for CPE using phase-contrast microscopy. Similar general tests are recommended by government agencies in cases where cell lines are to be used for biological production work (Code of Federal Regulations on Animals and Animal Products, 9 CFR 113.34–113.52, revised Jan. 1, 1978; Code of Federal Regulations on Food and Drugs, Subchapter F on Biologics, 21 CFR 630.13 b–c, revised Apr. 1, 1979; IABS (1989); Coriell, 1973; Lubiniecki and May, 1985). Procedures for reverse transcriptase assays to detect oncogenic viruses are also being applied at the ATCC for Certified Cell Lines (CCL category).

Because endogenous and most exogenous retroviruses produce no morphological transformation or cytopathology in infected cells, the production of such viruses by cell cultures is generally undetectable except by serological or biochemical means. At ATCC the concentration of particulate material from culture supernates and assay for viral RNA-directed DNA polymerase (RDDP) provide a sensitive and reliable means for detecting retrovirus production by cultured cells.

One or more of the procedures outlined below is currently being applied to all cell lines accessioned for the ATCC repository. Tests for specific viruses may be applied through collaborations as described above.

1. Examination of Established Cultures for Overt Cytopathogenic Effect or Foci

Steps

1. Hold each flask or bottle so that light is transmitted through the monolayer and look for plaques, foci, or areas that lack uniformity. If frozen stocks of cells are to be examined, pool and mix the contents of about 5% of the ampoules from each lot using a syringe with a cannula. Establish cultures for morphological examinations and for tests in sections below, using progeny from such pooled populations.

2. Using an inverted microscope, equipped with phase-contract optics wherever possible, examine cell culture vessels individually, paying special attention to any uneven areas in gross morphology observed in step 1. Check first using low power. If the cell line is suspect, subculture taking the appropriate safety precautions. Prepare coverslip cultures for further examination. Alternatively, autoclave and discard all suspect cultures. (Stainless-steel collection and sterilizing pans for this purpose can be obtained from the Orem Medical Company.)

3. Remove fluid from coverslip cultures that require additional study. Treat

with neutral buffered Formalin or other suitable fixative. Prepare a wet mount and examine under high power. (Consult Rovozzo and Burke, 1973; Bang, 1966; and Rapp and Melnick, 1966, for examples of cytopathogenic effects and further details.)

2. Application of the Hemadsorption Test

Steps

1. Establish test cultures in T-25 flasks using an inoculation density such that the monolayers become confluent in 48 to 72 hr.

2. Prepare washed red blood cell suspensions on the day the test is to be performed. Pack the erythrocytes from 5 ml of the purchased suspensions by centrifugation at 100 g and resuspend in 35 ml Hanks' saline without divalent cations. Repeat three times and resuspend the final pellet to yield a 0.5% suspension (v/v) of red blood cells in saline.

3. Remove the culture fluid and rinse the test monolayers with 5 ml Hanks' saline minus divalent cations.

4. Add 0.5 ml each of the suspensions of chick, guinea pig, and human type O erythrocytes from step 2. Then place the flask with monolayer down at 4°C for 20 min.

5. Observe macroscopically and microscopically under low power for clumping and adsorption of red blood cells to the monolayer.

6. Repeat steps 2–4 on all test cultures not exhibiting hemadsorption before recording a negative result. [A suitable positive control can be established by infecting a flask of rhesus monkey kidney cells with 0.2 ml of undiluted ATCC VR-95 (influenza virus strain A/PR/8/34) 48 to 72 hr before testing.]

3. Egg Preparation

Steps

1. Drill a small hole in the egg air sac (blunt end) using the electric drill (Cole–Parmer) and a $\frac{1}{16}$-in. burr-type bit or an 18-gauge needle. in this and subsequent operations, work with sterile instruments. Swab areas of the shell to be drilled with 70% ethanol before and after each manipulation. The drill bits may be placed in 70% ethanol before use.

2. Using the candling lamp (Nasco), locate the area of obvious blood vessel development, and at a central point carefully drill through the shell, leaving the shell membrane intact.

3. Place 2 or 3 drops of Hanks' saline on the side hole and carefully pick through the shell membrane with a 26-gauge syringe needle. The saline will seep in and over the chorioallantoic membrane (CAM) to facilitate its separation from the shell membrane.

4. Apply gentle suction to the hole in the air sac using a short piece of rubber tubing with one end to the mouth and the other pressed to the blunt end of the egg. Use the candling lamp to monitor formation of the artificial air sac over the CAM.

5. Seal both holes with squares of adhesive or laboratory tape and incubate the eggs horizontally at 37°C. We have found that standard cell culture incubators and walk-in rooms are entirely adequate for egg incubations. High-humidity or air/CO_2 boxes are not satisfactory.

4. Egg Inoculations

Steps

1. Obtain suspensions of test cells in the appropriate growth medium and adjust the concentration such that 0.2 ml contains 0.5 to 1×10^7 cells.

2. Remove the seal from side holes in the embryonated eggs and inject 0.2 ml of the cell suspension onto the CAM of each of 5 to 10 eggs.

3. Using the candling lamp, examine the embryos 1 day after adding the cell suspension; discard any embryos that have died. Repeat the examination periodically for 8 to 9 days.

4. If embryos appear to be viable at the end of the incubation period, open the eggs over the artificial air sac and examine the CAM carefully for edema, foci, or pox. Check the embryo itself for any gross abnormalities such as body contortions or stunting.

5. In cases in which viral contamination is indicated, repeat steps 1–4 both with a second aliquot of the suspect cells and with fresh fluid samples from eggs in which the embryos have died or appear abnormal. Positive controls may be established by inoculating eggs with influenza virus, Newcastle disease virus, and/ or Rous sarcoma virus.

5. Cocultivation Trials

Steps

1. Select two appropriate cell lines for cocultivation with each cell line to be tested. The lines chosen will depend on the species from which the test cell line originated. For example, for a human cell line, one could cocultivate with ATCC CCL 75 (WI-38), ATCC CCL 171 (MRC-5), or primary human embryonic kidney (HEK) cells. A cell line from a second species of choice in this example could be ATCC CCL 81 (Vero) originating from the African green monkey.

2. Inoculate a T-75 flask with 10 cells from each line in a total of 8 ml of an appropriate growth medium. In some cases, the inocula may have to be adjusted in an attempt to maintain both cell populations during the cocultivation period. For example, if a very rapidly proliferating line is cocultivated with a test line that multiplies slowly, the initial ratio of the former to the latter could be adjusted to 1:10. Similarly, the population that multiplies slowly might have to be reintroduced to the cocultivation flasks if it were being overgrown by the more rapidly dividing cells.

3. Change the culture fluid twice weekly and subcultivate the population as usual soon after it reaches confluence.

4. Examine periodically for CPE and hemadsorption over a 2- to 3-week period at minimum, using procedures described above.

Viral isolates may be identified through standard neutralization (hemadsorption inhibition, plaque inhibition, hemagglutination inhibition) or complement fixation tests. The ATCC Virology Department retains and distributes antisera to many viral serotypes, and identification can readily be accomplished.

6. Reverse Transcriptase Assays

Positive serological assays for retrovirus antigens in cells and cell packs indicate that a retrovirus genome is present, but these assays do not indicate whether release of progeny virus particles is occurring. We find that concentration of particulate material from culture supernates and assay for viral RDDP (Baltimore, 1970; Temin and Mizutani, 1970) provide a sensitive and reliable means for detecting retrovirus production by cultured cells.

a. Preparation of Cell Cultures

Cell cultures to be examined for the production of retrovirus should be cultured by the methods and in the media that are optimal for the particular cells. It is important that the cells be in good condition and not undergoing degeneration and autolysis.

Steps

1. When adherent cell cultures are about 50 to 60% confluent, or when suspension cultures are at a cell density about 50% of the maximum, completely replace the medium and reincubate the cultures.

2. Harvest fluid approximately 24 hr after feeding.

b. Processing of Culture Fluid

Steps

1. Collect culture medium aseptically.

2. Clarify medium by centrifugation at 1000 to 3000 g for 10 min at 4°C. Decant and save the clarified supernates and discard sedimented materials.

3. The clarified medium contains 0.15 M NaCl; add 5.0 M NaCl to a final concentration of 0.5 M NaCl. Calculate the volume of 5.0 M NaCl according to the formula $0.15(V_1) + 5.0(V_2) = 0.5(V_1 + V_2)$, where V_1 is the volume of clarified culture fluid, and V_2 is the volume of 5.0 M NaCl to be added. Mix well. If the medium becomes cloudy after addition of NaCl, centrifuge at 10,000 g for 10 min and save the supernate.

4. To 2 vol of clarified supernate containing 0.5 M NaCl, add 1 vol 30% PEG 6000 in 0.5 M NaCl. Mix well.

5. Allow precipitation to occur for at least 1 hr while holding in wet ice. At this point samples may be held overnight at 4°C if necessary.

6. Centrifuge at 7000 g for 10 min.

7. Decant and discard the supernates.

8. Drain the pellets thoroughly while holding at 4°C.

9. Resuspend the pellets in 50% (v/v) buffer A (0.05 M Tris–HCl, pH 7.5, 0.1 M KCl, 0.5 mM EDTA, 10 mM DTT, 0.05% v/v Triton X-100, and 50% glycerol). Care must be taken to ensure that pellets are completely resuspended.

10. Store resuspended pellets at −20°C. Aliquots are used for RDDP assays.

c. Assay of RNA-Directed DNA Polymerase Activity

This procedure is based on that of (Gallagher and Gallo, 1975).

Solutions

1. *Stock mix:* 0.5% (v/v) Triton X-100, 1.13 M KCl.

2. *Template-primer solutions (P-L Biochemicals):* MIX A: Combine 1 mg/ml poly(rA)·poly(dT)$_{12-18}$ with 0.01 M Tris–HCl, pH 7.5, and 0.1 M NaCl. MIX B:

TABLE IV Contents of RNA-Directed DNA Polymerase Assays for Three Samples

Tube No.	Medium concentrate	Sample volume	Mix A	Mix B	Cocktail
1	1	5 μl	10 μl	—	85 μl
2	1	5 μl	—	10 μl	85 μl
3	2	5 μl	10 μl	—	85 μl
4	2	5 μl	—	10 μl	85 μl
5	3	5 μl	10 μl	—	85 μl
6	3	5 μl	—	10 μl	85 μl
7	Negative control	5 μl[a]	10 μl	—	85 μl
8	Negative control	5 μl[a]	—	10 μl	85 μl
9	Positive control	5 μl[b]	10 μl	—	85 μl
10	Positive control	5 μl[b]	—	10 μl	85 μl

[a] Buffer A–glycerol 1:1 as used for resuspending PEG precipitates.
[b] PEG-precipitated particles from medium collected from known retrovirus (e.g., murine leukemia virus)-producing cells.

Combine 1 mg/ml poly(dA)·poly(dT)$_{12-18}$ with 0.1 M NaCl and 0.01 M Tris–HCl, pH 7.5.

3. *Working mixtures of template-primer solutions:* Mix stock mix and template-primer solutions in 3:2 (v/v) ratio.

4. *Reaction cocktail:* Evaporate 250 μl [^{3}H]TTP (carrier-free, New England Nuclear 221-X) to dryness under vacuum. Redissolve in 720 μl H_2O before adding the following components (volumes given are for 10 tubes): 1.0 M Tris–HCl, pH 7.8 (40 μl); 0.2 M dithiothreitol (40 μl); 0.01 M MnCl$_2$ (50 μl). Add MnCl$_2$ last (just before initiating reactions).
/academic/m7616/c197/365

Steps

1. Distribute culture medium concentrates and positive and negative control samples into siliconized 10 × 75-mm assay tubes. (a) For positive controls, use concentrates prepared from culture media of cell cultures known to be producing retroviruses. (b) For negative controls, use buffer A–glycerol (Table IV).

2. Add appropriate template-primer mix to each tube and mix with Vortex mixer. Hold tubes in wet ice for 15 min.

3. Initiate reactions by adding reaction cocktail to each tube and mixing. Allow reactions to proceed for 30 min in 37°C water bath.

4. At the end of incubation period, remove tubes to ice bath; terminate reactions by adding 25 μl per tube 0.1 M EDTA (Sethi and Sethi, 1975).

5. Spot 100 μl from each tube onto appropriately numbered DE-81 filters. Allow liquid to soak into filters.

6. Wash batches of filters with gentle manual swirling in at least 10 ml (per filter) of 5% (w/v) Na$_2$HPO$_4$·7H$_2$O. Repeat for a total of six washes (Sethi and Sethi, 1975).

7. Wash twice with distilled H_2O and twice with 95% ethanol and arrange filters on cardboard covered with absorbent paper. Dry thoroughly under a heat lamp.

8. Place each filter in a separate numbered scintillation vial, add 10 ml PPO–

POPOP scintillation cocktail (Betafluor) to the vial, and count in liquid scintillation counter (Beckman LS-3133) using tritium window.

Comments

A number of precautions must be observed in the interpretation of the results obtained in this assay. If the cultures to be tested are very heavy and undergoing autolysis, a large amount of cellular DNA-directed DNA polymerase may be associated with microsomal particles in the culture medium. These particles are concentrated by the polyethylene glycol procedure just as virus particles are. Because cellular DNA polymerases do not exhibit an absolute specificity for a DNA template, a certain level of [³H]TMP ([³H]thymidylate) incorporation directed by an RNA template will result from cellular polymerase activity. If a high level of DNA-directed cellular polymerase activity is present in medium concentrates, the (sometimes high) degree of incorporation by these enzymes can mask true RDDP activity, which may be present. Consequently, it is important that media be collected from healthy, actively growing cultures.

It must be remembered that enzymes that catalyze the polymerization or terminal addition of [³H]TMP with a poly(rA)·oligo(dT) template-primer are not exclusively viral (Fridlender *et al.,* 1972; Harrison *et al.,* 1976). Poly(rA) DD·CC oligo(dT) is generally employed because the activity of retroviral RDDP is usually greater with that template-primer than it is when measured by incorporation of dGMP (deoxyguanylate) directed by poly(rC)·oligo(dG) or by methylated derivatives of the poly(rC) template; however, DNA synthesis directed by poly(rC)·oligo(dG) is more specific for viral enzyme. Consequently, medium concentrates that show incorporation of [³H]TMP with the poly(rA) template should be tested for incorporation of [³H]dGMP directed by a poly(rC) template.

Incorporation of isotopic precursors into macromolecular form is generally detected by precipitation of macromolecules with trichloroacetic acid after the enzymatic reaction is terminated. Although we find background levels of radioactivity to be somewhat higher by the use of adsorption to and elution from ion-exchange filter paper, the ion-exchange procedure obviates the need for a filtration manifold, which is generally employed for acid precipitation. Also, the batch method employed allows many more samples to be efficiently processed.

IV. General Comments

Microbial contamination of cell lines is still an extremely serious problem. Mycoplasmal infection has been especially well studied, and the incidence of problems documented through government-funded programs. Screening results reported within the past decade showed that as many as 11% of cultures tested were infected with one or more species of mycoplasma (Del Guidice and Gardella, 1985). It is *absolutely imperative* that cell lines used in research or production work be tested routinely for such adventitious infection. The comparative cost in time and materials is extremely small. Rewards in terms of research or production reliability are substantial.

Testing for viral infection is more problematical in that it is expensive and multiple tests are required to provide even a limited degree of assurance on freedom from infection. We recommend consideration of screening on a case-by-case basis depending on anticipated use for the line, funding available, and a risk-versus-benefit analysis. Of course a potential health hazard for cell culture technicians is one major concern.

Finally it is also *critically important* to verify the identity of cell lines employed.

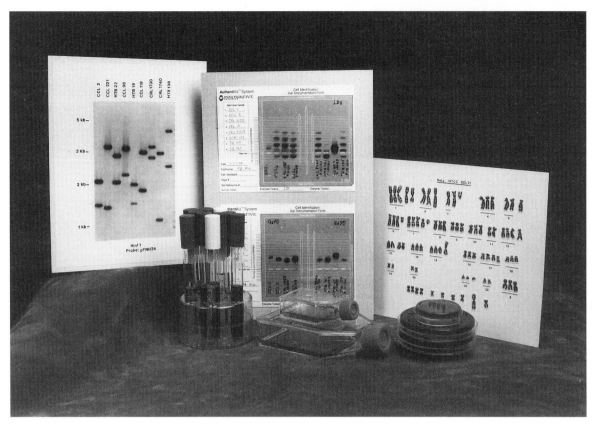

FIGURE 1 Appropriate quality control for cell lines includes multiple tests for microbial contamination (foreground center); verification of cell line species, for example, by isoenzymology (center background); and cell line identification by DNA fingerprinting (left) and/or by detailed cytogenetic analysis (right). Rationale and methods are described elsewhere (Hay, 1992; Hay *et al.*, 1992).

Hukku *et al.* (1984) document the incidence of cross-contamination of cell lines, reporting misidentifications in excess of 35%.

Thus a reasonably rigorous authentication program must include not only reliable tests to ensure absence of microbial infections (including mycoplasma) but also cell species verification. Figure 1 illustrates representative data involving microbial culture tests, isoenzymology to verify species, and cytogenetic analyses plus DNA fingerprinting to confirm cell identity. Methods are detailed elsewhere (Hay *et al.*, 1992) as are precautions required to avoid operator-induced contamination during routine processing (Hay, 1991).

REFERENCES

Aaronson, S. A., Todaro, G. J., and Scolnick, E. M. (1971) Induction of murine C-type viruses from clonal lines of virus-free BALB/3T3 cells. *Science* **174**, 157–159.

Baltimore, D. (1970) RNA-dependent DNA polymerase in virions of RNA tumor viruses. *Nature (London)* **226**, 1209–1211.

Bang, F. B. (1966) Effects of invading organisms on cells and tissues in culture. *In* "Cells and Tissues in Culture" (E. N. Willmer, ed.), pp. 151–261. Academic Press, New York.

Bolin, S. R., Ridpath, J. F., Black, J., Macy, M., and Roblin, R. (1994) "Survey of Cell Lines in the American Type Culture Collection Collection for Bovine Viral Diarrhea Virus." In press.

Caputo, J. (1988) Biosafety procedures in cell culture. *J. Tissue Culture Methods* **11,** 223–228.

Cassol, S. A., Poon, M-C., Pal, R., Naylor, M. J., Culver-James, J., Bowen, T. J., Russel, J. A., Krawetz, S. A., Pon, R. T., and Hoar, D. I. (1989) Primer mediated enzymatic amplification of cytomegalovirus (CMV) DNA. *J. Clin. Invest.* **83,** 1109–1115.

Coriell, L. L. (1973) Methods of prevention of bacterial, fungal and other contaminations. *In* "Contamination in Tissue Culture" (J. Fogh, ed.), pp. 29–49. Academic Press, New York.

Del Giudice, R. A., and Gardella, R. S. (1984) Mycoplasma infection of cell culture: Effects, incidence and detection. *In* "*In Vitro* Monograph, 5. Uses and Standardization of Vertebrate Cell Culture," pp. 104–115. Tissue Culture Association, Gaithersburg, MD.

Dilworth, S., Hay, R. J., and Daggett, P.-M. (1979) Procedures in use at the ATCC for detection of protozoan contaminants in cultured cells. *TCA Manual* **5,** 1107–1110.

Docherty, J. J., and Chopan, M. (1974) The latent herpes simplex virus. *Bacteriol. Rev.* **38,** 337–355.

Fridlender, B., Fry, M., Bolden, A., and Weissbach, A. (1972) A new synthetic RNA-dependent DNA polymerase from human tissue culture cells. *Proc. Natl. Acad. Sci. USA* **69,** 452–455.

Fogh, J. (1973) Contaminants demonstrated by microscopy of living tissue cultures or of fixed and stained tissue culture preparations. *In* "Contamination in Tissue Culture" (J. Fogh, ed.), pp. 65–106. Academic Press, New York.

Friedman, R. M., and Ramseur, J. M. (1979) Mechanisms of persistent infections by cytopathic viruses in tissue culture. *Arch. Virol.* **60,** 83–103.

Gallagher, R. E., and Gallo, R. C. (1975) Type C RNA tumor virus isolated from cultured human acute myelogenous leukemia cells. *Science* **187,** 350–353.

Harasawa, R., Kazumasa, H., Tanabe, H., Takada, Y., and Mizusawa, H. (1994) Detection of adventitious pestivirus in cell cultures by polymerase chain reaction using nested-pair primers. *Jpn. Tissue Culture Assoc. J.,* in press.

Harasawa, R., Mizusawa, H., Nozawa, K., Nakagawa, T., Asada, K., and Kato, I. (1993) Detection and tentative identification of dominant mycoplasma species in cell cultures by restriction analysis of the 16S–23S rRNA intergenic spacer regions. *Res. Microbiol.* **144,** 489–493.

Harrison, T. A., Barr, R. D., McCaffrey, R. P., Sarna, G., Silverstone, A. F., Perry, S., and Baltimore, D. (1976) Terminal deoxynucleotidyl transferase in AKR leukemia cells and lack of relation of enzyme activity to cell cycle phase. *Biochem. Biophys. Res. Commun.* **69,** 63–67.

Hay, R. J. (1991) Operator-induced contamination in cell culture systems. *In* "Virological Aspects of the Safety of Biological Products." *Aeres-Sorono Symp. Dev. Biol. Stand.* **75,** 193–204.

Hay, R. J. (1992) Cell line preservation and characterization. *In* "Animal Cell Culture: A Practical Approach" (R. I. Freshney, ed.), 2nd ed., Ch. 4, pp. 95–148. IRL Press, Washington, DC.

Hay, R. J., Caputo, J., and Macy, M. (1992) "ATCC Quality Control Methods for Cell Lines," 2nd ed. ATCC, Rockville, MD.

Hay, R. J., Macy, M. L., and Chen, T. R. (1989) Mycoplasma infection of cultured cells. *Nature* **339,** 487–488.

Holmgren, N. B. (1973) Contamination in tissue culture by parasites. *In* "Contamination in Tissue Culture" (J. Fogh, ed.) pp. 195–203. Academic Press, New York.

Hukku, B., Halton, D. M., Mally, M., and Peterson, W. D., Jr. (1984) Cell characterization by use of multiple genetic markers in eukaryotic cell cultures. *In* "Eukaryotic Cell Cultures, Basics and Applications" (R. T. Acton and J. D. Lynn, eds.), pp. 13–31. Plenum Press, New York.

IABS (1989) "Continuous Cell Lines as Substrates for Biologicals." IABS Symposium on Developments in Biological Standardization, Vol. 70. Karger, Basel.

Jahnes, W. G., Fullmer, H. M., and Li, C. P. (1957) Free-living amoebae as contaminants in monkey kidney tissue culture. *Proc. Soc. Exp. Biol. Med.* **96,** 484–488.

LeDuc, J. W., Smith, G. A., Macy, M. L., and Hay, R. J. (1985) Certified cell lines of rat origin appear free of infection with hantavirus. *J. Infect. Dis.* **152,** 1081–1082.

Lubiniecki, A. S., and May, L. H. (1985) Cell bank characterization for recombinant DNA mammalian cell lines. *Dev. Biol. Stand.* **60,** 141–146.

Ou, C-Y., Kwok, S., Mitchell, S. W., Mack, D. H., Sninsky, J. J., Krebs, J. W., Feorino, P., Warfield, D., and Schochetman, G. (1988) DNA amplification for direct detection of HIV-1 in DNA of peripheral blood mononuclear cells. *Science* **239,** 295–297.

Rapp, F., and Melnick, J. L. (1966) Cell, tissue and organ cultures in virus research. *In* "Cells and Tissues in Culture" (E. N. Willmer, ed.), pp. 263–316. Academic Press, New York.

Rovozzo, G. C., and Burke, C. N. (1973) "A Manual of Basic Virological Techniques." Prentice-Hall, Englewood Cliffs, NJ.

Sethi, V. S., and Sethi, M. L. (1975) Inhibition of reverse transcriptase activity of RNA tumor viruses by fagaronine. *Biochem. Biophys. Res. Commun.* **63,** 1070–1076.

Temin, H. M. (1974) On the origin of RNA tumor viruses. *Annu. Rev. Genet.* **8,** 155–177.

Temin, H. M., and Mizutani, S. (1970) RNA-dependent DNA polymerase in virions of Rous sarcoma virus. *Nature (London)* **226,** 1211–1213.

Ulrich, P. P., Bhat, R. A., Seto, B., Mack, D., Sninsky, J., and Yvas, G. N. (1989) Enzymatic amplification of hepatitis B virus DNA in serum compared with infectivity testing in chimpanzees. *J. Infect. Dis.* **160,** 37–43.

Weiss, S. H., Goedert, J. J., Gartner, S., Popovic, M., Waters, D., Markham, P., Veronese, F. M., Gail, M. H., Barkley, W. E., Gibbons, J., Gill, F. A., Leuther, M., Shaw, G. M., Gallo, R. C., and Blattner, W. A. (1988) Risk of human immunodeficiency virus (HIV-1) infection among laboratory workers. *Science* **239,** 68–71.

Willaert, E., Stevens, A. R., and Tyndall, R. L. (1978). *Acanthamoeba royreba* sp. from a human tumor cell culture. *J. Protozool.* **25,** 1–14.

SECTION B

Primary Cultures from Embryonic Tissues

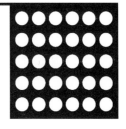

Primary and Extended Culture of Embryonic Mouse Cells: Establishment of a Novel Cell Culture Model of Apoptosis and Neural Differentiation

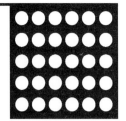

Deryk T. Loo and Carl W. Cotman

I. Introduction

Cultured rodent cells provide a powerful model to address cellular and molecular biology questions unapproachable using animal models. One approach is to use established cell lines that have been derived from tumorigenic material or transformed by chemical or genetic manipulation. A second approach is to use cells obtained from normal animal tissue directly and grown in culture either short term (primary culture) or long term (multipassage culture). Embryonic rodent tissue has proven to be a good source of cells for several reasons. Embryonic rodent cells are available in large quantities, they are relatively easy to culture, and culture conditions are easy to replicate since the age and genetic background of the embryos used may be controlled.

In this article we outline methods used for the primary and extended culture of mouse embryo cells both in conventional serum-containing medium (Todaro and Green, 1963) and in serum-free medium in which serum is replaced by a defined set of growth supplements (Barnes, 1987; Loo *et al.*, 1987). By controlling the culture medium used, one may select for cell populations of interest. Using a defined serum-free medium, we established a mouse embryo cell line [serum-free mouse embryo (SFME)] (Loo *et al.*, 1987) which we are currently using as a model to study (1) mechanisms of cell death and (2) neural cell differentiation. SFME cells undergo apoptotic cell death when deprived of trophic factor support (Rawson *et al.*, 1990; 1991b). Additionally, SFME cells express the gene encoding nestin (Loo *et al.*, 1994), a neuroepithelial stem cell marker (Lendahl *et al.*, 1990), and under defined conditions they express markers characteristic of either astrocytes or neurons (Sakai *et al.*, 1990, D.T.L. and C.W.C., unpublished data), suggesting that SFME cells may represent a pluripotent neural precursor cell type. Thus, the use of specific defined medium formulations may allow for the establishment of novel cell lines which will serve as valuable experimental models.

II. Materials and Instrumentation

Dulbecco's modified Eagle's medium (DMEM, Cat. No. 12100-046), Ham's F12 (Cat. No. 21700-075), calf serum (CS, Cat. No. 16170-011), and fetal calf serum (FCS, Cat. No. 16000-028) are obtained from Gibco-BRL. Insulin (Cat. No. I-

5500), transferrin (Cat. No. T-2252), fibronectin (Cat. No. F-1141), penicillin (Cat. No. P-3032), ampicillin (Cat. No. A-9393), streptomycin (Cat. No. S-9137), sodium selenite (Cat. No. S-5261), sodium bicarbonate (Cat. No. S-5761), Hepes (Cat. No. H-9136), trypsin (Cat. No. T-8128), and soybean trypsin inhibitor (Cat. No. T-9003) are obtained from Sigma Chemical Company. Epidermal growth factor (EGF, Cat. No. 01-101) is obtained from Upstate Biotechnology Inc. Sterilization filters (Cat. No. 120-0020) and cryopreservation vials (Cat. No. 5000-0020) are obtained from Nalgene. Various culture vessels, disposable pipets and centrifuge tubes are obtained from Falcon–Becton Dickinson Labware.

III. Procedures

A. TISSUE DISSOCIATION

Routinely, 16- to 18-day-old mouse embryos are used for primary cultures of mouse embryo cells. The goal of this procedure is to obtain a suspension of cells that consists of single cells and small clusters of cells. Do not overly mince or trypsinize the tissue. Excessive processing will result in lower cell viability. It is our experience that a large proportion of the cells plated that remain viable and are capable of being passaged migrate from small clumps of attached cells.

Solutions

1. *Calcium/magnesium-free phosphate-buffered saline (CMF-PBS):* To make 1 liter, dissolve 0.2 g KCl, 0.2 g KH_2PO_4, 8.0 g NaCl, and 2.16 g $Na_2HPO_4 \cdot 7H_2O$ in 900 ml purified water. Adjust pH to 7.4, add purified water to 1-liter final volume, filter-sterilize, and store in aliquots at 4°C.

2. *1.5 M Hepes:* To make 100 ml, dissolve 35.74 g Hepes in 80 ml purified water. Adjust pH to 7.4 with NaOH, add water to 100 ml, and store in 20-ml aliquots at −20°C.

3. *Penicillin, ampicillin, streptomycin stocks:* Dissolve 1.2 g penicillin, 0.25 g ampicillin, and 2.0 g streptomycin individually in 100 ml purified water. Store in 20-ml aliquots at −20°C.

4. *0.2% Trypsin solution:* To make 100 ml, dissolve 0.2 g trypsin in 90 ml CMF-PBS. Add EDTA (0.5 *M* stock) to a final concentration of 1 m*M*; then add CMF-PBS to a final volume of 100 ml. Filter-sterilize and store at −20°C.

5. *Trypsin inhibitor:* To make 100 ml, dissolve 100 mg trypsin inhibitor in 100 ml F12/DMEM. Filter-sterilize and store at −20°C.

6. *Insulin stock:* To make 50 ml, dissolve 50 mg insulin in 20 m*M* HCl. Filter-sterilize and store in 3-ml aliquots at −80°C. Store working stock at 4°C.

7. *Transferrin stock:* To make 50 ml, dissolve 125 mg transferrin in F12/DMEM. Filter-sterilize and store in 3-ml aliquots at −80°C. Store working stock at 4°C.

8. *Epidermal growth factor stock:* Add 2.0 ml sterile CMF-PBS to a vial containing 100 μg of sterile epidermal growth factor. Store at 4°C.

9. *HDL stock:* See Loo *et al.* (1989) for detailed preparation procedures.

10. *10^{-5} M Sodium selenite stock:* Dissolve 17.3 mg sodium selenite in 100 ml purified water to obtain a 10^{-3} *M* solution. Dilute 1 ml of the 10^{-3} *M* solution in 99 ml purified water to obtain a 10^{-5} *M* working stock solution. Filter-sterilize and store at 4°C.

TABLE I   Components of Medium and Serum-Free Supplements

| | Concentration | | |
Component	Stock	Final	Solvent
Hepes (pH 7.4)	1.5 M	15 mM	Water
Penicillin	20,000 U/ml	200 U/ml	Water
Ampicillin	2.5 mg/ml	25 μg/ml	Water
Streptomycin	20 mg/ml	200 μg/ml	Water
Insulin	1 mg/ml	10 μg/ml	20 mM HCl
Transferrin	2.5 mg/ml	10 μg/ml	F12:DMEM
Epidermal growth factor	50 μg/ml	50 ng/ml	PBS
High-density lipoprotein	10–20 mg/ml	20 μg/ml	NaCl/EDTA
Selenium	10 μM	10 nM	Water
Fibronectin	1 mg/ml	10 μg/ml	F12:DMEM

11. *Serum-free medium:* The basal culture medium is a 1:1 mixture of DMEM, containing 4.5 g/liter glucose, and Ham's F12 (F12:DMEM) supplemented with 15 mM Hepes, pH 7.4, 1.2 g/liter sodium bicarbonate, penicillin, streptomycin, and ampicillin. Purify water used for medium and medium supplements by triple glass distillation or passage through a high-quality water purification system and use immediately following purification as trace microbial contamination may lead to pyrogen contamination of the medium. Dissolve a 1-liter packet of DMEM powdered medium and a 1-liter packet of F12 powdered medium in 1.8 liters of purified water. Add 20 ml 1.5 M Hepes solution, 20 ml each of penicillin, ampicillin, and streptomycin solutions, and 2.4 g sodium bicarbonate. Adjust pH to 7.4 with HCl or NaOH, add purified water to 2-liter final volume, filter the medium immediately through 0.2-μm tissue culture filters, and store in disposable 250-ml plastic tissue culture flasks at $-20°C$. Storage in reusable glass bottles is not recommended due to complications in cleaning and sterilization and the possibility of contamination by materials previously stored in the bottles. Thawed medium should be stored at 4°C and used within 3 weeks.

F12:DMEM culture medium is supplemented with bovine insulin, human transferrin, mouse epidermal growth factor (EGF), human high-density lipoprotein (HDL) (Loo *et al.*, 1989), and sodium selenite, and cells are plated onto fibronectin-precoated culture vessels (Table I). Do not dilute serum-free supplements into culture medium stocks for future use as they are not stable long term in culture medium and bind to polystyrene plastic. Instead, add insulin, transferrin, EGF, and HDL individually from concentrated stock solutions directly to tissue culture vessels. Sodium selenite may be added to medium stocks. Store stock solutions of medium supplements in disposable polypropylene tubes. Avoid repeated freeze–thaw cycles. Disposable plastic pipettes and culture vessels are recommended as glass culture ware may introduce contaminating pyrogens or detergents which are extremely toxic to serum-free cultured cells.

12. *Serum-containing medium:* DMEM containing 15 mM Hepes, penicillin, ampicillin, streptomycin, and 1.2 g/liter sodium bicarbonate is routinely used for culturing mouse embryo cells in serum containing medium. Prepare DMEM medium as described above and supplement with 10% (v/v) calf or fetal calf serum. Batches of serum vary in composition from lot to lot. It is worthwhile to test new lots of serum for proper growth characteristics and obtain bulk quantities of desirable lots.

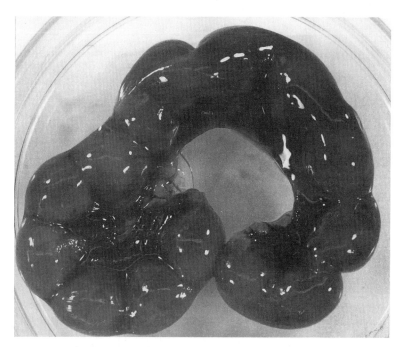

FIGURE 1 Photograph showing mouse uteri filled with embryos.

Steps

1. Cells to be grown under serum-free conditions are plated onto fibronectin-precoated culture vessels. Precoating must be done prior to cell preparation. To precoat culture vessels add bovine fibronectin to culture vessels at 10 μg/ml in F12:DMEM medium for 1–2 hr at 37°C in a 5% CO_2 atmosphere. We routinely precoat in half the volume used for cell plating (5 ml/75-cm^2 flask). Following precoating, aspirate the fibronectin solution from the culture vessel and wash once with fresh medium. Precoated culture vessels may be used immediately or stored dry for several days at room temperature.

2. Sacrifice the animal by cervical dislocation or CO_2 asphyxiation.

3. Immediately following sacrifice, swab the ventral surface of the animal with 70% ethanol and aseptically remove the uteri filled with embryos (Fig. 1). Keep embryos on ice until dissociation.

4. Using forceps and scissors, remove the embryos from the uterus and free them from surrounding membranes. Rinse embryos by placing them in a culture dish containing CMF-PBS. Repeat several times.

5. Transfer embryos to a fresh culture dish and mince with scissors. Mince the tissue until it is fine enough to be pipetted (clumps are about 1 mm in diameter).

6. Add 5 ml trypsin solution. Incubate the plate at 37°C in the hood. Incubating the plate on top of a heating block works well. Pipet the digestion periodically.

7. Follow the progression of the digestion by observing the suspension under the microscope. Do not trypsinize for more than 10–15 min.

8. Stop the digestion when the bulk of the suspension consists of single cells and small clumps of cells by adding 5 ml of trypsin inhibitor solution to the digestion. If the cultures are to be grown in serum-containing medium, substitute medium containing 10% serum for trypsin inhibitor solution.

9. Transfer the suspension to a centrifuge tube and allow large chunks to settle out. Transfer the supernatant to a fresh centrifuge tube and pellet the cells in a benchtop centrifuge.

10. Resuspend the cell pellet in a small volume of culture medium and estimate the cell number by counting with a hemocytometer.

11. Plate cells onto fibronectin-precoated culture vessels at a density of 1–2 $\times 10^5$ cells/cm^2. Subsequent cell plating will be at a much lower density; however, the initial plating must be dense since most cells will not attach to the substrate or grow. Add appropriate medium supplements to the cultures and incubate at 37°C in a 5% CO_2 atmosphere. If the cultures are to be grown in serum-containing medium no precoating of the culture vessel is necessary. It is advantageous to plate the cells initially in a smaller volume of medium than would normally be used. If a small volume of medium is used, the individual cells and small clumps of cells will have a greater chance of contacting and adhering to the plastic surface. Several hours after plating additional medium may be added to the cultures.

12. Change the culture medium 8–24 hr after the initial plating to remove cell debris and unattached cells.

B. SERIAL PASSAGING MOUSE EMBRYO CULTURES

Primary cultures of mouse embryo cells consist of a diverse population of cell types (Fig. 2). Subsequent passaging of the cells results in the selection of distinct homogeneous populations of cells (Fig. 2). The cell population that develops on serial passaging of the culture is dependent on the medium used for culturing. Careful selection of specific medium may allow for the selection of cell populations of interest. One strategy is to choose a serum-free medium that has been developed to support the growth of established cell lines (Barnes, 1987; Barnes and Sato, 1980). One may then attempt to culture mouse embryo cells in this medium or a derivative formulation, with the goal of selecting for cells that express properties of the cell line for which the medium was developed. In establishing the serum-free mouse embryo cell line (SFME) we used F12:DMEM supplemented with insulin, transferrin, EGF, HDL and a fibronectin substrate (Loo *et al.*, 1987). These cells display many unique properties not expressed by cells that have been derived in serum-containing medium. SFME cells have been cultured for more than 200 generations without entering a growth crisis phase and have retained a predominantly diploid genome (Fig. 3) (Loo *et al.*, 1987). SFME cells have a strict requirement for EGF; EGF withdrawal leads to cell death which follows an apoptotic pathway (Rawson *et al.*, 1990; Rawson *et al.*, 1991b). Additionally, SFME cells are acutely growth inhibited by serum (Loo *et al.*, 1987; Rawson *et al.*, 1991a). Thus, culturing mouse embryo cells in the presence of serum or in the absence of EGF would select against the cell type represented by SFME cells. We previously reported that serum or transforming growth factor β induces SFME cells to express glial fibrillary acidic protein (Sakai *et al.*, 1990), an intermediate filament expressed by astrocytes. Recently we have found that SFME cells express the gene encoding nestin (Loo *et al.*, 1994), a neuroepithelial stem cell marker (Lendahl *et al.*, 1990), suggesting that SFME cells may represent a pluripotent neural precursor cell type.

In contrast to SFME cells, serum-derived mouse embryo cells often lose proliferative potential following several divisions and enter a growth crisis phase where cell division is negligible (Todaro and Green, 1963) (Fig. 3). Continued culture of these cells often leads to the appearance of a subpopulation of immortalized cells which resume proliferation in serum-containing medium (Todaro and Green, 1963). It has been suggested that the population that emerges has somehow adapted to the culture

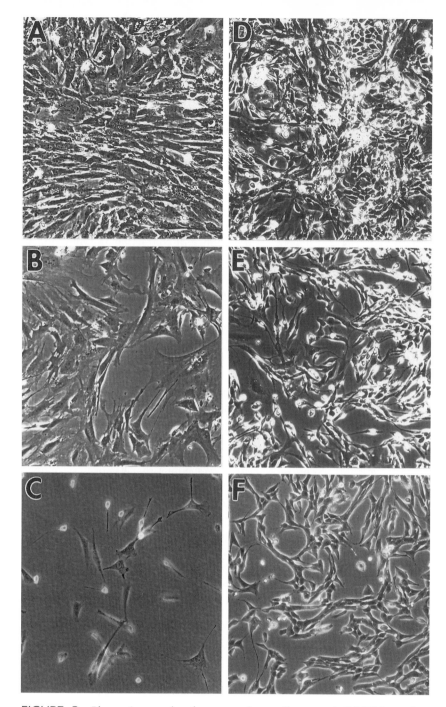

FIGURE 2 Photomicrographs of mouse embryo cells grown in DMEM supplemented with 10% CS (A–C) or in F12:DMEM supplemented with insulin, transferrin, EGF, and HDL on fibronectin-precoated flasks (D–F). Primary cultures (A, B), early-passage cultures (one or two passages) (C, D), late-passage cultures (>40 passages) (E, F).

conditions imposed on it and thus overcomes inhibitory effects of the serum (Barnes, 1987). Consistent with this idea, cells derived in this manner are genetically abnormal, usually possessing a tetraploid number of chromosomes and gross chromosomal abnormalities, and are often tumorigenic (Todaro and Green, et al., 1963).

The primary culture should be passaged once the culture has become 80–100% confluent. Depending on the dissociation and plating technique this will occur 2 to

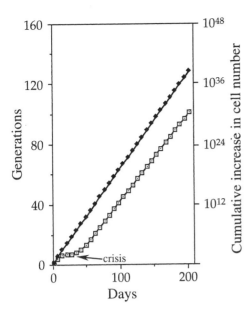

FIGURE 3 Representative graph showing growth of mouse embryo cells on successive transfer in DMEM supplemented with 10% CS (open squares) or in F12:DMEM supplemented with insulin, transferrin, EGF, and HDL on fibronectin-precoated flasks (filled squares).

7 days following the initial plating. Prior to passaging, the culture medium may become acidic quite rapidly. Monitor the pH of the medium and change the medium when it becomes acidic. Remove approximately 90% of the medium by aspiration and replace the medium with fresh medium and supplements. Do not attempt to remove all of the medium from cultures grown serum-free because this may result in drying out of the cells and loss of viability.

Steps

1. Aspirate the culture medium from the culture vessel. Add a small volume of room temperature trypsin solution to the vessel (1.0 ml/75-cm^2 flask). Immediately begin monitoring the trypsinization by microscopic examination. When the majority of cells have detached from the plastic (1–3 min), gently tap the vessel against the lab bench to dislodge the remaining adherent cells. Cultures grown in serum-containing medium may require longer trypsinization at 37°C.

2. Add an equal volume of trypsin inhibitor solution to the vessel and transfer the cell suspension to a centrifuge tube. Wash the vessel with a small volume of medium and pool with the cell suspension. For serum-containing cultures DMEM containing 10% serum may be substituted for trypsin inhibitor solution.

3. Pellet the cell suspension and resuspend in 1–2 ml of culture medium. Plate the desired number of cells in a fresh culture vessel. Precoat the culture vessel with fibronectin if the cells are to be grown under serum-free conditions. Change the medium when it becomes acidic or at least every 3 days. Subsequent passages should be performed using a consistent passaging regimen. The cell population will become increasingly homogeneous over two to four passages.

C. LONG-TERM STORAGE OF CULTURED CELLS

Cultured cells may be stored frozen indefinitely in liquid nitrogen.

Solutions

1. *Serum-free freezing medium:* Dissolve DMSO at a final concentration of 10% (v/v) in F12:DMEM. Filter-sterilize and store in aliquots at $-20°C$.

2. *Serum-containing freezing medium:* Dissolve DMSO at a final concentration of 10% (v/v) in FCS. Filter-sterilize and store in aliquots at $-20°C$.

Steps

1. Resuspend cell pellets in freezing medium at a density of $10^5 - 10^7$ cells/ml and transfer to cryogenic vials.

2. Encase the vials in styrofoam (a sandwich of two styrofoam culture tube racks works well) and allow to freeze slowly overnight at $-80°C$.

3. The following day, transfer the vials to liquid nitrogen.

4. When reinitializing cultures from frozen stocks thaw the cells quickly by constant agitation in a 37°C water bath. Remove the cells from the freezing medium by centrifugation and culture as described above.

IV. Comments

By use of the culture approach outlined in this article, primary and multipassage cultures of embryonic mouse cells may be established in serum-containing or serum-free medium. Cultures established using this approach provide valuable models to explore the regulation of cell function. Using a defined serum-free medium we established the SFME cell line which displays unique properties that we have been able to exploit to study mechanisms of programmed cell death and neural differentiation. Cultures established using other serum-free formulations may lead to the development of new cell lines which express unique properties and will serve as valuable experimental models.

V. Pitfalls

1. The use of high-quality reagents and tissue culture ware is essential. Contaminants such as detergents and bacterial endotoxins are extremely toxic to cells cultured in the absence of serum. Do not wash glassware, stir bars, etc., used to prepare media for serum-free cell culture with detergent; thoroughly rinse only with high-quality water.

2. Serum-free supplements such as peptide growth factors have a high affinity for plastic surfaces and should be stored at 4°C or frozen in small aliquots in polypropylene tubes. Serum-free supplements cannot be added to stocks of medium; they must be added directly to cultures.

3. High-density cultures rapidly deplete medium of peptide growth factors and other serum-free supplements, making frequent medium changes essential.

REFERENCES

Barnes, D. (1987) Serum-free animal cell culture. *BioTechniques* **5**, 1–9.

Barnes, D., and Sato, G. (1980) Methods for growth of cultured cells in serum-free medium. *Anal. Biochem.* **102**, 255–270.

Lendahl, U., Zimmerman, L. B., and McKay, R. D. G. (1990) CNS stem cells express a new class of intermediate filament protein. *Cell* **60**, 585–595.

Loo, D., Rawson, C., Ernst, T., Shirahata, S., and Barnes, D. (1989) Primary and multipassage culture of mouse embryo cells in serum-containing and serum-free medium. In "Cell Growth and Division: A Practical Approach" (Baserga, R., ed.), pp. 17–35. IRL Press, Oxford.

Loo, D. T., Fuquay, J. I., Rawson, C. L., and Barnes, D. W. (1987) Extended culture of mouse embryo cells without senescence: Inhibition by serum. *Science* **236**, 200–202.

Loo, D. T., Althoen, M. C., and Cotman, C. W. (1994) Down regulation of nestin by TGF-β or serum in SFME cells accompanies differentiation into astrocytes. *Neuroreport,* in press.

Rawson, C., Loo, D., Helmrich, A., Ernst, T., Natsuno, T., Merrill, G., and Barnes, D. (1991a) Serum inhibition of proliferation of serum-free mouse embryo cells. *Exp. Cell Res.* **192**, 271–277.

Rawson, C. L., Loo, D. T., Duimstra, J. R., Hedstrom, O. R., Schmidt, E. E., and Barnes, D. W. (1991b) Death of serum-free mouse embryo cells caused by epidermal growth factor deprivation. *J. Cell Biol.* **113**, 671–680.

Rawson, C., C.-Smith, C., and Barnes, D. (1990) Death of serum-free mouse embryo cells caused by epidermal growth factor deprivation is prevented by cycloheximide, 12-O-tetradecanoylphorbol-13-acetate, or vanadate. *Exp. Cell Res.* **186**, 177–181.

Sakai, Y., Rawson, C., Lindburg, K., and Barnes, D. (1990) Serum and transforming growth factor B regulate glial fibrillary acidic protein in serum-free-derived mouse embryo cells. *Proc. Natl. Acad. Sci. USA* **87**, 8378–8382.

Todaro, G. J., and Green, H. (1963) Quantitative studies of the growth of mouse embryo cells in culture and their development into established lines. *J. Cell Biol.* **17**, 299–313.

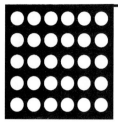

Tissue Culture of Embryonic Stem Cells

Martin Evans

I. Introduction

Pluripotential cells may be isolated from preimplantation embryos and retain their ability to differentiate and, in particular, to repopulate a host blastocyst to give rise to a chimeric mouse through passage in tissue culture. The use of these embryonic stem cells of mice as a route to somatic and germ line transgenesis has allowed several new approaches to experimental mammalian genetics. These cells provide a bridge between the whole animal and cells in tissue culture. The large number of cells that may be used and their ease of handling *in vitro* greatly facilitate the isolation of specific genetic modifications.

The introduction of genetic modification which may be induced, screened, or selected in culture to embryonic stem cells of the mouse provides a method for specific modification of endogenous chromosomal loci to manipulate and test gene function in the context of the whole animal. These methods, which include gene targeting by homologous recombination, provide a finer level of genetic manipulation than available in most other higher organisms and have great importance for an analysis of mammalian genetic function. This manipulative ability also provides a precise experimental tool for other biological studies and a method to create animal models of specific human diseases. Although detailed fine-grain genetic modification is possible most studies to date are using constructs designed to knock out gene function.

Embryonic stem (ES) cells are fastidious, and to keep them in a condition that maintains their normal karyotype and developmental capacity, great attention should be paid to culture conditions. It is not difficult to adapt ES cells to suboptimal conditions of culture usually either by very prolonged passage or through a "crisis" and then to derive a strain that is much more tolerant of these conditions. Almost universally such strains have lost or have seriously reduced competence for full differentiation and, in particular, for germ-line chimerism. They will NOT, therefore, be a useful stock with which to initiate gene manipulation experiments. Even with the best intentions and efforts conditions of culture are likely to fluctuate and to be suboptimal at times; it is therefore useful to maintain fairly early-passage frozen stocks of any particular cell line.

There are two major requirements for ES cell culture in the context of their use as genetic vectors: (1) The cells are maintained in their undifferentiated and totipotential state. (2) The cells retain a normal karyotype which is a prerequisite for germ-line transmission.

The original and still the best general method for maintenance of these cells is coculture with a mitotically inactivated "feeder layer" of fibroblasts. Several types of cells can provide this feeder function; the most widely used and tested are either the established cell line STO or primary embryo fibroblasts. It is now known that one of the most important factors supplied by these feeder layers is the growth factor LIF, and supplementation of the medium with recombinant LIF is now an alternative to the use of feeders. In my experience this can be satisfactory but I still find that the feeder layer approach works more reliably for maintenance of the full pluripotency of these cells. There are times when the use of feeder-free conditions is useful and LIF supplementation is then a boon. Although feeder use is an added procedure it is unwise to discard it merely on the grounds of convenience. It appears that many ES cell lines do grow better on feeders than with only LIF, whereas others can be switched between the two conditions with little trouble.

For any serious long-term investment in ES cells it is wise to expand and freeze ES cells over several passages, checking the karyotype and germ-line transmission. Only ES cells with proven karyotype and germ-line transmission properties should be used for experiments in which germ-line transmission is required.

II. Materials and Instrumentation

It may seem odd to mention washing up first, but ES cells are very sensitive indeed to traces of detergent left on glassware by washing protocols or washing machines. This has proved to be the most common source of problems with ES culture. It can manifest itself as an apparently toxic component, e.g., PBS, which may be traced to the residues in the bottles and caps used or to the water used for making medium, which may have been stored and autoclaved in washed glass bottles. Other common detergent problem areas arise with the use of glass measuring pipettes and so-called prewashed glass Pasteur pipettes. As most laboratory detergents are alkaline a very simple and sensitive test for contamination is to fill or wash the item with pure distilled water containing a small amount of phenol red. Purplish swirls coming from the item are indicative of contamination. Completely clean glassware has no effect on the color of the pH indicator.

One solution is to use new plasticware throughout, but this is not necessary so long as the problem is recognized and appropriate washing and rinsing are instituted. I find that the "disposable" Corning glass pipettes are very good and may be recycled repeatedly if required.

The descriptions here assume that tissue culture facilities are available. These may be elaborate or relatively simple, but it must be borne in mind that long-term culture is intended and so contamination is a severe problem. It is advisable to dedicate a room to ES cell culture. Apart from this the standard equipment, incubators and phase-contrast microscopes are required together with sterilization facilities.

Disposable tissue culture plasticware, tissue culture media, sera, and chemicals are all available from a range of reputable suppliers.

III. Procedures

A. PASSAGING AND MAINTENANCE OF ES CELLS

The key feature of ES cell propagation is that it is important not to allow the cultures to become too crowded or too sparse during routine culture. Either situation sets up conditions in which selection for abnormal (fast growing, aneuploid) cells can occur. A corollary is that the conditions employed for detachment and replating of ES cells should be chosen to maintain high plating efficiencies. When in good health ES cells grow with a population doubling time of about 14–20 hours. In practice, therefore, it is necessary to subculture ES cells about every 3 days and to change the medium frequently to prevent acidification. Cultures should be examined daily and the feeding and passage routine adjusted as necessary. An example of good, typical, healthy ES cells growing on a STO feeder layer is shown in Fig. 2. It is unwise in general to attempt to rescue cultures that show contamination, but in valuable cases gentamicin and kanamycin prove to be useful and nontoxic antibiotics. The only possible method to salvage a culture that has become contaminated with yeast or mold is rigorous washing in PBS followed by subcloning by picking up single cells with a micropipette. Contamination of cultures with bacteria at any time should be taken as a warning that mycoplasma contamination is also possible. This is usually disastrous to the cells' properties, and all cultures should be destroyed and replaced if mycoplasma contamination is detected.

B. PASSAGING ES CELL CULTURES

Solutions

1. *PBS:* made up from separate AnalaR ingredients or tablets and autoclaved. PBS stocks are stored and used at room temperature.

2. *Trypsin–EDTA:* 0.125% trypsin, 0.2 g/liter. EDTA in Ca^{2+}/Mg^{2+}-free PBS. Filter-sterilize and store in aliquots at $-20°C$. Trypsin–EDTA can be optionally supplemented with 2% chick serum (TVP). Thaw aliquots overnight and store at 4°C before use. TVP may be slightly better for getting quasi-single cell suspensions from ES cells. *Note:* Substitution of EGTA for EDTA is an improvement.

3. *Gelatin treatment of tissue culture dishes:* Allows improved ES cell growth. This should be carried out before feeder layer preparation or use of naked plasticware. Cover the tissue culture grade surface with a 0.1% sterile solution of swine type II gelatin (Sigma) in water for a few minutes. Then aspirate the solution and use the dish or flask immediately. Do not pretreat and dry the dishes.

4. *Tissue culture media:* The medium used for culture is Dulbecco's modified Eagle's medium (DMEM), high-glucose, low-pyruvate formulation. It is supplemented with nonessential amino acids (NEAAs) and a mixture of nucleosides (adenosine, guanosine, cytidine, and uridine) to a final concentration of 30 μM and thymidine to a final concentration of 10 μM. Fetal calf serum 10% and newborn calf serum 10% are used together with 10^{-4} M 2-mercaptoethanol. It is vital that the quality of the serum used is pretested, and batches of both fetal and newborn calf serum should be purchased only after careful and rigorous testing.

It is a mistake to imagine that the higher price of fetal calf serum necessarily makes it better. Some newborn sera are excellent and some fetal calf sera are extremely toxic to ES cells! (See Section H for serum test method).

For optimal growth, a 1:1 mixture of DMEM with Ham's F12M medium may be used. This peculiar mixture gives a compromise between the high-yielding DMEM, originally designed for maximal growth of tissue culture cell lines for virus production, and the finely balanced Ham's F12, originally developed for clonal growth of cells. ES cells grow happily in DMEM alone but better in DMEM + NEAA and better still in DMEM/F12. The only snag with the latter is that it becomes acidified faster and the medium needs to be changed more frequently.

These media may be prepared "in house" most conveniently from premixed powder. Alternatively, 10× concentrates may be used or medium bought in ready-to-use at 1× concentration. The water used must be of the highest purity, and glassware cleanliness is critical.

Make up of medium

DMEM (or DMEM/F12).

Glutamine (stored frozen as 100× concentrate of 200 mM).

β-Mercaptoethanol to a final concentration of 10^{-4} M, either 4 μl neat in 500 ml or from a 10^{-2} (100×) concentrate (prepared by adding 72 μl to 100 ml PBS).

10% calf serum and 10% fetal calf serum.

Nonessential amino acids (DMEM) from 100× concentrate.

Nucleosides from 100× concentrate (if required).

Antibiotics (if required)—use only penicillin, streptomycin, kanamycin, or gentamicin; do not use antimycotics, as these cause a high incidence of chromosomal anomalies.

LIF, if used, is added from appropriate stock; do not store unfrozen for longer than 1 week.[1]

Steps

1. Aspirate growth medium and add 10 ml of PBS. I use the PBS at room temperature but others prefer 4°C.

2. Aspirate PBS and add 5 ml cold trypsin–EGTA, wait a few seconds, and aspirate trypsin–EGTA to leave a film covering the cells. Trypsinize at room temperature for most situations, but we have found that trypsinization at 37°C is better for cells about to be injected into a blastocyst and is good for other purposes where a single-cell suspension is important.

3. Monitor under the microscope. The cells begin to round up and colonies start to detach.

4. Tap the flask or rock the dish to dislodge cells; check under the microscope to ensure that all the cells have detached.

5. Quickly add 10 ml growth medium to the flask and pipette up and down a few times to generate single cells and only a few small clumps (monitor under microscope). *Note:* If you passage the cells as large clumps they will differentiate.

6. Place the resuspended cells in a 10-ml centrifuge tube (universal) and pellet in the bench centrifuge (1000 rpm, 5 min).

7. Suck off the medium and resuspend the pellet in 10 ml growth medium.

8. Count the cells in a hemocytometer or Coulter counter and calculate number of cells per milliliter.

9. Aliquot the appropriate number of cells into flasks/plates for passage/ experimentation.

[1] LIF can be purchased commercially (as ESGRO from AMRAD Corporation) or produced fairly simply in house from eukaryotic or prokaryotic expression vectors. Which source you use is up to you. A third source of LIF is conditioned medium from cell lines, in particular, the Buffalo Rat Liver (BRL) cell line. Use of BRL media (normally 60% by volume, appendix below) as the sole source of LIF requires that large stocks of BRLs are on tap as the source of conditioned medium, which can again be time consuming. However, BRL medium does contain soluble factors, other than LIF, which seem beneficial to ES cells, and an intermediate position recommended for some ES cell lines (e.g., E14) is to grow the cells in medium supplemented with 10% BRL medium (by volume) and LIF. In the end the choice of conditions should be dictated by whatever works best (by actual test!) in your laboratory and with your particular ES cell lines.

10. Check that cells are attaching about 30–60 min after replating.

11. For routine maintenance change the medium on day 2 and subculture on day 3.

Use the following rule of thumb numbers for replating:

Confluent 25-cm^2 flask = approximately 5×10^6 cells: seed with 8×10^5 cells/10 ml.

Confluent 75-cm^2 flask = approximately $1–2 \times 10^7$ cells: seed with 3×10^6 cells/ 30 ml.

Confluent 175-cm^2 flask = approximately 4×10^7 cells: seed with 6×10^6 cells/ 70 ml.

Confluent 9-cm-diameter dish = approximately 2×10^7 cells: seed with 3×10^6 cells.

C. PREPARATION OF FEEDER LAYERS FROM STO CELLS

STO cells are routinely grown in DMEM supplemented with 10% NCS. Cultures of STO cells should be passaged promptly when they reach confluency to prevent the accumulation of noncontact-inhibited cells in the population. Feeders are prepared in the following manner.

Solutions

1. *PBS:* Make up from separate AnalaR ingredients or tablets and autoclave. Store PBS stocks and use at room temperature.

2. *DMEM + 10% calf serum:* See above.

3. *Mitomycin C:* Make up at 2 mg/ml in PBS and stored in the dark at 4°C for up to 2 weeks.

4. *Trypsin–EDTA:* 0.125% trypsin, 0.2 g/liter EDTA in Ca^{2+}/Mg^{2+}-free PBS. Filter-sterilize and store in aliquots at −20°C.

Steps

1. Remove the medium from a confluent 10-cm dish of STO cells and replace with DMEM/10% NCS plus 10 μg/ml mitomycin C (Sigma).

2. Incubate plates for 2–3 hr. Avoid longer exposure to mitomycin C.

3. Remove mitomycin C from the STO cells and wash each plate three times with 10 ml of PBS.

4. Trypsinize the cells and mix with DMEM/10% NCS to stop the trypsin activity.

5. Pellet the cells by centrifugation (1000 rpm, 5 min) and resuspend the cells in DMEM/10% NCS at 3×10^5 cells/ml.

6. Seed the cells onto gelatinized plates at a dilution of 5×10^4 cells per square centimeter.

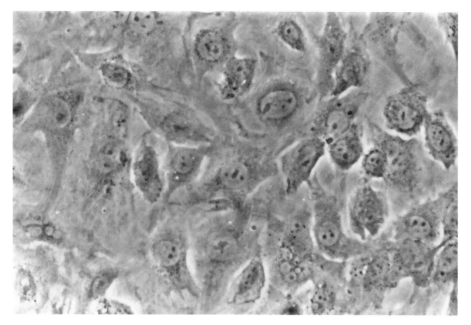

FIGURE 1 Phase-contrast appearance of cells of a STO feeder layer 3 days after preparation. Note that the cells cover the plastic surface and are epithelioid and largely nonoverlapping. This appearance should persist for at least 6 days.

7. Twelve hours later check that enough cells have been seeded to form a monolayer. Feeder layers can be used up to 1 week after their preparation.[2]

D. FEEDER LAYERS FROM PRIMARY EMBRYO FIBROBLASTS

Some workers prefer to use primary embryo fibroblasts to prepare feeder layers rather than cells as they feel that better ES cell growth can be obtained. This may reflect abused STO cells, however, rather than an intrinsic superiority of primary embryo fibroblasts. Primary fibroblasts have the considerable disadvantage that they have a limited culture life span (around 20 cell divisions).

Solutions

See Section C.

Steps

1. Kill a pregnant mouse on the 13th or 14th day of pregnancy.

2. Remove the uterine horns as aseptically as possible into a 10-cm bacteriological petri dish containing 10 ml PBS.

3. Cut open the uterine walls to release the embryos and transfer the embryos with the associated placentae and fetal membranes to a fresh dish of PBS.

---

[2] Be suspicious of feeder layers that fail to survive for more than 5 days when incubated. They are probably not well contact inhibited and should be replaced with a new stock. Good STO cell cultures grow as contact-inhibited 3T3 cultures and should form a pavement monolayer at confluence. An example of the appearance of the cells in a good STO feeder layer is shown in Fig. 1. There should be few elongated cells and very little cell piling. A confluent 9-cm dish should yield no more than 8×10^6 cells. If the cultures become denser or overgrown with elongated cells they may be recloned and flat colonies selected.

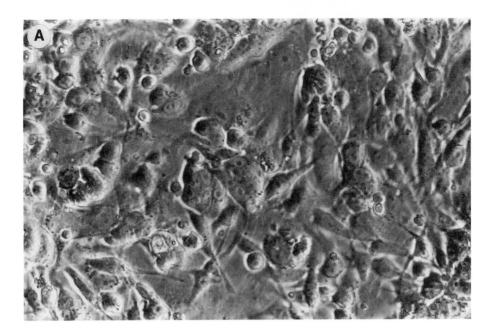

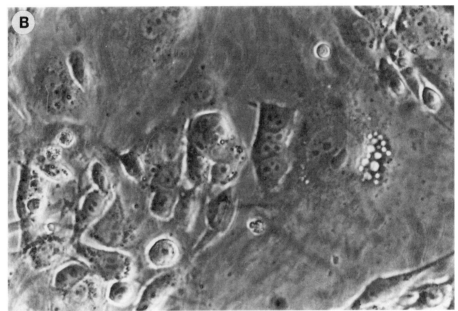

FIGURE 2 ES cells growing on the above feeder layer 30 hr after passage. Note the small colonies of ES cells. At this density of plating not all colonies are clonal as the cells attach to the substratum slowly after passage and may aggregate with each other.

4. Dissect the embryo free from the placenta and membranes and remove and discard the soft tissues of the embryo (e.g., heart, liver, and other viscera). Wash the carcass twice in PBS.

5. Mince the carcass with fine scissors in 2 ml trypsin–EDTA. Incubate for 5 min at 37°C and neutralize the trypsin with 8 ml DMEM/10% NCS.

6. Transfer the cell suspension to a sterile 15-ml centrifuge tube and allow any large pieces of tissue to settle at the bottom of the tube. Remove the supernatant and plate into a 10-cm tissue culture dish.

7. Change medium 24 hr later. When the plates are confluent expand the cultures. At this stage the cells can be frozen for recovery and used at a

later stage.

8. Feeder layers are prepared using the method described for STO cells. *Note:* The cell density will have to be increased two- to threefold to ensure a monolayer.

E. DIFFERENTIATION OF ES CELLS IN CULTURE

ES cells have the capacity to differentiate readily in culture into a wide variety of differentiated cell types. This will occur in the absence of chemical inducers such as retinoic acid (RA). Indeed, one of the difficulties in growing ES cells is to prevent this spontaneous differentiation.

F. FORMATION OF SIMPLE EMBRYOID BODIES

Solutions

1. *Trypsin–ED(G)TA:* See above.
2. *Culture medium:* DMEM + 10% fetal or newborn calf serum (batch dependent).

Steps

1. Remove feeder cells from the ES cell culture by passaging once on gelatinized plates. This step is not necessary if the ES cells have been grown without feeders in the presence of LIF.

2. Trypsinize the cells briefly so that small clumps of cells are still present. Neutralize the trypsin with DMEM/10% serum and plate onto bacteriological petri dishes. Each 10-cm dish should contain approximately 3×10^6 cells.

3. The clumps of cells will adhere together to form small aggregates. Culture for 4–5 days. By this time the aggregates (termed *simple embryoid bodies*) will have formed a distinct outer layer of large endoderm cells. The parietal endoderm cells secrete a layer of basement membrane material termed *Reichert's membrane,* which can be seen as a dark layer separating the endoderm cells from the undifferentiated inner cells.

4. If the simple embryoid bodies are left in culture for a further 10–14 days they will develop fluid-filled cavities and are now termed *cystic embryoid bodies.* During this period it will be necessary to change the medium every 4–5 days. To do this transfer the embryoid bodies and medium to a 15-ml centrifuge tube and allow the embryoid bodies to sink to the bottom of the tube. Carefully aspirate the old medium from the tube, leaving the embryoid bodies in a small volume of medium at the bottom of the tube. Add 10 ml of fresh medium and transfer the embryoid bodies in this medium back into the petri dish.

5. To assess the differentiation potential of an ES cell line it is necessary to plate the simple embryoid bodies onto a tissue culture dish in fresh medium so that attachment can occur and differentiated cell types can grow out onto the substrate. Culture of attached embryoid bodies will give rise to a wide spectrum of cell types including nerve, cardiac and skeletal muscle, cartilage, and endoderm. Individual cell types can be identified by immunofluorescence staining with cell type-specific antibodies.

G. KARYOTYPING

All ES cell lines and targeted clones should be karyotyped reasonably frequently to ensure that they have not lost the normal chromosome complement or acquired any gross chromosomal abnormalities. Simple chromosome counts are sufficient to determine the modal number (40) and estimate the range of variability in the population. G-banding should also be performed to detect any chromosomal abnormalities. It is important that the ES cells are in a state of active growth to obtain sufficient mitotic spreads. Good results are obtained using cultures subcultured 1–2 days before harvest and grown in DMEM/10% NCS, 10% FCS.

1. Preparation of Mitotic Spreads

Solutions

1. *Colcemid stock solution:* Make up 5 μg/ml in distilled water and store in aliquots at $-20°$C.

2. *KCl 0.56% solution.*

3. *100% pure dry methanol:* Buy this in small bottles so that the stock has never been opened for too long. Methanol is highly hygroscopic and will very soon pick up water from the atmosphere. Note too that methanol vapor is highly toxic.

4. *Glacial acetic acid.*

5. *Carnoy's fixative* (3:1 v/v absolute methanol:glacial acetic acid): Make up from the two components not more than a few hours before use and chill to $-20°$C.

A good supply of *clean* glass microscope slides is also needed.

Steps

1. Add colcemid (Sigma) to a final concentration of 0.05 μg/ml to a 6-cm plate of exponentially growing ES cells. Incubate at 37°C for 1 hr.

2. Trypsinize the cells and resuspend in 10 ml of 0.56% (w/v) KCl solution. Leave cells at room temperature for a total of 12 min (including the centrifugation time below).

3. Pellet the cells by gentle centrifugation (500 rpm, 5 min) and aspirate as much of the KCl solution as possible. Add freshly prepared ice-cold Carnoy's fixative (3:1 v/v absolute methanol:glacial acetic acid) gently flick and whirl tube to avoid cell clumping.

4. After 5 min at room temperature, pellet the cells and change the fixative. Repeat and resuspend the cells in 0.5–1 ml of fixative.

5. Apply small single drops of the cell suspension onto precleaned slides. Air-dry and observe the slides under phase contrast ($\times$200) to check the spreads. The cleanliness of the slide surface is paramount. Use prewashed slides and, if in difficulty, rewash them in hot detergent followed by extensive hot distilled water rinses. Alternatively, wash the slides with Carnoy's fixative wipe and dry. The droplet for metaphase spreading should spread out across the slide immediately and with a very flat edge meniscus. If this does not happen, either the slides are still dirty (check by testing the spreading of a small drop of neat freshly prepared fixative) or the cell suspension still contains too much residual water; centrifuge and resuspend in fresh fixative.

2. G-Banding

Solutions

1. *2× SSC.*

2. *0.25% trypsin in PBS.* (Not trypsin–EDTA.)

3. *5% calf serum in PBS.*

4. *6.8 Giemsa buffer:* Make up from Gurr buffer tablets available from BDH.

5. *5% Giemsa stain in 6.8 buffer:* This *must* be used within 30 min of being diluted.

Steps

1. Allow the slides to "mature" at room temperature for 2–3 days.

2. Bake the slides at 60°C for at least 12 hr.

3. Incubate the slides at 60°C in 2 × SSC for 1 hr.

4. Rinse slides for 10 min in running tap water followed by three rinses in distilled water. Do not allow slides to dry.

5. Dip slides in ice-cold 0.25% trypsin in PBS. The length of time the slides need to be left in the trypsin must be determined empirically, but a few seconds is usually adequate for ES cells. Overtrypsinization results in a distorted morphology and blurring of the bands. Undertrypsinization fails to fuse the chromatids and gives less distinct banding.

6. Following trypsinization place the slides through an ordered series of Coplin jars containing:

    5% NCS in PBS to arrest trypsin activity

    pH 6.8 buffer rinse

    5% Giemsa stain in 6.8 buffer for 10 min (must be freshly made up)

    pH 6.8 buffer rinse

    Distilled water rinse

7. Air-dry the slides and observe under oil immersion. Photograph suitable metaphase spreads.

H. COLONY-FORMING ASSAY FOR ES CELLS

The colony-forming assay described below can be used, with variations, for several purposes: testing serum batches, titrating LIF stocks, testing differentiation capacity of ES cells (see also Section E), and testing plating efficiencies (This can be applied to a wide variety of tests, e.g., for the adverse effects of detergent in other solutions such as batches of PBS.)

Solutions

1. *Standard tissue culture reagents:* See above.

2. *Serum batches or other reagents for test.*

Steps

1. Set up experimental media in six-well cluster dishes (2 ml/well) at twice the intended final concentration of additives and equilibrate in the incubator at 37°C in 5% CO_2 in air before use. Use duplicate (or better triplicate) wells for each condition and appropriate controls (e.g., known "good" serum batch). For serum batch testing (or plating test) use basal growth medium supplemented with the serum batch at 5% (by volume), 10% (by volume), and 20% (by volume). For LIF titration add LIF over a range of dilutions; for COS-LIF use COS conditioned media at 1/500, 1/1000, 1/5000, and 1/10,000 dilutions. For prokaryotic LIF use a range of dilutions from 20 ng/ml (1 nM) to 1 ng/ml (50 pM). For differentiation conditions add 10% FCS and without LIF.

2. Disperse ES cell stock culture (Section A) on day 2 after plating (i.e., semiconfluent), ensuring as close to a single-cell suspension as possible. Count and resuspend in basal growth medium at a density of 10^3 cells/ml.

3. Add 2 ml of cell suspension to each well (making 4 ml total volume 1× concentration of additives) and return to incubator.

4. Incubate for 5 days at 37°C, in 5% CO_2 in air.

5. Fix and then stain plates with Giemsa. ES cell colonies can be identified by characteristic morphology and dark staining properties. Differentiated colonies are more pale. Count the total number of colonies (=plating index) and the proportion of ES cell colonies. For FCS batch testing, the plating efficiency is the relevant parameter (along with colony size); for LIF testing, the proportion of differentiated colonies is the relevant parameter.

I. PRODUCTION OF BRL CONDITIONED MEDIUM

BRL cell conditioned medium is a valuable adjunct for ES cell culture, not only as a source of LIF, but also because it contains other soluble factors (IGF-II, kit ligand) which have beneficial effects on ES cell viability. Depending on the exact requirements medium can be conditioned in the presence of FCS (batch tested for ES cell growth) or in basal medium supplemented with transferrin. BRL is a very hardy cell line and can be held at confluence for several weeks without noticeable loss of viability or degradation of medium quality. The medium can be 'harvested' at regular intervals.

Solutions

1. *Standard tissue culture reagents:* See above.

2. *Collection medium:* DMEM, serum free or with 1% serum may be used.

Steps

1. Grow BRL cells to confluence in 75 ml growth medium with 10% FCS in 175-cm^2 tissue culture flasks. The exact number of flasks depends on your estimated usage. The "yield" from one flask is 25 ml/day.

2. Change medium to 75 ml collection medium. If collecting serum-free medium, discard first collection.

3. On day 3, pour off medium into sterile bottle (taking care not to spill medium on the cap region of the flask) and replace with 75 ml fresh medium.

4. Filter conditioned medium into sterile 100-ml bottles and store at −20°C.

BRL medium can be thawed in 37°C water bath and subsequently stored for up to 1 week at 4°C without deterioration in performance.

5. Repeat steps 3 and 4 until BRL monolayer begins to break up.

J. G418 SELECTION OF ES CELLS

Neomycin resistance is a popular and effective positive selection method for stable integration of DNAs into ES cells, and forms the basis of the majority of targeting strategies described to date. The input DNA construct is designed such that either the majority (PNS selections) or a proportion (promoter trapping strategies) of integration events results in expression of the bacterial neomycin resistance gene. Cells expressing *Neo* can then be selected by their ability to grow in G418. The main drawback of *Neo* selection is that it takes a few days to take hold on a population of cells, so transfected cells have to be plated at densities that will accommodate a few days' growth before the cells become confluent. An additional issue is that as the selection progressively takes hold, the dishes fill up with debris from dead cells and so the medium must be changed frequently to prevent injury to resistant cell colonies. Finally, some colonies can take ages to die; you can become unduly euphoric (or depressed) if you count resistant colonies after a week of selection—most of them will have gone a few days later. For this reason it is wise to keep cells under selection for at least 12–14 days to be confident you have eliminated all the stragglers and to include a control (nontransfected) plate of cells in each experiment. You can take off the selection when the control plates are completely dead. ES cells should be passaged at least once in the absence of G418 before using for microinjection.

An important technical issue is that different batches of G418 vary in potency for different cell types so each batch should be titrated in a trial transfection on the appropriate target cell to determine the optimal concentration for selection. The optimal concentration usually varies between 50 and 200 µg/ml of active G418 (read the label on the bottle!) for ES cells and can be higher for fibroblasts. If you are planning on using *Neo* selection a lot, buy G418 in large amounts from a single batch so you do not use it all up running tests before you get to do the experiment (or run out halfway through). Each titration should include, in parallel, cells transfected with an appropriate resistance plasmid (e.g., PGK-*Neo*) and non-transfected control cells. The optimal concentration is that which gives complete killing of control cells and maximum number of resistant colonies after 14 days of selection. For promoter trapping selection strategies, where the "strength" of the target promoter is unknown, the optimal concentration of G418 is the lowest one that kills all the control cells. It may also be necessary to perform trial selections with different G418 concentrations with the experimental plasmid.

Solutions

1. *Tissue culture reagents:* See above.

2. *G418 stock:* Make up in PBS at 100× the concentration to be used, usually approximately 20 mg/ml. G418 is available as Genticin from Gibco.

Steps

1. Transfect your target cells by whatever means appropriate. Keep an aliquot ($\frac{1}{10}$th) of cells back for selection controls.

2. Plate into 10-cm dishes at a density of approximately 10^6 cells/plate in 10 ml growth medium.

3. Change medium on day 3 to 10 ml growth medium + G418 (concentration determined by experiment).

4. On days 4 to 7 change to 10 ml fresh growth medium with G418 each day.

5. On days 8 to 14 change to 10 ml growth medium with G418 on alternate days.

Selected colonies should become visible in the dissecting microscope by day 10 and macroscopically scorable by day 14. G418 can be left out of the medium after all the cells on the control (nontransfected) plates have gone. Viable colonies have a "bright" appearance under the dissecting microscope (illumination from beneath). Colonies that are dying or dead are brown or yellow, and the cells appear shriveled.

K. REPLICA PLATING OF CLONES DIRECTLY ON PICKING

It is possible to replicate clones of ES cells into two or three 96-well multiwell dishes directly, therefore enabling storage of early freezes of multiple clones without much bother and allowing growth in replica plates for analysis.

Solutions

1. *Standard tissue culture reagents.*

2. $\frac{1}{10}$ *diluted trypsin–EGTA:* See above. Dilute with PBS.

3. *Freezing medium:* 10% dimethylsulfoxide in DMEM with 20% serum.

4. *STO feeder cells in suspension* (immediately after mitomycin C treatment): Concentration of 2×10^5/ml.

Steps

1. Prepare a 96-well round-bottomed multiwell dish (non-tissue-culture grade but sterile) with aliquots of 35 μl of $\frac{1}{10}$ diluted trypsin–EGTA.

2. Wash the medium from the dish containing the clones with PBS and then cover the clones with a further 10 ml of PBS.

3. Using a dissecting microscope and a 20-μl Pipetman set for about 5 μl, pick off the clones and eject them one-by-one into the wells of the multiwell dish. If you are reasonably fast and you have plenty of clones, it will take no more than 10–15 min to fill the dish, and if you use a lid, evaporation of the trypsin–EGTA solution is not a problem.

4. Using an eight-way pipettor, resuspend the clones by pipetting up-and-down with 200 μl of a suspension of STO feeders in full ES growth medium. The STOs should be at a concentration of about 2×10^5/ml so that on plating out, each multiwell should get $1–2 \times 10^4$ STO feeders. If you are splitting more than two ways adjust accordingly.

5. Transfer 100 μl to each of two replica multiwell dishes or 70 μl to each of three.

6. Incubate in CO_2 incubator and top-up the medium with another 100 μl after cells have attached.

7. Feed regularly and when a healthy culture is established (2–3 days). Freeze one plate by changing medium to 10% DMSO and freezing in −70°C freezer.

8. Passage and/or analyze the remaining plate.

IV. Comments

The use of ES cells for genetic manipulation of mice involves skills in molecular biology, tissue culture, embryo manipulation, and animal husbandry and genetics. As such it is often a difficult task to keep all these aspects of the experimental system working together and well. As has been alternatively expressed, "Gene targeting is a team activity." The protocols presented here are simple and work well, but there needs to be a continuing effort to maintain the culture conditions at their optimum if all the effort put into, e.g., the molecular biology of targeting, is not to be frustrated.

V. Pitfalls

Cultures of these cells are not reagents but living systems with fragile properties. They should be viewed as an experiment. Therefore, appropriate controls are needed and it is highly advisable to test the whole system in your lab under your conditions before trusting it.

ACKNOWLEDGMENTS

The protocols described have been developed over a number of years and represent the work of many people. Much of this manuscript derives from protocols gathered and written for three Wellcome Trust Summer Schools on gene targeting and I would like to gratefully acknowledge the contribution of Dr. John Heath and Dr. Bill Colledge and their generous permission to adapt the documents we prepared together.

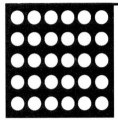

Isolation and Culture of Germ Cells from the Mouse Embryo

Massimo De Felici

I. Introduction

During the last 10 years developments in methods for isolation and culture of germ cells from the mouse embryo have allowed significant advances in our understanding of the process of early mammalian gametogenesis (for a recent review, see De Felici et al., 1992). Such techniques have provided the opportunity to pursue important questions regarding the life cycle of the germ line and have allowed students of the development of the germ line to move from the field of descriptive embryology to that of molecular biology. Moreover, the recent finding that embryonic stem (ES)-like cell lines which can be used for transgenic technology have been obtained by culturing primordial germ cells (PGCs) (Matsui et al., 1992; Resnick et al., 1992; see also other relevant articles in this volume) promises a further increase in the number of laboratories interested in using techniques for isolation and in vitro culture of mouse PGCs.

II. Materials and Instrumentation

EDTA (Cat. No. E-6635), trypsin (type XII-S, Cat. No. T-2262), penicillin G (Cat. No. P-3032), streptomycin sulfate (Cat. No. S-9137), L-glutamine (Cat. No. G-5763), sodium pyruvate (Cat. No. P-4562), sodium lactate (Cat. No. L-1375), MEM non-essential amino acids (Cat. No. M-7145), phenol red (Cat. No. P-4758), Dulbecco's modified Eagle's medium (Cat. No. D-5536), poly-L-lysine (MW > 500,000, Cat. No. P-5899), fast red TR salt (Cat. No. F-8764), fast blue BB salt (Cat. No. F-3378), naphthol AS-BI alkaline solution (Cat. No. 86-1), DNase (Cat. No. DN-EP), and forskolin (Cat. No. F-6886) are purchased from Sigma. Hepes (Cat. No. 391338) is from Calbiochem. NaCl "AnalarR" (Cat. No. 10241), KCl "AnalarR" (Cat. No. 10198), $Na_2HPO_4 \cdot 2H_2O$ "AnalarR" (Cat. No. 10383), KH_2PO_4 "AnalarR" (Cat. No. 10203), D-glucose "AnalarR" (Cat. No. 10117), $CaCl_2 \cdot 2H_2O$ "AnalarR" (Cat. No. 10070), $MgSO_4 \cdot 7H_2O$ "AnalarR" (Cat. No. 10151), $NaHCO_3$ "AnalarR" (Cat. No. 10247), and paraffin oil (Cat. No. 29436) are from BDH Laboratory Supplies. Bovine serum albumin (BSA, Cat. No. 103700) is from ICN Biomedicals. Heat-inactivated fetal calf serum (FCS, Cat. No. 29-102-49) and horse serum (HS, Cat. No. 29-219-49) are provided by Flow Laboratories. Percoll (Cat. No. 17-0891-01) is from Pharmacia. Recombinant mouse stem cell factor (SCF, Cat. No. 1832-01) and recombinant human leukemia inhibitory factor (LIF, Cat. No. 1999-01) are from Genzyme.

Fine scissors (Cat. No. S-4146), dissection forceps (Cat. No. F-3767), and No. 5

TABLE I M2 Medium[a]

Component	g/liter ultrapure H_2O
NaCl	5.534
KCl	0.356
KH_2PO_4	0.162
$MgSO_4 \cdot 7H_2O$	0.294
$CaCl_2 \cdot 2H_2O$	0.252
Glucose	1.000
Sodium pyruvate	0.036
Penicillin G	0.060
Streptomycin	0.050
$NaHCO_3$	0.338
Hepes	5.940
Phenol red	0.010
Bovine serum albumin	1.000
Sodium lactate (60% syrup)	3.145 ml/liter ultrapure H_2O

[a] Check that the pH is 7.2–7.3 and sterilize by 0.25-μm filtration. Store at 4°C for 1 month.

watchmaker's forceps (Cat. No. T-4412) are from Sigma. Disposable needles (25 gauge, Cat. No. 300600), 60- or 100-mm Falcon petri dishes (for embryo collection, Cat. Nos. 1007 and 1029, respectively), 35-mm Falcon tissue culture dishes (Cat. No. 3001), 24-well Falcon Multiwell (Cat. No. 3047) and 96-well Falcon Micro Test III (Cat. No. 3072) tissue culture plates, and Falcon polystyrene tubes (Cat. No. 2058) are provided by Becton Dickinson. Eppendorf tubes (1.5 ml) are from Eppendorf. Micropipettes (diameter about 20–30 μm) are drawn by hand from glass Pasteur pipettes using a microflame. A convenient holder for the micropipette can be constructed from tubing and a mouthpiece.

Other equipment includes an Eppendorf or equivalent 100-μl fixed-volume pipette; a stereomicroscope (the author uses a Wild M5 (from Leica, maximum magnification ×100 and equipped with both incident and transmitted light sources, the latter preferably with a movable mirror); Milli-Q filter (Millipore) for ultrapure H_2O preparation; and a humidified 37°C incubator with an atmosphere of 5% CO_2 in air.

III. Procedures

A. ISOLATION OF PGC-CONTAINING TISSUES FROM 8.5- AND 10.5-DAYS POSTCOITUS (dpc) EMBRYOS

At these stages germ cells, known as primordial germ cells (PGCs), are characterized by active migration and extensive proliferation. They cannot be purified and are collected together with heterogeneous somatic cell populations present along their migratory pathway. The regions dissected away from the embryo (allantois and the posterior primitive streak from 8.5-dpc embryos and dorsal mesoderm and associated tissues from 10.5-dpc embryos) correspond to the localization of migrating PGCs.

Solutions

1. *Dissection M2 medium:* Modified Krebs–Ringer solution with some of the bicarbonate replaced by Hepes buffer (Table I) (Quinn *et al.*, 1982).

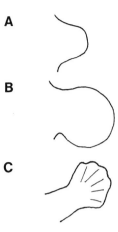

FIGURE 1 Morphology of hindlimb bud of mouse embryo at 10.5 (A), 11.5 (B), and 13.5 (C) dpc.

2. *Trypsin/EDTA solution:* A solution of 1 mM EDTA–2.5 mg/ml trypsin is prepared in M2 without Ca^{2+} and Mg^{2+} and bovine serum albumin.

3. *Culture medium:* Minimum essential medium with Earle's salts supplemented with 4 mM L-glutamine, 0.25 mM sodium pyruvate, 60 μg/ml penicillin, 50 μg/ml streptomycin, nonessential amino acids, 20 mM Hepes, pH 7.4, 25 mM sodium bicarbonate, 5% horse serum, and 2.5% heat-inactivated fetal calf serum. Dulbecco's modified Eagle's medium with sodium bicarbonate, supplemented with 4 mM L-glutamine, 0.25 mM sodium pyruvate, and 10% FCS can also be employed.

4. *Chromogenic solution for alkaline phosphatase detection:* Immediately before use dissolve 1 mg/ml fast red TR salt or fast blue BB salt in distilled water and add 40 μl/ml naphthol AS-BI alkaline solution.

Steps

1. Lay the freshly killed animal on its back and soak the abdomen with 70% alcohol. Naturally mated pregnant CD-1 mice are employed in the author's laboratory. The morning of a vaginal plug is found is considered 0.5 day post coitum (dpc). The developmental stage of embryos can be precisely determined by observing the morphology of the hindlimb bud (Fig. 1).

2. Pinch up the skin of the abdomen region between thumb and forefinger of both hands and pull it toward the head and tail until the abdomen is completely exposed and the fur is well out of the way.

3. Using forceps and fine scissors cut the body wall, push the coil of gut out of the way, and locate the two horns of the uterus.

4. Remove the uterus intact by cutting across the cervix and the two uterotubal junctions and trim away the fat and mesentery with fine scissors.

5. Transfer the uterus in a 60- or 100-mm petri dish in a volume of M2 medium sufficient to immerse the tissues completely, and remove any residual fat and mesentery. Transfer it to a second dish of medium and conduct all subsequent operations under the dissecting microscope.

6. Cut into individual decidua and remove the muscle layer with watchmaker's forceps.

7. Dissect the decidua as follows. Start by cutting off the mesometrial one-

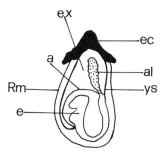

FIGURE 2 Schematic drawing showing the disposition of the embryo and membranes at 8.5 dpc. a, amnios; al, allantois; e, embryo; ec, ectoplacental cone; ex, exoceloma; ys, yolk sac; Rm, Reichert's membrane.

third of the decidua using forceps, pull the two halves of the remaining decidual tissues apart with forceps, and gently shell out the embryo.

8. Dissect the embryo from its surrounding membranes (Reichert's membrane, visceral yolk sac, and amnios, Figs. 2, 3A, and 3B) with watchmaker's forceps.

9. Locate the allantois in the caudal region of an 8.5-dpc embryo, and use two 25-gauge needles to hold the embryo and isolate the entire allantois and the posterior primitive streak (Fig. 3C).

10. The procedure for dissecting 10.5-dpc embryos is similar to that of steps 1–8, but there is relatively much less decidual tissue surrounding the larger embryos. After removal of the embryo's membranes, cut with scissors the anterior half of the embryo just below the armpits. Transfer to a dish of fresh medium the posterior half of the embryo and turn it onto its back. Under the stereomicroscope, hold the embryo fragment with the watchmaker's forceps and make a cut along the ventral midline. Remove viscera, and using the tips of the No. 5 forceps, peel away the dorsal mesentery and associated tissues from the more dorsal tissue of the embryo (Fig. 4).

11. Using a 100-μl Eppendorf pipette transfer to fresh medium the tissues dissected in steps 1–3, and then transfer them to a 1.5-ml Eppendorf tube containing 0.5 ml of a solution of trypsin–EDTA. After 1–2 min incubation at room temperature carefully remove the enzyme solution and wash the tissues two times with 1 ml of culture medium. Leave the tissues in about 100 μl of medium and pipette up and down with the Eppendorf pipette for their complete dispersion (about 10 strokes are usually sufficient).

12. Add culture medium to dilute the cell suspension and culture the cells under one of the conditions described in Sections D and E.

13. PGCs in the monodispersed cell suspension can be identified by their alkaline phosphatase (APase) content, and counted as follows. Transfer an aliquot (about 10–20 μl) of the cell suspension in serum-free medium to a polylysinated glass coverslip prepared following incubation for 1 hr at room temperature with 200 μg/ml poly-L-lysine in distilled water, three washings in distilled water, and air-drying. Cells will stick in a few minutes and can then be fixed (4% paraformaldehyde in PBS for 2–3 min). Wash three times with M2 or PBS and incubate in the dark in the chromogenic solution for APase detection. All steps are carried out at room temperature. APase-positive PGCs strongly stain red (fast red) or blue (fast blue) after 20–30 min (Fig. 5).

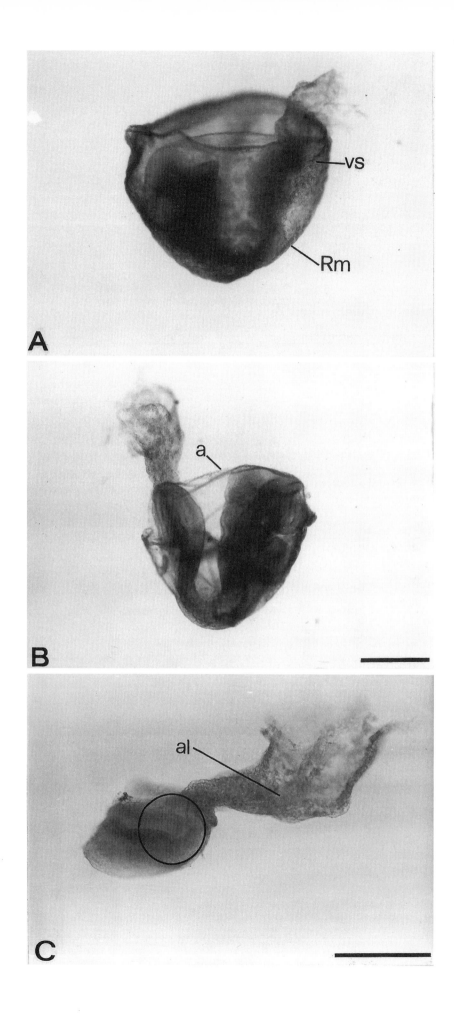

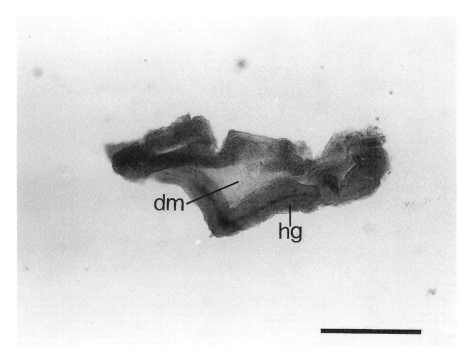

FIGURE 4 Dorsal mesentery (dm) and part of the gut dissected from a 10.5-dpc embryo. hg, hind gut. Bar = 0.25 mm.

Comments

Approximately 20–30 and 250–300 PGCs can be obtained from each 8.5- and 10.5-dpc embryo, respectively.

Pitfalls

The APase staining solution must be used within 15–30 min from preparation. The presence of serum in the medium reduces PGC attachment to poly-L-lysine-coated coverslips.

B. ISOLATION OF GERM CELLS FROM 11.5- TO 13.5-dpc EMBRYOS

Around 11.5 dpc, PGCs begin to colonize gonadal ridges and are called prospermatogonia in the male and oogonia in the female. They lose their motile phenotype but continue to proliferate until 13–14 dpc, reaching the maximum number of about 25,000 per embryo (Tam and Snow, 1981). On entering meiotic prophase (around 13.5 dpc), oogonia become primary oocytes.

FIGURE 3 Final stages in the dissection of allantois and posterior primitive streak from an 8.5-dpc mouse embryo. (A) Embryo within the Reichert's membrane (Rm) and visceral yolk sac (vs). (B) Visceral yolk sac has been opened, revealing amnios (a) and the embryo within. (C) Allantois (al) and posterior primitive streak dissected. The circle indicates the area where PGCs are found. Bar = 0.5 mm for A and B and 0.25 mm for C.

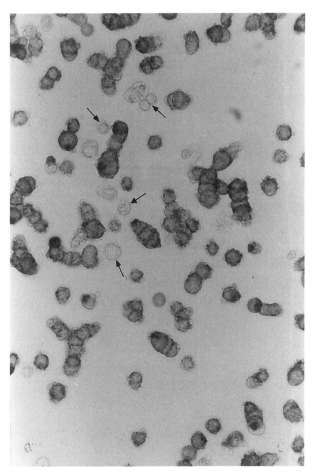

FIGURE 5 PGCs purified from an 11.5-dpc embryos and stained for APase. Unlabeled somatic cells are indicated by arrows.

Steps

1. Dissect the embryos as indicated in steps 1–6 of Section A. Alternatively to the procedure described in step 6, in this stage embryos with attached placenta can be dissected by cutting the antimesometrial wall of the uterus with the tips of scissors.

2. Remove Reichert's membrane, the visceral yolk sac, and the amnios by cutting away the embryo at the junction with the placenta with watchmaker's forceps, and proceed as in step 10 of Section A.

3. Remove the liver and intestine with watchmaker's forceps and identify the gonadal ridges lying on the dorsal wall of the embryo on either side of the abdominal aorta and adjacent to the mesonephroi (Fig. 6). Slide the tips of the forceps behind each gonadal ridge and mesonephros and cut them from the embryo.

4. Transfer the gonadal ridges and mesonephroi to fresh medium. Using needles, dissect the gonadal ridges from the mesonephroi while pressing the latter down on the plastic culture dish.

5. Dissociate the gonadal tissues following the procedure described in step 11 of Section A.

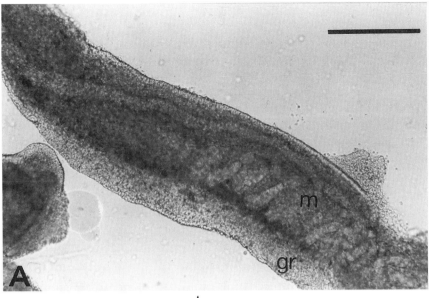

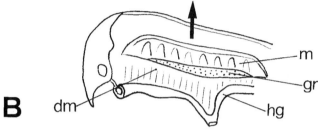

FIGURE 6 (A) Gonadal ridge and mesonephros dissected from an 11.5-dpc embryo. (B) Schematic drawing of the gonadal ridge location in the dorsal wall of the posterior half of an 11.5-dpc embryo after removal of the liver and part of the viscera. m, mesonephros; gr, gonadal ridge; dm, dorsal mesentery; hg, hindgut. Bar = 0.25 mm.

Comments

From about 12.5 dpc onward, the testis can be identified by the presence of sex cords, which give it a striped appearance, and the ovary, by its granular aspect and smaller size (Fig. 7). Germ cells constitute about 20–30% of the total cell population, and average numbers of 1000 (11.5 dpc), 8000 (12.5 dpc), and 12,000 (13.5 dpc) PGCs per gonad can be obtained.

C. PURIFICATION OF GERM CELLS FROM 11.5- TO 13.5-dpc EMBRYOS

According to McCarrey *et al.* (1987), a 99% pure population of 12.5- to 13.5-dpc germ cells can be sorted out from the cell suspension obtained as described in step 11 of Section A. To this purpose, germ cells must be labeled with fluorescent monoclonal antibody EMA-1 and separated from somatic cells using a fluorescence-activated cell sorter.

I describe here an easier and more rapid procedure to obtain relatively pure germ cells (about 70–80%) from 11.5- to 13.5-dpc gonads.

Solutions

1. *EDTA in phosphate-buffered saline:* The formula is given in Table II.
2. *Percoll solution:* Percoll is made isosmotic with M2 by adding 9 parts (v/v)

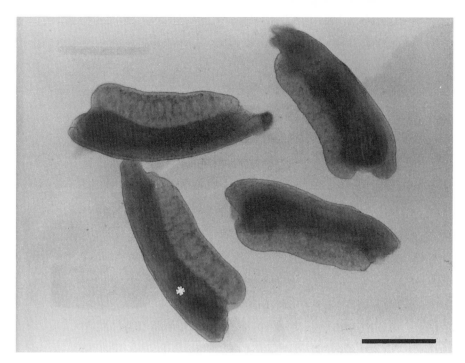

FIGURE 7 Testes (left) and ovaries (right) with attached mesenephroi (asterisk), isolated from 12.5-dpc embryos. Bar = 0.5 mm.

of Percoll to 1 part (v/v) of 10× concentrated M2. Solutions of stock isosmotic Percoll are diluted to lower concentrations (12, 25, and 65%) simply by diluting with normal-strength M2.

Steps

1. After step 3 of Section B, transfer gonadal ridges to EDTA–PBS solution for 15 min at room temperature. Return the ridges to M2 or to culture medium.

2. Using two 25-gauge needles hold and puncture the gonadal ridges. This releases germ cells but few of the somatic cells.

3. From this cell suspension germ cells can be further purified (up to 90%)

TABLE II PBS–EDTA Solution for Germ Cell Isolation[a]

Component	g/100 ml ultrapure H_2O
EDTA	0.01
NaCl	0.80
KCl	0.02
$Na_2HPO_4 \cdot 2H_2O$	0.115
KH_2PO_4	0.02
Glucose	0.02
Phenol red	0.001

[a] The final EDTA concentration is 0.01%. Check that the pH is 7.2–7.3. Sterilize by 0.25-μm filtration. The solution is stored at 4°C and can be used for at least 1 month.

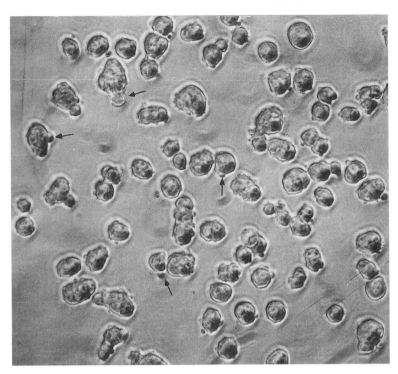

FIGURE 8 Germ cells from 12.5-dpc embryos purified by the EDTA–Percoll method. Note surface blebbing in most cells (arrows).

using a simple discontinuous gradient of Percoll (De Felici and McLaren, 1982). Briefly, collect the cell suspension obtained in step 2 with a mouth-operated glass micropipette and resuspend it in a 25% Percoll solution (final concentration), containing 2.5% FCS and 10 μg/ml DNase; place 1.5 ml of a 65% Percoll solution in a Falcon plastic tube (Cat. No. 2058) and gently layer the cell suspension on top of it; overlay the cell suspension with 1 ml of 12% Percoll; centrifuge at 200 g for 20 min at room temperature in a swinging-bucket bench-top centrifuge; discard the top 2.6 ml and collect germ cells in the next 0.5 ml.

4. If only a few hundred cells are needed, germ cells can be singly collected with a mouth-operated glass micropipette under the stereomicroscope, as they are easily identified by their morphology; they are large and have a smooth, often blebby surface (Fig. 8). Almost 100% of the cells collected in such fashion are APase positive.

Comments

With the EDTA-puncturing method, approximately 400 (11.5 dpc), 3000 (12.5 dpc), and 8000 (13.5 dpc) germ cells per gonad can be obtained (purity 70–80%); 20–25 stabs are sufficient to release germ cells. A heavier puncturing releases more germ cells but also increases the contamination with somatic cells.

The EDTA–Percoll procedure allows one person in a total time of 2–3 hr to collect up to 3000, 20,000, or 50,000 viable germ cells from five 11.5-, 12.5-, or 13.5-dpc embryos, respectively, a reasonable single-sex yield from a pregnant female.

Pitfalls

Avoid incubation of gonads in EDTA solution for more than 15–20 min; this may be harmful to cells. To release the greatest possible number of PGCs, puncture gonads immediately after EDTA treatment, as this treatment is rapidly reversible.

D. CULTURE OF PGC-CONTAINING TISSUES FROM 8.5- TO 11.5-dpc EMBRYOS

Steps

1. Make a suitable dilution with culture medium of the cell suspension obtained as reported in Section A, to obtain an almost confluent somatic cell monolayer after 1 day of culture. We usually seed cells obtained from 2 and 1 embryo, for 8.5- and 10.5–11.5 dpc embryos, respectively, into each well of a 96-well Falcon tissue culture plate in 250 μl of medium.

2. To improve PGC survival and proliferation add to the culture medium 10 ng/ml stem cell factor (SCF) also known as mastocyte growth factor (MGF), stem factor (SF), or kit ligand (KL), 20 ng/ml leukemia inhibitory factor (LIF) also known as differentiation-inhibiting activity (DIA), and 20 μM forskolin (FRSK).

3. After 1–3 days of culture (with daily changes of medium), identify PGCs by APase staining (see Section A).

Comments

If cells are cultured in the absence of growth factors and FRSK, the number of APase-positive cells progressively declines and after 3 days of culture it is less than 10% (8.5-dpc PGCs), about 20% (10.5-dpc PGCs) or less than 10% (11.5-dpc PGCs) the initial value. On the other hand, after 3 days of culture in the presence of LIF, SCF, and FRSK, the numbers of 8.5- and 10.5-dpc PGCs are about 4- and 2.5-fold higher than at the beginning of the culture, respectively; the number of 11.5-dpc PGCs declines to about 35% the initial value (Dolci *et al.*, 1993).

Pitfalls

If a confluent somatic cell monolayer does not form, PGC survival is poor already after 1 day of culture even in the presence of SCF, LIF, and FRSK.

E. COCULTURE OF PGC-CONTAINING TISSUES (8.5–11.5 dpc) OR PURIFIED GERM CELLS (11.5–13.5 dpc) ON A TM$_4$ CELL FEEDER LAYER

Steps

1. Feeder layers of TM$_4$ cells (a cell line derived from mouse Sertoli cells, available from American Type Culture Collection) are prepared by seeding 0.25 or 0.5 ml of cell suspension (about 10^5 cell/ml, in modified MEM supplemented with 5% HS and 2.5% FCS, see Section A) into the wells of 96- or 24-well Falcon tissue culture plates, respectively. After 1 day, TM$_4$ cells form nearly confluent monolayers that can be maintained for 3 additional days (daily changes of medium).

2. Seed PGC-containing tissue suspensions (about 0.5–1 embryo equivalent per well) or purified PGCs (about 10^3 cells/well) onto nearly confluent TM$_4$ cell feeder layers.

3. To improve PGC survival and proliferation, add to the culture medium 20 ng/ml LIF and 20 μM FRSK.

4. After 1–3 days of culture, identify PGCs by APase staining (see Section A).

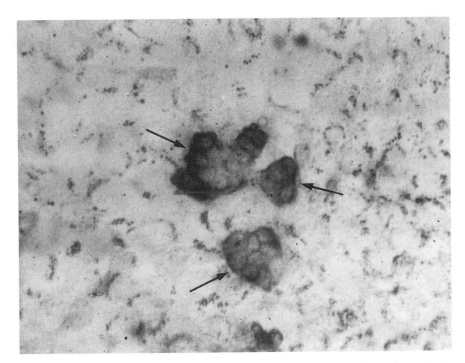

FIGURE 9 Colonies of APase-positive 10.5-dpc PGCs (arrows) after 3 days of culture on TM₄ cell feeder layers.

Comments

These are the best culture conditions for long-lasting survival and proliferation of PGCs. In the laboratory of the author, TM₄ cell feeder layers have been routinely employed to culture PGCs up to 3 days. Initially, PGCs are identifiable as single cells which eventually form colonies by aggregation or clonal division (Fig. 9). If longer culture periods (up to 7–9 days) are needed (i.e., to develop EG cells from PGCs), X-irradiated or mitomycin C-treated STO cell feeder layers or an Sl⁴-m220 cell line, which stably expresses membrane-bound murine SCF, should be used (Matsui *et al.,* 1992; Resnick *et al.,* 1992).

F. CULTURE OF ISOLATED GERM CELLS FROM 13.5-dpc OR OLDER EMBRYOS

When cultured in the absence of somatic cells, PGCs isolated from 11.5- and 12.5-dpc embryos survive for a few hours only (De Felici and McLaren, 1983) and rapidly undergo apoptosis (Pesce *et al.,* 1993). From 13.5 dpc onward, however, cultured germ cells survive for 3–4 days, undergoing some mitotic proliferation and meiotic progression (De Felici and McLaren, 1983; Wabik-Sliz and McLaren, 1984).

Steps

1. Plate about 10^4 germ cells/ml in modified DMEM (see Section A) with 10% FCS in 96-well tissue culture dish (250 μl/well) and carry out the culture in 5% CO_2/air in a humidified incubator at 37°C.

2. Alternatively, culture germ cells in 100-μl drops of the same medium in 35-mm Falcon petri tissue culture dishes under paraffin oil.

Comments

Under such culture conditions most of the germ cells fail to adhere to the plastic surface and form clumps of several cells. On the contrary, contaminating somatic cells attach to the culture dish and spread.

ACKNOWLEDGMENTS

I thank Dr. Maurizio Pesce for help in preparing this article and Professor Gregorio Siracusa and Susanna Dolci for critical reading of the manuscript. Work performed in the author's laboratory has been supported by grants: MURST (40% and 60%) and CNR Progetto Finalizzato FAT.MA No. 93.00738.PF41.

REFERENCES

De Felici, M., and McLaren, A. (1982) Isolation of mouse primordial germ cells. *Exp. Cell Res.* **142**, 476–482.

De Felici, M., and McLaren, A. (1983) *In vitro* culture of mouse primordial germ cells. *Exp. Cell Res.* **144**, 417–427.

De Felici, M., Dolci, S., and Pesce, M. (1992) Cellular and molecular aspects of mouse primordial germ cell migration and proliferation in culture. *Int. J. Dev. Biol.* **36**, 205–213.

Dolci, S., Pesce, M., and De Felici, M. (1993) Combined action of stem cell factor, leukemia inhibitory factor and cAMP on *in vitro* proliferation of mouse primordial germ cells. *Mol. Reprod. Dev.* **35**, 134–139.

Matsui, Y., Zsebo, K., and Hogan, R. (1992) Derivation of pluripotential embryonic stem cells from murine primordial germ cells in culture. *Cell* **70**, 841–847.

McCarrey, J. R., Hsu, K. C., Eddy, E. M., Klevecs, R. R., and Bolen, J. L. (1987) Isolation of viable mouse primordial germ cells by antibody-directed flow sorting. *J. Exp. Zool.* **242**, 107–111.

Pesce, M., Farrace, M. G., Piacentini, M., Dolci, S., and De Felici, M. (1993) Stem cell factor and leukemia inhibitory factor promote primordial germ cell survival by suppressing programmed cell death (apoptosis). *Development* **118**, 1089–1094.

Quinn, P., Barros, C., and Whittingham, D. G. (1982) Preservation of hamster oocytes to assay the fertilization capacity of human spermatozoa. *J. Reprod. Fertil.* **66**, 161–168.

Resnick, J. L., Bixler, L. S., Cheng, L., and Donovan, P. (1992) Long-term proliferation of mouse primordial germ cells in culture. *Nature* **359**, 550–551.

Tam, P. P. L., and Snow, M. H. L. (1981) Proliferation and migration of primordial germ cells during compensatory growth in mouse embryo. *J. Embryol. Exp. Morphol.* **64**, 133–147.

Wabik-Sliz, B., and McLaren, A. (1984) Culture of mouse germ cells from fetal gonads. *Exp. Cell Res.* **154**, 530–536.

SECTION C

Cultures of Specific Cell Types

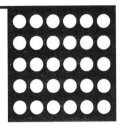

Cultivation of Human Epidermal Keratinocytes with a 3T3 Feeder Layer

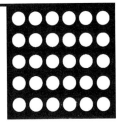

Fiona M. Watt

I. Introduction

There are many techniques for culturing human epidermal keratinocytes (see also articles by John P. Daley and Jean M. Donovan and by Craig Meyers, Mark G. Frattini, and Laimonis A. Laimins in this volume), but the method I describe here is the one devised by Jim Rheinwald and Howard Green (Rheinwald and Green, 1975). With this method, keratinocytes grow as multilayered sheets in which proliferation is confined to the basal layer and terminal differentiation takes place in the suprabasal layers, thus mimicking the spatial organization of normal epidermis. The cultures have a range of applications in basic research and in the clinic. They are used to study the factors that regulate stem cell proliferation, the initiation of terminal differentiation and tissue assembly, as well as the process of neoplastic transformation (Watt, 1989; Jones and Watt, 1993). Practical applications include the treatment of burn victims with cultured autografts (Compton *et al.*, 1989) and, potentially, the use of transduced keratinocytes as vehicles for gene therapy (see, e.g., Gerrard *et al.*, 1993).

What follows is a description of the procedures my laboratory uses to initiate and maintain cultures of keratinocytes from neonatal foreskins; it is based on the original Rheinwald and Green method, which has been progressively improved over the years as described by Rheinwald (1989). The key component of the culture system is the presence of a feeder layer of 3T3 cells that supports the growth of keratinocytes from clonal seeding densities.

II. Materials and Instrumentation

FAD powder [three parts Dulbecco's modified Eagle's medium (DMEM) and 1 part Ham's F12 medium (F12) supplemented with 1.8×10^{-4} M adenine] can be purchased from Imperial Laboratories. Alternatively, F12 (powder, Cat. No. 3-751) and DMEM (powder, Cat. No. 3-450) can be bought separately from Imperial Laboratories and adenine can be purchased from Boehringer-Mannheim (Cat. No. 102-067) (Lewes, Bell Lane, East Sussex, UK). Penicillin and streptomycin can be purchased from Imperial Laboratories (Cat. No. 4-804-07). A suitable supplier of fetal calf serum (FCS) and newborn calf serum (NCS) is Imperial Laboratories (FCS: Cat. No. 6-000-14, NCS: Cat. No. 6-010-14). Hydrocortisone is purchased from Calbiochem Novabiochem (UK) Ltd. (Cat No. 386 698). Cholera enterotoxin is from ICN Biomedicals Ltd. (Cat. No. 190329). Epidermal growth factor (EGF) is purchased from Austral Biologicals (Cat. No. GF-010-9). Insulin is purchased from Sigma Chemical Company Ltd. (Cat. No. I 5500).

Mitomycin C is obtained from Sigma (Catalog No. M0503). Trypsin (0.25%) can be purchased from Imperial Laboratories (Cat. No. 4-770-07). EDTA (2%) can also be obtained from Imperial Laboratories (Cat. No. 4-778-07). Mikrozid is purchased from Sanofi Winthrop Medicare. Dimethyl sulfoxide, (DMSO, D/4121) is obtained from FSA Laboratory Supplies. CelStirs are made by Wheaton, USA (Catalog No. 356533; Wheaton products are available through Jencons Scientific Ltd.). Cryotubes are purchased from Nunc (Cat No. 3-63401).

III. Procedures

A. THE FEEDER LAYER

Solutions

1. *Culture medium for 3T3 J2 cells:* This consists of DMEM supplemented with 100 IU/ml penicillin, 100 μg/ml streptomycin, and 10% newborn calf serum. It is essential to batch-test the serum for optimal growth of 3T3 J2.

2. *Trypsin/EDTA:* Mix 1 part 0.25% trypsin and 4 parts 0.02% EDTA [e.g., 2% stock diluted 1:100 with phosphate buffered saline (PBS)]. The same solution is used to harvest keratinocytes.

3. *Phosphate-buffered saline:* To make 1 liter, dissolve 0.2 g KCl, 0.2 g KH$_2$PO$_4$, 8.0 g NaCl, and 2.16 g Na$_2$HPO$_4 \cdot$7H$_2$O in 900 ml distilled water. Adjust pH to 7.4, add distilled water to 1-liter final volume, autoclave, and store at room temperature.

4. *Mitomycin C in PBS:* Prepare a stock solution of 0.4 mg/ml in PBS. Filter sterilize and store in aliquots at $-20°$C.

1. Cells

The J2 clone of random-bred Swiss mouse 3T3 cells was selected to provide optimal feeder support of keratinocytes (Rheinwald, 1989). The cells are maintained by weekly passaging at 1:10 to 1:20 dilution. Fresh cells are thawed every 3 months, since with prolonged passaging the cells start to senesce or undergo spontaneous transformation.

2. Preparing the Feeder Layer

Steps

1. To irreversibly inhibit proliferation, add mitomycin C (final concentration, 4 μg/ml) to confluent flasks of 3T3 J2 and incubate for 2 hr at 37°C.

2. Remove the medium, rinse the cells once with 0.02% EDTA, and then harvest in trypsin/EDTA. The optimal density of the feeder layer is one-third confluent (Rheinwald and Green, 1975; Rheinwald, 1989); hence each mitomycin C-treated flask is effectively split 1:3.

3. The feeders can be used immediately (i.e., plated at the same time as the keratinocytes) or prepared 1–2 days before they are required; if prepared in advance they are maintained in DMEM + 10% NCS. The feeder layer should not be prepared more than 2 days before use, because the feeder cells will start to degenerate.

B. KERATINOCYTE CULTURE MEDIUM

Solutions

1. *Hydrocortisone:* Prepare a 5 mg/ml stock in absolute ethanol. Store at −20°C.

2. *Cholera enterotoxin:* Prepare a 10^{-5} M stock in distilled water. Store at 4°C.

3. *EGF:* Prepare a 100 μg/ml stock in FAD + FCS. Store at −20°C.

4. *Insulin:* Prepare a 5 mg/ml solution in 5 mM hydrochloric acid. Store at −20°C.

Steps

1. The basic medium consists of three parts DMEM and 1 part F12 supplemented with 1.8×10^{-4} M adenine (FAD), 100 IU/ml penicillin, and 100 μg/ml streptomycin. Store at 4°C.

2. FAD is supplemented with 10% FCS. It is essential to batch test the serum for its ability to support high colony-forming efficiency, rapid growth, and serial passage of keratinocytes. The serum batches that are optimal for keratinocytes tend to be completely unsuitable for fibroblastic cells or hybridomas. FCS is stored at −20°C before use.

3. FAD + FCS is further supplemented with HICE cocktail, consisting of hydrocortisone (0.5 μg/ml), insulin (5 μg/ml), cholera enterotoxin (10^{-10} M), and EGF (10 ng/ml) (all final concentrations).

4. Complete medium (FAD + FCS + HICE) is stored at 4°C and used within 1 week.

C. SOURCE OF KERATINOCYTES

The starting source of keratinocytes is neonatal foreskin obtained from routine circumcisions. When handling any human tissue it is essential to take appropriate precautions against transmission of infectious agents. The foreskin is obtained as soon as possible after circumcision and transferred to the laboratory dry in a sterile Bijou. If it cannot be used immediately, it is stored overnight at 4°C.

D. ISOLATION OF KERATINOCYTES

Solutions

1. *PBS containing 100 IU/ml penicillin and 100 μg/ml streptomycin.*

Other solutions are as described in Procedures A and B.

Steps

1. Rinse the foreskin thoroughly in PBS containing 100 IU/ml penicillin and 100 μg/ml streptomycin.

2. Transfer the tissue to a 100-mm-diameter petri dish, epidermis down. Remove as much connective tissue (muscle and dermis) as possible using sterile curved scissors.

3. Transfer the epidermis and remaining connective tissue to a fresh dish and chopped into fine pieces (1–3 mm^2) using scalpels.

4. Flood the dish with 10 ml trypsin/EDTA, and transfer the solution containing pieces of skin with a wide-bore Pasteur pipette to a sterile CelStir. A CelStir is an autoclavable glass vessel containing a magnet suspended by a rod from the lid. Solutions are introduced and removed via a side arm in the vessel.

5. Incubate the CelStir at 37°C for 30 min on a magnetic stirrer; allow the lumps of tissue to settle out and remove the supernatant.

6. Add fresh trypsin/EDTA and repeat the procedure.

7. Determine the number of cells in the supernatant with a hemocytometer (see article by Ariana Celis and Julio E. Celis in this volume); collect the cells by centrifugation and resuspend in FAD + FCS + HICE. There are usually no cells from the first incubation, then $1–5 \times 10^6$ per subsequent incubation.

8. After four or five incubations the yield starts to decline; discard any remaining lumps of tissue.

9. Pool cells from each incubation and seed onto the feeder layer at a density of 5×10^5 per 75-cm^2 flask. The average yield per foreskin is approximately $5 \times 10^6–10^7$ cells.

10. After 2–3 days small colonies of keratinocytes are visible, surrounded by 3T3 J2 feeder cells (Fig. 1a). Over the following week, individual colonies expand, displacing the feeder layer and merging with one another. At confluence virtually no feeder cells remain (Fig. 1b). Feed the cells with fresh medium three times per week.

E. PASSAGING KERATINOCYTES

Solutions are as described in Procedures A and B.

Steps

1. Passage keratinocytes prior to confluence (approximately 7–10 days after plating). Remove the medium and rinse the cultures once with 0.02% EDTA.

2. Add fresh EDTA and incubate the cultures at 37°C for about 5 min. Then selectively detach the feeders by gentle aspiration with a pipette (Rheinwald, 1989).

3. To detach the keratinocytes, add trypsin/EDTA (see Procedure A, Solution 2) to the flasks and incubate at 37°C for about 10 min.

4. Transfer the cells to a centrifuge tube; use a small volume of culture medium to rinse the flask and then add it to the tube, inactivating the trypsin.

5. Recover the cells by centrifugation, count in a hemocytometer, and resuspend in complete medium.

6. Cells can be passaged at a density of $1–2 \times 10^5$ per 75-cm^2 flask.

F. FROZEN STOCKS OF KERATINOCYTES AND 3T3 J2 CELLS

Solution

1. *10% DMSO/90% fetal calf serum.*

Steps

1. We use most of the primary keratinocyte cultures to prepare frozen stocks; experiments are carried out on second and subsequent passages.

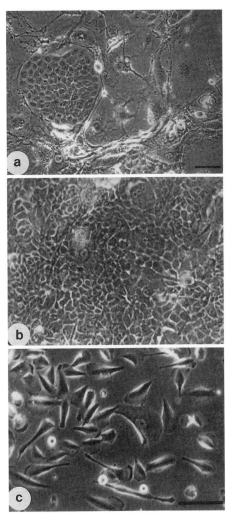

FIGURE 1   Phase-contrast micrographs of keratinocytes (a, b) and ndk (c). (a) Colony of keratinocytes surrounded by 3T3 J2 feeder layer. Reproduced, with permission, from Watt, F. M. (1988) *BioEssays* 8, 163–167. Scale bar = 100 μm. (b) Confluent sheet of keratinocytes (c) ndk cells. Scale bar in b and c = 50 μm. b and c reproduced from Adams and Watt (1988) with copyright permission of the Rockefeller University Press.

2. For freezing, harvest the keratinocytes as described above, but resuspend at 10^6/ml in 10% DMSO, 90% fetal calf serum.

3. Place 1 ml of cell suspension in each 1.8-ml Nunc CryoTube.

4. Place the tubes in a rubber rack wrapped in cotton wool overnight at −70°C and then transfer to liquid nitrogen (see also article by Ariana Celis and Julio E. Celis in this volume).

5. Freeze the 3T3 J2 cells in the same way.

IV. Comments

It is possible to obtain up to 100 population doublings of neonatal foreskin keratinocytes prior to senescence (Rheinwald, 1989). The number of passages prior to senescence varies between cell strains: 5 is the minimum, 10 the average, and numbers greater than 20 have been observed occasionally. The same basic culture procedure can be used to grow keratinocytes from adults (although the number of population doublings obtained will be somewhat reduced) and from other stratified squamous epithelia such as the lining of the mouth and the exocervix (Rheinwald, 1989).

V. Pitfalls

1. Under these culture conditions fibroblast contamination is very rarely a problem, because the feeder layer suppresses the growth of any human fibroblasts isolated from the skin at the same time as the keratinocytes (Rheinwald and Green, 1975). We have, however, noted that some strains of keratinocytes contain ndk-like cells. The original strain of cells known as ndk (for nondifferentiating keratinocytes) outgrew the normal keratinocytes in the culture at passage 3 (Adams and Watt, 1988); we have not seen this in other keratinocyte strains, but we do not recommend using keratinocyte cultures containing ndk-like cells for experiments. The ndk cells have a distinctive morphology (Fig. 1c) and although they have a number of characteristics of normal keratinocytes, such as expression of keratins 5, 14, 6, and 16 in culture, they do not undergo terminal differentiation and have some properties that are not shared with normal keratinocytes, such as production of scatter factor/hepatocyte growth factor (Adams *et al.,* 1991) and expression of the $\alpha_V\beta_1$ and $\alpha_V\beta_3$ integrins (Adams and Watt, 1991).

2. When keratinocytes are plated in culture there is selective attachment of the basal cells, but within 1 day the cultures consist of a mixture of basal and terminally differentiating keratinocytes (e.g., Jones and Watt, 1993). Seeding keratinocytes at high density appears, in our experience, to promote terminal differentiation and is not, therefore, the answer if you are in a hurry to obtain more cells.

3. Since keratinocytes are maintained in culture for long periods it is essential to be scrupulous in sterile technique and laboratory cleanliness to avoid fungal or bacterial contamination. We spray our incubators three times a week with Mikrozid.

4. Finally, it is essential to be well organized and plan your experiments in advance. It takes about 10 days from plating for keratinocytes to be ready for use and sufficient feeders must be available on the days when keratinocytes are ready for passaging.

REFERENCES

Adams, J. C., Furlong, R. A., and Watt, F. M. (1991) Production of scatter factor by ndk, a strain of epithelial cells, and inhibition of scatter factor activity by suramin. *J. Cell Sci.* **98,** 385–394.

Adams, J. C., and Watt, F. M. (1988) An unusual strain of human keratinocytes which do not stratify or undergo terminal differentiation in culture. *J. Cell Biol.* **107,** 1927–1938.

Adams, J. C., and Watt, F. M. (1991) Expression of β_1, β_3, β_4, and β_5 integrins by human epidermal keratinocytes and non-differentiating keratinocytes. *J. Cell Biol.* **115,** 829–841.

Compton, C. C., Gill, J. M., Bradford, D. A., Regauer, S., Gallico, G. G., and O'Connor, N. E. (1989). Skin regenerated from cultured epithelial autografts on full-thickness burn wounds from 6 days to 5 years after grafting. A light, electron microscopic and immunohistochemical study. *Lab. Invest.* **60,** 600–612.

Gerrard, A. J., Hudson, D. L., Brownlee, G. G., and Watt, F. M. (1993) Towards gene therapy for haemophilia B using primary human keratinocytes. *Nature Genet.* **3,** 180–183.

Jones, P. H., and Watt, F. M. (1993) Separation of human epidermal stem cells from transit amplifying cells on the basis of differences in integrin function and expression. *Cell* **73**, 713–724.

Rheinwald, J. G. (1989) Methods for clonal growth and serial cultivation of normal human epidermal keratinocytes and mesothelial cells. In "Cell Growth and Division. A Practical Approach" IRL Press, Oxford. (R. Baserga, ed.), pp. 81–94.

Rheinwald, J. G., and Green, H. (1975) Serial cultivation of strains of human epidermal keratinocytes: The formation of keratinizing colonies from single cells. *Cell* **6**, 331–344.

Watt, F. M. (1989) Terminal differentiation of epidermal keratinocytes. *Curr. Opin. Cell Biol.* **1**, 1107–1115.

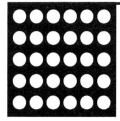

Growth of Human Keratinocytes in Serum-Free Medium

John P. Daley and Jean M. Donovan

I. Introduction

There are two principal methods for growing normal human keratinocytes in the tissue culture laboratory (see also articles by Fiona M. Watt and by Craig Meyers *et al.* in this volume). The first and oldest is the tissue explant method, discussed by Breidahl *et al.* (1989). The second method involves enzymatically dissociating the epidermis into a cell suspension and growing the keratinocytes as a suspension of single cells. In pioneering studies, Rheinwald and Green (1975) demonstrated that normal human keratinocytes could be enzymatically dissociated into a suspension of cells and grown in the tissue culture laboratory. Their procedure required that the dissociated cells be plated onto lethally irradiated mouse 3T3 cells in media containing several defined and undefined supplements [e.g., epidermal growth factor (EGF), cholera toxin, hydrocortisone, and fetal calf serum]. Ham and his colleagues demonstrated that the need for irradiated 3T3 cells could be eliminated if several defined supplements (e.g., trace elements, ethanolamine, phosphoethanolamine, triiodothyronine, and hydrocortisone) and one undefined component [i.e., bovine pituitary extract or (BPE)] were added to the defined basal medium MCDB 153 (Tsao *et al.*, 1982; Boyce and Ham, 1983). Commercially produced media are now available that allow the researcher to grow normal human keratinocytes in the laboratory without the need for an irradiated layer of feeder cells (Daley *et al.*, 1990).

II. Materials and Instrumentation

Neonatal foreskins are obtained from the nursery of a local hospital and used within 5 days of surgical excision. Gibco Keratinocyte-SFM (Cat. No. 320-7005PJ; recombinant EGF and BPE are supplied with the basal medium), gentamicin (Cat. No. 600-5750AD), Soybean trypsin inhibitor (Cat. No. 840-7075II), trypsin–EDTA (Cat. No. 610-5300AG), Dulbecco's phosphate-buffered saline without Ca^{2+} or Mg^{2+} (Cat. No. 310-4190AG), mouse type IV collagen (Cat. No. 680-3018IV) are purchased from Gibco-BRL.

Portable pipet-aid (Cat. No. 13-681-19), sterile disposable pipettes (5, 10, and 25 ml) (Cat. Nos. 13-675-22, 13-675-20, and 13-668-2), pipet tips (200 and 1000 μl; Cat. Nos. 21-197-8H and 21-197-8J), and sterile 15- and 50-ml polypropylene centrifuge tubes (Cat. Nos. 05-538-53D and 05-538-55) are obtained from Fisher Scientific. Gilson pipetmen (P20, P200, and P1000) were obtained from Rainin Instruments. Sterile tissue culture flasks (T25 and T75; Cat. Nos. 25103-25 and 25113-75) and sterile culture dishes (60 × 15 and 100 × 20 mm; Cat. Nos. 25010 and 25020) were obtained from Corning. Dispase (Cat. No. 40235) was obtained from Collaborative Research. Dissecting scissors (3.5 in.), dissecting forceps (4.75 in.), and straight forceps (4 in.) (Catalog Nos. 160-213, 160-52, and 160-15) were obtained from George Tiemann and Company. The IEC Centra-8R centrifuge was from Damon/IEC.

III. Procedures

NOTE

All tissue or cells of human origin should be considered potentially infectious and handled according to the CDC/NIH publication **"Biosafety in Microbiological and Biomedical Laboratories,"** HHS Publication No. (NIH) 88-8395.

A. CELL DISSOCIATION METHOD (DISPASE/TRYPSIN) FOR GROWING PRIMARY HUMAN KERATINOCYTES

Solutions

1. *Foreskin collection and transport medium:* Gibco Keratinocyte-SFM (without recombinant EGF or BPE), supplemented with 5 µg/ml of gentamicin.

2. *Fully supplemented Gibco keratinocyte-SFM:* Gibco Keratinocyte-SFM supplemented with recombinant EGF (0.1 ng/ml), BPE (25 µg/ml), and gentamicin (5 µg/ml).

3. *Dulbecco's phosphate-buffered saline (DPBS) without Ca^{2+} or Mg^{2+}:* To prepare 1× DPBS from a 10× concentrate (Gibco-BRL) dilute 1:10 with sterile distilled water.

4. *DPBS (without Ca^{2+} or Mg^{2+}) supplemented with gentamicin:* DPBS supplemented with either 5 or 20 µg/ml of gentamicin.

5. *0.05% trypsin, 0.53 mM EDTA:* Use as supplied by Gibco-BRL as a 1× solution.

6. *Dispase solution:* Dispase (100 ml of 5000 caseinolytic units/ml) is thawed on arrival and divided into 5-ml aliquots in 15-ml sterile centrifuge tubes. The material is refrozen and stored at −20°C until use. At the time of use, 5 ml of Dispase is thawed and mixed with 5 ml of Gibco Keratinocyte-SFM (without BPE or recombinant EGF).

7. *Soybean trypsin inhibitor:* Dissolve 1 g of Gibco soybean trypsin inhibitor (SBTI) in 100 ml of DPBS (without Ca^{2+} or Mg^{2+}). Sterile-filter the solution with a 0.2-µm cellulose acetate filter and store at 4°C or aliquot and store frozen at −20°C until use. If material is stored at 4°C, we routinely make fresh stock every 2 weeks. Frozen aliquots have been kept for up to 6 to 8 weeks before use.

8. *Collagen/DPBS:* Murine Collagen IV is supplied frozen at a concentration of 1 mg/ml. To make 50 ml at a final concentration of 5 µg/ml, dilute 50 µl of collagen to 50 ml with sterile DPBS.

---

1. Handling of Tissue(s) and Preparation of Cell Suspension for Growing Dissociated Primary Cells

Steps

1. At the hospital nursery, individual foreskins are placed into sterile 50-ml test tubes containing 10–15 ml cold collection/transport medium and kept at 4°C until use.

2. At the laboratory, each foreskin is rinsed in 5–10 ml of DPBS (without Ca^{2+} or Mg^{2+}) supplemented with gentamicin (20 µg/ml) for 30 min, at room temperature. With a pair of sterile forceps, each foreskin is transferred into a second antibiotic rinse for 5–10 min.

3. Using sterile surgical instruments, remove any fatty or other extraneous tissue from each foreskin.

4. Cut each foreskin into two to four pieces of approximately equal dimensions, dependent on the size of the tissue.

5. Dilute 5–10 ml of Dispase with an equal volume of Gibco Keratinocyte-SFM. Place this solution into a sterile 60-mm culture dish.

6. At this point, Pool all the foreskins and place each piece of tissue, dermis side down, into the 60-mm culture dish containing the Dispase solution. Seal the dish with Parafilm and incubate at 4°C for 18 hr. *We pool the cells from 5 to 10 donors for our experiments.*

7. Remove the pieces of tissue from the Dispase solution and place in 5–10 ml DPBS (without Ca^{2+} or Mg^{2+}) containing 20 µg/ml gentamicin.

8. Using a pair of sterile, fine-pointed forceps, separate the upper epidermis from the underlying dermis of each piece of tissue. Place the resulting epidermal sheets into a 100-mm culture dish containing 5 ml of trypsin–EDTA (0.05%, 0.53 mM EDTA).

9. Incubate the epidermal sheets at 37°C for 10–15 min. Gently pipette the tissue/cells every 2–3 min with a sterile, disposable 2-ml pipette.

10. Add 5 ml of the sterile soybean trypsin inhibitor to the culture dish to neutralize the trypsin.

11. Transfer the cells/SBTI from the culture dish to a sterile 50-ml centrifuge tube containing 10 to 15 ml of the SBTI solution. *At the end of the incubation period, several small pieces of "intact" tissue may still be present in the culture dish. Try not to include these intact pieces of tissue when transferring the cell suspension to the 50-ml centrifuge tube.*

12. Centrifuge the cell suspension for 10 min at room temperature at 85 g.

13. Decant the supernatant and gently resuspend the cell pellet in 5–10 ml of Gibco Keratinocyte-SFM (without BPE or recombinant EGF).

14. Count an aliquot of the cells using a hemocytometer (see article by Ariana Celis and Julio E. Celis in this volume). *We do not include in our cell count the more flattened and irregularly shaped differentiated/cornified cells but only those smaller more regularly shaped cells.*

15. Add the appropriate volume of fully supplemented Gibco Keratinocyte-SFM to the T25 or T75 culture vessel(s) and seed each vessel with an aliquot of the cell suspension. *For primary cells (i.e., cells going into culture for the first time), we use a seeding density of 3–5 $\times$ 10³ cells/cm² of surface area.*

16. Incubate the culture vessel(s), loosely capped, in a 5% CO_2 incubator at 37°C.

17. Fluid change the culture vessel(s) with a complete change of fully supplemented medium every 48–72 hr.

18. Passage the cells when they have grown to 75–80% confluency.

2. Handling and Preparation of Tissue(s) for Growth of Keratinocytes from Tissue Explants

a. Collagen coating of tissue culture plates

Steps

1. Prepare enough collagen/DPBS solution, at a final concentration of 5 μg/ml, to coat each 100-mm dish with 5 ml of the solution.

2. Place 5 ml of the collagen/sterile H_2O solution into each 100-mm tissue culture dish to be used. Wet the entire growth surface with the mixture by gently tilting the dish.

3. Incubate the dish/collagen for 30 min at room temperature. We leave the culture dishes in the biological safety cabinet for this incubation.

4. Following incubation, remove the collagen solution from each culture dish. Wash each dish with 5 ml of sterile H_2O. Leave the H_2O in the dish until you are ready to place the tissue pieces on to the dish.

B. PREPARATION OF NEONATAL FORESKINS FOR TISSUE EXPLANT METHOD

Solutions are as described under Protocol A.

Steps

1. The neonatal foreskins used for growing human keratinocytes from tissue explants are collected and initially prepared as is steps 1–3 above and then treated according to steps 2–10 below.

2. Rinse each foreskin, individually, in absolute ethanol by submerging the tissue for a maximum of 60 sec and immediately rinse the foreskin in DPBS. *This step must be done very carefully*; do not *submerge the tissue for more than 60 sec.*

3. Place the foreskin, dermis side down, on the surface of a sterile plastic culture dish. Using a sterile scalpel (we use a No. 22 round blade), cut the tissue into small (approximately 2-cm^2) squares of tissue.

4. Briefly rinse the squares of tissue in DPBS/gentamicin (5 μg/ml) and then place them in a sterile, dry culture dish to drain.

5. Remove the rinse water from the culture dish and transfer the tissue squares to a collagen-coated culture dish using sterile, fine-tipped forceps. Place them, dermis side down, arranged symmetrically around the dish (8–10 pieces per 100-mm dish).

6. Incubate the explant containing dishes for 30 min at 37°C, **without** tissue culture medium.

7. Following the above incubation, **very carefully and slowly** add 7 ml of fully supplemented Gibco Keratinocyte-SFM to the dish. *This is best achieved by using a sterile 10-ml disposable plastic pipette. Place the tip of the pipette on the* *surface of the culture dish and let the medium flow from the pipette so that the liquid slowly surrounds,* **but does not cover,** *the attached squares of tissue.*

8. Incubate the dish at 37°C in 5% CO_2 for 24 hr and then carefully add an additional 3 ml of medium to each dish.

9. Incubate the dishes as described above for 5–7 days before feeding the culture dishes with fresh, fully supplemented medium. Thereafter, feed the cultures with fresh medium every 48–72 hr.

10. We passage the keratinocytes in these explant cultures when the outgrowing cells from the most active tissue pieces begin to overlap.

C. SERIAL PASSAGING OF NORMAL HUMAN KERATINOCYTES BEYOND THE PRIMARY OR FIRST PASSAGE

Solutions are as described under Protocol A.

Steps

1. Remove the medium and tissue fragments from the culture vessel(s) and rinse the vessel(s) with DPBS (without Ca^{2+} or Mg^{2+}).

2. Add enough trypsin–EDTA to cover the surface of the vessel(s) and incubated for 10–15 min at 37°C. *Check the culture vessel(s) approximately every 5 min until the majority of the cells are detached and floating.*

3. Add 10–20 ml of soybean trypsin inhibitor to each culture vessel to neutralize the trypsin.

4. Centrifuge the cells at 85 *g* for 10 min.

5. Decant the supernatant and very gently resuspend the cell pellet(s) in 3–5 ml of fully supplemented Gibco Keratinocyte-SFM.

6. Count an aliquot of cells using a hemocytometer.

7. Aliquot fully supplemented Gibco Keratinocyte-SFM into T25 or T75 flasks.

8. Transfer an aliquot of cells to each culture vessel so that the cell density is $1–3 \times 10^3$ cells/cm². Incubate the culture vessels, loosely capped, in a 37°C, 5% CO_2 incubator.

9. Feed the culture vessels with a complete change of fully supplemented medium every 48–72 hr.

10. Passage the cells when they reach 75–80% confluency.

IV. Comments

By use of the protocols described in this article, normal human keratinocytes can be grown as primary cells and serially passaged. Color Plate 1 is a photomicrograph of a colony of primary keratinocytes, grown for 7 days as a cell suspension, demonstrating the typical "cobblestone" appearance. Color Plate 2 and 3 demonstrate the typical pattern of keratinocyte outgrowth from explants of neonatal foreskins at days 2 and 11 in culture.

V. Pitfalls

1. The major pitfalls when using either the dissociated cell or explant method of growing human keratinocytes in serum-free medium is the critical dependency of cell growth on BPE and EGF. Supplementing the basal medium with a less than optimal concentration of either component can significantly affect the growth rate and morphology of the cells. BPE at too high a concentration results in the inhibition of cell growth, whereas EGF at too high a concentration can result in the cells having an "abnormal" or "unhealthy" morphology in culture.

2. A major technical pitfall in growing keratinocytes from tissue explants is the tendency of the explant to become "unstuck" when the culture dishes are being handled. One needs to treat these cultures very gently when feeding or making observations under the microscope.

3. When growing keratinocytes from tissue explants, one frequently observes that not all the fragments of tissue have keratinocytes migrating from them. It is also observed that cells may not be migrating from and growing around a given explant in a uniform or symmetrical fashion. Pitfalls 2 and 3 are major factors, negatively impacting on the use of explants in quantitative studies.

REFERENCES

Boyce, S., and Ham, R. J. (1983) Calcium-regulated differentiation of normal human epidermal keratinocytes in chemically defined clonal culture and serum-free serial culture. *J. Invest. Dermatol.* **81**, 33S–40S.

Breidahl, A. F., Judson, R. T., and Clunie, G. J. (1989) Review of keratinocyte culture techniques: Problems of growing skin. *Aust. N.Z. J. Surg.* **59**, 458–497.

Daley, J. P., Hawley-Nelson, P., and Epstein, D. A. (1990) Growth of human epidermal keratinocytes in keratinocyte serum-free medium. *Focus* **12**, 68–71.

Rheinwald, J. G., and Green, H. (1975) Serial cultivation of strains of human epidermal keratinocytes: The formation of keratinizing colonies from single cells. *Cell* **6**, 331–344.

Tsao, M. C., Walthall, B. J., and Ham, R. G. (1982) Clonal growth of normal human epidermal keratinocytes in a defined medium. *J. Cell. Physiol.* **110**, 219–229.

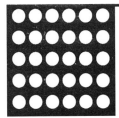

Isolation of Hepatocytes

Per O. Seglen

I. Introduction

Intact, isolated hepatocytes can be prepared in large quantity by the application of collagenase treatment (Howard and Pesch, 1968) to the perfused liver (Berry and Friend, 1969). Systematic studies of the collagenase perfusion technique (Seglen, 1972, 1973a,b) have established that optimal results are obtained by a two-step procedure, in which the isolated rat liver is perfused first with a Ca^{2+}-free buffer (or with EGTA) to separate the desmosomal cell contacts, then with collagenase *and* Ca^{2+} (an obligatory activator of the enzyme) to dissolve the extracellular matrix. The two-step procedure can be performed with a very simple perfusion apparatus (Seglen, 1976) and results in the complete dissociation of the liver (~100% yield) within 10–15 min, usually with 90–95% of the hepatocytes remaining structurally intact (Seglen, 1976). While most experimental studies have been performed with rat hepatocytes, the procedure is, with minor adjustments (such as the use of individual lobes or liver pieces instead of the whole liver), applicable to any animal, including humans (Müller *et al.*, 1976; Walton and Cowey, 1979; Reese and Byard, 1981).

II. Materials and Instrumentation

A. REAGENTS AND MATERIALS

Collagenase type IV (Cat. No. C5138) and other biochemicals were obtained from Sigma Chemical Company. Nylon filters (Nytal) of 100- and 250-μm mesh width were from Schweizer Seidengazefabrik AG, Thal, Switzerland, and the stainless-steel net (0.67-mm mesh width) used in the liver support dish was from F. Burmeister A/S (Cat. No. 18/8-25). Square (10 × 10-cm) plastic dishes (Cat. No. 109) were from Sterilin Ltd. The 1.19 × 1.50-mm nylon tubing used for portal cannulation was taken from a Portex Intravenous Cannula Set (Cat. No. E1045) from Portex Ltd. The perfusion pump, a Multifix M 80 equipped with a 1:36 gear (Cat. No. M 850:2), and silicone rubber tubing of various sizes were purchased from Heigar & Company. Custommade glassware was from JM Glassteknikk Skandinavia A/S. Dogs' combs of stainless steel were purchased in a pet shop, and every second comb tooth removed to obtain sufficient spacing (2–3 mm).

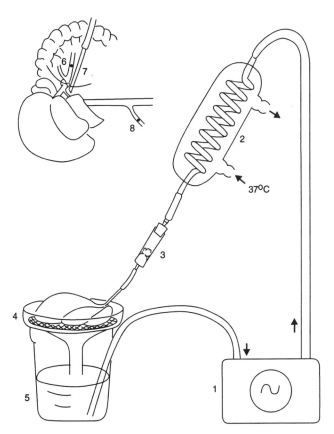

FIGURE 1 Perfusion apparatus. (1) perfusion pump; (2) heating unit; (3) filter/cannula unit; (4) liver support dish; (5) perfusate reservoir. The *inset* illustrates the cannulation of the portal vein; (6) insertion site for portal cannula; (7) prepositioning of the portal cannula tip just past the portal ligature; (8) suitable heparin injection site (iliolumbar vein).

B. PERFUSION APPARATUS

The standard apparatus (Fig. 1) has been designed for rat liver perfusion and should be scaled up or down for use with larger or smaller animals. It consists of the following parts:

1. *Perfusion pump:* A perstaltic pump of variable capacity (10–70 ml/min) is equipped with 2 × 4-mm silicone rubber tubing. The tubing should be as short as possible, and in one piece, to prevent gas trapping and bubble formation.

2. *Heating unit:* A water-jacketed glass coil is connected to a thermostated circulating water bath, maintaining the perfusate temperature at 37°C. The coil is custommade of 2 × 4-mm glass tubing, consisting of 22–24 turns, with a coil diameter of 3 cm and a coil length of 10 cm. The heating unit is clamped to a flexible lamp holder which allows movement in all directions, thus facilitating an exact positioning of the portal cannula.

3. *Filter/cannula unit:* A combined filter/bubble trap/cannula unit is made of a 5-cm piece of 8 × 10-mm silicone rubber tubing, stoppered with 1.5-cm rubber bungs at both ends. The bungs are pierced with stainless-steel tubing cut from a 1.5 × 1.9-mm Wasserman cannula. At one end of the unit the steel tube is covered with 1 × 3-mm silicone rubber tubing and connected to the 2 × 4-mm efflux tubing (about 10 cm) from the heated coil (this bung remains permanently connected with the coil unit); at the other end the steel tube is connected by a 3-

cm piece of 1×3-mm silicone rubber tubing to the portal cannula. The cannula is a 3- to 4-cm piece of autoclavable 1.2×1.5-mm Portex nylon tubing, cut at the tip at an angle of approximately 45°. A small cotton wool plug is used as filter; the unit should be filled with perfusion fluid before insertion of the cotton to avoid air trapping.

C. LIVER SUPPORT DISH

The isolated liver is supported on a disk-shaped stainless-steel net (to ensure effective capillary drainage from the cut portal vein orifice), lying in a custommade glass dish, 8 cm in diameter, with a conical outlet. The dish is placed on top of a 150-ml beaker serving as a reservoir for the recirculating perfusate. To establish recirculation, the end of the tubing leading to the pump is simply immersed into the reservoir.

D. OPERATING STAGE

A stainless-steel tray (preferably one that can contain about 500 ml of fluid) is used as support for the rat during operation.

III. Procedures

A. PERFUSION

Solutions

Concentrated stock solutions are stored in 15-ml glass tubes as frozen 10-ml portions sufficient for one cell preparation.

1. *Calcium concentrate:* 4.5 g $CaCl_2 \cdot 2H_2O$; H_2O to 500 ml.

2. *Ca/Mg concentrate:* 1.3 g $MgCl_2 \cdot 6H_2O$ and 1.8 g $CaCl_2 \cdot 2H_2O$; H_2O to 500 ml.

3. *Perfusion buffer concentrate:* 207.5 g NaCl, 12.5 g KCl, 60.0 g Hepes, and 6 g solid NaOH; H_2O to 1000 ml.

4. *Suspension buffer concentrate:* 40.0 g NaCl, 4.0 g KCl, 1.5 g KH_2PO_4, 1.0 g Na_2SO_4, 72.0 g Hepes, 69.0 g Tes, 65.0 g Tricine, and 21.0 g solid NaOH; H_2O to 1000 ml.

5. *Collagenase buffer concentrate:* Dissolve 1.25 g collagenase (Sigma type IV) in 200 ml H_2O; then add 1.75 g $CaCl_2 \cdot 2H_2O$. Dissolve 10 g NaCl, 1.25 g KCl, 60.0 g Hepes, and 6.6 g solid NaOH in 250 ml H_2O. Mix the two solutions and add H_2O to 500 ml. Filter the solution through a millipore serum filter.
The final buffers are routinely made by dilution and mixing of the concentrates on the day before cell isolation and stored overnight at 0°C or 37°C as specified.

6. *Perfusion buffer:* 20 ml perfusion buffer concentrate, H_2O to 500 ml; pH 7.4 at 37°C. Saturate the buffer with oxygen by bubbling. Cover the bottle opening with Parafilm, in which a small puncture is made for outlet of excess gas on heating. Store overnight at 37°C. This prolonged temperature equilibration prevents the bubble formation often observed on rapid heating.

7. *Collagenase buffer (0.05% collagenase):* 10 ml collagenase buffer concentrate, H_2O to 50 ml; pH 7.6 at 37°C. Store at 0°C in a 50-ml measuring

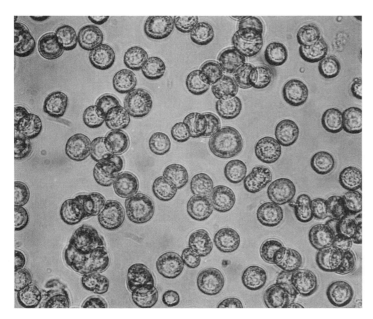

FIGURE 2   Final preparation of isolated rat hepatocytes. ×230.

cylinder covered with Parafilm. The buffer should be warmed to and maintained at 37°C for at least 15 min prior to use.

Steps

1. Heat the perfusion buffer to 37°C and pump it (at low speed) directly from the bottle into the apparatus. Fill the detached filter unit with fluid and insert the cotton wool plug (air-free); then assemble the unit.

2. Place the rat in a 5-liter glass beaker inside a fume hood and anesthetize it by pouring 8–10 ml ethyl ether onto a twice-folded filter paper over the opening of the beaker. Cover with a lid. Wait 2–3 min until the rat has just fallen asleep; then transfer it to the operating stage and maintain a very light anesthesia by placing the rat's snout just inside a 100-ml beaker containing a cotton wool pad moistened with 2.5 ml ether. The liver should have a light red color; if it turns purple the anesthesia is too deep.

3. Open the rat's abdomen by a long, transverse cut, and flap the intestines over to expose the portal vein area. Use two small pieces of filter paper to tear apart the loose connective tissue covering the right iliolumbar vein (Fig. 2) and inject about 1000 units of heparin while holding the vein firmly in place with forceps. Close the injection site with a small arterial clamp.

4. Place a loose ligature around the portal vein just below the last of its tributaries (Fig. 1, inset), using a crescent-shaped 3-cm-long surgical needle and 4-O USP gauge surgical silk thread. Align the portal cannula along the portal vein and adjust its position to ensure that the tip of the portal cannula will be just inside the ligature. Start the perfusate flow at a moderate rate (20 ml/min).

5. Hold the distal end of the portal vein and one end of the ligature firmly with one hand. With fine scissors, make a deep cut in the lower caval vein (to allow perfusate efflux); then (immediately) another cut halfway through the portal vein 5–10 mm above the ligature (Fig. 1, inset). Quickly insert the portal cannula and push it until its orifice has just passed the ligature. The cannula must not be pushed past the first portal branch, in which case perfusate flow to the right anterior lobe will be impeded. Tie the ligature firmly to secure the cannula.

6. Gradually increase the perfusate flow to wash out the blood from the liver. The washout can be aided by varying the perfusion pressure with a fingertip at the caval efflux site, but excessive liver distention must be avoided. When the liver is completely blanched and has acquired a light tan color, cut the upper caval vein just below the diaphragm and increase the perfusate flow to 50 ml/min.

7. Dissect out the liver with blunt-end scissors. Cut completely through both ends of the caval vein, the portal vein, and the biliary duct (distal to the portal ligature). Cut all the thin ligaments that connect the liver to the intestines and to the abdominal wall; do not attempt to sever them by tearing, as this will most likely disrupt the liver capsule rather than the ligaments. When the liver is freed from the carcass, let it hang from the portal cannula and untwist any twisted lobes. Place the liver on its support dish on top of a beaker and continue perfusion until most of the perfusion buffer has been consumed.

8. Stop the perfusate flow momentarily and switch the pump inlet to a 150-ml beaker containing 50 ml of warm (37°C) collagenase buffer. Fill the apparatus and the liver with this buffer at low pump speed while letting the residual perfusion buffer run to waste. Place the dish on top of the collagenase buffer reservoir, and increase the pump speed to 50 ml/min.

9. Continue perfusion with recirculating collagenase buffer for 5–10 min or until rupture of the portal vein occurs. During this period the liver should swell uniformly to approximately twice its original size.

B. LIVER DISSOCIATION AND HEPATOCYTE PURIFICATION

Solutions

1. *Suspension buffer:* 20 ml suspension buffer concentrate and 10 ml Ca/Mg concentrate, H_2O to 200 ml; pH 7.6 at 37°C. Store at 0°C. Pyruvate 20 mM can be included as a standard source of energy if desired.

2. *Wash buffer:* 20 ml perfusion buffer concentrate and 10 ml calcium concentrate, H_2O to 500 ml; pH 7.4 at 37°C. Store at 0°C.

3. *Trypan blue solution (0.6%, isotonic):* Dissolve 150 mg trypan blue and 120 mg NaCl in 25 ml H_2O under heating; filter the solution and store as frozen 2-ml aliquots. Mix three parts with one part of cell suspension.

Steps

1. Transfer the liver to a wide Petri dish (e.g., a square 10 × 10-cm Sterilin plastic dish) containing 80 ml ice-cold suspension buffer and detach it from the portal cannula. Hold the liver firmly in the portal connective tissue with forceps and rake out the cells gently with a dog's comb; avoid tissue squeezing. Avoid combing of any infarcted or poorly perfused regions. If the perfusion has been successful, all hepatocytes should go into suspension, leaving only a white remnant of connective and vascular tissue.

2. Filter the suspension through a 250-μm nylon filter (cut as a 15-cm disk) to remove connective tissue debris and cell clumps. The filter is pressed against the inside bottom and walls of a 150-ml plastic beaker by means of a plastic or stainless steel cylinder. Lift the filter slowly up through the cell suspension, under agitation, to avoid squeezing the cells through the filter.

3. Incubate the cells in a 20-cm glass Petri dish at 37°C on a tilting platform (low speed, approximately 10 tilts per minute) for 30 min, to allow damaged cells

to repair, dissolve, or aggregate. After this preincubation, cool the cells to 0°C by placing the dish on ice water under gentle agitation. Filter the suspension through a double-layered nylon filter (250 μm/100 μm).

4. Purify the hepatocytes by four centrifugations at 0°C in flat-bottomed 150-ml beakers (~40 ml in each beaker, e.g., 400 rpm for 2 min), with gentle resuspension in ~40 ml ice-cold wash buffer each time. The flat bottom of the beaker facilitates resuspension of sedimented cells with a minimum of mechanical stress. Finally resuspend the sedimented cells in ice-cold suspension buffer at the cell concentration desired. A photomicrograph of purified rat hepatocytes is shown in Fig. 2. The appropriate centrifugation conditions must be worked out empirically for the particular combination of centrifuge, rotor, and vessel used. Requirements for purity versus yield must also be taken into account: longer centrifugation times will give a higher cell yield, but a lower hepatocyte purity. For most purposes a yield of 30–50% with a hepatocyte purity of around 95% (by cell number) will be adequate. As a general rule, the centrifugation speed should be kept low (200–500 rpm) to minimize mechanical damage to the cells.

5. Check the quality (viability) of the final cell suspension by trypan blue exclusion. Mix 100 μl cell suspension with 300 μl isotonic 0.6% trypan blue solution and count under the microscope (in a Bürker chamber). It should be possible to routinely prepare cell suspensions with better than 90% viability (percentage of trypan blue-excluding cells).

IV. Comments

Hepatocytes are structurally fragile and should always be handled gently. Vigorous pipetting, shaking, shearing, or foaming must be avoided; all equipment in contact with cells must be clean and detergent free. Hepatocytes are, furthermore, metabolically active and should be kept at 0°C when not used in experiments (since there is some metabolic activity even at 0°C, an energy source such as pyruvate should be included during long-term storage). Sedimented cells, in particular, may rapidly become anoxic and die at elevated temperatures.

V. Pitfalls

1. The surgical procedures require considerable skill, which can be acquired only through practice. Particular attention should be paid to the maintenance of a *light* ether anesthesia: the liver color should be a light red, not dark red or purple (which would indicate a disturbed liver circulation). While injection anesthesia is technically easier, it stresses the animal, which in turn may lead to impaired portal circulation through adrenergic vasoconstriction.

2. Injection of heparin into the very thin-walled iliolumbar vein can be difficult. Clean exposure of the vein by teasing apart the overlying connective tissue with filter paper is important, as is insertion of the injection needle parallel to the vein, to make sure it does not go through. The vessel must be held firmly by forceps to prevent it from being pushed away by the injection needle.

3. Insertion and fixation of the portal cannula is the single most difficult step. The cutting and the insertion must be done quickly, before the portal vein collapses and bleeding impairs visibility. It is essential to prealign the portal cannula with the utmost precision, so that it will assume the correct position inside the vein even when it is out of sight and no longer held by hand. The cannula must be inserted almost parallel to the portal vein, not at an angle. Some

wiggling may be necessary to get the cannula in; it must not be pushed too forcibly, or the vein may rupture. Throughout the cannulation step the distal end of the portal vein must be held firmly with one hand so as to keep the vein straight.

4. A major source of variability in liver cell preparation is the quality of the collagenase. Commercially available collagenase preparations vary considerably in their liver dispersion efficiency, there being no obvious correlation between this efficiency and the specific enzymatic activity or purity indicated by the manufacturer. It is advisable to test several different enzyme batches and to order larger quantities of batches found suitable.

REFERENCES

Berry, M. N., and Friend, D. S. (1969) High-yield preparation of isolated rat liver parenchymal cells. A biochemical and fine structural study. *J. Cell Biol.* **43**, 506–520.

Howard, R. B., and Pesch, L. A. (1968) Respiratory activity of intact, isolated parenchymal cells from rat liver. *J. Biol. Chem.* **243**, 3105–3109.

Müller, P., Singh, A., Orci, L., and Jeanrenaud, B. (1976) Secretory processes, carbohydrate and lipid metabolism in isolated mouse hepatocytes. Aspects of regulation by glucagon and insulin. *Biochim. Biophys. Acta* **428**, 480–494.

Reese, J. A., and Byard, J. L. (1981) Isolation and culture of adult hepatocytes from liver biopsies. *In Vitro* **17**, 935–940.

Seglen, P. O. (1972) Preparation of rat liver cells. I. Effect of Ca^{2+} on enzymatic dispersion of isolated, perfused liver. *Exp. Cell Res.* **74**, 450–454.

Seglen, P. O. (1973a) Preparation of rat liver cells. II. Effect of ions and chelators on tissue dispersion. *Exp. Cell Res.* **76**, 25–30.

Seglen, P. O. (1973b) Preparation of rat liver cells. III. Enzymatic requirements for tissue dispersion. *Exp. Cell Res.* **82**, 391–398.

Seglen, P. O. (1976) Preparation of isolated rat liver cells. *Methods Cell Biol.* **13**, 29–83.

Walton, M. J., and Cowey, C. B. (1979) Gluconeogenesis by isolated hepatocytes from rainbow trout *Salmo gairdneri. Comp. Biochem. Physiol. B* **62**, 75–79.

Isolation and Culture of Oval Cells from Carcinogen-Treated Rats

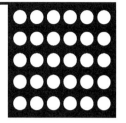

Pablo Steinberg

I. Introduction

Hepatocellular and cholangiocellular carcinomas are the two most frequently observed epithelial tumors in the liver. It is now well established that the development of hepatocellular tumors in various experimental models is preceded by a focal glycogenosis (Bannasch, 1968). Furthermore, cytomorphological and cytochemical studies show that a sequence of changes takes place, leading from clear and acidophilic glycogen storage foci through mixed cell foci and neoplastic nodules to hepatocellular adenomas and carcinomas (Bannasch *et al.,* 1980; Hacker *et al.,* 1982; Steinberg *et al.,* 1991). On the other hand, the first stage in cholangiocarcinogenesis is the proliferation of so-called oval cells (Bannasch and Massner, 1976; Steinberg *et al.,* 1991). Oval cells are liver epithelial cells, which seem to derive from cells forming the Hering canals or cells located near these canals in the portal spaces of the liver. Thereafter, cholangiofibroses, cystic cholangiomas, cholangiofibromas, and, after long lag periods, cholangiocarcinomas develop (Bannasch and Massner, 1976; Steinberg *et al.,* 1991). There is no doubt that the earliest foci seen during the development of hepatocellular carcinomas, the clear and acidophilic glycogen storage foci, are composed of parenchymal cells. However, a controversial question remains to be answered: Do the parenchymal cells within these foci originate from preexisting parenchymal cells or could they originate from oval cells? Experiments to settle this issue can be carried out only if highly purified oval cell preparations and oval cell cultures are available. The oval cell isolation procedure described herein, a modification of the method of Yaswen *et al.* (1984), consists of four steps: collagenase perfusion of the liver, collagenase–pronase E digestion of the minced liver tissue, Nycodenz density gradient centrifugation, and centrifugal elutriation (Pack *et al.,* 1993).

II. Materials and Instrumentation

L-Alanine (Cat. No. A-7627), L-aspartic acid (Cat. No. A-9256), L-asparagine (Cat. No. A-0884), L-citrulline (Cat. No. C-7629), L-cysteine (Cat. No. C-7880), L-histidine (Cat. No. H-8125), L-glutamic acid (Cat. No. G-1251), L-glutamine (Cat. No. G-3126), glycine (Cat. No. G-7126), L-isoleucine (Cat. No. I-2752), L-leucine (Cat. No. L-8000), L-lysine (Cat. No. L-5626), L-methionine (Cat. No. M-9625), L-ornithine (Cat. No. O-2375), L-phenylalanine (Cat. No. P-2126), L-proline (Cat. No. P-0380), L-serine (Cat. No. S-4500), L-threonine (Cat. No. T-8625), L-tryptophan (Cat. No. T-0254), L-tyrosine (Cat. No. T-3754), L-valine (Cat. No. V-0500),

Hepes (Cat. No. H-3375), EGTA (Cat. No. E-4378), EDTA (Cat. No. ED2SS), insulin (Cat. No. I-5500), hydrocortisone 21-hemisuccinate (Cat. No. H-4881), DL-ethionine (Cat. No. E-0626), and deoxyribonuclease I (Cat. No. D-0876) were purchased from Sigma. Dulbecco's modified Eagle's medium (DMEM 10-fold concentrated, Cat. No. 042-02501M), streptomycin (Cat. No. 066-01860B), and penicillin G (Cat. No. 066-01830E) were obtained from Gibco-BRL; Ham's F10 medium (Cat. No. F-0715) and fetal bovine serum (Cat. No. S-0115) from Biochrom; collagenase (Cat. No. 103578) from Boehringer-Mannheim; pronase E (Cat. No. 7433.0001) from Merck; Nycodenz from Nycomed AS; and the choline-deficient diet (Cat. No. C-1030) from Altromin. Petri dishes (94-mm diameter, Cat. No. 633171) and centrifugation tubes (Cat. No. 188261 for volumes up to 15 ml and Cat. No. 227261 for volumes up to 50 ml) were purchased from Greiner. For sterilization by filtration, disposable sterile bottle-top filters (0.22 μm, Cat. No. 25975-45) from Ciba Corning and disposable filter holders (0.2 μm, Cat. No. 462700) from Schleicher und Schuell were used. For elutriation a JE-6B rotor (Cat. No. 347514) with a standard separation chamber (Cat. No. 347986) was used in a J-6M/E Beckman centrifuge (Cat. No. 348279) from Beckman.

III. Procedures

A. ANIMALS AND DIET

Male outbred Sprague–Dawley rats (130–150 g body weight) are housed in plastic cages on a fixed day and night cycle and fed ad libitum a choline-deficient diet supplemented with 0.1% (w/w) DL-ethionine (CDE diet, prepared by Altromin, Lage, Germany) for 6 weeks. Within this period a massive proliferation of oval cells occurs in the livers of these animals (Steinberg *et al.*, 1991). The choline-deficient diet also has a limited amount of methionine (0.16% w/w) compared with the standard diet (0.86% w/w), because of the efficient endogenous synthesis of choline from methionine in the rat.

B. NONRECIRCULATING COLLAGENASE PERFUSION OF THE RAT LIVER

Solutions

1. *Glucose stock solution:* To make 1 liter, dissolve 9 g of D-glucose in distilled water and adjust to a total volume of 1 liter. Autoclave and store at 4°C.

2. *HEPES stock solution:* To make 1 liter, solubilize 60 g Hepes in distilled water and adjust to a total volume of 1 liter. Adjust pH to 7.4, autoclave, and store at 4°C.

3. *Krebs–Henseleit buffer:* To make 1 liter, add 70 g NaCl, 1.72 g KCl, and 1.6 g KH$_2$PO$_4$ to distilled water, adjust pH to 7.4, and bring to a total volume of 1 liter. Autoclave and store at 4°C.

4. *EGTA stock solution:* To make 100 ml, dissolve 4.8 g EGTA in distilled water and adjust to a total volume of 100 ml. Autoclave and store at 4°C.

5. *Insulin stock solution:* Dissolve 50 mg insulin in 25 ml distilled water. Add 5 drops of a 10 N NaOH solution and sterilize by filtration using a 0.2-μm filter. Aliquot and store at −20°C.

6. *Glutamine stock solution:* Solubilize 29.9 g L-glutamine in 1 liter distilled water and sterilize by filtration using a 0.2-μm filter. Aliquot and store at −20°C.

7. *Amino acid stock solution:* To make 1 liter, dissolve 0.27 g L-alanine, 0.55 g L-methionine, 0.14 g L-aspartic acid, 0.65 g L-ornithine, 0.40 g L-asparagine, 0.55 g L-phenylalanine, 0.27 g L-citrulline, 0.55 g L-proline, 0.14 g L-cysteine, 0.65 g L-serine, 1.00 g L-glutamic acid, 1.35 g L-threonine, 1.00 g glycine, 0.65 g L-tryptophan, 0.40 g L-isoleucine, 0.55 g L-tyrosine, 0.80 g L-leucine, 0.80 g L-valine, and 1.30 g L-lysine in 1 liter distilled water. Adjust pH upward until the solution clears (approximately pH 10.5). After the amino acids are in solution, readjust the pH to 7.4 with concentrated HCl. Sterilize by filtration using a 0.2-μm filter and store at 4°C.

8. *Penicillin G/streptomycin stock solution:* Dissolve 1 million units penicillin G and 1 g streptomycin in 100 ml of 0.9% (w/v) NaCl. Sterilize by filtration using a 0.2-μm filter, aliquot, and store at −20°C.

9. *CaCl$_2$ stock solution:* To make 1 liter, add 30.5 g $CaCl_2 \cdot 2H_2O$ to distilled water and bring to a total volume of 1 liter. Autoclave and store at 4°C.

10. *Preperfusion solution:* To make 300 ml of preperfusion solution take 186 ml of glucose stock solution, 30 ml of Hepes stock solution, 30 ml of Krebs–Henseleit buffer, 45 ml of amino acid stock solution, 1.5 ml of insulin stock solution, 0.7 ml of glutamine stock solution, 3 ml of penicillin G/streptomycin stock solution, and 1.2 ml of EGTA stock solution. Stir, sterilize by filtration using a 0.2-μm filter, and keep in a water bath at 37°C.

11. *Perfusion solution:* To make 400 ml of perfusion solution take 248 ml of glucose stock solution, 40 ml of Hepes stock solution, 40 ml of Krebs–Henseleit stock solution, 60 ml of amino acid stock solution, 2 ml of insulin stock solution, 4 ml of glutamine stock solution, 1 ml of penicillin G/streptomycin stock solution, 9.6 ml of CaCl$_2$ stock solution, and 400 mg collagenase. Stir, sterilize by filtration using a 0.2-μm filter, and keep in a water bath at 37°C.

Steps

1. Perfuse the liver *in situ* through the portal vein with the preperfusion solution in a nonrecirculatory way for 20 min at an infusion rate of 1 ml/min/g liver.

2. Perfuse the liver *in situ* through the portal vein with the perfusion solution in a nonrecirculatory way for 30 min at an infusion rate of 1 ml/min/g liver.

C. COLLAGENASE–PRONASE E DIGESTION OF THE MINCED LIVER TISSUE

Solutions

1. *NaHCO$_3$ stock solution:* To make 1 liter, add 75 g NaHCO$_3$ to distilled water and bring to a total volume of 1 liter. Sterilize by filtration using a 0.2-μm filter and store at 4°C.

2. *Complete DMEM:* To make 500 ml of complete DMEM take 50 ml of DMEM 10-fold concentrated, 10 ml of glutamine stock solution, 24.5 ml of NaHCO$_3$ stock solution, 5 ml of penicillin G/streptomycin stock solution, and 410 ml of distilled water.

3. *Digestion medium:* Add 100 mg collagenase, 100 mg pronase E, 4 mg deoxyribonuclease I, and 470 mg Hepes to 100 ml of complete DMEM. Sterilize by filtration using a 0.2-μm filter and keep on ice.

Steps

1. Mince the perfused liver in 25 ml of the digestion medium.

2. Incubate in a shaking bath at 37°C for 20 min.

3. Remove carefully the supernatant, add ice-cold complete DMEM containing 3% (v/v) fetal bovine serum to a final volume of 50 ml, and centrifuge at 400 g for 5 min at 4°C.

4. With the undissociated tissue repeat twice steps 2 and 3, thereby adding each time 25 ml of fresh digestion medium.

D. NYCODENZ DENSITY GRADIENT CENTRIFUGATION

Solutions

1. *Gey's balanced salt solution (GBSS):* To make 1 liter, dissolve 8 g NaCl, 0.37 g KCl, 0.07 g MgSO$_4$·7H$_2$O, 0.15 g NaH$_2$PO$_4$·H$_2$O, 0.03 g KH$_2$PO$_4$, 0.22 g CaCl$_2$·2H$_2$O, 0.21 g MgCl$_2$·6H$_2$O, 0.227 g NaHCO$_3$, and 1 g D-glucose in 1 liter distilled water, adjust pH to 7.4, sterilize by filtration using a 0.2-μm filter, and store at 4°C.

2. *28.7% (w/v) Nycodenz solution:* Add 50 g Nycodenz to 166.66 ml of GBSS without NaCl. Stir, sterilize by filtration using a 0.2-μm filter, aliquot in 14-ml fractions, and store at −20°C.

Steps

1. Resuspend each of the three pellets in 45 ml of GBSS and centrifuge at 400 g for 5 min at 4°C.

2. Combine the pellets in a final volume of 11 ml of GBSS and mix with 14 ml of the 28.7% (w/v) Nycodenz solution.

3. Cover the layer with 2 ml of GBSS and centrifuge at 400 g for 15 min at 4°C.

4. Remove the upper layer, which is enriched with liver nonparenchymal cells, and centrifuge at 400 g for 5 min at 4°C.

E. CENTRIFUGAL ELUTRIATION

Solution

1. *Elutriation medium:* To make 2 liters, dissolve 80 mg deoxyribonuclease I in complete DMEM, add 60 ml fetal bovine serum, and bring to a total volume of 2 liters with complete DMEM.

Steps

1. Disinfect the elutriation rotor (Color Plate 4a and b) by running 70% v/v ethanol through it. Drain the ethanol out of the rotor before overnight storage.

2. Pump elutriation medium at a flow rate of 10 ml/min into the elutriation system.

3. Set a centrifugation temperature of 10°C and accelerate the elutriation rotor to 2500 rpm.

4. Calibrate pump flow rates of 13.5, 19, 22, 26, 30, and 39.5 ml/min.

5. Resuspend the nonparenchymal cell-enriched pellet in 5 ml of elutriation medium.

6. Load the cell suspension into the elutriation system at an initial flow rate of 10 ml/min.

7. Collect six 150-ml fractions using flow rates of 13.5, 19, 22, 26, 30, and 39.5 ml/min. In the fraction eluting at a flow rate of 39.5 ml/min 90% of the cells are oval cells (see Comments).

F. OVAL CELL CULTURING

Solutions

1. *Hydrocortisone stock solution:* Dissolve 50 mg hydrocortisone 21-hemisuccinate in 100 ml complete DMEM. Sterilize by filtration using a 0.2-μm filter and store at $-20°$C.

2. *EDTA solution:* Dissolve 25 mg EDTA in 100 ml phosphate-buffered saline solution (PBS; 8 g NaCl, 0.2 g KCl, 0.2 g KH_2PO_4, and 2.31 g $Na_2HPO_4 \cdot 12H_2O$ in 1 liter distilled water).

3. *Complete Ham's F-10 medium:* Add 10 ml glutamine stock solution and 5 ml penicillin G/streptomycin stock solution to 500 ml Ham's F-10 medium.

4. *Complete cell culture medium:* To make 500 ml, combine 225 ml of complete DMEM, 225 ml of complete Ham's F-100 medium, 50 ml of fetal bovine serum, 0.5 ml of hydrocortisone stock solution, and 0.25 ml of insulin stock solution.

Steps

1. Plate the fraction eluting at a flow rate of 39.5 ml/min, which is highly enriched with oval cells, at a density of 5×10^6 cells/94-mm untreated Petri dish in complete cell culture medium.

2. To eliminate the contaminating fibroblasts from the (nearly confluent) primary oval cell cultures, remove the complete cell culture medium, wash the cells three times with PBS, add the EDTA solution, and incubate for 5 min at 37°C. Fibroblasts are detached from the Petri dishes. Wash three times with PBS and then add fresh complete cell culture medium.

3. Culture the cells at 37°C in a humidified atmosphere of 5% CO_2, change the complete cell culture medium every 3–4 days, and passage once a week on plastic at a split ratio of 1:10 (Color Plate 5).

IV. Comments

Oval cells are identified as such in the elutriated fractions according to the following criteria: (1) cell diameter ranging from 10 to 15 μm; (2) presence of cytokeratin 19; (3) presence of γ-glutamyltranspeptidase activity; (4) presence of albumin; (5) absence of peroxidase activity. Morphometric data on the cells can be obtained by using a Coulter counter, whereas the presence or absence of albumin, cytokeratin 19, γ-glutamyltranspeptidase and peroxidase in these cells is monitored by means of conventional enzyme cytochemical and immunocytochemical techniques (Pack *et al.*, 1993). With the protocol described in this article the largest percentage of cells (90%) fulfilling the five above-mentioned criteria is consistently found in the fraction eluting at a flow rate of 39.5 ml/min. This fraction is contaminated with Kupffer cells and fibroblasts, but no liver parenchymal cells are observed.

The plating efficiency is low (10–20%) and cannot be increased by precoating the Petri dishes with collagen or fibronectin. The low plating efficiency is most probably due to the use of pronase E in the cell procedure; pronase E is a protease from *Streptomyces griseus* that selectively disrupts the plasma membrane of liver parenchymal cells without affecting oval cells. Alternative isolation methods, in which pronase E has been omitted, fail to yield highly purified oval cell fractions.

Williams' medium E can also be used to culture oval cells. To make the complete cell culture medium, combine 500 ml of Williams' medium E, 55 ml of fetal bovine serum, 5 ml of glutamine stock solution, 2.5 ml of insulin stock solution, and 700 mg gentamicin sulfate.

V. Pitfalls

1. Two critical modifications of the method described by Yaswen *et al.* (1984) are the centrifugation of the nonparenchymal cell suspensions in a Nycodenz density gradient before centrifugal elutriation and the reduction of the fetal bovine serum content in the elutriation medium from 10 to 3% (v/v). Without these two modifications no successful elutriation can be accomplished.

2. The procedure described herein allows complete digestion of the liver of rats fed the CDE diet for up to 6 weeks (Pack *et al.*, 1993) and about 70×10^6 cells/ rat liver can be recovered in the fraction eluting at a flow rate of 39.5 ml/min. If the feeding period is increased, proliferating fibroblasts and cholangiocellular lesions (cholangiofibroses and cholangiofibromas) completely distort the architecture of the lobes and the number of isolated oval cells strongly decreases. However, even in animals fed the CDE diet for 14–22 weeks $15–30 \times 10^6$ cells/ rat liver can still be obtained with this isolation procedure.

REFERENCES

Bannasch, P. (1968) The cytoplasm of hepatocytes during carcinogenesis. Electron- and light-microscopical investigations of the nitrosomorpholine-intoxicated rat liver. *Recent Res. Cancer Res.* **19**, 1–100.

Bannasch, P., and Massner, B. (1976) Histogenese und Cytogenese von Cholangiofibromen und Cholangiocarcinomen bei Nitrosomorpholin-vergifteten Ratten. *Z. Krebsforsch.* **87**, 239–255.

Bannasch, P., Mayer, D., and Hacker, H. J. (1980) Hepatocellular glycogenesis and hepatocarcinogenesis. *Biochim. Biophys. Acta* **605**, 217–245.

Hacker, H. J., Moore, M. A., Mayer, D., and Bannasch, P. (1982) Correlative histochemistry of some enzymes of carbohydrate metabolism in preneoplastic and neoplastic lesions in the rat liver. *Carcinogenesis* **3**, 1265–1272.

Pack, R., Heck, R., Dienes, H. P., Oesch, F., and Steinberg, P. (1993) Isolation, biochemical characterization, long-term culture, and phenotype modulation of oval cells from carcinogen-fed rats. *Exp. Cell Res.* **204**, 198–209.

Steinberg, P., Hacker, H. J., Dienes, H. P., Oesch, F., and Bannasch, P. (1991) Enzyme histochemical and immunohistochemical characterization of oval and parenchymal cells proliferating in livers of rats fed a choline-deficient/DL-ethionine-supplemented diet. *Carcinogenesis* **12**, 225–231.

Yaswen, P., Hayner, N. T., and Fausto, N. (1984) Isolation of oval cells by centrifugal elutriation and comparison with other cell types purified from normal and preneoplastic livers. *Cancer Res.* **44**, 324–331.

In Vitro Culture of Mouse Fetal Choroid Plexus Epithelial Cells

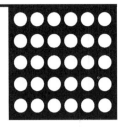

Elizabeth Stadler, Tim Thomas, and Marie Dziadek

I. Introduction

The choroid plexus forms the barrier between the blood and the cerebrospinal fluid (CSF), and is part of the important blood–brain barrier system which maintains a relatively constant fluid environment within the central nervous system compared with the changing composition of the blood plasma. The choroid plexus in each cerebral ventricle consists of a single layer of cuboidal, polarized secretory epithelium associated with highly vascularized stromal tissue. The blood–CSF barrier is formed by tight junctions between cells at the ventricular surface of the choroid plexus epithelial layer. The choroid plexus epithelium is the major site of CSF production, particularly the essential carrier proteins necessary for transport of molecules such as iron, copper, and thyroid hormone across the blood–brain barrier (Davson *et al.*, 1987).

The molecular mechanisms that regulate the production of CSF proteins and the mechanisms that control the transport functions of the choroid plexus epithelium are best studied in a culture system, using either intact choroid plexus tissue in organ culture (Agnew *et al.*, 1984) or isolated choroid plexus epithelial cells (Crook *et al.*, 1981; Nathanson and Chun, 1989; Tsutsumi *et al.*, 1989). We have recently shown that the mouse fetal choroid plexus synthesizes and secretes the same pattern of proteins as does the adult choroid plexus (Thomas *et al.*, 1992). When fetal choroid plexus epithelial cells are isolated and cultured on a reconstituted basement membrane substrate, they form vesicles of highly polarized epithelial monolayers with an internal lumen, which have an ultrastructural morphology similar to that of the fetal choroid plexus epithelium *in vivo*, and synthesize and secrete the same pattern of proteins (Thomas *et al.*, 1992). These cells can also be maintained as a polarized monolayer on the surface of a substrate containing a mixture of collagen I and basement membrane gels (Stadler, Thomas, and Dziadek, in preparation). These cultures allow the study of factors that regulate gene expression and those that control the transport functions of the choroid plexus epithelium.

II. Materials and Methods

Dulbecco's modified Eagle's medium (DMEM, Cat. No. D5172301), trypsin (Cat. No. 9362901), 200 mM glutamine solution (Cat. No. 09871901), penicillin G (Cat. No. 09587501), streptomycin (Cat. No. 9470201), versene solution (Cat. No. 0711901), and phenol red (1% solution, Cat. No. 09811301) are obtained from Commonwealth Serum Laboratories. Powdered DMEM is obtained from ICN Biomedicals (Cat. No. 1033120). Fetal calf serum (Cat. No. 2006140PJ) is obtained from Gibco-BRL and sodium bicarbonate (Cat. No. 10247) from BDH Chemicals. Collagen I from rat tail tendons (Cat. No. 40236), basement membrane Matrigel (Cat. No. 40234), and dispase (Cat. No. 40235) are purchased from Collaborative Research. Crystalline bovine serum albumin (Cat. No. A3156), sodium lactate syrup (Cat. No. L4263), Hepes (Cat. No. H0763), and pancreatin (Cat. No. P 1750) are obtained from Sigma Chemical Company.

Tissue culture 35-mm dishes (Cat. No. 153066), 100-mm dishes (Cat. No. 150350), four-well multidishes (Cat. No. 176740), and 2.0-ml cryotubes (Cat. No. B-63401) are obtained from Nunc. Sterile plastic 14-ml tubes (Cat. No. 2001) are obtained from Becton Dickinson and acrodisc syringe filters (0.22 μm, Cat. No. 3504192) and acrocap filters (0.22 μm, Cat. No. 3504480) from Gelman Sciences. Litmus paper (Cat. Nos. 9542, 9543) was supplied by Merck. All other chemicals mentioned in the sections on Solutions and Substrates were obtained from BDH Chemicals Australia, Pty Ltd.

III. Procedures

A. DISSECTION OF FETAL CHOROID PLEXUS

Solutions

1. *Dulbecco's phosphate-buffered saline (PBS):* To make 1000 ml PBS dissolve the following ingredients in autoclaved Milli Q-filtered (Millipore) or double-distilled water to a final volume of 1000 ml: 8.0 g NaCl; 0.2 g KCl; 1.15 g Na_2HPO_4 (anhydrous); 0.20 g KH_2PO_4; 0.132 g $CaCl_2 \cdot 2H_2O$; 0.10 g $MgCl_2 \cdot 6H_2O$. Omit $CaCl_2 \cdot 2H_2O$ and $MgCl_2 \cdot 6H_2O$ for Ca^{2+}, Mg^{2+}-free PBS. Solution can be filter-sterilized or autoclaved. Store at 4°C.

2. *M2 culture medium:*

Stock A (10×): To make 100 ml of 10× concentrated stock A, mix the following ingredients and make up to a volume of 100 ml with sterile (autoclaved Milli Q filtered or double-distilled) water: 5.534 g NaCl; 0.356 g KCl; 0.162 g KH_2PO_4; 0.294 g $MgSO_4 \cdot 7H_2O$; 4.347 g (3.29 ml) Na lactate syrup; 1.00 g D-glucose; 0.06 g penicillin G; 0.5 g streptomycin.

Stock B (10×): Dissolve 2.106 g $NaHCO_3$ and 0.010 g phenol red in 100 ml of sterile water.

Stock C (10×): Dissolve 0.036 g Na pyruvate in 10 ml sterile water.

Stock D (10×): Dissolve 0.252 g $CaCl_2 \cdot 2H_2O$ in 10 ml sterile water.

Stock E (10×): Dissolve 5.957 g Hepes and 0.01 g phenol red in 100 ml sterile water and adjust pH to 7.4.

To make 10 ml of M2 medium, add together 1.0 ml stock A, 0.16 ml stock B, 0.10 ml stock C, 0.10 ml stock D, and 0.84 ml stock E. Dissolve 40 mg crystalline bovine serum albumin (BSA) in 7.8 ml water and add to the other ingredients. Filter-sterilize the medium into sterile 14-ml plastic culture tubes using 0.22-μm acrodisc or acrocap filters. Medium can be stored at −20°C.

Steps

1. Naturally mated 8 to 12-week-old female mice (outbred or inbred strains) are killed by cervical dislocation on day 12.5 of pregnancy. The morning of the vaginal plug is designated as day 0.5 of pregnancy.

2. Dissections are preferably carried out under a laminar flow hood. Swab the animal with 75% ethanol and make a midline incision to expose the reproductive tract. Dissect the fetuses from the uterine horns into a sterile 100-mm Petri dish containing sterile Dulbecco's phosphate-buffered saline (PBS) (with or without Ca^{2+}, Mg^{2+}).

3. Use fine scissors and watchmaker's forceps to open the uterine horns and release the fetuses. Separate these from the placenta and extraembryonic membranes and place into another culture dish containing sterile PBS.

4. Dissect the hindbrain choroid plexus from each fetus (Fig. 1) using fine watchmaker's forceps under a dissecting microscope (Wild stereo dissecting microscope, Leitz) placed in the laminar flow hood, and transfer the tissue into sterile Hepes-buffered M2 medium on a 37°C warming plate. Pool the hindbrain choroid plexuses from fetuses of four pregnant mice (32–40 fetuses).

B. ISOLATION OF EPITHELIAL CELLS

Solutions

1. *Dulbecco's modified Eagle's medium:* Heat-inactivate fetal calf serum in a water bath at 56°C for 30 min. To 100 ml of 1× DMEM add 10 ml heat-inactivated fetal calf serum, 2 ml 2 mM glutamine, 3 ml 7.5% sodium bicarbonate, 6 mg penicillin G, and 10 mg streptomycin. Medium containing glutamine can be stored at 4°C for up to 2 weeks.

2. *Pancreatin/trypsin:* To make 100 ml of 2.5% pancreatin/0.5% trypsin, dissolve 2.5 g pancreatin and 0.5 g trypsin in 100 ml Dulbecco's Ca^{2+}, Mg^{2+}-free PBS. The solution is cloudy and particulate. Spin down any undissolved material at 16,000 rpm at 4°C (Sorvall RC5C centrifuge, SS34 rotor). Remove the supernatant and repeat the centrifugation step. Sterilize the enzyme solution by filtration.

3. *Trypsin/versene:* To make 100 ml of 0.1% trypsin/versene add 10 ml versene solution (10× concentrated) and 0.8 ml of reconstituted trypsin powder (12.5% w/v) to 89.2 ml of sterile distilled water. This gives a final concentration of 0.1% trypsin and 0.2 g/liter EDTA. Store aliquoted at −20°C.

4. *Matrigel:* Matrigel can be purchased from Collaborative Research or prepared from the mouse Engelbreth Holm Swarm tumor as described by Kleinman *et al.* (1986). Store Matrigel at −20°C and thaw at 4°C just before use. Dispense 150 μl to each culture well in a four-well multidish using a sterile pipette tip. Gel at 37°C for 1 hr before seeding cells.

5. *Collagen I gel:* Rat tail collagen I can be purchased as a 3 mg/ml preparation in acetic acid from Collaborative Research or prepared from rat tail tendons as described by Elsdale and Bard (1972). To make up the collagen gel substrate, the acidic collagen I solution (in acetic acid, pH 5–6) is brought to neutral pH by adding 10× DMEM and NaOH. (a) To make up a stock of 10× DMEM, add 3.7 g NaHCO$_3$ to one satchet of DMEM powder (1000 ml equivalent) and dissolve in 100 ml sterile water. Filter-sterilize into 10-ml aliquots and store at −20°C. To 10 ml 10× DMEM add 10 μl of 1% phenol red and 1.0 ml heat-inactivated FCS. Add sterile 5.0 M NaOH in 50-μl drops with a P200 Gilson pipette, mixing well between each addition, until the concentrate is at pH 8.5. Litmus paper is used to check the pH. As a final check, add 10 μl 10× DMEM, pH 8.5, to 60 μl collagen I solution pH 5.0, mix, and check that the resulting gel is at pH 7.4 using litmus paper. The color of the gel should be within the normal color range of DMEM at pH 7.4. Store the DMEM concentrate in 2-ml aliquots at −20°C. Each aliquot can be thawed and refrozen several times. (b) To

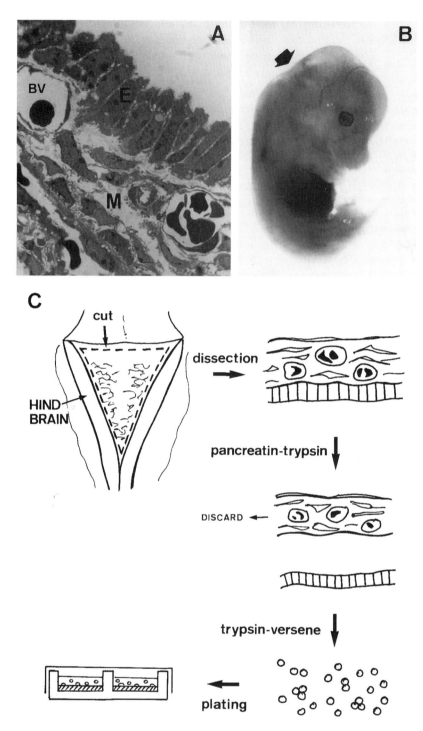

FIGURE 1 (A) Histological section through the choroid plexus showing the epithelium (E), mesenchymal cells (M), and blood vessels (BV). (B) Position of the hindbrain choroid plexus (arrow). (C) Diagram showing the procedure for dissection of the hindbrain choroid plexus, indicating the region of the brain that is dissected (dorsal view) and separation of the epithelial layer.

make up the collagen gel substrate, in a sterile cryotube on ice mix 1.5 ml acidified collagen I preparation and 270 μl 10× DMEM/FCS/NaOH stock concentrate. Mix by gently pipetting using a P1000 Gilson with sterile tip. Use immediately or store at −20°C. To reuse, thaw at 4°C and keep on ice.

6. *Mixed collagen I and Matrigel substrate:* To make a 33% Matrigel/67% collagen I mixed substrate, add 100 μl of collagen I and 50 μl Matrigel to the culture dish placed on ice. Mix by gently pipetting up and down, avoiding the formation of air bubbles. Use the Gilson tip to spread the mixture evenly over the surface of the culture well. Allow to gel at 37°C for 1 hr before seeding cells.

Steps

1. Use a P1000 Gilson pipette with sterile tip to transfer all tissue to a 35-mm culture dish containing 1.0 ml 2.5% pancreatin/0.5% trypsin in Ca^{2+}, Mg^{2+}-free PBS, and incubate at 4°C for 30 min. Then transfer the tissue (using a sterile tip) to a 35-mm dish containing M2 medium at room temperature.

2. Separate the epithelial layer of each tissue piece from the underlying vascularized mesenchyme (see Fig. 1) using sharp tungsten needles. Needles are made by fixing fine tungsten wire in glass rods and sharpening by electrolysis in 1.0 *M* NaOH. The epithelium is separated in sheets (two or three pieces for each choroid plexus).

3. Transfer the epithelial sheets using a Gilson pipette to fresh M2 medium at room temperature, and check under the dissecting microscope to ensure that no mesenchymal tissue is present.

4. Collect the clean epithelial sheets with minimal medium into a Gilson pipette tip and transfer into a sterile 14-ml tissue culture tube. Add 0.5 ml 0.1% trypsin/versene solution and incubate the tissue at 37°C for 2 min, or until the epithelial sheets are just starting to break up after gentle shaking.

5. Add 1.0 ml DMEM plus 10% FCS to the tube and centrifuge the cells at 150 *g* for 3 min. Discard the supernatant and gently resuspend the cells in 4.0 ml DMEM plus 10% FCS.

6. Take a small aliquot of the dispersed cells using a sterile Pasteur pipette and determine the cell number using a hemocytometer (see article by Ariana Celis and Julio E. Celis). The total cell number obtained from 8–10 fetuses (one pregnant mouse) is $1–2 \times 10^5$. This isolation procedure results in greater than 95% of cells being viable.

7. Plate the cells onto four-well multidishes containing substrates of 100% Matrigel or a mix of 33% Matrigel and 67% collagen I gel. Plate the cells in 1.0 ml of medium in each well, at $1–2 \times 10^5$ cells/ml, and culture at 37°C in a humidified atmosphere of 5% CO_2.

8. Change the medium every second day.

IV. Comments

Fetal choroid plexus epithelial cells attach and grow well on the Matrigel and mixed collagen I/Matrigel substrates, but not on a collagen I substrate alone (Thomas *et al.,* 1992). After 2 days in culture on both substrates cells are rounded, phase light single cells or small aggregates. On Matrigel some of these aggregates are starting to form vesicles (Fig. 2). After 4 days in culture cells on the collagen I/ Matrigel mix have formed monolayer patches, which become more extensive over subsequent days in culture (see Fig. 2). During this time cells on Matrigel have formed expanded vesicles of various sizes (see Fig. 2).

Several batches of Matrigel have been tried and consistent results have been obtained. Cells can be cultured on these substrates for at least 5–6 weeks; however, the collagen I/Matrigel mixed substrates can lift off or tear after several weeks in

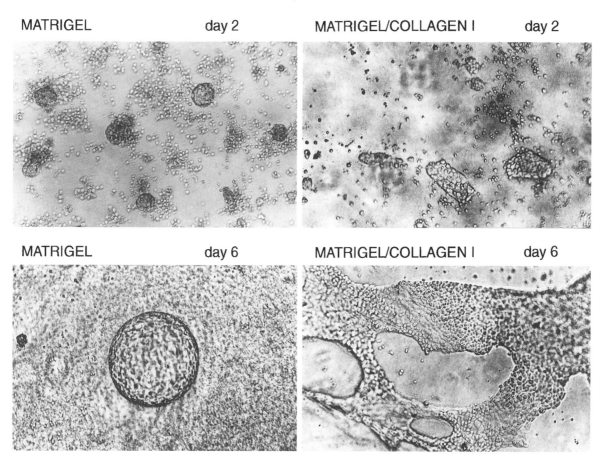

MATRIGEL   day 2   MATRIGEL/COLLAGEN I   day 2

MATRIGEL   day 6   MATRIGEL/COLLAGEN I   day 6

FIGURE 2   Morphology of cultured mouse fetal choroid plexus epithelial cells.

culture. Cells grown as monolayers on collagen I/Matrigel mixed substrate can be passaged after dissociation from the substrate with 0.1% trypsin/versene. Add 1.0 ml of trypsin/versene to each well and incubate at 37°C until the cells start to lift off the substrate (3–5 min). Cells grown on Matrigel become embedded in the matrix and are difficult to dissociate from the matrix in a viable state, even with dispase.

Contamination by mesenchymal cells is minimal or nonexistent if care is taken during epithelial separation; however, any mesenchymal cells remaining in the epithelial preparation do not proliferate on the extracellular matrix substrates used and are therefore usually a negligible contaminant.

It should be noted that dissection of the choroid plexus from mouse embryos and separation of the epithelial layer can be carried out under clean, nonsterile conditions on a laboratory bench. In these circumstances it is necessary to use sterile instruments (soaked in 75% ethanol) and media to which antibiotics (penicillin, streptomycin) have been added. If the dissections and isolation of epithelial cells are performed under sterile conditions in a laminar flow hood, it is not necessary to add antibiotics to the culture media.

Cells can be fixed and processed for histology and electron microscopy using routine procedures, providing that solvents that dissolve the plastic culture dish are not used. Fixation causes the substrates to become more rigid and slightly brittle and allows them to be easily removed from the dishes using fine forceps. Matrigel tends to fragment easily, and should be handled more carefully.

Tissue-specific gene expression (e.g., transthyretin, ceruloplasmin, IGFII) can be analyzed by Northern blot hybridization of the total RNA purified from each culture well. The recovery of total RNA is estimated from the amount of *Escherichia coli* RNA recovered after addition of 10 μg to the culture well prior to cell lysis. Total RNA is purified after dissolution of the extracellular matrix substrate and lysis of cells in 7.5 *M* guanidine hydrochloride, using a modification of the method of Chirgwin *et al.* (1979) as described in Thomas *et al.* (1992). The yield of RNA and the amount of total RNA per culture well can be determined by probing Northern gel filters with oligonucleotide probes complementary to *E. coli* 23 S ribosomal RNA and mouse 28 S ribosomal RNA. The amount of tissue-specific mRNAs can be quantitated relative to total RNA after Northern blot hybridization using cDNA probes and correction for yield. Our studies have shown that transthyretin mRNA levels in choroid plexus epithelial cells are maintained over a 6-day culture period at the 12.5-day fetal *in vivo* levels (Thomas *et al.*, 1992).

V. Pitfalls

1. Since the initial embryo dissections are from a nonsterile animal, always use sterile solutions and clean instruments. Take care to remove the uterus without touching the animal fur. Swab the animal with 75% ethanol before commencing the dissection.

2. Do not leave the choroid plexus tissue or isolated epithelial sheets in the enzyme solutions for longer periods than required for tissue separation or cell dissociation, since this will greatly reduce subsequent cell viability.

3. Change the medium gently using a sterile Pasteur pipette, as the substrate can easily lift off the culture dish during medium changes if this is not done carefully.

4. Variability of cell morphology (a mixture of vesicles and monolayer patches) can occur in a culture dish if the collagen I and Matrigel are not well mixed.

REFERENCES

Agnew, W. F., Alvarez, R. B., Yuen, T. G. H., Abramson, S. B., and Kirk, D. (1984) A serum-free culture system for studying solute exchanges in the choroid plexus. *In Vitro* **20,** 712–722.

Chirgwin, J. M., Przybyla, A. E., MacDonald, R. J., and Rutter, N. J. (1979) Isolation of biologically active ribonucleic acid from sources enriched in ribonuclease. *Biochemistry* **18,** 5294–5299.

Crook, R. B., Kasagamin, H., and Prusiner, S. B. (1981) Culture and characterization of epithelial cells from bovine choroid plexus. *J. Neurochem.* **37,** 845–854.

Davson, H., Welch, K., and Segal, M. B. (1987) "Physiology and Pathophysiology of the Cerebrospinal Fluid." Churchill Livingston, Edinburgh.

Elsdale, T., and Bard, J. (1972) Collagen substrata for studies on cell behaviour. *J. Cell Biol.* **54,** 626–637.

Kleinman, H. K., McGarvey, M. L., Hassell, J. R., Star, V. L., Cannon, F. B., Laurie, G. W., and Martin, G. M. (1986) Basement membrane complexes with biological activity. *Biochemistry* **25,** 312–318.

Nathanson, J. A., and Chun, L. L. Y. (1989) Immunological function of the blood–cerebrospinal fluid barrier. *Proc. Natl. Acad. Sci. USA* **86,** 1684–1688.

Thomas, T., Stadler, E., and Dziadek, M. (1992) Effects of the extracellular matrix on fetal choroid plexus epithelial cells: Changes in morphology and multicellular organization do not affect gene expression. *Exp. Cell Res.* **203,** 198–213.

Tsutsumi, M., Skinner, M. K., and Sanders-Bush, E. (1989) Transferrin gene expression and synthesis by cultured choroid plexus epithelial cells. *J. Biol. Chem.* **264,** 9626–9631.

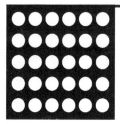

Isolation and Culture of Type II Pulmonary Epithelial Cells

Stephen R. Rannels and D. Eugene Rannels

I. Introduction

The alveolar surface of the lung is covered by two populations of pneumocytes, type I and type II epithelium. The type I cell, which accounts for most of the alveolar surface area and provides a highly specialized barrier for gas exchange (Rannels *et al.*, 1991), is poorly understood. Although approaches to type I cell purification have been discussed, they have not been applied widely because of the lack of phenotypic markers to monitor isolation procedures (Dobbs *et al.*, 1988; Danto *et al.*, 1992). In contrast, the type II cell has been studied extensively, largely because of the development of reliable procedures for its isolation and primary culture. Investigations based on the use of purified populations of cultured type II cells have provided convincing evidence to support a role for the pneumocytes both in the maintenance of normal lung function and in the response of the lung to injury (for review, see Rannels and Rannels, 1989).

While type II cells can be isolated by a variety of approaches, the protocols used most commonly are modifications of the gradient method of Dobbs and Mason (1979) or of the panning method of Dobbs *et al.* (1986). Purification of the cells based on density gradient centrifugation is reliable and consistent, with yields of 30 to 40×10^6 type II cells per rat of 230 g body weight. Isolation procedures applied to a minimum of three to four rats provide the best results, as lower cell yields are common with the use of fewer animals. The protocol below is designed to obtain a maximal cell yield from the lungs of six rats.

II. Materials and Instrumentation

Materials

Calbiochem: DNase I (Cat. No. 260912); *Corning:* culture flask, 75 cm² #25115; *Costar:* culture plate, 24-well #3424; disposable serological pipette #4101; *Elastin Products Inc:* elastase #E-134; *Falcon:* cellulose nitrate membrane filter, 0.22 μm, #7105; conical tube, 50 ml, #2070; culture dish, 100 mm, #3003; culture plate, six-well, #3046; *Fisher:* BaSO₄, #B68-500; NaCl, #S271-3; NaHCO₃, #S233-50; *Fort Dodge Laboratories:* pentobarbital, #1206-1E; *Gibco:* Dulbecco's minimal essential medium (DMEM), #430-1600EC; Hanks' balanced salt solution (HBSS), #310-4185AG; Joklik's modified Eagle's medium (JMEM), #410-2300EC; *HyClone Laboratories Inc:* fetal calf serum (FCS), #A-1115-L; *ICN Biochemicals* (Flow Laboratories): amphotericin B, #16-723-48; newborn calf serum (NCS), #29-121-54; trypan blue, #195532; *Nalgene:* Erlenmeyer flask, #100-4116C; *Pharmacia:* Percoll,

#17-0891-01; density marker beads, #17-0549-01; *Sigma:* gentamicin sulfate, #G3632; penicillin/streptomycin, #P3539; trypsin inhibitor, #T9128; *Tetko:* HC-160 nylon mesh, #3-160-53.

Instrumentation

Baker Co: EdgeGARD tissue culture hood, #EG6320; *Biomedical Research Instruments:* blunt-tip scissors, 4.5 in., #11-3020; curved 4-in. forceps, plain, #10-2350; curved 4-in. forceps, toothed, #10-2460; *Codman:* scissors, 8 in., #36-5051; *Dupont Instruments:* Sorvall centrifuge, #RT6000D; rotor, #H1000B; *Fisher:* bull dog clamp, 2.25 in., #13-812-4; hemocytometer, HyLite, #02-671-10; hemostat, 5 in., #13-812-8; hemostat, 5.5 in., #13-812-24; vortex, #12-812; *Forma Scientific:* CO_2 incubator, #3159; *HUB Surgical:* OO suture, #A-55; *Lab-Line Instruments:* water bath, #3535; *Small Parts Inc:* tracheal cannula tubing, #K-HTX-14.

III. Procedures

All procedures detailed below are based on preparation of type II cells from the lungs of six rats of approximately 230 g body weight.

Solutions

1. *Culture medium:* Prepare DMEM and JMEM according to the specifications of the manufacturer. Amphotericin B and antibiotics are added in the following concentrations: amphotericin B, 2.5 mg/liter; gentamicin sulfate, 50 mg/liter; penicillin, 10^5 units/liter; streptomycin, 100 mg/liter. Warm the medium to 37°C before use.

2. *Trypsin inhibitor/DNase:* For the lungs of six rats, dissolve 72 mg trypsin inhibitor and 7.5 mg DNase in 45 ml JMEM. Filter-sterilize, then add 45 ml newborn calf serum. Steps 1 and 2 are performed before removal of the lungs is begun.

3. *Elastase/BaSO$_4$:* Prepare a stock aqueous solution of $BaSO_4$ in advance. Dialyze a concentrated solution of $BaSO_4$ against water, then adjust to a final concentration of 20% and autoclave. Add 225 μl of the sterile $BaSO_4$ to 90 ml JMEM for a final concentration of 0.05%. Add elastase to a final concentration of 25 units/ml (1 unit solubilizes 1 mg elastin in 20 min at 37°C, pH 8.8) based on the activity of the concentrated commercial elastase preparation. Calculate the required volume of concentrated elastase solution as follows:

$$\frac{(25 \text{ U/ml})(6 \text{ rats})(15 \text{ ml/rat})}{(\text{units/mg elastase})(\text{mg elastase/ml})}$$

4. *Percoll solution:* Stock Percoll is used to dilute a 10-fold (10×) concentrated solution of Hanks' balanced salts. For example to prepare 20 ml of Percoll solution, mix 18 ml Percoll with 2 ml 10× Hanks'. Store at 4°C until the gradients are prepared by dilution with JMEM to final densities of 1.04 and 1.08 g/ml.

5. *Percoll gradients:* One discontinuous Percoll gradient is required for each three pairs of lungs. Isolation of cells from six rats thus requires two gradients containing 8 ml of each density solution. To prepare two gradients, mix 12.2 ml of Percoll solution (from step 4) with 5.5 ml JMEM for a final density of 1.08 g/ml; mix 5.6 ml of Percoll solution with 11.3 ml JMEM to yield a density of 1.04 g/ml. (These calculations are based on a stock Percoll density of 1.129 g/ml; this

value must be verified with each new order of Percoll.) To prepare the gradient, carefully layer 8 ml of 1.04 density solution over 8 ml of 1.08 density solution in a conical 50-ml plastic cell culture tube.

Animals

Male Sprague–Dawley rats (200–250 g body weight) obtained from Charles River Laboratories are housed under controlled conditions (72 ± 2°F, 50 ± 20% humidity) in rooms ventilated with fresh air at 12 to 15 complete changes per hour. Rats are provided free access to Purina Lab Chow and water. The automatically controlled photoperiod provides 12 hr light (0700–1900) and 12 hr dark without twilight. Rats are anesthetized with an intraperitoneal injection of sodium pentobarbital (60 mg/kg body weight).

Steps

The first steps in cell isolation are to clear blood from the pulmonary capillaries and fluid from the alveolar spaces prior to intratracheal infusion of elastase. Elastase digestion at the alveolar surface disrupts the integrity of the extracellular matrix, thereby freeing cells that line the airways and alveolar compartments. Type II cells are separated subsequently by density centrifugation and differential attachment.

1. Expose the trachea at the throat by separating overlying muscle medially using a curved forceps. Slip the forceps under the trachea (do not include esophagus) and insert a double ligature. Place a small cut between two tracheal rings and insert a sterile 1.5-in. stainless-steel cannula fitted with tygon tubing to permit attachment to a 10-ml syringe. Secure the cannula tightly with the two OO silk ties already in place.

2. Open the abdomen and chest along the sternum, making an initial small incision through the left diaphragm below the xiphoid process. After the lungs collapse, cut the sternum anteriorly to the neck. Next cut the diaphragm along its margin; do not touch the lungs. Clamp a hemostat along each of the cut edges of the ribs and sternum; reflect the ribs laterally to open the thorax. Do not bend the ribs back too far, as they will fracture and puncture the lungs during subsequent inflation. Figure 1 illustrates the completed surgical procedure for lavage and clearing of the lungs.

3. Clear blood from the pulmonary vasculature by inserting an 18-gauge needle, connected to a source of 0.15 N NaCl 30 cm above the heart, into the right ventricle. Take care not to puncture the posterior wall of the heart and to direct the needle toward the right atrium for optimal clearing. Adjust the inflow line to lie parallel to the body of the rat, secure it temporarily, and begin the saline infusion. Inflate and deflate the lungs several times with 10 ml of air from the tracheal syringe; then maintain inflation during vascular clearing. Make an incision in the abdominal aorta to permit outflow of saline from the system after the liver appears granular and engorged. Do not cut the inferior vena cava, as back pressure in the venous system helps to clear the pulmonary vasculature more effectively. Next, clamp the vena cava near the liver below the diaphragm to prevent backflow of hepatic fluids; then cut the vena cava above the hemostat. Inflate and deflate the lungs several times until they are white. If small areas of the parenchyma still remain pink, they probably will not clear. These erythrocytes will be partially separated on the Percoll gradient. Clamp the saline feed line, remove the needle from the heart, and promptly cut the left ventricle to prevent retrograde entry of blood into the pulmonary circulation, as the heart may still contract.

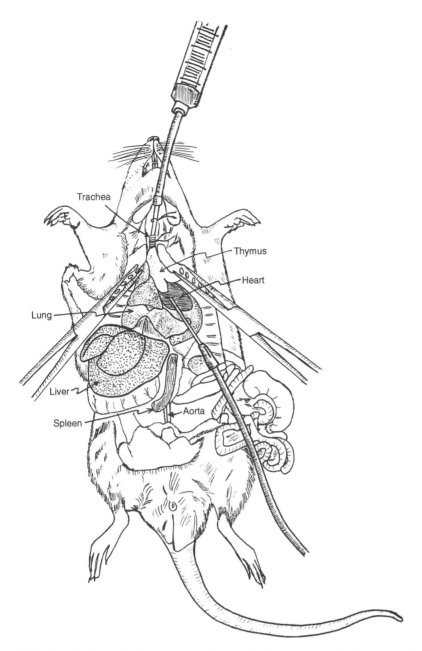

FIGURE 1 Completed surgery for lavage of the airways and clearing of the pulmonary vasculature. The figure is discussed in the text.

4. Carefully dissect the heart–lung complex from the chest by pulling the cannula gently forward and cutting the tissue free from the dorsal thoracic wall using a small blunt-tipped scissors. Do not puncture the lungs.

5. Using a syringe attached to the tracheal cannula, lavage the airways with three to six separate 10-ml volumes of saline to clear alveolar macrophages. Next, remove the syringe and close the tubing with a bulldog clamp; hang the lungs over the edge of a 400-ml beaker containing enough JMEM to cover the tissue. Raise and lower the lungs gently in the JMEM to free any external blood clots. Complete this entire procedure for each rat; then transfer the lungs into a sterile environment for all subsequent steps. Glass and plastic ware must be sterile for the remaining steps; forceps and scissors are dipped in ethanol and flame-sterilized.

6. Type II cells are isolated from each pair of lungs by intratracheal instillation of porcine pancreatic elastase in JMEM containing $BaSO_4$, prepared as above. $BaSO_4$ increases the density of the remaining alveolar macrophages, which phagocytose the particles throughout the procedure. Instill 10 ml of enzyme solution via the tracheal cannula: attach a 10-ml syringe, hold it vertically, pipette the elastase solution into the syringe barrel, and allow it to enter the lung by gravity. Insert the plunger to push any remaining solution slowly into the lung. Pull 3 to 4 ml of solution (plus a few air bubbles) back into the syringe, then push the fluid into the lung again to ensure that enzyme is well distributed. Do not introduce air into the lung. Fold the end of the tygon tubing to prevent leakage, clamp with a bulldog, and then lower each lung into JMEM. Treat all lungs in the same manner in sequence. Incubate the beaker containing the tissues in a water bath at 37°C for 15 min; then add 5 more ml of elastase solution to each lung in the same sequence and incubate for an additional 15 min.

7. Terminate proteolysis by intratracheal infusion of 15 ml JMEM solution containing trypsin inhibitor, DNase, and newborn calf serum. Transfer the lungs to an empty beaker.

8. Carefully dissect each lung free from trachea, heart, thymus, and other tissues; remove the major airways. This dissection should be performed in a 100-mm plastic tissue culture dish. Transfer all fluids that accumulate during the dissection to a 250-ml beaker. Place all the dissected lungs into the same beaker and mince into small pieces (1–2 mm) with sharp scissors. Fluids released during mincing, which contain cells, are pipetted from beneath the floating lung fragments and transferred to a sterile 250-ml plastic flask to facilitate further mincing of the tissue. Transfer the minced tissue to the flask and vortex the resulting suspension for 5 min on speed 6 to 7 before filtering it through sterile HC160 Nitex bolting nylon. Filter by gravity only; rinse the mince with JMEM. Pellet the cells from the eluate by centrifugation in a 50-ml conical tube at 400 g for 10 min. The tissue remaining on the nylon filter is a good source for isolation of fibroblasts by collagenase digestion.

9. Type II cells may aggregate within the viscous DNA released during mincing of the lung tissue; thus DNA must be hydrolyzed so that individual cells can be separated efficiently during density centrifugation. Resuspend the cell pellets into 40 ml of JMEM containing 80 μg/ml DNase; incubate at 37°C for 15 min, then at room temperature for 15 min. If cell clumping or viscous material remains, add several milligrams of DNase and incubate an additional 5 to 10 min.

10. While the cells incubate in Step 9, prepare an appropriate number of discontinuous Percoll gradients, as described above. Layer 20 ml of cell suspension over the 16-ml discontinuous gradient; centrifuge at 400 g for 20 min in a refrigerated (4°C) tabletop centrifuge. Two main cell layers will resolve: the upper layer contains dead cells and cell debris; the layer resting on the gradient interface contains more than 90% type II cells. Some type II cells will form aggregates which separate easily during resuspension. Carefully remove the top layer of the gradient by suction to within about 1 cm of the second layer; then collect the type II cells (including those clumped on the side of the tube) using a sterile 10-ml pipette. Be careful not to collect any $BaSO_4$ or erythrocytes from the bottom of the tube. Combine the cell fractions from two gradients (about 20 ml) in a 50-ml conical tube and fill the tube with JMEM. Invert the tube to mix and dilute the high-density Percoll; then pellet the type II cells by centrifugation at 400 g for 10 min.

11. Resuspend the cell pellets in DMEM containing 10% fetal calf serum (50

ml for 6 rats). Place 25 ml of the suspension in a 250-ml tissue culture flask and incubate in a CO_2 incubator for 15 min at 37°C. Be certain to loosen the cap of the flask to facilitate gas exchange. After 15 min, tighten the cap and pan the cells free of the surface by rocking and rotating back and forth. Next turn the flask over so the cells can adhere to the opposite fresh surface during a second 15-min interval. After again panning the unattached cells, remove them from the flask. Cells that have attached to the flask surfaces are largely pulmonary macrophages and fibroblasts.

12. Cells recovered from the differential attachment steps are 95–98% viable, as determined by trypan blue exclusion. Count these cells on a hemocytometer and dilute them to the required plating density for primary culture using DMEM containing 10% FCS or another medium appropriate for cell culture.

IV. Comments

Optimal cell yields are obtained from the lungs of healthy rats. Prepare cells within days after animal delivery; extended housing of rats results in lowered cell yield and purity. Preparation of type II cells from the lungs of six rats, as described, can be performed in 6 to 7 hr by an experienced technician. If help is available for the surgical procedures, the size of the preparation could be doubled without a substantial additional time requirement.

It is advisable to test individual lots of elastase before purchasing the enzyme. Most suppliers will provide a sample for preliminary evaluations of cell yield, purity, and viability. This approach reveals substantial differences in the utility of the enzyme preparations on the commercial market. The least expensive enzyme is not necessarily the best purchase.

Isolation procedures based on cell density offer the disadvantage that subpopulations of pneumocytes of unusual densities may not be recovered efficiently at the Percoll gradient interface. If type II cells are to be isolated from groups of treated animals in which cell sizes may differ (Uhal et al., 1989), consider density-independent isolation procedures (Dobbs et al., 1986).

Conditions of cell culture will vary according to specific requirements. Type II cells flatten and lose characteristic phenotypic features with time of culture on plastic (Dobbs et al., 1985, 1988); they remain rounded or in clusters on floating collagen membranes (Shannon et al., 1992) or on the EHS sarcoma matrix (Rannels et al., 1987; Shannon et al., 1990). The serum concentration and the plating density also are important considerations. High and low plating densities of approximately 2×10^5 or 2×10^4 cells/cm^2 of culture surface, respectively, have been used by many investigators. Figure 2 shows a high-density culture of type II cells after 36 hr on a plastic surface.

V. Pitfalls

The major problems encountered in the above procedures are poor clearing of the vasculature and low cell yield. Poor vascular clearing is often associated with low cell yield.

1. If the lungs clear poorly, consider the following:
   a. When the tracheal cannula is pushed beyond the bifurcation of the main bronchi it will prevent uniform flow of air or liquids into the lung. Grind a shallow groove $\frac{1}{8}$ in. from the end of the tracheal cannula; use this

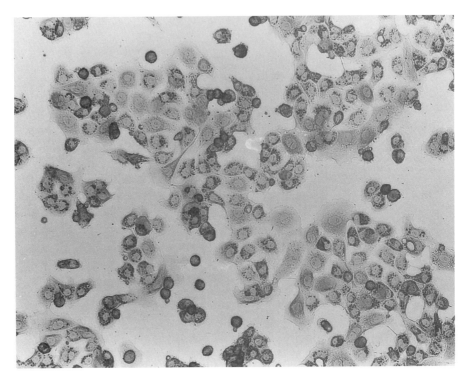

FIGURE 2 Type II cells in primary culture. Cells isolated and purified as described in the text were plated in DMEM at a density of $2 \times 10^5/\text{cm}^2$ on tissue culture plastic. After 36 hr, the cells were stained with osmium tetroxide to highlight the lamellar bodies.

groove to secure one of the ligatures and to prevent slippage in the latter steps of the procedure.

b. The tip of the saline inflow needle should lie freely in the right ventricle pointing toward the pulmonary vessels, not against the back wall of the heart. A small change in needle direction can improve clearing of the lungs dramatically.

c. Allow liver to engorge with fluid before cutting the abdominal aorta.

d. If part of the lung has ruptured, as indicated by hissing or bubbling of air or by loss of saline during the subsequent lavage, too much force may have been used for inflation or infusion of liquids. Perform these steps more gently and slowly. Verify that lungs were not punctured by a broken rib.

e. Allow the heart to help clear the lungs; poor clearing will result if the rat is too deeply anesthetized or dead.

2. If the final type II cell yield is low, consider the following:

a. Mincing may not be adequate. Type II cells disrupted by elastase cannot escape the parenchyma during vortexing if the pieces are too large. Too much mincing causes excessive cell damage and DNA release, which traps the cells in viscous aggregates. Keep the scissors sharp.

b. Vortexing must be rigorous enough to swirl the mince suspension up the sides of the flask.

c. Be certain that the final $BaSO_4$ concentration is 0.05%. Too much barium can disrupt the Percoll gradient, allowing cells that should layer at the interface to sediment further. Indistinct cell layers often indicate mixing at the interface. Be careful to pour the gradients and layer cell suspensions slowly. It may be necessary to calibrate the gradients using marker beads of known density.

d. During macrophage depletion (Step 11), lower the flask slowly to the horizontal position on the incubator shelf. To avoid loss of material, do not allow the cell suspension to enter the neck of the flask. In addition, panning the cells from each surface of the flask must be sufficiently rigorous that cells swirl freely into the medium. Type II cells remaining in the flask are a common cause of low yield. If in doubt concerning the efficiency of this step, use a microscope to view the cells that remain in the flask to confirm that they are macrophages.

ACKNOWLEDGMENTS

The authors thank Cara L. Osborne and Ellen B. Wolpert for their help in preparation of the manuscript. This work is supported by Grants HL-31560 and HL-42482 from the National Institutes of Health.

REFERENCES

Danto, S. I., Zabski, S. M., and Crandall, E. D. (1992) Reactivity of alveolar cells in primary culture with type I monoclonal antibodies. *Am. J. Respir. Cell Mol. Biol.* **6**, 296–306.

Dobbs, L. G., Gonzales, R., and Williams, M. C. (1986) An improved method for isolating type II cells in high yield and purity. *Am. Rev. Respir. Dis.* **134**, 131–145.

Dobbs, L. G., and Mason, R. J. (1979) Pulmonary alveolar type II cells isolated from rats. Release of phosphatidylcholine in response to β-adrenergic stimulation. *J. Clin. Invest.* **147**, 378–387.

Dobbs, L. G., Williams, M. C., and Brandt, A. E. (1985) Changes in biochemical characteristics and pattern of lectin binding of alveolar type II cells with time in culture. *Biochim. Biophys. Acta* **846**, 155–166.

Dobbs, L. G., Williams, M. C., and Gonzales, R. (1988) Monoclonal antibodies specific to apical surfaces of rat alveolar type I cells bind to surfaces of cultured, but not freshly isolated, type II cells. *Biochim. Biophys. Acta* **970**, 146–156.

Rannels, D. E., and Rannels, S. R. (1989) Influence of the extracellular matrix on type 2 cell differentiation. *Chest* **96**, 165–173.

Rannels, D. E., Stockstill, B., Mercer, R. R., and Crapo, J. D. (1991) Cellular changes in the lungs of adrenalectomized rats following left pneumonectomy. *Am. J. Respir. Cell Mol. Biol.* **5**, 351–362.

Rannels, S. R., Yarnell, J. A., Fisher, C. S., Fabisiak, J. P., and Rannels, D. E. (1987) Role of laminin in maintenance of type II pneumocyte morphology and function. *Am. J. Physiol.* **253**, C835–C845.

Shannon, J. M., Emrie, P. A., Fisher, J. H., Kuroki, Y., Jennings, S. D., and Mason, R. J. (1990) Effect of a reconstituted basement membrane on expression of surfactant apoproteins in cultures of adult rat alveolar type II cells. *Am. J. Respir. Cell Mol. Biol.* **2**, 183–192.

Shannon, J. M., Jennings, S. D., and Neilsen, L. D. (1992) Modulation of alveolar type II cell differentiated function in vitro. *Am. J. Physiol.* **262**, L427–L436.

Uhal, B. D., Rannels, S. R., and Rannels, D. E. (1989) Flow cytometric identification and isolation of hypertrophic type II pneumocytes after partial pneumonectomy. *Am. J. Physiol.* **257**, C528–C536.

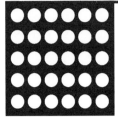

Maintenance of Human Diploid Fibroblast-like Cells in Culture

Robert T. Dell'Orco

I. Introduction

Human diploid fibroblast-like cells (HDF) maintained *in vitro* have been used as an experimental model system in biomedical research for more than 30 years (see also article by Vincent J. Cristofalo in this volume). The impetus for the widespread use of these rather fastidious cells can be traced to their proposed use to study senescence at a cellular level (Hayflick and Moorhead, 1961; Hayflick, 1965). Their acceptance for aging research led to their increased availability and the development of culture conditions which now make their maintenance in culture routine. This availability has allowed investigators to employ normal human cells instead of immortalized populations to study fundamental biological processes without the possible interference of abnormal metabolic activities. Although HDF have a limited proliferative potential in culture, they are in many cases the cells of choice when investigators attempt to define normal cellular function at a molecular, biochemical, or cellular level.

II. Materials and Instrumentation

The culture medium is the original formulation of McCoy's Medium 5a which is obtained from Gibco-BRL (Cat. No. 0865066) and contains fetal bovine serum from Hyclone (Cat. No. A1111-L), streptomycin sulfate USP from Pfizer (Cat. No. 1626), penicillin G from Squibb (Cat. No. C2621A), and sodium bicarbonate from Fisher (Cat. No. 9233). Pronase is obtained from Calbiochem (Cat. No. 53702) and is dissolved in calcium- and magnesium-free Earle's balanced salt solution from Gibco-BRL (Cat. No. 310-4150AJ). Both the medium and the pronase are filter-sterilized with 0.2-μm filters from Gelman (Cat. No. 12158). Compressed gas is a custom mixture of 8% carbon dioxide, 19% oxygen, and 73% nitrogen which is obtained locally. Sterile cell scrapers are obtained from Sigma (Cat. No. C 2802) and 75-cm^2 plastic culture flasks are obtained from Falcon (Cat. No. 3023). Sterile 10-ml pipettes are obtained from various suppliers. An inverted microscope is used for the routine observation and monitoring of culture conditions (Olympus Model CK). Water used for the preparation of the culture medium is first treated by reverse osmosis and then by a five-stage Milli-Q Plus system from Millipore (Cat. No. ZD40 115 95).

III. Procedures

A. SUBCULTIVATION AND REFEEDING STEPS

Solutions

1. *Water:* The water used for the preparation of the culture medium should be treated for cell culture uses. The water used in this procedure is treated by reverse osmosis followed by treatment with a five-bowl Milli-Q Plus system. The Milli-Q system contains two ion-exchange cartridges, two cartridges for removal of organics, and a final 0.22-μm filter. The final product water should have at least 18-MΩ resistance and should be periodically tested for total dissolved solids and pyrogens.

2. *Pronase:* Dissolve 50 mg of pronase in 100 ml calcium- and magnesium-free Earle's balanced salt solution (pH 7.0–7.2) for a 0.05% solution. Filter sterilize and store at 4°C.

3. *McCoy's Medium 5a containing 10% FBS and antibiotics:* Dissolve a 1-liter package of powdered medium 5a, 2.2 g of sodium bicarbonate, 50 mg of streptomycin, and 50,000 units of penicillin in 800 ml of water treated for cell culture uses. Adjust the pH of the medium to 7.0 with 1 N NaOH or 1 N HCl at room temperature. The pH will increase 0.2 to 0.4 unit with filtration and incubation at 37°C; this will bring the final pH to the optimum for HDF of between 7.2 and 7.4. Bring the volume to 1 liter by the addition of 100 ml of fetal bovine serum and water. Filter-sterilize and store at 4°C.

Steps

1. Remove pronase and culture medium from 4°C and bring to room temperature.

2. Decant medium from a confluent T-75 culture of HDF, add 5 ml of 0.05% pronase to the flask, and incubate for 1 min at room temperature.

3. Decant pronase solution but continue incubation at room temperature for 2 to 3 min at which time the cells will begin to be released from the growth surface. This step can be monitored by observation with an inverted microscope. Once cells begin to detach, strike the flask against the palm of the hand three to four times to aid cell release.

4. Add 10 ml of McCoy's Medium 5a containing 10% FBS and antibiotics to the culture flask. Ensure that all the cells have been released from the growth surface by scraping the surface of the flask with a sterile cell scraper.

5. Use a sterile 10-ml pipette and a pipetting aid to disperse the cells into a single-cell suspension. Place the pipette tip slightly above the bottom of the flask and pipette the cell suspension up and down 10 times.

6. Remove an aliquot of the cell suspension (1.0, 1.25, 2.5, or 5 ml) and place it into a sterile T-75 flask that contains 25 ml of fresh McCoy's Medium 5a containing 10% FBS and antibiotics. Direct a stream of compressed gas into the flask for 10 sec, tighten the cap securely, and place in a 37°C incubator.

7. Two days after subcultivation, refeed the new culture with fresh medium. Remove the spent medium with a sterile 2-ml pipette attached to a vacuum flask. Add 25 ml of fresh McCoy's Medium 5a containing FBS and antibiotics and gas with compressed gas for 10 sec. Direct the stream of gas against the top of the flask away from the cell sheet. Return the culture to the incubator.

8. Refeed the culture again 4 days after subcultivation; however, do not gas at

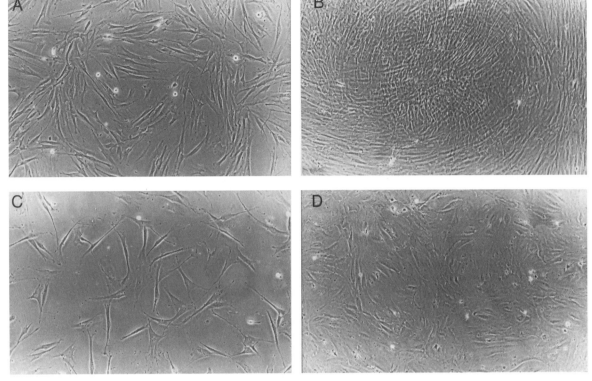

FIGURE 1   Morphology of low- and high-PD HDF in culture (100×). Low-PD cells during log phase of growth (A) and at confluence (B); high-PD cells during log phase of growth (C) and at confluence (D).

this refeeding. Withdraw spent medium, add 25 ml of fresh medium, and continue incubation at 37°C.

9. A confluent monolayer will be formed 7 days after subcultivation and the culture will be available for a subsequent transfer. This subculture regime can continue until the cells are unable to form a confluent monolayer in 2 weeks following the addition of 5 ml of cell suspension when subcultured. The culture is refed every 2 or 3 days during this 2-week period with 25 ml of fresh medium with gassing.

IV. Comments

HDF (Fig. 1) exhibit a limited proliferative potential in culture and the extent of this *in vitro* life span is determined by the number of replicative events achieved by the population (Dell'Orco *et al.,* 1973). The maximum number of replicative events in which any strain of HDF can participate is related to several factors, including the age of the donor from which the cells are obtained, the tissue of origin, and the biopsy site. The life span of HDF is measured in terms of population doublings (PDs), the number of times the population has to double to form a confluent monolayer following subculture into a culture vessel of equivalent surface area. Thus, according to the procedure described here, the introduction of 1.25 ml of cell suspension from a confluent T-75 culture into another T-75 flask would result in a 1:8 split ratio. For the seeded cells to form another confluent monolayer, the population would have to divide three times and 3 PDs would be added to the age of the cells with this subcultivation and the formation of the subsequent monolayer.

Cells at lower PDs proliferate more rapidly and a higher proportion of their cells are capable of initiating replicative DNA synthesis and dividing. Therefore, cells closer to their establishment from primary culture, low PD, are split at higher split ratios, 1:10 or 1:8. With successive subcultivation, the growth rate slows and the number of cells capable of synthesizing DNA is reduced (Cristofalo and Sharf, 1973). This usually occurs when the cells have completed 75 to 80% of their maximum *in vitro* life span; at this time, the split ratio is reduced to 1:4. When cells near the end of their *in vitro* life span, the split ratio is further reduced to 1:2. When the cells are no longer capable of undergoing one PD in 2 weeks with refeeding every 2 to 3 days, the culture is said to be "senescent" or "phased out." At this point, the cells are still viable and can be maintained with refeeding for extended periods; however, they have reached the end of their replicative, *in vitro* life span.

V. Pitfalls

1. The time and temperature used for the enzymatic release of HDF from the growth surface should be tightly controlled. Incubation of cells in the presence of pronase or other proteolytic enzymes for longer periods or at higher temperatures can result in cellular damage and a reduction in growth potential.

2. Stock cultures should be periodically tested to ensure that they are free of mycoplasma contamination.

3. The culture medium used in this protocol contains 10% FBS. Because of the expense of FBS, several attempts have been made to replace FBS with combinations of hormones, growth factors, and basic alterations in medium composition. Some of the formulations will sustain the growth of HDF for limited periods; however, none have been completely satisfactory in maintaining the long-term growth characteristics provided by FBS.

REFERENCES

Cristofalo, V. J., and Sharf, B. B. (1973) Cellular senescence and DNA synthesis. *Exp. Cell Res.* **76**, 419–427.
Dell'Orco, R. T., Mertens, J. G., and Kruse, P. F., Jr. (1973) Doubling potential, calendar time, and senescence of human diploid cells in culture. *Exp. Cell Res.* **77**, 356–360.
Hayflick, L. (1965) The limited in vitro lifetime of human diploid cell strains. *Exp. Cell Res.* **37**, 614–636.
Hayflick, L., and Moorhead, P. (1961) The serial cultivation of human diploid cell strains. *Exp. Cell Res.* **25**, 585–621.

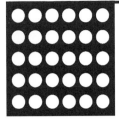

Isolation of Osteoclasts and Osteoclast Plasma Membranes

Miep Helfrich, Takuya Sato, Ken-ichi Tezuka,
Masayoshi Kumegawa, Stephen Nesbitt,
Michael Horton, and Patricia Collin-Osdoby

I. Introduction

Bone is a complex tissue consisting of various cell types and abundant mineralized extracellular matrix. Osteoclasts, the cells responsible for bone resorption, reside among osteoblasts, osteocytes, bone marrow cells, and bone marrow stromal cells, and osteoclast numbers are low when compared with these other cell types. This, taken together with the fact that osteoclasts adhere avidly to the bone matrix and, because of their size and high content of proteolytic enzymes, are fragile, complicates isolation of pure osteoclasts, in particular in numbers large enough to allow biochemical and molecular analyses. However, in the absence of cell lines with characteristics of mature osteoclasts and uncertainty over the exact nature of the osteoclast-like cells formed in long-term marrow cultures, isolation of mature osteoclasts directly from bone remains the best way to obtain authentic osteoclasts. Various strategies are currently in use to isolate osteoclasts. The choice of method depends largely on the required yield and purity of the osteoclasts and on the species studied. Here we have selected four methods for detailed description, one well-established protocol (based on Chambers and Magnus, 1982, Section IIIA) and three relatively recent methods (Sections IIIB–D), which can be applied to mammalian and/or avian osteoclasts and yield preparations of varying osteoclast purity. Other methods, however, exist and are currently used and we recommend a more comprehensive discussion of these as further introduction (Osdoby *et al.*, 1992).

For many biological and functional assays only relatively small numbers of osteoclasts are required which can be obtained by mechanical disaggregation from the epiphyses of mammalian or avian long bones, usually from newborn rat, rabbit, or chick. In such studies osteoclast purity can be compromised, because the cells are microscopically identified and selected among the coisolated adherent cell types and therefore isolation protocols can be relatively simple (Protocol A).

For biochemical and molecular studies, however, much larger numbers of osteoclasts of a high purity are required. Until recently, large numbers of viable osteoclasts could be obtained only from birds (chick and quail), but now isolation of large numbers of rabbit osteoclasts of high purity has also been described (Tezuka *et al.*, 1992). This method takes advantage of the fact that, in this species in particular, adherent nonosteoclastic cells can be selectively removed by enzymatic treatment (Protocol B).

The availability of monoclonal antibodies that react specifically with osteoclasts has enabled development of immunomagnetic separation protocols. We describe a method for purification of viable chick osteoclasts that uses both density gradients and immunomagnetic separation and gives high yield and viability (Collin-Osdoby *et al.*, 1991, protocol D). Similarly, immunomagnetic isolation can be used to obtain specifically osteoclast-derived plasma membranes from a crude membrane preparation. This method, given in Protocol C, has advantages when it is difficult, or unnecessary, to obtain viable osteoclasts in the numbers required for biochemical analysis and has already been successfully applied to the biochemical study of adhesion receptors on human osteoclastoma-derived osteoclasts (Nesbitt *et al.*, 1993).

II. Materials and Instrumentation

Minimal essential medium (Cat. No. 21050-014), M199 Earle's medium (Cat. No. 31100-027, or 21157-029 for phenol red-free), penicillin and streptomycin (PS, Cat. No. 15070-022), antibiotic/antimycotic (Cat. No. 15240-021), Hanks' balanced salt solution (HBSS, Cat. No. 11201-019), glutamine (Cat. No. 25030-024), $NaHCO_3$ (Cat. No. 11810-025), and Hepes (Cat. No. 11344-025) are obtained from Gibco. α-Modified minimum essential medium (α-MEM, Cat. No. 10-311-22) is from Flow Laboratories. Fetal calf serum (FCS), tissue culture grade, e.g., from Gibco (Cat. No. 10106-078), Filtron (Cat. No. 110-1120B), or Irvine Scientific (Cat. No. 3000). Trypan blue (Cat. No. T-6146), EDTA (Cat. No. E-6511), phenylmethylsulfonyl fluoride (PMFS, Cat. No. P-7626), sodium deoxycholate (DOC, Cat. No. D-6750), aprotinin (Cat. No. A-6279), phosphate-buffered saline (PBS, Cat. No. P-4417, or prepare as in Protocol D), Trizma base (Cat. No. T-1503), Tris–HCl (Cat. No. T-7149), sodium azide (Cat. No. S-2002), and pronase E (Cat. No. P-6911) are from Sigma. Sodium dodecyl sulfate (SDS, Cat. No. 44544) is from BDH. Nonidet-P40 (NP-40) is from Calbiochem (Cat. No. 492017). Heparin (1000 USP U/ml) is from Upjohn Company (Cat. No. 0268-07). Collagenase (type 3) and trypsin (TRL3) are from Worthington Biochemical Corporation (Cat. Nos. LS04182 and LS03707, respectively). Protein A–Sepharose beads (Cat. No. 17-0780-01) and Percoll (Cat. No. 17-0891-01) are from Pharmacia. Sheep anti-mouse conjugated immunomagnetic M-450 beads and M-280 Dynabeads (Cat. Nos. 110-01 and 112.01, respectively) are from Dynal. Ascites of monoclonal antibody 13C2 to the vitronectin receptor is available from Dr. M. A. Horton, ICRF, Hemopoiesis Research Group, St. Bartholomew's Hospital, West Smithfield, London. Anti-osteoclast monoclonal antibody 121F is available from Dr. Philip Osdoby, Department of Biology, Washington University, St. Louis, Missouri. Rabbit anti-mouse immunoglobulin (Ig) is obtained from Dakopatts (Cat. No. Z259). Falcon tissue culture plastics are from Becton Dickinson. Magnets (35-lb pull) are from Edmund Scientific (Cat. No. R42,098) or use tube racks from Advanced Magnetics (BioMag Separator, Cat. No. 4102S) or from Dynal (Cat. No. 120.04). Nitex filters, 350 and 110 μm, are from Tetko, Inc. (Cat. Nos. 3-350-36 and 3-112-50, respectively). Instruments and nonspecific supplies (check for each protocol) include forceps, scissors, scalpels, bacteriological-grade petri dishes, bottles, 50-ml centrifuge tubes with caps, 500-ml beakers, filters, 3-ml syringes, 18-gauge needles, and pipettes (all sterile), Eppendorf tubes (1.5 ml), hemocytometer, dry ice, alcohol (70% ethanol), Vortex mixer, refrigerated centrifuge with swinging-bucket rotor (e.g., HB-4), rotary shaker, sterile hood, and tissue culture incubator. Glass coverslips and devitalized bovine cortical bone slices (prepared by user) are optional.

III. Procedures

A. ISOLATION OF OSTEOCLASTS FROM NEWBORN RAT LONG BONES

Solution and Animals

1. *Culture medium:* Supplement MEM with 100 IU/ml penicillin, 100 µg/ml streptomycin, 2 mM L-glutamine, and 10% FCS.
2. *Animals:* Newborn rats, up to 48 hr old.

Steps

Use sterile technique and instruments.

1. Sacrifice rats by decapitation, and wipe the skin with alcohol. Cut off all limbs; keep on ice in petri dish.
2. Dissect out tibiae, femora, humeri, ulnae, and radii using fine forceps and a scalpel. Remove most soft tissue. Keep dissected bones in PBS on ice.
3. Quickly curette the bones into 1–2 ml of MEM in a petri dish holding one bone at a time with fine forceps. Use 1 ml of medium for long bones of four rats.
4. Take the released cell suspension into a small tube; if necessary, break up clumps by gently pipetting up and down several times with a plastic pipette or an automatic pipette fitted with a 1-ml pipette tip (not smaller), and let bone debris sediment for 15 sec.
5. Take the supernatant, add MEM/FCS/PS to the desired volume, and plate out the cell suspension immediately onto glass coverslips, bone wafers, or directly into a tissue culture plate, as required.
6. After 30–60 min gently wash off the nonadherent cells with warm MEM/FCS/PS, add fresh medium, and maintain the cells at 37°C in a humidified atmosphere of 5–10% CO_2.

Comments

Using this protocol small numbers of osteoclasts can be reproducibly obtained (several hundred per newborn rat). One hour after plating, osteoclasts will be well spread out and can easily be identified by phase-contrast microscopy among other adherent cell types (Fig. 1). Short settling times favor osteoclasts over other cell types, but absolute yields are reduced.

The method works equally well with newborn rabbit (1–2 days) long bones as an osteoclast source, where larger numbers of osteoclasts can be obtained (see also Protocol B); with chick long bones (18 days *in ovo* or older, see also Protocol D), in which case great care has to be taken to break up clumps in step 4 and cells should be allowed to adhere for 90 min in step 6 before rinsing; and with human fetal long bones (lower osteoclast yield, again allow to adhere for at least 90 min before rinsing).

Osteoclasts isolated in this way can, for example, be plated out onto bone wafers and used in bone resorption assays (culture at 10% CO_2 or use "low-pH medium" as in Protocol D; Arnett and Dempster, 1986; Arnett *et al.*, 1994); plated out onto precoated plastic surfaces and used in adhesion studies (Helfrich *et al.*, 1992); and plated out onto glass coverslips and used in single-cell physiology (Shankar *et al.*, 1993) and in many other assays such as immunocytochemistry, *in situ* hybridization, histochemistry, and single-cell molecular techniques (see Osdoby *et al.*, 1992).

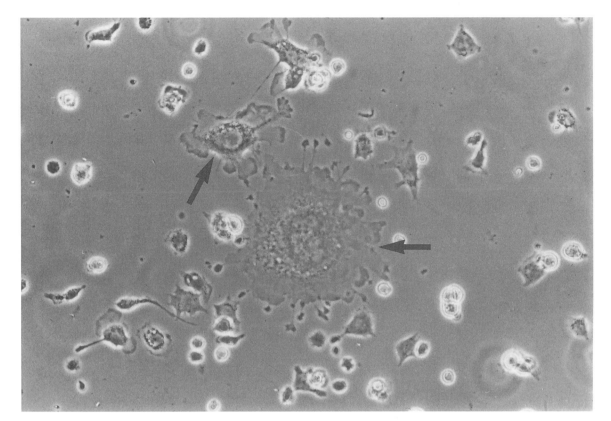

FIGURE 1   Low-power phase-contrast view of rat osteoclasts (arrows), isolated as described in Protocol A, spread out among other adherent cells on a glass coverslip 1 hr after plating out. Nonadherent cells have been washed off.

Pitfalls

Rat osteoclasts adhere very avidly to most types of tissue culture plastic. It is therefore advised to use bacteriological-grade plastic and not to have serum present during the isolation procedure. It is essential that steps 3–5 are performed quickly to prevent osteoclasts from sticking to the petri dish during step 3. For the same reason, large numbers of rat long bones should be curetted in batches and the cell suspensions kept on ice until pooled.

B. ISOLATION OF LARGE NUMBERS OF PURE RABBIT OSTEOCLASTS

Animals

1. Ten-day-old rabbits (100–110 g body weight).

Steps

Use sterile technique and instruments.

1. Sacrifice rabbits with ether and wipe the skin with alcohol.

2. Dissect out tibiae, femora, humeri, ulnae, radii, and scapulae using forceps and scissors. Remove soft tissues from the bones and pool dissected bones in ice-cold α-MEM. Proceed with steps 3–8 using the bones of one rabbit at a time.

3. Mince the bones from one rabbit with scissors in a 35-ml beaker containing 5.0 ml of α-MEM for about 2 min.

4. Add 5 ml of α-MEM, let bone debris sediment for 10 sec, and then decant the cell fraction into a 50-ml tube on ice.

5. Repeat this procedure of mincing and decanting three or four times to obtain unfractionated bone cells.

6. Agitate remaining bone fragments mildly in 35 ml of α-MEM with a Vortex mixer for 30 sec.

7. Save the cell fraction in a 50-ml tube after sedimentation (1 g) for 2 min.

8. Plate the cells in α-MEM containing 5% FCS at a density of $6-8 \times 10^7$ cells in 10 ml into a 90-mm plastic culture dish (expect $4-6 \times 10^8$ cells/rabbit).

9. Let the cells adhere for 3 hr at 37°C in a humidified atmosphere of 5% CO_2.

10. Remove the medium containing the nonadherent cells. Replace it with 10 ml of fresh medium, and culture the cells for an additional 20 hr.

11. Wash off nonadherent cells two or three times with PBS.

12. Add PBS containing 0.001% Pronase E and 0.02% EDTA to the adherent cells and incubate them for 3–5 min at 37°C.

13. Wash off nonadherent cells several times with PBS.

14. Plates will now contain pure populations of osteoclasts.

Comments

Using this protocol large numbers of pure osteoclasts (purity 95%) can be reproducibly obtained: $2.5-3.5 \times 10^5$ osteoclasts (15–25.3 mg total RNA) at 24 hr after plating. Centrifugation steps are avoided because they damage cells and reduce the osteoclast yield. Short settling times favor osteoclasts, but the absolute yield is reduced: $1.6-1.9 \times 10^5$ osteoclasts (10.2–13.5 mg total RNA) at 8 hr after plating. More osteoclasts can be obtained from a 10-day-old rabbit than from rabbits of other ages. During prolonged culture of mixed bone cell populations nonosteoclastic multinucleated cells may form; however, the multinucleated cells isolated using this method (24 hr culture) have been shown to be genuine osteoclasts by the following criteria: they have tartrate-resistant acid phosphatase activity (Fig. 2), have calcitonin (CT) receptors by autoradiography, and respond to CT by contracting. The amount of cAMP is increased by addition of CT. A few isolated cells (1–2%) can be removed from the culture dishes with additional Pronase–EDTA treatment; these show bone-resorbing activity when cultured onto bone slices and this activity is suppressed by CT.

This method may be applicable to other animals, except chickens. Chick osteoclasts do not show the high affinity to a plastic substratum. Pure osteoclasts can also be isolated from rats, but only in small numbers.

As large numbers of osteoclasts are obtained by this procedure, these isolated cells can be useful for molecular studies to isolate cDNA clones coding for osteoclast-specific genes (Tezuka et al., 1992), for molecular or biochemical studies to examine the presence of hormones or cytokines and their receptors, and as immunogens to establish monoclonal antibodies.

Pitfalls

Osteoclasts in bone tissues appear to degenerate very rapidly after death. It is therefore advisable to remove the cells from the bone rapidly and mildly (steps 1–

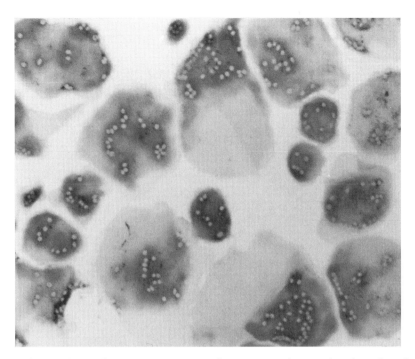

FIGURE 2 Light microscopic view of a pure population of multinucleated rabbit osteo-clasts (prepared as described in Protocol B) stained for tartrate-resistant acid phosphatase [Reproduced, with permission, from Tezuka *et al.* (1992).]

3). For the same reason bone tissues should be minced with sharp scissors. The cell suspension should be kept in iced tubes because rabbit osteoclasts adhere avidly to plastic.

C. IMMUNOMAGNETIC ISOLATION OF HUMAN OSTEOCLAST PLASMA MEMBRANES FROM OSTEOCLASTOMAS

Tissue

1. Giant cell tumor of the bone (osteoclastoma) obtained immediately after surgical removal. Tissue can be snap frozen in liquid nitrogen and stored frozen at −50°C until use.

Preparatory Steps

1. Prepare membranes from the osteoclastoma and establish osteoclast levels by vitronectin receptor (VNR) titration (Nesbitt and Horton, 1992).

2. Choose a suitable protein label for the membrane preparation, e.g., radioactive label ^{125}I (Hames and Rickwood, 1981) or nonradioactive label biotin (Nesbitt and Horton, 1992).

Solutions

Use glass-distilled water for all.

1. *RIPA lysis buffer:* Stock solutions: 15.8 g Trizma–HCl in 100 ml is 1 *M*, 12.1 g Trizma base in 100 ml is 1 *M*. Mix to obtain a 1 *M* Tris stock solution of pH 8.0, i.e., 20 ml of 1 *M* Trizma base and 40 ml of 1 *M* Trizma–HCl. For 1

liter of 2× RIPA lysis buffer dissolve 20 ml Tris stock, pH 8.0, 20 ml NP-40, 2 g SDS, 17.5 g NaCl, 0.4 g sodium azide, and 20 g DOC in 1 liter of distilled water. Just before use dilute 1:2 with distilled water and add 1% aprotinin (1:100 from stock solution, as purchased from Sigma) and 1 mM PMSF (1:200 from a freshly prepared stock solution of 200 μM in methanol, 34.84 mg/100 μl).

2. *Wash solution:* Prepare PBS as in Protocol D or from PBS tablets as per instructions; add 1 ml sodium azide from a 10% stock solution (10 g/100 ml water) per 200 ml PBS.

Immunoisolation Steps

1. Take 100 μl ($\cong$2 mg) of sheep anti-mouse IgG M-280 Dynabeads into a 1.5-ml Eppendorf tube, resuspend in 1 ml of wash (PBS, 0.05% azide), and vortex.

2. Isolate beads by magnetic separation for 1 min, using the Dynal magnet.

3. Pour off the wash and repeat the washing procedure.

4. Resuspend the isolated bead slurry in 1 ml (3.3 mg) 13C2 mouse monoclonal antibody ascites containing 0.05% azide. Vortex and allow to mix for 6 hr at 4°C.

5. Remove unbound antibody by magnetic separation.

6. Repeat the washing procedure on the antibody-coated beads four times with washing for 2 min apiece and mixing at room temperature. A final wash should proceed for 15 min.

7. Isolate the antibody-coated beads and resuspend in a 1-ml suspension (in wash buffer) of labeled osteoclastoma membranes ($\cong$1 mg protein). Allow the antibody beads and membranes to mix for 16 hr at 4°C.

8. Separate antibody beads with attached osteoclast membranes magnetically and remove the unbound membranes.

9. Wash the bead isolate gently (without vortexing to avoid physical disruption of the bead–membrane complex). Perform three wash cycles, mixing for 15 min, at 4°C.

10. Elute the osteoclast membranes from the antibody beads by placing in 1 ml of 1× RIPA lysis buffer. Vortex for 1 min and mix for a further 15 min, at 4°C.

11. Isolate the beads, collect the osteoclast membrane lysate, and leave on ice.

12. *Note:* Antibody may leach from the antibody beads into the lysate during the isolation procedure; therefore, preclear the lysate with 100 ml of protein A–Sepharose beads coated with rabbit anti-mouse immunoglobulin. Allow the preclearance to proceed for 60 min, with mixing, at 4°C, and repeat the preclearance twice.

13. Aliquot and freeze the osteoclast membrane lysate for storage at −50°C.

14. Biotin-labeled membrane preparations isolated by this method require the addition of glycerol to a 5% (v/v) final lysate concentration prior to their frozen storage. Also avoid repeated freeze–thawing. This step aids preservation of the biotin label.

Comments

By using the high specificity of VNR expression on the osteoclast plasma membrane, one can effectively isolate these from a heterogeneous membrane preparation

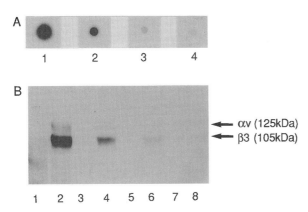

FIGURE 3   Assessment of immunoisolated VNR on osteoclast membranes (immunomagnetically sorted as described in Protocol C) from a biotinylated osteoclastoma membrane preparation. (A) Dot-blot analysis (dots 1–4) of consecutive osteoclast membrane isolates. Each dot constitutes 0.2% of the total membrane lysate. (B) VNR immunoprecipitation analysis (lanes 1–8). Antibodies: negative control, normal mouse serum (lanes 1, 3, 5, 7), and 23C6 anti-VNR antibody (lanes 2, 4, 6, 8). Membrane lysates used were first (lanes 1, 2), second (lanes 3, 4), third (lanes 5, 6), and fourth (lanes 7, 8) isolates. All samples were reduced and run for 2 hr in a 7.5% SDS–PAGE gel. Ten percent biotinylated membrane lysate was run in each lane and the protein visualized by streptavidin–horseradish peroxidase-enhanced chemiluminescence. Film exposure time was 45 min. VNR αv and β3 bands are marked by arrows and their estimated molecular weight (in kilodaltons) is stated. Densitometry assessment on the immunoprecipitated VNR calculated the total osteoclast membrane yield at 57% extraction level from the osteoclastoma. [Modified with permission, from Nesbitt *et al.* (1993).]

using immunomagnetic anti-VNR antibody-coated beads as stated above. Theoretically, other osteoclast-specific antibodies may also be used (see Protocol D and James *et al.*, 1991). To maximize osteoclast membrane yields the immunoisolation procedure can be repeated several times on the unbound membranes remaining after each magnetic isolation (Fig. 3A). Membrane inversion restricts yields to approximately 50%. The isolated osteoclast membrane proteins were judged to be of high purity by the nonselection of several membrane molecules known to be present on other cell types in the osteoclastoma (Nesbitt *et al.*, 1993).

The yields of osteoclast membrane have proved sufficient to facilitate extensive biochemical study involving affinity chromatography and immunoprecipitation SDS–polyacrylamide gel electrophoresis (PAGE) techniques to identify osteoclast plasma membrane molecules and their associated molecules (Nesbitt *et al.*, 1993). Analysis of associated molecules requires nonionic lysis buffers, e.g., 100 mM octyl-β-glucopyranoside (OGP), 1% NP-40 (avoid SDS, DOC, and high-salt buffers).

Intact osteoclastoma osteoclasts have been isolated by techniques similar to those reported here and in Protocol D using a different monoclonal antibody (James *et al.*, 1991). Osteoclastoma is the only source of large numbers of human osteoclasts, but the tumor is rare and the viability of the osteoclasts is often low. Therefore, for biochemical analysis of membrane proteins, the present method offers practical advantages over isolation of intact osteoclasts; the osteoclastoma tissue can be stored frozen until use and high yields of osteoclast plasma membranes are obtained independent of the viability of the osteoclasts.

Pitfalls

1. It is a prerequisite to assess platelet levels for each tumor membrane isolate as platelets exhibit very low levels of VNR expression and therefore may contaminate the osteoclast isolate. Osteoclast isolates prepared from several osteoclastomas to date and screened for the highly expressed platelet molecule gpIIb have proved negative at the detection limit of 1 ng. If present, platelet membrane contamination can be removed using a preclearing immunoisolation for gpIIb expression or by manganese-dependent RGD affinity chromatography (Kirchhofer et al., 1991).

2. Antibody contamination of the osteoclast membrane lysate can be reduced by the preclearance stated in step 12. A low antibody level still may remain sometimes, providing a minor artifact of 13C2 antibody-bound VNR protein. This contaminant within an immunoprecipitation SDS-PAGE analysis can be excluded by virtue of its molecular weight and weak expression (Nesbitt et al., 1993). Additionally, this antibody contaminant may partially interfere in affinity chromatography experiments, reducing overall protein yields, or limit subsequent attempts to generate amino acid sequence data from the isolated osteoclast membrane proteins.

D. IMMUNOMAGNETIC ISOLATION OF CHICK OSTEOCLASTS

Solutions

Use glass-distilled water for all.

1. *Phosphate-buffered saline (PBS):* 9 g NaCl, 0.385 g KH_2PO_4, and 1.25 g $KHPO_4$ per liter, pH 7.2 (using 10 N NaOH).

2. *Hanks' balanced salt solution (HBSS):* Dissolve packet in 990 ml of water, add 10 ml antibiotic/antimycotic and 3.5 g $NaHCO_3$, check pH 7.2, sterile-filter one batch, and prepare another to store at 4°C without sterilization.

3. *Moscona's low bicarbonate (MLB):* Add 8 g NaCl, 0.2 g KCl, 50 mg NaH_2PO_4, 0.2 g $NaHCO_3$, 2 g dextrose, 10 ml antibiotic/antimycotic, 990 ml water, check pH 7.2, and sterile-filter.

4. *Moscona's low bicarbonate–EDTA (MLBE):* Dissolve 1 g EDTA in 15 ml 1% KOH, add to 1 liter of solution 3, check pH 7.2, and sterile-filter.

5. *Collagenase:* Stock is 0.5 mg/ml in HBSS. Dilute 2 parts of stock with 1 part of MLB for use.

6. *Trypsin:* Stock is 1% in MLB. Dilute 11.25 ml of stock with 37.5 ml MLBE and 201.5 ml MLB for use.

7. *Percoll:* Dissolve 1 package HBSS powder (for 1 liter) in 640 ml water, add 0.35 g $NaHCO_3$ and 10 ml antibiotic/antimycotic, and sterile-filter. For 35% Percoll, mix 65 ml of this solution with 35 ml of Percoll. For 6% Percoll, mix 83 ml of the HBSS solution with 17 ml of 35% Percoll–HBSS. Adjust pH of both 35 and 6% Percoll solutions to pH 7.2 and sterile-filter.

8. *Trypan blue:* 0.4 g trypan blue and 0.9 g NaCl in water. Sterile-filter.

9. *OC culture medium:* To 1 liter M199 Earle's medium without phenol red, add 700 mg $NaHCO_3$, 2.38 g Hepes, pH to 6.8, and 25 ml antibiotic/antimycotic. To 100 ml, add 5 ml FCS (charcoal stripped for use in modulator studies).

Animals

1. *Chicks:* Fifteen hatchlings fed a normal diet for 4–6 days, then switched to a low-calcium feed (Purina, ≤0.2% calcium) for 4 weeks.

Steps

1. Set up, just prior to dissection, forceps and scissors in alcohol and prechilled buffers on ice. Readjust pH of MLB if necessary. Fill several ice containers. Place petri dishes with HBSS on ice.

2. Prepare anti-osteoclast immunomagnetic beads: swirl and withdraw 250 μl of goat anti-mouse immunomagnetic bead suspension from stock bottle, resuspend in PBS and sort with a hand-held magnet three times to wash, resuspend beads in 200 μl PBS, and add 25 μl of purified mouse monoclonal antibody 121F ($\cong$600 μg Ig). Incubate 3–6 hr at 4°C with end-over-end mixing until needed in step 13.

3. Euthanize chicks with CO_2 gas by placement in a covered box containing a small plastic tub of dry ice in water for about 5 min.

4. To expedite dissection, several people wearing alcohol-rinsed gloves should each remove a group of birds from the box, alcohol squirt the wings and legs of each bird just prior to its dissection, rapidly remove the tibiae and humeri using the alcohol-soaked scissors and forceps, clean off extraneous soft tissue without removing the bone ends which are replete with osteoclasts, and place the bones in HBSS-filled petri dishes on ice.

5. Holding one bone at a time with alcohol-rinsed forceps over another dish of HBSS, poke both bone ends and quickly flush the marrow out using an 18-gauge needle attached to a 3-ml syringe filled and refilled several times with HBSS from the dish, and then replace the bone in the original dish of HBSS. Repeat for each bone.

6. Remove any remaining extra tissue, shake bones gently to wash in eight 50-ml centrifuge tubes, each containing 40 ml HBSS, and place bones in new dishes of HBSS on ice to split longitudinally with scissors.

7. Transfer the split bones to eight 50-ml tubes with 35–40 ml HBSS to cover bones, shake vigorously for 30 sec, pass the supernatant sequentially through 350- and 110-μm Nitex filters over plastic beakers on ice, repeat shaking of bones in 35 ml MLB, filter into the same beakers, disperse filtered solution into 50-ml centrifuge tubes, and spin at 210 g for 10 min at 4°C. This crude fraction contains the majority of the nonviable osteoclasts and a minor proportion of the viable osteoclasts.

8. Incubate bones in eight 50-ml tubes each containing 35 ml of 0.333 mg/ml collagenase in HBSS/MLB for 30 min at 37°C. Then shake gently, discard this solution, incubate bones for 15 min in 35 ml MLB, and switch bones to 35 ml/ tube 0.045% trypsin in MLB/MLBE for 30 min at 37°C to obtain viable osteoclasts.

9. Vigorously shake bones for 3 min, pour solution through a 350-μm Nitex filter into a plastic beaker on ice containing 1 ml of heparin and 5 ml of FCS, immediately refill the tubes containing bones with 20 ml of MLB to shake an additional 3 mins, divide the filtered solution into two parts and pass through 110-μm Nitex filters into two beakers on ice, and finally disperse filtrates into twelve 50-ml centrifuge tubes held on ice. The solution from the second 3-min shaking and a third 1-min shaking is similarly filtered through the 350- and 110-μm filters, then added to the tubes on ice.

10. Centrifuge the filtrates at 300 g for 10 min at 4°C, pour off lipid pad and supernatant, wipe out lipid and matrix material with a tissue before inverting tubes, resuspend each pellet with a 10-ml pipette in 2–5 ml MLB (use only wide-bore pipettes to avoid osteoclast fragmentation), transfer to six new 50-ml tubes, add 0.1 ml heparin per tube, fill tubes to 50 ml with MLB, invert to mix, and

centrifuge again to wash. If osteoclasts are to be cultured, initiate sterile technique and solutions at this point.

11. Resuspend each pellet in 5 ml of 35% Percoll, combine into one new tube and add 0.6 ml heparin, briefly vortex at low speed, divide into four 50-ml tubes, raise volumes with additional 35% Percoll to 10 ml each, very slowly overlay each tube with 3 ml of HBSS, and centrifuge at 440 g in a swinging-bucket rotor for 20 min at 4°C.

12. Remove tubes without disturbing gradients, withdraw the interface and top 5–8 ml into four new tubes on ice containing 25 ml HBSS, fill with HBSS to 50 ml, discard pellets, and centrifuge at 300 g for 10 min at 4°C. Meanwhile, set up four tubes containing 10 ml 6% Percoll on ice.

13. Resuspend each pellet thoroughly in 3 ml HBSS using a 10-ml pipette, combine and briefly vortex (if clumping is a problem add 0.12 ml heparin), overlay 3–3.5 ml on each 6% gradient tube, and let stand undisturbed on ice for 1 hr for osteoclasts to penetrate the Percoll. Meanwhile, wash immunomagnetic beads three times with 1% FCS in HBSS, resuspend in a drop of the same, and hold on ice.

14. Carefully remove the top 4 ml and discard, combine bottom fractions in pairs, dilute with HBSS to 50 ml, and centrifuge at 300 g for 10 min at 4°C.

15. Resuspend pellets containing viable osteoclast populations in 10 ml HBSS total, transfer to another 50-ml tube, add washed monoclonal antibody-coupled immunomagnetic beads, and incubate the tube slanted at a sharp angle in an ice bucket set on a rotary shaker at 100 rpm for 30 min.

16. Stand tube upright in ice with a magnet taped to the lower part of the tube or stand tube in a magnetic tube rack buried in ice. Magnetically sort bound from unbound cells for 3–5 min, slowly remove unbound cells with a 10-ml pipette being careful not to pull any magnetic beads into the pipette, remove magnet (or take tube out of magnetic stand), and add 50 ml HBSS. Invert tube a few times to mix gently, resort, and repeat washing three to five times. As each wash is withdrawn into another tube, sort this with another magnet to recover any lost beads, wash, and add back to original tube.

17. Resuspend bead-bound cells in 2–5 ml prewarmed OC medium or HBSS, remove a 0.1-ml aliquot, and add 0.1 ml of 0.4% trypan blue to this to assess osteoclast yield, viability (unstained cells), and purity in a hemocytometer. Cells may be used immediately for physiological, biochemical, or molecular studies, or snap-frozen and stored at −70°C with or without a cocktail of protease inhibitors. To culture the osteoclasts, use:

a. 5.0 ml culture medium for 0.2 ml per well in 20 wells of a 48-well culture plate (with a bone slice in the well for resorption analysis). Add any modulators either immediately or after overnight incubation for osteoclast attachment at 37°C in a humidified incubator in 95% air/5% CO_2, harvest cells after 24–72 hr for biochemical, molecular, or resorption analysis, and harvest medium for determination of secreted or released osteoclast products,

b. 5.0 ml culture medium for 0.5 ml per well in 10 wells of a 24-well dish (with glass coverslips in wells for histochemical, enzymatic, or immunocytochemical analyses if desired).

Comments

Immunomagnetic sorting of osteoclast preparations enables rapid purification of osteoclasts from mixed cell populations. The use of 121F antibody-coupled beads

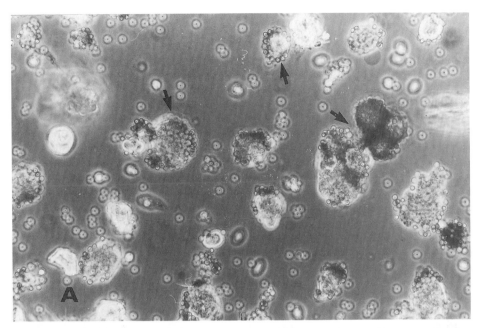

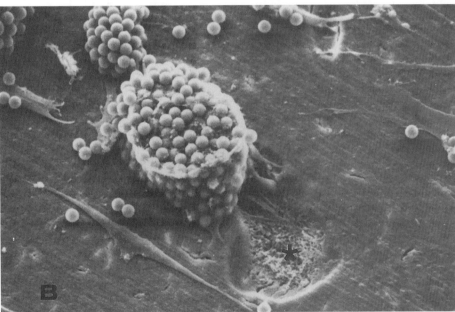

FIGURE 4 (A) Low-power phase-contrast view of chick osteoclasts placed in culture immediately after immunomagnetic isolation with antibody 121F-coated magnetic beads as described in Protocol D. Osteoclasts (arrows) have bound large numbers of magnetic beads. (B) A scanning electron micrograph of an immunomagnetically sorted chick osteoclast, cultured for 48 hr on a slice of bovine cortical bone. Large numbers of magnetic beads are still bound to the surface of the cell and have been internalized; however, this has not interfered with the resorbing activity of the osteoclasts. The asterisk indicates a resorption pit excavated by this cell. Original magnification, ×960. [Reproduced, with permission, from Collin-Osdoby et al. (1991).]

is not species restricted and can effectively collect osteoclasts from chicken, rat, or human osteoclastomas. Other anti-osteoclast-specific antibodies (e.g., 35L, 75B) are equally capable of sorting osteoclasts. Although immunomagnetic sorting of osteoclasts from highly impure populations (e.g., step 10) can be performed, and may be best for such purposes as the rapid isolation of cells for extraction of undegraded RNA, the final purity ($\geq 90\%$) achieved is greater for immunomagnetic sorting of partially purified (6% Percoll) isolated osteoclasts (Fig. 4A). Typical preparations from 15 chickens yield $1-2 \times 10^6$ osteoclasts with a viability of $\geq 95\%$; however, many factors impact on the yield, purity, and viability and these parameters are partially at odds with one another. Optimal results are obtained if the chick feed (and water) is low in calcium to increase osteoclast numbers and the points listed below are followed. For many purposes, the 6% Percoll isolated cells themselves are sufficient. To maximize the use of these animals, the nonviable cells from step 7 are routinely 35 and 6% Percoll purified by another worker in parallel to serve as a biochemical source of osteoclast material (Oursler *et al.*, 1991a), and the marrow cells are Ficoll–Hypaque fractionated for culture of the mononuclear cells as a model of *in vitro* osteoclast development (Oursler *et al.*, 1991b). The low-pH medium described here for osteoclast culture enhances their bone pit resorption and is therefore recommended over α-MEM with serum.

Pitfalls

1. The immunomagnetic isolation of osteoclasts is in itself quick, but the preparation of 35 or 6% Percoll separated osteoclast populations prior to the immunosorting takes considerable time. Crude preparations can also be immunosorted but purity is reduced, and matrix reassembly is more problematic.

2. Osteoclast viability is dependent on the speed of the preparation. Therefore, several people should complete the dissections within 20–30 min; steps 3–7, 8, and 9–14 should take no longer than 1, 1.5, and 3 hr, respectively; and the osteoclasts should be ready for culture 7–7.5 hr after starting dissection. To maintain viability, cells should be kept on ice, pipetted only with wide-bore or 10-ml pipettes, and gently resuspended. If several people are not available for dissection, scale down the preparation.

3. Osteoclast purity depends on completely removing all extraneous tissue from the bones before shaking, thoroughly resuspending cells and adding heparin to avoid cell clumps, performing all steps on ice to inhibit internalization of antibody-coated beads and matrix reassembly which entraps osteoclasts with contaminating cells, and carefully overlaying or withdrawing fractionated cells from gradients. It is important during the immunomagnetic bead incubation (step 15) that the cells be well dispersed and that mixing is sufficient for efficient capture of large numbers of osteoclasts but not so vigorous that bead binding is inhibited or reversed. Red blood cells constitute the major contaminating cells in the 6% Percoll or immunosorted osteoclasts but are easily removed as nonadherent cells with the medium after overnight culture.

4. Immunosorting may not be advisable if antibody beads bound to the osteoclasts alter the physiological response under study. Although many can be removed by moderate vortexing of the cells, it is not possible to remove all the beads without severely damaging the cells. To date, however, no interference with osteoclast resorption or modulator responses has been observed despite the phagocytosis of bound beads by immunosorted osteoclasts in culture (Fig. 4B).

REFERENCES

Arnett, T., and Dempster, D. (1986) Effect of pH on bone resorption by rat osteoclasts in vitro. *Endocrinology* **119**, 119–124.
Arnett, T. R., Boyde, A., Jones, S. H., and Taylor, M. L. (1994) Effects of medium acidification

by alteration of carbon dioxide or bicarbonate concentrations on the resorptive activity of rat osteoclasts. *J. Bone Min. Res.* **9**, 375–379.

Chambers, T., and Magnus, C. (1982) Calcitonin alters behaviour of isolated osteoclasts. *J. Pathol.* **136**, 27–39.

Collin-Osdoby, P., Oursler, M. J., Webber, D., and Osdoby, P. (1991) Osteoclast-specific monoclonal antibodies coupled to magnetic beads provide a rapid and efficient method of purifying avian osteoclasts. *J. Bone Min. Res.* **6**, 1353–1365.

Hames, B. D., and Rickwood, D. (eds.) (1981) "Gel Electrophoreses of Proteins." Oxford University Press, New York.

Helfrich, M. H., Nesbitt, S. A., Dorey, E. L., and Horton, M. A. (1992) Rat osteoclasts adhere to a wide range of RGD (Arg–Gly–Asp) peptide-containing proteins, including the bone sialoproteins and fibronectin via a $\beta3$ integrin. *J. Bone Min. Res.* **7**, 335–343.

James, I. E., Walsh, S., Dodds, R. A., and Gowen, M. (1991) Production and characterisation of osteoclast-selective monoclonal antibodies that distinguish between multinucleated cells derived from different human tissues. *J. Histochem. Cytochem.* **39**, 905–914.

Kirchhofer, D., Grzesiak, J., and Pierschbacher, M. D. (1991) Calcium as a potential physiological regulator of integrin-mediated cell adhesion. *J. Biol. Chem.* **266**, 4471–4477.

Nesbitt, S., and Horton, M. (1992) Non-radioactive biochemical characterisation of membrane proteins using enhanced chemiluminescence. *Anal. Biochem.* **206**, 267–272.

Nesbitt, S., Nesbit, M., Helfrich, M., and Horton, M. (1993) Biochemical characterisation of human osteoclast integrins. *J. Biol. Chem.* **268**, 16737–16745.

Osdoby, P., Krukowski, M., and Collin-Osdoby, P. (1992) Experimental systems for studying osteoclast biology. *In* "Biology and Physiology of the Osteoclast" (B. R. Rifkin and C. V. Gay, eds.), pp. 1–32. CRC Press, Boca Raton, FL.

Oursler, M., Collin-Osdoby, P., Anderson, R., Li, L., Webber, D., and Osdoby, P. (1991a) Isolation of avian osteoclasts: Improved techniques to preferentially purify viable cells. *J. Bone Min. Res.* **6**, 375–385.

Oursler, M. J., Collin-Osdoby, P., Li, L., Schmitt, E., and Osdoby, P. (1991b) Evidence for an immunological and functional relationship between superoxide dismutase and a high molecular weight osteoclast plasma membrane glycoprotein. *J. Cell. Biochem.* **46**, 331–344.

Shankar, G., Davison, I., Helfrich, M. H., Mason, W. T., and Horton, M. A. (1993) Integrin receptor-mediated mobilisation of intranuclear calcium in rat osteoclasts. *J. Cell Sci.* **105**, 61–68.

Tezuka, K., Sato, T., Kamioka, H., Nijweide, P. J., Tanaka, K., Matsuo, T., Ohta, M., Kurihara, N., Hakeda, Y., and Kumegawa, M. (1992) Identification of osteopontin in isolated rabbit osteoclasts. *Biochem. Biophys. Res. Commun.* **186**, 911–917.

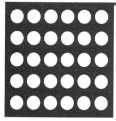

Culturing of Human Umbilical Vein and Dermal Microvascular Endothelial Cells

Ey∂finnur Olsen

I. Introduction

Endothelial cells (ECs) appear in the middle of the third week of development in the visceral mesoderm of the human embryo where they are derived from the angiogenic cell cluster. ECs participate in many aspects of human biology, such as hemostasis, vasomotor control, immune functions (Roitt, 1988), inflammation (Hurley, 1985), and angiogenesis, and are essential to the blood–brain barrier (Betz and Goldstein, 1986). Furthermore, in common diseases such as atherosclerosis (Ross, 1993), hypertension, and diabetes mellitus, there are pathological alterations in their function(s). Exchange of metabolites between the blood and tissues takes place at the level of capillaries and ECs play important regulatory functions. In larger vessels and the heart the main function of the ECs is to provide a nonthrombogenic surface as well as numerous regulatory substances.

Endothelial cells cover the internal surfaces of arteries, arterioles, capillaries, venules, the heart, and the lymphatic vessels. The arteries, veins, and heart contain, in addition to ECs, a wall consisting mainly of smooth muscle cells and heart muscle cells, respectively, whereas capillaries and lymph vessels consist predominantly of ECs.

Endothelial cells from larger vessels and the heart can be isolated by first washing the lumen of the vessel followed by enzymatic release, whereas preparation of ECs from microvessels poses a considerable challenge since perfusion of microvessels is very difficult. In the latter case, it is more practical to squeeze out segments of microvessels from the tissue and then separate them from extracellular matrix components and contaminating cells by centrifugation and selective trypzination.

II. Materials and Instrumentation

Cell culture-grade collagenase, type XI (Cat. No. C-9497), was from Sigma, fetal calf serum (Cat. No. S 0115), Dulbecco's modified Eagle's medium (10×) (Cat. No. F-0455), L-glutamine (Cat. No. K-0282), penicillin–streptomycin (Cat. No. A-2213), and sodium bicarbonate (Cat. No. L-1713) were from Biochrom KG; polyclonal antibodies against von Willebrand factor (Cat. No. A-082) were from DAKO; trypsin (Cat. No. 03-046-5B) was from Biological Industries; culture dishes were from Nunc; 96-well microtiter plates were from Greiner; 50-ml conical centrifuge tubes (Cat. No. 227270) were from Greiner; disposable needles (1.1 × 40 mm, Cat. No. 301500) were from Becton Dickinson Fabersanitas and needle holders (Cat.

No. 13-312-12) with a notch provided for the cannula were obtained from Martin Medizin-Technik.

III. Procedures

A. ISOLATION OF HUMAN UMBILICAL VEIN ENDOTHELIAL CELLS

Solutions

1. *Water for cell culture medium:* Distill tap water three times and then autoclave for 30 min at 120°C. Keep at 4°C until use.

2. *Hanks' balanced salt solution (HBSS, Ca^{2+} and Mg^{2+} free, 1×):* 5.4 mM KCl, 4.4 mM KH_2PO_4, 136.9 mM NaCl, and 2.7 mM Na_2HPO_4. To make 1 liter add 400 mg KCl, 60 mg KH_2PO_4, 8000 mg NaCl, and 62.1 mg $Na_2HPO_4 \cdot H_2O$. After dissolving, autoclave solution for 30 min at 120°C and then readjust volume with sterile water to the volume prior to autoclaving or alternatively sterile-filter solution. Keep HBSS at 4°C until use.

3. *0.25% trypsin solution:* 2.5% trypsin stock solution is diluted with HBSS to 0.25%. To make 250 ml add 25 ml of 2.5% stock solution and complete to 250 ml with sterile HBSS. Divide into aliquots of convenient size (e.g., 20 ml) and keep at −20°C until use.

4. *Culture medium:* Dulbecco's modified Eagle's medium containing 10% (v/v) fetal calf serum, sodium bicarbonate at 0.3% (w/v) final concentration, L-glutamine at 2 mM final concentration, and penicillin–streptomycin at final concentrations of 100 U and 100 μg/ml respectively. To make 500 ml of medium add 50 ml of 10× stock solution of Dulbecco's modified Eagle's medium, 50 ml of fetal calf serum, 20 ml of 7.5% (w/v) sodium bicarbonate, 5 ml of 200 mM L-glutamine, and 5 ml of penicillin–streptomycin (penicillin, 10,000 U/ml; streptomycin, 10,000 μg/ml), and 370 ml of autoclaved water.

Steps

1. Keep the umbilical cord in sterile HBSS. Human umbilical vein endothelial cells (HUVECs) should be isolated within 10 hr of delivery.

2. Cut 1–2 cm off at each end of the umbilical cords to ensure sterility (Fig. 1A) and cut away regions of the cords that have been in contact with clamps.

3. Cannulate the vein immediately (Fig. 1C) at both ends with blunt needles (1.1-mm outer diameter; disposable needles are easily blunted by smoothing the edge with a file) and keep them in place with the needle holders provided with a notch for the cannula (Fig. 1D).

4. Perfuse the vein with sterile HBSS until the solution is free of red blood cells.

5. Flush the vein with air and fill it with 0.25% trypsin solution prewarmed to 37°C. Plug the needles (with stoppers from disposable infusion sets) (Figs. 1B, E) and incubate the cord in a humified 37°C incubator for 15 min.

6. Massage the cord with your fingers (Fig. 1F) before recovering the trypsin solution (Fig. 1G).

7. Flush the vein with air and collect the effluent in a sterile 50-ml conical centrifuge tube.

8. Flush the vein with an additional 50–100 ml of HBSS and collect the effluent in sterile 50-ml conical centrifuge tubes.

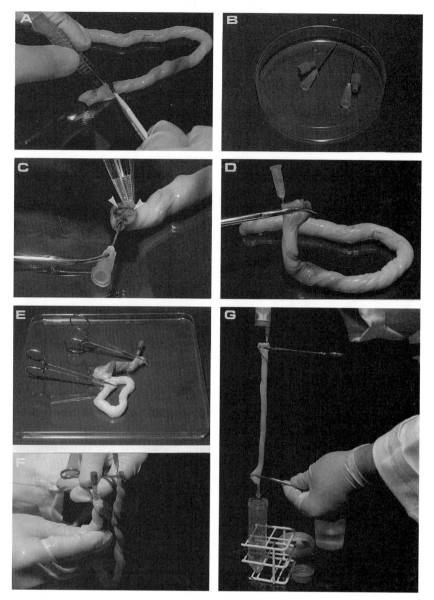

FIGURE 1 (A) Cutting the end off the umbilical cord. (B) Blunt-ended needles and stoppers. (C) Cannulating the vein; The arteries are indicated by arrows. (D) Cannula inserted and held in place by needle holder. (E) Umbilical cord ready to be incubated. (F) Massaging of cord to release cells. (G) Flushing of cord and recovery into a 50-ml centrifuge tube.

9. Centrifuge the cell suspension at 500 g for 10 min.

10. Wash the cells by resuspending the pelleted cells in HBSS and centrifuge at 500 g for 10 min.

11. Repeat the washing procedure in step 10 twice.

12. Resuspend the pellet in culture medium and filter the cells through a piece of sterile gauze (10 × 10 cm, sterilized at 160°C for 30 min wrapped in aluminum foil) (Fig. 2). Plate cells on glass coverslips placed in 50-mm tissue culture dishes for immunofluorescence analysis or seed cells in microtiter wells for labeling.

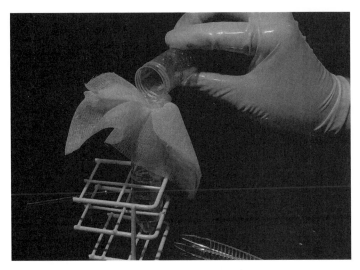

FIGURE 2   Filtration through sterile gauze.

B. HUMAN DERMAL MICROVASCULAR ENDOTHELIAL CELLS

Solution

1. *Collagenase solution:* 0.2% (w/v) collagenase dissolved in Dulbecco's modified Eagle's medium containing 5% fetal calf serum, sodium bicarbonate at 0.3% (w/v) final concentration, L-glutamine at 2 mM final concentration and penicillin–streptomycin at final concentrations of 100 U and 100 μg/ml respectively. To make 250 ml add 500 mg of cell culture-tested collagenase, 25 ml of 10× stock solution of Dulbecco's modified Eagle's medium, 12.5 ml of fetal calf serum, 10 ml of 7.5% (w/v) sodium bicarbonate, 2.5 ml of 200 mM L-glutamine, and 2.5 ml of penicillin–streptomycin (10,000 units/ml, 10,000 μg/ml). After dissolving, complete to 250 ml with sterile water.

Other solutions and media are as described in protocol A.

Steps

1. Cut normal adult skin obtained after surgical operations (e.g., reduction mammaplasty) into strips 3–4 mm wide. Place in tissue culture flasks containing 30–40 ml of collagenase solution and incubate at 4°C for about 72 hr.

2. Peel off the epidermis from the dermis with the aid of two fine forceps. Discard the epidermis.

3. Wash the dermis once in HBSS. Press segments of dermal microvessels into prewarmed culture medium by gently applying 3 or 4 strokes to the exposed dermal surface with the handle of a sterile plastic tweezer (Fig. 3).

4. Filter the resulting suspension through a piece of sterile gauze (10 × 10 cm) and centrifuge for 10 min at 500 g.

5. Resuspend the pellet in culture medium and filter the cells through a piece of sterile gauze (10 × 10 cm) and plate cells on coverslips placed in 50-mm culture dishes for immunofluorescence analysis or seed cells in microtiter wells for labeling.

6. Select colonies on the basis of morphological appearance.

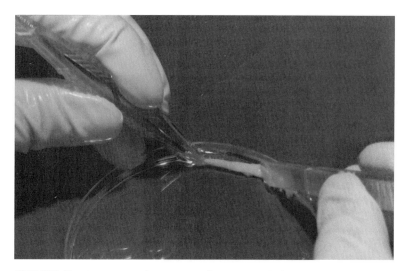

FIGURE 3   Squeezing of segments of microvessels from dermal strip.

7. Transfer selected coverslips to new culture dishes containing complete medium.

8. In addition, it may be necessary to apply selective trypzination and/or selective attachment to isolate colonies of ECs.

IV. Comments

Endothelial cells can be identified using fluorescence microscopy by their ability to synthesize von Willebrand factor (Fig. 4A) and to bind *Ulex europaeus I* agglutinin, a lectin specific for some α-L-fucose-containing glyco compounds (Holthöfer *et al.,* 1982). By use of electron transmission microscopy ECs can be identified by the presence of Weibel–Palade bodies (Weibel and Palade, 1964), an organelle specific for ECs. In culture ECs display a characteristic (see Fig. 4B) appearance which is a good day-to-day indicator of the cell type. Megakaryocytes produce von Willebrand factor but this rarely gives rise to doubts as to the cell type isolated, as megakaryocytes are usually present only in bone marrow or liver, and in cases where it may be a potential contaminant of an isolate the morphology and size would reveal the heterogeneity of the culture.

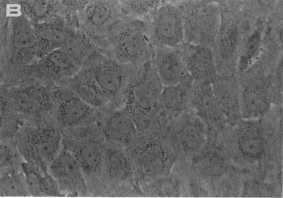

FIGURE 4   (A) Immunofluorescence, von Willebrand factor. (B) Phase-contrast micrograph showing appearance of human umbilical vein endothelial cells.

When obtaining tissues from humans, either patients or healthy volunteers, it is essential that international and local ethical standards are kept. Most countries have signed the Helsinki Declaration II which has sections describing recommendations regarding basic principles of clinical research and biomedical research. The implementation of the Helsinki Declaration II may differ in details in various countries, but it is the responsibility of the researcher to make sure that these rules are followed.

V. Pitfalls

1. Keep the time from tissue isolation to isolation of cells as short as possible to maximize the yield of cells.

2. Leukocytes and red blood cells may adhere to ECs from larger vessels or microvessels but usually detach in a day or two and can be washed away by several changes of medium.

3. Cultures of microvessel ECs may be contaminated with fibroblasts that easily outgrow ECs in culture media such as Dulbecco's modified Eagle's medium with 10% fetal calf serum. Segments of microvessels can be enriched for by short centrifugation (less than 1 min at 500 g) or by gravity (by leaving the tubes in vertical position for 10–15 min), as vessel segments sediment more quickly than single cells. In addition it may be necessary to apply selective trypsinization, taking advantage of the fact that fibroblasts tend to detach more quickly than ECs.

4. As sample specimens obtained from surgical departments may not be handled with the same care with respect to sterility as the patient, one must always make use of antibiotics in the culture medium, usually penicillin and streptomycin suffice.

REFERENCES

Betz, A. L., and Goldstein, G. W. (1986) Specialized properties and solute transport in brain capillaries. *Annu. Rev. Physiol.* **48**, 241–250.

Holthöfer, H., Virtanen, I., Kariniemi, A. L., Hormia, M., Linder, E., and Miettinen, A. (1982) *Ulex europaeus* I lectin as a marker for vascular endothelium in human tissues. *Lab. Invest.* **47**, 60–66.

Hurley, J. V. (1985) Inflammation. In J. R. Anderson (ed.), "Muir's Textbook of Pathology," pp. 4.5–4.17. Edward Arnold, London.

Roitt, I. (1988) "Essential immunology," 6th ed. Oxford: Blackwell Scientific.

Ross, R. (1993) The pathogenesis of atherosclerosis: A perspective for the 1990s. *Nature* **362**, 801–809.

Weibel, E. R., and Palade, G. E. (1964) New cytoplasmic components in arterial endothelia. *J. Cell Biol.* **23**, 101–112.

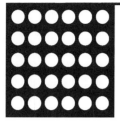

Isolation and Proliferation of Adult Mammalian Central Nervous System Stem Cells

Brent A. Reynolds, Catherine Leonard, and Samuel Weiss

I. Introduction

In mammalian tissues, where differentiated cells have a relatively short life span, cells are constantly being replaced. A notable example is the hematopoietic system where eight distinct lineages are generated from a relatively small population of founding cells referred to as *stem cells* (Potten and Loeffler, 1990). Unlike the hematopoietic system, the mature mammalian central nervous system (CNS) has very little to no cell turnover and does not generate new cells following injury. This has led to the assumption that the CNS does not contain stem cells and that it does not have the potential to replace cells lost to injury or disease.

We have isolated from the embryonic and adult mammalian CNS a cell that exhibits stem cell-like characteristics *in vitro* and can be differentiated into neuronal and glial cells (Reynolds *et al.,* 1992; Reynolds and Weiss, 1992). The presence of a putative stem cell in the adult CNS, with the potential to generate new neurons, raises a number of interesting therapeutic possibilities. These include the establishment of adult-derived CNS stem cell lines to be used as a source of tissue for neuronal transplantation or the proliferation and differentiation of the stem cell *in vivo* to replace cells lost to injury or disease.

II. Materials and Instrumentation

DMEM (Cat. No. 430-2100 EB), F12 nutrient mixture (Cat. No. 430-1700 EB), glutamine (Cat. No. 320-5030 AG), and penicillin–streptomycin (Cat. No. 600-5070 AG) are obtained from Gibco. Epidermal growth factor (EGF, Cat. No. 01-40001) is from Collaborative Research. Ovomucoid (Cat. No. 109878) is obtained from Boehringer-Mannheim. Insulin (Cat. No. I-5500), putrescine (P-7505), progesterone (P-6149), sodium bicarbonate (S-5761), glucose (G-8270), transferrin (T-2252), Hepes buffer (H-3375), selenium (SQ-133), trypsin (T-1005), hyaluronidase (H-6254), and kynurenic acid (K-3375) are from Sigma. Spinner flasks (25 ml) used in the tissue dissociation step are obtained from Bellco Glass Company (Cat. No. 1967-00025). A Plexiglas stand for holding vials and equipped with tubing for oxygenation was homemade (Fig. 1).

III. Procedures

Cell dissociations are adapted from Kay and Wong (1986) and Fraser and Mac-Vicar (1991).

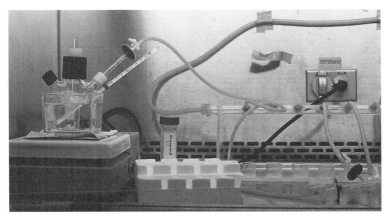

FIGURE 1 Experimental setup for the isolation of cells from the adult mouse CNS, performed in a sterile culture hood.

Solutions

1. *Artificial CSF (aCSF):* To make 1 liter of regular aCSF, mix 700 ml double-distilled (dd)H_2O, 62 ml of a 2 M stock solution of NaCl, 5 ml of a 1 M stock solution of KCl, 1.3 ml of a 1 M stock solution of $MgCl_2$, 169 ml of a 155 mM stock solution of $NaHCO_3$, 10 ml of a 1 M stock solution of glucose, and 18 ml of a 108 mM stock solution of $CaCl_2$. Bubble the aCSF with 95% O_2/5% CO_2 for 15 min, adjust the pH to 7.35, and make up to 1 liter volume with ddH_2O. To make 1 liter of high-Mg^{2+}/low-Ca^{2+} aCSF, follow the procedure as above but increase the volume of $MgCl_2$ added to 3.2 ml and reduce the volume of $CaCl_2$ added to 0.926 ml.

2. *10× stock solution of DMEM/F12:* Add 77 g DMEM and 53 g F12 nutrient mix to 1 liter sterile distilled water and stir to dissolve.

3. *10× stock solution of hormone mix (HM):* Combine 20 ml 10× DMEM/F12, 4 ml 30% glucose, 3 ml 7.5% $NaHCO_3$, 1 ml 1 M Hepes, and 150 ml sterile ddH_2O. To this above solution add

200 mg transferrin: Empty the contents of each bottle into the 1× medium; then rinse with the medium to remove all the powder.

50 mg insulin: Add 2 ml 0.1 N HCl (previously filter-sterilized) to a 50-mg vial of insulin. Once it has dissolved, add 18 ml of sterile ddH_2O. Add this to the 1× medium.

19.32 mg putrescine dissolved in 20 ml sterile ddH_2O.

20 μl 3×10^{-3} M selenium: Add 1.93 ml sterile ddH_2O to a 1-mg vial, mix, and transfer to a small sterile tube. Store at −20°C. The solution can be reused.

20 μl 2×10^{-3} M progesterone: Add 1.59 ml 95% ethanol to a 1-mg vial, mix, and transfer to a small sterile tube. Store this at −20°C. The solution can be reused.

Once all five ingredients have been added to the 1× medium, filter-sterilize the whole solution using a 0.2-μm filter and divide it into 50-ml aliquots; store frozen at −20°C.

4. *Working solution of DMEM/F12/HM:* To make 500 ml of medium, filter-sterilize the following into an autoclaved bottle: 224 ml ddH_2O, 50 ml 10× DMEM/F12, 10 ml 30% glucose, 7.5 ml 7.5% $NaHCO_3$, 2.5 ml 1 M Hepes, 6 ml 200 mM glutamine, 150 ml ddH_2O, and 50 ml 10× HM.

Steps

1. Add 2 ml of penicillin–streptomycin to 100 ml aCSF in a sterile graduated cylinder. Filter this through a 0.2-μm pore-size syringe filter into two sterile 50-ml tubes. Repeat for high-Mg^{2+}/low-Ca^{2+} aCSF. Oxygenate all four tubes for 15–20 min.

2. Weigh out the following enzymes into a 50-ml sterile tube: 40 mg trypsin, 20 mg hyaluronidase, 6 mg kynurenic acid. Add 30 ml of high-Mg^{2+}/low-Ca^{2+} aCSF and shake gently to dissolve.

3. Transfer the enzyme solution into the spinner flask and cap it. Set the flask in a water bath at 30°C on a stir plate. Insert a Pasteur pipette into one of the side-arms of the flask and use this to gently oxygenate the solution (95% O_2/5% CO_2).

4. To prepare for the dissection, half-fill one 75-mm and two 35-mm petri dishes with regular, oxygenated aCSF. Clean the dissection microscope with 70% isopropanol and place it in the culture hood. Also have ready the following sterile dissection instruments: large rat-tooth forceps, rongeurs, fine forceps, and Vannas scissors.

5. Outside the hood, have ready a pair of large dissection scissors and rat-tooth forceps, a 75-mm petri dish, and a wash bottle with 70% ethanol. Kill two mice by cervical dislocation. Remove the heads, skin them, and place them on the petri dish. Rinse with 70% ethanol to sterilize. Further dissection steps should be performed in the culture hood.

6. Expose the brain using rongeurs; then rinse the surface with oxygenated aCSF from a Pasteur pipette. Remove the brain completely and transfer it to the 75-mm petri dish containing aCSF. Rinse the brain and transfer it again to a 35-mm dish.

7. Under the microscope, dissect out the whole striatum using fine forceps and Vannas scissors (Paxinos and Watson, 1982). Transfer the striata to the second 35-mm dish and using the Vannas scissors cut each striatum into 10–20 thin pieces.

8. Using a wide-bore graduated pipette, transfer the chopped striata into the spinner flask containing the equilibrated enzyme mixture. Set the shaker and oxygenation so that the motion is very gentle and not too many bubbles form. Allow this to stir for 1.5 hr.

9. Transfer the tissue to a centrifuge tube containing 4–5 ml of DMEM/FI2/HM with trypsin inhibitor (ovomucoid 0.7 mg/ml). Triturate the tissue 25 times with a fire-narrowed cotton-plugged Pasteur pipette.

10. Allow the triturated solution to settle; then remove half of the supernatant to another centrifuge tube. Add 2 ml more of the ovomucoid-containing medium and triturate about 25 times. Allow any undissociated tissue to settle, remove the supernatant, and combine with the first supernatant.

11. Spin the dissociated cells at 400 rpm for 5 min.

12. The supernatant will be somewhat cloudy and a thin wispy pellet will be visible at the bottom of the tube. Carefully aspirate as much of the supernatant as possible and resuspend the cells in 20 ml of DMEM/FI2/HM containing EGF at 20 ng/ml.

13. Plate the cells in 35-mm culture dishes, adding 2 ml of cell suspension to each dish. Wait 4–5 min for the cells to settle; then aspirate most of the medium and replace it with fresh DMEM/FI2/HM/EGF.

14. Culture at 37°C in a humid, field atmosphere of 5% CO_2.

IV. Comments

Using the described procedure results in the generation of 200–400 clonally derived spheres (Reynolds and Weiss, 1992). Indirect immunocytochemical analysis with antibodies that recognize antigens found in differentiated CNS cells (i.e., for neurons—neuron-specific enolase, neurofilament; astrocytes—glial fibrillary acidic protein; oligodendrocytes—myelin basic protein, galactocerebroside) reveals that cells within the sphere are not differentiated. In fact, virtually all of the cells within the spheres are immunoreactive for nestin, an intermediate filament protein found in undifferentiated CNS cells (Lendahl *et al.*, 1990). We have been able to differentiate embryonic and adult neurospheres using a number of different paradigms (Reynolds and Weiss, 1993). Common to all the differentiation protocols is the attachment of the undifferentiated spheres to a coated substrate (i.e., poly-L-ornithine, laminin, fibronectin). Hence, this procedure allows one to isolate stemlike cells from the adult CNS and proliferate them *in vitro,* generating a large number of progenitor cells that can differentiate into neurons and glial cells. This technique may prove to be a valuable model system for investigating and manipulating undifferentiated progenitor cells and represents a potential source of cells for neuronal transplantation.

V. Pitfalls

1. Be careful not to transfer any hair during the dissection procedures as this will increase the risk of bacterial or fungal contamination (steps 5–7).

2. While dissociating the striatal tissue do not let the temperature rise above 36°C or fall below 28°C (step 8).

3. If after spinning the dissociated cells (step 11) the pellet is quite large, too much debris is present. If this is the case remove the supernatant, resuspend the cells, and spin a second time (repeat if necessary).

4. Do not plate cells onto culture dishes that have been pretreated with poly-L-ornithine, as this seems to inhibit proliferation of the stem cell (step 13).

5. It is advisable to remove the medium and replace with fresh DMEM/F12/HM/EGF after the cells are first plated so as to decrease the amount of debris in the culture (which also inhibits division of the stem cell) (step 13).

ACKNOWLEDGMENTS

This work was supported by the Medical Research Council of Canada (MRC). B.A.R. is a recipient of a studentship from the Alberta Heritage Foundation for Medical Research (AHFMR). S.W. is an AHFMR Scholar and an MRC Scientist.

REFERENCES

Fraser, D. D., and MacVicar, B. A. M. (1991) Low-threshold transient calcium current in rat hippocampal lacunosum-moleculare interneurons: Kinetics and modulation by neurotransmitters. *J. Neurosci.* **11**, 2812–2820.

Kay, A. R., and Wong, R. K. S. (1986) Isolation of neurons suitable for patchclamping from adult mammalian central nervous system. *J. Neurosci. Methods* **16**, 227–238.

Lendahl, U., Zimmerman, L. B., and McKay, R. D. G. (1990) CNS stem cells express a new class of intermediate filament protein. *Cell* **60**, 585–595.

Paxinos, G., and Watson, C. (1982) "The Rat Brain in Stereotaxic Coordinates." Academic Press, New York.

Potten, C. S., and Loeffler, M. (1990) Stem cells: Attributes, cycles, spirals, pitfalls and uncertainties. Lessons for and from the Crypt. *Development* **110**, 1001–1020.

Reynolds, B. A., Tetzlaff, W., and Weiss, S. (1992) A multipotent EGF-responsive striatal embryonic progenitor cell produces neurons and astrocytes. *J. Neurosci.* **12**, 4568–4574.

Reynolds, B. A., and Weiss, S. (1992) Generation of neurons and astrocytes from isolated cells of the adult mammalian central nervous system. *Science* **255**, 1707–1710.

Reynolds, B. A., and Weiss, S. (1993) EGF-responsive stem cells in the mammalian central nervous system. *In* "Restorative Neurology and Neuroscience," Vol. 6: "Neuronal Cell Death and Repair" (A. C. Cuello, ed.), pp. 247–255. Elsevier, Amsterdam.

Clonal Cultures *in Vitro* for Hemopoietic Cells Using Semisolid Agar Medium

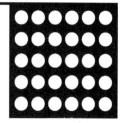

Gregory R. Johnson

I. Introduction

The past 10 years have witnessed an exponential increase in knowledge of the regulation of hemopoiesis. At lease 18 cytokines (interleukins, erythropoietin, and colony-stimulating factors) have been identified, molecularly cloned, and expressed. Many of these hemopoietic growth factors are now being used in a clinical situation. They have been found to be very useful in correcting anemia and white cell deficiencies either in chronic disease or following acute treatment (e.g., chemotherapy, bone marrow transplantation).

The discovery of hemopoietic growth factors was greatly facilitated by the ability to grow hemopoietic cells *in vitro*. These assays enable undifferentiated hemopoietic precursors to proliferate and differentiate into all of the hemopoietic lineages. Especially valuable has been the development of clonal cultures for hemopoietic precursor cells. These assays rely on immobilization of the cells in a semisolid nutrient medium. In the presence of appropriate growth factors, these cells proliferate and produce a clonal colony of differentiated cells. By the counting of colonies it is possible to infer the number of precursor cells in the starting cell population. This is possible because a linear relationship exists between the number of colonies formed and the number of cells cultured. By comparison, liquid suspension cultures do not allow enumeration of precursor cell numbers as the progeny can intermingle. The second feature of clonal cultures is the dose–response relationship that exists between amount of growth factor and number of colonies stimulated. This dose–response relationship is sigmoidal, having a linear phase and a plateau phase. The linear portion of the curve can be used to determine the amount of growth factor activity, and in cultures as described here 50 units of growth factor activity corresponds to the amount of activity stimulating 50% of maximal colony numbers. More detailed information on hemopoietic colony formation and cytokines can be found in the sources listed under References.

II. Materials and Instrumentation

A. SEMISOLID AGAR MEDIUM CULTURES

Iscove's modified Dulbecco's medium powder with L-glutamine and 25 mM Hepes buffer (IMDM, Cat. No. 430-2200 EL from GIBCO, for 5 liters of single-strength medium). DEAE-dextran (Cat. No. D-9885, Sigma), L-asparagine (Cat. No. A4284,

Sigma), β-mercaptoethanol (Cat. No. 10247 BDH AnalaR), penicillin G (Cat. No. P3032 Sigma), streptomycin sulfate (Cat. No. S91367, Sigma), and agar (Bacto-Agar, Cat. No. 0140-01 Difco). Hemopoietic growth factors can be purchased from a number of commercial suppliers (e.g., Genzyme). For routine cultures, conditioned medium can be prepared from a number of tissues (see below). Fetal calf serum can be obtained from a number of suppliers, but requires pretesting (see below). Petri dishes 35–36 mm and 100 mm (can be obtained from a variety of suppliers and are bacteriological grade; tissue culture grade is not required. For viable cell counting, eosin (Cat. No. 34197, BDH) is required.

B. CONDITIONED MEDIUM

The following items were obtained from the suppliers indicated: Iscove's modified Dulbecco's medium powder with L-glutamine and 25 mM Hepes buffer (IMDM, Cat. No. 430-2200 EL, GIBCO), β-mercaptoethanol (Cat. No. M-7522, Sigma), sodium bicarbonate (NaHCO$_3$, Cat. No. 10247, BDH), penicillin G (Cat. No. P3032, Sigma), streptomycin sulfate (Cat. No. S91367, Sigma), and pokeweed mitogen (Cat. No. 670-5360AC, GIBCO). Fetal calf serum (FCS) can be obtained from various suppliers and batches can be selected only by prior testing; if a batch is available that is known to support colony formation, then this can be used to prepare conditioned media. A variety of flasks can be used to prepare pokeweed mitogen-stimulated spleen cell conditioned medium (PWM-SCM) for murine cultures, although we routinely use 1- to 2-liter glass flasks fitted with a cotton bung to allow gas diffusion. For preparation of human placenta conditioned medium a variety of flasks can also be used but we routinely use disposable 75-cm^2 tissue culture flasks (Cat. No. 25110-75, Corning).

C. INSTRUMENTATION

A stereomicroscope (SZ, Olympus), CO$_2$ incubator (many brands are available and it is recommended that one with stainless-steel water jackets be obtained) are needed. In addition, to minimize desiccation of cultures an incubator without an inbuilt fan is preferred. The standard light microscope for cell counting must have $\times$20 and $\times$40 objectives. Graduated, glass blow-out pipettes in volumes of 1, 5, 10, and 20 ml. volumes. For concentration of conditioned media, an Amicon hollow-fiber concentrator (Model DC2A) fitted with a HIP10 membrane is used.

III. Procedures

A. METHOD FOR ESTABLISHING AND SCORING AGAR–MEDIUM CULTURES

Solutions

1. *IMDM for agar cultures (AIMDM):*

IMDM	35.32 g
H$_2$O	780 ml
Penicillin (60 mg/ml)	1.0 ml
Streptomycin (100 mg/ml)	0.4 ml
DEAE-dextrin (50 mg/ml solution)	3.0 ml
L-Asparagine	0.4 g
NaHCO$_3$	9.8 g
β-Mercaptoethanol	11.8 μl

Place 780 ml water into a liter beaker and add a magnetic stirrer. Gradually add preweighed powder while stirring. Add other reagents while continually stirring. Medium is prepared endotoxin-free, filter-sterilized, sterility-checked by culturing and distributed in 100-ml aliquots. These are sealed and stored at 4°C. Each preparation of AIMDM should be batch-tested against that currently in use, before routine use. The pH should be around 7.1. This cannot be adjusted if incorrect. The osmolarity of the prepared medium should be 290–300.

2. *Agar:* 0.6 g agar and 100 ml H_2O. Weigh agar into a 500-ml flask, add 100 ml Milli-Q water, and plug flask loosely. Bring to boil for 2 min over gas flame. Prepare immediately before culturing and maintain at 45°C in water bath. Each new lot of agar should be batch-tested against that currently in use, prior to routine use.

3. *Fetal calf serum:* FCS is used as a source of nutrients in cell cultures. Batches of FCS are extensively tested prior to purchase, for optimal results, in semisolid cultures. They are also titrated to determine optimal concentration (final concentration usually 15–30%). The storage/shelf-life of FCS at −20°C is at least 2 years, and at −70°C, as long as 10 years. Centrifugation may be necessary to remove any sediment that forms after thawing. It is otherwise ready for use.

4. *Eosin for viable cell counts:* Prepare stock solution, 10% eosin-yellow powder (weight/volume) in normal saline; keep at 4°C. Mix 0.2 ml stock eosin solution with 8.6 ml normal saline and 1.5 ml FCS to prepare working solution. Store frozen.

5. *Hemopoietic growth factors:* If purchased commercially, these should be pretested to determine amount required for optimal colony formation. If conditioned media are prepared (see below), these also require prior titration to determine optimal concentration for maximal colony stimulation. These stimuli should be divided into aliquots at a concentration at least 10-fold higher than that to be used finally in the culture dish. They can be stored frozen, but once thawed should not be refrozen as this can result in loss of activity.

6. *Single-strength Iscove's modified Dulbecco's medium:* Add entire amount of IMDM powder (88.3 g) to 4.8 liters of double-distilled, deionized water and mix with gentle stirring. Rinse inside of container to remove all traces of powder. Add 15.12 g $NaHCO_3$ and stir. Add 29.5 μl of β-mercaptoethanol, 2.5 ml of penicillin (60 mg/ml stock solution), and 1 ml of streptomycin (100 mg/ml stock solution). Keeping container sealed, mix solution, filter-sterilize, and store in 500-ml aliquots in sealed bottles at 4°C.

7. *Pokeweed mitogen:* This should be prepared immediately prior to use. Any material not used should be discarded. Make up powder with 5 ml of double-distilled, deionized water. Remove from container and dilute 1:15 (v/v) in double-distilled water.

Steps

1. Warm AIMDM to room temperature.

2. Prepare agar solution.

3. Count viable cells using hemocytometer (see also article by Ariana Celis and Julio E. Celis in this volume) and eosin.

4. Draw culture layout, in book, showing culture dish number, stimuli for each culture dish, and number of cells for each culture dish.

5. Place required number of culture dishes on incubator tray and number lids individually according to culture book.

6. Add required stimuli to appropriate culture dishes as described in culture book. Usually for each culture, the required amount of stimulus is added in 0.1 ml per culture dish. This amount can be less but should not be exceeded as the agar will not gel.

7. Add AIMDM, fetal calf serum, agar, and cells (in this order) to tube or flask and mix by vortexing. It is essential that the cells are added last to this mixture, as only after mixing of the reagents is the medium at single strength. For each group of cultures, allow 1 ml of agar medium for each culture, plus at least 1 ml extra for wastage in pipetting. For each 1 ml culture, mix reagents in the following proportions: 0.3 ml AIMDM, 0.2 ml FCS, 0.5 ml agar, 0.1 ml cells in normal saline. These proportions give a final concentration of fetal calf serum of approximately 20% (by volume). If by pretesting, lower or higher concentrations of FCS are required, adjust the amount of AIMDM accordingly, so that the amount of AIMDM and FCS equals 0.5 ml for each 1 ml of culture.

8. Aliquot 1-ml volumes into petri dishes and swirl to mix stimuli and agar medium containing cells.

9. Allow mixture to gel and place in fully humidified incubator containing 5–10% CO_2 in air.

10. After required incubation period (normally 7 days for murine cultures and 14 days for human cultures) remove cultures from incubator and count colonies using an Olympus SZ stereomicroscope. Murine colonies are defined as having greater than 50 cells and human colonies as having greater than 40 cells (some investigators count human colonies as having greater than 20 cells). The microscope is placed on a black background and the concave side of the mirror is adjusted until the cells appear white against a black background.

B. PREPARATION OF CONDITIONED MEDIA

Although specific stimuli may be required, for many situations, and always for use as a positive control, a variety of conditioned media containing hemopoietic growth factors can be prepared. The following are examples of conditioned media, one suitable for human cultures and the other suitable for murine cultures.

1. Preparation of Human Placenta Conditioned Medium

Steps

1. Obtain placenta should be within 9 hr of birth. Place on large sterile tray in biological safety cabinet.

2. Using sterile instruments, remove outer layer of placenta. Assume that this portion is not sterile. Instruments can be kept sterile by periodically returning them to boiling water.

3. Cut portions (1 cm^3) of exposed placenta, and place in 100-mm petri dish containing 10 ml IMDM. Limit each petri dish to contain 8–10 pieces.

4. Having removed sufficient pieces of placenta, rinse each piece through three changes of IMDM in 100-mm petri dishes to remove most of the blood.

5. Place 18–20 pieces of placenta into tissue culture flasks (75 cm^2, Cat. No. 25110-75, Corning) in 60 ml IMDM with 5% (v/v) FCS.

6. The placental cultures, with the caps loosely sealed, are placed in an incubator at 37°C fully humidified and containing 5–10% CO_2 in air.

7. After incubation, harvest the medium free of placenta by pouring the contents of each flask through cotton gauze into a collection flask. Centrifuge the medium at 12,000 g and store the supernatant at −20°C until 4–5 liters has accumulated.

8. Then concentrate the placenta conditioned medium approximately 10-fold using a hollow-fiber concentrator (this type of concentrator is preferred because of the relatively large volumes involved).

9. Filter-sterilize the concentrate and then test by titration into human bone marrow semisolid agar cultures. Ideally, batches of conditioned media should, on titration, produce a sigmoid dose–response relationship with number of colonies formed. At maximal colony numbers stimulated, there should be a plateau in numbers of colonies formed, and there should be no sign of high-dose inhibition.

2. Preparation of Murine Pokeweed Mitogen-Stimulated Spleen Cell Conditioned Medium

Steps

1. Prepare a single-cell suspension of murine spleen cells, either by testing the spleen tissue with needles or forcing it through a fine steel mesh.

2. Place the spleen cells in a tube and allow it to stand for 5 min to allow larger tissue fragments to settle. Remove the supernatant and determine viable cell numbers.

3. Make up the cells to 2 × 10^6/ml in IMDM containing 10% FCS. (The concentration of FCS should be as low as possible and can be determined only by preliminary testing.) Then add pokeweed mitogen (0.05 ml of a 1:15 dilution of freshly prepared stock is added for each milliliter of culture medium).

4. Incubate the cells in medium for 7 days at 37°C in a fully humidified incubator containing 5–10% CO_2 in air. The cells can be incubated in a variety of containers. We routinely use 2-liter flasks, with cotton bungs, containing 250 ml of medium.

5. After incubation harvest the conditioned medium and centrifuge at 3000 g to remove cellular debris. Then concentrate the medium 10-fold as described above for human placenta conditioned medium.

6. Titrate the concentrated PWM-SCM into cultures of murine bone marrow cells to determine the concentration required to give plateau numbers of colonies.

7. The conditioned medium can then be diluted to a concentration 10 times that required for maximal colony formation, divided into 20-ml aliquots, and stored at −20°C until required. Once thawed the PWM-SCM should be stored at 4°C.

IV. Pitfalls

1. Numerous pitfalls are associated with these procedures. A major problem involves the selection of a suitable FCS. If possible, a known positive sample should be obtained from a colleague, for use as a control when testing new batches.

2. The agar needs to be boiled, to ensure it is properly dissolved. For this

reason it is recommended that a gas flame be used. The agar will initially bubble up, and care must be taken to prevent it from overflowing the flask. Once the bubbling has subsided, the agar should be boiled for 1 min to sterilize. The agar cannot be dissolved completely by autoclaving and this method should not be used.

3. It is imperative that the incubator being used is fully humidified, as desiccation of the cultures will prevent colony growth. With satisfactory cultures, a small volume of liquid will be evident at the edge of the agar medium when the cultures are tilted. If desiccation has occurred, the surface of the agar medium will not be smooth and shiny, but will display irregularities. To prevent desiccation, the incubator should contain one or more large open trays containing double-distilled water. Humidity can be improved by pumping the air–gas mixture into the incubator via a tube immersed in one of the trays of water. Many incubators are fitted with a fan to produce a uniform atmosphere within the closed incubator. This can also cause desiccation of cultures and the fan may have to be disconnected.

4. The possibility of cultures drying out is increased by increasing the incubation time. For cultures in excess of 7 days it is good policy to place the culture dishes in a 100-mm petri dish (two cultures per 100 mm dish) containing a third 35-mm culture dish, without a lid, and H_2O.

5. When establishing the cultures, problems can arise due to the temperature of the agar. If too cold, it will gel prematurely and not allow immobilization of cells. If too hot, it will kill the cells. It is recommended that the agar be maintained at 45°C and the AIMDM and FCS be allowed to warm to room temperature (18–20°C). When agar, medium, and FCS are mixed, the temperature of the solution will be less than 37°C and will not kill the cells, but will still be above the gelling temperature of the agar. Once cells have been added to the agar medium mixture and mixed, they must be aliquoted to the culture dishes prior to the agar gelling to allow mixing of agar medium, cells, and stimulus previously placed in the culture dish.

REFERENCES

Atkinson, K. (1993) Cytokines in bone marrow transplantation. *Today's Life Sci.* 5, 28–38.

Clark, S. C., and Kamen, R. (1987) The human hematopoietic colony-stimulating factors. *Science* 236, 1229–1237.

Mertelsmann, R., Herrman, F., Hecht, T., and Schulz, G. (1990) Hematopoietic growth factors in bone marrow transplantation. *Bone Marrow Transplant.* 6, 73–77.

Metcalf, D. (1984) "The Hemopoietic Colony Stimulating Factors." Elsevier, Amsterdam.

Metcalf, D. (1985) The granulocyte–macrophage colony stimulating factors. *Science* 229, 16–22.

Metcalf, D. (1986) How reliable are *in vitro* clonal cultures? Some comments based on hemopoietic cultures. *Int. J. Cell Cloning* 4, 287–294.

Metcalf, D. (1991) The control of granulocytes and macrophages: Molecular, cellular and clinical aspects. *Science* 254, 529–533.

Nicola, N. A. (1989) Hemopoietic cell growth factors and their receptors. *Annu. Rev. Biochem.* 58, 45–77.

Nicola, N. A. (1991) Receptors for colony stimulating factors. *Br. J. Haematol.* 77, 133–138.

Sheridan, W. P., Morstyn, G., Wolf, M., Lusk, J., *et al.* (1989) Granulocyte colony-stimulating factor and neutrophil recovery after high dose chemotherapy and autologous bone marrow transplantation. *Lancet* 2, 891–895.

Properties of Isolated Sertoli Cells

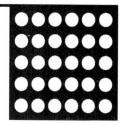

Pierre S. Tung and Irving B. Fritz

I. Introduction

We initially describe techniques for the isolation and culture of purified populations of Sertoli cells from testes of immature rats. We then discuss variations in procedures suitable for the isolation of Sertoli cell-enriched preparations from testes of adult rats, mice, and rams. We subsequently outline techniques that optimize the maintenance of the histotype of Sertoli cells during culture; that influence cell–cell and cell–substratum interactions; that modify morphogenetic characteristics and spreading behavior; and that permit investigations of secretion or transport by Sertoli cells. In addition, we describe markers for the identification of Sertoli cells and other types of testicular cells which may be present in Sertoli cell-enriched preparations in culture.

The rat testis may be separated into three parts: (1) the tunica albuginea (or the capsule) and blood vessels of the testis; (2) the seminiferous tubule, consisting of the peritubular tissue and the seminiferous epithelium; (3) the interstitial tissue.

The tunica albuginea is a sheath of firm connective tissue highly vascularized by branches of spermatic blood vessels. The tunica albuginea and the major blood vessels can be readily removed with fine forceps and scissors.

The periphery of the seminiferous tubule in adult rats is confined by peritubular boundary tissue and associated components of the "limiting membrane." This "limiting membrane" consists of the basal lamina and a framework of connective fibers, together with the fibroblast-like peritubular myoid cells. The peritubular tissue is removed by sequential enzymatic treatment by methods described below. The remaining epithelium consists of Sertoli cells and germinal cells. Distinctive junctional complexes are present between adjacent Sertoli cells in testes of pubertal and sexually mature rats. These tight junctions between interdigitating Sertoli cells do not readily allow separation of individual cells. Instead, aggregates are usually prepared for Sertoli cell culture. Hyaluronidase digestion facilitates dissociation of peritubular and germ cells from Sertoli cell aggregates, reduces the size of the aggregates, and promotes spreading. For the isolation of Sertoli cells from testes of adult animals, calcium- and magnesium-free solutions are employed, with the exception of the collagenase solution, to facilitate retraction of the elaborate cytoplasmic extensions and to weaken junctional complexes between Sertoli cells. As Sertoli cells spread out during culture, forming monolayers, a few germinal cells may remain attached to the free surfaces of Sertoli cells, but no germinal cells remain attached to the substratum.

The interstitial tissue constitutes the skeletal framework of the testis. It consists of cells and of loose connective tissue that supports the blood vessels, lymphatics, and nerves of the testis. The following groups of cells are present in the interstitium: Leydig cells, fibroblasts, macrophages, lymphocytes, and mast cells. The interstitial tissue can be dissociated from seminiferous tubules by trypsin digestion, as described below.

II. Materials and Instrumentation

Hanks' balanced salt solution (HBSS, Cat. No. 310-4020AK), calcium- and magnesium-free HBSS (Cat. No. 310-4170AG), trypsin (Cat. No. 610-5090AG), calf serum (Cat. No. 200-6200AJ), fetal bovine serum (Cat. No. 200-6140AJ), Eagle's minimum essential medium with glutamine (MEM, Cat. No. 320-1095PK), nonessential amino acids (Cat. No. 320-1051AG), penicillin (Cat. No. 860-1830 MJ), streptomycin (Cat. No. 860-1860 IM), and fungizone (Cat. No. 600-5295AE) are purchased from Gibco. Mickel Mechanical tissue slicer (Cat. No. 23-40-100-2) is purchased from Brinkman. DNase (type I, Cat. No. D-4263), soybean trypsin inhibitor (Cat. No. T-9003), collagenase (type I, Cat. No. C-0130), testicular hyaluronidase (type IS, Cat. No. H-3506), bovine serum albumin (BSA, Cat. No. A-2153), EGTA (Cat. No. E-4378), elastase (Cat. No. E-8140), and cytosine arabinoside (Cat. No. C-6760) are purchased from Sigma. Laminin (Cat. No. 40232) and Matrigel (Cat. No. 40234) are supplied by Collaborative Research. Millicell-HA inserts (Cat. No. PIHA 01250) are supplied by Millipore Corporation.

III. Procedures

A. TESTES FROM RATS AT EARLY STAGES OF PUBERTY

Solutions

Store at 4°C.

1. *HBSS.*
2. *HBSS containing 0.25% trypsin and 10 μg/ml DNase.*
3. *HBSS containing 1 mg/ml collagenase.*
4. *HBSS containing 1 mg/ml bovine testicular hyaluronidase and 1 mg/ml collagenase.*
5. *Calcium- and magnesium-free HBSS containing 0.1 mM EGTA:* To make 1 liter, solubilize 38 mg of EGTA in calcium- and magnesium-free HBSS and adjust to a total volume of 1 liter.
6. *HBSS containing 1% BSA.*

Steps

Purified populations of Sertoli cells may be most readily isolated from testes of young (8- to 30-day-old) rats, using procedures initially reported by Dorrington and Fritz (1975) and subsequently modified by Tung *et al.* (1984), as follows.

1. Swab the abdomen of the rats with 70% ethanol, and dry with sterile cotton.

2. Surgically remove testes from freshly decapitated young rats, using clean techniques, and place testes into petri dishes containing sterilized HBSS.

3. Hold the capsule at one pole of the testis with fine forceps, make an incision with fine scissors the length of the testis just below the capsule, and then use a second pair of forceps to tease out the seminiferous tubules and interstitial tissue while continuing to hold the capsule at the pole of the capsule with the first pair of tweezers. In this way, the major blood vessels should remain with the capsule as testis tissue is extruded.

4. Blot the tissue briefly on tissue paper to remove excess HBSS, and then place the testis onto HBSS-moistened filter paper in a petri dish.

5. Cut into 0.5-mm tissue fragments, using a tissue slicer.

6. Immediately transfer the testicular mince (about 1.6 g wet weight from ten 20-day-old rats) to a 125-ml Ehrlenmeyer flask, containing 50 ml sterilized HBSS having 0.25% trypsin and 10 μg/ml DNAase. Incubate for 30 min at 32°C in a shaking (60 oscillations/min) water bath. The DNase is crucial to destroy DNA liberated from damaged cells. Without DNase, cells in the preparations stick together tightly.

7. Transfer the tissue and enzyme solution into a 50-ml polyethylene tube, and let settle for 5 min at room temperature.

8. Aspirate and discard about 25 ml of the relatively clear supernatant fraction. Add an amount of soybean trypsin inhibitor sufficient to stop the actions of trypsin.

9. Filter the testis fragments through a 1-mm mesh screen to remove undigested portions, adjust to 20 ml with HBSS, and let settle for 5 min.

10. Aspirate and discard the relatively clear supernatant portion, and then resuspend the fragments in 20 ml fresh HBSS.

11. Sediment and resuspend again, and then resuspend the fragments in 20 ml HBSS containing 1 mg/ml collagenase.

12. Transfer the contents to a 125-ml Ehrlenmeyer flask, and incubate for 30 min at 32°C with shaking (60 oscillations/min). Transfer contents to a 50-ml plastic centrifuge tube.

13. Centrifuge (2 g for 2 min), and discard supernatant fraction. Resuspend aggregates in 20 ml HBSS containing 1 mg/ml bovine testicular hyaluronidase and 1 mg/ml collagenase (type I), and incubate for 30 min.

14. Centrifuge (2 g for 2 min), discard supernatant, and take aggregates up in 20 ml HBSS containing 10 mg/ml BSA.

15. Centrifuge (2 × 2 g, 2 min), discard supernatant fraction, and disperse cell aggregates.

16. Agitate gently (20 times) with a Pasteur pipette in Ca^{2+}- and Mg^{2+}-free HBSS containing 0.1 mM EGTA. When larger aggregates and/or more germinal cells are desired, hyaluronidase and the last step for dispersing cell aggregates in EGTA may be deleted; however, the Sertoli cell-enriched preparations contain more fibroblasts if these steps are not included.

17. Centrifuge the cell suspension (60 g for 2 min), discard the supernatant fraction, wash the pellet with 1% BSA in HBSS, and again centrifuge.

18. Resuspend 1 vol of washed cell aggregates in 9 vol of MEM.

19. For contiguous cultures, seed 15 μl of cell suspension per square centimeter of substratum surface. This yields a density of approximately 1×10^6 cells/cm^2. For lower cell densities the suspension volumes may be accordingly adjusted.

B. TESTES FROM ADULT RATS, MICE, OR RAMS

Solutions

1. *HBSS containing 2 mg/ml collagenase and 1 mg/ml elastase.*

2. *Matrigel 1:20 dilution in HBSS.*

3. *Other solutions:* (See Section A).

Steps

For preparing Sertoli cells from testes of mature animals, the following modifications are required to reduce cell injury and to facilitate cell attachment and spreading (Tung *et al.*, 1987):

1. With the exception of collagenase digestion, which is calcium dependent, the buffer used (HBSS) is replaced by calcium- and magnesium-free HBSS containing 0.1 mM EGTA.

2. At step 4 of the procedure in Section A, the solution used for tissue digestion contains 2 mg/ml collagenase and 1 mg/ml elastase; and the incubation time is extended to 60 min to remove the peritubular tissue, which is thickened and more resistant to enzyme digestion in testes of adult animals.

3. In testes of seasonal breeders such as rams, Sertoli cells from animals killed during times of quiescent spermatogenesis are far less elaborate in cytoplasmic structure than Sertoli cells from testes in which spermatogenesis is active. The former more closely resemble Sertoli cells prepared from testes of immature rats described above.

4. Coating the substratum surface with an appropriate extracellular matrix (ECM) component, such as laminin, promotes cell attachment and spreading. For this purpose, a reconstituted basement membrane preparation, Matrigel, is suggested, using a 1:20 dilution for incubation (3 hr at 4°C), then air-drying on the surface of the tissue culture vessel. Gelated Matrigel facilitates maintenance of histotype in contiguous cultures (Hadley *et al.*, 1985).

C. CULTURE CONDITIONS

Solutions

1. *MEM:* Store at 4°C.
2. *Calf serum:* Store at 4°C.

Steps

Sertoli cells prepared from pubertal and adult animals are usually incubated at 32°C in a water-saturated atmosphere of 95% air and 5% CO_2. The medium, with or without calf serum (10% v/v), is replenished every 2–3 days during culture. The composition of the medium greatly influences the behavior and topography of Sertoli cells. Characteristics of Sertoli cells maintained under "basal conditions" are those observed in purified or in Sertoli cell-enriched preparations maintained in standard MEM supplemented with nonessential amino acids, glutamine (4 mM), penicillin, streptomycin, and fungizone (100 units/ml, 100 μg/ml, and 2.5 μg/ml, respectively).

IV. Comments

A. BEHAVIOR OF SERTOLI CELLS IN CULTURE

When plated at subconfluent to confluent densities in standard MEM, Sertoli cell aggregates readily attach to polystyrene and glass surfaces. In the following 1–2 days, Sertoli cells continue to migrate from the aggregates, gradually assuming a

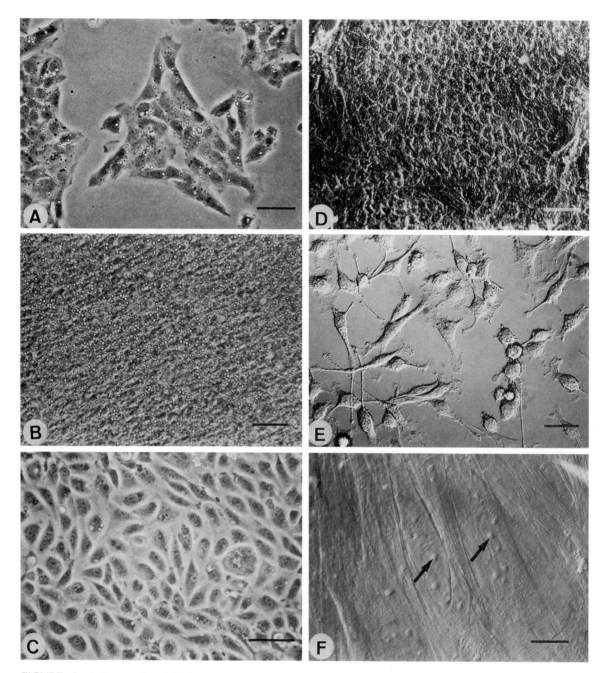

FIGURE 1 Micrographs with phase-contrast (A, B) or Nomarski (D) optics, showing cell–cell association pattern in sparse (A), contiguous (B), or confluent (D) cultures of Sertoli cells. In addition, cultures of endothelial cells are shown in a phase-contrast micrograph (C), and cultures of fibroblast-like peritubular cells are illustrated under Nomarski optics (E, F). All cells were maintained in MEM containing 10% calf serum. They were fixed either at 4 days (A–D, F) or at 8 hr (E) after seeding. Note the plaquelike structure of Sertoli cells (B, D). Contrast this with peritubular cells (F) having an extremely attenuated, fibroblast-like cell shape and prominent nucleoli (arrows in F). Bar = 40 μm.

flat squamous form, and forming colonies of compact monolayer cells (Fig. 1A). Sertoli cells that have migrated from cell aggregates do not crisscross one another and never form multilayers. They tend to form pavement-type borders with adjacent Sertoli cells. Monolayers formed by cells that have spread out from adjacent aggregates tend to join, thus fusing patches of small colonies into a large plaque. In

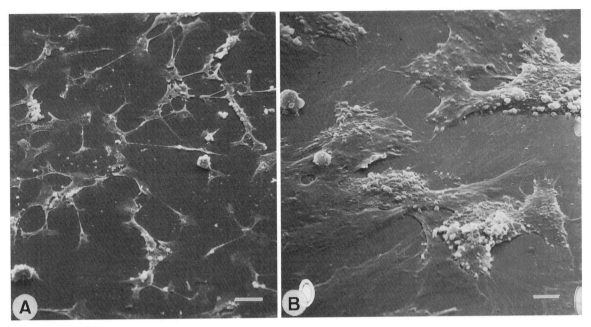

FIGURE 2 Scanning electron micrographs of Sertoli cells in subconfluent cultures in the absence (B) or presence of 5 μg/ml ovine FSH in serum-free MEM during the last 24 hr (A). Cells were fixed 3 days after seeding. Bar = 10 μm.

contiguous cultures, cell borders do not appear definitive, except when viewed under Normarski optics (compare Fig. 1B with Fig. 1D). In the presence of FSH and calf serum, Sertoli cells from testes of immature rats proliferate and can be maintained for 3–4 weeks in primary cultures (Griswold *et al.*, 1977). Efforts to obtain secondary cultures are rarely successful because Sertoli cells from testes of rats older than 14 days have an extremely low mitotic rate (Tung *et al.*, 1975).

Prior to the formation of a contiguous monolayer, or in subconfluent cultures, Sertoli cells prepared from testes of 20-day-old rats are responsive to the addition of FSH or dibutyryl cAMP. The pronounced morphological changes observed in cells maintained in standard MEM (Tung *et al.*, 1975) include the formation of astrocytic-type cytoplasmic processes (compare Figs. 2A and B). These changes in cell shape are completely blocked when 10% calf serum or antiproteases such as α_2-macroglobulin are added to the culture medium. Sertoli cells are the only cell type in the testis that manifest morphological changes in response to FSH (Tung and Fritz, 1977).

B. PROMOTION AND MODIFICATION OF HISTOTYPE

Sertoli cells seeded on polystyrene or glass surfaces do not retain their normal *in situ* histotype. ECM components isolated from the basement membrane of rat seminiferous tubules, or from Matrigel, have been shown to promote maintenance of the normal histotype with retention of polarized structures (Tung and Fritz, 1987; Hadley *et al.*, 1985). With low concentrations of air-dried Matrigel as substratum, the migration and flattening of sparsely seeded Sertoli cells are enhanced, thereby facilitating investigation of the intracellular localization of cytoskeletal proteins (Figs. 3A and D), laminin (Fig. 3E), and other markers (Tung *et al.*, 1987, 1988).

For investigations of long-term morphogenetic behavior, it has proven useful to plate Sertoli cells (isolated from testes of immature rats) on top of feeder layers of preexisting peritubular cells (600 Sertoli cell aggregates and 5000 peritubular cells

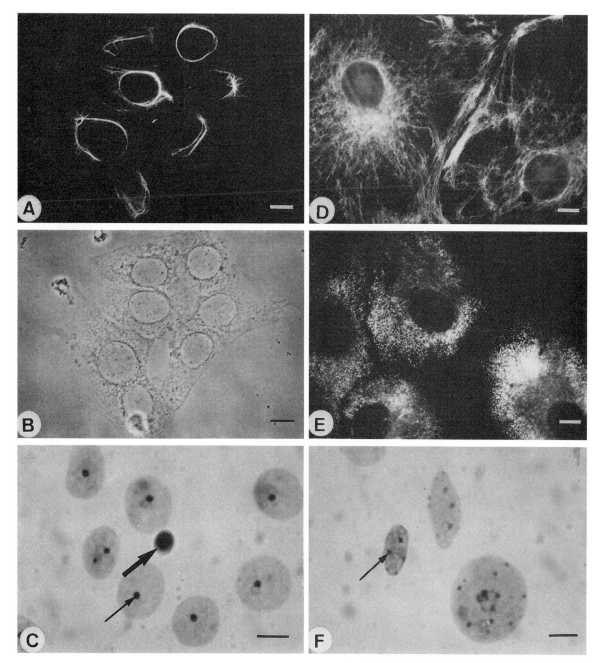

FIGURE 3 Indirect immunofluorescence micrographs, showing the localization of vimentin (A, D) and laminin (E) in Sertoli cells seeded sparsely on coverslips coated (air-dried) with 1:20 (v/v) Matrigel and maintained for 1 day (A) and 4 days (D, E). (B) Phase-contrast micrograph showing the same field as in A. (C, F) Feulgen-stained preparations of Sertoli cells (C) and peritubular cells (F), respectively. The small arrow in C and F indicates a satellite karyosome; the large arrow in C, a germinal cell nucleus. Bar = 10 μm.

per square centimeter, respectively). A morphogenetic cascade takes place in this coculture system resulting in the formation of structures resembling germ-free seminiferous tubules (Fig. 4) (Tung and Fritz, 1987).

Sertoli cells, seeded at 0.6 to 1 × 10^6 cells/cm^2 on Matrigel-coated membrane within a two-chambered system (Millicell-HA, Millipore Corp.), exhibit polarized cytoplasmic structures and biological functions. These include bidirectional endocytosis, polarized secretions, and transcellular transport systems (for review, see Dja-

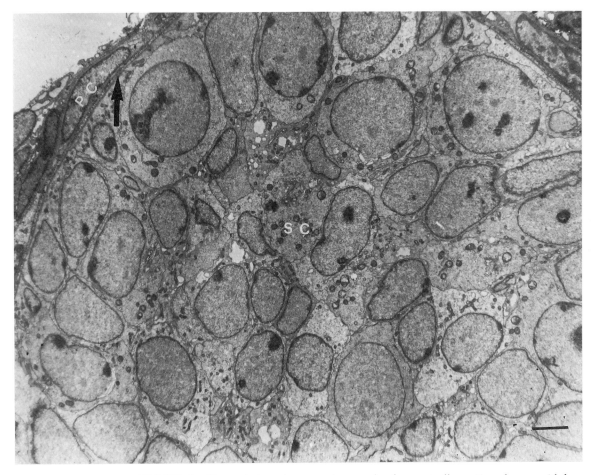

FIGURE 4   Transmission electron micrograph of a vertically sectioned organoid formed by Sertoli cells and peritubular cells, isolated from testes of 8-day-old rats and maintained in coculture for 8 days in MEM containing 10% fetal bovine serum. SC, reaggregated Sertoli cells; PC, peritubular cells; arrow, basement membrane. Bar = 2 μm.

kiew and Onoda, 1993). Polarized functions of Sertoli cells are further promoted when cocultured with peritubular cells previously seeded on the lower surface of the membrane which supports Sertoli cells.

C. ASSESSMENT OF TISSUE PREPARATIONS AND CELLS IN CULTURE

Properties of testicular cells, isolated from 20-day-old rats and maintained in culture at subconfluent density in standard MEM containing 10% calf serum (Figs. 1–4) are summarized in Table I.

V. Pitfalls

1. When major blood vessels are not excluded from the tissue preparation, endothelial cells may appear in the culture; however, smooth muscle cells and fibroblasts in the vascular wall are removed by collagenase and subsequent washings.

2. In Sertoli cell-enriched aggregates maintained in culture in the presence of

TABLE I Characteristics in Culture of Anchorage-Dependent Somatic Cells from Testes of Immature Rats

Property	Sertoli cells	Fibroblastic cells[a]	Endothelial cells[b]
Initial pattern of colonies	Each aggregate forms one patch containing a cluster of closely adherent cells (Fig. 1A).	Cells freely disperse, forming homogenous layer(s) on the entire substratum (Figs. 1E, F).	Small colonies form, consisting of polygonal patches containing clusters of associated cells (Fig. 1C).
Cell–cell association	Spread cells appose each other in a monolayer; cell borders are not always definitive (Figs. 1A, B, D). Residual germinal cells may remain attached to free surfaces during initial period of culture.	Cells rarely form close approximations with each other. They crisscross often (Figs. 1E, F), forming multiple layers, and they never associate with germinal cells.	Cells from the same vessel segment associate together with clear, definitive mosaic-like borders (Fig. 1C). They never associate with germinal cells.
Shape of single nondividing cells	Squamous and moderately flattened, round to polygonal (Figs. 1A, 2B).	Ranging from bipolar, cylindrical, triangular, stellate, to polyhedral. They are extremely attenuated in sparse culture (Fig. 1F).	Ranging from round to polygonal, with flattened periphery and mounded centers (Fig. 1C).
Cytochemical markers	Express vimentin, often arranged in a perinuclear ring (Fig. 3A) in contiguous cultures and in early stages (0–48 hr after plating) of subconfluent cultures. Vimentin becomes uniformly distributed in long-term subconfluent cultures (Fig. 3D). Express laminin and type IV collagen, detectable in Golgi apparatus and exocytic vesicles (Fig. 3E). Factor VIII is not detectable.	Express vimentin filaments, uniformly distributed throughout cytoplasm; fibronectin; and type I, III, and IV collagen; but not factor VIII. Peritubular myoid cells also express the α SM isotype of actin. Leydig cells can be identified by 3β-hydroxysteroid dehydrogenase expression.	Express vimentin filaments, uniformly distributed throughout cytoplasm; laminin; and factor VIII.
Nucleolus	One or two nucleoli per nucleus.	Multinucleoli are common, prominent in attenuated cells (Fig. 1F).	Nucleolus not prominent.

TABLE I   *Continued*

Property	Sertoli cells	Fibroblastic cells[a]	Endothelial cells[b]
Ultrastructural characteristics[c]	One to two satellite karyosomes, tripartite in adult rats. Nucleus has characteristic infoldings. Discontinuous heterochromatin clumps are present in periphery. SER is moderately to well developed, and RER is not dilated. Lipid droplets often appear in cytoplasm.	Multi-karyosome common. Nucleus is oblong and elongated with no deep indentations. Thin continuous heterochromatin is present in periphery. Binucleated cells and polyploids are common in long-term culture. RER is abundant, often dilated in peritubular myoid cells which also exhibit dense myofilament bands. Lipid droplets rarely appear, except in Leydig cells.	Nucleus is round to oblong, having a prominent heterochromatin rim in the periphery. SER is elaborate, and RER is not dilated. Lipid droplets rarely appear.

[a] If present, fibroblast-type cells are usually found in the "outskirts" of Sertoli cell colonies in subconfluent cultures or underlying Sertoli cell monolayer in confluent cultures.

[b] Endothelial-type cells appear only when major blood vessels have not been excluded from the preparation. Smooth muscle cells in the vascular wall are removed by collagenase and subsequent washings.

[c] For detailed descriptions of the morphology of cells fixed *in situ*, see Fawcett (1975); for further ultrastructural characterization of cells in culture, see Tung *et al.* (1975) and Solari and Fritz (1978).

serum, contaminating fibroblasts will proliferate unless inhibitors are added. For example, if L-valine is replaced with D-valine, the growth of fibroblast-type cells is suppressed. When serum is included in the culture medium under those conditions, the serum should be dialyzed to remove free amino acids. Cytosine arabinoside (3 μg/ml) also suppresses fibroblast growth in Sertoli cell-enriched preparations maintained in serum-rich medium.

REFERENCES

Djakiew, D., and Onoda, M. (1993) Multichamber cell culture and directional secretion. *In* "The Sertoli Cell" (L. D. Russell and M. D. Griswold, eds.), pp. 181–194. Cache River Press, Clearwater, FL.

Dorrington, J. H., and Fritz, I. B. (1975) *Endocrinology* 96, 879–889.

Fawcett, D. W. (1975) The ultrastructure and functions of Sertoli cells. *In* "Handbook of Physiology: Section 7" (R. O. Greep and D. W. Hamilton, eds.), vol. 5, pp. 21–55. American Physiological Soc., Washington, D.C.

Griswold, M. D., Solari, A., Tung, P. S., and Fritz, I. B. (1977) *Mol. Cell. Endocrinol.* 7, 151–165.

Hadley, M. A., Byers, S. W., Suarez-Quian, C. A., Kleinman, H. K., and Dym, M. (1985) *J. Cell Biol.* **101**, 1511–1522.

Solari, A., and Fritz, I. B. (1978) *Biol. Reprod.* **18**, 329–345.

Tung, P. S., Choi, A. H. C., and Fritz, I. B. (1988) *Anat. Rec.* **220**, 11–21.

Tung, P. S., Dorrington, J. H., and Fritz, I. B. (1975) *Proc. Natl. Acad. Sci. USA* **72**, 1838–1842.

Tung, P. S., and Fritz, I. B. (1977) Isolation and culture of testicular cells: a morphological characterization. *In* "Techniques of Human Andrology" (E. S. E. Hafez, ed.), pp. 125–146. North-Holland, Amsterdam.

Tung, P. S., and Fritz, I. B. (1987) *Dev. Biol.* **120**, 139–153.

Tung, P. S., Rosenior, J., and Fritz, I. B. (1987) *Biol. Reprod.* **36**, 1297–1312.

Tung, P. S., Skinner, M., and Fritz, I. B. (1984) *Biol. Reprod.* **30**, 199–211.

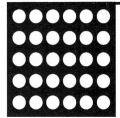

Culture of Ovarian Granulosa Cells: Calcium Imaging at the Single-Cell Level

Jorge A. Flores and Johannes D. Veldhuis

I. Introduction

Porcine granulosa cells can be easily harvested and cultured from individually dissected or pooled follicles. Under the experimental conditions described in this article, cytoplasmic free calcium ion concentrations ($[Ca^{2+}]_i$) appear to be regulated in single cells by a variety of specific hormones known to be key regulators of ovarian cell physiology (Flores *et al.*, 1990, 1991, 1992a,b; Wang *et al.*, 1989). Gonadotropins (Fig. 1), angiotensin II, endothelin-1, and luteinizing hormone-releasing hormone (LHRH) all appear to modulate $[Ca^{2+}]_i$ in cultured granulosa cells.

II. Materials and Instrumentation

A. REAGENTS AND HORMONES

Ovine follicle-stimulating hormone (NIADDK-oFSH-17, potency equals 20× NIH-FSH-S1 units/mg) is from the Hormone Distribution Office, National Pituitary Agency, NIAMDD, NIH. The acetoxymethyl ester form of fura 2/AM (Cat. No. 344905) is from Calbiochem Corporation. Methyl sulfoxide (Cat. No. EK 112 2852) and sodium bicarbonate ($NaHCO_3$, Cat. No. S-233) are from Fisher Scientific. Bovine albumin fraction V (BSA, Cat. No. 4503), EGTA (Cat. No. E3257), Hepes (Cat. No. 845-1344), and porcine insulin (Cat. No. I3505) are purchased from Sigma Chemical Company. Fetal bovine serum (FBS, Cat. No. 200-6140), Eagle's minimum essential medium (MEM, Cat. No. 410-1500EH), and penicillin–streptomycin (Cat. No. 600-5140PG) can be purchased from Gibco Laboratories. Tissue culture chamber slides (Cat. No. 177372) are purchased from Lab-Tek, Nunc, Inc. Microscope coverglass (Cat. No. 3206) is from Clay Adams. Double-coated Scotch tape (Cat. No. 665) is from Commercial Office Supply Division.

B. INSTRUMENTATION

A Zeiss Axioplan microscope (Carl Zeiss, Inc.) set up for epifluorescence microscopy has been adapted for Ca^{2+} imaging. The excitation light is supplied by a high-pressure xenon arc UV lamp, and the excitation wavelengths are selected by 360- and 380-nm filters (2-nm half-bandwidth; Corion) mounted in a manually controlled

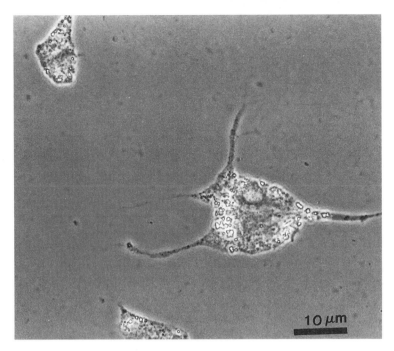

FIGURE 1 Cultured swine granulosa cells used for calcium imaging.

rotating filter wheel (MAC 2000, Ludl Electronic Products) between the UV lamp and the microscope. The fluorescence emitted by the fura-2 within the cells is collected by the objective (Nikon UV-F, ×20) and passed through a barrier filter (490–600 nm transmission) to the face of a silicon-intensified target (SIT) camera (series 68, DAGE-MTI Inc.). The resultant video signal is stored on broadcast-quality tape at 33 frames per second (U-matic Vo-5600, Sony Corp.).

III. Procedures

A. CULTURE OF GRANULOSA CELLS

Solutions

1. *Hepes:* To make 1 M stock solution, dissolve 23.83 g of Hepes in 100 ml distilled water.

2. *Hepes-buffered MEM:* To 600 ml of distilled water, add powdered MEM to prepare 1 liter of medium. While stirring, add 26.25 ml 1 M Hepes, 10 ml penicillin–streptomycin, and adjust pH to 7.4 using 1 N NaOH. Add 1.0 g BSA and distilled water to bring volume to 1 liter. Sterilize by filtration using a 0.2-μm filter and store at 4°C.

3. *Bicarbonate-buffered MEM:* To 4.5 liters of distilled water, add powdered MEM to prepare 5 liters of medium. While stirring, add 11 g sodium bicarbonate, and adjust pH to 7.4 using 1 N NaOH. Add distilled water to bring to 5 liters.

4. *Insulin stock:* To make 1 mg/ml stock, dissolve 10 mg of insulin in 10 ml of 0.01 M HCl. Sterilize through a 0.2-μm filter. Aliquot and store at −20°C.

5. *Penicillin–streptomycin stock:* To make penicillin (50,000 units/ml)–streptomycin (50 mg/ml) stock, dissolve 5 million units of penicillin and 5 g of

streptomycin in 100 ml of 0.9% NaCl. Sterilize through a 0.2-μm filter. Aliquot and store at 20°C.

6. *FSH stock:* To make 0.25 mg/ml stock solution, add 1 ml of 0.9% NaCl to FSH vial. Aliquot and store at 20°C.

7. *Bicarbonate-buffered MEM supplemented with 3% FBS, oFSH (200 ng/ml), and insulin 3 (μg/ml):* To make 100 ml, mix 97.3 ml bicarbonate-buffered MEM, 3.0 ml, FBS, 40.0 μl, FSH and 30.0 μl insulin.

Steps

1. Collect swine ovaries at a local abattoir in ice-cold 0.9% NaCl and transport to the laboratory in an ice box.

2. Obtain granulosa cells from well-vascularized, medium-sized follicles (3–5 mm in diameter) by fine-needle aspiration of the follicular fluid. Follicular fluid aspiration is done under aseptic conditions working in a laminar-flow hood.

3. Centrifuge the pooled follicular fluid at 500 g (2000 rpm) for 10 min at 4°C.

4. Discard the follicular fluid and wash the pelleted granulosa cells three times with Hepes-buffered MEM.

5. Count the cells using a hemocytometer and adjust the cell density to 1.0 $\times$ 10^5 cells/ml with bicarbonate-buffered MEM supplemented with 3% (v/v) FBS, oFSH (200 ng/ml), and porcine insulin (3 μg/ml).

6. Add the granulosa cell suspension (1.5 ml) to tissue culture chamber slides. Maintain the cell cultures in a humidified incubator (37°C, 95% air, 5% CO_2) for 48–72 hr. Prior to the calcium experiments, transfer the tissue chamber slides containing the cultured cells to serum-free Hepes-buffered MEM with 0.1% BSA, and build a Cunningham chamber on each slide as described below.

B. CUNNINGHAM CHAMBERS

Steps

1. Aspirate the Hepes-buffered MEM from the tissue chamber slide, leaving only a thin film above the cell monolayer.

2. Remove the tissue chamber from each slide. Except for 10 cm of the center area, wipe the slide off with a folded Kimwipes tissue until completely dry.

3. Place a piece of double-coated Scotch tape at each dry side bordering the cell monolayer.

4. Carefully, trying not to trap air bubbles, place a cover glass on the Scotch tape and press it down (Fig. 2). This creates a chamber with an approximate volume of 60 μl. Return the slides to the incubator after building the Cunningham chambers.

C. FURA 2/AM LOADING

Solution

1. *Fura 2/AM stock:* Protect fura 2/AM from light as much as possible. To make a 500 μM stock solution, dissolve 1 mg of fura 2/AM in 1.96 ml DMSO. Vortex well and store at −20°C in 5-μl aliquots.

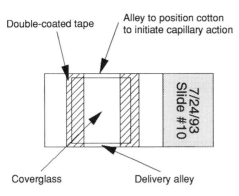

Double-coated tape

Alley to position cotton to initiate capillary action

7/24/93 Slide #10

Coverglass

Delivery alley

FIGURE 2 Cunningham chamber.

Steps

1. Thaw one 5-μl aliquot of the stock fura 2/AM at 500 μM in methyl sulfoxide at room temperature.

2. Add 45 μl Hepes-buffered MEM with 0.1% BSA to the 5 μl fura 2/AM and vortex. If kept in the dark this solution can be used to prepare the final 1 μM fura 2/am solution at least twice.

3. Add 10 μl of this fura 2/AM solution to 490 μl Hepes-buffered MEM with 0.1% BSA. This final fura 2/AM solution at 1 μM is used to load the cultured granulosa cells.

4. Exchange of medium within the Cunningham chamber with the 1 μM fura 2/AM solution is accomplished by capillarity. Capillary action is initiated by touching one end of the Cunningham chamber with a Kimwipes tissue. The fura 2/AM solution is delivered at the other end of the Cunningham chamber. At least 180 μl of the fura 2/AM solution is delivered in this manner.

5. Incubate granulosa cells loaded with 1 μM fura 2/AM for 20 min at 37°C.

6. Wash the cells with Hepes-buffered MEM with 0.1% BSA and incubate for a further 20 min at 37°C to allow time for cytoplasmic deesterification of the fura 2/AM dye.

D. CALCIUM MEASUREMENTS

Steps

1. Following dye loading, place the Cunningham chamber on the stage of a Zeiss Axioplan microscope (Fig. 3).

2. Place a broadcast-quality tape in the video recorder unit.

3. Adjust the gain and kilovoltage in such manner that the intensity of the fluorescent signal is in the working range of the image analyzer unit.

4. Select fields for recording on the basis of fluorescence signal quality. Once a satisfactory microscopy field is found, turn the play/recorder on.

5. When delivery of stimulatory substances is desired, exchange of medium within the Cunningham chamber is accomplished by capillarity. Capillary action is created by placing a small piece of cotton at one end of the chamber at the beginning of each trace. For a typical delivery, 60 μl of medium is carefully deposited at the other end of the chamber. Fura 2 emission at 360-nm excitation wavelength (Ca^{2+}-independent) is recorded at the beginning and at the end of

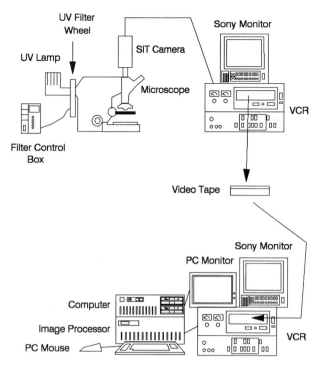

FIGURE 3 Fluorescent microscope setup.

each trace to evaluate fura 2/AM leakage and/or photobleaching. Sequential monitoring of changes in $[Ca^{2+}]_i$ after hormonal stimulation of granulosa cells is followed as fura 2/AM emission at 380-nm excitation.

E. DATA ANALYSIS

Steps

1. Turn on the video recorder and digital analyzer units.

2. Place the broadcast-quality tape containing the desired images in the video recorder, and turn on the play function.

3. The recorded video signal corresponding to an individual cell is captured and digitized using software (RADTIME) run on a QX-7 image analysis system (Quantex Corp.). This software creates an ASCII file of the mean radiance within the cell of interest and an area of background for substraction.

4. Export the ASCII file to a spreadsheet program (Lotus 1-2-3, Vol. 2.0, Lotus Development Corp.), where the 380-nm fluorescence values are corrected for background and then converted to ratio values using the equation $R = F_0/F_i$, where F_0 is the initial 380-nm emission intensity, and F_i is the 380 nm fluorescence at time i. The data in graphic form (Fig. 4) represent the plot of the converted fluorescence ratio (y axis) over time (x axis).

IV. Comments

With the protocol described in this article, cultured swine granulosa cells can be used to study the participation of Ca^{2+} in the signal transduction mechanism em-

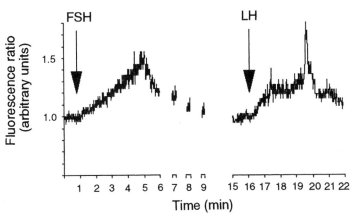

FIGURE 4 Ability of follicle-stimulating hormone (FSH) and luteinizing hormone (LH) to initiate Ca^{2+} transients in a single porcine granulosa cell, as indicated by the increased fluorescence ratio after gonadotropin exposure. FSH (10 ng/ml) was delivered at 45 sec, and the fluorescence was monitored continuously for 6 min after fura 2 excitation at 380 nm. At 7, 8, and 9 min the fluorescence was monitored at 20-sec windows. Cells were washed at 10 min with Hepes-buffered MEM with 0.1% BSA. At 15 min the fluorescence was again monitored continuously for another 7 min. LH (10 ng/ml) was delivered at 15 min and 45 sec.

ployed by a variety of ovarian modulators. This approach is particularly suitable to understand acquisition of specific aspects of signal transduction necessary for cell-to-cell communication and granulosa cell differentiation. Cell heterogeneity even within a single ovarian follicle can also easily be approached using the described protocol.

V. Pitfalls

Although this protocol is very well suited to gaining an understanding of signal transduction mechanisms at the single-cell level in ovarian cells, we still have the critical technical difficulty of assessing secretion at the same temporal and single-cell level at which the second messengers are measured. Resolution of this technical difficulty constitutes one of the major challenges in this area of research.

REFERENCES

Flores, J. A., Quyyumi, S., Leong, D. A., and Veldhuis, J. D. (1992a) Actions of endothelin-1 of swine ovarian (granulosa) Cells. *Endocrinology* **131**, 1350–1358.

Flores, J. A., Sharma, O. P., Leong, D. A., and Veldhuis, J. D. (1992b) Luteinizing hormone and endothelin-1 induce calcium release in porcine granulosa cells at different stages of development. *In* "IX Ovarian Workshop, Serono Symposia, July 1992, Chapel Hill, North Carolina," p. 30, Abstract 19. Serono Symposia, USA, Chapel Hill, NC.

Flores, J. A., Veldhuis, J. D., and Leong, D. A. (1990) Follicle stimulating hormone evokes an increase in intracellular free calcium ion concentrations in single ovarian (granulosa) cells. *Endocrinology* **127**, 3172–3179.

Flores, J. A., Veldhuis, J. D., and Leong, D. A. (1991) Angiotensin II induces calcium release in a subpopulation of single ovarian (granulosa) cells. *Mol. Cell. Endocrinol.* **81**, 1–10.

Wang, J., Baimbridge, K. G., and Leung, P. C. K. (1989) Perturbation of intracellular calcium ion concentration in single rat granulosa cells by angiotensin II. *Endocrinology* **124**, 1094–1096.

SECTION D

Cell Separation
Techniques

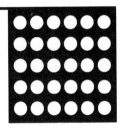

Isolation of Peripheral Blood Mononuclear Cells and Identification of Human Lymphocyte Subpopulations by Multiparameter Flow Cytometry

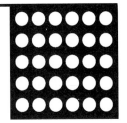

Marianne Hokland, Hanne Jørgensen, and Peter Hokland

I. Introduction

Peripheral blood is the primary source of lymphoid cells for investigation of the human immune system. The distribution of lineage-associated membrane proteins on isolated human leukocyte subpopulations has emerged as an important preliminary tool for investigating their function (Barclay *et al.*, 1993). Density gradient centrifugation on a mixture of Ficoll and sodium metrizoate of a density of 1.077 g/liter is a simple and rapid method for purifying peripheral blood mononuclear cells (PBMNCs), which takes advantage of the density differences between leukocyte subsets and other blood elements (Bøyum, 1964). Thus, while PBMNCs and platelets collect on top of the gradient due to their low density, granulocytes sediment to its bottom due to their higher density (Fig. 1). In addition, the Ficoll sucrose polymer aggregates the erythrocytes so that they, too, traverse the gradient. Platelets can subsequently be separated from the PBMNCs by low-force washing or, if complete removal is necessary, by centrifugation through a fetal calf serum (FCS) cushion. The PBMNC population thus obtained from a healthy donor consists of about 5% B lymphocytes, 5–15% monocytes, 60–70% T lymphocytes, and 5–15% natural killer (NK) cells (Reichert *et al.*, 1991).

The introduction of flow cytometry (FCM) with immunofluorescence staining techniques has revolutionized the analysis of cell surface antigen expression (elegantly reviewed by Shapiro, 1983). By use of this methodology, the frequency distributions of up to four different fluorochromes as well as forward and side scatter (showing cell size and granularity, respectively) are simultaneously used to characterize each cell. Thus, the fast analysis of large numbers of cells combined with the quantitative data output yields results vastly superior to those of the more cumbersome immunofluorescence microscopy.

The development of monoclonal antibodies (MoAbs) against lymphocyte differentiation antigens has provided useful reagents for identifying T-cell, B-cell, myelomonocytic, and NK cell populations. Such MoAbs can be obtained commercially (and, in some instances, from cell banks), and FCM is now the established method for detection of these cell types, be they normal or malignant (Quirke and Dyson, 1986; Colvin and Preffer, 1987).

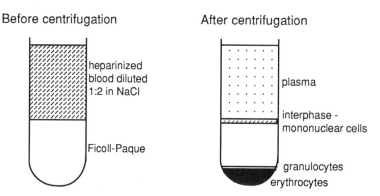

Before centrifugation

heparinized
blood diluted
1:2 in NaCl

Ficoll-Paque

After centrifugation

plasma

interphase -
mononuclear cells

granulocytes
erythrocytes

FIGURE 1 Heparinized human peripheral whole blood diluted 1:2 in 0.9% NaCl layered on a Ficoll–Paque gradient and the distribution of the leukocytes after centrifugation.

We provide here the basic tools for isolation of PBMNCs from peripheral blood and, moreover, exemplify the power of multiparameter FCM by identification of the CD56+/CD3− NK cell population. The latter procedure was chosen, because it involves two-color labeling and necessitates extensive electronic gating.

II. Materials and Instrumentation

A. REAGENTS

Heparinized blood is obtained by venipuncture. Heat-inactivated (1 hr, 56°C) human AB serum is obtained from the local blood bank. Sodium chloride (0.9%), sodium azide (0.1%), formaldehyde (1% in PBS, pH 7.0), and phosphate-buffered saline (PBS, pH 7.4), are purchased from local producers. Preservative-free Heparin Leo (5000 IU/ml) is from Løvens Kemiske Fabrik. Ficoll–Paque solution (density 1.077 g/liter, Code No. 17-0840-02) is obtained from Pharmacia. Heat-inactivated (1 hr, 56°C) FCS (Code No. S-0001a) is purchased from Sera-Lab. MoAbs [IgG$_1$ fluorescein isothiocyanate (FITC) control (Cat. No. X927), IgG$_{2\alpha}$ R-phycoerythrin (RPE) control (Cat. No. X950), CD45 FITC/CD14 RPE (Cat. No. FR700), CD56 RPE (Cat. No. R890), and CD3 FITC (Cat. No. F818)] are from DAKO.

B. INSTRUMENTATION

The temperature-controlled centrifuge (Beckman GS-6R) was purchased from Beckman Instruments, Inc., and a Vortex mixer from Snijders. Conical centrifuge tubes (10 ml), plastic tubes (4 ml), and plastic pipettes, all sterile, were purchased from Nunc. Adjustable-volume (5–50 μl, 250–1000 μl, and 1–5 ml) micropipettes were obtained from Finnpipette (Labsystems Oy), and the flow cytometer is a Coulter Elite purchased from Coulter Electronics Ltd.

III. Procedures

A. SEPARATION OF HUMAN MONONUCLEAR CELLS BY FICOLL– PAQUE DENSITY GRADIENT CENTRIFUGATION

Solutions

1. *0.9% Sodium chloride:* To make 1 liter, dissolve 9.0 g NaCl in distilled water to a total volume of 1 liter. Store at 4°C.

2. *Phosphate-buffered saline, pH 7.4:* To make 1 liter, add 0.34 g of KH_2PO_4, 1.58 g of K_2HPO_4, and 8.0 g of NaCl to distilled water, adjust pH to 7.4 and bring to a total volume to 1 liter. Store at 4°C.

Steps

1. Draw blood by sterile venipuncture into a syringe containing sufficient preservative-free heparin to yield a final concentration of 2 IU/ml.

2. Mix blood with an equal volume of 0.9% NaCl and carefully layer 5 ml onto 3 ml Ficoll–Paque in a 10-ml conical tube so that the interface is maintained intact (Fig. 1).

3. Centrifuge the tube at 400 g for 25 min at room temperature. Carefully harvest PBMNCs from the interphase using a Pasteur pipette (Fig. 1), yielding as little contamination as possible of either Ficoll–Paque or plasma.

4. As the presence of some Ficoll–Paque is unavoidable, add four to five times the volume of PBS containing 2% human AB serum (PBS–AB). Mix well to disperse the remaining Ficoll–Paque before further centrifugation at 200 g for 12 min.

5. After decanting the supernatant resuspend PBMNCs in 10 ml PBS–AB for a further two washing cycles at 100 g for 8 min (to get rid of thrombocytes).

6. Resuspend PBMNCs in PBS–AB to a concentration of 1×10^7/ml before use.

B. IDENTIFICATION OF HUMAN CD56+/CD3− NATURAL KILLER CELLS BY FLOW CYTOMETRY

Natural killer cells are lymphoid cells that do not rearrange immunoglobulin and T-cell-receptor genes and express neither their products nor a complete CD3 complex on their surface (Fitzgerald-Bocarsly *et al.,* 1988). Though no single antigen unequivocally identifies them, the vast majority of human NK cells express the CD56 antigen (Griffin *et al.,* 1983). From an immunological point of view, two main functions are connected to NK cells: an antineoplastic effect and an antimicrobial effect toward parasites, bacteria, and viruses. Furthermore, NK cells seem to play an important role in extramedullary, physiological hematopoiesis (for a review, see Ritz *et al.,* 1988).

For most purposes, unconjugated MoAbs can be used in a standard indirect fluorescence technique. For double- or triple-labeling purposes, however, it is necessary to use directly conjugated antibodies to minimize unspecific binding. To obtain accurate frequencies of lymphocyte subsets such as NK cells, it is furthermore necessary to exclude monocytes from the flow cytometric analysis of PBMNCs.

Solutions

1. *0.1% Sodium azide:* For a 20% stock solution, dissolve 50 g sodium azide in distilled water to a total volume of 250 ml. Dilute this solution 1:200 with PBS (pH 7.4) for 0.1% sodium azide and store at 4°C.

2. *Phosphate-buffered saline, pH 7.0:* To make 1 liter, add 0.34 g KH_2PO_4, 1.58 g of K_2HPO_4, and 8.0 g NaCl to distilled water, adjust pH to 7.0, and bring to a total volume of 1 liter. Store at 4°C.

3. *1% Formaldehyde:* To make 100 ml add 2.7 ml of 37% formaldehyde (Sigma, F1635) to 97.3 ml PBS, pH 7.0. Store at 4°C.

Steps

1. 1×10^6 cells (100 μl of a 1×10^7/ml PBMNC suspension) in PBS–AB are needed per aliquot.

2. To one of each vial containing 1×10^6 cells is added (a) 10 μl CD45FITC/CD14RPE (DAKO), (b) 10 μl IgG$_{2a}$RPE (DAKO) (isotype control for CD56RPE), (c) 10 μl IgG$_1$FITC (DAKO) (isotype control for CD3FITC), (d) 10 μl CD56RPE (DAKO), (e) 10 μl CD3FITC (DAKO), (f) 10 μl CD56RPE (DAKO) and 10 μl CD3FITC (DAKO).

3. Mix on a Vortex mixer and incubate in the dark for 15 min at room temperature.

4. Wash cells twice in PBS–AB at 300 g for 5 min.

5. While tube is placed on a Vortex mixer fix cells by adding 200 μl 1% formaldehyde in PBS with 0.1% sodium azide.

6. *Flow cytometric analysis:* The suggested settings for running samples on a Coulter Elite machine are forward scatter 760 V, side scatter 660 V, PMT2 (FITC) 1000 V, and PMT3 (RPE) 1180 V. Although different instruments may vary, these relative levels should provide some guidelines.

Run vial (a) and acquire 40,000 cells in a forward vs 90° (side) scatter histogram and set a bitmap gate around the lymphocyte population thus excluding monocytes (Fig. 2A).

Export lymphocyte scatter signals to a FITC vs RPE histogram and establish lymphocyte gate criteria as >95% cells positive for the panleukocyte CD45 marker and <5% cells positive for the monocyte marker CD14 (Fig. 2B). (Normally, results are much better with >99% CD45+ and <1% CD14+ cells).

Run isotype controls (b) and (c) and define a limit between positive and negative cells (normally at 1–3% positive cells) (Fig. 2E). Controls should always match the isotype and the fluorochrome of the reactive MoAbs to be analyzed!

As emission spectra of FITC and RPE overlap, run samples (d) and (e) to determine fluorescence compensation by subtracting a certain percentage of the FITC signal from the photomultiplier, which receives the RPE signal (and vice versa). An example of CD3-FITC-labeled cells before and after compensation for RPE (analysis on lymphocyte gate defined above) is shown in Figs. 2C and 2D. Compensation is optimal when less than 1% FITC signal is seen in the RPE channels.

Finally, the double-labeled cells, vial (f), can now be analyzed (Fig. 2F). Quadrant 1 contains the CD56+/CD3− (NK) cell population (22% of the cell population analyzed), quadrant 2 contains the CD56+/CD3+ (5%) (mainly non-MHC-restricted T cells). Finally, quadrant 4 contains the CD56−/CD3+ T cells (62%).

IV. Comments

To quality-control the FCM it is advisable to adjust settings daily according to a standard preparation of fluorescent beads (Standard-Brite, Coulter PN 6604146), so that the fluorescence intensity measured in a given channel remains constant. When working with human blood cells or infectious agents, biosafety practices must always be followed. If further culturing is necessary, all solutions and equipment must be sterile and proper sterile technique must be used accordingly.

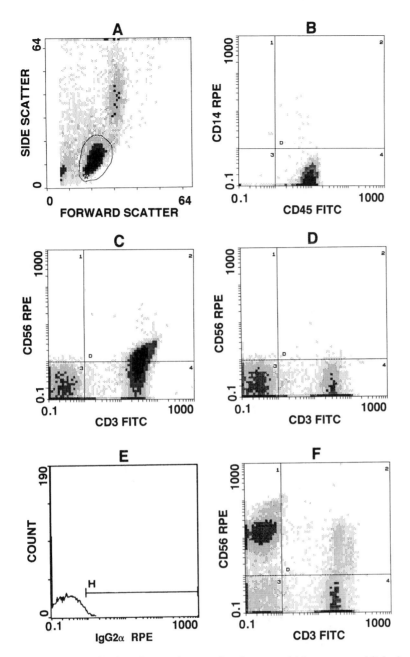

FIGURE 2   The lymphocyte bitmap for data acquisition was established running sample (a) using forward and 90° side scatter (A). The lymphocyte population in the bitmap shown in A is displayed on a dot plot (B) to make sure that >95% of the population is CD45+ and <5% of the population is CD14+. Fluorescence compensation is usually not needed for RPE-labeled cells; however, for brightly stained FITC cells (in this example the CD3FITC), it is usually necessary to compensate electronically for spectral overlap into the red PMT (C and D, Appendix I). Depending on the sample, it may be necessary to subtract from 1 to 30% of the green (FITC) signal from the red (RPE) signal. The fluorescence compensation from the control screen is selected. When adjusting the fluorescence compensation, subtract just enough signal (red/green) to bring the green signals just within the cursors enclosing quadrant 4 (the green-only domain) (D). The gate of the isotype control vial of CD56 (=IgG2α RPE) (E) is used to distinguish negative CD56 cells from positive cells (as well as the CD3 isotypic counterpart, IgG). The test sample is run (F) showing 22% CD56+/CD3− (~NK cells), 5% CD56+/CD3+ 1 (~non-MHC-restricted T cells), and 62% CD56−/CD3+ (~T cells).

V. Pitfalls

1. The yield and purity of PBMNCs depend on the efficiency of red cell removal. When erythrocytes in whole blood are aggregated, a small fraction of the lymphocytes (Hokland and Heron, 1980) are trapped in the clumps and, therefore, sediment with the erythrocytes. Cell loss during the first wash after Ficoll–Paque might also be a problem when the cell solution is not thoroughly mixed.

2. Other sources of PBMNCs, for example, defibrinated blood, can be used to get rid of platelets; however, defibrination can cause agglutination of the mononuclear cells. Moreover, the low centrifugation force during the second and third washing cycles (as suggested here) leaves the bulk of platelets in the supernatant. Finally, although defibrinated blood usually gives a "clean" PBMNC suspension, the yield is lower and there may be selective losses of some subsets.

3. As binding characteristics of a given MoAb can change when it is combined with other antibodies (due to, e.g., steric hindrance), unconjugated CD3 should ideally be added to vials (b) and (d). Likewise, unconjugated CD56 should be added to (c) and (e).

4. Although conjugated MoAbs are fairly costly, fluorochrome conjugation of MoAbs should be attempted in the single lab only when done on a regular basis.

5. Many antigens are present on leukocytes in densities so low that identification of a clear-cut positive fraction might not be possible (e.g., CD56 on NK cells in this chapter). This is a reflection of the biology of this protein. Do not attempt to obtain a clean separation between positive and negative cells in such instances by increasing the voltage of the photomultipliers. It will only result in higher background.

REFERENCES

Barclay, A. N., Birkeland, M. L., Brown, M. H., Beyers, A. D., Davis, S. J., Somoza, C., and Williams, A. F. (1993) "The Leukocyte Antigen FactsBook." Academic Press, London/New York.

Bøyum, A. (1964) Separation of white blood cells. *Nature* **204**, 793–794.

Colvin, R. B., and Preffer, F. I. (1987) New technologies in cell analysis by flow cytometry. *Arch. Pathol. Lab. Med.* **111**, 628–632.

Fitzgerald-Bocarsly, P., Herberman, R. B., Hercend, T., Hiserodt, J., Kumar, V., Lanier, L., Ortaldo, J., Pross, H., Reynolds, C., Welsh, R., and Wigzell, H. (1988) A definition of natural killer cells. *Immunol. Today* **9**, 292–296.

Griffin, J. D., Hercend, T., Beveridge, R., and Schlossman, S. F. (1983) Characterization of an antigen expressed by human natural killer cells. *J. Immunol.* **130**, 2947–2951.

Hokland, P., and Heron, I. (1980) The Isopaque–Ficoll method re-evaluated: Selective loss of autologous rosette-forming lymphocytes during isolation of mononuclear cells from human peripheral blood. *Scand. J. Immunol.* **11**, 353–356.

Quirke, P., and Dyson, J. E. (1986) Flow cytometry: Methodology and applications in pathology. *J. Pathol.* **149**, 79–87.

Reichert, T., DeBruyère, M., Deneys, V., Tötterman, T., Lydyard, P., Yuksel, F., Chapel, H., Jewell, D., Van Hove, L., Linden, J., and Buchner, L. (1991) Lymphocyte subset reference ranges in adult caucasians. *Clin. Immunol. Immunopathol.* **60**, 190–208.

Ritz, J., Schmidt, R. E., Michon, J., Hercend, T., and Schlossman, S. F. (1988) Characterization of functional surface structures on human natural killer cells. *Adv. Immunol.* **42**, 181–212.

Shapiro, H. M. (1983) "Practical Flow Cytometry," 2nd ed. Alan R. Liss, New York.

Purification of Functionally Active Epidermal Langerhans Cells Using Immunomagnetic Beads

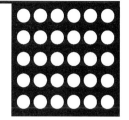

Jenny Morris and Anthony Chu

I. Introduction

Epidermal Langerhans cells are the most peripheral representatives of the dendritic family found in very low (0.5–2%) numbers in the epidermis (Gommans *et al.,* 1985) Langerhans cells do not divide in culture or maintain their phenotype in culture for more than a few weeks (Demidem *et al.,* 1986). To investigate fully their functions and interactions with other epidermal cell populations it is essential that they can be purified. To date many techniques have been tried with variable success (Schuler *et al.,* 1983; Morhenn *et al.,* 1983; Teunissen *et al.,* 1988; Wood *et al.,* 1985). The most promising technique employed seems to be that using monoclonal antibody-bound magnetic beads (Hanau *et al.,* 1987; Schmitt *et al.,* 1989). With this technique Langerhans cells can be selected efficiently and with purity; however, once attached to Langerhans cells the beads cannot be detached, and although many studies can be performed on this population, the beads can affect the function of the isolated cells and do, for example, reduce the alloantigen presenting capacity of Langerhans cells (Morris *et al.,* 1992).

The technique described here employs a relatively new reagent (Detachabead) that allows the detachment of Dynabeads from positively selected cells. Detachabead is a polyclonal antibody that has been produced by immunizing goats or sheep with mouse Fab fragments. It was specifically developed to be used with beads coated with antibodies directed against T- and B-cell markers and, initially, seemed to work only with IgM class antibodies (subsequently some IgG class antibodies have been found to detach). Dynal markets a mouse IgM anti-human class II coated bead for tissue typing, and this reagent is employed to select Langerhans cells from epidermal cell suspensions, relying on the fact that Langerhans cells are the only cells in normal epidermis that express this marker.

II. Materials and Instrumentation

Class II Dynal Beads (Cat. No. 210.03), Detachabead solutions (Cat. No. 125.02), and magnets (Cat. No. MCP6) were obtained from Dynal UK Ltd, dispase (Cat. No. 165859) was obtained from Boehringer-Mannheim. Trypsin/EDTA (10× solution, Cat. No. 043 05400), fetal bovine serum (Cat. No. 013 06290), RPMI 1640 (Cat. No. 041 01870), penicillin–streptomycin (Cat. No. 043 05070), Fungizone (amphotericin B, Cat. No. 043 05290), and L-glutamine (Cat. No. 043 05030) were obtained from Gibco UK Ltd. Phosphate-buffered saline (PBS) tablets (Cat. No. 28 10305) were supplied by Oxoid UK, and calcium- and magnesium-free PBS tablets (Cat. No. 8 103 05) were obtained from ICN Flow Laboratories UK. Acridine orange (Cat. No. A6014), ethidium bromide (Cat. No. E8751), choleratoxin (Cat. No. C3012), and hydrocortisone (Cat. No. H4881) were obtained from Sigma UK. Tissue culture flasks, petri dishes, tips, tubes, and microfuge tubes were supplied by Gibco UK Ltd.

III. Procedures

A. PREPARATION OF A SINGLE-CELL SUSPENSION OF EPIDERMAL CELLS

Preparation is carried out in a class II laminar airflow cabinet.

Solutions

1. *Decontamination medium:*
RPMI-1640
    + Penicillin (500 units/ml and streptomycin (500 μg/ml)
    + Fungizone (amphotericin B), 25 μg/ml

2. *Dispase solution:* Make up a stock solution of 20 μg/ml dispase using deionized water, filter-sterilized by passage through a 0.2-μm filter, aliquot into suitable volumes (1 and 5 ml depending on size of skin specimens encountered), and store at −20°C. This stock solution should be diluted 1:10 in phosphate-buffered saline (PBS) when required. Do not repeat freeze–thaw this reagent.

3. *Phosphate-buffered saline:* Both PBS and calcium and magnesium-free PBS were obtained in tablet form; dissolve one tablet in 100 ml of deionized water and sterilize the resulting solution by autoclaving.

4. *Acridine orange/ethidium bromide:* To make the 100× stock solution, combine 50 mg ethidium bromide (Sigma) and 15 mg acridine orange (Sigma) dissolved in 1 ml of ethanol and make up to 50 ml in distilled water; store this solution frozen in the dark. Prepare the working solution by diluting the stock solution 1:100 (v/v) in PBS; store the resulting solution for up to 1 month at room temperature in the dark.

NOTE

Caution: Acridine orange and ethidium bromide have been found to be highly mutagenic and should be handled with care.

---

5. *Trypsin/EDTA:* Dilute 10× stock solutions 1:10 in calcium- and magnesium-free PBS as required.

Steps

1. On receipt, separate the skin from the underlying subcutaneous fat, cut into pieces of managable size, and decontaminate for 30 min.

2. Then cut the skin into shallow strips (approximately 2–3 mm wide and 1–3 cm long), wash in PBS, and incubate at 4°C overnight in dispase solution. (A warm incubation step may be performed in preference to a cold incubation, in

which case the skin should be incubated at 37°C for 2–3 h, but in our hands we have noticed that such an incubation results in reduced viability).

3. After incubation the epidermis can be readily separated from the dermis using fine forceps. Incubate the epidermis at 37°C for 15–20 min in trypsin/EDTA; then manually disrupt the epidermis by repeatedly passing it (three to five times) through a syringe.

4. Remove the nondissociated tissue by passing it through gauze that has been rinsed through with 5 ml of FBS (this stops nonspecific binding to the gauze and inactivates the trypsin).

5. Wash the cells twice in RPMI by centrifugation at room temperature at 400 g for 5 min.

6. Check viability using a mixture of acridine orange and ethidium bromide. Mix equal volumes of cells and acridine orange/ethidium bromide working solution and observe using a standard fluorescence microscope. The differential uptake of the two dyes (Mishell *et al.*, 1980) allows the identification of viable and nonviable cells. Both live and dead cells take up acridine orange, which intercalates into DNA, staining it green. Ethidium bromide is taken up only by nonviable cells and intercalates into DNA making it appear orange, overwhelming the acridine orange. Consequently a dead cell will have an orange nucleus, and living cell nuclei will fluoresce bright green.

B. LANGERHANS CELL SEPARATION PROCEDURE

Solutions

1. *Growth medium:*
   RPMI 1640
   + 10% Fetal bovine serum
   + L-Glutamine (to a final concentration of 2 mM)
   + Penicillin (50 units/ml) and streptomycin (50 μg/ml)
   + Choleratoxin (50 ng/ml)
   + Hydrocortisone (5 μg/ml)

(Hydrocortisone may be omitted; it is used in the medium to reduce keratinization and should be used if long-term keratinocyte cultures are to be grown.)

2. *Phosphate-buffered saline:* Obtain PBS in tablet form; dissolve one tablet in 100 ml of deionized water and sterilize the resulting solution by autoclaving.

Steps

1. Seed the cells at $1–5 \times 10^6$/ml in growth medium and incubate at 37°C for 3 days in a humidified chamber containing 5% CO_2/95% air.

2. After 3 days remove the nonadherent cells; the Langerhans cells can be isolated from this population. The adherent population contains no Langerhans cells but long-term keratinocyte cultures can be obtained from these.

3. Harvest the nonadherent population after 3 days; wash by centrifugation at 400 g for 5 min at room temperature in PBS with 2% FBS and resuspend at 5×10^7 ml in cold (4°C) PBS containing 2% FBS.

4. Use 2×10^8 Dynal beads per milliliter of epidermal cells (giving a bead-to-Langerhans cell ratio of between and 1:10 and 1:40 depending on the number of

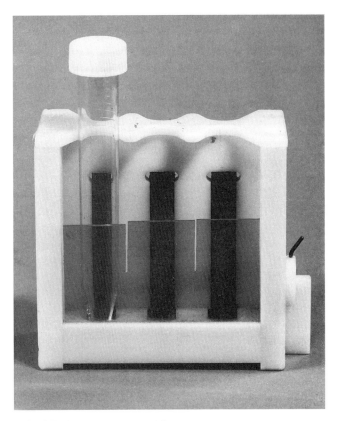

FIGURE 1 Magnetic particle concentrator.

Langerhans cells present). Wash the beads in PBS with 2% FBS three times using the magnet separation device (Fig. 1).

5. Mix the beads and cells together in a tube, and rotate at 4°C for 30 min.

6. Select the bead bound cells using the magnet, by repeated passage past the magnet, washing with PBS 2% FBS (×10).

7. Collect the bead-positive population into a microfuge tube and concentrate them by centrifugation at 400 g for 5 min (check the bead-positive population and retrieve any beads remaining using the magnet). At this stage, small volumes of each population can be checked for "purity"; that is, the bead-positive population should not contain cells that have not bound to beads. If any nonbound cells remain in the positive population then the cells need to be washed and reconcentrated using the magnet.

8. Once washed, resuspend the bead bound cells in 50 μl of RPMI + 2% FBS medium. It is important at this stage to ensure that the cells are as concentrated as possible, as this facilitates detachment of the beads.

9. Add one unit (10 μl) of detachabead to the beads and mix well by repeated pipetting (×3); rotate the microfuge tube at room temperature for 45 min.

10. Draw the reaction mixture into a micropipette and dispense three times.

11. Remove the beads from the cells using the magnet. Again, take great care to ensure that all the beads are removed; this is achieved by repeated passage past the magnet as before.

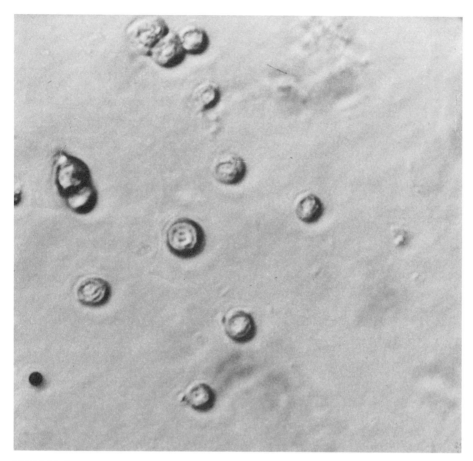

FIGURE 2   Epidermal Langerhans cells after separation (×400).

12. Remove the Detachabead from the dissociated cells by washing twice with RPMI containing 2% FBS and use the cells as required (Fig. 2).

13. Test for purity using indirect immunofluorescence and FACS analysis. Purity is consistently >95%.

IV. Comments

This technique allows the isolation of antibody and bead-free Langerhans cells. Although yields are very variable, in our laboratory sufficient cells are obtained to conduct functional studies on these cells.

V. Pitfalls

1. As the beads used in this technique are marketed for a different purpose (tissue typing), that is, one requiring high-affinity binding of the monoclonal antibody and cells, high avidity of the class II antibody results in relatively poor detachment of the beads. Some degree of batch-to-batch variability was initially observed, although more recently this has been reduced and has resulted in a much lower cell yield (10–20% of potential cells). It is important that each batch of beads be assessed to obtain maximum yield of Langerhans cells. The balance between using sufficient beads to pull the Langerhans cells out of the suspension and using few enough to totally detach with the Detatchabead is critical and will vary from batch to batch. An increase in yield of Langerhans cells can be obtained if the presence of beads on the Langerhans cells is not a problem, in which case it would be better to select Langerhans cells on CD1a, either using an indirect technique in which anti-CD1a is bound to the Langerhans cell and an anti-mouse immunoglobulin-coated bead is used to select the antibody bound cells or using a directly conjugated bead system with an anti-CD1a monoclonal antibody directly conjugated to Dynal beads. There also exists the risk that non-Langerhans cells will be inadvertently selected as HLA DR is not specific for Langerhans cells. There is an obvious need for an IgM class anti-CD1a monoclonal antibody that would overcome some of these problems.

2. Although the phenomenon of clumping was observed with freshly isolated cells, it was not fully investigated and by altering conditions it may well be overcome.

REFERENCES

Demidem, A., Faure, M., Dezutter-Dambuyant, C., and Thivolet, J. (1986) Loss of allogeneic T cell activating ability and Langerhans cell markers in human epidermal cell cultures. *Clin. Immunol. Immunopathol.* **38**, 319–326.

Gommans, J. M., van-Erp, P. E., Forster, S., Boezeman, J., and Mier, P. D. (1985) Isolation and preliminary biochemical characterization of the human epidermal Langerhans cell. *J. Invest. Dermatol.* **85**, 191–193.

Hanau, D., Schmitt, D. A., Fabre, M., Bury, R., and Cazenave J. P. (1987) Fast isolation of human epidermal Langerhans cells by immunomagnetic particles. *J. Invest. Dermatol.* **89**, 327.

Mishell, B. B., Shiigi, S. M., Henry, C., Chan, E. L., North, J., Gallily, R., Slomich, M., Miller, K., Marbrook, J., Parks, D., and Good, A. H. (1980) Preparation of mouse cell suspensions. *In* "Selected Methods in Cellular Immunology" (B. B. Mishell and S. M. Shiigi, eds.), pp. 21–22. W. H. Freeman, New York.

Morhenn, V. B., Wood, G. S., Engleman, E. G., and Oseroff, A. R. (1983) Selective enrichment of human epidermal cell populations using monoclonal antibodies. *J. Invest. Dermatol.* **81**, 127s–131s.

Morris, J. F., Alaibac, M., Jia, M. H., and Chu, T. (1992) Purification of functional active epidermal Langerhans cells: A simple and efficient new technique. *J. Invest. Dermatol.* **99**, 237–240.

Schmitt, D. A., Hanau, D., and Cazenave, J. P. (1989) Isolation of epidermal Langerhans cells. *J. Immunogenet.* **16**, 157–168.

Schuler, G., Aubock, J., and Linert, J. (1983) Enrichment of epidermal Langerhans cells by immunoadsorption to *Staphyloccus aureus* cells. *J. Immunol.* **130**, 2008–2010.

Teunissen, M. B. M., Wormmeester, J., Martien, M. T., Kapsenberg, M. L., and Bos, J. D. (1988) Enrichment of unlabelled human Langerhans cells from epidermal cell suspensions by discontinuous density gradient centrifugation. *J. Invest. Dermatol.* **91**, 358–362.

Wood, G. S., Kosek, J., Butcher, E. C., and Morhenn, V. B. (1985) Enrichment of murine and human Langerhans cells with solid phase immunoabsorption using pan-leukocyte monoclonal antibodies. *J. Invest. Dermatol.* **84**, 37–40.

SECTION **E**

Model Systems to Study Differentiation

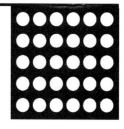

Nonterminal and Terminal Adipocyte Differentiation of Murine 3T3 T Mesenchymal Stem Cells

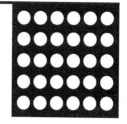

Hanlin Wang, Dawn B. Sturtevant, and Robert E. Scott

I. Introduction

Murine 3T3 T mesenchymal stem cells can be induced to differentiate into various cell types but they show a predilection to undergo adipocyte differentiation (Filipak et al., 1989). Under the experimental conditions described in this article, rapidly growing cells first leave the proliferative cycle and enter a quiescent state. This predifferentiation growth arrest state represents a distinct G_1 cell cycle restriction point which is a prerequisite for adipocyte differentiation. Thereafter, the adipocyte differentiation occurs and two distinct populations of adipocytes can be obtained: nonterminally and terminally differentiated adipocytes. Both types of adipocytes express a similar morphology, but nonterminally differentiated cells retain their proliferative potential, whereas terminally differentiated cells do not. Thus, nonterminally differentiated adipocytes can be induced to dedifferentiate and return to the proliferation state or to irreversibly lose their proliferative potential and undergo terminal differentiation (Scott et al., 1982; Hoerl and Scott, 1989). As this multistep process of adipocyte differentiation has been defined in detail (Fig. 1), it has been used as a valuable in vitro model system to study molecular mechanisms of cellular differentiation, neoplastic transformation, and differentiation-associated tumor suppressor activity (Minoo et al., 1989; Scott et al., 1989; 1993; Wang and Scott, 1991; Sparks et al., 1992).

II. Materials and Instrumentation

Citrate-anticoagulated platelet-poor human plasma is obtained from Blood Bank. Dulbecco's modified Eagle's medium (DMEM, Cat. No. D5648), $BaCl_2$ (Cat. No. B0750), heparin (sodium salt, Cat. No. H8514), d-biotin (Cat. No. B4639), insulin (Cat. No. I6634), penicillin G (Cat. No. P3032), and streptomycin sulfate (Cat. No. S9137) are purchased from Sigma. Fetal bovine serum (FBS, Cat. No. A-1111-L) is from HyClone. EDTA (Cat. No. 8993-01) is obtained from J. T. Baker. Sodium citrate (Cat. No. 0754) and NaCl (Cat. No. 7581) are from Mallinckrodt, and sodium bicarbonate (Cat. No. S233) is from Fisher Scientific.

Bacteriological petri dishes (100-mm Lab-Tek sterlstar plates, ethylene oxide-sterilized, Cat. No. D1907) are purchased from Baxter Scientific Products. Tissue culture plates (100-mm, Cat. No. 3100) and bottle filters (0.2 μm, Cat. Nos. 8330

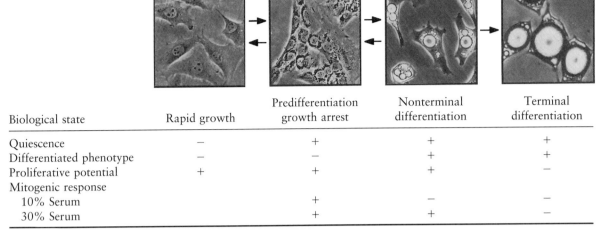

Biological state	Rapid growth	Predifferentiation growth arrest	Nonterminal differentiation	Terminal differentiation
Quiescence	−	+	+	+
Differentiated phenotype	−	−	+	+
Proliferative potential	+	+	+	−
Mitogenic response				
10% Serum		+	−	−
30% Serum		+	+	−

FIGURE 1   Model illustrating the multistep process of 3T3 T adipocyte differentiation.

for 500 ml and 8310 for 100-ml) are from Costar. Dialysis tubing with a 3500 molecular weight cutoff (Spectra/Por 3, Cat. No. 132725) is provided by Spectrum.

III. Procedures

A. PREPARATION OF THE CITRATE ELUATE OF BARIUM-PRECIPITATED HUMAN PLASMA AT HIGH pH

Solutions

1. *1 M BaCl$_2$:* To make 1 liter, solubilize 244.3 g of BaCl$_2$ in distilled water and adjust to a total volume of 1 liter. Store at 4°C.

2. *0.9% NaCl–20 mM sodium citrate solution:* To make 1 liter, add 9 g of NaCl and 5.9 g of sodium citrate to distilled water, adjust pH to 7.4, and bring to a total volume of 1 liter. Store at 4°C.

3. *3.8% sodium citrate stock solution:* To make 5 liters, dissolve 190 g of sodium citrate in distilled water and adjust to 5 liters. Store at 4°C.

Steps

1. Thaw citrated, platelet-poor human plasma overnight at 4°C (start with 210 ml).

2. Centrifuge at 4°C for 20 min at 1500 g (3000 rpm in GS-3 rotor) to remove any precipitate. Save and use the supernatant for subsequent steps.

3. Adjust supernatant to pH 8.6 with 10 N NaOH.

4. To the supernatant, add 1 M BaCl$_2$ slowly to a final concentration of approximately 0.1 M (add 21 ml of BaCl$_2$ to the 210 ml of plasma). Thereafter a precipitate should form.

5. Readjust pH to 8.6 with 10 N NaOH and gently stir the solution for 30 min at 4°C.

6. Centrifuge the suspension at 4°C for 25 min at 4000 g (5000 rpm in GS-3 rotor).

7. Decant the supernatant and save the pellet.

8. Partially solubilize the pellet by adding one-third the original plasma volume of 0.9% NaCl–20 mM sodium citrate (70 ml). Use a rubber policeman to help solubilization.

9. Stir the suspension at 4°C for 45 min.

10. Centrifuge at 4°C for 25 min at 4000 g to remove additional precipitates.

11. Dialyze the supernatant at 4°C for 8–12 hr with constant stirring against 10 liters of 0.19% (6.5 mM) sodium citrate (pH 7.4) in Spectra/Por 3 dialysis tubing with a 3500 molecular weight cutoff. *To make 10 liters of 0.19% sodium citrate (pH 7.4),* add 500 ml of 3.8% sodium citrate stock solution to 9500 ml of distilled water; adjust pH to 7.4 (~5 drops of 6 N HCl).

12. Repeat step 11 two times.

13. Divide this dialyzed plasma fraction (designated CEPH) into ~40-ml aliquots and store at −20°C.

B. INDUCTION OF NONTERMINAL DIFFERENTIATION

Solutions

1. *−30% DMEM:* To 600 ml of distilled water, add powdered DMEM used to prepare 1 liter of medium. While gently stirring, dissolve 3.7 g sodium bicarbonate and adjust pH to 7.2 using 1 N HCl. Add additional distilled water to bring the medium volume to 700 ml. Sterilize immediately by filtration using a 0.2-μm filter and store at 4°C.

2. *Heparin stock solution:* To make 1000 units/ml stock solution, dissolve 100,000 units of heparin in 100 ml of phosphate-buffered saline (PBS). Store at room temperature.

3. *Biotin stock solution:* To make 10^{-3} M stock solution, dissolve 24.4 mg of *d*-biotin in 100 ml of 0.1 N NaOH. Filter using a 0.2-μm bottle filter and store at 4°C.

4. *Penicillin–streptomycin stock:* To make the penicillin (50,000 units/ml)– streptomycin (50 mg/ml) stock, dissolve 5 million units of penicillin and 5 g of streptomycin in 100 ml of 0.9% NaCl. Sterilize through a 0.2-μm filter. Aliquot and store at −20°C.

5. *Insulin stock:* To make a 5 mg/ml stock, dissolve 50 mg of insulin in 10 ml of 0.01 M HCl. Sterilize through a 0.2-μm filter. Aliquot and store at −20°C.

6. *0.1% EDTA:* To make 4 liters, dissolve 4 g of EDTA in 3200 ml distilled water (to help dissolve EDTA, adjust pH to 8.0 and stir at room temperature for 30 min and then return to pH 7.4). Then add 400 ml of 10× PBS (pH 7.4) and bring to a total volume of 4 liters with distilled water. Sterilize using a 0.2-μm bottle filter and store at room temperature.

Steps

1. Subconfluent cells that are growing in DMEM/10% FBS are refed with fresh DMEM/10% FBS the day before the experiment.

2. Thaw CEPH at room temperature and prepare differentiation-inducing medium. *To make 100 ml of differentiation-inducing medium containing 25% CEPH,* combine 70 ml −30% DMEM, 1 ml biotin stock, 3 ml heparin stock, 0.2

ml penicillin–streptomycin stock, and 25 ml CEPH. Filter through a 0.2-μm filter and add 20 μl of insulin stock.

3. Detach cells by incubating with 0.1% EDTA (10 ml/150-cm^2 flask) at 37°C until cells come off or are rounded up (~10–30 min). Hit flask a few times to completely detach cells.

4. Count cell number using a hemacytometer and centrifuge cell suspension at 500 g (~1500 rpm) for 5 min at room temperature.

5. Resuspend the cell pellet in differentiation-inducing medium (DMEM/25% CEPH) and replate cells onto 100-mm Lab-Tek bacteriological petri dishes at 10^4 viable cells/cm^2 with 8–10 ml of medium per dish.

6. Culture at 37°C in a humidified atmosphere of 5% CO_2 for 6–8 days.

C. INDUCTION OF TERMINAL DIFFERENTIATION

Solution

1. *Dialyzed human plasma (dHP):* Dialyze citrated platelet-poor human plasma at 4°C in Spectra/Por 3 dialysis tubing with 3500 molecular weight cutoff against 10 liters of 0.19% (6.5 mM) sodium citrate (pH 7.4) with constant stirring. Change dialysis solution every 8–12 hr (three changes). Store dHP at −20°C in ~40-ml aliquots.

Steps

1. Thaw dHP at room temperature and prepare terminal differentiation-inducing medium. *To make 100 ml of terminal differentiation-inducing medium,* combine 70 ml −30% DMEM, 1 ml biotin stock, 3 ml heparin stock, 0.2 ml penicillin–streptomycin stock, and 25 ml dHP. Filter through a 0.2-μm filter.

2. Detach nonterminally differentiated adipocytes induced in DMEM/25% CEPH as described in Procedure B by incubation with 0.1% EDTA (5 ml/dish) at 37°C until cells detach (~10 min).

3. Centrifuge the cell suspension at 300 g (~1200 rpm) for 10 min at room temperature.

4. Resuspend the cell pellet in terminal differentiation-inducing medium (DMEM/25% dHP) and replate cells onto tissue culture plates at a density of 10^4 cells/cm^2.

5. Culture at 37°C in a humidified atmosphere of 5% CO_2 for 3–4 days.

IV. Comments

With the protocol described in this article, adipocyte differentiation can be easily monitored and quantitated under a phase microscope as cells are cultured at low density. Cells are designated as "adipocytes" if they acquire numerous golden and refractile cytoplasmic lipid droplets (Fig. 1). Oil red O staining, by which lipid droplets are stained red, can also be used to help identify differentiated cells. In certain experiments, adipocyte differentiation can be monitored by assaying enzymatic activity or gene expression of enzymes involved in adipogenesis, such as lipoprotein lipase and glycerol-3-phosphate dehydrogenase (Krawisz and Scott, 1982; Sparks *et al.*, 1992).

Nonterminally and terminally differentiated adipocytes are distinguished by their proliferative capacity. In our laboratory, we routinely establish their proliferative capacity by passing adipocytes onto tissue culture plates and culturing in DMEM containing 30% FBS, 50 μg/ml insulin, and 2.5 μCi/ml [^{3}H]thymidine for 40 hr. The ability of cells to proliferate is then assayed by autoradiographic measurement of [^{3}H]thymidine incorporation into DNA using Kodak NTB-2 emulsion (Hoerl and Scott, 1989; Wang and Scott, 1991). By definition, adipocytes that synthesize DNA are nonterminally differentiated, whereas cells that cannot proliferate are terminally differentiated. It is thought that a plasma protein that is present in dHP but is removed during preparation of CEPH, aproliferin, induces the irreversible loss of cellular proliferative potential associated with terminal differentiation (Wier and Scott, 1986). Therefore, adipocytes cultured in CEPH-containing medium can remain at the nonterminally differentiated state for many days without losing their proliferative potential as long as the CEPH used is free of aproliferin.

It must be stressed that preparations of both nonterminally and terminally differentiated cells actually represent enriched cell populations rather than absolutely pure cultures. For example, a typical terminal differentiation specimen may contain 10–20% undifferentiated cells and 80–90% adipocytes of which 90–95% are terminally differentiated. A typical nonterminal differentiation specimen may contain 10–20% undifferentiated cells and 80–90% adipocytes of which 5–10% are terminally differentiated.

V. Pitfalls

1. The ability of 3T3 T cells to differentiate decreases progressively during prolonged passage and culture. New stock cultures of rapidly growing cells should therefore be thawed every 12 weeks from liquid nitrogen storage and maintained at low density by passage when less than 70% confluent. Cells passed for more than 12 weeks show a decreased ability to differentiate.

2. When inducing nonterminal differentiation, increasing cell density ($>10^4$ cells/cm^2) will decrease differentiation efficiency.

3. Ethylene oxide-treated bacteriological plates should be employed to obtain maximum differentiation.

4. Different CEPH and dHP preparations vary in their ability to promote differentiation so each preparation should be pretested.

REFERENCES

Filipak, M., Estervig, D. N., Tzen, C-Y., Minoo, P., Hoerl, B. J., Maercklein, P. B., Zschunke, M. A., Edens, M., and Scott, R. E. (1989) Integrated control of proliferation and differentiation of mesenchymal stem cells. *Environ. Health Perspect.* **80**, 117–125.

Hoerl, B. J., and Scott, R. E. (1989) Nonterminally differentiated cells express decreased growth factor responsiveness. *J. Cell. Physiol.* **139**, 68–75.

Krawisz, B. R., and Scott, R. E. (1982) Coupling of proadipocyte growth arrest and differentiation. I. Induction by heparinized medium containing human plasma. *J. Cell Biol.* **94**, 394–399.

Minoo, P., Sullivan, W., Solomon, L. R., Martin, T. E., Toft, D. O., and Scott, R. E. (1989) Loss of proliferative potential during terminal differentiation coincides with the decreased abundance of a subset of heterogeneous ribonuclear proteins. *J. Cell Biol.* **109**, 1937–1946.

Scott, R. E., Estervig, D. N., Tzen, C-Y., Minoo, P., Maercklein, P. B., and Hoerl, B. J. (1989) Nonterminal differentiation represses the neoplastic phenotype in spontaneously and simian virus 40-transformed cells. *Proc. Natl. Acad. Sci. USA* **86**, 1652–1656.

Scott, R. E., Hoerl, B. J., Wille, J. J., Jr., Florine, D. L., Krawisz, B. R., and Yun, K. (1982)

Coupling of proadipocyte growth arrest and differentiation. II. A cell cycle model for the physiological control of cell proliferation. *J. Cell Biol.* **94,** 400–405.

Scott, R. E., Tzen, C-Y., Witte, M. M., Blatti, S., and Wang, H. (1993) Regulation of differentiation, proliferation and cancer suppressor activity. *Int. J. Dev. Biol.* **37,** 67–74.

Sparks, R. L., Allen, B. J., and Strauss, E. E. (1992) TGF-β blocks early but not late differentiation-specific gene expression and morphologic differentiation of 3T3 T pro-adipocytes. *J. Cell. Physiol.* **150,** 568–577.

Wang, H., and Scott, R. E. (1991) Insulin-induced mitogenesis associated with transformation by the SV40 large T antigen. *J. Cell. Physiol.* **147,** 102–110.

Wier, M. L., and Scott, R. E. (1986) Aproliferin—A human plasma protein that induces the irreversible loss of proliferative potential associated with terminal differentiation. *Am. J. Pathol.* **125,** 546–554.

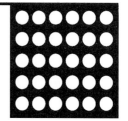

Cell Systems for *ex Vivo* Studies of Myogenesis: A Protocol for the Isolation of Stable Muscle Cell Populations from Newborn to Adult Mice[1]

Christian Pinset and Didier Montarras

I. Introduction

The tissue culture approach has been particularly fruitful for the study of skeletal muscle differentiation. The most popular sources of myoblasts have been birds (chick and quail) and rodents (rat and mouse); however, myoblasts from other origins, including human, *Xenopus*, lizard, pig, calf, rabbit, and ostrich (this list is not exhaustive), are also being cultured. Intriguingly, only cultures derived from rodents (rat and mouse) have led to the isolation of permanent myogenic cell lines (Yaffé, 1968; Yaffé and Saxel, 1977; Linkhart *et al.,* 1981; Pinset *et al.,* 1991). Although developing muscles are the source of myoblasts, adult muscles provide myosatellite cells, the mononucleated stem cells that are mobilized in muscle regeneration. Since the pioneering work of Irwin Konigsberg (Konigsberg, 1963), a great deal of information has been learnt on how cultured muscle cells retain the ability to both proliferate and differentiate. These *ex vivo* studies have established that the differentiation of proliferating mononucleated myoblasts requires the arrest of cells in the G_1 phase of the cell cycle, the coordinate activation of a battery of genetically unlinked muscle-specific genes, and the formation of syncytia (the myotubes) by fusion. Myogenic cell systems continue to provide a dramatic contribution to the understanding of determination and differentiation, and three cell lines (C3H 10T1/2, C2, and L6) are at the origin of the discovery of the myogenic regulatory factors of the MyoD family (Davis *et al.,* 1987; Wright *et al.,* 1989; Emerson, 1993, for review). Muscle cells in culture have also provided insights into the role of growth factors and hormones during myogenesis. For example, it has been shown that basic fibroblast growth factor (bFGF) and insulin-like growth factors (IGFs), which both are produced by muscle cells, exert opposite effects on differentiation. Although bFGF prevents differentiation (Linkhart *et al.,* 1981), IGFs stimulate it (Florini *et al.,* 1991).

The protocol presented here highlights improvements made by ourselves to classical procedures described by Konigsberg in Volume 58 of "Methods in Enzymology" (Ham and McKeehan, 1979). The procedure allows the isolation and the establishment of myogenic cell populations from mice. Mice were chosen because of the many mutants already available, a number that is increasing through transgenesis.

[1] We dedicate this article to the memory of Irwin Konigsberg.

II. Materials and Instrumentation

Dulbecco's modified Eagle's medium (DMEM, Cat. No. 0810D) and Molecular and Cellular Developmental Biology 202 medium (MCDB 202, Cat. No. 3300D) are obtained from Biochrom. Ultroser (steroid-free, Cat. No. 260303) is from Sepracor and it can also be purchased from Gibco Europe. Sodium insulin (Cat. No. 86004) is from Bayer Diagnostic. Dimethylsulfoxide (DMSO, Cat. No. 2950) and Gelatine (Cat. No. 4078) are purchased from Merck. Phosphate-buffered saline (Cat. No. D-5773), collagenase type V (Cat. No. C-9263), and EDTA (Cat. No. ED2SS) are obtained from Sigma. Trypsin (Cat. No. 109819) is from Boehringer-Mannheim. Mowiol (Cat. No. 4.88) and bisbenzimide (Cat. No. 33342) are from Hoechst. Monoclonal antibody against troponin T (Cat. No. N355), anti-mouse IgG antibody coupled to biotin (Cat. No. RPN 481), and streptavidin coupled to Texas red (Cat. No. RPN 1233) are purchased from Amersham. Giemsa's stain R (Cat. No. 3.20313) is from Rhône Poulenc.

Standard plastic tissue culture dishes for adherent eucaryotic cells (diameter: 10.5 and 3.5 cm); 24-well plates; Pyrex cylinders (height 0.8 cm, diameter 0.5 cm); silicon vacuum grease (Beckman) used to isolate colonies; cryogenic tubes; inverted light microscope equipped with phase contrast, X10 wide-field eyepieces, and X6 and X16 objectives; laminar flow hood; incubator allowing growth of the cells at 37°C in a humidified atmosphere + 7.5% CO_2.

Tools for dissection: small scissors, fine forceps, pins, scalpels, all sterilized by autoclaving.

III. Procedures

A. ISOLATION OF CELLS FROM MUSCLES

Solutions

1. *DMEM and MCDB 202 media:* Sterilize by filtration and store at 4°C in the dark. Sterile solutions of antibiotics are added to the medium just before use (final concentrations: penicillin 200 units/ml and streptomycin 0.2 mg/ml).

2. *Selected fetal calf serum (FCS):* A good serum should support clonal growth and differentiation of the mouse myogenic cell line C_2 (Yaffé and Saxel, 1977).

3. *Ultroser steroid free:* Dissolve in sterile water according to the manufacturer's instructions.

4. *Na insulin:* Solubilize in water at 10 mg/ml, sterilize by filtration, and store in aliquots at −20°C. Insulin solutions should be stored in plastic, not glass, to avoid adsorption.

5. *Phosphate-buffered saline (PBS):* Dissolve pellets, autoclave, and store at +4°C.

6. *Trypsin:* Prepare 0.2% (w/v) trypsin in PBS, 0.1% (w/v) trypsin in MCDB 202 medium. Sterilize these stock solutions by filtration and store at −20°C.

7. *Type V collagenase:* Prepare 0.05% (w/v) collagenase in MCDB 202 medium. Sterilize this stock solution by filtration and store at −20°C.

8. *Versene:* PBS containing 2 mM EDTA. To make 1 liter, add 0.67 g of EDTA to 1 liter of PBS. Autoclave and store at 4°C.

9. *Giemsa dye:* Dissolve in water (10% v/v).

10. *Collagen:* Collagen can be prepared from adult rat tendons. After sterile

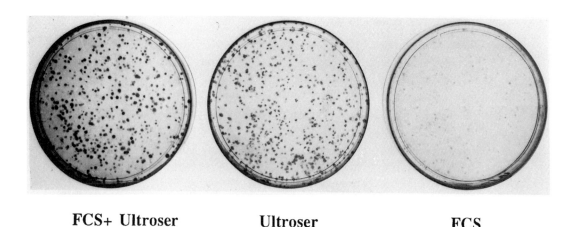

FCS+ Ultroser   **Ultroser**   **FCS**

FIGURE 1 Influence of serum and serum substitute on the proliferation of newly isolated mouse muscle cells. The figure represents a secondary culture of cells isolated from the leg muscle of a 3-week-old mouse. Cells plated at low density (500 cells per 10-cm dish) were allowed to grow as indicated in the protocol. After 10 days, the cells were fixed and stained with Giemsa. The number and the size of the colonies indicated that the serum substitute (Ultroser) in combination with the fetal calf serum provides better conditions for proliferation.

dissection, place tendons from two tails in 250 ml of 10 mM acetic acid. Stir the suspension for 24 h at 4°C and then clarify by a short centrifugation at 5000 rpm. The final concentration of collagen is usually close to 1 mg/ml. This solution is stored at 4°C. For coating, dilute collagen to 1/100 (v/v) in cold DMEM, incubate the dishes for 1 hr at 37°C, remove the medium, and let the dishes dry in the hood for a couple of hours or longer. Collagen can also be obtained from commercial sources and must be tested.

Steps

1. Kill the mice by asphyxiation with CO_2 and sterilize in 70% (v/v) ethanol in the hood. Cells can be prepared by sterile dissection (in the hood) of the muscles from the posterior legs of one mouse (from newborn to adult). Muscle tissue free of skin and bones is minced and digested five times for 5 min in 5 ml of enzymatic mix at room temperature with gentle shaking: *Enzymatic mix:* 20 ml of 0.1% (w/v) trypsin and 20 ml of 0.05% (w/v) collagenase, both prepared in MCDB 202 medium, are mixed before use.

2. After each digestion, the tissue fragments are pelleted by a very mild centrifugation (2 min at 100 rpm) and the action of the enzymes is stopped by the addition of 1 ml of FCS. At the end of the digestion process, four-fifths of the cells are pelleted by centrifugation at 800 g for 10 min and frozen (see below). The rest of the cells are plated on 10 collagen-coated dishes (diameter 10 cm) containing proliferation medium. At this very low cell density cells will form colonies. *Proliferation medium:* For 100 ml, mix DMEM 40 ml, MCDB 202 40 ml, FCS 20 ml, and Ultroser 2 ml.

3. After 5 days, cells are fed fresh proliferation medium and a few days later the cells are subcultured in growth medium on collagen-coated dishes. In no circumstances should cells be allowed to reach high density. For this, at each passage, a few thousand cells can be plated in 10-cm dishes and subcultured every 4 days. Cells are detached from the dishes in the presence of trypsin–Versene. Mix 0.1% (w/v) trypsin in PBS with an equal volume of Versene and store at 4°C for a few days. Complete detachment of the cells should be rapid and must be controlled under the microscope (Fig. 1).

B. FREEZING AND THAWING OF CELLS

Cells can be efficiently frozen prior to cultivation. This is particularly convenient when a limited number of animals are available.

Solution

1. *Freezing solution:* Fetal calf serum containing 10% (v/v) DMSO.

Steps

1. Resuspend noncultured cells in 5 ml of fetal calf serum containing 10% (v/v) DMSO and freeze in aliquots of 1 ml in cryogenic tubes in two steps: 24 hr at $-80°C$; permanent storage in liquid nitrogen.

2. Thaw the cells directly at 37°C. Add 4 ml of medium to the cell suspension to reduce serum concentration.

3. Centrifuge for 10 min at 800 g to eliminate DMSO.

4. Resuspend the cell pellet in 50 ml of growth medium (see above) and plate the cells in five collagen-coated dishes (diameter 10 cm). The same protocol is used to freeze cultured cells or cell lines at later stages (C_2, Sol 8, etc).

C. PROTOCOLS FOR DIFFERENTIATION

Morphological differentiation, the fusion of mononucleated myoblasts into multi-nucleated myotubes, can easily be followed under the microscope on living cells or after fixation and staining of the cells with Giemsa.

Solution

1. *Differentiation medium:* A mixture of DMEM and MCDB 202 media (1/1) supplemented with 2% (v/v) FCS and 10 μg/ml insulin. At this concentration, insulin mimics the positive effect of IGFs on differentiation.

1. Colony Assay

This assay is used to determine the frequency of cells forming myotubes within a population. This assay can also be used to ring isolate colonies.

Steps

1. Plate the cells at the density of 100 cells per 10-cm dish on 10 collagen-coated dishes in proliferation medium.

2. After 5 days, feed the cells with fresh proliferation medium. At this stage, colonies are usually easily detected.

3. Allow the colonies to grow for 4 to 5 more days. At this time, cells can be either kept in proliferation medium without changing it or fed with differentiation medium. Morphological differentiation is analyzed during the next 3 days.

a. Ring Isolation of Colonies

This procedure can be applied to colonies where differentiation has already started. Numerous unfused cells (myoblasts) will continue to proliferate. This allows the isolation of myogenic colonies in one step.

Steps

1. Mark the position of the colonies to be isolated on the bottom of the dish.

2. Aspirate the medium.

3. Press down in the dish a glass cylinder bearing a continuous bead of silicon grease to encompass the colony.

4. Add a drop of Trypsin–Versene and monitor the detachment of the cells under the microscope.

5. Resuspend the cells in 10 ml of proliferation medium and plate in two collagen-coated dishes (diameter 5 cm).

b. Isolation of Myogenic Clones

Steps

1. Plate the cells at the density of 0.5 to one cell per well on 24-well plates under the culture conditions described for proliferation.

2. Identify the myogenic clones.

2. Mass Culture Assay

This assay provides a sufficient number of cells to purify materials (DNA, RNA, proteins) required for biochemical studies.

Steps

1. Plate the cells on collagen-coated dishes in proliferation medium at the density of 10^5 cells per 10-cm dish.

2. Let the cells grow for several days. Spontaneous differentiation frequently occurs after prolonged growth (5 to 8 days) in proliferation medium; however, after 4 to 5 days of growth, differentiation can be stimulated by feeding the cells with differentiation medium (see Section C1).

All the protocols described for proliferation and differentiation of newly isolated muscle cells can be applied to myogenic cell lines (C_2, Sol 8); however, in this case the use of collagen-coated dishes and Ultroser is not obligatory.

3. Immunostaining

The fusion process is not an obligatory event for differentiation. Thus, the extent of differentiation in a culture can be determined by *in situ* immunostaining of the cells with an antibody recognizing a protein strictly characteristic of differentiated muscle cells. We describe here this procedure for the detection of troponin T.

Solutions

1. *Mounting medium:* To 2.4 g of mowiol, add 6 g of glycerol, 6 ml of H_2O, and 12 ml of 0.2 M Tris buffer, pH 8.5. Incubate the solution at 50°C for 1 hr or

longer with occasional shaking to dissolve the mowiol. Clarify the mixture by centrifugation (5000 rpm, 5 min). Store in aliquots at −20°C.

2. *Bisbenzimide:* Dissolve 10 mg of bisbenzimide in 10 ml of ethanol. Clarify by centrifugation for 5 min at 5000 rpm; store this stock solution at 4°C in the dark.

Steps

1. Grow the cells as desired for proliferation and/or differentiation on 3.5-cm dishes.

2. After two PBS washes, fix the cells for 2 min in a 1/1 (v/v) mixture of methanol and acetone stored at −20C°.

3. Wash the cells thrice with PBS and twice with PBS containing 0.2% (w/v) gelatin.

4. Dilute the monoclonal antibody directed against troponin T to 1/50 in PBS/gelatin and add 50 μl to each dish. Allow to react for 40 min at room temperature.

5. Repeat step 3.

6. Dilute the second antibody (anti-mouse IgG antibody coupled to biotin) to 1/50 in PBS/gelatin. Add 50 μl to each dish. Allow to react as in step 4.

7. Repeat step 3.

8. Dilute streptavidin coupled to Texas red to 1/100 in PBS gelatin. Add 50 μl to each dish. Allow to react as in step 4.

9. Wash thrice with PBS. A DNA-specific fluorescent dye (bisbenzimide, Hoechst 33342) is added at 1 μg/ml to the penultimate PBS wash to stain nuclei.

10. Prior to observation, cells are mounted in mowiol solution. Add a drop to each dish and cover with a glass coverslip (Fig. 2).

NOTE Cells should not be allowed to dry at any step.

IV. Comments

The improvements that we have made to classical protocols can be summarized as follows.

1. Better digestion conditions: the use of growth medium (MCDB 202) buffered with Hepes, instead of PBS, and digestion for shorter periods.

2. Addition to the growth medium of the serum substitute Ultroser, which is composed of a mixture of growth factors: We have tested several commercial serum substitutes and, to date, Ultroser has given the best results (see Fig. 1).

3. Platings at very low density and subsequent cultivation at low density: This protocol has allowed us to isolate myogenic cell populations from all mouse strains so far studied (seven to date). The percentage of myogenic cells (cells forming myotubes) in such populations was always very high. The ability to proliferate and the myogenic characteristics of the cells were stable: no sign of

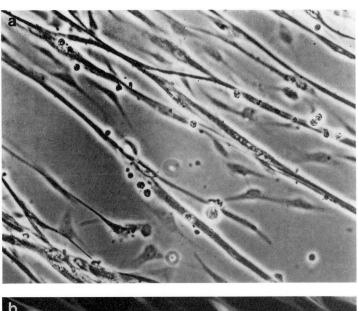
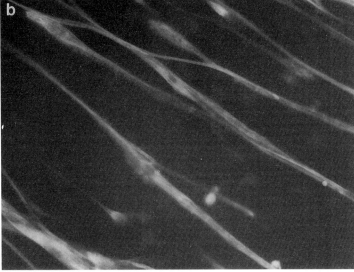

FIGURE 2 Immunostaining of differentiated muscle cells with a troponin T antibody. A muscle cell population obtained from a 3-week-old wild-type mouse was allowed to differentiate after 10 subcultures and processed for immunostaining as described. A large proportion of cells retained the ability to differentiate through the subculturing process. (a) Phase contrast. (b) Immunofluorescence.

crisis or loss of "myogenicity" after several months in culture. These cells are also suitable for transfection studies.

ACKNOWLEDGMENTS

We thank Dr Robert Kelly for critical reading and J. Gex and M Adjemian for preparing this manuscript. The authors are supported by grants from the Centre National de la Recherche Scientifique, the Institut Pasteur, and the Association Française contre les Myopathies.

REFERENCES

Davis, R. L., Weintraub, H., and Lassar, A. B. (1987) Expression of a single transfected cDNA converts fibroblasts to myoblasts. *Cell* **51,** 987–1000.

Emerson, C. P., Jr. (1993) Skeletal myogenesis: Genetics and embryology to the fore. *Curr. Opin. Genet. Dev.* **3,** 265–274.

Florini, J. R., Magri, K. A., Ewton, D. Z., James, P. L., Grindstaff, K., and Rotwein, P. S. (1991) "Spontaneous" differentiation of skeletal myoblasts is dependent upon autocrine secretion of insulin-like growth factor-II. *J. Biol. Chem.* **266,** 15917–15923.

Ham, R. G., and McKeehan, W. L. (1979) Media and growth requirements. *In* "Methods in Enzymology" (W. B. Jakoby and Ira H. Pastan, eds.), Vol. 58, pp. 44–93. Academic Press, New York.

Konigsberg, I. R. (1963) Clonal analysis of myogenesis. *Science* **140,** 1273–1284.

Linkhart, T. A., Clegg, C., and Hauschka, S. D. (1981) Myogenic differentiation in permanent clonal mouse myoblast cell lines: Regulation by macromolecular growth factors in the culture medium. *Dev. Biol.* **86,** 19–30.

Pinset, C., Mulle, C., Benoit, P., Changeux, J. P., Chelly, J., Gros, F., and Montarras, D. (1991) Functional adult acetylcholine receptor develops independently of motor innervation in Sol 8 mouse muscle cell line. *EMBO J.* **10,** 2411–2418.

Wright, W. E., Sassoon, D. A., and Lin, V. K. (1989) Myogenin, a factor regulating myogenesis, has a domain homologous to MyoD. *Cell* **56,** 607–617.

Yaffé, D. (1968) Retention of differentiation potentialities during prolonged cultivation of myogenic cells. *Proc. Natl. Acad. Sci. USA* **61,** 477–483.

Yaffé, D., and Saxel, O. (1977) Serial passaging and differentiation of myogenic cells isolated from dystrophic mouse muscle. *Nature* **270,** 725–727.

Induction of Cell Differentiation in Human HL-60 Promyelocytic Leukemia Cells: Quantitation of a Myeloid Specific Antigen, MRP-8/MRP-14 Protein Complex

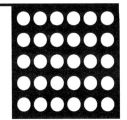

Shinichi Murao, Mamoru Nakanishi, Seiya Matsumoto, Norifumi Ueda, and Eliezer Huberman

I. Introduction

Cultured cells, including human HL-60 promyelocytic leukemia cells, are useful in studying the control of cell growth and differentiation (Huberman and Callaham, 1979). These cells can respond to certain chemicals by acquiring either a granulocyte-like (Collins *et al.*, 1980) or a monocyte- or macrophage-like phenotype (Murao *et al.*, 1983). These mature phenotypes can be characterized and set apart by a number of differentiation markers. A helpful tool in detecting such markers are murine monoclonal antibodies (MoAbs) prepared against intracellular proteins that specify peripheral blood granulocytes, monocytes, and macrophages (Murao *et al.*, 1989). We describe procedures for the induction of differentiation in HL-60 cells and for the quantitation of a myeloid maturation-specific antigen designated MRP-8/MRP-14 (migration inhibitory factor-related proteins) (Lagasse and Clerc, 1988) (Fig. 1).

II. Materials and Instrumentation

RPMI-1640 medium (Cat. No. 320-1875AJ), penicillin G (Cat. No. 860-1840MJ), streptomycin sulfate (Cat. No. 860-18601J), and fetal bovine serum (FBS, 200-6140AJ) are purchased from Gibco-BRL. DMSO (Cat. No. D8779), Tris (Cat. No. T1503), polyoxyethylenesorbitan monolaurate (Tween 20, Cat. No. P1379), sodium azide (Cat. No. 52002), mycophenolic acid (Cat. No. M5255), and bovine serum albumin (BSA, Cat. No. A7888) are from Sigma Chemical Company. *p*-Nitrophenyl phosphate, disodium salt (PNPP, Cat. No. 147-02343), all-*trans*-retinoic acid (Cat. No. 182-01111), phorbol 12-myristate 13-acetate (PMA, Cat. No. 163-14851), and 1,25-dihyroxyvitamin D_3 [1,25-$(OH)_2D_3$, Cat. No. 031-14851] are from Wako Chemical.

Bacteriological petri dishes (60 mm, Cat. No. 628102, and 90 mm, Cat. No.

The submitted manuscript has been authored by a contractor of the U.S. Government under contract No. W-31-109-ENG-38. Accordingly, the U.S. Government retains a nonexclusive, royalty-free license to publish or reproduce the published form of this contribution, or allow others to do so, for U.S. Government purposes.

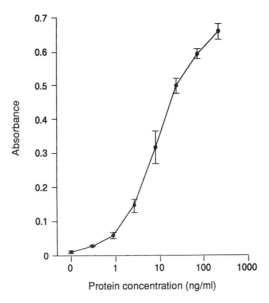

FIGURE 1   Standard curve of the MRP-8/MRP-14 complex. The coating antibody is rabbit anti-MRP-8. The incubation time of the substrate is 20 min.

663102), 96-well ELISA plates (Immulon 600, Cat. No. 655061), centrifuge tubes (15 ml, Cat. No. 188271), and microtubes (1.5 ml, Cat. No. 616-201, and 0.75 ml, Cat. No. 667-201) are from Greiner. Biotin-labeled anti-mouse IgG1 (Cat. No. 61-0140) and alkaline phosphatase-labeled avidin (Cat. No. 43-4422) are from Zymed. The ultrasound tissue homogenizer (Sonifier 250) is from Branson. The ELISA reader, Multiscan Bichromatic (Cat. No. L-5111617), and Multichannel Pipette (Cat. No. L4143037) are from Lab System. A Universal Shaker SHK-U4 is from IWAKI. A cell counter, Coulter Counter Model D, is from Coulter Electronics. HL-60 cells were provided by Dr. Robert Gallo (National Cancer Institute).

III. Procedures

A. TISSUE CULTURE AND INDUCTION OF CELL DIFFERENTIATION

Solutions

1. *Culture medium:* Add 0.5 ml of penicillin G (2×10^5 units/ml), 0.5 ml streptomycin sulfate (200 g/ml), 2 ml L-glutamine (200 mM), and 50 ml fetal bovine serum into 500 ml RPMI-1640 medium. All solutions are sterile when purchased. Store at 4°C.

2. *Stock solution:* Dissolve PMA, 1,25-$(OH)_2D_3$, and retinoic acid in DMSO at a concentration of 1 mg/ml. Transfer aliquots of 100 μl of each solution into sterile microtubes and store at -70°C. The solution can be stored for about 6 months.

3. *Working solution:* We treat HL-60 cells with two or three different concentrations. Examples of appropriate concentrations are shown in Table I. In this section, an example of 1,25-$(OH)_2D_3$ is described. Mix 10 μl of 1,25$(OH)_2D_3$ stock solution with 990 μl of RPMI-1640 medium (diluent 1). Further dilute diluent 1 with 4 vol of RPMI-1640 medium to make diluent 2 (20 μg/ml). Make diluent 3 (6 μg/ml) and diluent 4 (0.2 μg/ml) from diluent 2 before use. In general, a series of concentrations, including those that inhibit cell multiplication, should be used to identify potential chemical inducers of

TABLE I Recommended Concentrations to Induce Differentiation
in HL-60 Cells

Chemicals	Concentration[a]	Differentiation	Reference
PMA	1–5 nM	Macrophage-like	Huberman and Callaham, 1979
1,25-$(OH)_2D_3$	10–100 nM	Monocyte-like	Murao et al., 1983
Retinoic acid	100–1000 nM	Granulocyte-like	Collins et al., 1980
Mycophenolic acid	3–10 μM	Granulocyte-like	Collart and Huberman, 1990
DMSO	1.2–1.3%	Granulcoyte-like	Collins et al., 1980

[a] Appropriate concentrations may vary depending on the subclones of HL-60 provided.

differentiation. Differentiating characteristics should be detected at concentrations that inhibit about 50% of cell multiplication.

Steps

1. Prepare stock cells (1.4×10^6 to 1.6×10^6/ml, 50 ml) in five 90-mm dishes and dilute with fresh culture medium. Adjust cells to a concentration of $1.0–1.5 \times 10^5$/ml and split into 50-mm dish (5 ml each) the day before the experiment.

2. Treat cells with 100 μl of 1,25-$(OH)_2D_3$ diluents 2, 3, and 4. The final concentrations are 10, 30, and 100 nM, respectively.

3. Culture cells at 37°C in an atmosphere of 5% CO_2 in air in humidified incubator for 4–6 days.

4. Collect cells every day. Count cell number and examine a series of differentiation markers (Table II).

B. CHARACTERIZATION OF CELLS

Chemically treated HL-60 cells can be induced to differentiate in a dose- and time-dependent manner. To evaluate the phenotypic changes associated with this differentiation, a series of biochemical assays and histochemical and immunohisto-chemical stainings are examined (see Table II). We recommend two or three different

TABLE II Characterization of Differentiating HL-60 Cells

Characteristic	Gr[a]	Mo[b]/Mc[c]	Reference
Nonspecific esterase	±	+++/+++	Yam et al., 1971
Lysozyme	±	+++/+++	Sigma Chemical Company Bulletin L-6876
Nitroblue tetrazolium test	++	+/±	Collins et al., 1980
Attachment	−	+/+++	Huberman and Callaham, 1979
Phagocytosis	±	+/+++	Huberman and Callaham, 1979
OKM₁ MoAb (CD11b)	+++	+++/++	Foon et al., 1982
NM-6 MoAb	+++	+++/−	Murao et al., 1989

[a] Granulocyte-like cells; treated with 1.3% DMSO.
[b] Monocyte-like cells; treated with 100 nM 1,25-$(OH)_2D_3$.
[c] Macrophage-like cells; treated with 5 nM PMA.

assays or stainings for identifying granulocyte-like, monocyte-like, or macrophage-like phenotypes. References of each assay or staining procedure are listed in Table II. Here, we describe the procedures to measure the amount of MRP-8/MRP-14 complex in differentiating HL-60 cells.

C. QUANTITATION OF MRP-8/MRP-14 COMPLEX (TWO-ANTIBODY SANDWICH METHOD)

1. Preparation of Cellular Extracts

Solutions

1. *Phosphate-buffered saline (PBS):* To make 1 liter of stock solution ($\times 10$), add 80 g of NaCl, 2 g of KCl, 2 g of KH_2PO_4, and 11.25 g of Na_2HPO_4, and bring to a total volume of 1 liter.

2. *Extraction buffer:* To make 100 ml extraction buffer, add 5 ml of 1 M Tris–HCl (pH 7.4), 200 μl of 500 mM EDTA, and 1 ml Triton X-100. Bring to 100 ml with distilled water. Store at 4°C.

Steps

All procedures are performed in a cold room or on ice, unless otherwise noted.

1. Transfer HL-60 cells to a 15-ml centrifuge tube from tissue culture dishes. Use a rubber policeman to detach cells from the dish if necessary. Count cells with a Coulter cell counter and centrifuge cells at 1000 g for 5 min. Save 1 ml of supernatant from each culture in a 1.5-ml microtube and store at −70°C.

2. Wash cells twice with 5 ml of PBS, and transfer to a 1.5-ml microtube. Centrifuge at 2000 g for 2 min and remove supernatant.

3. Add 0.5 ml of extraction buffer and process with an ultrasound homogenizer for 10 sec, twice. Agitate the cell suspension with a rotary shaker (60 rpm) for 2 hr.

4. Centrifuge tubes at 12,000 rpm for 15 min. Save the supernatant, and store at −70°C.

2. Two-Antibody Sandwich Assay

Solutions

In following solutions, we indicate appropriate volumes that are enough for four assay plates.

1. *Coating buffer:* To make 1 liter, add 8.4 g of $NaHCO_3$ and 0.2 g of sodium azide, adjust pH to 9.6 with 1 M Na_2CO_3 (10.1 g/100 ml distilled water), and bring to a total volume of 1 liter.

2. *Diluent buffer:* To make 1 liter, add 6.6 g of 1 M Tris, 203 mg of $MgCl_2 \cdot 6H_2O$, 8.76 g of NaCl, 0.5 ml of Tween 20, and 0.2 g of sodium azide, and adjust pH to 8.1 with 12 N HCl and volume to 1 liter with distilled water.

3. *Washing buffer:* To make 1 liter, add 0.515 g of $NaH_2PO_4 \cdot 2H_2O$, 2.4 g of $Na_2HPO_4 \cdot 12H_2O$, 8.5 g of NaCl, and 0.5 ml of Tween 20, and adjust to 1 liter with distilled water.

4. *Blocking buffer:* Dissolved 0.5 g BSA in 50 ml of diluent buffer before use.

5. *Rabbit anti-MRP-8 or anti-MRP-14 solutions:* Prepare antisera to MRP-8 and MRP-14 by the method described by Harlow and Lane (1988). The IgG fraction is purified by a protein A–Sepharose column chromatography, reconstructed with PBS, and stored at −70°C. To make 50 ml of working solution, dilute 67 μl of serum with 50 ml of dilution solution (1:750 dilution).

6. *Standard antigen solution:* Purification of the antigen, MRP-8/MRP-14 complex, is described elsewhere (Murao *et al.*, 1989). The purified MRP-8/MRP-14 complex is concentrated (100 μg/ml) and stored at −70°C. To make 2 ml of working solution (300 ng/ml), mix 6 μl of stock solution with 2 ml of diluent buffer just before use.

7. *NM-6 MoAb solution:* NM-6 MoAb is prepared from ascites by inoculating NM-6 hybridoma cells into Balb/c mice. NM-6 MoAb (IgG1) is purified by protein A–Sepharose column chromatography, concentrated (2 mg/ml), and stored at −70°C. To make a working solution dilute 50 μl of NM-6 MoAb with 50 ml of PBS (1:1000 dilution) before use.

8. *Biotin-conjugated anti-mouse IgG solution:* Dilute 50 μl biotin-conjugated anti-mouse IgG1 (stock) in 50 ml PBS before use.

9. *Avidin–peroxidase solution:* Dilute 25 μl avidin–peroxidase solution (stock) in 50 ml PBS before use.

10. *Substrate buffer:* To make 1 liter, dissolve 4.2 g of $NaHCO_3$ and 2.03 g of $MgCl_2$, adjust pH to 9.8 with 2 M NaOH (8 g of NaOH in 100 ml of distilled water), and bring to a total volume of 1 liter.

11. *Substrate solution:* Dissolve 500 mg of PMPP in 50 ml substrate buffer before use.

Steps

All procedures are performed at room temperature except step 1. In each well, 100 μl of reaction solution is added with an eight-barrel micropipette unless otherwise indicated. The plates are agitated for periods indicated on the universal shaker at 100 rpm. Between each step, wells are washed three times with 200 μl of washing solution.

1. Coat 96-well ELISA plates with rabbit anti-MRP-8 or MRP-14 antibody solutions at 4°C overnight.

2. Block titer plates with 1% BSA (100 μl) for 2 hr.

3. In each antibody-coated 96-well ELISA plate, fill 24 wells (lanes 1, 2, and 3 from A to H) with standard antigen solutions. The standard solution (300 ng/ml) is poured into wells A and is diluted stepwise from wells B to wells G with 2 vol of PBS at each step. The final concentrations of standard solutions from well A to well H are 300.0, 100.0, 33.3, 11.1, 3.7, 1.2, 0.4, and 0.0 ng/ml, respectively. The supernatants of culture media and cellular extracts are also diluted stepwise to 1:30, 1:90, 1:270, and 1:810 and incubated in wells of lanes 4 to 12 from wells A to D, or wells E to H, respectively, in the same manner. Incubate these antigen and sample solutions for 2 hr.

4. Incubate NM-6 MoAb solution for 2 hr.

5. Incubate biotin-labeled anti-mouse IgG1 solution for 1.5 hr.

6. Incubate avidin–alkaline phosphatase solution for 1 hr.

7. Incubate substrate solution, and immediately insert a 96-well ELISA plate

into the reader. Read absorbance (690 and 450 nm) 10, 20, and 30 min after the substrate solution is inoculated and obtain specific absorbance by differentiating values at 450 nm from values at 690 nm.

IV. Comments

MRP-8 and MRP-14 are marker proteins that characterize myelomonocytic cell differentiation (Lagasse and Clerc, 1988; Murao *et al.*, 1989). Both have calcium-binding domains and are highly similar to S-100 proteins. MRP-8 and MRP-14 usually form a complex of molecular weight of 36,000–38,000 on sodium dodecyl sulfate–polyacrylamide gel electrophoresis. Their biological function is still unknown.

V. Pitfalls

1. HL-60 cells are maintained in logarithmically growing phase. If the cells are kept under confluent conditions, a significant number of cells spontaneously differentiate.

2. When thawing materials (antibodies, antigen, or samples), mix well before diluting or processing for the next step.

3. Incubation time in steps 3–6 can be shortened to half of the indicated periods. In this case, the sensitivity to detect the minimum amount of antigen may be lowered.

REFERENCES

Collart, F., and Huberman, E. (1990) Expression of IMP dehydrogenase in differentiating HL-60 cells. *Blood* 75, 570–576.
Collins, S. J., Bonder, A., Ting, R., and Gallo, R. C. (1980) Induction of morphological and functional differentiation of human promyelocytic leukemia cells (HL-60) by compounds which induce differentiation of murine leukemia cells. *Int. J. Cancer* 25, 213–218.
Foon, K. A., Schroff, R. W., and Gale, R. P. (1982) Surface markers on leukemia and lymphoma: Recent advances. *Blood* 60, 1–19.
Harlow, E., and Lane, D. (1988) "Antibodies: A Laboratory Manual," pp. 53–117. Cold Spring Harbor Laboratory Press, Cold Spring Harbor, NY.
Huberman, E., and Callaham, M. F. (1979) Induction of terminal differentiation in human promyelocytic leukemia cells by tumor-promoting agents. *Proc. Natl. Acad. Sci. USA* 76, 1293–1297.
Lagasse, E., and Clerc, G. (1988) Cloning and expression of two human genes encoding calcium-binding proteins that are regulated during myeloid differentiation. *Mol. Cell. Biol.* 8, 2402–2410.
Murao, S., Collart, F. R., and Huberman, E. (1989) A protein containing the cystic fibrosis antigens is an inhibitor of protein kinases. *J. Biol. Chem.* 264, 8356–8360.
Murao, S., Gemmell, M. A., Callaham, M. F., Anderson, N. L., and Huberman, E. (1983) Control of macrophage cell differentiation in human promyelocytic HL-60 leukemia cells by 1,25-dihydroxyvitamin D_3 and phorbol-12-myristate-13-acetate. *Cancer Res.* 43, 4989–4996.
Yam, L. T., Li, C. Y., and Crosby, W. H. (1971) Cytochemical identification of monocytes and granulocytes. *Am. J. Clin. Pathol.* 55, 283–290.

Differentiation of Murine Erythroleukemia Cells (Friend Cells)

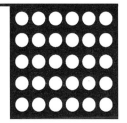

Victoria M. Richon, Richard A. Rifkind, and Paul A. Marks

I. Introduction

Murine erythroleukemia cells (MELCs) are virus-transformed erythroid precursor cells that can be induced to differentiate by a variety of chemicals, including dimethyl sulfoxide and a group of polar/apolar compounds, of which hexamethylene bisacetamide (HMBA) has been most extensively studied (Friend *et al.,* 1971; Marks and Rifkind, 1978). Commitment to terminal differentiation is the irreversible capacity to express the differentiated phenotype, including globin gene expression and loss of proliferative capacity, despite removal of the inducer (Gusella *et al.,* 1976; Fibach *et al.,* 1977). Induction of differentiation is a multistep process characterized by an initial latent period (10–12 hr) during which a number of morphological and metabolic changes occur, including activation of membrane-associated protein kinase C and modulation of expression of a number of genes, such as c-*myb*, c-*myc*, c-*fos*, and p53, but the cells do not commit to terminal cell division nor do they express the globin genes. Following the latent period with continued culture with inducer there is progressive, apparently stochastic, recruitment of cells to commit to terminal differentiation (Rifkind and Marks, 1993). MELCs are a useful model system to investigate the mechanism by which proliferating transformed precursor cells in a differentiation lineage withdraw from the cell division cycle and express the genes characteristic of the normal differentiated phenotype.

II. Materials and Instrumentation

Hexamethylene bisacetamide (Cat. No. H-6260), hydrogen peroxide (Cat. No. H-1009), and benzidine dihydrochloride (Cat. No. B-3383) were obtained from Sigma. Minimum essential medium alpha (MEM-alpha, Cat. No. 410-2000) was obtained from Gibco. Methylcellulose (Cat. No. M-352) was obtained from Fisher. Fetal calf serum (Cat. No. A-1111-L) was obtained from HyClone. Glycerol (Cat. No. 2136-01) was obtained from Baker. The 35 × 10-mm tissue culture dishes with grid (Cat. No. 174926) were obtained from Nunc.

III. Procedures

A. MAINTAINING CELL CULTURES

Solution

1. *Complete medium:* MEM-alpha supplemented with 10% fetal calf serum. The fetal calf serum is heat-inactivated for 30 min at 56°C, aliquoted, and stored at −20°C. The complete medium is stored at 4°C for up to 1 month.

Steps

1. Initiate cell cultures at 1×10^5 cells/ml complete medium and incubate at 37°C in 5% CO_2.

2. Passage cells every 2 or 3 days. Cells have a cell cycle time of 10 to 12 hr. Logarithmic growth of cells in culture without HMBA begins about 12 hr after onset of culture. Cell density growth arrest generally occurs between 48 and 60 hr when cells reach a density of $2-4 \times 10^6$ cells/ml.

3. Discard cells after about 40 passages, at which time thaw a low-passage culture to minimize progressive changes in phenotype and differentiation capacity.

B. FREEZING CELLS

Solution

1. *Freezing medium:* MEM-alpha, 10% fetal calf serum, 10% glycerol. To make 100 ml, add 80 ml MEM-alpha, 10 ml fetal calf serum, and 10 ml glycerol. Filter-sterilize as described above and store at 4°C.

Steps

1. Pass day 2 cells at 2×10^5 cells/ml in complete medium in a total volume of 5.0 ml or more, depending on the number of vials of early passage cells to be frozen.

2. After a 24-hr growth period at 37°C, pellet cells by centrifugation at 800 rpm for 5 min. Resuspend cell pellet in 5.0 ml of freezing medium.

3. Dispense 1.0 ml/vial (Nalgene, Cat. No. 5000-0012).

4. Cool cells gradually (30 min 4°C, 1 hr −20°C) and store in liquid nitrogen.

5. To grow cells after removal from liquid nitrogen, thaw vial quickly in 37°C water bath with agitation.

6. Transfer contents to centrifuge tube containing 5 ml complete medium at 37°C and centrifuge at 800 rpm for 5 min.

7. Resuspend cell pellet in 5 ml complete medium and incubate at 37°C in 5% CO_2.

C. HEXAMETHYLENE BISACETAMIDE INDUCTION OF DIFFERENTIATION OF MURINE ERYTHROLEUKEMIA CELLS

Solution

1. *HMBA:* 200 mM HMBA in unsupplemented MEM-alpha. Sterilize the solution by filtration (Nalgene, 0.45 μm, Cat. No. 245-0045) and store at 4°C for up to 1 month.

Steps

1. Initiate a culture of day 2 cells ($1-2 \times 10^6$ cells/ml) at 1×10^5 cells/ml in complete medium containing 5 mM HMBA.

2. Measure the extent of differentiation at various time intervals, for example, every 12 hr or 24 hr after initiation of culture, using either the benzidine assay to measure hemoglobin accumulation or the commitment assay to determine the

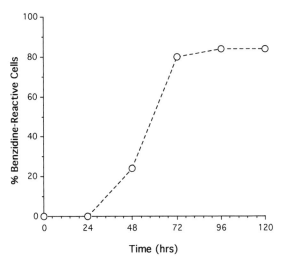

FIGURE 1 Kinetics of HMBA-induced accumulation of hemoglobin-producing cells as determined by the benzidine assay. MELCs (DS19/sc9) are cultured with 5 mM HMBA and the percentage of benzidine-reactive cells is determined at the times indicated.

irreversible capacity to express hemoglobin and proliferate. These assays are described below.

D. BENZIDINE LIQUID STAINING TO MEASURE HEMOGLOBIN ACCUMULATION

Solution

1. *Benzidine stock solution:* 0.2% benzidine dihydrochloride in 0.5 M acetic acid. Store at 4°C for up to 2 months in a dark bottle.

Caution: Take care in handling benzidine dihydrochloride because it is a suspected carcinogenic agent.

NOTE

Steps

1. Prepare staining solution by adding 0.1 ml of 30% hydrogen peroxide to 5 ml benzidine stock solution. This solution must be made fresh.

2. Add equal amount of the above solution to cell culture (usually 0.1 ml of each).

3. Let stand 5 min at room temperature for color development.

4. Score by counting a total of at least 100 cells using a hemocytometer and standard microscope with 10× eyepiece and 10× and 40× objectives. Score the blue cells as benzidine positive.

5. The results of a typical experiment are shown in Fig. 1.

E. COMMITMENT ASSAY TO MEASURE LOSS OF PROLIFERATIVE CAPACITY AND HEMOGLOBIN ACCUMULATION

Solutions

1. *2× MEM-alpha:* Dissolve one envelope of powder in distilled water (approximately 400 ml). Add 3.7 g $NaHCO_3$ and bring volume up to 500 ml

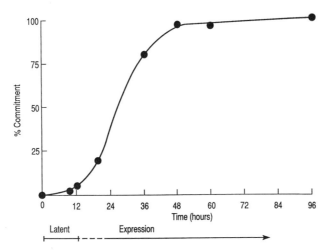

FIGURE 2 Kinetics of HMBA-induced commitment as determined by the commitment assay. MELCs (DS19/Sc9) are cultured with 5 mM HMBA and commitment is determined at the times indicated.

with distilled water. The pH should be approximately 7.0. Sterilize by filtration (Nalgene, 0.45 μm). Store at 4°C.

2. *Methylcellulose:* Autoclave at 4 g in a 500-ml Erlenmeyer flask with stirring bar.

3. *150 ml autoclaved, distilled H_2O.*

Steps

1. Dissolve methylcellulose in 100 ml hot sterile H_2O and mix well.

2. When solution is at room temperature, add 100 ml 2× MEM-alpha and mix for 2 days at 4°C (final concentration 2% methylcellulose).

3. Pour 34 ml into sterile 50-ml centrifuge tubes. This solution can be stored at −20°C for up to 1 year.

4. Thaw methylcellulose solution at 37°C, add 6.0 ml fetal calf serum (final concentration 15%), mix well, and remove bubbles by centrifugation.

5. Carefully pour 3 ml methylcellulose solution into a sterile 5-ml syringe (Becton Dickinson, Cat. No. 9603) with plunger removed, and cap in place.

6. Add to this syringe 15,000 cells (5000/ml methylcellulose). Add cells that have been incubated without or with inducer in suspension culture for the appropriate time (usually 0–48 hr), wash once in complete medium, and resuspend at 1×10^6 cells/ml in complete medium.

7. Carefully insert plunger by inverting syringe and loosening cap. Insert plunger only so far that it does not fall out. Tighten the cap and mix the contents by inverting syringe 15 to 20 times.

8. Plate 1 ml per plate (Falcon 35 × 10-mm plates).

9. Incubate plates for 5 days at 37°C in 5% CO_2.

10. After 5 days, stain the colonies for hemoglobin-containing cells. Prepare the staining solution as described above for the benzidine assay. Carefully add 1 ml of staining solution to each plate and let stand for 5 min.

11. Colonies are scored as committed if they contain fewer than 32 cells and are benzidine positive (blue). Colonies in methylcellulose are visualized using an inverted microscope with 10× eyepiece and 4× and 10× objectives. The results from a typical experiment are shown in Fig. 2.

IV. Comments

The differentiation assays described have been successfully used to test a variety of new inducing agents for their ability to induce terminal differentiation of MELCs (Breslow *et al.,* 1991). A number of variant cells have been derived from the parental cell line, DS19/Sc9, with respect to sensitivity to induction by HMBA. These MELC variants include a cell line, R1, derived from DS19/Sc9 by selection for resistance to HMBA (Marks *et al.,* 1983). Another variant was derived from DS19/Sc9 by selection for resistance to low levels (2–5 μg/ml) of vincristine (Melloni *et al.,* 1988). Vincristine-resistant DS19/Sc9 cells can be induced to differentiate with accelerated kinetics of commitment compared with the parental DS19/Sc9 cells.

V. Pitfalls

1. Fetal calf serum should be tested prior to use. Some batches of fetal calf serum do not sustain cell growth and/or induced differentiation and should not be used. Maintain cells with passage in the test lot of fetal calf serum for at least 2 weeks prior to carrying out differentiation assays.

2. Each lot of methylcellulose must be tested to determine the optimal concentration for forming distinct colonies while obtaining high plating efficiency (50–80%).

REFERENCES

Breslow, R., Jursic, B., Fa Yan, Z., Friedman, E., Ngo, L., Rifkind, R. A., and Marks, P. A. (1991) New more potent cytodifferentiating agents related to hexamethylene bisacetamide. *Proc. Natl. Acad. Sci. USA* 88, 5542–5546.

Fibach, E., Reuben, R. C., Rifkind, R. A., and Marks, P. A. (1977) Effect of hexamethylene bisacetamide on the commitment to differentiation of murine erythroleukemia cells. *Cancer Res.* 37, 440–444.

Friend, C., Scher, W., Holland, J., and Sato, T. (1971) Hemoglobin synthesis in murine erythroleukemia cells *in vitro:* Stimulation of erythroid differentiation by dimethylsulfoxide. *Proc. Natl. Acad. Sci. USA* 68, 378–382.

Gusella, J., Geller, R., Clarke, B., Weeks, V., and Housman, D. (1976) Commitment to erythroid differentiation by Friend erythroleukemia cells: A Stochastic Analysis. *Cell* 9, 221–229.

Marks, P. A., Chen, Z. X., Banks, J., and Rifkind, R. A. (1983) Erythroleukemia cells: Variants inducible for hemoglobin synthesis without commitment to terminal cell division. *Proc. Natl. Acad. Sci. USA* 80, 2281–2284.

Marks, P. A., and Rifkind, R. A. (1978) Erythroleukemic differentiation. *Annu. Rev. Biochem.* 47, 419–448.

Melloni, E., Pontremoli, S., Damiani, G., Viotti, P., Weich, N., Rifkind, R. A., and Marks, P. A. (1988) Vincristine-resistant erythroleukemia cells have marked increased sensitivity to hexamethylene bisacetamide induced differentiation. *Proc. Natl. Acad. Sci. USA* 85, 3835–3839.

Rifkind, R. A., and Marks, P. A. (1993) Induced differentiation: Molecular mechanism and therapeutic potential. *In* "Proceedings of the Vth Esteve Foundation Symposium on the Pharmacology of Cell Differentiation," pp. 223–233. Elsevier Science, Amsterdam.

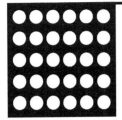

Cultured PC12 Cells: A Model for Neuronal Function and Differentiation

Kenneth K. Teng and Lloyd A. Greene

I. Introduction

Since its initial description and characterization in 1976 (Greene and Tischler, 1976), the rat pheochromocytoma PC12 cell line has become a commonly employed model system for studies of neuronal development and function. In particular, PC12 cells have been a convenient alternative to cultured neurons for studying the trophic and differentiative actions of nerve growth factor (NGF; reviewed by Levi-Montalcini and Angeletti, 1968; Levi and Alemá, 1991). When cultured in serum-containing medium, PC12 cells adopt a round and phase-bright morphology and proliferate to high density. Under these conditions, PC12 cells display many of the properties associated with immature adrenal chromaffin cells and sympathicoblasts. When challenged with physiological levels of NGF, these cells cease division, become electrically excitable, extend long branching neurites, and gradually acquire many characteristics of mature sympathetic neurons. Several attributes of the PC12 cells have led to their widespread popularity in neurobiological research. These include their relatively high degree of differentiation before and after NGF treatment, homogeneous response to stimuli, availability in large numbers for biochemical studies, and suitability for genetic manipulations. Here we detail experience gained with this cell line in terms of tissue culture requirements and treatment with NGF, as well as quantitative assessment of NGF actions. In addition, we describe some of the potential difficulties that one may encounter when culturing PC12 cells and suggest possible means to avoid or ameliorate these problems. The reader is referred to several prior articles (Greene and Tischler, 1982; Greene et al., 1987, 1991) for a more in-depth discussion of the properties and experimental exploitation of the PC12 cell line.

II. Materials and Instrumentation

RPMI-1640 medium is purchased from GIBCO Laboratories, (Cat. No. 430-3200EB) in powder form. Donor horse serum (Cat. No. 12-44977P), fetal bovine serum (Cat. No. 12-10377P) and penicillin–streptomycin (Cat. No. 59-60277P) are obtained from JRH Biosciences. It is recommended that sera be prescreened for their capacity to promote PC12 cell growth and maintenance. The horse serum should be heat-inactivated in a 56°C water bath for 30 min before use.

Tissue culture plasticware is obtained from Falcon/Becton Dickinson and Company. Freezing vials are purchased from Nunc (Cat. No. 377267). Millipak-60 filters (0.22 μm, Cat. No. MPGL06SH2) are from Millipore. Filter units (0.45 μm, Cat.

No. 245-0045) are obtained from Nalgene Company. Ethylhexadecyldimethylammonium bromide (Cat. No. 1179712) is purchased from Eastman Kodak Company.

The 2.5 S NGF is prepared from adult male mouse submaxillary glands as described by Mobley *et al.* (1976). The glands can be purchased from Bioproducts for Science (Cat. No. 516) and stored at −80°C until use. NGF stocks (250 µg/ml, in pH 5.0 acetate buffer) are stored at −80°C and, once thawed, can be kept at 4°C. NGF may also be purchased from a variety of commercial suppliers including Boehringer-Manheim and Upstate Biotechnology, Inc.

Rat tail collagen is prepared in 0.1% acetic acid as previously described (Greene *et al.*, 1991) from the tendons of rat tails (see Fig. 14.2 of Kleitman *et al.*, 1991, for a photographic illustration of the procedure for exposing and removing rat tail tendons). Aliquots of collagen stock are stored at −20°C. Once thawed, the stock can be stored for up to several months at 4°C. One large tail furnishes approximately 200 ml of stock collagen. Sterile technique should be employed throughout the preparation.

III. Procedures

A. ROUTINE TISSUE CULTURE TECHNIQUES

Solutions

1. *Complete growth medium:* Prepare RPMI-1640 medium according to the supplier's protocol in reverse osmosis/Milli-Q water. After addition of sodium bicarbonate (2 g/liter), penicillin (final concentration 25 U/ml), and streptomycin (final concentration 25 µg/ml), sterilize the medium by filtration through a Millipak-60 filter unit, dispense into 500-ml autoclaved bottles, and store in the dark at 4°C. The bottles should be dedicated to tissue culture only and should be cleaned by thorough rinsing without soap or detergent. To make up complete growth medium, add 50 ml of heat-inactivated horse serum and 25 ml of fetal bovine serum to 500 ml of RPMI-1640 medium. Store complete growth medium at 4°C.

2. *Medium for freezing of cells:* Mix 1 vol of DMSO with 9 vol of complete growth medium. This medium should be freshly prepared for immediate use only.

3. *Diluted collagen solution:* Prepare a 30% ethanol solution with autoclaved reverse osmosis/Milli-Q water. Mix in an appropriate volume of the collagen stock. The optimal final dilution of the collagen should be empirically determined by testing various concentrations for their capacity to foster cell attachment and NGF-promoted neurite outgrowth (cf. Greene *et al.*, 1991). At too low a dilution, adhesion to substrate is poor, whereas at too high a concentration, neurite outgrowth is impeded and cells are difficult to dislodge for subculture (see below). Typically, a 1:50 dilution of the stock is optimal. Unused portions of the diluted collagen solution can be stored at 4°C for 1–2 days.

Steps

1. Add the diluted collagen solution to plastic tissue cultureware (10 ml/150-mm dish, 5 ml/100-mm dish, 1 ml/35-mm dish, 0.5 ml/well of 24-well culture plate). Leave uncovered to air-dry overnight in a tissue culture hood. Collagen-coated dishes are stored at room temperature and should be used within 1 week after preparation.

2. Feed PC12 cells three times a week with complete growth medium. Remove approximately two-thirds of the culture medium from each plate and replace with

fresh complete growth medium (10 ml for 150-mm dishes, 5 ml for 100-mm dishes, 1.5 ml for 35-mm dishes). The medium should be added gently and from the side of the tissue culture dish. The feeding schedule should be kept rigid for maximum cell viability. Maintain PC12 cells in a 37°C incubator with a water-saturated, 7.5% CO_2 atmosphere.

3. PC12 cells are passaged (subcultured) when the cultures are 80–90% confluent. Dislodge the cells from the surface of the dish by repeatedly and forcefully triturating the culture medium directly onto the cells (use 10-ml pipettes for 150- and 100-mm dishes; use fire-polished Pasteur pipettes with reduced bore size for 35-mm dishes). Forceful aspiration also decreases cell clumping. Mix the culture medium containing detached PC12 cells with fresh complete medium in a 1:3 or 1:4 ratio. Then plate the PC12 cells onto collagen-coated dishes; the passage number of the newly plated PC12 cells should be increased by one. As the cell doubling time is 3–4 days, subculture every 7–10 days.

4. Stock cultures of PC12 cells are frozen at high density ($>5 \times 10^6$ cells/ml; see below for cell counting procedure) as follows. Dislodge cells from tissue culture dish as above, pellet by centrifugation at room temperature for 10 min at 500 g, and remove the medium. Add the appropriate volume of freezing medium (described above) and resuspend the cell pellet. Aliquot into a Nunc freezing vial (1 ml/vial) and transfer to a −80°C freezer for at least 1 day. For high-viability long-term storage, the vials should be maintained in liquid nitrogen. The vials should not be permitted to warm up during transfer to liquid nitrogen (e.g., transfer on dry ice).

5. Thaw frozen PC12 cell stocks (in freezing vials) rapidly in a 37°C water bath (2–3 min). Immediately transfer the cells into 9 vol of complete growth medium. Pellet the cells by centrifugation at room temperature for 10 min at 500 g. Discard the supernatant. Resuspend the cell pellet in fresh, complete growth medium and plate cells on collagen-coated dishes.

B. PROMOTION AND ASSESSMENT OF NERVE GROWTH FACTOR-DEPENDENT NEURITE OUTGROWTH

Solution

1. *Low serum medium:* Mix 1 ml of heat-inactivated horse serum per 100 ml of RPMI-1640 medium. Store at 4°C.

Steps

1. Dislodge PC12 cells from stock culture dishes and triturate well using a Pasteur pipette with reduced bore size to break up cell clumps. Then plate the cells at low densities (5×10^6 cells per 150-mm dish, $1–2 \times 10^6$ cells per 100-mm dish, $2–5 \times 10^5$ cells per 35-mm dish; see cell counting procedure below) on collagen-coated dishes in medium supplemented with NGF (50–100 ng NGF/ml of medium). Just before use NGF should be diluted from the stock into the medium in plastic containers (NGF binds to glass surfaces). Diluted solutions of NGF are not stable. Although neurite outgrowth is satisfactory in complete growth medium, low serum medium is recommended instead to economize on serum as well as to reduce cell clumping. Once plated, the cultures should be maintained in a 37°C incubator with a water-saturated, 7.5% CO_2 atmosphere and should be fed three times per week as described above. Neurite-bearing cells should be noticeable within 1–3 days of NGF treatment and the numbers of

PC12 cells with neurites should increase progressively with time of NGF exposure. By 7–10 days of treatment, at least 90% of the cells should generate neurites (Fig. 1).

2. To determine the numbers of neurite-bearing PC12 cells after NGF treatment, observe cultures with a phase-contrast microscope under high magnification (e.g., 320×). Within a random field, use a multichannel laboratory counter to register the numbers of cells that possess at least one neurite greater than 20 μm (about two cell body diameters) in length. Also, in the same field, count the numbers of cells without neurites or with neurites less than 20 μm in length. Randomly choose another area of the culture and continue counting until the total number of cells assessed exceeds 100. For consistent results, count only discernible and/or single cells, but not cell clumps.

3. To measure neurite length and the rate of neurite elongation, observe cultures using an eyepiece equipped with a calibrated micrometer. The latter is used to measure the entire length of randomly chosen neurites. At least 20–25 neurites are measured per culture. The rate of neurite elongation is determined from a plot of mean neurite length versus time of NGF treatment. A typical rate for PC12 cells is 40–50 μm/day.

4. Neurite regeneration assays are carried out with NGF-pretreated PC12 cell cultures. Treat the cells first with NGF for 7–10 days as described in step 1 of this section. Then rinse the cultures five times with medium (without NGF) while the cells are still attached to the substrate. Mechanically dislodge the cells from the dish by trituration through a Pasteur pipette (fire-polished to reduce the bore size) and wash five times in medium (without NGF) by repeatedly centrifuging at 500 g for 10 min at room temperature. Then plate the washed cells at low density ($\approx 10^5$ cells/35-mm dish) in medium (complete or low serum) in the presence or absence of NGF (see step 1 of this section). Examine the cultures 24 hr later and score for percentage of neurite-bearing cells or cell clumps. Because NGF-treated PC12 cells tend to aggregate, it is often necessary to score clumps rather than single cells. The ability of NGF to induce neurite regeneration from PC12 cells is determined by subtracting the number of neurite-bearing cells in culture medium without NGF from the number of neurite-bearing cells in NGF-containing culture medium. For well-washed cultures, the background value

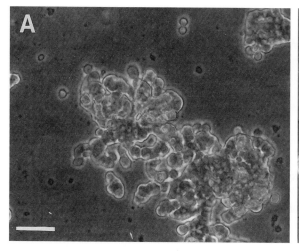 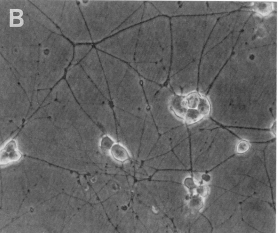

FIGURE 1   Morphologies of PC12 cells before and after NGF treatment. (A) Phase-contrast photomicrograph of non-NGF-treated (naive) PC12 cells. (B) Phase-contrast photomicrograph of PC12 cells treated with 50 ng/ml NGF for 14 days. Note that on long-term NGF treatment, PC12 cells elaborate a dense network of neurites. Bar = 50 μm.

(neurite regeneration without NGF) should be about 10%, whereas with NGF, 80–100% of the cells or cell clumps should regenerate neurites. The regeneration protocol can be used as a quantitative bioassay for NGF (Greene *et al.*, 1987).

C. ASSESSMENT OF THE SURVIVAL-PROMOTING ACTIONS OF NERVE GROWTH FACTOR

Solutions

1. *Nucleus counting solution stock (Soto and Sonnenschein, 1985):* Dissolve 5 g ethylhexadecyldimethylammonium bromide and 0.165 g NaCl in 80 ml of reverse osmosis/Milli-Q water. Add 2.8 ml glacial acetic acid and 1 drop bromophenol blue. Bring final volume to 100 ml and filter through a 0.45-μm filter unit. Store the solution at room temperature.

2. *Working nucleus counting solution (Soto and Sonnenschein, 1985):* Mix PBS (10 ml), 10% Triton X-100 (5 ml), 1 M MgCl$_2$ (200 μl), and nucleus counting solution stock (10 ml) with enough reverse osmosis/Milli-Q water so that the final volume is 100 ml. Pass through a 0.45-μm filter unit. Store the working nucleus counting solution at room temperature.

Steps

1. To determine the numbers of PC12 cells suspended in culture or other medium, pellet the cells by centrifugation, aspirate to remove the medium, and resuspend the cells in a known volume of the working nucleus counting solution. This solution provides a homogeneous suspension of intact nuclei which are quantified using a hemocytometer (see also article by Ariana Celis and Julio E. Celis). To count cells attached to a substrate, remove the medium and replace with a known volume of working nucleus counting solution. Resuspend the resulting nuclei by trituration and quantify with a hemocytometer.

2. Wash PC12 cells with serum-free RPMI medium five times while still attached to culture dishes and then, after detachment by trituration, wash another five times in serum-free RPMI medium by centrifugation/resuspension. Resuspend the cells in RPMI-1640 medium with or without NGF or other potential trophic agents. Plate the cells in collagen-coated 24-well culture plates in 0.5 ml of medium (0.5–1.0 × 10^5 cells/well). Exchange medium three times per week. Carry out cell counts by removing the medium, adding working nucleus counting solution (250 μl), and counting intact nuclei. Typically, without trophic substances such as NGF, 50% of the cells die by 24 hr of serum deprivation and 90% by 3–4 days.

IV. Comments

By adhering to the above-described protocols, our laboratory has been able to maintain (for the past 17 years) PC12 cell stocks that are consistently responsive to NGF and that present a stable phenotype; however, a survey of the literature concerning the use of PC12 cells occasionally reveals conflicting or inconsistent results between laboratories. One possible cause may be the generation of variant "PC12 cell" lines. Like other continuous cell lines, PC12 cells are subject to spontaneous mutations and clonal PC12 cell variants have been identified from past studies. The introduction of nonstandard culture methods (e.g., changing sera, medium, substrate) can favor the selection of such variants over the wild-type population.

Although the use of "variant" PC12 cell lines does not necessarily undermine the validity of the data generated with them, it can give rise to uncertainty or confusion when one attempts to integrate/reproduce the findings from various reports. It is therefore our suggestion that a uniform standard of culturing PC12 cells be adopted for studies with this cell line.

Another cautionary note on the use of the PC12 cell line is that although it is a convenient model system for studying neuronal development and function, it is not a full substitute for "bona fide" nerve cells. Therefore, whenever feasible, experimental results obtained with PC12 cells should be verified or compared with those for representative neurons.

V. Pitfalls

1. Poor survival or growth of stock cultures has three possible causes: (i) the initial plating density is too low; (ii) the horse serum is not properly heat-inactivated or is of insufficient quality (the latter is the usual cause for failure to thrive); (iii) the culture medium is outdated (the glutamine has degraded).

2. The most probable cause of poor cell adherence is an insufficient level of collagen as the substrate.

3. A poor NGF response is indicated by the continuous proliferation of PC12 cells in NGF-containing medium and by the lack of neurite-bearing cells even after long-term NGF treatment. Possibly the initial plating density is too high or the NGF may be inactive. This would also lead to poor NGF-promoted cell survival in serum-free culture medium. In addition, the collagen concentration on the dishes may be too high or too low or the collagen has deteriorated, and the cultures may contain a large proportion of nonresponsive variants (in this case, start with cell stock of lower passage number).

4. Spontaneously arising PC12 cell variants are indicated by the presence of flat (phase-dark), rapidly dividing, non-NGF-responsive cells. Alternatively, contaminating variants may appear spiky in morphology (process-bearing), even in the absence of NGF. The best solution is to replace the entire stock with PC12 cells from an earlier passage and to adopt culture conditions that do not favor selection of variants.

5. More than 50% of PC12 cells in serum-free medium alone without NGF should die within 24 hr of plating; however, PC12 cells at high density are capable of conditioning the culture medium and this retards death. Therefore, if cultures exhibit a delay in serum-free cell death, the experiment should be repeated with a lower density of cells. Alternatively, delay of cell death could be due to an insufficient washout of serum.

6. Generally, it is prudent to discard contaminated cultures and replace with fresh PC12 cell stock; however, if it is necessary to rescue a nonreplaceable culture (such as cell line established from transfection experiments), the following treatments may be effective in removing common sources of contamination (see also article by Robert J. Hay): (i) Yeast: treat the culture with 1% Fungizone (final concentration) in complete medium. (ii) Mold: remove the contaminant by aspiration; alternatively, use a Pasteur pipette to remove some of the PC12 cells from a small unaffected area of the dish, replate the cells onto a new dish, and then treat the cells with 1% fungizone in complete medium. (iii) Bacteria: a combination of antibiotics and bacterial static (see Sambrook *et al.*, 1989, for appropriate doses) may be added to the culture; PC12 cells can tolerate ampicillin, kanamycin, spectinomycin, tetracycline, and chloramphenicol.

REFERENCES

Greene, L. A., Aletta, J. M., Rukenstein, A., and Green, S. H. (1987) PC12 pheochromocytoma cells: Culture, nerve growth factor treatment, and experimental exploitation. *In* "Methods in Enzymology" (D. Barnes and D. A. Sirbasky, eds.), Vol. 147B, pp. 207–216. Academic Press, San Diego.

Greene, L. A., Sobeih, M. M., and Teng, K. K. (1991) Methodologies for the culture and experimental use of the PC12 rat pheochromocytoma cell line. *In* "Culturing Nerve Cells" (G. Banker and K. Goslin, eds.), pp. 207–226. MIT Press, Cambridge, MA.

Greene, L. A., and Tischler, A. S. (1976) Establishment of a noradrenergic clonal line of rat adrenal pheochromocytoma cells which respond to nerve growth factor. *Proc. Natl. Acad. Sci. USA* **73**, 2424–2428.

Greene, L. A., and Tischler, A. S. (1982) PC12 pheochromocytoma cultures in neurobiological research. *Adv. Cell. Neurobiol.* **3**, 373–414.

Kleitman, N., Wood, P. M., and Bunge, R. P. (1991) Tissue culture methods for the study of myelination. *In* "Culturing Nerve Cells" (G. Banker and K. Goslin, eds.), pp. 337–377. MIT Press, Cambridge, MA.

Levi, A., and Alemá, S. (1991) The mechanism of action of nerve growth factor. *Annu. Rev. Pharmacol. Toxicol.* **31**, 205–228.

Levi-Montalcini, R., and Angeletti, P. U. (1968) Nerve growth factor. *Physiol. Rev.* **48**, 534–569.

Mobley, W. C., Schenker, A., and Shooter, E. M. (1976) Characterization and isolation of proteolytically modified nerve growth factor. *Biochemistry* **15**, 5543–5552.

Sambrook, J., Fritsch, E. F., and Maniatis, T. (1989) "Molecular Cloning: A Laboratory Manual," 2nd ed. Cold Spring Harbor Laboratory, Cold Spring Harbor, NY.

Soto, A. M., and Sonnenschein, C. (1985) The role of estrogen on the proliferation of human breast tumor cells (MCF-7). *J. Steroid Biochem.* **23**, 87–94.

Growing Madin–Darby Canine Kidney Cells for Studying Epithelial Cell Biology

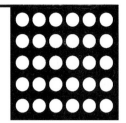

Kai Simons and Hilkka Virta

I. Introduction

Epithelial cells display a structural and functional polar organization (Simons and Fuller, 1985). In these cells, the plasma membrane can be divided into two distinct domains, the apical membrane and the basolateral membrane, each containing different sets of proteins. The apical membrane facing a secretory or an absorptive lumen is delimited by a junctional complex from the basolateral membrane. The tight junction (zonula occludens) is the most apical member of the complex. It is found at the intersection between the apical and the lateral plasma membranes and joins each cell to its neighbors, thus limiting the diffusion of molecules between the luminal and serosal compartments (Gumbiner, 1987). This junction also prevents the lateral diffusion of membrane proteins from one domain to another, thus maintaining their unique composition. Immediately basal to the tight junctions is the intermediate junction (zonula adherens or belt desmosomes). The other, more basal junctional elements are desmosomes (maculae adherentes) and gap junctions which attach the lateral membranes of adjacent cells to each other. The junctional complex is involved in sealing the epithelium; it prevents molecules from diffusing between adjacent cells. The basolateral membrane faces the bloodstream and is involved in cell–cell contact and cell adhesion to the basement membrane.

For most studies on epithelial cell polarity cultured cells have been used. These cells are superior to the cells obtained from tissues because they can be grown under carefully controlled conditions and are easily manipulated. The cell population is homogeneous. Biosynthetic experiments using pulse–chase techniques with radioactive precursors can be accomplished at an analytical level with a short time resolution. Endocytosis and transcytosis can also be studied. The most well-studied epithelial cell is the Madin–Darby canine kidney (MDCK) cell. This cell line is derived from normal dog kidney (McRoberts *et al.,* 1981). An unusual feature of these cells is that while in culture they retain many differentiated properties characteristic of kidney epithelial cells. Among these are an asymmetric distribution of enzymes and vectorial transport of sodium and water from the apical to the basolateral faces. The latter gives rise to "domes" or "blisters" in confluent cultures, which are transient areas where collected fluid has forced the monolayer to separate from the substratum. Morphologically the cells resemble a typical cuboidal epithelium with microvilli on the apical side of the cells. Two different strains of the MDCK cell are known (Richardson *et al.,* 1981; Balcarova-Ständer *et al.,* 1984). Strain I cells are derived from a low-passage MDCK cell stock and these cells form a tight epithelium with transepithelial resistance above 2000 ohm·cm². Strain II cells form a monolayer of lower resistance of 100–200 ohm·cm². MDCK strain II cells have been used primarily for studies of the cell biology of epithelial cells. Transcytosis is, however, more conveniently studied in MDCK strain I cells because of their high electrical resistance.

Several factors are important for optimal expression of the epithelial phenotype *in vitro* (Simons and Fuller, 1985). A primary consideration is the polarity of nutrient uptake. *In vivo*, many nutrients reach the epithelial sheet from the basolateral side, which faces the blood supply; however, when epithelial cells are cultured on glass or plastic, they are forced to feed from the apical surface, which faces the culture medium. Hence, the basolateral surface becomes isolated from the growth medium as the monolayer is sealed by the formation of tight junctions. To grow properly the epithelial sheet must remain somewhat leaky, or expose basolateral proteins responsible for uptake of nutrients and binding of growth factors on the apical side.

These problems can be overcome simply by growing the epithelial cells on permeable supports, such as polycarbonate and nitrocellulose filters. Epithelial cells form monolayers with a higher degree of differentiation when the basolateral surface is directly accessible to the growth medium. This is evident from the morphology of the cells, their increased responsiveness to hormones, and the exclusion of basolateral proteins from their apical surfaces.

II. Materials and Instrumentation

Minimal essential medium with Earle's salt (MEM) is purchased as a powder (Cat. No. To 31-10) from Biochrom, and mixed with Milli-Q-filtered H_2O, and sterile-filtered. Glutamine (200 mM, Cat. No. 043-05030H), penicillin (10,000 IU/ml)–streptomycin (10,000 μg/ml) (Cat. No. 043-05140 H), trypsin (0.05%)/EDTA (0.02%) (Cat. No. 043-05300H), and phosphate-buffered saline (PBS, Cat. No. 041-04040H) are from Gibco-BRL. The Transwell polycarbonate filters (2.45 cm, Cat. No. 3412, and 10 cm, Cat. No. 3419) are from Costar. Tissue culture flasks (75 cm², Cat. No. 153732) are from Nunc. The glass petri dishes (140 mm diameter and 30 mm high) for holding six 2.4-cm Transwell filters are Schott Glasware.

The laminar flow hood (Steril Gard Hood Model VMB-600) is from Baker. The CO_2 incubator (Model 3330) is from Forma Scientific. The inverted Diavert microscope is from Leitz. The electrical resistance measuring device (EVOM) is from World Precision Instruments. The centrifuge (Type 440) is from Hereaus-Christ.

III. Procedures

A. GROWING MADIN–DARBY CANINE KIDNEY CELLS ON PLASTIC

The MDCK I and II cells are passaged every 3–4 days up to 25 passages. One flask is usually split into five new flasks. MDCK II cells usually form domes within 2 days of splitting, whereas MDCK I cells do not blister.

Solutions

1. *MEM growth medium:*

	Stock	Volume/liter
5% fetal calf serum (MDCK II)	100%	50 ml
10% fetal calf serum (MDCK I)	100%	100 ml
2 mM glutamine	200 mM	10 ml
100 IU/ml penicillin–100 μg/ml streptomycin	100×	10 ml

2. Phosphate-buffered saline (PBS).

3. 0.05% trypsin/0.02% EDTA.

Steps

1. Wash hands and wipe laminar flow hood with 70% ethanol. Warm all solutions to 37°C. All manipulations are done in the laminar flow hood. When splitting the cells, remove the growth medium from the 75-cm^2 flasks containing the confluent layer of MDCK cells and add 10 ml PBS. Rinse and discard wash solution.

2. Add 5 ml trypsin/EDTA solution, seal flask, and incubate for 10–15 min at room temperature (until small patches of cells are rounded up but not yet detached from the flask).

3. Remove the trypsin/EDTA solution and add 1.5 ml of fresh trypsin/EDTA. Reseal the flask and incubate at 37°C for 10–15 min (MDCK II) or 25–30 min (MDCK I). At this point the cells should flow down the bottom of the flask when the flask is turned up. Hit the flask hard against the palm of your hand.

4. Add 10 ml prewarmed MEM growth medium and resuspend the cells with a sterile 10-ml pipet (at least five times up and down). Check in the inverted microscope that the cells are not sticking to each other.

5. Plate 2 ml of the cell suspension in a new 75-cm^2 flask containing 20 ml of MEM growth medium.

B. SEEDING MDCK CELLS ON POLYCARBONATE FILTERS

Solutions

1. MEM growth medium containing 10% fetal calf serum, penicillin–streptomycin, and 2 mM glutamine: See Solution A1.

2. Phosphate-buffered saline (PBS).

3. 0.05% trypsin/0.02% EDTA.

Steps

1. Seed the cells on the filters at high density, higher than that achieved by confluent cells on plastic. The cells form tight junctions within 24 hr and reach maximum tightness on the filters in 4 days. During this time cell density increases to more than five times that achieved on plastic. We place the filters in the petri dishes containing growth medium. For seeding we use one 75-ml flask, containing a confluent layer of MDCK I and II cells, for 2.4-cm-diameter filters (Transwell 3412). If you use large 10-cm-diameter filters (Transwell 3419), seed one 75-cm^2 culture flask of MDCK cells into each large filter.

2. Pour off medium from the culture flask and rinse cells with 10 ml of warm PBS. Pour off PBS.

3. Add 5 ml of warm trypsin/EDTA to cells. Leave in laminar flow hood.

4. After 15 min remove the trypsin/EDTA with a pipette, add 1.5 ml of trypsin/EDTA, put the flask into a CO_2 incubator (37°C) for 10–15 min (MDCK II) or 25–30 min (MDCK I).

5. Remove flask (cells should be loose). Hit the flask hard against your palm. Add 10 ml of warm growth medium, and suspend cells by pipetting up and down

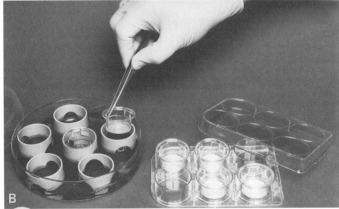

FIGURE 1 (A) The glass petri dish contains six filter holders for Transwell 3412 filters. (B) The glass petri dish contains one filter holder for one Transwell 2419 filter.

with a 10-ml pipette. Put suspension into 50-ml Falcon tube and centrifuge 5 min at 1000 rpm in Heraus-Christ centrifuge.

6. Remove supernatant and suspend cells in 9.5 ml of growth medium.

7. Pour 90 ml medium into glass petri dish containing six Transwell 3412 filters. Use 140 ml for one Transwell 3419 filter. The petri dishes contain filter holders specially made to fit either 3412 or 3419 filters (Fig. 1). These units are autoclaved before use. Place filters into filter holders and allow filters to get wet from the bottom with medium. This should be done while the cells are in the centrifuge.

8. Add 1.5 ml cell suspension to each filter in its holder. Use six Transwell 3412 filters or one Transwell 3419 filter per petri dish. Be careful not to spill cells over the edge of the filter holder.

9. Swirl petri dish gently to remove any trapped air from beneath filters.

10. Place the petri dish with the filters in the CO_2 incubator.

11. Leave for 3–4 days in the incubator. No medium change is required during this time.

C. TRANSEPITHELIAL RESISTANCE MEASUREMENT

Steps

1. Transepithelial resistance of filter-grown MDCK cells is measured with EVOM "chopstick" electrodes. Each leaf has an outer and an inner electrode.

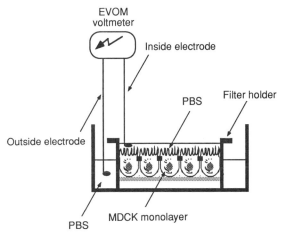

FIGURE 2 Scheme illustrating the setup for measuring electrical resistance.

The outside electrodes are small silver pads for passing current through the membrane sample. Inside electrodes are small Ag/AgCl voltage sensors.

2. To test the instrument, switch the mode switch to R and turn the power on. Push the test R button. With the range switch in the 2000 V position, the meter will read 1000 (±1 digit). In the 20 k range, the meter will read 1.00. The meter is now ready for use.

3. To test the electrodes, insert the small telephone-type plug at the end of the chopsticks electrode cable into the jack on the front panel of the EVOM. Place the tips of the electrodes into 0.1 M KCl. Switch the mode switch to Volts. Turn the power switch on. The digital panel meter may read 1 or 2 mV owing to the asymmetry of the voltage sensor pair. After 15 min, adjust this voltage to 0 mV with the screwdriver adjustment labeled "Zero V."

NOTE

If the electrode asymmetry potential difference exceeds the zero adjustment range, the central electrodes may be dirty or contaminated.

---

4. Measure resistance. The electrode set is designed to facilitate measurements of membrane voltage and resistance of cultured epithelia in culture cups by dipping one stick electrode inside the cup on top of the cell layer and the second stick electrode in the external bathing solution.

NOTE

The stick designated for external use is slightly longer than its companion (Fig. 2).

To measure resistance, immerse the electrode pair again into electrolyte, and set the mode switch to "Ohm." The display should read zero; if not, adjust the display to zero with the Ohms Zero screwdriver adjustment. Push the measure R button. A steady ohm reading of the resistance should result.

Example:

(a) Measure resistance R from solution + sample membrane support ... 109

(b) Measure resistance R from solution + membrane support + tissue ... 189

(c) Subtract (a) from (b) ... $189 - 109 = 80$, R (tissue) $= 80$ V

(d) Calculate resistance × area product

$$\text{resistance} \times \text{area}$$
$$= 1.2 \text{ cm} \times p \times r^2$$
$$= 80 \text{ V} \times 3.14 \times (1.2 \text{ cm})^2$$
$$= 361.9 \text{ V cm}^2$$

5. When moving the electrodes from one dish to another it is best not to rinse electrodes with distilled water. If it is necessary to wash the electrodes between measurements, they should be rinsed with the membrane perfusate (e.g., PBS). Do not hit the cell layer with the internal electrode when making a measurement. Small differences in the apparent fluid resistance may occur if the depth to which the electrodes tips are immersed varies. If the tips are unusually dirty, a light and very brief sanding with a fine nonmetallic abrasive paper will clean the sensor tip. For sterilization the electrodes may be soaked in alcohol or bactericides. After sterilization, the electrodes should be rinsed extensively with sterile perfusing solution or 1 M KCl.

IV. Comments

The cell layer on the filter cannot be observed in the inverted microscope because the filters are not transparent. Transparent filters are also commercially available but they are more expensive than the polycarbonate ones; however, either the cells in one filter can be stained or the transepithelial resistance can be measured to ensure that the layer is intact. Our experience is that when one filter in the petri dish checks out, the other filters will also be fine.

It is recommended that MDCK cells not be used for more than 20–25 passages. New stock cells should then be thawed from liquid nitrogen storage.

We use filter holders for growing MDCK cells on either 2.4- or 10-cm polycarbonate filters. It is possible to grow the cells in either the six-well plate for the Transwell 3412 filter or in the petri dish supplied with the Transwell 3419 filters. Under these latter culture conditions the growth media have to be changed every day; otherwise the cells do not get enough nutrients and do not grow to optimal density. The problems with changing the medium every day are, first, the extra work involved, and second, the considerably increased risk of contamination. Therefore, we prefer to place filter holders in petri dishes into which one can add enough growth medium to last 4 days.

REFERENCES

Balcarova-Ständer, J., Pfeiffer, S. E., Fuller, S. D., and Simons, K. (1984) Development of cell surface polarity in the epithelial Madin–Darby canine kidney (MDCK) cell line. *EMBO J.* **3,** 2687–2694.

Gumbiner, B. (1987) Structure, biochemistry and assembly of epithelial tight junctions. *Am. J. Physiol.* **253,** C749–C758.

McRoberts, J. A., Taub, M., and Saier, M. H., Jr. (1981) The Madin–Darby canine kidney (MDCK) cell line. *In* "Functionally Differentiated Cell Lines" (G. Sata, ed.), pp. 117–139. Alan Liss, New York.

Richardson, J. C. W., Scalera, V., and Simmons, N. L. (1981) Identification of two strains of MDCK cells which resemble separate nephron tubule segments. *Biochim. Biophys. Acta* **673**, 26–36.

Simons, K., and Fuller, S. D. (1985) Cell surface polarity in epithelia. *Annu. Rev. Cell. Biol.* **1**, 243–288.

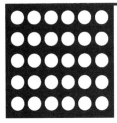

In Vitro Studies of Epithelium-to-Mesenchyme Transitions

Ana Maria Vallés, Jean Paul Thiery, and Brigitte Boyer

I. Introduction

Although epithelial cells are particularly cohesive with defined junctions and multiple adhesive mechanisms, they can remodel extensively during morphogenetic processes. The epithelial–mesenchymal transition (EMT) is one of the most profound modifications that allow cells to separate from an epithelial structure and form another tissue at a different site in the embryo (Trelstad *et al.,* 1982; Hay, 1991). The newly formed mesenchymal cells have lost apical–basal polarity and specialized contacts with neighboring cells and the basal lamina. The reverse process, mesenchymal–epithelial transition (MET), also occurs during embryogenesis as a mechanism for the establishment of transient as well as definitive epithelia. Several histogenetic processes involve repeated EMT and MET (Ekblom, 1992). *In vivo,* epithelial plasticity has been more extensively studied in amphibians, fishes, and birds (Thiery *et al.,* 1985); however, experimental *in vitro* approaches have also been developed to characterize and manipulate the parameters of EMT in defined systems (Zuk *et al.,* 1989; Burdsal *et al.,* 1993; Reichmann *et al.,* 1992). Accordingly, the role of certain growth factors in the promotion of EMT has been described using *in vitro* models (Potts and Runyan, 1989; Vallés *et al.,* 1990). We therefore analyze here the different techniques by which *in vitro* EMTs can be evaluated.

A. MORPHOLOGICAL TRANSFORMATIONS

As a first approach, EMT can be analyzed in terms of modifications in cell morphology, observed by light and electron microscopy (Fig. 1). In sparse cultures, epithelial cells grow as islets of polygonal cells in close apposition. Because of the presence of junctions between adjacent cells, intercellular spaces are reduced. Cultures of high cell density appear as cobblestone-like monolayers. EMT can be induced by extracellular matrix (ECM) components such as collagens, fibronectin, laminin, and soluble factors such as epidermal growth factor (EGF), hepatocyte growth factor/scatter factor (HGF/SF), fibroblast growth factors (FGFs), and transforming growth factors (TGFs) α and β. The range of active concentrations of these growth factors is usually 1 to 100 ng/ml. Certain growth factors, such as FGFs, have to be stabilized by the addition of heparin at 10 μg/ml. Initial experiments should determine the lag period before morphological changes are first noticed: depending on the cell type, this period ranges from 2 hr to several days. After EMT has occurred, cells acquire a fibroblast-like appearance, characterized by an elongated morphology with pseudopodial protrusions. In sparse cultures, these cells

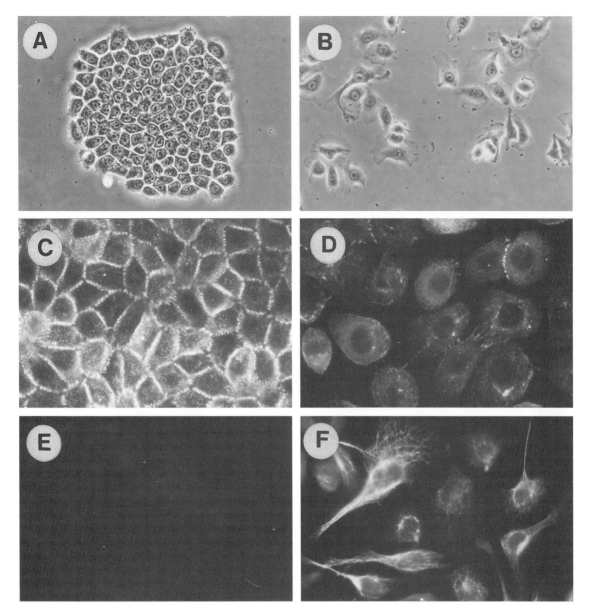

FIGURE 1 Morphological and immunofluorescence studies of EMT. (A, B) Light microscopy of (A) epithelial cells converted into (B) mesenchymal-like cells. (C–F) Immunofluorescent labeling of (C, E) epithelial and (D, F) fibroblast-like cells stained with (C, D)
anti-desmoplakin antibody and (E, F) anti-vimentin antibody. Note the internalization of
desmosome immunoreactivity in the dissociated cells (D) and the absence of vimentin immuno-
labeling in epithelial cells (E).

are clearly separated by large intercellular spaces. Cultures of high cell density do
not regain the characteristic pavement-like aspect of epithelial monolayers; instead,
cells have the tendency to crawl over one other. One expected consequence of the
morphological modifications arising during EMT is the loss of epithelial apical–
basal polarity, which is replaced by a fibroblastic front end–back end polarity. At
the electron microscopy level, microvilli disappear from the apical surface, and the
Golgi apparatus located at the apical pole of the nucleus in epithelial cells is now
found in the cytoplasm at the front end of fibroblast-like cells. Tight junctions that
seal the apical part of the lateral membranes in epithelial cells, thereby constituting
the structural barrier between the apical and basolateral domains of the plasma

membrane, disappear during EMT. Moreover, other types of epithelial junctions such as desmosomes, which constitute a belt connecting epithelial cells together, are no longer found at the periphery of the fibroblast-like cells.

B. MARKERS OF DIFFERENTIATION

Epithelial and fibroblastic cells can be distinguished on the basis of expression of proteins specific for either the epithelial or fibroblastic state of differentiation. The pattern of expression of these proteins can be analyzed by different techniques, such as immunofluorescence, immunoprecipitation, immunoblotting, Northern blotting, and polymerase chain reaction (PCR), which are not detailed here. All epithelial cells express intermediate filaments of the keratin type, whereas vimentin filaments are the hallmark of cells derived from mesenchymal tissues (see Fig. 1); however, keratin filaments can persist in cells transformed into fibroblasts without effect on the EMT, providing that vimentin is also expressed (Boyer et al., 1989). Furthermore, it should be stressed that some epithelial cell lines can express vimentin. Extracellular matrix components are also different: many types of epithelial cells in vitro synthesize a matrix rich in collagen IV and laminin, whereas fibroblastic cells express fibronectin.

Epithelial cells are tightly interconnected by junctional complexes. As EMT produces fibroblastic cells with the tendency not to form cohesive structures, intercellular junctions are expected to disappear from the cell periphery. This means that proteins that are specifically assembled in these junctional complexes must undergo a process of negative regulation leading to their loss of expression or loss of function. It is therefore necessary to test for the expression of ZO-1, localized in tight junctions; E-cadherin, found in adherens-type junctions; and desmoplakin and desmoglein, two components of desmosomes (see Fig. 1). As tight junctions are involved in the establishment of the epithelial permeability barrier, the disappearance of ZO-1 is accompanied by the loss of transepithelial resistance as well as the free passage of radiolabeled markers and ions across epithelial monolayers cultured on permeable filters (Bomsel et al., 1989). The disappearance of cell–cell junctions is often accompanied by the loss of protein polarity: among the proteins that are localized mainly at the apical surfaces of epithelial cells are dipeptidyl peptidase IV and N-CAM; Na^+, K^+-ATPase and E-cadherin segregate in the lateral membranes.

The choice of techniques and markers of differentiation is restricted by the availability of reagents (e.g., antibodies) that react with the species under study.

II. Materials and Instrumentation

The growth factors acidic FGF (Cat. No. 01-116), basic FGF (Cat. No. 01-111), TGF-α (Cat. No. 01-165) TGF-β (Cat. No. 01-134), and insulin-like growth factors I (Cat. No. 01-141) and II (Cat. No. 01-142) can be purchased from Upstate Biotechnology, Inc. (UBI). EGF (Cat. No. E-1257), heparin (Cat. No. H-3393), and Coomassie brilliant blue R-250 (Cat. No. B-0149) are from Sigma Chemical Company. Dulbecco's modified Eagle's minimal essential medium (10× concentrated, Cat. No. 042-02501H) is from Gibco BRL-Life Technologies Inc.

Multidish 24-well tissue culture plates (Cat. No. 1-43982) are from Nunc InterMed. Pipetman and yellow tips are from Gilson Medical Electronics. Falcon 35-mm bacterial petri dishes (Cat. No. 1008) are from Becton Dickinson Labware. (Lincoln Park, NJ, USA). Parafilm is from American National Can Company.

Extracellular matrix components such as collagen type I (Cat. No. C-7661), Fibronectin (Cat. No. F-1141), laminin (Cat. No. L-2020), and gelatin (Cat. No. G-9391) are from Sigma. Basement membrane Matrigel (Cat. No. 400234B) is from

Collaborative Biomedical Products–Becton Dickinson Biomedical Research. Filters (type HA, 0.45-μm pore size, Cat. No. HAWP 142 50) are from Millipore Corporation. The Sykes–Moore chamber (Cat. No. 1943-11111) and 25-mm coverslips (1943-22222) are from Bellco Glass Inc. The Diaphot TMD inverted microscope is from Nikon (Tokyo, Japan). Video camera (Cat. No. WV BL 200), time-lapse video recorder (Cat. No. AG-6720), and monitor screen (Cat. No. WV 5410) are from Panasonic Matsushita Electric Industrial Company. Gyrotory shaker, Model G2, is from New Brunswick Scientific.

III. Procedures

A. TESTS OF CELL MOTILITY

1. Wound Colonization Assay

Solution

1. *Coomassie blue fixative:* To make 1 liter, solubilize 1 g of Coomassie blue in a fixative solution of 100 ml acetic acid, 400 ml ethanol, and 600 ml distilled water. Filter solution.

Steps

1. Establish confluent cell cultures are in 24-well plates and arrest by serum starvation for 24 hr.

2. Gently scratch the cell cultures with a Gilson pipet yellow tip, to produce a "wound" devoid of cells.

3. Rinse the wells twice with 1 ml of medium to remove all cellular debris.

4. Add the medium containing motility factors to be tested or plain medium to the wells.

5. Incubate the plates overnight and examine by phase-contrast microscopy the next morning.

6. Stain and fix cell cultures with a solution of Coomassie blue for 5 min followed by extensive washes with tap water.

7. Keep the dried plates at room temperature and rehydrate prior to microscopic examination (Fig. 2).

Comments

Several cell cultures can be compared at the same time under the same experimental conditions. Quantification of "wound repair" is possible by measuring the areas free of cells before and after overnight incubation. Measurements can be done by taking pictures of the cell cultures and cutting out and weighting the pieces of photographic paper corresponding to the wounds or, alternatively, by digitalizing the wound areas and analyzing them with morphological analysis software, which is now available in the market. This method does not allow the speed of locomotion to be estimated.

Pitfalls

1. It should be noted that for some cell lines that do not move under serum-free conditions, the experiment should be conducted in the presence of serum. In

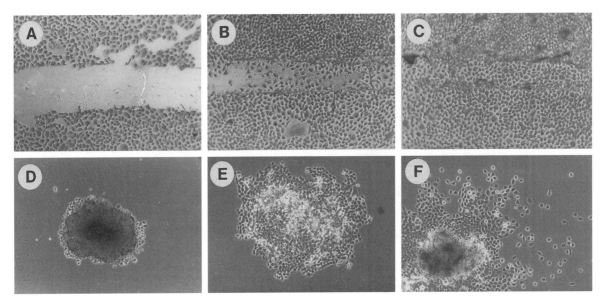

FIGURE 2 Motility and dispersion assays. (A–C) Wound healing of cell monolayers after overnight incubation under standard conditions (A) and increasing concentrations of scattering factor (B, C). (D–F) Dispersion of an aggregate of cells under exposure to a scatter factor photographed at different times after deposition on a permissive substrate: (D) initial attachment of the aggregate, (E) collapse of aggregate after 8 hr in culture, (F) dispersion of isolated cells after 24 h.

that case, it is necessary to check that wound healing does not result from cell proliferation.

2. It is also important to verify that the serum used in the culture medium does not contain factors that dissociate the cells before addition of the scatter factors to be tested.

3. The rate of wound colonization greatly depends on cell density: it is therefore important to first evaluate the number of cells to be seeded that will give rise to a minimum level of wound repair under basal conditions. If different cell lines are compared with respect to their ability to repair wounds, their cell densities at the time of scratching of the monolayer must be identical.

2. Video Microcinematography

Steps

1. Seed 50,000 trypsinized cells on a glass coverslip of 25-mm diameter placed in a 35-mm petri dish, and allow to attach for several hours at 37°C in a humidified atmosphere equilibrated with CO_2.

2. Mount the glass coverslip in a Sykes–Moore chamber (Fig. 3).

3. Fill the chamber with complete medium (with or without scatter factor) previously equilibrated with CO_2 at 37°C by using a 2-ml syringe and a 23-gauge sterile needle.

4. Place the chamber under an inverted microscope equipped with a video camera connected to a time-lapse video recorder and to a monitor screen (Fig. 4).

5. Film cell cultures at 37°C for several hours. With the Panasonic AG-6720 time-lapse video recorder, recording is done by setting the 480-hr intermittent recording mode and analysis is done by accelerating the tape to normal speed.

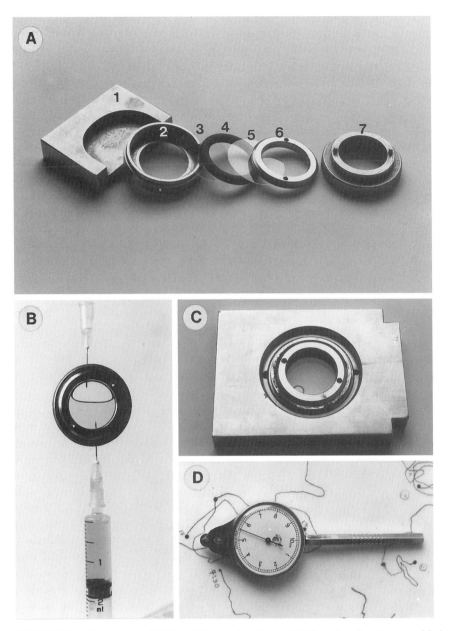

FIGURE 3 Mounting of Sykes–Moore chamber. (A) The chamber is assembled in the following order: the inferior metal part (2) is put on the wrench assembly device (1), and the 25-mm coverslip (3) to which cells are attached is placed in it, followed by the silicon gasket (4), a second coverslip (5), and the upper metal part of the chamber (6). Unit is sealed by screwing the top using the wrench device (7). Do not seal the device too tight to avoid breaking the coverslips. (B) The gasket is penetrated by a 25-gauge needle to gain entrance to the culture area. Four holes are provided equidistantly around the chamber. Overpressure is eliminated by inserting a second needle in the opposite hole. (C) The mounted chamber is placed in a metal holder for viewing on microscope stage. (D) Map measurer on tracing paper on which cell motility pathways were traced.

6. Place tracing paper on the screen and trace the displacement of at least 20 individual cells onto the paper. Measure the distance traveled by each cell, expressed in centimeters, using a map measurer (see Fig. 3) and convert these measurements to micrometers per hour by the following formula: speed of locomotion (μm/hr) = distance (cm) $\times 10^4$/hours of recording $\times$ objective magnification $\times$ zoom.

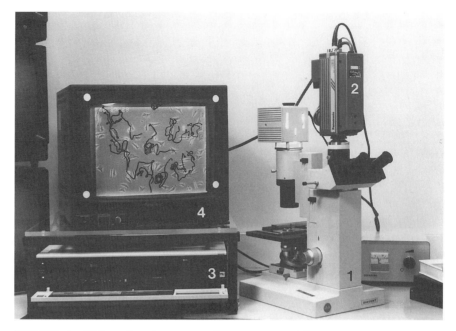

FIGURE 4 Video microcinematography equipement. The camera (2) is mounted on the inverted microscope (1), connected to a video recorder (3) and a monitor screen (4). Tracing paper is taped on the screen to draw the accelerated movement of cells.

Comments

This method provides a dynamic view of the transition, permitting measurement of the lag time before cells start moving, and gives a rough estimate of cell division.

Pitfalls

1. Expensive equipment is required.

2. The major problem is maintaining cells at 37°C throughout the recording period. Some cells are sensitive to the progressive loss of CO_2 inside the chamber. Such cells would require a special device allowing constant flow of medium with CO_2.

3. This method is time consuming and does not allow different conditions to be compared at the same time.

3. Other Tests

Several other cell motility assays have been successfully used. Among them is the Boyden chamber (Imhof *et al.*, 1990). The Boyden chamber is best suited for chemotactic migration but has also been used for nondirected cell locomotion. The "phagokinetic" track assay (Albrecht-Bühler and Goldman, 1976) is a simple method for measuring motility of freshly trypsinized cells. It relies on the displacement of colloidal gold particles by motile cells, leaving traces that can easily be visualized by light microscopy.

B. TESTS OF CELL DISPERSION

There are several assays that estimate the ability of cells to scatter, a property that implies both cell motility and cell dissociation. These assays are therefore appropriate for studies of EMT.

1. Dispersion of Aggregates on Bidimensional Substrates

Dispersion of cells can be studied by two different techniques: cellular aggregates (Tucker *et al.*, 1990) and explant cultures (Zuk *et al.*, 1989).

Solutions

1. *3 mg/ml collagen stock solution:* To make a collagen stock solution, dissolve 5 mg of collagen in 1.67 ml of 3% acetic acid. Store at $-20°C$ in small aliquots.

2. *0.1% gelatin solution:* To make 1 liter, dissolve 1 g of gelatin in PBS. Heat the solution until gelatin is dissolved. Store at 4°C.

Steps

1. To prepare substrates, incubate Falcon bacterial petri dishes (35 mm) for 2 hr at 37°C with either 1 ml of 20 μg/ml purified fibronectin or laminin in distilled H_2O or 1 ml of 0.1% gelatin.

2. Dissolve collagens in PBS to make a concentration of 0.1 mg/ml. Deposit a drop of substrate onto the bacterial petri dish, spread with a bent Pasteur pipet and allowed to dry under sterile air flow.

3. Rinse all substrates several times with PBS. Alternatively, complex substrates like Matrigel, prepared according to manufacturer's instructions, may be used.

4. To obtain cell aggregates, inoculate $1–1.5 \times 10^6$ trypsinized cells per milliliter into sterile 25-ml silicon-treated Erlenmeyer screw-capped flasks, containing medium preequilibrated for 30 min in a CO_2 incubator, and transfer to a rotatory shaker.

5. Maintain the cells at 37°C with constant shaking (75 rpm) for at least 24 hr.

6. After sedimentation of the spheroids, carefully aspirate about 10 cellular aggregates with a Pasteur pipet and deposit them onto 35-mm bacterial petri dishes previously coated with ECM components (see steps 1–3) (Fig. 5).

7. To prepare explant cultures, seed cells on tissue culture dishes coated with basement membrane components such as Matrigel, a preparation of ECM proteins extracted from the Engelbreth–Holm–Swarm (EHS) mouse sarcoma tumor (Kleinman *et al.*, 1986), or ECM substrates, and grow to confluency.

8. After 1 day of confluency, cut 1-mm^2 pieces of cells and place them flat with the apical surface toward the substrate; incubate for 1–2 hr in 500 μl of culture to allow attachement of explant.

9. Add the remainder of the medium (with or without scatter factors) and culture the cells for up to 3 weeks.

10. Analyze epithelial outgrowth by measuring the diameter of the cellular monolayer developing around the central mass of the aggregate or explant as a function of time (Fig. 2). Individual cell emigration is quantified using video time-lapse equipement as described above. In this case, petri dishes are filled to the top with CO_2-equilibrated medium and sealed with Parafilm.

Comments

Using this technique it is possible to compare many different samples treated under various conditions. Quantification is feasible. It is a good method for studying additional effects of ECM and soluble factors in the promotion of cell dispersion.

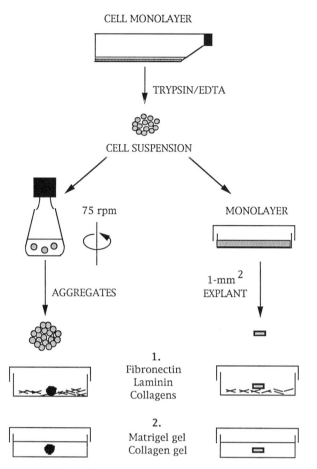

CELL MONOLAYER

TRYPSIN/EDTA

CELL SUSPENSION

75 rpm

MONOLAYER

AGGREGATES

1-mm^2
EXPLANT

1.
Fibronectin
Laminin
Collagens

2.
Matrigel gel
Collagen gel

FIGURE 5 Schematic representation of the experimental procedure for cell dispersion assay. Freshly trypsinized cells are either grown as monolayer or inoculated in Erlenmeyer flasks for aggregate formation. Pieces of explant culture and cell aggregates can then be placed (1) on ECM proteins such as fibronectin, laminin, and collagens or (2) on Matrigel and collagen gels and analyzed by time-lapse video microscopy.

Pitfalls

Cells that do not form compact aggregates have the tendency to spontaneously fall apart during the manipulation of aggregates and therefore give rise to false patterns of emigration.

2. Dispersion of Aggregates in Tridimensional Substrates

Solution

1. *Collagen gels:* Prepare collagen gels by mixing 8 vol of collagen type 1 (in the range 1–4 mg/ml) in acetic acid with 1 vol of 0.1 *N* NaOH and 1 vol of 10× concentrated DMEM. To form 1-mm-thick gels in 24-well plates, use 1 ml gel solution per well.

Steps

1. Cell aggregates and explants can be included within collagen gels or Matrigel. In this case, preculture explants on precoated Millipore filters instead of precoated petri dishes; prepare aggregates exactly as described above.

2. Gently suspend about 10 aggregates or one explant in the collagen gel solution. Incubate plates at 37°C for 1 hr prior to addition of 1 ml of complete medium (with or without scattering factors).

3. Alternatively, mix cells with undiluted Matrigel under the conditions recommended by the manufacturer. Briefly, thaw Matrigel overnight at 4°C, mix with the aggregates on ice, and distribute 1 ml/well in a 24-well plate. Polymerize at 37°C for 1 hr prior to addition of ~1 ml of complete medium on top of the gel.

4. Analyze cell dispersion by light microscopy, focusing at different planes below the surface of the gel.

Comments

This is the method of choice for reproducing *in vivo* conditions; however, quantification of dispersion is difficult and biochemical analysis of scattered cells is almost impossible. It should be noted that for most cell types, complete dispersion is not observed, thus impairing en masse analyses of the population.

3. Other Methods

An alternative method for cells that do not form tight aggregates has been described by Varani and colleagues (Varani *et al.,* 1978). This technique consists of forming semisolid droplets of cells included in low-melting-point agarose. These droplets are deposited on the various substrates and analyzed as described above.

Attempts to mimick *in vivo* situations have led to the development of interesting assays to study the influence of the normal environment on the pattern of cell dispersion. In that respect, Tucker and co-workers (1991) confronted, in organotypic cultures, aggregates of cells with explants of normal tissue and studied the behavior of these cells. Many other systems can be developed by adapting this method to the cells and tissues of interest.

ACKNOWLEDGMENTS

We thank D. Morineau for photographic assistance. Work in the author's laboratory is supported by the Centre National de la Recherche Scientifique (CNRS), the Association pour la Recherche contre le Cancer (ARC 6455), the Ligue Française contre le Cancer (National Committee and Committee of Paris), and the National Institutes of Health (2 RO1 CA-49417-04).

REFERENCES

Albrecht-Bühler, G., and Goldman, R. D. (1976) Microspike mediated particle transport towards the cell body during early spreading of 3T3 cells. *Exp. Cell Res.* **97,** 329–339.

Bomsel, M., Prydz, K., Parton, R. G., Gruenberg, J., and Simons, K. (1989) Endocytosis in filter-grown Madin–Darby canine kidney cells. *J. Cell Biol.* **109,** 3243–3258.

Boyer, B., Tucker, G. C., Vallés, A. M., Franke, W. W., and Thiery, J. P. (1989) Rearrangements of desmosomal and cytoskeletal proteins during the transition from epithelial to fibroblastoid organization in cultured rat bladder carcinoma cells. *J. Cell Biol.* **109,** 1495–1509.

Burdsal, C. A., Damsky, C. H., and Pederson (1993) The role of E-cadherin and integrins in mesoderm differentiation and migration at the mammalian primitive streak. Development **118,** 829–844.

Ekblom, P. (1992) Renal development. *In* "Physiology and Pathophysiology" (D. W. Seldin and G. Giebisch, eds.), pp. 475–501. Raven Press, New York.

Hay, E. D. (1991) "Cell Biology of Extracellular Matrix." Plenum Press, New York.

Imhof, B., Dargemont, C., Deugnier, M.-A., and Dunon, D. (1990) A chemotactic assay enabling recovery of cells after migration. *In* "Immunological Methods" (I. Lefkovits and B. Pernis, eds.), Vol. IV, pp. 235–249. Academic Press, San Diego.

Kleinman, H. K., McGarvey, M. L., Hamel, J. R., Star, V. L., Cannon, F. B., Laurie, G. W., and Martin, G. R. (1986) Basement membrane complexes with biological activity. *Biochemistry* **25**, 312–318.

Potts, J. D., and Runyan, R. B. (1989) Epithelial–mesenchymal cell transformation in the embryonic heart can be mediated, in part, by transforming growth factor β. *Dev. Biol.* **134**, 392–401.

Reichmann, E., Schwarz, H., Deiner, E. M., Leitner, I., Eilers, M., Berger, J., Busslinger, M., and Beug, H. (1992) Activation of an inducible c-FosER fusion protein causes loss of epithelial polarity and triggers epithelial–fibroblastoid cell conversion. *Cell* **71**, 1103–1116.

Thiery, J. P., Duband, J. L., and Tucker, G. C. (1985) Cell migration in the vertebrate embryo: Role of cell adhesion and tissue environment in pattern formation. *Annu. Rev. Cell Biol.* **1**, 91–113.

Trelstad, R. L., Hayashi, A., Hayashi, K., and Donahoe, P. K. (1982) The epithelial–mesenchymal interface of the male rat mullerian duct: Loss of basement membrane integrity and ductal regression. *Dev. Biol.* **92**, 27–40.

Tucker, G. C., Boyer, B., Gavrilovic, J., Emonard, H., and Thiery, J. P. (1990) Collagen-mediated dispersion of NBT-II rat bladder carcinoma cell line. *Cancer Res.* **50**, 129–137.

Tucker, G. C., Delouvée, A., Jouanneau, J., Gavrilovic, J., Moens, G., Vallés, A. M., and Thiery, J. P. (1991) Amplification of invasiveness in organotypic cultures after NBT-II rat bladder carcinoma with in vitro scattering factors. *Invasion Metast.* **11**, 297–309.

Vallés, A. M., Boyer, B., Badet, J., Tucker, G. C., Barritault, D., and Thiery, J. P. (1990) Acidic fibroblast growth factor is a modulator of epithalial plasticity in a rat bladder carcinoma cell line. *Proc. Natl. Acad. Sci. USA* **87**, 1124–1128.

Varani, J., Orr, W., and Ward, P. R. (1978) A comparison of the migration patterns of normal and malignant cells in two assay systems. *Am. J. Pathol.* **90**, 159–171.

Zuk, A., Matlin, K. S., and Hay, E. D. (1989) Type I collagen gel induces Madin–Darby canine kidney cells to become fusiform in shape and lose apical–basal polarity. *J. Cell Biol.* **108**, 903–919.

SECTION **F**

Immortalization of Cells

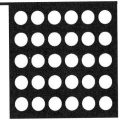

Inducible Immortalization of Cells from Transgenic Mice Expressing Simian Virus 40 under *lac* Operon Control

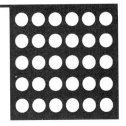

Ruth Epstein-Baak

I. Introduction

An inducible transgenic mouse system has been established in which the expression of the simian virus 40 (SV40) large T antigen (TAg) integrated into the germline is regulated by the *lac* operon (Epstein-Baak *et al.*, 1992). When the nonmetabolizable inducer isopropyl thiogalactoside (IPTG) is present, fibroblasts cultured from the tails of these mice proliferate and display a transformed phenotype as a consequence of the expression of the SV40 TAg. Cells grown in the absence of inducer display the normal differentiated phenotype, undergo senescence within 2 months of culture, and provide a control for studying the molecular mechanisms underlying neoplastic transformation. The regulatory system is reversible in that removal of the inducer causes a reemergence of the differentiated phenotype. This reversibly inducible system adds another dimension to those currently available in which SV40 is the regulated transgene (Brinster *et al.*, 1984; Jat *et al.*, 1991), as the bacterial regulatory element is completely foreign and easily manipulated. Many cell types from these transgenics are amenable to approaches similar to that delineated here for culturing lines from murine tail explants.

II. Materials and Instrumentation

RPMI-1640 medium (Cat. No. 12-167B), 200 mM glutamine (Cat. No. 17-605A), penicillin–streptomycin (Cat. No. 17-603A), 50× essential amino acids (Cat. No. 13-606A), nonessential amino acids (Cat. No. 13-114A), and 10× phosphate-buffered saline (PBS) without calcium (Cat. No. 16-006Y) were purchased from BioWhittaker. Collagenase (type I, Cat. No. C-0130), 10× trypsin/EDTA (Cat. No. T-9395), Evans blue (Cat. No. E-2129), and 0.4% trypan blue (Cat. No. T-8154) are from Sigma. IPTG (Cat. No. 5529UA) and minimum essential medium (MEM) with Earle's salts (Cat. No. 320-1090) are from Gibco-BRL. PAB108 culture supernatant is from cells obtained from American Type Tissue Collection (Cat. No. TIB-230). Fluorescein isothiocyanate (FITC)-conjugated goat anti-mouse IgG is from TAGO (Cat. No. 6240). Tissue culture plates (Cat. No. 3424) are from Costar.

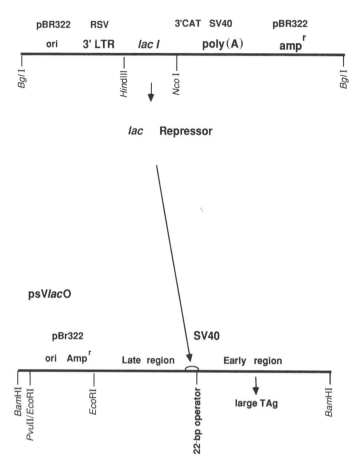

pRSV 1

psV*lac*O

FIGURE 1 The inducible cells described in the text are obtained from transgenic mice that have cointegrated the 5.7-kb pRSV-1 plasmid (Hu and Davidson, 1987) that encodes the *lac* repressor (regulated by promoter sequences found within the 3' LTR of the Rous sarcoma virus) and the 6.4-kb pSV*lac*O plasmid containing the SV40 early region. A 22-bp synthetic *lac* operator sequence has been cloned into an *Xho*I site present within the origin of replication, upstream of the SV40 large TAg encoding region of pSV*lac*O (Brown *et al.*, 1987). It is to this *lac* operator sequence that the *lac* repressor binds, thus preventing transcription of the SV40 TAg. The consequent inhibition of TAg synthesis is relieved in the presence of the inducer, IPTG, because the *lac* repressor undergoes a conformational change and can no longer bind to the *lac* operator sequence.

III. Procedures

A. CONSTRUCTION OF TRANSGENIC MICE

A vector containing the *lac* repressor under control of the Rous sarcoma virus 3' LTR (Hu and Davidson, 1987) and a plasmid containing the bacterial *lac* operator/promoter region linked to the SV40 large TAg (Brown *et al.*, 1987) were purified twice by CsCl density gradient sedimentation and once further by sucrose gradient centrifugation. The linearized DNAs were coinjected at a ratio of 10:1, respectively, into single-cell embryos derived from superovulated ICR/Hsd female mice (Harlan Spraque Dawley, Inc., Indianapolis). These constructs (Fig. 1) have been described in detail (Epstein-Baak *et al.*, 1992; Hu and Davidson, 1987; Brown *et al.*, 1987).

Standard methods for microinjection of the oocytes were used as reviewed by Jon W. Gordon (this volume) and described by Hogan *et al.* (1986).

B. PREPARATION OF CELL LINES FROM TAIL EXPLANTS

Solutions

1. *Balanced salt solution (BSS):* BSS (Mishell and Dutton, 1967) is made up from two 10× stocks. *Solution I* contains 10.0 g dextrose, 0.6 g KH_2PO_4, 3.58 g $Na_2HPO_4 \cdot 7H_2O$, and 20 ml of 0.5% phenol red solution. *Solution II* contains 1.86 g $CaCl_2 \cdot 2H_2O$, 4.0 g KCl, 2.0 g $MgCl_2 \cdot 6H_2O$, and 2.0 g $MgSO_4 \cdot 7H_2O$. Dissolve the components of each stock solution and bring each up to 1000 ml with double-distilled water. A 1× BSS is made by adding sequentially 10 ml each of solutions I and II to 80 ml double-distilled water (final pH 7.2–7.4, conductivity 14–16 mOsm).

2. *Supplemented RPMI medium:* RPMI medium is supplemented with fetal calf serum qualified to support the *in vitro* growth of splenic lymphocytes (Mishell and Dutton, 1967) as well as selected myeloma and fibroblast lines. To make supplemented RPMI medium, combine 100 ml RPMI, 15 ml Mishell–Dutton nutritive cocktail (see step 4), 1.25 ml 100× β-2-mercaptoethanol (see step 3), 1.25 ml penicillin–streptomycin (5000 units/ml penicillin, 5000 μg/ml streptomycin), and 1.25 ml glutamine (200 mM).

3. *100× 2-mercaptoethanol:* Dilute 10 μl of 2-mercaptoethanol (14.2 M) into 28 ml BSS. Store at 4°C.

4. *Mishell–Dutton nutritive cocktail:* To make 500 ml of cocktail combine 5 g dextrose, 350 ml MEM, 50 ml essential amino acids (50×), 25 ml nonessential amino acids (100×), and 75 ml $NaHCO_3$ (7.5%). Filter-sterilize and store at −20°C.

5. *1 M IPTG:* Dissolve 1 g in 4.2 ml double-distilled water, filter-sterilize, and store at −20°C.

6. *Trypsin:* Dilute 10× stock 1:10 in PBS without calcium.

Steps

1. After washing the tail of a donor mouse with 70% EtOH, cut a fragment approximately 1 cm long from the tip with a razor blade, and rinse and mince it in BSS (into small pieces, 0.5–2 mm). Transfer the pieces to 24-well Costar plates containing 0.5 ml of RPMI-1640 medium (one to three pieces per well).

2. Add collagenase to obtain a final concentration of 1 mg/ml and incubate cultures overnight in an incubator (5% CO_2 in air).

3. To induce the expression of the SV40 large TAg, add 5 μl of 1 M IPTG/ml of culture medium (final concentration of 5 mM). Do not add to control cultures.

4. After 24 hr, aspirate medium containing collagenase by holding the pipette to the side of the dish. Replace with 1.0 ml of supplemented RPMI containing IPTG (I^+) or not (as in I^0 negative controls). Cells should be fed initially twice a week by aspirating approximately 80% of the medium. Medium containing 5 mM IPTG should be added fresh at each feeding.

5. When cells reach confluence [10^6/ml, usually by week 2, (Figure 2)] they should be trypsinized. First, aspirate the medium and any nonadherent cells. Then add sequentially 0.5 ml 4 mM EDTA (made in PBS without Ca^{2+}) and an equal volume of 2× trypsin (stock diluted to 2× in 0.85% NaCl). Incubate for approximately 5 min. Check by viewing under the microscope that cells are

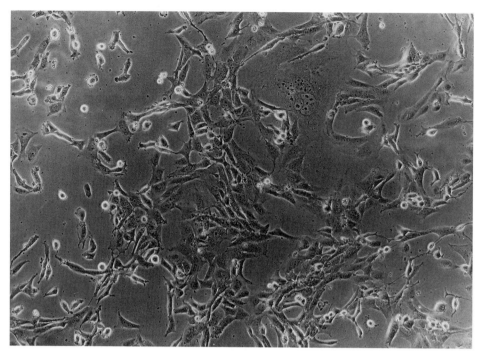

FIGURE 2 Shown here are cells grown in the presence of IPTG derived from the inducible SV40 murine transgenic line 425. Cells are morphologically distinct from uninduced cells which exhibit contact inhibition. Foci of disorganized stacking are observed in the induced cells which exhibit a reduction of fibronectin synthesis.

detaching. When cells become nonadherent, pipette them into a 15-ml conical tube containing supplemented RPMI medium, and centrifuge for 7 min at 200 g. Resuspend in 1.0 ml of supplemented medium, count in 0.4% trypan blue (see article by Ariana Celis and Julio E. Celis), and plate at a concentration of no less than 8×10^4/ml for maintenance. Passage cells before they reach saturation density (3–4 days), to minimize selection of IPTG-independent mutants (SV40 constitutive variants). The doubling time for cells cultured under these conditions is 18–24 hr, unless IPTG is present in the culture, in which case there is a shorter division time. Cell lines should be frozen as soon as possible.

C. CLONING OF CULTURED CELLS

It is critical that cloning of cells that display the reversible phenotype be accomplished prior to further characterization (see Pitfalls). Cloning at limiting dilution may be performed as early as the first or second passage. Although a discussion of the statistical theory underlying this technique is beyond the scope of this article, it is important to note that the distribution of cells follows a Poisson distribution. The procedure involves culturing a cell population at progressively lower densities, until the cells of interest occur at a frequency of less than one per well (see Henry *et al.*, 1980, for a more complete discussion).

Steps

1. Seed 96-well plates with cells in log phase (2–3 days after last passage) over a concentration range spanning 0.5–100 cells/ml (plate 0.2 ml/well).

2. Select clones from wells plated at a concentration that yields more than 37% negative wells. At this concentration the remaining cells will contain cells

that arise from either one or two progenitors. Therefore, colonies arising from this concentration or lower are preferred for obtaining clonal derivatives. Allow cells in selected wells to reach near confluency, trypsinize, and plate the entire contents of the well into a chamber of a Costar 24-well plate (use 0.5 ml medium at first; then add more medium as cells grow).

3. Freeze as soon as possible, especially those cultures growing in the absence of IPTG (I^0), as they have limited growth potential.

D. MONITORING SV40 LARGE TAG EXPRESSION BY IMMUNOFLUORESCENCE

By the end of the second week, the expression of SV40 TAg in induced cultures (those with IPTG present, I^+) can be detected by immunofluorescence. Large TAg can be observed microscopically as early as 2 days after addition of IPTG to cells established in the absence of inducer. Removal of IPTG produces a reduction of SV40 mRNA within 4 days and a reduction in fluorescent staining visible by day 7.

Solutions

1. *Tris-buffered glycerol:* Add 5.0 ml of 1.0 M Tris, pH 8.5, to 90 ml of glycerol and 5.0 ml of H_2O.

2. *PBS–azide:* Make a 10% stock of sodium azide, and dilute 1:500 in 1× PBS.

3. *Evans blue:* Make a 0.06% stock by dissolving 0.06 g in 100 ml water.

Steps

1. Trypsinize cells as above, and dilute to 5×10^4 cells/ml.

2. Plate 0.2 ml/well in duplicate on Nunc chamber slides.

3. When cells are almost confluent ($<10^6$/ml), remove chamber walls from slide, and wash slide in PBS (1× without azide) for 1 min.

4. Fix in 95% EtOH for 5 min.

5. Incubate slide in Evans blue for 3 min.

6. Wash in PBS–azide (0.02%) and incubate for 20 min with mouse monoclonal antibody PAB108 (see Comments). Wash slide for 30–60 min with PBS–azide.

7. Incubate with FITC-conjugated goat anti-mouse IgG for 20 min, and wash once more for 30–60 min.

8. Mount coverslips with Tris-buffered glycerol.

IV. Comments

This transgenic mouse system provides the prototype for designing additional transgenic systems which can be generated to permit the cloning *in vitro* of cells of any type at any stage of differentiation, provided that the oncogene is expressed in that lineage. The utility of these methods in generating cell lines of interest can be greatly enhanced by specifically tailoring the mice by either the substitution of other oncogenes for SV40 or the directed expression of the TAg by replacement with a cell-specific promoter.

PAB108 recognizes a denaturation-resistant determinant found on the NH$_2$-terminal end of the SV40 large and small T antigens (Gurney *et al.*, 1986).

V. Pitfalls

1. The frequency of IPTG-independent cell lines increases progressively with time, probably because of the accumulation of operator-constitutive mutants, which results in TAg expression without addition of IPTG. Cultures grown without inducer generally stop growing by 40 generations, unless such mutants are present. Occasionally, cultures grown in the presence of inducer become IPTG independent, but in general the major problem occurs when control cells are grown in the absence of inducer, because there is a selection pressure for such mutants to take over the culture. Establishing new stocks from cells frozen early after growth in the absence of inducer minimizes the latter problem. Working with cells cloned in the presence of inducer (and screened for IPTG dependence, i.e., TAg negative without inducer) minimizes the likelihood of such IPTG-independent colonization. In making *lac* operon-controlled transgenic mice in the future, the inclusion of multiple operators upstream of the regulated transgene may reduce the "leakiness" in the system.

2. It should be noted that removal of inducer does not result in the disappearance of large TAg in all cells. After 30 days, 20–30% of the cells remain positive for the TAg, as measured by fluorescent staining. The retention of the transformed phenotype, as measured in assays that score single cells (focus formation, anchorage-independent growth, TAg staining), may reflect the heterogeneity in the population (i.e., possible differences in thresholds of transformation). Cloning the cell lines immediately after establishment may therefore minimize problems that arise as a result of heterogeneity.

REFERENCES

Brinster, R. L., Chen, H. Y., Messing, A., Van Dyke, T., Levine, A. J., and Palmiter, R. D. (1984) Transgenic metallothionein growth hormone SV40 thymidine kinase fusion-gene. *Cell* 37, 367–379.

Brown, M., Figge, J., Hansen, U., Wright, C., Kuan-Teh, J., Khoury, G., Livingston, D. M., and Roberts, T. M. (1987) *Lac* repressor can regulate expression from a hybrid SV40 early promoter containing a *lac* operator in animal cells. *Cell* 9, 603–612.

Epstein-Baak, R., Lin, Y., Bradshaw, V., and Cohn, M. (1992) Inducible transformation of cells from transgenic mice expressing SV40 under Lac operon control. *Cell Growth Diff.* 3, 127–134.

Gurney, E. G., Tamowski, S., and Deppert, W. (1986) Antigenic binding sites of monoclonal antibodies specific for simian virus 40 large T antigen. *J. Virol.* 57, 1168–1172.

Henry, C., Marbrook, J., Vann, D. C., Dankward, K., and Wofsy, C. (1980) Limiting dilution analysis. *In* "Selected Methods in Immunology" (B. B. Mishell, and S. M. Shiigi, eds.), pp. 138–152. W. H. Freeman, San Francisco.

Hogan, B., Constantini, F., and Lacy, E. (1986) "Manipulating the Mouse Embryo." Cold Spring Harbor Laboratory Press, Cold Spring Harbor, NY.

Hu, M. C-T., and Davidson, N. (1987) The inducible *lac* operator–repressor system is functional in mammalian cells. *Cell* 48, 555–566.

Jat, P. S., Noble, M. D., Ataliotis, P., Yugiro, T., Yannoutsos, N., Larsen, L., and Kioussis, D. (1991) Direct derivation of conditionally immortal cell lines from an H-2K^b-tsA58 transgenic mouse. *Proc. Natl. Acad. Sci. USA* 88, 5096–5100.

Mishell, R. I., and Dutton, R. W. (1967) Immunization of dissociated spleen cell cultures from normal mice. *J. Exp. Med.* 126, 423–442.

Immortalization of Rat Ventral Prostate Epithelial Cells Using Simian Virus 40 T Antigen

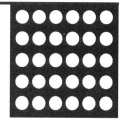

Debra A. Gordon and Roger L. Miesfeld

I. Introduction

The prostate is a small gland located at the base of the bladder in human males which secretes ions and specific proteins into the semen. Recently, this gland has become a focus of attention because a significant number of men (1 of 4) in developed countries will exhibit clinical symptoms of prostatic origin (Carter and Coffey, 1990). The major diseases of the prostate, benign prostatic hyperplasia and prostatic adenocarcinoma, both involve abnormal cellular proliferation.

Much of our knowledge of prostate development and function, particularly its hormonal control, has been gained through the use of intact animal models, primarily dog and rat. Comparatively little is known, however, about the cellular and molecular mechanisms underlying normal prostate cell growth partly due to the paucity of *in vitro* cell models.

A number of methods have been developed to isolate primary cultures of prostate epithelial and/or stromal cells (e.g., Montpetit and Tenniswood, 1989). The limited lifetimes of primary cells, however, makes them unsuitable for most molecular genetic studies. To address this problem, we have taken advantage of the fact that cells from several different tissues have been successfully immortalized by the expression of simian virus 40 (SV40) T antigen (e.g., Chou, 1985). Using a method of rat ventral prostate (RVP) epithelial cell isolation modified from Montpetit and Tenniswood (1989), in combination with transfection of a plasmid expressing SV40 T antigen, we have established numerous RVP cell lines (Rundlett *et al.*, 1992). ·

II. Materials and Instrumentation

Male Sprague–Dawley rats (300–324 g) were obtained from Harlan Sprague–Dawley. Fibronectin (Cat. No. F-4759), sodium chloride (Cat. No. S-5886), potassium chloride (Cat. No. P-5405), monobasic (Cat. No. S-5011) and dibasic (Cat. No. S5136) sodium phosphate, and Hepes (Cat. No. H-9136) were purchased from Sigma. Fungizone (Cat. No. 600-5295AE), penicillin G (potassium salt, Cat. No. 860-1840MJ), streptomycin sulfate (Cat. No. 860-1860IM), Geneticin (G418, Cat. No. 860-1811-II), trypan blue (Cat. No. 630-5250AE), Cell-Porator (Cat. No. 1600-AA), and electroporation cuvettes (Cat. No. 1601-AB) were from Gibco BRL. Collagenase A (Lot No. 11827, Cat. No. 118927) and dispase (grade II, Cat. No. 165859) were from Boehringer-Mannheim. Falcon brand tissue culture supplies, including

T-25 culture flasks (Cat. No. T4160-25), 60-mm culture plates (Cat. No. T4155-2), and 100-mm culture plates (Cat. No. T4155-3A) were purchased from Baxter. Baxter was also the supplier of 50-ml polypropylene screw-cap centrifuge tubes (Cat. No. C3920-50), surgical instruments (tissue forceps, Cat. No. D2567-2A; splinter forceps, Cat. No. D2559-1A; Mayo scissor, Cat. No. D2655-1A, Spencer stitch scissor, Cat. No. D2675-1A), and anhydrous D-glucose (Cat. No. 34912-500-NY). Dulbecco's modified Eagle's medium (low glucose pyruvate, Cat. No. 9416) was from Irvine Scientific. Calf bovine serum (Cat. No. A-2151-L) was obtained from Hyclone. Percoll (Cat. No. 17-0891-01) was purchased from Pharmacia. Nalge Company was the supplier of the Oak Ridge polycarbonate 50-ml centrifuge tubes with polypropylene caps (Cat. No. 3118-0050). A hemocytometer was purchased from Fisher (Cat. No. 02-671-10). The plasmid pSV3neo was obtained from American Type Culture Collection (Cat. No. 37150).

III. Procedures

NOTE

Caution: Except where noted, all solutions should be sterilized by 0.2-μm filtration, and procedures should include sterile technique.

A. FIBRONECTIN COATING OF 60-MM TISSUE CULTURE PLATES

Solution

1. *Fibronectin solution:* 1 mg/ml fibronectin, 0.1 M NaCl, 50 mM Tris–HCl, pH 7.4. Reconstitute lyophilized powder to 1 mg/ml fibronectin with sterile double-distilled H$_2$O (ddH$_2$O).

Steps

1. Dilute fibronectin stock solution to 10 μg/ml with sterile ddH$_2$O.

2. Pipette 3 ml of diluted solution into a 60-mm culture plate and coat the entire surface. Allow fibronectin solution to remain in the plate for 2–5 min.

3. Remove the liquid from the plate by pipette and allow the plate to dry overnight in a sterile environment. Each 3 ml of fibronectin solution can be used to coat three to five culture plates. Store fibronectin-coated plates at 4°C under sterile conditions.

B. COLLECTION AND DIGESTION OF PROSTATE TISSUE

Solutions

1. *10× Hanks' buffered saline (HBS) solution:* 1.3 M NaCl, 30 mM KCl, 40 mM D-glucose, 0.25 M Hepes, and 10 mM sodium phosphate, pH 7.4. To make 100 ml of the solution, dissolve 7.60 g NaCl, 0.22 g KCl, and 0.72 g anhydrous D-glucose in ddH$_2$O; then add 25 ml of a 1 M stock solution of Hepes, pH 7.4, and 1 ml of a 1 M stock sodium phosphate buffer solution, pH 7.4. Bring to 100-ml final volume with ddH$_2$O. Store at 4°C.

2. *Pen/Strep solution:* 10.1 U/μl penicillin G and 7.55 mg/ml streptomycin sulfate. To make 10 ml of solution, dissolve 63.1 mg of the potassium salt of

penicillin G (1600 U/mg) and 0.1 g streptomycin sulfate (755 μg active drug/mg powder) in ddH$_2$O. Bring to 10-ml final volume with ddH$_2$O. Dispense into 1- to 5-ml aliquots and store at -20°C.

3. *Fungizone solution:* 250 μg/ml amphotericin B and 205 μg/ml desoxycholate. Rehydrate lyophilized powder as directed by manufacturer. Dispense into 1-ml aliquots and store at -20°C.

4. *Supplemented HBS solution:* 0.101 U/μl penicillin G, 75.5 μg/ml streptomycin, 0.01$\times$ Fungizone in 1$\times$ HBS, pH 7.4. To make 20 ml of the solution, combine 17.6 ml ddH$_2$O, 2 ml of 10$\times$ HBS, 200 μl of Fungizone solution, and 200 μl of Pen/Strep solution. It is unnecessary to filter-sterilize this solution; however, it is important to make this solution just prior to use.

5. *Dulbecco's modified Eagle's medium (DMEM):* Prepare DMEM according to the manufacturer's directions. Store at 4°C.

6. *Wash medium:* 1% calf bovine serum (CBS) in DMEM. Make 35 ml just prior to use.

7. *Collagenase solution:* 100 mg/ml collagenase A in 20 mM Hepes, pH 7.4. Dissolve 100 mg lyophilized enzyme in 20 mM Hepes, pH 7.4. Bring to 1-ml final volume with 20 mM Hepes, pH 7.4. Store at 4°C.

8. *Dispase solution:* 100 mg/ml dispase in 20 mM Hepes, pH 7.4. Dissolve 100 mg lyophilized enzyme in 20 mM Hepes, pH 7.4. Bring to 1-ml final volume with 20 mM Hepes, pH 7.4. Store at 4°C.

9. *Digestion medium:* DMEM containing 10% CBS, 1 mg/ml collagenase A, 1 mg/ml dispase, 0.01$\times$ Fungizone, 0.101 U/μl penicillin G, 75.5 μg/ml streptomycin. To make 20 ml of the solution, combine 17.2 ml DMEM, 2.0 ml CBS, 200 μl collagenase A solution, 200 μl dispase solution, 200 μl Fungizone solution, and 200 μl Pen/Strep solution. Make this medium just prior to use.

Steps

1. Make up supplemented HBS, digestion medium, and wash medium. Keep these solutions on ice until needed.

2. Collect four male rats from the animal facility. Euthanize *one* animal by CO$_2$ asphyxiation.

3. Work rapidly at this point to avoid extensive tissue anoxia. Place the animal on its back in a clean, aseptic area. Grasp the skin overlying the pubis with tissue forceps and cut through the skin and underlying connective tissue using a large scissor. Blunt dissect the abdominal musculature until the bladder is visible. The ventral prostate in the rat is a small, pinkish, two-lobed gland located ventral and posterior to the bladder (Chaisson, 1980). Grasp the lobes of the prostate with a small forcep and cut the gland free using a small scissor. If performed properly, there should minimal bleeding with this procedure.

4. Place the isolated prostate tissue into 20 ml ice-cold supplemented HBS, and repeat the isolation procedure (one-at-a-time) on the remaining three rats.

Steps B5–7 and C3–15 should be performed in a laminar flow hood or other sterile environment.

NOTE

---

5. Transfer the prostates and supplemented HBS into a 10-mm culture plate. Mince the tissue into 1- to 2-mm^3 pieces using a sterile disposable scalpel. In this

process, remove connective tissue from glandular material using the point of the scalpel. Discard fragments of connective tissue. Careful attention at this step will expedite subsequent steps. Transfer minced tissue to a T-25 culture flask using a plastic pipette.

6. Tilt the T-25 flask such that tissue pieces settle in one corner. Carefully remove the overlying solution by suction or with a pipette. Add 10 ml wash medium to the flask and repeatedly pipette tissue pieces up and down. This serves to break down larger pieces. Repeat this step twice more using fresh wash medium.

7. Carefully remove all of the Wash Medium. Add 10 ml of digestion medium to the remaining tissue fragments. Tightly cap the T-25 flask and seal with Parafilm. Agitate the flask for 12–16 hr at room temperature or for 4–5 hr at 37°C. Depending on the activity of the proteolytic enzymes, the time and/or temperature of this digestion step may need to be adjusted.

C. ISOLATION AND ELECTROPORATION OF EPITHELIAL CELLS

Solutions

1. *Stock isotonic Percoll (SIP) solution:* 90% Percoll and 1× HBS. Prepare 125 ml of this solution by adding 12.5 ml 10× HBS to 112.5 ml Percoll. Make fresh just prior to use.

2. *Growth medium:* DMEM containing 10% CBS, 0.101 U/μl penicillin G, 75.5 μg/ml streptomycin. To make this solution, add 50 ml CBS and 5 ml Pen/ Strep solution to 445 ml DMEM. Store at 4°C.

3. *Geneticin (G418) solution:* 300 mg/ml active drug in ddH$_2$O. Store at −20°C.

Steps

1. Review the general scheme shown in Fig. 1.

2. Autoclave six 50-ml Oak Ridge polycarbonate centrifuge tubes with screw-on caps.

3. Check the status of the digestion reaction. Pipette the mixture up and down several times. The solution should have the smooth consistency of a single-cell suspension and there should be no obvious tissue pieces. Place a small drop of the suspension on a microscope slide and check that the majority of cells are viable. If necessary, modify the digestion time or temperature (do not exceed 37°C) to meet these conditions.

4. Prepare the SIP solution and 200 ml 1× HBS. Use 1× HBS to make the following SIP dilutions:

Final % Percoll	Volume of SIP (ml)	Volume of 1× HBS (ml)
20	7.0	24.5
30	10.5	21.0
40	14.0	17.5
45	15.75	15.75
50	17.5	14.0
55	19.25	12.25
60	21.0	10.5

5. Pipette 4 ml of 1× HBS into each of six 50-ml Oak Ridge polycarbonate centrifuge tubes. Create a gradient by *underlaying* 4 ml of the 20% Percoll

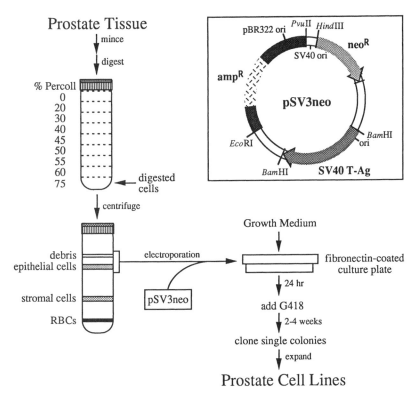

Prostate Tissue

Prostate Cell Lines

FIGURE 1   Schematic for the immortalization of prostate epithelial cells. Percoll gradient-enriched epithelial cells are transfected with the plasmid pSV3neo and plated in the presence of the cytotoxic agent G418. Only those cells that integrate the plasmid into the genome survive this selection. A detailed map of the pSV3neo plasmid is shown in the inset.

solution in each of the tubes. Be careful not to mix the layers. Repeat this procedure using progressively more concentrated Percoll solutions. Increasing care is required to slip the pipette down the side of the tube and through the mounting gradient with each subsequent layer. **Do not** pipette the last bit of Percoll out of the tip to avoid bubbles which will disturb the gradient. Set completed gradients aside temporarily and prepare the prostate cell suspension.

6. Transfer the digested cell suspension to a 50-ml polypropylene screw-cap tube. Centrifuge at 400 g for 10 min. Remove the supernatant. Carefully resuspend the cells in 4 ml 1× HBS, and then add 20 ml SIP. Gently mix to obtain a homogeneous cell suspension with a final Percoll concentration of 75%.

7. Underlay each of the six Percoll gradients prepared in step 5 with an equal volume (approximately 4 ml) of the cell suspension.

8. Centrifuge the gradients at 400 g for 30 min at 4°C. Turn off the brake and allow the rotor to coast to a stop.

9. Carefully, so as not to disturb the gradient, remove and discard the top clear layer of each gradient. Enriched epithelial cells band near the top of the gradient (see Fig. 1). Depending on the resolution, there may be one thick band or two closely spaced bands of cells in this region of the gradient. Remove the epithelial cell band(s) with a pipette. Combine fractions from three gradients together in 50-ml polypropylene screw-cap tubes.

NOTE

There may be a weak band containing cellular debris above the epithelial cell band. It is easiest to include this debris with the desired band of cells.

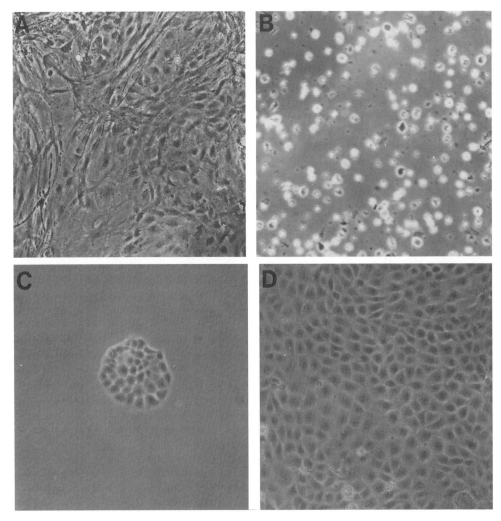

FIGURE 2 Time course of pSV3neo-transfected prostate cells. (A) Twenty-four hours after transfection and in the absence of G418, a heterogeneous population of cells are attached to the culture plate. (B) Five days following G418 addition, the majority of cells die. (C) Single colonies of immortalized cells arise after 2 weeks under G418 selection. (D) Single colonies are cloned and expanded to yield independent prostate cell lines, such as the one shown.

10. Dilute the contents of each polypropylene tube by no more than 50% with 1× HBS. Pellet the cells at 2500 g for 15 min at 4°C.

11. Carefully aspirate the supernatant and resuspend the cells in 10 ml 1× HBS. Determine the number of viable cells using trypan blue and a hemocytometer.

12. Centrifuge the cell suspension at 400 g for 10 min at 4°C. Remove and discard the supernatant and repeat this wash step with 1× HBS. Resuspend the final cell pellet to 5 × 10⁶ cells/ml in 1× HBS.

13. Place 1 ml of cell suspension into an electroporation cuvette. Add 100 μg of pSV3neo and electroporate the cells according to the manufacturer's instructions. The optimum conditions (μF, V) for electroporation must be determined for each machine and cell type. Consult the Cell-Porator manual for details.

14. Allow the cells to sit, in the cuvettes, at room temperature for 10 min following electroporation. In this time, add 4–5 ml growth medium to several 60-mm fibronectin-coated culture plates.

15. Seed each culture plate with 0.5 ml electroporated-cell suspension. As electro-

poration kills many of the cells, it is difficult to judge the number of viable cells in this volume. The optimum cell density is in the range of $0.5-1 \times 10^6$ viable cells/plate.

16. Place the cells in a 37°C incubator with 5% CO_2 atmosphere. After 24 hr, add fresh growth medium and G418 to a final concentration of 250 μg active drug/ml. Replace G418-containing growth medium every 2–3 days, as needed.

17. After several (2–3) weeks under G418 selection, single colonies will arise (Fig. 2C). These may be cloned using standard tissue culture methods (e.g., Freshney, 1987).

IV. Comments

We have also used this protocol to established cell lines from regressed prostates of castrated rats and regenerating prostates of testosterone-treated castrates (Rundlett *et al.*, 1992).

V. Pitfalls

1. Sterilize all solutions except supplemented HBSS.

2. Removal of prostates from the animals may be done aseptically; however, sterile technique must be used in all other steps of the procedure.

3. Making the Percoll gradient is one of the most difficult and critical steps of the procedure. Be careful not to mix adjacent layers of Percoll. Proceed slowly and avoid air bubbles in the tip of the pipette. It may be useful to practice setting up a gradient prior to sacrificing animals.

ACKNOWLEDGMENTS

The authors thank Dr. Xi-Ping Wu and Dr. Stephen Rundlett for assistance in this work. This work was supported by grants to R.L.M. from the American Cancer Society (NP-702), National Science Foundation (DCB-9105007), and Arizona Disease Control Research Commission (0-052). D.A.G. is supported by a postdoctoral fellowship from the Cancer Research Foundation of America. R.L.M. is a scholar of the Leukemia Society of America, and gratefully acknowledges the generous contribution of the Del Webb Foundation in providing the necessary seed money to initiate this project.

REFERENCES

Carter, H. B., and Coffey, D. S. (1990) The prostate. *Prostate* **16**, 39–48.
Chaisson, R. B. (1980) "Laboratory Anatomy of the White Rat," 4th ed. Brown, Dubuque, IA.
Chou, J. Y. (1985) Establishment of rat fetal liver lines and characterization of their metabolic and hormonal properties: Use of temperature sensitive SV40 virus. *In* "Methods in Enzymology" (L. Birnbaumer and B. W. O'Malley, eds.), Vol. 109, pp. 385–396. Academic Press, San Diego.
Freshney, R. L. (1987) "Culture of Animal Cells: A Manual of Basic Technique," 2nd ed., pp. 137–147. Wiley–Liss, New York.
Montpetit, M. L., and Tenniswood, M. P. (1989) Separation of mature rat ventral prostate epithelial and fibroblast cells. *Prostate* **15**, 315–325.
Rundlett, S. E., Gordon, D. A., and Miesfeld, R. L. (1992) Characterization of a panel of rat ventral prostate epithelial cell lines immortalized in the presence or absence of androgens. *Exp. Cell Res.* **203**, 214–221.

SECTION G

Cell Cycle Analysis

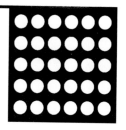

Cell Cycle Analysis by Flow Cytometry

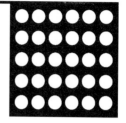

Zbigniew Darzynkiewicz

I. Introduction

A great variety of flow cytometric methods for cell cycle analysis have been developed during the past 25 years. These techniques can be grouped into three categories. The first comprises methods that rely on a single-time measurement of cell populations and provide no direct information on cell cycle kinetics. This analysis may be either univariate, based on measurement of DNA content alone (e.g., Crissman and Tobey, 1974), or multivariate, when another cell feature is measured in addition to DNA. The additional feature(s) provides information about a particular metabolic or molecular feature(s) of the cell that generally correlates with a rate of cell progression through the cycle or cell quiescence (review, Darzynkiewicz, 1990). Hence, although such measurements per se cannot reveal whether the cell actually progresses through the cycle or not, the kinetic information is inferred from the DNA content (cell cycle position) and from the metabolic or molecular profile of that cell.

In the second category are methods that combine time-lapse measurements of cells synchronized in the cycle prior to the study or whose progression through the cycle was perturbed, e.g., halted by the agent arresting them at a specific point of the cycle (*stathmokinesis*) (Darzynkiewicz *et al.*, 1987).

Methods in the third category rely on analysis of DNA replication in conjunction with DNA content measurements. In these methods, incorporation of the DNA replication marker 5′-bromo-2′-deoxyuridine (BrdUrd) is related to the position of the cell in the cycle. Incorporation of BrdUrd is detected either by cytochemical methods based on the use of the DNA dyes whose fluorescence is quenched by BrdUrd (e.g., Rabinovitch *et al.*, 1988) or after partial denaturation of DNA, by BrdUrd antibodies (e.g., Dolbeare *et al.*, 1983). The time-lapse measurements of the cohort of BrdUrd-labeled cells allow one to estimate their rate of progression through different points of the cell cycle. Direct information on cell cycle kinetics can thus be obtained with the use of methods in either the second or third category.

Only a few selected methods, representing examples from each category, are presented in this article. More detailed descriptions of these and other methods, their applicability to different cell systems, and their advantages and limitations are presented in several chapters of the methodology books (Gray and Darzynkiewicz, 1987; Darzynkiewicz and Crissman, 1990).

II. Materials and Instrumentation

The materials listed for each of the different procedures can be purchased from the following sources: Triton X-100 (Cat. No. X-100), Pipes (Cat. No. P 3768),

RNase A (Cat. No. R 5000), and 5-bromo-2'-deoxyuridine (BrdUrd, Cat. No. B 5002) from Sigma Chemical Company; DAPI 4',6'-diamidino-2-phenylindole (DAPI, Cat. No. D 1306), propidium iodide (PI, Cat. No. P-1304), and high-purity acridine orange (AO) (Cat. No. A-1301) from Molecular Probes; formaldehyde (methanol free, ultrapure generally used where the depolymerized paraformaldehyde is specified, Cat. No. 4018) from Polysciences Inc.

The greatest selection of monoclonal and polyclonal antibodies applicable to cell cycle analysis are offered by DAKO Corporation, Sigma Chemical Company, Upstate Biotechnology Incorporated, (UBI), and PharMingen.

A variety of flow cytometers from different makers can be used to measure cell fluorescence following staining according to the procedures listed below. The scope of this article does not allow description of these models. The manufacturers of the most common flow cytometers are Becton Dickinson Immunocytometry Systems, Coulter Corporation, and PARTEC GmbH.

The software to deconvolute the DNA content frequency histograms, to estimate the proportions of cells in the respective phases of the cycle, is available from Phoenix Flow Systems and Verity Software House.

III. Procedures

A. UNIVARIATE ANALYSIS OF CELLULAR DNA CONTENT

Progression through S phase and mitosis (cytokinesis) results in changes in cellular DNA content. The cell's position in the cycle can therefore be estimated on the basis of the DNA content measurement. A variety of fluorochromes and numerous methods are used for DNA content analysis. A simple protocol described below, which can be modified to accommodate different dyes, has been developed and applied to numerous cell types (Darzynkiewicz *et al.*, 1984).

1. Procedure of Cell Staining with DAPI

Solutions

1. Triton X-100, 0.1% (v/v, final concentration).
2. $MgCl_2$, 2 mM.
3. NaCl, 0.1 M.
4. Pipes buffer, 10 mM, pH 6.8.
5. DAPI, 1 μg/ml (2.85 μM).

Steps

1. Admix 0.2 ml of cell suspension (10^5–10^6 cells, either directly withdrawn from tissue culture or prefixed in suspension in 70% ethanol and then rinsed and suspended in buffered saline) with 2 ml of staining solution prepared as above.

2. Transfer sample to the flow cytometer and measure cell fluorescence. Maximum excitation of DAPI, bound to DNA, is at 359 nm, and emission, at 461 nm. Use a combination of appropriate dichroic mirrors and emission filters to measure cell fluorescence at 450–500 nm. For excitation, use the available UV light laser line at the wavelength nearest 359 nm. When a mercury arc lamp serves as the excitation source, use a UG1 excitation filter.

3. The data acquisition software of most flow cytometers/sorters allows one to record the fluorescence intensities (the integrated area of the electronic pulse

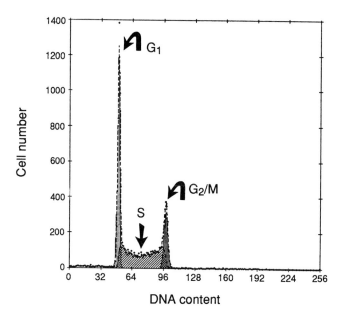

FIGURE 1 Frequency distribution–DNA content histogram of human leukemic HL-60 cells, stained with DAPI as described in the protocol. The "Multicycle" deconvolution program (Phoenix Flow Systems) has been used to identify subpopulations of G_1, S, and G_2/M cells, differing in DNA content, as shown.

signal) of 10^4 or more cells per sample. The data are presented as DNA content–frequency histograms (Fig. 1). The data analysis software packages (e.g., Bagwell, 1993) that deconvolute the frequency histograms either are included with the purchase of the flow cytometer or are commercially available from other vendors, as listed under Materials and Instrumentation. Such programs should be used to estimate the percentage of cells in $G_{0/1}$ (generally represented by the first peak on the histograms, which these programs integrate under the assumption of the Gaussian distribution), S and $G_2 + M$ (the second peak, Fig. 1).

2. Staining with Propidium Iodide

If excitation with UV light is not possible, the procedure given above for DAPI can be modified to apply PI as the DNA fluorochrome. To this end, instead of DAPI, PI is present in the staining solution at a concentration of 10 μg/ml. This solution also contains 20 units/ml of the DNase-free RNase A. The cells should be incubated in the staining solution for 30 min at room temperature, in the dark, prior to measurement.

Maximum excitation of PI, bound to DNA, is at 536 nm and emission is at 617 nm. Blue (488 nm) or green light lines of lasers are optimal for PI excitation. Emission is measured using the long-pass 610-nm filter. The data acquisition and analysis is as described above for DAPI-stained cells.

B. MULTIPARAMETER ANALYSIS

There are several methods that rely on multiparameter analysis that not only distinguish cells differing in their DNA content, but can also identify quiescent or mitotic cells. One such method is based on analysis of the sensitivity of DNA to denaturation which varies with cell progression through the cycle (Darzynkiewicz, 1990). Bivariate analysis of DNA content and the proliferation of associated antigens

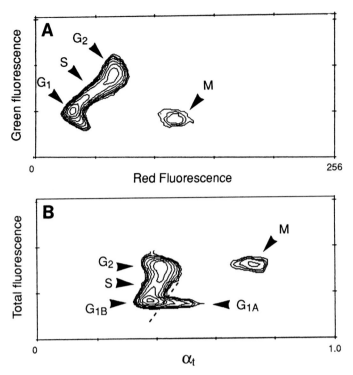

FIGURE 2 Bivariate analysis of red and green fluorescence of HL-60 cells stained with AO after incubation with RNase A and partial denaturation of DNA with 0.1 M HCl. The green fluorescence represents AO interactions with double-stranded DNA sections; the red fluorescence represents AO binding to denatured DNA. Cells in mitosis show higher red and lower green fluorescence than G_2 cells, indicative of more extensive DNA denaturation (A). When the data are expressed as total fluorescence (green + red; correlating with total DNA content) vs α_t (α_t = ratio of red to total fluorescence intensities), the latter representing the fraction of denatured DNA, the phases of the cell cycle, as shown in (B), can be distinguished with better clarity. The discrimination between early G_1, postmitotic cells (G_{1A}), still having condensed chromatin, and late G_1 cells (G_{1B}), with the most decondensed chromatin, is also apparent (broken line).

is another approach that makes it possible, e.g., to distinguish between proliferating and quiescent cells (Bauer, 1990; Celis *et al.*, 1984; Gerdes *et al.*, 1983).

1. Changes in Chromatin Condensation during the Cell Cycle Detected by DNA Denaturation

Nuclear chromatin undergoes condensation during the cell cycle. In mitosis the chromatin is maximally condensed, whereas the most decondensation is observed at the time of entrance to S phase (Bruno *et al.*, 1991). Chromatin of G_0 cells is also highly condensed, although less so than in mitosis. These changes in chromatin condensation are detected by altered DNA *in situ* sensitivity to denaturation. Analysis of DNA denaturability is done with the use of the metachromatic fluorochrome acridine orange, which differentially stains double-stranded vs denatured DNA (Fig. 2). After cell fixation and incubation with RNase, the cells are exposed to 0.1 M HCl to partially denature the DNA. The staining with AO is done at low pH to prevent DNA renaturation. The method allows discrimination between cells in G_0, G_1, S, and G_2 phases and in mitosis (Darzynkiewicz, 1990) (Fig. 2).

Solutions

1. *AO stock solution:* 1 mg AO dissolved in 1 ml of distilled water, and kept in dark at +4°C. AO of the highest purity should be used.

2. *Staining solution:* prepared by mixing 90 ml of 0.1 M citric acid with 10 ml of 0.2 M Na_2PO_4 and adding 0.6 ml of the AO stock solution (final AO concentration is 6 μg/ml, i.e., 20 μM; pH 2.6).

Steps

1. Fix cells in suspension in 70% ethanol for at least 2 hr.

2. Centrifuge cells at 300 g for 5 min. Resuspend cell pellet (10^6 to 2×10^6 cells) in 1 ml of Hanks' buffered salt solution (HBSS) and add 100 units of DNase-free RNase A.

3. Incubate at 37°C for 1 hr. Centrifuge and resuspend in 0.5 ml of HBSS.

4. Add 0.2 ml of this suspension to 0.5 ml of 0.1 M HCl, at room temperature.

5. After 30 sec add 2 ml of the staining solution, at room temperature.

6. Transfer the sample to the flow cytometer and measure cell fluorescence. Optimal excitation of AO is with blue light (488-nm laser line or BG 12 excitation filter). Measure the green fluorescence of AO, reflecting the interaction of this dye with double-stranded DNA, at a bandwidth between 515 and 545 nm. The red fluorescence, representing AO binding to denatured DNA, is measured with a long-pass filter above 640 nm.

7. The data can be transformed to represent total cell fluorescence (red + green) vs α_t, where total fluorescence is proportional to total DNA content in the cell and α_t is the fraction of denatured DNA, as shown in Fig. 2 (Darzynkiewicz, 1990). Some data analysis programs can be modified to allow this conversion. Software for the data conversion to α_t is also commercially available (Phoenix Flow Systems).

This method is very sensitive to variations in AO concentration, pH, and ionic strength, and therefore some instruments require adjustment of the AO concentration in the staining solution to compensate for dye diffusion from the sample to the sheath fluid (Darzynkiewicz, 1990). The assay is limited to cells that do not contain large amounts of glycosaminoglycans or keratins, inasmuch as these compounds also stain with AO. Because AO binds to the tubing of flow cytometers, which may adversely affect measurement of weak immunofluorescence in subsequent samples, rinsing with a bleaching solution followed by 70% ethanol and saline is advised.

2. Simultaneous Measurement of DNA and Individual Intracellular Proteins

The expression of various proteins often varies during the cell cycle, as well as in cycling and quiescent cells. The cellular content of such proteins therefore provides information on the proliferative status of the cell. Because antibodies against many such proteins are now commercially available, immunocytochemical detection of these proteins is possible. The most common markers of proliferating cells are: (a) the proliferating cell nuclear antigen (PCNA) (Celis *et al.,* 1984; see also article by Julio E. Celis and Peder Madsen in this volume), the antigen detected by Ki-67 antibody (Gerdes *et al.,* 1983), and (c) p120 nucleolar antigen (Freeman *et al.,* 1991; see Fig. 3).

Methods for detection of the proliferation-associated proteins and, in particular, the choice of optimal fixative vary depending on the particular antigen (Bauer, 1990). The method described below, with minor modifications, has been applied to several antigens (e.g., Bruno *et al.,* 1991).

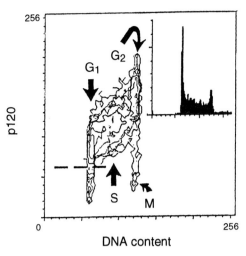

FIGURE 3 Bivariate analysis of the expression of the proliferation-associated nucleolar p120 antigen (Freeman *et al.*, 1991) and DNA content in human leukemic MOLT-4 cells. A decrease in p120 is apparent during transition from G_1 to M, and early G_1—postmitotic—cells (below the broken line) have decreased p120 compared with late G_1 cells. A DNA frequency histogram of these cells is shown in the inset.

Solutions

1. *Fixative:* 0.5% formaldehyde in Hanks' buffered salt solution (HBSS), pH 7.4.
2. *Rinsing solution:* 0.1% Triton X-100, 0.5% bovine serum albumin, and 0.1% sodium azide in HBSS.

Steps

1. Fix in suspension 1×10^6 to 2×10^6 cells in 1 ml of the formaldehyde fixative for 15 min, on ice. Add 5 ml of ice-cold HBSS. Spin at 400 *g* for 5 min.

2. Resuspend cells in 5 ml of the rinsing solution, and keep on ice for 5 min. Centrifuge.

3. Resuspend cell pellet in 100 μl of the rinsing solution that contains the primary antibody. Follow instructions supplied by the vendor regarding the final titer of the supplied antibody (the range 1:40 to 1:100 is often recommended). Incubate 30–60 min at room temperature with gentle agitation. Add 2 ml of rinsing solution. Centrifuge.

4. Use the isotype immunoglobulin as a negative control. Process exactly as in step 3.

5. Resuspend cells in 100 μl of rinsing solution that contains the fluoresceinated secondary antibody, generally at a final 1:20 to 1:40 dilution. Incubate at room temperature for 1 hr with gentle agitation. Centrifuge.

6. Resuspend cells in 1 ml HBSS containing 5 μg/ml of PI and 20 units of RNase A. Keep in the dark at room temperature for 1 hr. Use excitation with blue light (488 nm) and measure cell fluorescence in green (FITC, 530 ± 15 nm) and red (PI, >620 nm) wavelengths.

C. ANALYSIS OF CELL CYCLE KINETICS

1. Stathmokinetic Approach

In a classical stathmokinetic experiment the agent arresting cells in mitosis (e.g., colcemid or vinblastine) is added into the culture during the exponential phase of cell growth and the proportion of cells in mitosis is estimated as a function of the time of arrest. The slope of the plot of the accumulation of cells in mitosis during stathmokinesis reveals the rate of cell entry into mitosis ("mitotic rate," "cell birth rate").

Flow cytometric analysis of the stathmokinetic experiment can be based either on quantification of the increased proportions of cells in $G_2 + M$ (by DNA content measurement and univariate data analysis) or by enumeration of cells in M (by selective staining of M cells, e.g., as shown in Fig. 4, and multivariate analysis of such data). Depletion of the G_1 compartment, as well as the rate of cell progression through S phase, can also be measured during stathmokinesis (Darzynkiewicz *et al.*, 1987). The scheme of a simple stathmokinetic *in vitro* experiment is described next.

Solutions

Depending on the method used to stain DNA, appropriate solutions, e.g., as described in procedures listed above, should be applied.

Steps

1. To the exponentially and asynchronously growing cell culture add the stathmokinetic agent (e.g., colcemid, vinblastine, or nocodazole) at the concentration that arrests all cells entering mitosis and yet does not perturb the progression through other phases. Different cell types show different sensitivities to particular agents and pilot experiments testing different concentrations of the agents are often needed to estimate the efficiency of the cell arrest.

2. Collect cells hourly, during a time interval equivalent to approximately one-third of the cell doubling time, and fix them in suspension.

3. Use either the flow cytometric staining techniques that allow identification of cells in G_1, S, and $G_2 + M$ (e.g., as in Fig. 1), or multiparameter analysis, which allows one to distinguish M cells (e.g., as in Fig. 2).

4. Use the data analysis programs that allow quantitation of the percentages of cells in the respective phases of the cycle, per each sample.

5. Plot the data as in Fig. 4. From the graphic display estimate the cell cycle parameters, as shown in this figure. A more extensive analysis of the stathmokinetic experiment has been presented before (Darzynkiewicz *et al.*, 1987).

2. BrdUrd Incorporation

Incubation of cells in medium containing BrdUrd results in incorporation of this analog in place of thymidine during DNA replication (S phase). The incorporated BrdUrd can be detected either cytochemically, by virtue of its propensity to quench the fluorescence of several DNA fluorochromes such as Hoechst 33358 and acridine orange (Latt, 1977), or immunocytochemically, using poly- or monoclonal antibodies developed against this precursor (Fig. 5) (see also article by Julio E. Celis and Peder Madsen in this volume).

Continuous or pulse–chase cell labeling with BrdUrd, followed by detection of BrdUrd simultaneously with measurement of cellular DNA content and bivariate data analysis (Dolbeare *et al.*, 1983), allows one to estimate a variety of cell cycle parameters. The protocol of Dolbeare *et al.* (1983), modified by Moran *et al.* (1985), to dissociate histones by HCl prior to DNA denaturation and use low-ionic-strength buffer for DNA denaturation by heat is given below. DNA denaturation by acid (HCl) gives more satisfactory results in some cell types.

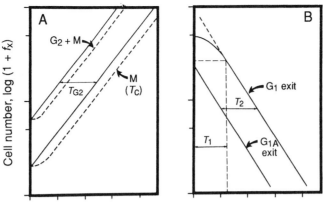

Time of stathmokinesis (hr)

FIGURE 4 Scheme of analysis of the stathmokinetic experiment. The asynchronously and exponentially growing cell cultures are treated with a metaphase-arresting, stathmokinetic agent and subsequently sampled and analyzed to obtain the percentages of cells in the respective phases of the cell cycle (e.g., as in Fig. 2). The percentages of cells in the respective phases (expressed as fraction of total, f_x), at a given time point of mitotic arrest, are then plotted as $\log(1 + f_x)$. The rate of entrance to M (or G_2 + M slope) reveals the duration of the cell cycle (T_c). The duration of G_2 (T_{G_2}) is estimated as the time–distance of the G_2 + M vs M slopes (A). After administration of the stathmokinetic agent, the M arrest is generally delayed (A, broken line). Because the stathmokinetic agent prevents cell entrance to G_1, the rates of cell exit from G_1 can also be estimated (B). The stochastic component of the rate of cell exit from G_1 manifests as the straight slope and is expressed as the half-life of cell residence in G_1 or in G_{1A}, whereas duration of the nonstochastic component of G_1 is represented by T_1 or T_2 (Darzynkiewicz et al., 1987).

a. Thermal denaturation of DNA

Solutions

1. *DNA denaturation buffer:* 0.1 mM Na-EDTA in 1 mM Na-cacodylate; final pH 6.0

2. *Diluting buffer:* Hanks' buffered salt solution (HBSS) containing 0.1% Triton X-100 and 0.5% bovine serum albumin (BSA).

Steps

1. Incubate cells with 10–30 μg/ml BrdUrd under lightproof conditions.

2. Fix cells in suspension in 70% ethanol.

3. Centrifuge cells (1–2 × 10^6) at 300 g for 5 min, resuspend cell pellet in 1 ml of diluting buffer containing 100 units of RNase A, and incubate at 37°C for 30 min.

4. Centrifuge cells (400 g, 5 min) and suspend cell pellet in 1 ml of ice-cold 0.1 M HCl containing 0.1% Triton X-100. After 1 min centrifuge cells again. Drain thoroughly and resuspend in 5 ml of DNA denaturation buffer.

5. Centrifuge cells again, and resuspend cell pellet in 1 ml of DNA denaturation buffer.

6. Heat cells at 90 or 95°C for 5 min; then place on ice for 5 min. Add 5 ml of diluting buffer. Centrifuge.

7. Drain well; suspend cells in 100 μl of anti BrdUrd, dissolved in dilution buffer, for 30 min at room temperature (follow the instructions provided by the supplier regarding the dilution, time, and temperature of incubation with anti-BrdUrd).

8. Add 5 ml of dilution buffer, centrifuge.

9. Suspend in 100 μl of goat anti-mouse IgG labeled with fluorescein (dissolved in dilution buffer); incubate 30 min at room temperature.

10. Add 5 ml of diluting buffer, centrifuge, drain, and resuspend in 1 ml of this buffer containing 5 μg/ml of PI.

11. Measure BrdUrd-associated green fluorescence and DNA-associated red fluorescence as described above in Procedure C2.

b. Denaturation of DNA by HCl

Solutions

1. *Diluting buffer:* same as for thermal denaturation of DNA (see Procedure C2a).

Steps

1. Follow steps 1–3 as described above for thermal denaturation of DNA.

2. Centrifuge cells (400 g, 5 min), and resuspend cell pellet in 1 ml of 2 M HCl. After 20 min at room temperature add 5 ml of HBSS, centrifuge, and drain well. Resuspend cells in 5 ml of 0.2 M phosphate buffer at pH 7.4, to neutralize traces of the remaining HCl.

3. Follow steps 7–11 as described above for thermal denaturation of DNA (see Procedure C2a).

The scope of this article makes it impossible to describe all the possibilities of analysis of a variety of the cell cycle parameters based on BrdUrd incorporation,

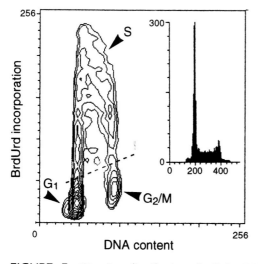

FIGURE 5   Bivariate distribution of cellular DNA content and BrdUrd incorporation. HL-60 cells were incubated with BrdUrd for 30 min and fixed, DNA was denatured by acid, the incorporated BrdUrd was detected by the monoclonal antibody (Becton Dickinson), and DNA was counterstained with PI, as described in the procedure.

after either the pulse–chase or continuous cell labeling. The readers are advised to consult Gray *et al.* (1990) and Crissman and Steinkamp (1990) for a more detailed description of these methods.

IV. Comments

Each of the described methods yields a different degree of information on the cell cycle. Choice of the method should therefore be dictated primarily by the need to learn particular details of cell cycle kinetics. Univariate DNA content analysis provides estimates of cell percentages in $G_{0/1}$, S, and $G_2 + M$ and, when combined with measurements of cell proliferation rates (doubling times) and growth fraction, may reveal the durations of these phases. Bivariate or multivariate analyses, by taking into account, in addition to DNA content, the presence of other cell constituents or metabolic differences, allow one to discriminate between G_2 and M or G_1 and G_0 cells. It is expected that methods based on detection of the proliferation-associated cell cycle phase-specific proteins (e.g., cyclin E or B, DNA polymerase α), by virtue of providing information about expression of these proteins, will be increasingly used as an adjunct to DNA content measurement in standard assays of the cell cycle. Most kinetic information is available from assays based on stathmokinesis or BrdUrd incorporation. These latter techniques are especially suitable to study cells *in vitro* and investigate perturbation of the cell cycle induced by drugs or physical factors.

V. Pitfalls

1. Each approach has different types of limitations and possible pitfalls. As mentioned, the univariate DNA content measurements, unless combined with analysis of cell growth curves, do not reveal cell kinetics. The kinetics is generally inferred from the fraction of cells in S, G_2, and M phases, under the assumption that all cells do progress through the cell cycle and that length of G_1 is variable while durations of S, G_2, and M are relatively constant. The cells can, however, be "frozen" in the cycle, e.g., when treated with a drug that arrests them in all phases of the cycle at the same time, and thus be indistinguishable from proliferating cells. The most frequent pitfall of most methods is inaccurate measurement of DNA content. The most common cause of this is inappropriate adjustment of optics and/or fluidics of the flow cytometer. The accuracy of measurements is generally expressed as a coefficient of variation (CV) of the mean value of the fluorescence of uniform population, e.g., as of DNA content of G_1 cells. The results are unacceptable if the CV of the mean value of DNA of G_1 population is larger than 7–8%; ideally it should be below 2%.

2. A common pitfall in the analysis of proliferation-associated antigens is inappropriate cell fixation. The formaldehyde fixation, as presently described, is optimal in the case of some antigens, whereas other antigens require a mixture of ethanol and acetone, methanol, etc. Pilot experiments, testing different fixatives and different means of cell permeabilization, should be performed in the case of each new antigen. Many monoclonal antibodies commercially available have been developed to proteins in a denatured state and are useful for immunoprecipitation or Western blotting, but may not be used for immunocytochemistry.

3. In the case of BrdUrd techniques, the unpredictable variable that affects cell stainability is variation in chromatin structure between different cell types. Hence, the methods should often be optimized for a particular cell type by testing different temperatures of DNA denaturation (80–100°C) or different strengths of HCl used to induce DNA denaturation (1–4 M).

ACKNOWLEDGMENT

This work was supported by NCI Grant RO1 96704.

REFERENCES

Bagwell, C. B. (1993) Theoretical aspects of flow cytometry data analysis. *In* "Clinical Flow Cytometry. Principles and Application" (K. D. Bauer, R. E. Duque, and V. T. Shankey, eds.), pp. 41–61. Williams & Wilkins, Baltimore.

Bauer, K. D. (1990) Analysis of proliferation associated antigens. *In* "Flow Cytometry" (Z. Darzynkiewicz and H. A. Crissman, eds.), pp. 235–247. Academic Press, San Diego.

Bruno, S., Crissman, H. A., Bauer, K. D., and Darzynkiewicz, Z. (1991) Changes in cell nuclei during S phase: Progressive chromatin condensation and altered expression of the proliferation-associated nuclear proteins Ki-67, Cyclin (PCNA), p105 and p34. *Exp. Cell Res.* **196,** 99–106.

Celis, J. E., Bravo, R., Larsen, P. M., and Fey, S. J. (1984) Cyclin: A nuclear protein whose level correlates directly with proliferative state of normal as well as transformed cells. *Leukemia Res.* **8,** 143–157.

Crissman, H. A., and Steinkamp, J. A. (1990) Cytochemical techniques for multivariate analysis of DNA and other cellular constituents. *In* "Flow Cytometry and Sorting" (M. R. Melamed., T. Lindmo, and M. L. Mendelsohn, eds.), pp. 227–247. Wiley–Liss, New York.

Crissman, H. A., and Tobey, R. A. (1974) Cell cycle analysis in 20 minutes. *Science* **184,** 1297–1298.

Darzynkiewicz, Z. (1990) Probing nuclear chromatin by flow cytometry. *In* "Flow Cytometry and Sorting" (M. R. Melamed., T. Lindmo, and M. L. Mendelsohn, eds.), pp. 315–340. Wiley–Liss, New York.

Darzynkiewicz, Z., and Crissman, H. A. (eds.) (1990) "Flow Cytometry." Academic Press, San Diego.

Darzynkiewicz, Z., Traganos, F., and Kimmel, M. (1987) Assay of cell cycle kinetics by multivariate flow cytometry using the principle of stathmokinesis. *In* "Techniques in Cell Cycle Analysis" (J. W. Gray and Z. Darzynkiewicz, eds.), pp. 291–336. Humana Press, Clifton, N.J.

Darzynkiewicz, Z., Williamson, B., Carswell, E. A., and Old, L. J. (1984) Cell cycle-specific effects of tumor necrosis factor. *Cancer Res.* **44,** 83–90.

Dolbeare, F., Gratzner, H., Pallavicini, M., and Gray, J. W. (1983) Flow cytometric measurements of total DNA content and incorporated bromodeoxyuridine. *Proc. Natl. Acad. Sci. USA* **80,** 5573–5577.

Freeman, J. W., McGrath, P., Bonada, V., Selliah, N., Ownby, M., Maloney, T., Busch, R. K., and Busch, H. (1991) Prognostic significance of proliferation associated nucleolar antigen p120 in human breast carcinoma. *Cancer Res.* **51,** 1973–1978.

Gerdes, J., Schwab, U., Lemke, H., and Stein, H. (1983) Production of a mouse monoclonal antibody reactive with human nuclear antigen associated with cell proliferation. *Int. J. Cancer* **31,** 13–20.

Gray, J. W., and Darzynkiewicz, Z. (eds.) (1987) "Techniques in Cell Cycle Analysis." Humana Press, Clifton, N.J.

Gray, J. W., Dolbeare, F., and Pallavicini, M. G. (1990) Quantitative cell cycle analysis. *In* "Flow Cytometry and Sorting" (M. R. Melamed, T. Lindmo, and M. L. Mendelsohn, eds.), pp. 445–467. Wiley–Liss, New York.

Latt, S. A. (1977) Fluorometric detection of deoxyribonucleic acid synthesis: Possibilities for interfacing bromodeoxyuridine dye techniques with flow fluorometry. *J. Histochem. Cytochem.* **25,** 915–926.

Moran, R., Darzynkiewicz, Z., Staiano-Coico, L., and Melamed, M. R. (1985) Detection of BrdUrd incorporation by monoclonal antibodies: Role of DNA denaturation step. *J. Histochem. Cytochem.* **33,** 821–827.

Rabinovitch, P. S., Kubbies, M., Chen, Y. C., Schindler, D., and Hoehn, H. (1988) BrdU-Hoechst flow cytometry: A unique tool for quantitative cell cycle analysis. *Exp. Cell Res.* **174,** 309–318.

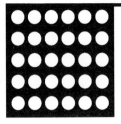

Preparation of Synchronous Populations of Mammalian Cells in Specific Phases of the Cell Cycle by Centrifugal Elutriation

R. Curtis Bird, Shiawhwa Su, and Gin Wu

I. Introduction

Centrifugal elutriation is the only method whereby large numbers of cells can be rapidly separated on the basis of size (Diamond, 1991). This method combines the ability to separate cells into sequential cell cycle phase populations of relatively high purity without the use of drugs or inhibitors (Bludau *et al.,* 1986; Braunstein *et al.,* 1982; Hann *et al.,* 1985; Iqbal *et al.,* 1984; Wu *et al.,* 1993; Brown and Schildkraut, 1979). The purity of the samples is relatively high and the cells proceed to grow, following separation, without a detectable lag period. Thus, centrifugal elutriation combines speed of separation of large numbers of cells with little or no perturbation of the cell growth cycle and avoids the use of agents that might induce artifact. As additional advantages centrifugal elutriation overcomes the limits on cell number imposed by fluorescence-activated cell sorting, the long separation times required for unit gravity sedimentation, as well as problems associated with osmotic stress in centrifugation media. The only real compromise is that the purity of the samples is somewhat lower than commonly achieved with alternative methods. The developmental history and theory of centrifugal elutriation have recently been reviewed (Conkie, 1985).

Synchronous fractions were analyzed, following elutriation, by flow cytometry and [^{3}H]thymidine incorporation (Wu *et al.,* 1993; Pai and Bird, 1994). Both means of analysis demonstrated that sequential fractions of elutriated cells represent sequential cell cycle phases as determined by analysis of cell volume, DNA content, and ability to incorporate thymidine during five sequential 1-hr periods following return to culture. From this analysis, cells collected at flow rates of 21–25 ml/min were designated the G_1-phase population, cells collected at flow rates of 29–35 ml/min were designated the S-phase population, and cells collected at flow rates of 43 ml/min were designated the G_2/M-phase population. Flow cytometric analysis, based on measurements of DNA content and cell volume, were also used to determine the levels of contamination of S-phase cells in the G_1-phase fractions (approximately 3%) and of G_1-phase cells in the S-phase cell population (approximately 10%) (Hann *et al.,* 1985). Thus, large populations of cells were rapidly separated into seven or eight synchronous fractions without the use of drugs and with low levels of contaminating cells.

II. Materials and Instrumentation

The centrifugal elutriator was obtained from Beckman Instruments (elutriator rotor assembly, Cat. No. JE-6B, was run in a Model J2-21 elutriation centrifuge). Accessories specified by the manufacturer were used throughout and the rotor was equipped with a standard separation chamber. A Masterflex digital peristaltic pump (Model 7523 fitted with a Model 7014-21 pump head, Cole–Parmer) was used to pump cells and media through the rotor.

Materials for cell culture included the α modification of Eagle's minimal essential growth medium (α-MEM, ICN Flow, Cat. No. 10-311-22), fetal bovine serum (FBS, Intergen, Cat. No. 1020-90), donor horse serum (DHS, ICN Flow, Cat. No. 29-211-49), 100× antibiotic/antimycotic solution (Gibco/BRL, Cat. No. 600-5240AG), 10× trypsin (Gibco/BRL, Cat. No. 610-5090), and Hanks' balanced salt solution (Sigma, Cat. No. H-8389). All plasticware was tissue culture grade (Corning Plasticware, Fisher Scientific). All other reagents were standard reagent grade and available from numerous sources. The water used throughout this procedure was ultrapure in quality and was prepared by ion-exchange chromatography (Barnstead Nanopure) to 18-MΩ resistance and then glass distilled to remove residual endotoxin and RNase activity. Solutions were sterilized by autoclaving or ultrafiltration (0.2 μm).

III. Procedures

A. CELL CULTURE

In this procedure the growth medium and elutriation medium were developed from standard protocols for the growth of HeLa cells (Pai and Bird, 1992). If different cell lines are employed, appropriate media should be substituted (see **Pitfalls**).

Solutions

1. *Growth and Elutriation Media:* Powdered α-MEM (10-liter pack) was dissolved in ultrapure water with 1× antibiotics and 22 g NaHCO$_3$ and made up to 10 liters. The medium was placed in a pressurizable vessel, filtered through a 0.2-μm filter (Millipore) by positive pressure into sterile 0.5-liter bottles, and stored at 4°C. Prior to use, FBS (10% v/v) was added to make growth medium or DHS (5% v/v) was added to make elutriation medium. Use of DHS greatly reduced the cost of elutriation without detectable effects on cell growth or quality of the fractionation (see **Pitfalls**).

2. 0.5 *M* Hepes: Dissolve 14.17 g Hepes buffer (Fisher, Cat No. BP310-100) in ~80 ml water and adjust pH to 7.2. Adjust volume to 100 ml, filter-sterilize, and store in the cold.

3. 0.5 *M* Na$_2$ EDTA: Begin to dissolve 14.61 g EDTA-free acid (Sigma, Cat. No. E-9884) in ~40 ml water with a magnetic stirrer. Monitor pH of the solution continuously while slowly adding 1 *M* NaOH (40 g/liter for 1 *M* stock) dropwise. Continue to adjust the pH up to ~8.0. As the EDTA dissolves, the pH will continue to fall. Carefully adjust the final pH to 8.0. Adjust volume to 100 ml, filter-sterilize, and store in the cold.

4. *Trypsin solution:* Add 8 ml of 2.5% trypsin stock solution (10×), 2 ml 0.5 *M* Hepes, pH 7.2, and 2 ml 0.5 *M* Na$_2$EDTA, pH 8.0, to a 100-ml bottle of

Hanks' salt solution. Make additions from sterile stock solutions maintaining sterility. Store in the cold.

5. 70% Ethanol: Combine 700 ml absolute (not denatured) ethanol with 300 ml water. Store in 0.5-liter bottles at room temperature.

Steps

1. Cultured HeLa S3 cells were grown in 20 ml of modified Eagle's α-MEM medium (Flow Laboratories) with 10% FBS and antibiotics in 15-cm-diameter culture plates at 37°C with 5% CO_2 and 100% humidity (Pai and Bird, 1992).

2. Collect cells at 60–70% confluence by trypsin digestion.

3. Concentrate cells by low-speed *centrifugation* (3000 g for 5 min) at 4°C and resuspend in 5 ml of ice cold α-MEM with 5% DHS for every 3 plates (15 cm). This medium is used throughout the elutriation procedure. Maintain the cells on ice until they are loaded into the elutriator. Harvest just before the rotor is filled with medium.

B. ELUTRIATION

Steps

1. Arrange the elutriation system as described in the schematic diagram (Fig. 1A). Assemble the elutriator rotor according to the manufacturer's directions (Fig. 1B). Lightly lubricate each O-ring, which seals the rotating assembly on top of the rotor, with silicone grease, taking care to wipe off any excess. Place lower washer and spring on top of the rotor followed by the outer ring and rotating seal. Note that the screw threads on the top assembly are reversed. Lightly tighten the top and check that the outer ring spins freely. Tighten the side-set screw and repeat the check for a freely spinning assembly. Loosen the lower washer inside the outer ring, half a turn. Check that the assembly spins freely, retighten the lower washer, and check that it spins freely again. Take care to ensure that the rotating seal connecting the rotor to the fluid lines is freshly cleaned and polished with the scintered glass plate and polishing paper provided. Only a lint-free tissue with an appropriate solvent (e.g., $CHCl_3$) should be used as even a small speck of lint can cause leakage. A *very thin* layer of silicone grease can be applied to the upper edge of the rotating seal to help create a good seal but all excess silicone must be removed. Stick the seal to the polypropylene disk on the bottom surface of the top of the seal assembly by gently seating the silicone on the seal with a half-turn. Carefully screw the top of the seal assembly onto the outer ring (note reverse threads) and hand tighten. This connection should not leak more than 1–3 ml during a normal elutriation run of <1 hr. Even very small leaks encountered at low initial flow rates can result in significant loss of fluid and cells toward the end of the run as the flow rate rises. If persistent leaks are encountered, reexamine the seal and check for a perfectly clean and even surface on both edges. If none of these measures adequately seals the rotor connections, replace the seal.

2. Assemble the elutriator chamber according to the manufacturer's directions (Fig. 1B). Ensure that both halves of the chamber are perfectly clean and that the polypropylene gasket is positioned to allow alignment of the sample tube. Tighten the screws to assemble but do not overtighten. Lightly lubricate both O-rings, on the base of the chamber assembly, with silicone grease, taking care to wipe off any excess. Insert the chamber and align the base pin and sample tube connections. Secure it in place with the metal plug. The screw threads on the plug

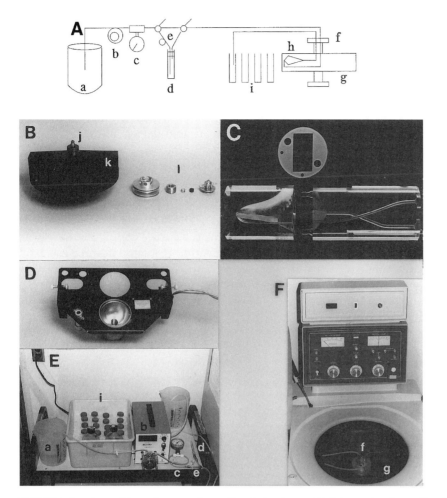

FIGURE 1 Assembly and setup of centrifugal elutriator. (A) Schematic of centrifugal elutriator. Elutriation medium is pumped from the reservoir beaker (a), by the peristaltic pump (b), through the pressure gauge (c), and the sample tube (d), or the bypass harness (e), through the rotating seal (f), and into the rotor (g). The sample is separated in the elutriation chamber (h) and pumped back to the sample collection tubes on ice (i). (B) Rotor and rotating seal assembly including O-rings on top of the rotor (j) which seal the rotating assembly to the rotor, the elutriation chamber (k), and from left to right, the outer ring, lower washer, spring that is placed inside the lower washer, rotating seal, and top of seal assembly (l). (C) Elutriation chamber showing left (outer) and right (inner) halves separated by the gasket (above). Note the actual separation chamber within the left side and the set screws and alignment pin extending beyond both edges of the right side of the chamber. (D) Strobe assembly located below the rotor. (E) Elutriation setup showing the reservoir beaker (a), peristaltic pump (b), pressure gauge (c), sample tube (d), bypass harness (e), and sample collection tubes (i). Note the positions of beakers to supply/accept media. (F) Elutriation centrifuge showing the complete rotating seal assembly (f) and elutriation rotor (g), with strobe wires/waste tubing extending through the right centrifuge wall and inlet/outlet tubing extending through the left centrifuge wall.

should be lubricated with Spincoat (Beckman) provided with the elutriator. Tighten with the tool provided but do not overtighten as the O-rings can be crushed.

3. Assemble the elutriator centrifuge according to the manufacturer's directions (Fig. 1C). Remove the high-speed rotor (if present) and wipe out any moisture in the centrifuge chamber. Install the strobe assembly in the centrifuge chamber and secure with thumb screws while ensuring it is centered over the rotor spindle in

the center (Fig. 1D). Feed both wire connections through the ports on the right side of the centrifuge chamber and secure them with the metal plate. Carefully place the rotor on the spindle in the center of the centrifuge and ensure that it spins freely. Connect the three pieces of silicone tubing to the rotor (inlet, outlet, and overflow) and feed them through the appropriate port (inlet and outlet to the left, overflow to the right with the wires). Ensure all are pulled tight enough so that none have any slack in them but not so tight as to pinch or pull off any of the connections. The overflow tube should wrap around the top of the seal assembly and pass under the inlet port (the upper of the two ports on the sides of the top of the seal assembly). Seal each of the ports around each tube and wire with a slit stopper, where they pass through the centrifuge chamber wall, to ensure good vacuum.

4. Prepare a large ice bucket containing two 0.5-liter bottles of elutriation medium, 30 sterile capped tubes (50 ml), and the cell suspension. Place the bucket on a cart or table next to the centrifuge with the pump and three 2-liter beakers one of which contains 1 liter of sterile water. Include a 20-ml syringe with an 18-gauge needle and the sample injection harness with a pressure gauge (Cole-Parmer, Cat. No. L-07380-75, Fig. 1E). If sterile samples are to be collected, an additional beaker of 70% ethanol and a bottle of sterile water must also be included. A sterile hood must be positioned next to the centrifuge to allow both reservoir beakers and samples to be collected under sterile conditions.

5. Clean the exterior of the silicone tubing with ethanol and place the inlet in the beaker containing the sterile water and the outlet in the empty beaker. The inlet tubing should also be installed into the pump head and attached to the sample application and bypass harness, with an inline pressure gauge, so that they are between the pump and the rotor (Fig. 1E). Begin pumping water through the rotor (which is stationary and the centrifuge is off, see **Pitfalls**) at 45 ml/min (>200 ml). Carefully observe the water as it fills the equipment (~100 ml) and dislodge any bubbles with gentle pressure on the tubing or tapping of other components. Release the air from dead spaces within the pressure gauge by pinching the tubing just after the gauge and rapidly releasing it. Do not let the pressure rise above 15 psi or tubing may burst. Adjust the stopcocks on the sample/bypass harness to allow the harness and sample tube to completely fill. Continue to pump water through the equipment until all bubbles have been cleared. Observe all connections, particularly at the rotor, for leaks.

6. Close the centrifuge door and start the rotor. Allow the speed to gradually rise and stabilize at 2000 rpm (±1 rpm is acceptable) at 4°C. Be sure to increase the speed slowly. Check each of the stoppers to ensure the seals are adequate to allow development of a vacuum in the centrifuge. Observe the chamber through the periscope and adjust the strobe firing timer to center the image. If the chamber appears to have a rod running along the center rather than two screws running near each edge, then the strobe is 180° out of phase with the rotor and is allowing visualization of the balance chamber. Continue to adjust the strobe until the chamber is visible. Check for bubbles at the outlet using the squeeze-and-release technique. Turn off the pump. If a slow leak occurs, the fluid will be drawn back up into the tube as the fluid leaks out of the system. The system is sealed if the fluid level in the outlet tube does not change.

7. If sterile collection is required, switch to 70% ethanol and pump 200 ml through the rotor followed by 200 ml of sterile water from a bottle in the laminar flow hood. Switch to elutriation medium (without DHS) on ice and pump 200 ml (if sterile collection is not required omit ethanol rinse). Be sure to include all sections of the sample injection harness, including the sample tube and the stopcocks, during the rinse with each of these solutions. Turn off the pump

before switching the stopcocks. Turn the pump off and change to elutriation medium with 5% DHS to prevent the cells from sticking. Pump 100 ml at 45 ml/min through the sample tube. At this point, two people are required to operate the system: one collects samples and one monitors rotor and pump speed as well as sample injection.

8. Disperse the trypsinized cells ($1-2 \times 10^8$), which have been held on ice in 5 ml of elutriation medium (containing 5% DHS), with seven gentle passes through an 18-gauge needle on a 20-ml syringe. Be careful not to introduce bubbles. Turn off the pump. Gently inject the cells into the sample tube (stopper up), allowing the cells to settle to the bottom. Turn the tube over and *gently* inject about 2 ml of air to act as a shock absorber against the pulsing peristaltic action of the pump. Adjust the pump, which is still off, to zero and then turn the pump on. Gradually adjust the pump up to 10 ml/min, being careful not to overshoot this value. Observe the sample tube and watch the cells enter the system. Take care to avoid pulsing of the medium or any residual pools of cells in the sample tube. Collect three tubes of 50 ml each in the sample collection tubes on ice. Once loaded, the harness can be set on the bench in a stable position which maintains the inverted orientation of the sample tube (stopper down). Carefully increase the pump speed to 15 ml/min. Do not overshoot. We collect G_1-phase cells between 21 and 25 ml/min, S-phase cells at 29–35 ml/min, and G_2/M-phase cells at 43 ml/min. Be prepared to work quickly at the end of an elutriation run as the flow rate becomes very fast and tubes containing elutriated cells fill at the rate of approximately one every minute. Following elutriation pellet the cells by centrifugation (3000 *g*, 5 min) and resuspend in growth medium. Adjust cell density with additional growth medium, after counting in a hemocytometer, and transfer to tissue culture dishes.

C. CELL CYCLE ANALYSIS

Parts of the synchronous cell fractions are fixed and analyzed by flow cytometry and the remaining cells are immediately prepared for RNA isolation or placed back into culture. Cultured cells are analyzed for their ability to synchronously enter S phase by determining the kinetics of [^{3}H]thymidine incorporation.

Solutions

1. *Phosphate buffered saline (PBS)*: Dissolve 0.71 g of Na_2HPO_4 (0.01 *M* final, Sigma, Cat. No. S-0876) and 4.5 g NaCl (0.9% w/v final) in ~400 ml water and adjust pH to 7.6. Adjust volume to 500 ml, filter-sterilize, and store in the cold.

2. *Staining solution*: Make 50 μg/ml propidium iodide and 40 μg/ml RNase A by diluting stock solutions. Add 111 μl PI stock (4.5 mg/ml, Sigma, Cat. No. P-4170) and 20 μl RNase A stock (20 mg/ml, Sigma, Cat. No. R-5125) to 10 ml water. Do not attempt to weigh RNase as any contamination of the laboratory will make future isolation of RNA very difficult. Open a 250-mg bottle in the fume hood and add 12.5 ml water. Cap and dissolve. Aliquot with a disposable pipette (tissue culture type) in 1-ml lots in microcentrifuge tubes. Store at $-20°C$. Use only disposable tubes and pipettes with RNase solutions and avoid any contamination or aerosols. Dissolve 100 mg of PI in 22.22 ml of water directly in the bottle. Do not weigh out. PI is extremely toxic and should be handled with care including the use of gloves. Be careful not to create aerosols or liberate dust from granular reagent. Dispose of all PI solutions and contaminated materials as hazardous waste. Use only disposable tubes and pipettes. Store PI at $-20°C$ in the dark as it is light sensitive.

3. *100% Trichloroacetic acid:* To a 500-g bottle of trichloroacetic acid (TCA, Sigma, Cat No. T-4885) add sufficient water to bring the volume in the bottle to approximately the shoulder. Add a stir bar, cap the bottle, and stir to dissolve the contents. Carefully adjust the volume to 500 ml. TCA is extremely caustic. Do not attempt to measure or weigh TCA granules. Use caution when pipetting the solution. TCA 100% is very stable when stored in the cold. Dilutions should be freshly prepared from the stock daily. Store dilutions on ice while in use and dispose of unused portions.

4. *[³H]Thymidine growth medium:* Add 10 μCi/ml [³H]thymidine (1 μCi/μl stock, Du Pont NEN, Cat. No. NET-027Z) directly to growth medium under sterile conditions at the rate of 10 μl/ml of medium. Prepare fresh only what is required daily.

5. *1.0 M Tris buffer:* Dissolve 60.55 g Tris buffer (Sigma, Cat No. T-8524) in ~400 ml water and adjust pH to 7.6. Adjust volume to 500 ml, filter-sterilize, and store in the cold.

6. *20% Sodium dodecyl sulfate:* Dissolve 20 g sodium dodecyl sulfate (SDS, Sigma, Cat. No. L-3771) in sterile water using a sterile beaker and a stir bar rinsed in ethanol. Adjust final volume to 100 ml. SDS cannot be autoclaved or filtered. Store at room temperature.

7. *TES buffer:* Add 10 mM Tris–HCl, pH 7.6 (1 ml of 1 M stock), 1 mM EDTA, pH 8.0 (0.5 ml of 0.5 M stock), and 1% SDS (5 ml of 20% stock) to 93.5 ml water, filter, and store at room temperature.

8. *4% Paraformaldehyde:* Dissolve 4 g paraformaldehyde (Sigma, Cat. No. P6148) in 100 ml water and stir to dissolve by gently heating to 60–65°C in a fume hood. This can take an extended period and the solution will still appear cloudy. Clarify by addition of a few drops of 1 M NaOH (up to ~20 drops). Cool before use and store at 4°C. Fixative fumes are extremely toxic. Always use in a fume hood and avoid any contact.

Steps

1. Cell cycle fractions are analyzed by flow cytometric analysis (Fig. 2). Wash approximately 5×10^5 cells by centrifugation and resuspend in ice-cold Hanks' balanced salt solution. Fix cells by adding an equal volume of ice-cold 4% paraformaldehyde. After 24 hr incubation at 4°C, collect the cells by centrifugation and resuspend in 2 ml of ice-cold PBS. Alternatively, fix cells by slow dropwise addition of 3 vol of 70% ethanol (−20°C) while applying continuous gentle agitation with a Vortex mixer. Allow cells to fix for at least 1 hr and then wash as described above. Approximately 30 min prior to flow cytometric analysis, add 3 ml of staining solution to each aliquot of 300 μl of cell suspension and incubate at room temperature. Analyze fluorescence on an Elite flow cytometer (Coulter).

2. Analyze acid-precipitable [³H]thymidine incorporation by synchronous cell populations by pulse-labeling each separated fraction of cells with 10 μCi/ml [³H]thymidine in complete growth medium for 1 hr at hourly intervals after return of the cells to culture. Place cells in 96-well plates (2×10^4/well) in 100 μl growth medium and incubate under normal growth conditions. Add 1 μCi [³H]thymidine to each well at the appropriate time and incubate 1 hr. Wash each cell fraction twice with Hanks' balanced salt solution, drain of fluid, lyse in 100 μl TES, load 100 μl of lysate onto a 2.4-cm filter paper circle (Whatman 540, Cat No. 1540-324) labeled with a No. 2 pencil, and allow to air dry. Precipitate samples with excess solutions of 200 ml for up to 50 filters for 20 min (do not exceed this time or the filters may be damaged): 20% TCA, 10% TCA, ethanol,

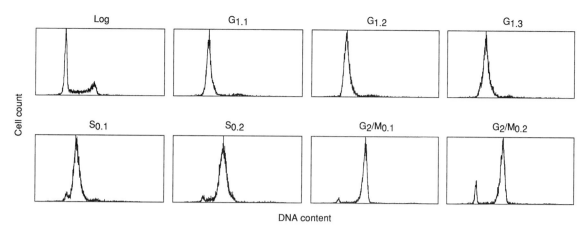

FIGURE 2 Flow cytometric analysis of cell cycle synchrony in sequential centrifugal elutriator fractions of HeLa S3 cells. Synchronous populations of HeLa S3 cells were selected by centrifugal elutriation of exponential cultures (log), and degree of synchrony was analyzed by flow cytometry. Cell number was plotted against DNA content based on propidium iodide fluorescence for each cell cycle fraction. Flow cytometric analysis of sequential G_1-phase fractions collected at flow rates of ($G_{1.1}$) 21 ml/min, ($G_{1.2}$) 23 ml/min, and ($G_{1.3}$) 25 ml/min. S-phase cells selected by centrifugal elutriation at flow rates of 29 ml/min ($S_{0.1}$), and 35ml/min ($S_{0.2}$) while G_2/M phase cells were collected at 43 ml/min.

ether, ethanol. Then air-dry and determine the radioactivity in each sample by liquid scintillation counting in 5 ml Aquasol 2 (Du Pont NEN, Cat. No. NEF-952) as previously described (Wu *et al.*, 1993).

IV. Comments

Using this protocol, it is possible to separate approximately 1×10^8 to 1×10^9 cells into up to eight sequential cell cycle phase fractions in about 40–60 min (sequential fractions designated $G_{1.1}$, $G_{1.2}$, $G_{1.3}$, $S_{0.1}$, $S_{0.2}$, G_2/$M_{0.1}$, G_2/$M_{0.2}$, see Fig. 2). The level of contamination of each fraction of cells, with those fractions preceding it, rose in later cell cycle fractions. The first fractions were of the highest purity (~97%, see Fig. 2), whereas purity of the fractions dropped in samples representing later times during the cell cycle. In G_2/M fractions significant numbers of cells synthesizing DNA are recovered though this activity declines rapidly once the cells are placed back in culture (Fig. 3). Only centrifugal elutriation can produce so many fractions of relatively high purity so quickly with little detectable lag in cell growth and no detectable drug/inhibitor-induced artifacts (see Fig. 3).

V. Pitfalls

1. It is critical that separations be attempted only with single-cell populations. Steps should be taken to ensure complete dissociation of cells liberated from tissues or culture. When in doubt, monitor dispersion microscopically.

2. Only Beckman neutral pH rotor detergent should be used to clean the rotor and separation chamber. It is particularly important to ensure that the sample tube at the outer edge of the separation chamber is soaked in detergent overnight to remove any cell debris that has accumulated as this will greatly affect flow rate as well as the fluid dynamics of sample loading in the chamber. This aperture is too small to be cleaned with a tool and no instrument that could scratch the

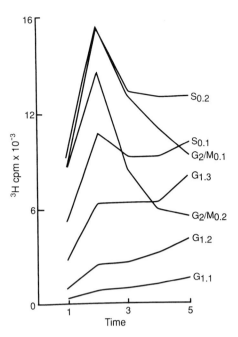

FIGURE 3 Analysis of synchrony of entry into DNA synthesis in centrifugal elutriation fractions of HeLa S3 cells. HeLa cells were separated into synchronous fractions by centrifugal elutriation, and kinetics of entry into DNA synthesis phase (S phase) was determined by measuring mean acid-precipitable [^{3}H]thymidine incorporation (10 μCi/ml in growth medium) for five sequential 1 hr incubations, in duplicate, for each cell cycle fraction identified in Fig. 2. Note that each cell fraction reaches S phase at sequentially later times after return to culture.

interior surface of the chamber should be applied. Be extremely careful with the separation chamber as overtightening of the screws or scratches to the surface will damage the chamber.

3. If alterations to the growth medium or elutriation medium are contemplated, the new medium must be tested to empirically determine at what flow rate cell cycle fractions elute. Even very small changes in medium formulation (e.g., as little as 0.5% change in DHS concentration) dramatically change the fluid dynamics of the elutriation system. Changes in cell loading density and temperature can also create detectable effects on elutriation profiles. A simple pilot experiment is usually sufficient to determine what effects such alterations have on elution flow rate if it is followed by analysis by flow cytometry.

4. All O-rings and gaskets should be inspected before each run to ensure they are in good condition. All worn seals should be replaced.

5. Failure to secure the wires and tubing connecting the rotor and strobe to the exterior of the centrifuge will result in them becoming wrapped around the rotor and seriously damaging the equipment.

6. We have replaced the Oakridge-style sample application tube supplied by the manufacturer with a straight glass test tube (13 × 100 mm) with the same size aperture at the top as the tube supplied. This eliminates the shoulder at the top of the Oakridge tube which can trap cells resulting in a continuous loading of cells throughout the elutriation procedure. The tube should be siliconized to within approximately 2 cm from the top with Sigmacote (Sigma, Cat. No. SL-2). Do not allow Sigmacote to contact the glass surface above this point as the stopper will no longer hold securely under pressure.

7. Monitor rotor speed frequently as fluctuations of only a small amount can greatly affect the efficiency of elutriation. It is particularly important to check rotor speed each time the refrigeration system cycles on.

8. If sterilization of the assembly is required, be sure that the centrifuge is turned off while the ethanol is in the system. Failure to observe this measure could result in a fire hazard. Alternatively, the system can be sterilized with 6% hydrogen peroxide while the centrifuge is running (Conkie, 1985).

ACKNOWLEDGMENTS

The authors thank Dr. Suresh Pai for consultation on this protocol and Randy Young-White for valuable technical support. This work was supported by the NIH (R15-GM47555), the NSF(RII-8610669), the USDA (92-03847), the Smokeless Tobacco Research Council Inc., and the Morris Animal Foundation.

REFERENCES

Bludau, M., Kopun, M., and Werner, D. (1986) Cell cycle-dependent expression of nuclear matrix proteins of Ehrlich ascites cells studied by in vitro translation. *Exp. Cell Res.* **165**, 269–282.

Braunstein, J. D., Schulze, D., DelGiudice, T., Furst, A., and Schildkraut, C. L. (1982) The temporal order of replication of murine immunoglobulin heavy chain constant region sequences corresponds to their linear order in the genome. *Nucleic Acids Res.* **10**, 6887–6902.

Brown, E. H., and Schildkraut, C. L. (1979) Perturbation of growth and differentiation of Friend murine erythroleukemia cells by 5-bromodeoxyuridine incorporation in early S phase. *J. Cell. Physiol.* **99**, 261–277.

Conkie, D. (1985) Separation of viable cells by centrifugal elutriation. *In* "Animal Cell Culture: A Practical Approach" (R. I. Freshney, ed.), pp. 113–124. IRL Press, Oxford.

Diamond, R. A. (1991) Separation and enrichment of cell populations by centrifugal elutriation. *In* "Methods: A Companion to Methods in Enzymology," Vol. 2, pp. 173–182. Academic Press, San Diego.

Hann, S. R., Thompson, C. B., and Eisenman, R. N. (1985) c-*myc* oncogene protein synthesis is independent of the cell cycle in human and avian cells. *Nature* **314**, 366–369.

Iqbal, M. A., Plumb, M., Stein, J., Stein, G., and Schildkraut, C. L. (1984) Coordinate replication of members of the multigene family of core and H1 human histone genes. *Proc. Natl. Acad. Sci. USA* **81**, 7723–7727.

Pai, S. R., and Bird, R. C. (1992) Growth of HeLa S3 cells cotransfected with plasmids containing a c-*fos* gene under the control of the SV40 promoter complex, pRSVcat, and G418 resistance. *Biochem. Cell Biol.* **70**, 316–323.

Pai, S. R., and Bird, R. C. (1994) Overexpression of c-*fos,* induces expression of the retinoblastoma tumor suppressor gene Rb in transfected cells. Submitted for publication.

Wu, G., Su, S., Kung, T.-Y. T., and Bird, R. C. (1993) Molecular cloning of G1 phase mRNAs from a subtractive G1 phase cDNA library. *Biochem. Cell. Biol.* **71**, 372–380.

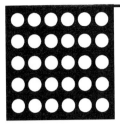

Synchronization of Normal Diploid and Transformed Mammalian Cells

Gary S. Stein, Janet L. Stein, Jane B. Lian, Thomas J. Last, Thomas Owen, and Laura McCabe

I. Introduction

Synchronized cells are required for defining regulatory mechanisms operative during specific periods of the cell cycle as well as at key transition points that separate G_1, S-, G_2, and mitosis. This article is restricted to methods that have proven to be effective for synchronizing continuously dividing normal diploid and tumor cells as well as for monitoring cell synchrony.

Synchronization of continuously dividing cells can be effectively achieved by imposing metabolic blocks that meet several criteria. First, cells must be arrested at a specific point in the cell cycle. Second, cells must be permitted to progress through other stages of the cell cycle to reach the arresting point. Third, the block must be rapidly reversible with minimal perturbations of biochemical, cellular, or molecular parameters of proliferation. Fourth, phenotypic properties characteristic of specialized cells that are expressed during proliferation should be minimally affected by the cell synchronization protocol.

Historically, the use of excess thymidine was the first widely accepted method for inducing cell synchrony and remains one of the most effective techniques (Bootsma et al., 1964; Terasima and Tolmach, 1963). By treatment with two sequential "thymidine blocks," a synchronous population of cells can be obtained at the beginning of S phase. This method can be used to synchronize both suspension and monolayer cells and is readily applicable to both normal diploid, transformed and tumor cells. It should be emphasized that for this method to function optimally all cells must be undergoing exponential growth. A description of the double thymidine block procedure has been reported for tumor cells by Stein and Borun (1972) and Holthuis et al. (1990) and for normal diploid cells by Holthuis et al. (1990).

The synchronization protocol is based on imposing the first thymidine block on exponentially growing cells for a minimum period equivalent to G_2 + M + G_1 but not to exceed 16 hr. The rationale is that by inhibiting ribonucleotide reductase activity, high concentrations of thymidine inhibit DNA synthesis in S-phase cells by depleting the nucleotide precursor pools of dCTP. Cells in G_2, M, and G_1 are not affected by excess thymidine treatment and continue to traverse the cell cycle until reaching the G_1–S phase boundary when the onset of DNA synthesis is inhibited. As a result, at completion of the initial thymidine block, approximately half of the cell population is uniformly distributed throughout S phase and the other half of the cell population is at the beginning of S phase (Fig. 1). The thymidine block is then released for a period exactly equivalent to S phase. This "release" permits the cells accumulated at the G_1–S phase boundary and those blocked throughout S

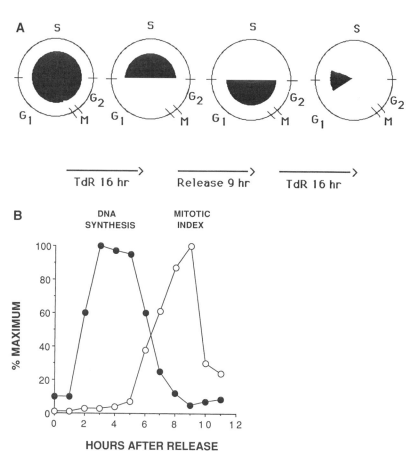

FIGURE 1 (A) Diagram of double thymidine (TdR) block method of cell synchrony. (B) DNA synthesis and mitotic index following release from second thymidine block are expressed as percentages of maximal [³H]thymidine incorporation or as a percentage of the maximal number of mitotic cells counted in a visual field.

phase to pass through S phase. Now, with half the cell population in early G_2 and other cells distributed between G_2, M, and G_1 a second thymidine block is imposed for a period equivalent to $G_2 + M + G_1$ but maximally 16 hr. At completion of the second thymidine block all cells are at the beginning of S phase. On release of the second thymidine block the cells synchronously traverse S, G_2, mitosis, and G_1.

Experience dictates that thymidine blocks should generally not exceed 16 hr to prevent breakdown of polyribosomes. The concentration of thymidine required to execute this synchronization procedure is dependent on the cell type. The appropriate thymidine concentration must be experimentally determined by defining the minimal concentration to inhibit DNA synthesis by 95% within 15 min but permit complete resumption of DNA synthesis in all cells immediately following removal of excess thymidine from the culture medium. We developed the protocol described in this article for synchronization of exponentially growing HeLa S3 human cervical carcinoma cells in monolayer or suspension culture and primary cultures of normal diploid rat osteoblasts or ROS 17/2.8 rat osteosarcoma cells in monolayer culture on coverslips, glass tissue culture plates, or plastic tissue culture dishes. This method is based on a doubling time of 20 hr with the following times associated with each stage of the cell cycle: G_1, 6 hr; S, 9 hr; G_2, 4 hr; and mitosis, 1 hr.

II. Materials and Instrumentation

Thymidine (Cat. No. T-9250) and deoxycytidine (Cat. No. D-8006) were obtained from Sigma. Suspension cultures of HeLa S3 cells are maintained in Joklik-modified Eagle's minimal essential medium purchased from Gibco Laboratories and supplemented with 3.5% fetal calf and 3.5% horse serum. Primary cultures of normal diploid, calvarium-derived rat osteoblasts are maintained in Eagle's minimal essential medium purchased from Gibco Laboratories and supplemented with 10% fetal bovine serum. ROS 17/2.8 rat osteosarcoma cells are maintained in F12 medium purchased from Gibco Laboratories and supplemented with 2% fetal calf and 5% horse serum. Monolayer cultures of HeLa S3 cells are maintained in Eagle's minimal essential medium purchased from Gibco Laboratories and supplemented with 3.5% fetal calf and 3.5% horse serum. Suspension cultures of HeLa S3 cells are maintained in erlenmeyer flasks or carboys ranging in size from 250 ml to 35 liters. A sterile magnetic stir bar is placed in the bottom of each flask and a sterile cotton plug is inserted in the neck of the flask. The flasks are placed on a magnetic stirrer and maintained at 37°C in a tissue culture incubator or "warm room." Monolayer cultures are maintained at 37°C in a tissue culture incubator with a moist 5% CO_2 atmosphere. [^{3}H]Thymidine (20 Ci/mmole) is obtained from DuPont NEN. Trichloroacetic acid (Cat. No. T-6399) and sodium dodecyl sulfate (SDS, Cat. No. L5750) are purchased from Sigma. Ecolume liquid scintillation counting cocktail is obtained from ICN Biomedicals, Inc. (Cat. No. 882470). Corning cellulose acetate membrane filter units (0.2 μm, Cat. No. 25970-33) are used for sterilization of all reagents and tissue culture media.

III. Procedures

A. DOUBLE THYMIDINE BLOCK SYNCHRONIZATION OF SUSPENSION CULTURES OF HeLa S3 CELLS

Solutions

1. *Thymidine:* Prepare a stock solution of 100 mM thymidine in serum-free medium and filter-sterilize. To make 100 ml of stock solution weigh 2.42 g of thymidine.

2. *Cell culture medium:* Dissolve powder medium in double glass-distilled water and filter-sterilize. Immediately prior to use supplement culture medium with serum, 2 mM L-glutamine, 1.5% penicillin, and 0.05% streptomycin.

Steps

1. Dilute exponentially growing cells at a concentration of 5×10^5/ml with fresh medium to a final concentration of 3.5×10^5 cells/ml, and add thymidine to a final concentration of 2 mM from a 50$\times$ stock solution prepared in serum-free medium.

2. Release the first thymidine block by pelleting the cells by centrifugation at 600 g for 5 min, carefully pouring off the growth medium and washing the cell pellet in 200 vol of serum-free medium at 37°C to maximally eliminate thymidine-containing medium in contact with the cell pellet. Resuspend the cells at a final concentration of 3.5×10^5 cells/ml in fresh growth medium containing 24 μM deoxycytidine.

3. After completion of the 9-hr release period, initiate a second thymidine block by diluting the suspension cultures with fresh medium to a final concentration of 3.5×10^5 cells/ml and adding thymidine to a final concentration of 2 mM.

4. Release the cells from the second thymidine block by centrifugation at 600 g for 5 min as described in step 2 and then resuspending the cells in fresh growth

medium containing 24 μM deoxycytidine at a final concentration of 3.5×10^5 cells/ml.

B. THYMIDINE SYNCHRONIZATION OF MONOLAYER CULTURES

Steps

1. Initiate a thymidine block in cultures at a cell density that will permit active growth throughout the time course of the synchronization procedure. The first thymidine block is imposed by removing the growth medium by aspiration and providing fresh medium containing 2 mM thymidine. The cells are blocked for 12–16 hr.

2. Release the cells from the first block for 9 hr by removing the thymidine-containing medium by aspiration and washing the monolayers twice with an equal volume of serum-free medium (at 37°C) prior to replacement with normal growth medium containing 24 μM deoxycytidine.

3. Following the 9-hr release period, impose a second thymidine block by adding thymidine to a final concentration of 2 mM from a 50× stock solution in serum-free medium.

4. After 12–16 hr, release the second thymidine block by removing the thymidine-containing medium by aspiration and washing the monolayers twice with an equal volume of serum-free medium (at 37°C) and feeding with normal growth medium containing 24 μM deoxycytidine.

C. MONITORING CELL SYNCHRONY

Solutions

1. *10% TCA:* To prepare 100% TCA, dissolve 500 g of TCA in 227 ml of water. Dilute TCA to 10% and store in an amber glass, covered vessel at 4°C.

2. *10% SDS:* To prepare 10% SDS dissolve 10 g SDS per 100 g of glass-distilled water. Store at room temperature.

Steps

Determination of DNA synthesis rate in suspension cultures

1. Add [³H]thymidine to 2 ml of cells to final concentration of 5 μCi/ml and incubate the cells at 37°C for 30 min with gentle agitation.

2. Pellet cells by centrifugation at 600 g for 5 min and remove the medium by aspiration.

3. Wash the cell pellet twice in ice-cold serum-free medium, followed each time by centrifugation at 4°C at 600 g for 5 min.

4. Resuspend the cell pellet in 6 ml of cold 10% TCA and maintain in an ice bath for at least 5 min.

5. Pellet the precipitate by centrifugation at 600 g for 5 min and remove the medium by aspiration.

6. Repeat steps 4 and 5.

7. Resuspend the pellet in 500 μl 10% SDS and transfer to a liquid scintillation vial.

8. Add 16 ml of Ecolume liquid scintillation counting cocktail to each vial. Radioactivity levels are quantitated in a liquid scintillation spectrometer.

DNA synthesis rate in monolayer cultures

9. Add [^{3}H]thymidine to the culture medium to a final concentration of 5 μCi/ml and incubate the cells at 37°C for 30 min.

10. Remove the culture medium by aspiration and rinse the monolayer twice with ice-cold serum-free medium.

11. Add 5 ml 10% TCA and maintain in ice bath for at least 5 min.

12. Remove TCA by aspiration.

13. Repeat steps 11 and 12.

14. Add 1 ml 10% SDS and maintain for 2 min at room temperature to solubilize TCA precipitates.

15. Assess incorporated radioactivity as described above (see step 8).

IV. Comments

During the past several years variations of the thymidine block procedure have been developed for synchronization of continuously dividing cells. Examples include substitution of aphidicolin (5 μg/ml for HeLa cells, osteosarcoma cells, or osteoblasts) or hydroxyurea (1 mM for HeLa cells, osteosarcoma cells, or osteoblasts) for thymidine during the second "S-phase block." Aphidicolin (Cat. No. A0781) and hydroxyurea (Cat. No. H8627) can be purchased from Sigma.

S phase can be followed by determining cellular levels of histone mRNA by Northern blot or slot-blot analysis using a ^{32}P-labeled histone gene probe (Plumb *et al.*, 1983). Although time consuming, autoradiography following [^{3}H]thymidine labeling of cultures provides the most direct approach to monitor cell synchronization, as visual examination of the autoradiographic preparations unquestionably indicates which cells are replicating DNA. The specific protocols for autoradiography of suspension and monolayer cultures have been described in an in-depth and comprehensive manner by Baserga and Malamud (1969). S-phase cells can also be visualized by *in situ* hybridization using a ^{35}S-radiolabeled histone gene probe (Pockwinse *et al.*, 1992). Although requiring specialized instrumentation, cell cycle progression may be monitored by fluorescence-activated sorting.

A 12- to 16-hr treatment of exponentially growing HeLa cells with 2 mM thymidine during the initial block will allow all cells that were in G_2, mitosis, or G_1 at the initiation of the block to progress to the G_1–S phase boundary, while cells undergoing DNA replication will be immediately arrested in S phase. Thus, at the completion of the first thymidine block, approximately 50% of the cells will accumulate at a G_1–S phase transition point and the other half of the cells will be arrested at various points in S phase.

A 9-hr release period from the first thymidine block permits all cells to exit S phase. Washing and resuspending the cells in media containing deoxycytidine facilitates rapid reversal of the thymidine block by compensating for effects of an expanded thymidine pool. The 50% of the cells that accumulated at the G_1–S phase boundary during the first thymidine block now will be in the initial segment of G_2, and those cells that were blocked at various points during S phase will be distributed between G_2, mitosis, and G_1.

A 12- to 16-hr treatment with excess thymidine during the second block accumulates all cells at the G_1–S phase boundary.

V. Pitfalls

1. It is essential to maintain the cells at 37°C throughout the synchronization procedure. Even a slight decrease in temperature will result in significant delays in cell cycle progression. Optimal conditions for cell synchronization are achieved by carrying out the entire procedure in a 37°C environmental room using an ambient temperature centrifuge for harvesting suspension culture cells.

2. Minimal concentrations of trypsin and/or EDTA should be used for subculturing monolayer cells prior to synchronization. Cell viability will be increased and exponential growth will resume with minimal delay.

3. When releasing thymidine-blocked suspension cells by centrifugation, the cell pellet should be adequately drained to maximize removal of thymidine-containing medium.

4. When adding or removing medium from monolayer cultures during synchronization steps, caution must be exercised to avoid disrupting the cultures and detaching the cells.

REFERENCES

Baserga, R., and Malamud, D. (1969) "Autoradiography." Hoeber, New York.

Bootsma, D., Budke, L., and Vos, O. (1964) Studies on synchronous division of tissue culture cells initiated by excess thymidine. *Exp. Cell Res.* **33**, 301–309.

Holthuis, J., Owen, T. A., van Wijnen, A. J., Wright, K. L., Ramsey-Ewing, A., Kennedy, M. B., Carter, R., Cosenza, S. C., Soprano, K. J., Lian, J. B., Stein, J. L., and Stein, G. S. (1990) Tumor cells exhibit deregulation of the cell cycle histone gene promoter factor HiNF-D. *Science* **247**, 1454–1457.

Pedrali-Noy, G., Spadari, S., Miller-Faures, A., Miller, A. O. A., Kruppa, J., and Koch, G. (1980) Synchronization of HeLa cell cultures by inhibition of DNA polymerase α with aphicicolin. *Nucleic Acids Res.* **8**, 377.

Plumb, M., Stein, J. L., and Stein, G. S. (1983) Coordinate regulation of multiple histone mRNAs during the cell cycle in HeLa cells. *Nucleic Acids Res.* **11**, 2391–2410.

Pockwinse, S. M., Wilming, L. G., Conlon, D. M., Stein, G. S., and Lian, J. B. (1992) Expression of cell growth and bone specific genes at single cell resolution during development of bone tissue-like organization in primary osteoblast cultures. *J. Cell. Biochem.* **49**, 310–323.

Stein, G. S., and Borun, T. W. (1972) The synthesis of acidic chromosomal proteins during the cell cycle of HeLa S3 cells. I. The accelerated accumulation of acidic residual nuclear protein before the initiation of DNA replication. *J. Cell Biol.* **52**, 292.

Terasima, T., and Tolmach, I. J. (1963) Growth and nucleic acid synthesis in synchronously dividing populations of HeLa cells. *Exp. Cell Res.* **30**, 344–362.

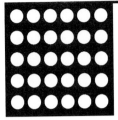

Synchronization of Transformed Human Amnion Cells by Mitotic Detachment

Julio E. Celis and Peder Madsen

I. Introduction

The life cycle of mammalian cells is divided into periods based on two landmarks, cell division at mitosis (M) and chromosomal DNA replication during S phase (Howard and Pelc, 1953). The gaps separating mitosis from S phase and the latter from mitosis have been designated G_1 and G_2, respectively. Normal as well as some transformed cells can enter a resting stage (G_0) on reaching confluency or by lowering the serum content of the medium, whereas most transformed cells are unable to do so (Baserga, 1978; Pardee et al., 1978, and references therein).

Mitotic "shake off" offers a simple and quick method to obtain a population of synchronized cells for cell cycle studies (see also articles by Gary S. Stein et al. and by Theresa Higgens and Enrique Rozengurt in this volume). The technique requires a cell line with loosely attached mitotic cells (Fig. 1A) as these can be easily detached by mechanical forces induced, for example, by shaking the tissue culture flask (Fig. 1B). Subsequent plating of the mitotic cells cells yields a population of cells that enter more or less synchronously into the G_1 phase of the cell cycle. The method does not make use of chemicals, which may have adverse effects.

Evaluation of cell cycle progression in a population of synchronized mitotic cells, is conveniently assessed by monitoring entry into S phase using autoradiography (see article by Theresa Higgens and Enrique Rozengurt in this volume). Alternatively, entry into S phase can be determined by immunofluorescence microscopy using EB PCNA/cyclin autoantibodies (Miyashi et al., 1978; Celis and Celis, 1985; Bravo, 1986) or anti-bromodeoxyuridine antibodies (Gratzner, 1982; Bravo and Macdonald-Bravo, 1987). Both procedures are easy to perform and yield essentially the same results.

II. Materials

5-Bromo-2'-deoxyuridine (Cat. No. B5002) and 5-fluoro-2'-deoxyuridine (Cat. No. F0503) were purchased from Sigma. Mouse monoclonal anti-bromodeoxyuridine (Cat. No. M744) and rhodamine-conjugated rabbit anti-mouse immunoglobulins (Cat. No. R270) were obtained from DAKO. Rhodamine-conjugated goat immunoglobulin to human IgG (Cat. No. 55202) was from Cappel and PCNA/cyclin autoantibodies (EB) were a gift from E. M. Tan (Scripps Clinic). Tissue culture dishes (40 mm, Cat. No. 153066) were from Nunc and the 25-cm² tissue culture flasks (Cat. No. 690160) from Greiner. All other reagents were as described in the article by

Ariana Celis and Julio E. Celis. Besides general tissue culture facilities (see article by Ariana Celis and Julia E. Celis in this volume) the procedures require a microscope equipped with fluorescence optics. For the experiments discussed below we used a Zeiss Axioplan microscope.

III. Procedures

A. SYNCHRONIZATION OF HUMAN AMNION CELLS BY MITOTIC DETACHMENT

Solutions

1. *Complete Dulbecco's modified Eagle's medium (DMEM):* Prepare as described in the article by Ariana Celis and Julio E. Celis.

Steps

1. Plate human amnion (AMA) cells in a 25-cm² flask as described in the article by Ariana Celis and Julio E. Celis in this volume.

2. Place the flask in a 37°C humidified 5% CO_2 incubator until the cells have reached the desired density (Fig. 1A).

3. Aspirate the medium with a Pasteur pipette connected to a vacuum line.

4. Add 10 ml of complete DMEM. Close the cap tightly and shake strongly by hand. Aspirate the foamy solution.

5. Repeat step 4 at least twice.

6. Add fresh complete DMEM (10 ml) and place the flask in the CO_2 incubator for at least 2 hr.

7. Remove the flask from the incubator, tighten the cap, and shake strongly by hand.

8. Collect the medium containing the mitotic cells in a conical sterile tube and centrifuge for 1 or 2 min in a bench-top centrifuge (2000–3000 rpm).

9. Aspirate the supernatant and gently resuspend the cells in 1 ml of complete DMEM. Place a drop in an object glass and cover with a coverslip. Observe under phase contrast (Fig. 1B). About 60% of the mitotic figures correspond to metaphases.

10. Add the whole of the cell suspension to a 60-mm tissue culture dish containing several sterile 12-mm round glass coverslips. Place in the CO_2 incubator.

B. IDENTIFICATION OF S-PHASE CELLS USING EB PCNA AUTOANTIBODIES

Solutions

1. *Hanks' buffered saline solution (HBSS) without Ca^{2+} and Mg^{2+}:* To make 1 liter 10× stock solution weigh 4 g of KCl, 0.6 g KH_2PO_4, 80 g NaCl, and 0.621 g of $Na_2HPO_4 \cdot 2H_2O$. Complete to 1 liter with distilled water.

2. *1× HBSS without Ca^{2+} and Mg^{2+}:* To make 1 liter of solution take 100 ml of the 10× stock and complete to 1 liter with distilled water.

3. *PCNA autoantibodies (EB):* Dilute 1:200 in HBSS.

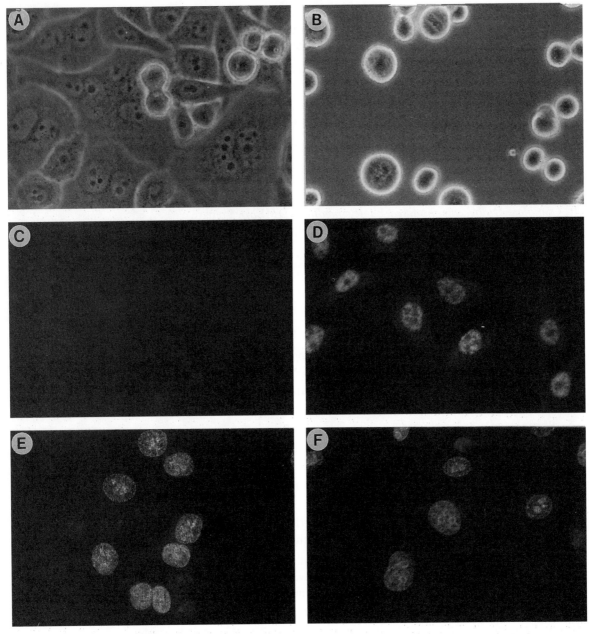

FIGURE 1 (A,B) Phase-contrast micrographs of (A) synchronous AMA cells and (B) mitotic AMA cells obtained by mitotic detachment. (C–E) Immunofluorescence micrographs of synchronized AMA cells reacted with PCNA antibodies at 2 (C), 8 (D), and 16 (E) hr after plating mitotic AMA cells. (F) As in E, but reacted with anti-bromodeoxyuridine antibodies.

4. *Rhodamine-conjugated goat immunoglobulins to human anti-human IgG:* Dilute 1:200 in HBSS.

5. *Methanol at −20°C.*

6. *Mouting medium (Gelvatol):* For preparation see article by Monika Herzog *et al.* in this volume.

Steps

1. Take coverslips seeded with mitotic AMA cells (from Protocol A) at 2-hr intervals and place them in 40-mm tissue culture dishes containing HBSS. Wash twice with HBSS. S phase starts about 7–9 hr after plating.

2. Discard the HBSS and add 3 ml of methanol at $-20°C$. Rock the dish and discard the methanol. Add 3 ml of fresh methanol at $-20°C$ and leave for 4 min at room temperature.

3. Discard the methanol and wash the monolayers three or four times with HBSS.

4. Pick the coverslip with the aid of a Dumont No. 5 forcep (see Fig. 3F in the article by Ariana Celis and Julio E. Celis in this volume) and dry it by touching the edge against a piece of tissue paper.

5. Place 10 μl of PCNA autoantibodies (1:200 dilution in HBSS) in a clean 40-mm tissue culture dish. Gently place the coverslip, cell side down, on top of the drop. Label both the bottom and the lid of the tissue culture dishes.

6. Cover the tissue culture dish with the lid and place it in a small plastic box containing pieces of wet tissue paper.

7. Incubate in a 37°C humidified 5% CO_2 incubator for 45 min.

8. At the end of the incubation add 2 ml of HBSS, pickup the floating coverslip with forceps, and place it, cell side up, in the bottom of the culture dish. Wash three times with HBSS.

9. Add 10 μl of rhodamine-conjugated rabbit anti-human IgG (1:200 dilution in HBSS) to the lid and gently place the coverslip, cell side down, on top of the drop.

10. Cover the lid with the bottom part of the dish and incubate in a 37°C humidified 5% CO_2 incubator for 45 min.

11. At the end of the incubation, add 2 ml of HBSS and wash the coverslip three times with HBSS. Finally wash once with distilled water.

12. Dry the coverslip by touching the edge of a tissue paper. Mount, cell side down, on an object glass containing a drop of mounting medium (see Fig. 3F of the article by Ariana Celis and Julio E. Celis in this volume). Dry for 30 min at 37°C or alternatively leave for several hours at room temperature.

13. Observe in a fluorescence microscope using a rhodamine filter. Figure 1 shows immunofluorescence micrographs of synchronized AMA cells stained at 2 (Fig. 1C), 8 (Fig. 1D), and 16 (Fig. 1E) hr after plating the mitotic cells.

C. IDENTIFICATION OF S-PHASE CELLS USING BrdU ANTIBODIES

Solutions

1. *50 mM 5-bromo-2'-deoxyuridine (stock solution):* To make 2 ml weigh 0.031 g, dissolve in distilled water, and complete to 2 ml.

2. *10 mM 5-fluoro-2'-deoxyuridine (stock solution):* To make 10 ml weigh 0.025 g, dissolve in distilled water, and complete to 10 ml.

3. *Labeling solution:* To make 10 ml add 10 μl of the 5-bromo-2'-deoxyuridine stock and 2 μl of the 5-fluoro-2'-deoxyuridine stock. Complete to 10 ml with complete DMEM.

4. *1.5 M Hydrochloric acid:* To make 10 ml take 1.36 ml of 37% HCl and add 8.64 ml of distilled water.

5. *Monoclonal mouse anti-bromodeoxyuridine:* Dilute 1:100 in HBSS.

6. *Rhodamine-conjugated rabbit immunoglobulins to mouse immunoglobulins:* Dilute 1:100 in HBSS.

Other solutions are as described in Protocol B.

Steps

1. Add 3 ml of the labeling solution to a 40-mm tissue culture dish containing the coverslips with the synchronized cells prepared in Protocol A. Incubate for 30 min at 37°C in a humidified 5% CO_2 incubator.

2. Aspirate the labeling medium and wash twice with HBSS.

3. Aspirate the HBSS and add 2–3 ml of methanol at −20°C. Rock the dish and discard the methanol. Add fresh methanol at −20°C and leave for 4 min at room temperature.

4. Aspirate the methanol and wash five times with HBSS.

5. Aspirate the HBSS and add 3 ml of 1.5 *M* HCl. Incubate for 40 min at 37°C.

6. Aspirate the HCl and wash five times with HBSS.

7. Place 20 μl of anti-bromodeoxyuridine antibodies (1:100 dilution in HBSS) in a clean 35-mm tissue culture dish. Gently place the coverslip, cell side down, on top of the drop. Label both the bottom and the lid of the tissue culture dishes.

8. Cover the tissue culture dishes with the lids and place them in a small plastic box containing pieces of wet tissue paper.

9. Incubate in a 37°C humidified 5% CO_2 incubator for 45 min.

10. At the end of the incubation add 2 ml of HBSS, pickup the floating coverslip with forceps, and place it, cell side up, in the bottom of the culture dish. Wash three times with HBSS.

11. Add 20 μl of rhodamine-conjugated rabbit anti-mouse immunoglobulins (1:50 dilution in HBSS) to the lid and gently place the coverslip, cell side down, on top of the drop.

12. Cover the lid with the bottom part of the dish and incubate in a 37°C humidified 5% CO_2 incubator for 45 min.

13. At the end of the incubation, add 2 ml of HBSS and wash the coverslip five times with HBSS. Finally wash once with distilled water.

14. Dry the coverslip by touching the edge of a tissue paper. Mount, cell side down, on a object glass containing a drop of mounting medium. Leave at room temperature for 10–20 min.

15. Observe in a fluorescence microscope using a rhodamine filter. Figure 1F is a photomicrograph of synchronized AMA cells stained 16 hr after plating the mitotic cells.

If necessary the procedure can be interupted after step 4 and the cells can be kept in HBSS at 4°C for several days.

IV. Comments

Using the procedures described in this article, it is possible to obtain a highly purified fraction of mitotic cells (Fig. 1B) that enters S phase in a more or less synchronized fashion (Figs. 1 D–F). The synchrony deteriorates, however, after the second S phase.

V. Pitfalls

1. Mitotic "shake off" can only be applied to monolayer cells that exhibit loosely attached mitotic figures and well-spread interphase cells.

2. The particular staining obtained with EB PCNA autoantibodies is not necessarily observed with other PCNA antibodies.

3. To avoid contamination, diluted antibodies should be kept at 4°C in the presence of 0.1% sodium azide.

REFERENCES

Baserga, R. (1978) Resting cells and G_1 phase of the cell cycle. *J. Cell Physiol.* **95**, 377–382.
Bravo, R., and Macdonald-Bravo, H. (1987) Existence of two populations of cyclin/proliferating cell nuclear antigen during the cell cycle: Association with DNA replication sites. *J . Cell Biol.* **105**, 1549–1554.
Bravo, R. (1986) Synthesis of the nuclear protein cyclin (PCNA) and its relation with DNA replication. *Exp. Cell Res.* **163**, 287–293.
Celis, J. E., and Celis, A. (1985) Cell cycle-dependent variations in the distribution of the nuclear protein cyclin proliferating cell nuclear antigen in cultured cells: subdivision of S phase. *Proc. Natl. Acad. Sci. USA* **82**, 3262–3266.
Gratzner, H. G. (1982) Monoclonal antibody to 5-bromo- and 5-iododeoxyuridine: A new reagent for detection of DNA replication. *Science* **218**, 474–475.
Howard, A., and Pelc, S. R. (1953) Synthesis of deoxyribonucleic acid in normal and irradiated cells and its relationship to chromosome breakage. *Heredity* **6**, 261–273.
Miyashi, K., Fritzler, M. J., and Tan, E. M. (1978) An autoantibody to a nuclear antigen in proliferating cell. *J. Immunol.* **121**, 2228–2234.
Pardee, A. B., Dubraw, R., Hamlin, J. L., and Kletzien, R. F. (1978) Animal cell cycle. *Annu. Rev. Biochem.* **47**, 715–750.

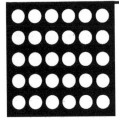

Stimulation of DNA Synthesis in Quiescent 3T3 Cells

Theresa Higgins and Enrique Rozengurt

I. Introduction

Growth factors and cytokines are implicated in a wide variety of physiological and pathological processes including embryogenesis, hemopoiesis, wound healing, immune responses, atherosclerosis, and neoplasia. Many studies of growth factors have used cultured fibroblasts such as Swiss 3T3 cells as a model system. These cells cease to proliferate in the G_0 phase of the cell cycle when they deplete the medium of its growth-promoting activity. Such quiescent cells can be stimulated to reinitiate DNA synthesis and cell division either by replenishing the medium with fresh serum or by adding polypeptide growth factors, neuropeptides, or pharmacological agents in serum-free medium (Rozengurt, 1985). Studies performed with combinations of growth factors have revealed an important aspect of their action: the existence of potent and specific synergistic interactions (Rozengurt, 1986, 1989). This finding suggested that growth factors bind to different receptors and generate multiple intracellular signals that interact synergistically to initiate a proliferative response (Rozengurt, 1986).

Synergistic effects are of crucial importance in assessing the growth-promoting activity of any agents in serum-free, chemically defined conditions. Indeed the mitogenic effects of a variety of factors including epidermal growth factor (Mierzejewski and Rozengurt, 1977), phorbol esters (Dicker and Rozengurt, 1978), vasopressin (Rozengurt *et al.*, 1979), cAMP-increasing agents (Rozengurt *et al.*, 1981), vasoactive intestinal peptide (Zurier *et al.*, 1988), diacylglycerols (Rozengurt *et al.*, 1984), bradykinin (Woll and Rozengurt, 1988), and endothelin (Fabregat and Rozengurt, 1990) could be revealed only when added in combination with an appropriate synergistic factor.

The following protocols describe the method by which Swiss 3T3 cells can be propagated in culture retaining both density-dependent inhibition of growth and responsiveness to multiple mitogenic agents, and the methods of determining the stimulatory and inhibitory effects of growth factors and cytokines on DNA synthesis of Swiss 3T3 cells.

II. Materials and Instrumentation

Chrome alum (chromic potassium sulfate), BDH Chemicals Ltd.

Developer, Kodak D19, Sigma Chemical Co. Ltd., Cat. No. P-5670.

Disodium hydrogen orthophosphate (Na_2HPO_4), BDH Chemicals Ltd., Cat. No. 102494C.

D-Glucose, BDH Chemicals Ltd., Cat. No. 10117.

Dulbecco's modified Eagle's medium (DMEM), Gibco BRL, Cat. No. 074-02100.

Ethylenediaminetetraacetic acid (EDTA, Versene), BDH Chemicals Ltd., Cat. No. 10093.

Ferrous sulfate (FeSO$_4$), Sigma Chemical Co. Ltd., Cat. No. F-7002.

Filter paper No. 1, Whatman International Ltd., Cat. No. 1001 185.

Film, fine-grain autoradiographic stripping plate AR10, Kodak Ltd. U.K., Cat. No. 3003522.

Fixer, Polymax, Kodak, Cat. No. 3648532.

Fetal bovine serum (FBS), Gibco BRL, Cat. No. 001-06290M.

Formaldehyde solution, BDH Chemicals Ltd., Cat. No. 10113 6C.

Gelatin (type B, bovine skin), Sigma Chemical Co. Ltd., Cat. No. G-9382.

Giemsa stain (crystalline), Sigma Chemical Co. Ltd., Cat. No. G-4507.

Liquid scintillation cocktail, Ultima Gold, Canberra Packard, Cat. No. 6013329.

[*Methyl*-^{3}H]thymidine, aqueous solution, 925 GBq/mmol, 25 Ci/mmol, Amersham International PLC, Cat. No. TRK 120.

Penicillin G (potassium salt), Sigma Chemical Co. Ltd., Cat. No. P-7794.

Phenol red (crystalline), BDH Chemicals Ltd., Cat. No. 200904U.

Potassium chloride (KCl), BDH Chemicals Ltd., Cat. No. 101984L.

Potassium dihydrogen orthophosphate (KH$_2$PO$_4$), BDH Chemicals Ltd., Cat. No. 10203.

Streptomycin sulfate, Sigma Chemical Co. Ltd., Cat. No. S-9137.

Sodium carbonate, anhydrous (Na$_2$CO$_3$), FSA Laboratory Supplies, Cat. No. S/2920.

Sodium chloride (NaCl), BDH Chemicals Ltd., Cat. No. 10241 AP.

Sodium dodecyl sulfate (SDS), BDH Chemicals Ltd., Cat. No. 44244 4H.

Sodium hydrogen carbonate (NaHCO$_3$), FSA Laboratory Supplies, Cat. No. S/4240.

Sodium hydroxide, pellets (NaOH), BDH Chemicals Ltd., Cat. No. 102524X.

Sodium sulfate (Na$_2$CO$_3$), FSA Laboratory Supplies, Cat. No. S/6640.

Thymidine, Sigma Chemical Co. Ltd., Cat. No. T-5018.

Trichloroacetic acid (TCA), FSA Laboratory Supplies, Cat. No. T/3000/53.

Trizma base. Sigma Chemical Co. Ltd., Cat. No. T-1503.

Trypsin (porcine, pancreatic), Difco.

Waymouths medium (MB752/1), Gibco BRL, Cat. No. 074-01400.

III. Procedures

A. MAINTENANCE OF STOCK SWISS 3T3 CELLS

Solutions

1. Phenol red (1%): Dissolve 10 g phenol red powder in 325 ml 0.1 *M* NaOH. Make up to 1 liter with distilled water. Filter through 0.2-μm filter, aliquot, and store at 4°C.

2. Versene, 0.2 g/liter in phosphate-buffered saline (PBS) without Ca^{2+} or Mg^{2+}: Dissolve 8 g NaCl, 0.2 g KCl, 1.15 g Na_2HPO_4, 0.2 g KH_2PO_4, 0.2 g EDTA (Versene), and 15 ml phenol red (1%) in 900 ml distilled H_2O (heat if necessary). Check that pH is 7.2 and adjust volume to 1 liter. Aliquot and autoclave at 121°C (15 lb pressure) for 15 min. Store at room temperature.

3. Trypsin (0.25% in Tris–saline): Dissolve 8 g NaCl, 0.1 g Na_2HPO_4 1 g D-glucose, 3 g Trizma base, 0.38g KCl, and 1.5 ml phenol red (1%) in 200 ml distilled H_2O. Add HCl to pH 7.7. Dissolve 2.5 g trypsin in 200 ml distilled H_2O; assist by bubbling air through the solution. Add dissolved trypsin to Tris–saline solution and make up volume to 1 liter. Check pH is still 7.7. Filter-sterilize, aliquot, and store at −20°C. Dilute with Versene to 0.05% for use.

4. Dulbecco's MEM: Make as per manufacturer's instructions but adding 3.7 g/liter $NaHCO_3$, 100 units/ml penicillin, and 100 mg/ml streptomycin. Supplement with 10% fetal bovine serum (FBS).

Steps

1. Wash subconfluent cultures of Swiss 3T3 cells in 100-mm Nunc dishes twice with 4 ml Versene at 37°C.

2. Incubate cells in 0.5 ml Trypsin/Versene mix at 37°C until cells detach when dishes are tapped (2–3 min). Care must be taken that all cells detach to avoid the selection of variants with altered adhesion properties. Usually two or three dishes are sufficient to yield 1×10^6 cells.

3. Collect cells in 5 ml/plate DMEM/FBS and count cell number using either a hemocytometer (see article by Ariana Celis and Julio E. Celis in this volume) or Coulter particle counter.

4. Replate cells onto 100-mm Nunc tissue culture dishes at 5×10^4 cells in 10 ml DMEM/FBS.

5. Culture at 37°C in a humidified atmosphere of 10% CO_2 for 3–4 days.

6. Repeat steps 1–5 every 3–4 days to maintain the cultures subconfluent. This is critical to avoid the emergence in the cell population of variants that are able to proliferate under crowded conditions and, consequently, have a relaxed density-dependent inhibition of growth.

B. PREPARATION OF SWISS 3T3 CELLS FOR EXPERIMENTAL PURPOSES

Solutions

The solutions are as described in Section A.

Steps

1. Refeed subconfluent cultures (3 days old) with fresh DMEM/FBS.

2. Culture at 37°C in a humidified atmosphere of 10% CO_2 for 2–3 days. At the end of this time the cultures should be confluent.

3. Trypsinize, collect, and count the cells as described in the previous section. Four dishes should yield approximately 8×10^6 cells. The saturation density of Swiss 3T3 cells should be about 3×10^4 cells/cm^2.

4. Replate cells onto 35-mm Nunc tissue culture dishes at 1×10^5 cells in 2.5 ml DMEM/FBS.

5. Culture at 37°C in a humidified atmosphere of 10% CO_2 for 6–8 days.

6. At the end of this time the cells will be confluent and quiescent, being arrested in G_1 as judged by the fact that fewer than 1% of the cells are labeled as determined by autoradiography (see below).

C. MEASUREMENT OF [³H]THYMIDINE INCORPORATION INTO ACID-INSOLUBLE MATERIAL

Solutions

1. [³H]Thymidine mix: To 9 ml distilled H_2O add 1 ml [*methyl*-³H]thymidine (1 mCi/ml, 37 Bq) and 100 μl thymidine at 10 mM. Sterilize by passing through a 0.2-μm filter and store at 4°C.

2. Waymouth's medium: Make up as per manufacturer's instructions but supplementing with 3.7 g/liter $NaHCO_3$ and 1.6 μM $FeSO_4$.

3. Assay medium: Mix DMEM 1:1 with Waymouth's medium and add 10 μl/ml of prepared [³H]thymidine mix.

4. Phosphate-buffered saline: Make PBS as previously described in Section A, step 2, without the addition of phenol red or Versene.

5. Trichloroacetic acid (5%): First make 50% by dissolving 500 g TCA crystals in 500 ml distilled H_2O. Make up volume to 1 liter. This is corrosive. Store at 4°C. Make a 1:10 dilution with distilled H_2O at 4°C for use.

6. Ethanol (70%): Mix 700 ml absolute ethanol with 300 ml distilled H_2O.

7. 0.1 M NaOH with 2% Na_2CO_3 and 1% sodium dodecyl sulphate: Dissolve 4 g NaOH pellets, 20 g Na_2CO_3, and 10 g SDS in 900 ml distilled H_2O. Make up volume to 1 liter.

Steps

1. Wash confluent, quiescent cultures of Swiss 3T3 cells in 35-mm Nunc dishes twice with DMEM at 37°C to remove residual serum.

2. Incubate cultures in 2 ml assay medium containing appropriate factors at 37°C in humidified atmosphere of 10% CO_2.

3. After 40 hr, wash cultures twice with ice-cold PBS and remove acid-soluble radioactivity by incubating for 20 min in 5% TCA at 4°C.

4. Wash cultures twice with ethanol and solubilize cells by a 30-min incubation in 1 ml 0.1 NaOH, 2% Na_2CO_5, and 1% SDS at 37°C.

5. Determine the radioactivity incorporated into the acid-insoluble material by liquid scintillation counting in an appropriate liquid scintillation cocktail (Ultima Gold).

6. The level of incorporation of [³H]thymidine into the cells induced by addition of medium containing 10% FBS causes maximum stimulation of DNA synthesis. The values given by other agents can be expressed as a percentage of this.

D. AUTORADIOGRAPHY OF LABELED NUCLEI

Solutions

1. Assay medium: Prepare as in the previous section, except add 5 μl/ml undiluted [*methyl*-³H]thymidine instead of the thymidine mix.

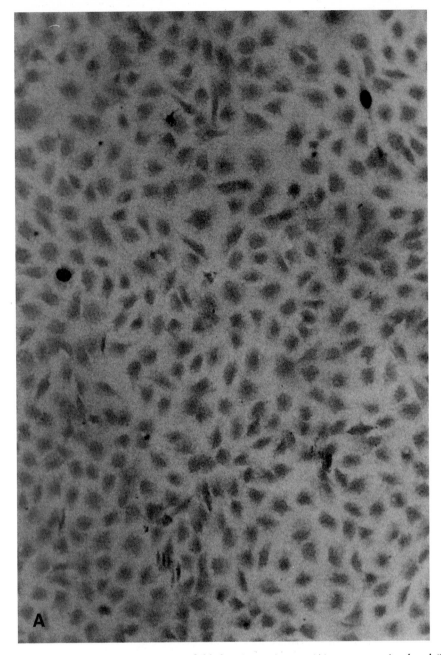

FIGURE 1 Typical microscopic field showing quiescent (A) or serum-stimulated (B) cells, labeled with [³H]thymidine and processed according to Section D.

    2. Formol saline: Dissolve 5 g NaCl and 15 g Na$_2$SO$_4$ in 400 ml distilled H$_2$O. Add 100 ml filtered formaldehyde and adjust volume to 1 liter. Store at 4°C.

    3. Tris–saline: Dissolve 8 g NaCl, 0.38 g KCl, 0.1 g NaH$_2$PO$_4$, 1 g D-glucose, 3 g Trizma base, and 1.5 phenol red (1%) in 900 ml distilled H$_2$O. Add HCl to pH 7.4 and make up to 1 liter with distilled H$_2$O. Filter-sterilize, aliquot, and store at 4°C.

    4. Chrome alum solution: Heat 5 g gelatin in 400 ml distilled H$_2$O to dissolve; dissolve 0.5 g chrome alum separately in 400 ml distilled H$_2$O. Mix the solutions when cool and make up volume to 1 liter with distilled H$_2$O. Store at 4°C.

    5. Developer: Make up Kodak D19 as per manufacturer's instructions.

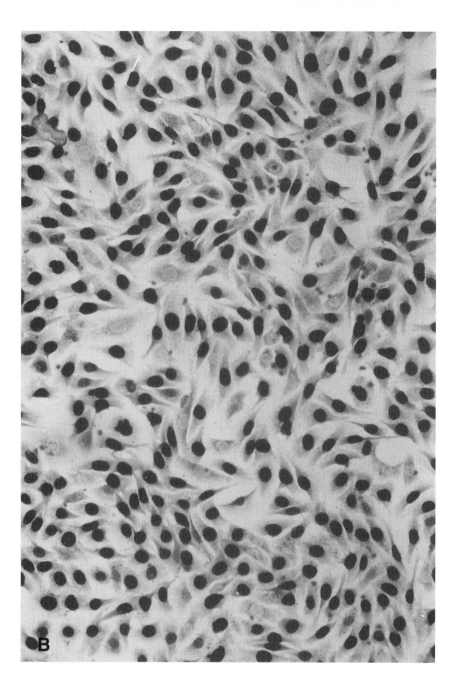

6. Fixer: Mix 100 ml Kodak Polymax fixer with 400 ml distilled H_2O immediately prior to use.

7. Giemsa's stain: Add 495 ml glycerol to 7.5 g Giemsa stain powder and heat for 90–120 min. Once cooled, add 495 ml methanol. Mix well and let stand at room temperature for 7 days. Filter through Whatman filter paper No. 1 and aliquot. Dilute 1:4 with distilled water for use.

Steps

1. Wash confluent, quiescent cultures of Swiss 3T3 cells in 35-mm Nunc dishes twice with DMEM at 37°C.

2. Incubate in 2 ml of assay medium containing appropriate factors.

3. After 40 hr, remove medium and fix cells in 2 ml formol saline at 4°C for 20 min.

4. Wash twice with Tris–saline at 4°C.

5. Extract the acid-soluble radioactivity with 5% TCA at 4°C using two 2-ml washes for 5 min each.

6. Wash three times with 70% ethanol and dry.

7. Write relevant details of treatment of cells on *side* of dish with an indelible pen.

8. Coat dishes with chrome alum and leave to dry. The residue after chrome alum has been poured on and poured back off will be sufficient.

9. Lay Kodak AR 10 stripping film onto dishes. In the dark, cut pieces of film approximately 4 cm². Fill dish with distilled H_2O and lay a piece of film on top, emulsion side down. When film has stretched pour off water and film will stick firmly to the base of the dish. Store in the dark for at least 1 week.

10. Develop in D19 for 4 min, wash in distilled H_2O for 2 min, and fix in Polymax for 5 min. Wash in tap water for 30 min.

11. Counterstain with Giemsa's and allow to dry.

Following this protocol the nuclei engaged in DNA synthesis become extensively labeled. A typical result is shown in Fig. 1. Labeled and unlabeled cells of at least 10 microscopic fields across a dish are counted and the results expressed as follows:

$$\% \text{ Labeled nuclei} = \frac{\text{number of labeled cells} \times 100}{\text{total number of cells in field}}$$

IV. Comments and Pitfalls

Swiss 3T3 cells have been selected for their ability to cease DNA synthesis at confluence. To maintain this fundamental property, the stock cultures of Swiss 3T3 cells should always be passaged before confluency and new stock cultures should be recovered from liquid nitrogen storage every 2 months.

It must be remembered that an apparent inhibition of DNA synthesis by putative antiproliferative agent might also be due to alterations in the transport of thymidine across the plasma membrane. One simple way to exclude the possibility of inhibition of thymidine transport being responsible for a reduction in [³H]thymidine incorporation is to vary the concentration of thymidine in the experiment (e.g., from 1 μM to 10 μM). If the apparent inhibition of DNA synthesis is entirely due to a decrease in thymidine transport, then the effect should be overcome by increasing the concentration of this nucleoside, thereby allowing it to permeate the membrane by simple diffusion. In addition, the results obtained by incorporation of [³H]thymidine should be compared with those obtained by autoradiography which is much less sensitive to changes in thymidine transport, especially after long times of exposure. Under normal conditions the results obtained by both methods should be strictly comparable. Figure 2 shows, as a typical example, the dose–response of platelet-derived growth factor (PDGF) for the stimulation of DNA synthesis assessed by either method. The half-maximum concentration of PDGF to induce DNA synthesis obtained from these procedures was the same (Fig. 2).

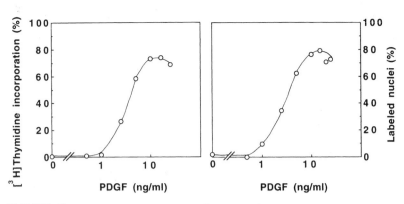

FIGURE 2 Dose–response curves of DNA synthesis in Swiss 3T3 cells stimulated with PDGF and assessed by either incorporation of [³H]thymidine into acid-insoluble material (left) or autoradiography (right).

REFERENCES

Dicker, P., and Rozengurt, E. (1978) Stimulation of DNA synthesis by tumour promoter and pure mitogenic factors. *Nature* **276,** 723–726.

Fabregat, I., and Rozengurt, E. (1990) Vasoactive intestinal contractor, a novel peptide, shares a common receptor with endothelin-1 and stimulates Ca^{2+} mobilization and DNA synthesis in Swiss 3T3 cells. *Biochem. Biophys. Res. Commun.* **167,** 161–167.

Mierzejewski, K., and Rozengurt, E. (1977) Density-dependent inhibition of fibroblast growth is overcome by pure mitogenic factors. *Nature* **269,** 155–156.

Rozengurt, E. (1985) The mitogenic response of cultured 3T3 cells: Integration of early signals and synergistic effects in a unified framework. *In* "Molecular Mechanisms of Transmembrane Signalling" (P. Cohen and M. Houslay, eds.), Vol. 4, pp. 429–452. Elsevier, Amsterdam.

Rozengurt, E. (1986) Early signals in the mitogenic response. *Science* **234,** 161–166.

Rozengurt, E. (1989) Signal transduction pathways in mitogenesis. *Br. Med. Bull.* **45,** 515–528.

Rozengurt, E., Legg, A., and Pettican, P. (1979) Vasopressin stimulation of 3T3 cell growth. *Proc. Natl. Acad. Sci. USA* **76,** 1284–1287.

Rozengurt, E., Legg, A., Strang, G., and Courtenay-Luck, N. (1981) Cyclic AMP: A mitogenic signal for Swiss 3T3 cells. *Proc. Natl. Acad. Sci. USA* **78,** 4392–4396.

Rozengurt, E., Rodriguez-Pena, A., Coombs, M., and Sinnett-Smith, J. (1984) Diacylglycerol stimulates DNA and cell division in mouse 3T3 cells: Role of Ca^{2+}-sensitive, phospholipid-dependent protein kinase. *Proc. Natl. Acad. Sci. USA* **81,** 5748–5752.

Woll, P. J., and Rozengurt, E. (1988) Two classes of antagonist interact with receptors for the mitogenic neuropeptides bombesin, bradykinin and vasopressin. *Growth Factors* **1,** 75–83.

Zurier, R. B., Kozma, M., Sinnett-Smith, J., and Rozengurt, E. (1988) Vasoactive intestinal peptide synergistically stimulates DNA synthesis in mouse 3T3 cells: Role of cAMP, Ca^{2+} and protein kinase C. *Exp. Cell Res.* **176,** 155–161.

SECTION H

Cytotoxic Assays

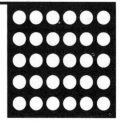

Quantitative Determination of Compound Cytotoxicity in Proliferating Cells: Monitoring DNA Synthesis by [3H]Thymidine Incorporation

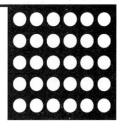

Kathy May

I. Introduction

Legislation demands that new therapeutic agents are subjected to rigorous cytotoxicity testing before they are progressed to the clinic. The development of cell culture techniques as alternatives to animal experiments has enabled primary investigations, at least, to be performed *in vitro* (Stenberg, 1986). Although *in vitro* cytotoxicity is not necessarily directly related to *in vivo* toxicity, it can indicate a selective mode of action for a compound (Stenberg *et al.*, 1986; Vere Hodge and Perkins, 1989). The cytotoxicity assay used depends largely on the information required for the agent under study. A range of parameters can be investigated, including cell viability (dye exclusion, cell counts), cell metabolism (dye reduction), and cell replication ([3H]thymidine incorporation). Incorporation of tritiated thymidine into nascent DNA provides a highly sensitive means of assessing cell proliferation. This extreme sensitivity has resulted in widespread use of the technique in the quantitative assessment of compound effects on the rate of cellular DNA synthesis (Moore and Randall, 1987; Bianchi and Fortunati, 1990).

II. Materials and Instrumentation

Human embryonic lung cells, MRC-5, were obtained from the ATCC (Cat. No. CCL 171). Tissue culture medium components were all from Life Technologies: fetal calf serum (Cat. No. 011-06290), heat inactivated at 56°C for 30 min, dispensed and stored at −20°C; Eagle's 10× minimum essential medium (MEM, Cat. No. 042-01435); sodium bicarbonate, 7.5% (Cat. No. 043-05080), and MEM nonessential amino acids (NEAA, Cat. No. 043-01140) stored at +4°C; penicillin/streptomycin solution (Cat. No. 043-05070) and 200 mM L-glutamine (Cat. No. 043-05030) stored at −20°C. Trypsin solution, 2.5% in normal saline, was also obtained from Life Technologies (Cat. No. 043-05090) and stored at −20°C. Dimethyl sulfoxide (DMSO) was from Sigma Chemical Company. This was aliquoted and autoclaved prior to use. [6-3H]Thymidine (TRA.306) was purchased from Amersham and scintillation fluid (Betaplate scint SC/9200) from LKB.

MRC-5 cells were maintained in Nunc (Gibco BRL) 80-cm² tissue culture flasks

(Cat. No. 1-53732A) and grown in Nunc microwell F96 plates (Cat. No. 1-67008A) for assay, and a Nunc Immunowash (Cat. No. 4-70173A) was used for medium aspiration. The automated cell harvester used and the liquid scintillation counter, 1205 Betaplate, were from LKB. Printed glass-fiber filtermats (1205-404) and bags (1205-411) for use with the 1205 Betaplate were supplied by Wallac Oy.

III. Procedures

A. PREPARATION OF MICROTITRATION PLATE CULTURES AND EXPOSURE TO A RANGE OF DRUG CONCENTRATIONS

Solutions

1. *Growth medium:* Eagle's MEM ($10\times$) 10%, sodium bicarbonate 3%, glutamine 1%, nonessential amino acids 1%, 1 M NaOH 0.5%, fetal calf serum 10%, and penicillin/streptomycin 1% (all v/v) are made up to required volume with sterile distilled water. The medium should be stored at $+4°C$ and warmed to $37°C$ prior to use. Medium prepared without serum (assay medium) should be used for diluting the [^{3}H]thymidine prior to use in the assay.

Steps

Aseptic conditions must be observed throughout. Test compounds need to be diluted in the cell growth medium. If solubility is a problem, DMSO can be used as follows.

1. Dissolve the test compounds at 10 mg/ml in DMSO. These stock solutions can be stored at $-20°C$ for future reference. Prepare a 200 μg/ml solution of each compound in cell growth medium. This is conveniently achieved by diluting 20 μl of a 10 mg/ml stock solution into 980 μl of growth medium.

2. Add 150 μl of the 200 μg/ml solutions to the top row of a microtiter plate in triplicate. Include a DMSO control in the assay and also cell controls.

3. Add 100 μl of growth medium to the other wells. Titrate test solutions, with the sequential transfer of 50-μl volumes, to give the following series of concentrations: 200, 60, 20, 6, . . . , 0.6 μg/ml. Place plate with loose-fitting lid in a $37°C$, 5% CO_2, humidified incubator, to equilibrate with CO_2 while the cell suspension is being prepared.

4. Trypsinize a confluent flask of MRC-5 cells and resuspend in growth medium at 1×10^5 cells/ml. Add 100 μl of cell suspension to each well of the assay plate to give 1×10^4 cells/well and final drug concentrations of 100, 30, 3, . . . , 0.3 μg/ml. If a slow-growing cell line is used in the assay rather than MRC-5 cells, increase the cell density to 2×10^5/ml.

5. Incubate at $37°C$, 5% CO_2, for 48 hr.

B. [6-^{3}H]THYMIDINE INCORPORATION AND SCINTILLATION COUNTING

Steps

1. Dilute [^{3}H]thymidine in serum-free assay medium. A working stock of 500 μCi can be made by adding 0.5 ml of the 2 Ci/mmol stock to 20 ml of assay

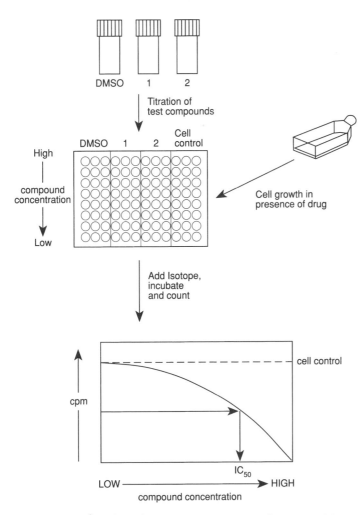

FIGURE 1   [³H]Thymidine incorporation assay for cytotoxicity.

medium. This can be stored at +4°C. Add 0.5 μCi of [6-³H]thymidine (20 μl working stock) per well. Incubate at 37°C, 5% CO_2, for 5 hr.

2. Remove the labeled medium from the microtiter plates with the immunowash aspirator.

3. Add 200 μl PBS per well, to wash the cell monolayer. To release the cells from the microdilution plate, remove the wash (with the aspirator) and replace with 50 μl 1% trypsin/PBS per well. Incubate at 37°C until the cells detach (about 10 min).

4. Use the automated cell harvester to lyse the cells with water and adsorb the DNA onto glass-fiber filters in the format of the microtiter plate. [6-³H]Thymidine incorporated into cellular DNA is retained on the filter while unincorporated material passes through.

5. Dry the filters in a warm-air oven for about 30 min (alternatively, filters can be microwaved, 2.5 min each side) and seal into a sample bag with 10 ml scintillant. The amount of [6-³H]thymidine present in each filter is determined by scintillation counting in the Betaplate liquid scintillation counter.

6. Take the means of the triplicate determinations and construct a graph of counts per minute (cpm) against compound concentration. Record cytotoxicity values as the concentration of compound (μg/ml) inhibiting cellular proliferation by 50% compared with the controls.

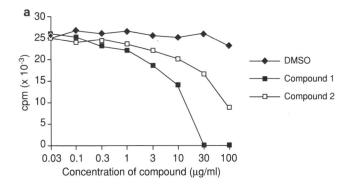

FIGURE 2   Representative cytotoxicity data for two test compounds. The graph (a) of cpm against compound concentration is used to obtain the IC_{50} values (b).

IV. Comments

If suspension cells are used in the assay, steps B2 and B3 are omitted. Test concentrations can be adjusted, according to the properties of the compound under investigation. Using the protocol described in this assay, it is possible to demonstrate the effects of compounds on cellular DNA synthesis. Indication of a selective mode of action can be gained and a putative therapeutic index determined for the test compound. The assay stages are presented diagramatically in Fig. 1 and representative data are given in Figs. 2a and 2b.

V. Pitfalls

1. To obtain maximum sensitivity, it is important for the cells to remain in exponential growth throughout. When different cell lines are being used, optimal seeding rates should be determined to ensure this is the case.

2. To gain accurate cytotoxicity values, complete solubility of the test compound must be ensured. Sonication is often useful. If DMSO or alternative solvents have to be used, appropriate diluent controls must be included. DMSO toxicity will vary with the cell type used, but assay concentrations greater than 1% should be avoided.

3. Ensure that all the cells have completely detached from the microtiter plates before harvesting onto the filters.

4. Thymidine analogs can appear artificially toxic in a [³H]thymidine assay due to competition effects on incorporation.

REFERENCES

Bianchi, V., and Fortunati, E. (1990) Cellular effects of an anionic surfactant detected in V79 fibroblasts by different cytotoxicity tests. *Toxicol. in Vitro* 4, 9–16.
Moore, R. C., and Randall, C. (1987) Different effects of 1-β-D-arabinofuranosylcytosine and aphidicolin in S-phase cells—Chromosome aberrations, cell cycle delay and cytotoxicity. *Mutat. Res.* 178, 73–80.

Stenberg, K. (1986) Cellular methods for measuring drug toxicity in vitro. *Trends Pharmacol. Sci.* **7**, 218–220.

Stenberg, K., Wangenheim, J., and Tribukait, B. (1986) Quantitative analysis of antiviral drug toxicity in proliferating cells. *Cell Biol. Toxicol.* **2**, 441–455.

Vere Hodge, R. A., and Perkins, R. M. (1989) Mode of action of 9-(4-hydroxy-3-hydroxy-methylbut-1-yl) guanine (BRL 39123) against herpes simplex virus in MRC-5 cells. *Antimicrob. Agents Chemother.* **33**, 223–229.

SECTION I

Senescence, Programmed Cell Death, and Others

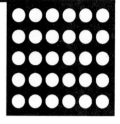

Serial Propagation of Human Fibroblasts for the Study of Aging at the Cellular Level

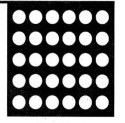

Vincent J. Cristofalo, Roberta Charpentier, and Paul D. Phillips

I. Introduction

Normal human diploid fibroblast-like cells (HDFs) are widely used to study *in vitro* cell aging, growth factor action, and cell proliferation. The finite replicative life span of HDFs in culture is characterized by a period of rapid proliferation followed by a decline in the rate of proliferation, after which the cultures can no longer be propagated (Hayflick and Moorhead, 1961). This decline in proliferative capacity is interpreted as an expression of aging at the cellular level (Hayflick, 1965). The proliferative rate and stage in the life history of a culture can be monitored best by well-controlled and reproducible cell culture procedures (Cristofalo and Sharf, 1973; Cristofalo and Charpentier, 1980). Standard subcultivation procedures to study aging in HDFs maintained in serum-supplemented medium and, for the short-term, in serum-free, chemically defined medium are described.

II. Materials and Instrumentation

Components of standard growth medium include Auto-Pow, an autoclavable formulation of Eagle's modified minimal essential medium (MEM) with Earle's salts, without glutamine and without sodium bicarbonate (Cat. No. 11-100-22) and Basal Medium Eagle (BME) vitamins (Cat. No. 16-004-49) from Flow Laboratories. Fetal bovine serum (FBS) is from a variety of suppliers and tested on a lot-by-lot basis. Sodium bicarbonate (Cat. No. S8875) and L-glutamine (Cat. No. G3126) are from Sigma Chemical Company.

Components of serum-free, chemically defined medium include modified basal medium MCDB-104 (where Na pantothenate is substituted for Ca pantothenate, without $CaCl_2$, without Hepes buffer, and without Na_2HPO_4; Formula No. 82-5006EA) from Gibco, and partially purified platelet-derived growth factor (PDGF, 3 μg/ml, Cat. No. P-8147), epidermal growth factor (EGF, 100 ng/ml, Cat. No. E-1257), insulin (INS, 5 μg/ml, Cat. No. I-6634), Transferrin (TRS, 5 μg/ml, Cat. No. T-2158), and dexamethasone (55 ng/ml, Cat. No. D-4902) from Sigma.

Dissociation medium components include NaCl (Cat. No. S-9625), KCl (Cat. No. P-5405), $NaH_2PO_4 \cdot H_2O$ (Cat. No. S-9638), glucose (Cat. No. G-6152), $10\times$ 2.5% trypsin in Hanks' saline without Ca^{2+} and Mg^{2+} (Cat. No. T-2904), and soybean trypsin inhibitor type I-S (Cat. No. T-6522) from Sigma. $50\times$ MEM amino acids

(Cat. No. B-6766) are from Sigma. 100× MEM vitamins (Cat. No. 16-004-49), and Phenol red (Cat. No. 16-900-49) are from Flow Laboratories. The Isoton II (Cat. No. 8546719) is from Coulter Electronics, Inc.

Tissue culture flasks (175 cm², Cat. No. 3028, 75 cm², Cat. No. 3024, and 25 cm², Cat. No. 3013), 24-well plates (Cat. No. 3047), and 15-ml conical plastic centrifuge tubes (Cat. No. 2097) are from Falcon Labware. Plastic pipettes (1 ml, Cat. No. 7553-F55, 5 ml, Cat. No. 7553-F80, and 10 ml, Cat. No. 7553-H65) are from Thomas Scientific. Filters (0.22 μm, Cat. No. 4619-B20) are from Sigma.

Laminar flow hoods (Sterilgard, Model VBM 400) are from Baker. The Coulter counter, Model ZM, is from Coulter Electronics, Inc. The inverted light microscope is from Nikon. Incubators (Model 3172) are from Forma Scientific. The refrigerated centrifuge, Model PR-J, is from International Equipment Company.

III. Procedures

A. CELL PROPAGATION IN SERUM-SUPPLEMENTED MEDIUM

This procedure is modified from those of Cristofalo and Charpentier (1980) and Phillips and Cristofalo (1989).

Solutions

1. *Incomplete medium:* To make 1 liter, add 9.4 g of Auto-Pow MEM powder and 10 ml BME vitamins to 854 ml deionized water. Mix thoroughly. Dispense 432 ml of this incomplete modified MEM into each 1-liter bottle. Screw the caps on loosely, apply autoclave tape to each bottle, and autoclave for 15 min at 121°C. When the sterilization cycle is finished, remove the bottles from the autoclave quickly, as prolonged heat destroys some medium components. With the caps still loose, place the vessels in the laminar flow hood and allow to cool to room temperature. When cooling is complete, tighten the caps and store the vessels at 4°C in the dark.

2. *Complete medium with 10% (v/v) FBS:* To each 1-liter bottle containing 432 ml of sterile but incomplete modified MEM medium, add 13 ml of a filter-sterilized solution of 7.5% (w/v) sodium bicarbonate, 5 ml of a filter-sterilized solution of 200 mM L-glutamine, and 50 ml of sterile FBS. Prepare complete medium fresh for each use. If stored longer than 1 week at 4°C, add 1 ml more of L-glutamine per 100 ml of complete medium at the time it is to be used.

3. *Ca²⁺- and Mg²⁺-free medium:* To make 1 liter add, in order, 6.8 g NaCl, 0.4 g KCl, 0.14 g NaH$_2$PO$_4$·H$_2$O, 1 g glucose, 20 ml of 50× MEM amino acids, 10 ml of 100× MEM vitamins, and 10 ml of a 0.5% (w/v) solution of phenol red to 900 ml of deionized water. Dilute to 1 liter with deionized water and filter-sterilize (0.20-μm pore size) under house vacuum. Store at 4°C.

4. *Trypsinizing solution:* To 40 ml of Ca²⁺- and Mg²⁺-free MEM add 5 ml of sterile 7.5% sodium bicarbonate. Add 5 ml of sterile 2.5% trypsin to a final pH of 7.4. Prepare fresh and keep on ice.

Steps

1. In a laminar flow hood, using sterile procedures, pour off the medium from the cell culture flask into a sterile beaker by decanting the fluid from the side opposite the cell growth surface. Alternatively, the medium can be aspirated from the growth vessel into a vacuum flask using a sterile Pasteur pipette.

2. Rinse the cell sheet twice with 4 ml each of the trypsinizing solution.

3. Remove the excess solution with a 1-ml pipette or by aspiration.

4. Add enough trypsinizing solution to just cover the cell sheet. For example, 2 ml is sufficient for a T-75 flask.

5. Secure the cap of the culture flask and place it in the incubator (37°C) for approximately 15 min. The cells will round up as they lift off the growth surface. Using the microscope, periodically check to see if the cells are detaching.

6. When all of the cells have detached from the growth surface as determined by inspection under the microscope, return the flask to the laminar flow hood. Carefully pipette complete medium (10% FBS-supplemented medium) down the growth surface of the vessel to wash down and collect the cells and to stop the trypsinization process. Record the volume of medium used. For a T-75 flask use 8 ml for a final harvest volume of 10 ml.

7. Before counting the cell harvest, break up the cell clumps by drawing the entire suspension into a 10-ml pipette and then allowing it to flow out gently against the wall of the vessel. Repeat the process at least three times. Repeat the same procedure using a 5-ml pipette to obtain a single-cell suspension. Until the procedure becomes routine, withdraw a sample, and check under the microscope to make sure that a single-cell suspension has been achieved. Keep the cells on ice during this process to inhibit cell reattachment.

8. Using sterile procedures, remove an aliquot from the suspension, then dilute in nonsterile Isoton in a counting vial. Typically, we dilute 0.5 ml of the cell suspension from a T-75 flask into 19.5 ml of Isoton.

9. Count the sample in a Coulter Counter and determine the number of cells in the harvest.

10. In the laminar flow hood, add complete medium to the culture vessels (0.53 ml/cm^2 of cell growth surface).

11. Resuspend the cell harvest with a pipette and inoculate each culture vessel at a constant density of 1×10^4 cells/cm^2 of growth surface.

12. Deliver a 95% air:5% CO$_2$ mixture by passing it through a sterile, cotton-filled CaCl$_2$ drying tube, through a sterile pipette into the gas phase in the cell culture flask. Flush directly over the medium surface for several seconds. Other than serum, dissolved CO$_2$ in equilibrium with HCO$_3^-$ represents the principal buffer system in the medium. As CO$_2$ is volatile, the gas phase in the flasks is adjusted to the proper pCO$_2$ to maintain the pH of the medium at 7.4. Close the flask tightly and incubate at 37°C.

13. Calculate the population doubling level (PDL) at each subcultivation directly from the cell count.

Example:

One week after seeding a T-75 flask with the standard inoculum of 7.5 $\times 10^5$ cells, the harvest contained 6.0×10^6 cells. The population doubling increase is calculated by the formula $N_H/N_I = 2^X$ (where N_H = cell harvest number, N_I = cell inoculum number, and X = the number of population doublings). Then, 6.0×10^6 cells/7.5×10^5 cells = 2^X, or $log(6 \times 10^6)$ $- log(7.5X^5) = X log 2$. Therefore, X = 3.

Add the new population doubling level to the previous population doubling level to arrive at the current cumulative population doubling level (CDPL) at seeding.

B. CELL PROPAGATION IN SERUM-FREE MEDIUM

This procedure is modified from those of Phillips and Cristofalo (1980) and Phillips and Cristofalo (1989).

Solutions

1. *Incomplete medium for serum-free cell propagation:* To prepare 1 liter of medium, add one packet of powdered MCDB-104 to 700 ml of deionized distilled water. Mix thoroughly. Add the following additional components in the order listed: 1.0734 g $Na_2HPO_4 \cdot 12H_2O$, 1.754 g NaCl, 1.0 ml of a 1 M $CaCl_2$ solution, and 1.176 g $NaHCO_3$. Bring the final volume to 1 liter with deionized distilled water. Filter-sterilize the medium through a 0.22-μm pore filter into sterile glass bottles. Final pH is 7.3 to 7.5. Store for up to 3 weeks at 4°C.

2. *Special medium for concentrated growth factor stock solutions:* To 900 ml of deionized distilled water add one packet of the MCDB-104, 1.0743 g $Na_2HPO_4 \cdot 12H_2O$, 11.9 g Hepes buffer, 1.0 ml of 1 M $CaCl_2$, and 25.0 ml of 1 M NaOH. Adjust the pH of the solution to 7.5 by titration with 1 M NaOH and bring the volume to 1 liter with deionized distilled water. Sterilize by filtration through a 0.22-μm filter. Store frozen until needed.

3. *Concentrated growth factor stock solutions:* Using sterile plastic pipettes, prepare growth factor stock solutions using the special medium, above, as follows: EGF at 2.5 μg/ml (100×), INS at 500 μg/ml (100×), TRS at 500 μg/ml (100×), and 5 mg/ml DEX in 95% ethanol, then diluted to 5.5 μg/ml with the special medium. DEX should be stored in sterile siliconized glass test tubes. PDGF readily adsorbs to glass surfaces; follow suppliers' instructions. Use PDGF at approximately 6 ng/ml if it is highly purified and at about 3 μg if it is only a crude, partially purified preparation. Dispense all stock solutions with sterile plastic pipettes into 0.5- to 1.0-ml sterile plastic test tubes and store at −20°C for short periods (up to 4 weeks) or at −70°C for longer periods (3–4 months).

4. *Complete medium for serum-free cell propagation:* For 100 ml of complete serum-free medium add the following to 94 ml of incomplete medium (MCDB-104): 2 ml PDGF stock solution, (final concentration 1 U/ml); 1 ml EGF stock solution (final concentration 100 ng/ml); 1 ml INS stock solution (final concentration 5 μg/ml); and 1 ml DEX stock solution (final concentration 55 ng/ml).

5. *Trypsin inhibition solution:* Add 100 mg of soybean trypsin inhibitor to 100 ml of incomplete medium (MCDB-104). Sterilize with a 0.22-μm Millipore filter. Dispense 8-ml portions into sterile plastic tubes and store at −20°C. When needed, thaw and dilute 1:1 with incomplete medium (MCDB-104).

Steps

1. Follow Step A1.

2. Follow Step A2 but use 10-ml quantities of the trypsinizing solution to rinse the cell sheet.

3. Follow Steps A3–A6, except the trypsin inhibition solution should be used instead of complete medium (10% FBS-supplemented medium) to wash and collect the cells from the growth surface of the flask. Mitogens present in the FBS may be sequestered inside of the cells or associated with their plasma membranes. The presence of even small quantities of serum complicates the interpretation of cell growth response results.

4. Follow Steps A7–A9.

5. Under sterile conditions, wash the cell harvest by centrifugation at 75 g for 5 min at 4°C.

6. Resuspend cells in 10 ml of incomplete medium (MCDB-104).

7. Centrifuge again at 75 g for 5 min at 4°C.

8. Resuspend cells in 7 to 10 ml of MCDB-104 (approximately 8×10^6 to 1×10^7 cells/ml).

9. Remove another 0.5-ml aliquot of the cell suspension and determine the cell number with the Coulter counter as before.

10. Follow Steps A10–A14.

IV. Comments

These procedures, developed over a 20-year period, provide reproducible results and an optimum growth environment for human diploid fibroblasts in both serum-containing and serum-free media. The major advantage to serum-containing medium is the ease with which the cells may be subcultivated to achieve their maximum proliferative potential. The advantage of the serum-free medium is its completely defined composition and the accompanying ability to rigorously control the regulation of cell proliferation and, presumably, other hormonally regulated functions.

Expect little or no increase in cell number within 24 hr of subcultivation. Between 20 and 50% of the cells do not survive subcultivation. Moreover, the first parasynchronous round of DNA synthesis does not begin until approximately 15 hr after seeding, and the first mitotic cells do not appear until 30 hr after seeding.

Using these procedures, cultures will attain their maximum proliferative capacity, which we determine as follows. The cell cultures are subcultivated weekly. When a confluent monolayer is not formed after 1 week, cultures are refed by replacing the spent medium with fresh complete medium employing the 5% CO_2 mixture as described. If the cells are not confluent after 3 weeks of refeeding, the culture is harvested anyway. If the population has not doubled during the 3 weeks of refeeding (i.e., for a T-75 flask, $N_H < 1.5 \times 10^6$ cells), then the cell line is considered to be phased out. In our laboratory, the average CPDL at "phase out" for WI-38 cells is 67.

V. Pitfalls

1. The trypsinization process may be speeded up by gently tapping the sides of the flask. Take care not to splatter the cells against the top and sides of the flask because this will lead to errors in determining the number of cells in the flask.

2. Do not attempt to freeze the incomplete medium (MCDB-104) because as it freezes, the pH rises. On thawing, salts will occasionally precipitate out of solution and may not redissolve. This medium is prepared in small batches and kept refrigerated for up to 3 weeks.

3. It is important to use the highest-quality deionized water for subcultivating cells in serum-free, chemically defined medium.

REFERENCES

Cristofalo, V. J., and Charpentier, R. (1980) A standard procedure for cultivating human diploid fibroblastlike cells to study cellular aging. *J. Tissue Culture Methods* 6, 117–121.

Cristofalo, V. J., and Sharf, B. B. (1973) Cellular senescence and DNA synthesis: Thymidine incorporation as a measure of population age in human diploid cells. *Exp. Cell Res.* 76, 419–427.

Hayflick, L. (1965) The limited in vitro lifetime of human diploid cell strains. *Exp. Cell Res.* 37, 614–636.

Hayflick, L., and Moorhead, P. S. (1961) The serial cultivation of human diploid cell strains. *Exp. Cell Res.* 25, 585–621.

Phillips, P. D., and Cristofalo, V. J. (1980) A procedure for the serum-free growth of normal human diploid fibroblasts. *J. Tissue Culture Methods* 6, 123–126.

Phillips, P. D., and Cristofalo, V. J. (1989) Cell culture of human diploid fibroblasts in serum-containing and serum-free media. *In* "Cell Growth and Division: A Practical Approach" (R. Baserga, ed.), pp. 121–132. IRL Press, Oxford/Washington, DC.

Morphological Criteria for Identifying Apoptosis

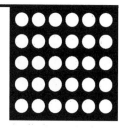

John F. R. Kerr, Clay M. Winterford,
and Brian V. Harmon

I. Introduction

Apoptosis was originally defined morphologically (Kerr *et al.*, 1972). More recently, agarose gel electrophoresis of extracted nuclear DNA has been widely used for its identification, the internucleosomal double-strand cleavage that accompanies this type of cell death resulting in the appearance of a distinctive oligonucleosomal "ladder" when ethidium bromide-stained gels are viewed in ultraviolet light (Wyllie, 1980). Such cleavage may not, however, always occur in cell death that would be regarded as being apoptotic on other grounds (Collins *et al.*, 1992; Ucker *et al.*, 1992), and morphological changes still provide the most reliable criteria for recognizing the process (see also article by Jonathan L. Tilly in this volume).

Apoptosis involves a series of consecutive, morphologically delineated phases, and it will be necessary to consider these in describing its diagnostic features. The latter are most clearly evident at the electron microscopic level. Nevertheless, with practice, apoptosis can often be recognized with confidence by light microscopy. It should be noted that the morphology of physiological cell death occurring in invertebrates differs in some respects from the stereotyped pattern that characterizes classical apoptosis in higher animals (Robertson and Thomson, 1982; Lockshin and Zakeri, 1991); we confine our account to the appearances observed in mammals. Additional illustrations of the morphology of apoptosis and comprehensive bibliographies supporting our descriptions can be found in reviews (Wyllie *et al.*, 1980; Kerr *et al.*, 1987; Walker *et al.*, 1988; Arends and Wyllie, 1991).

II. Morphological Recognition of Apoptosis

A. ELECTRON MICROSCOPY

Standard electron microscopic techniques are quite adequate for recognizing apoptosis.

In tissues, the process characteristically affects scattered single cells, rather than groups of contiguous cells, and there is no associated inflammation such as occurs with necrosis. The sequential ultrastructural events observed in the two types of cell death are shown in stylized form in Fig. 1.

Changes in the nucleus provide the first unequivocal evidence of the onset of apoptosis. The chromatin condenses and becomes segregated in sharply delineated masses that abut on the nuclear envelope. These masses have fairly smooth inner

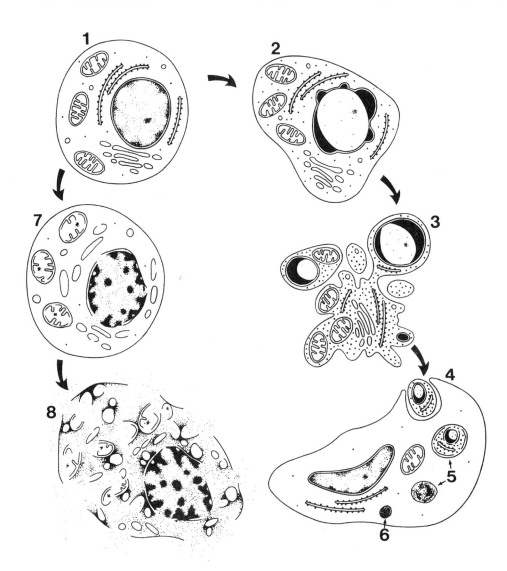

FIGURE 1 Sequence of ultrastructural changes in apoptosis (2–6) and necrosis (7,8). A normal cell is represented at 1. Early apoptosis (2) is characterized by segregation of the chromatin in sharply circumscribed masses that lie against the nuclear envelope, condensation of the cytoplasm, and convolution of the nuclear and cell outlines. In the next phase (3), the nucleus fragments and the cell as a whole buds to produce membrane-bounded apoptotic bodies of varying size and structure, which are phagocytosed (4) by nearby cells and degraded within lysosomes (5). Finally, the bodies are reduced to unrecognizable residues (6). In the irreversibly injured cell, the occurrence of necrosis (7) is accompanied by clumping of chromatin without marked changes in its distribution, the appearance of densities in the matrix of grossly swollen mitochondria, and focal disruption of membranes. At a later stage (8), organelles and membranes disintegrate, but the overall configuration of the cell is usually maintained.

contours, appear uniformly dense at low magnification, and are found to be made up of closely packed, fine granules at high magnification. The proportion of the nucleus that is occupied by condensed chromatin varies with cell type, being particularly high in lymphoid cells. The chromatin changes are often accompanied by convolution of the nuclear outline. Altered components of the nucleolus are visible

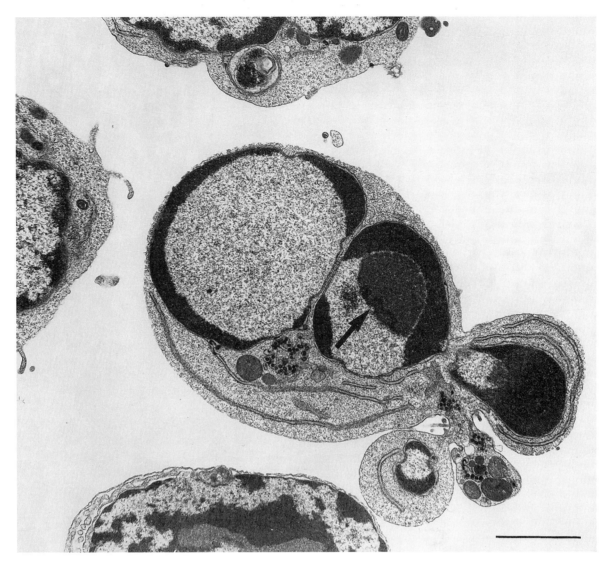

FIGURE 2 Apoptosis occurring spontaneously in culture of murine NS-1 cell line. Note the marked cell surface convolution, the membrane-enclosed nuclear fragments containing sharply segregated, compact chromatin, and the remnant of the nucleolar fibrillar center (arrow). Bar = 2 μm.

only in some planes of section; a characteristic feature of the process is the presence of a round or oval granular mass derived from the nucleolar fibrillar center lying closely applied to the inner edge of the condensed chromatin (Fig. 2 shows one of these masses at a slightly later stage of the process).

Simultaneously with the early events occurring in the nucleus, the cytoplasm condenses, and protuberances of varying size appear on the cell surface. Clear vacuoles may be evident in the otherwise dense cytoplasm, but their presence is inconstant. It should be stressed that relative cytoplasmic condensation in the absence of typical nuclear changes is not indicative of apoptosis, cytoplasmic density varying considerably from one cell to another in many normal tissues. The cytoplasmic condensation that accompanies apoptosis may be difficult to appreciate in cells dispersed in cultures. It is most clearly evident in tissues, where the dense apoptotic cells stand out against their unaffected neighbors (Fig. 3).

Rapid progression of the processes described above is associated with further convolution of the nuclear and cell outlines, followed by budding of the nucleus to

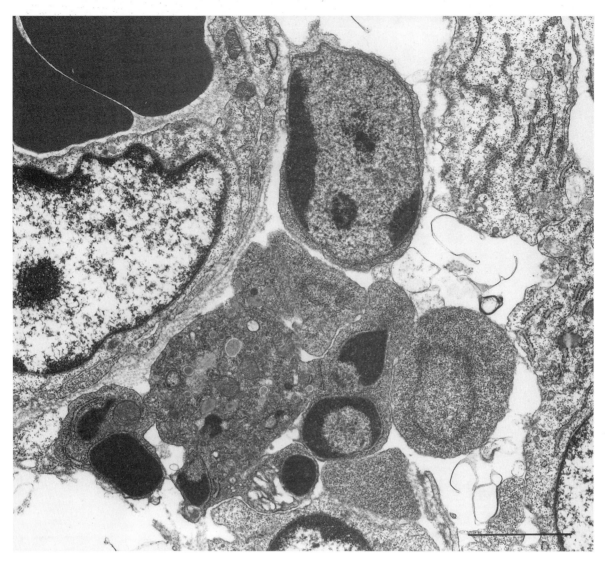

FIGURE 3 Apoptosis occurring in murine EMT6 sarcoma nodule 2 hr after heating at 44°C for 30 min. Condensation of the cytoplasm with preservation of the integrity of organelles, nuclear fragmentation, and budding of the cell as a whole to produce discrete, membrane-bounded apoptotic bodies are well shown. Bar = 2 μm.

produce discrete fragments that are still enclosed by a double-layered envelope (Fig. 2) and of the cell as a whole to produce membrane-bounded apoptotic bodies (Figs. 3 and 4). The characteristic sharp segregation of the condensed chromatin is maintained in the nuclear fragments, dense chromatin being confined to peripheral crescents in some and occupying most or all of the cross-sectional area in others (Figs. 2–4). The cytoplasmic organelles of newly formed apoptotic bodies remain well preserved (Fig. 3).

The number, size, and structure of the apoptotic bodies arising from a particular cell depend on the extent of nuclear and cellular budding that occurs. This, in turn, appears to be determined, at least in part, by the anatomical structure of the affected cell. Thus, cells with relatively voluminous cytoplasm often undergo extensive nuclear and cellular budding with the production of large numbers of apoptotic bodies, many but not all of which contain one or more nuclear fragments (Fig. 3); several of the bodies may be conspicuously larger than the rest. Small cells with scant

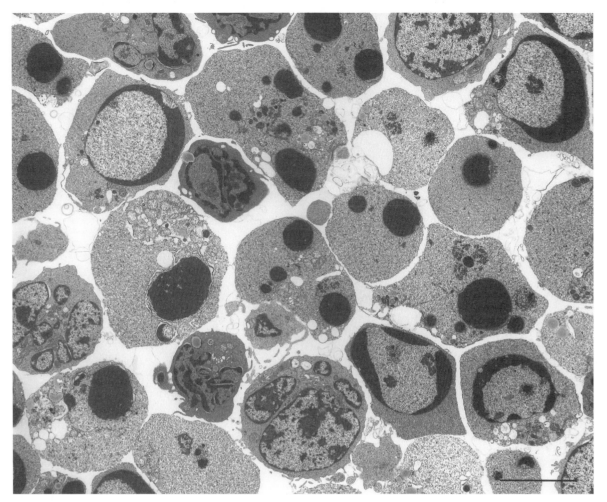

FIGURE 4 Numerous apoptotic bodies in culture of human Burkitt's lymphoma cell line (BM13674) 4 hr after heating at 43°C for 30 min. In some nuclear fragments, compact chromatin is confined to peripheral crescents; in others, it occupies virtually the whole cross-sectional area. Bar = 7 μm.

cytoplasm such as cortical thymocytes, on the other hand, often show restricted nuclear and cellular budding during apoptosis.

Within tissues, most apoptotic bodies are rapidly phagocytosed by resident macrophages (Fig. 5) or by other nearby cells, including epithelial cells; a few of those formed in single-layered epithelia may be shed from the surface. Inside phagosomes, the bodies undergo degenerative changes and are degraded by lysosomal enzymes derived from the ingesting cell (Fig. 6). The apoptotic origin of partly degraded phagocytosed bodies can often be inferred from the presence of remnants of dense chromatin masses (Fig. 6). Eventually, the bodies become unrecognizable by electron microscopy and are reduced to indigestible residues within telolysosomes.

Apoptotic bodies that escape phagocytosis, either because of their extrusion from epithelial surfaces or because of their dispersal in cell cultures, spontaneously undergo degenerative changes that resemble those occurring in necrosis. Such degenerate apoptotic bodies can be confidently distinguished from cells that have undergone necrosis *ab initio* if a nuclear remnant showing apoptotic-type chromatin changes is included in the plane of section (Fig. 7).

The onset of apoptosis in the individual members of a cell population is typically asynchronous. Various different phases of the process are therefore usually evident

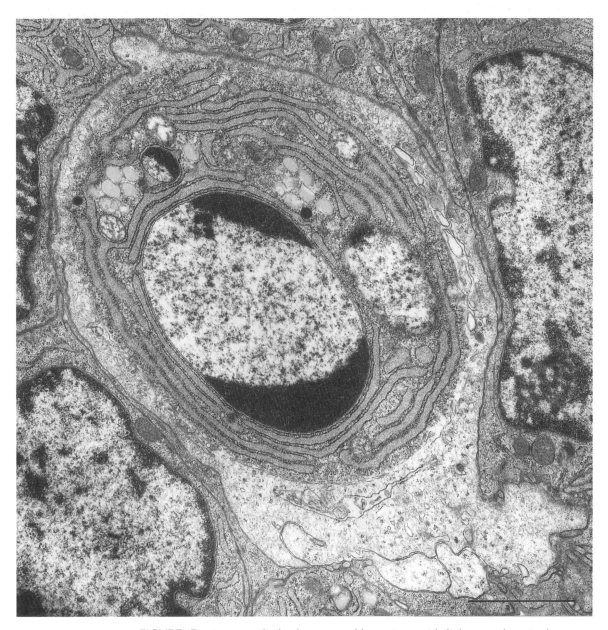

FIGURE 5 Apoptotic body phagocytosed by an intraepithelial macrophage in the rat ventral prostate 2 days after castration. Note the typical nuclear fragments and the well-preserved rough endoplasmic reticulum. Bar = 2 μm.

in any sample examined. The condensation and budding of a cell to form apoptotic bodies take only a few minutes, whereas degradation of phagocytosed bodies takes some hours. Thus, unless the sample happens to be taken very early in a wave of apoptosis, the more advanced stages of the process are encountered most frequently.

The ultrastructural appearance of necrosis (Fig. 8) is quite different from that of apoptosis (Fig. 1). Although clumping of chromatin occurs in necrosis, its distribution is not markedly altered as it is in apoptosis, and the edges of the clumps tend to be irregular in outline and relatively poorly defined (Fig. 8). Moreover, the nucleus does not bud to form discrete, membrane-enclosed fragments. At a later stage, the chromatin may largely disappear. The swollen necrotic cell tends to maintain its overall configuration, despite breakdown of plasma, nuclear, and organelle membranes (Fig. 8). The presence of densities in the matrix of mitochondria (Fig. 8)

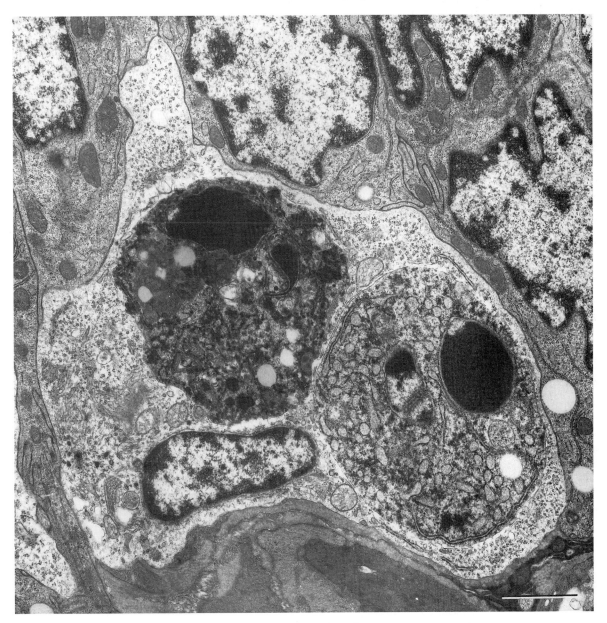

FIGURE 6 Partly degraded apoptotic bodies within macrophage lysosomes in same specimen as that illustrated in Fig. 5. Nuclear fragments containing characteristically segregated compact chromatin are still recognizable. Bar = 3 μm.

is characteristic. In tissues, groups of contiguous cells are classically affected and associated inflammation is usually evident. Removal of necrotic cells is accomplished exclusively by cells of the mononuclear phagocytic system.

B. LIGHT MICROSCOPY

The histological hallmark of the occurrence of apoptosis is the presence of discrete, well-preserved apoptotic bodies. Because of the speed with which the early stages of the process are completed, convoluted, budding cells are rarely seen. In the later stages, degradation of apoptotic bodies makes them progressively more difficult to recognize.

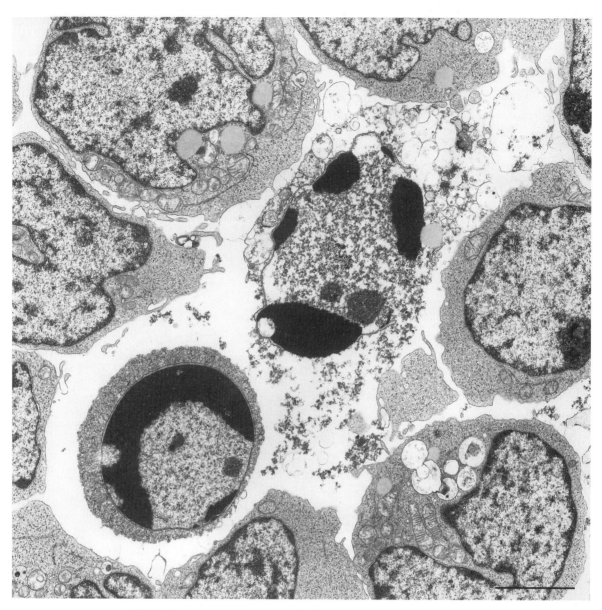

FIGURE 7 Apoptosis in human Burkitt's lymphoma cell line (BM13674) 6 hr after X-irradiation (5 Gy) *in vitro*. The lower apoptotic body is well preserved. The upper body shows supervention of degenerative changes similar to those found in necrosis, but a nuclear fragment with apoptotic-type chromatin segregation is still clearly recognizable within it. Bar = 3 μm.

The diversity of size and structure of apoptotic bodies revealed by electron microscopy is mirrored in their histological appearance (Fig. 9). They are usually roughly round or oval in shape. Where cellular budding has been relatively restricted during their formation, many tend to be only a little smaller than the cells of origin (Figs. 9B and C). Where cellular budding has been extensive, on the other hand, they often range widely in size (Fig. 9A). The degree of nuclear fragmentation is also very variable. For example, the apoptotic bodies derived from tumor cells illustrated in Fig. 9B contain numerous nuclear fragments, whereas those derived from cortical thymocytes illustrated in Fig. 9C comprise single dense chromatin masses surrounded by barely detectable cytoplasmic rims. Some quite large apoptotic bodies derived from cells with abundant cytoplasm may be devoid of nuclear fragments (Fig. 9A).

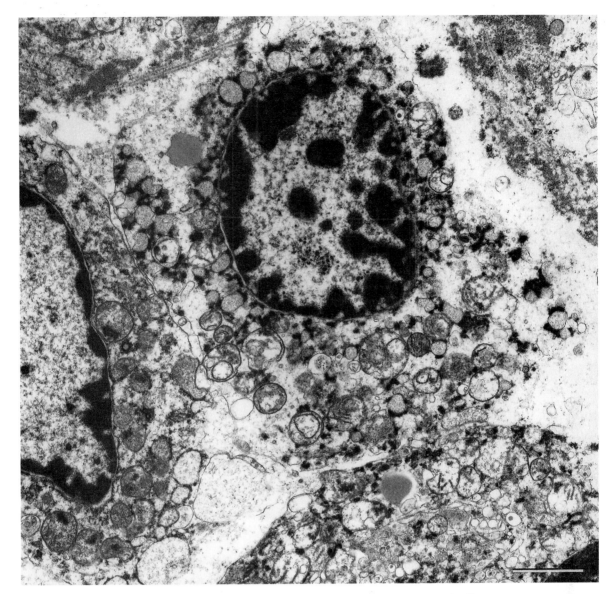

FIGURE 8   Confluent necrosis due to ischemia in a murine P-815 tumor growing in muscle. Note the ill-defined edges of the small chromatin clumps, the presence of densities in the matrix of some of the grossly swollen mitochondria, and the preservation of the overall configuration of the cells despite extensive breakdown of their membranes. Bar = 2 μm.

The characteristic segregation of chromatin in apoptotic nuclear fragments displayed by electron microscopy is evident by light microscopy only in very thin sections; in relatively thick sections and in smears, the fragments usually appear uniformly dense (Fig. 9).

In tissues, apoptotic bodies are frequently found grouped in clusters (Fig. 9A), but scattered, solitary bodies are also seen. It may be difficult to determine whether individual bodies have been phagocytosed or are still extracellular. Evidence of inflammation is characteristically absent. Infiltrating mononuclear leukocytes may, however, be present where apoptosis is being induced by cellular immune mechanisms.

The histological distinction of apoptosis from necrosis poses little difficulty in tissue sections; the involvement of groups of adjoining cells, the presence of inflammation, and the preservation of overall cell outlines without evidence of nuclear

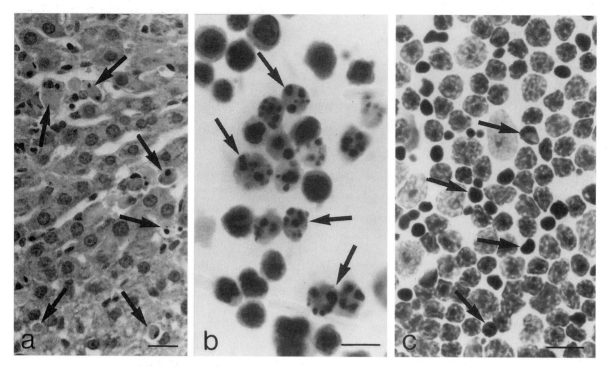

FIGURE 9 Histological appearance of apoptotic bodies (arrows). (A) Left lobe of rat liver undergoing atrophy 3 days after ligation of its portal venous supply. Hematoxylin- and eosin-stained paraffin section. Bar = 12 μm. (B) Overgrown culture of murine NS-1 cell line. Smear stained with hematoxylin and eosin. Bar = 10 μm. (C) Rat thymus 3 hr after injection of dexamethasone, 70 mg/kg. Although most of the nuclear fragments appear uniformly dense, marginated masses of chromatin are evident in two of them. Imprint stained by the Feulgen technique. Bar = 10 μm.

budding are all indicative of the latter process. Moreover, in relatively thin sections, the irregular clumping of nuclear chromatin evident in necrotic cells by electron microscopy (Fig. 8) is usually discernible. In smears of necrotic cells, however, the nuclear chromatin may appear uniformly dense, the nuclear appearance resembling that of apoptosis of small cells such as thymocytes, in which nuclear fragmentation is minimal (Fig. 9C). If there is doubt about the nature of cell death detected in smears, electron microscopy should be performed.

III. Comments

The morphological criteria outlined above should permit apoptosis to be recognized with certainty. Its quantification is, however, time consuming. Flow cytometry has recently been used for this purpose. It is likely to prove a useful technique in studies of apoptosis.

IV. Pitfalls

Partly degraded, phagocytosed apoptotic bodies and apoptotic bodies that have undergone secondary degeneration in cultures have sometimes been misidentified as necrotic cells. The distinction may indeed be difficult if nuclear remnants showing chromatin changes of the apoptotic type are not still detectable in the degenerate bodies. In these circumstances, it may be necessary to study samples taken at earlier times to elucidate the type of cell death occurring.

Phagocytosed apoptotic bodies can be mistaken for autophagic vacuoles. The presence of a nuclear fragment or of organelles that differ in structure from those of the cell in question clearly identifies the contents of a lysosome as heterophagic rather than autophagic. Unusually large size of a putative autophagic vacuole may also provide a clue to an apoptotic origin.

Lastly, so-called type B dark cells have been confused with apoptotic cells. The resemblance between the two is, however, only superficial (Walker *et al.*, 1988). Although the cytoplasm is condensed in type B dark cells, mitochondria are grossly swollen and cytoplasmic processes arising from the cell surface have usually become stretched out between adjacent cells. The nuclei show overall condensation and lack the distinctive chromatin segregation seen in apoptosis. The significance of type B dark cell formation is uncertain. It may represent a variant of necrosis (Walker *et al.*, 1988).

REFERENCES

Arends, M. J., and Wyllie, A. H. (1991) Apoptosis: Mechanisms and roles in pathology. *Int. Rev. Exp. Pathol.* **32**, 223–254.

Collins, R. J., Harmon, B. V., Gobé, G. C., and Kerr, J. F. R. (1992) Internucleosomal DNA cleavage should not be the sole criterion for identifying apoptosis. *Int. J. Radiat. Biol.* **61**, 451–453.

Kerr, J. F. R., Searle, J., Harmon, B. V., and Bishop, C. J. (1987) Apoptosis. *In* "Perspectives on Mammalian Cell Death" (C. S. Potten, ed.), pp. 93–128. Oxford University Press, Oxford.

Kerr, J. F. R., Wyllie, A. H., and Currie, A. R. (1972) Apoptosis: A basic biological phenomenon with wide-ranging implications in tissue kinetics. *Br. J. Cancer* **26**, 239–257.

Lockshin, R. A., and Zakeri, Z. (1991) Programmed cell death and apoptosis. *In* "Apoptosis. The Molecular Basis of Cell Death" (L. D. Tomei and F. O. Cope, eds.), pp. 47–60. Cold Spring Harbor Laboratory Press, Cold Spring Harbor, NY.

Robertson, A. M. G., and Thomson, J. N. (1982) Morphology of programmed cell death in the ventral nerve cord of *Caenorhabditis elegans* larvae. *J. Embryol. Exp. Morphol.* **67**, 89–100.

Ucker, D. S., Obermiller, P. S., Eckhart, W., Apgar, J. R., Berger, N. A., and Meyers, J. (1992) Genome digestion is a dispensable consequence of physiological cell death mediated by cytotoxic T lymphocytes. *Mol. Cell. Biol.* **12**, 3060–3069.

Walker, N. I., Harmon, B. V., Gobé, G. C., and Kerr, J. F. R. (1988) Patterns of cell death. *Methods Achiev. Exp. Pathol.* **13**, 18–54.

Wyllie, A. H. (1980) Glucocorticoid-induced thymocyte apoptosis is associated with endogenous endonuclease activation. *Nature (London)* **284**, 555–556.

Wyllie, A. H., Kerr, J. F. R., and Currie, A. R. (1980) Cell death: The significance of apoptosis. *Int. Rev. Cytol.* **68**, 251–306.

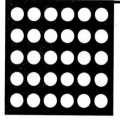

Use of the Terminal Transferase DNA Labeling Reaction for the Biochemical and *in Situ* Analysis of Apoptosis

Jonathan L. Tilly

I. Introduction

Apoptosis, a mode of physiological cell death used by multicellular organisms for normal tissue remodeling during embryogenesis and postnatal development, can be distinguished from necrotic or pathological cell death by several morphological and biochemical features (Kerr *et al.,* 1972; see also article by John F. Kerr *et al.* in this volume). Among these, the endonuclease-catalyzed, internucleosomal breakdown of nuclear DNA into oligonucleosomal fragments (180 to 200-bp multiples) is thought to herald the irrevocable commitment of cells to die via apoptosis (Wyllie, 1980). Although it has become evident that not all forms of physiological cell death are dependent on nuclear DNA breakdown (Ucker *et al.,* 1992; Schwartz *et al.,* 1993), the characteristic feature of internucleosomal DNA cleavage has been widely used as an early marker for apoptosis in many cell systems, including the thymus and gonads (Wyllie, 1980; Hughes and Gorospe, 1991; Tilly *et al.,* 1991; Tilly, 1993; Tapanainen *et al.,* 1993).

The conventional approach to detect the ladder pattern of internucleosomal DNA breakdown has relied on ethidium bromide staining of electrophoretically separated DNA and its subsequent visualization by UV transillumination (Wyllie, 1980). This methodology has several potential drawbacks, however, including a lack of sensitivity when analyzing small amounts of DNA or quantitating changes in the extent of DNA cleavage, and an inability to discriminate *in situ* the specific cell populations undergoing apoptosis. To overcome these problems, the application of the terminal transferase DNA labeling reaction for analyzing internucleosomal DNA fragmentation by both biochemical (extracted DNA; see Tilly and Hsueh, 1993: copyright, Wiley–Liss, 1993) and *in situ* (tissue localization; see Gavrieli *et al.,* 1992) approaches is detailed herein.

II. Materials

A. BIOCHEMICAL ANALYSIS OF DNA INTEGRITY

Terminal deoxynucleotidyl transferase (Tdt, 25 units/μl, Cat. No. 220-582), 5× concentrated Tdt enzyme reaction buffer (1 M potassium cacodylate, 125 mM Tris–HCl, 1.25 mg/ml bovine serum albumin, pH 6.6, supplied with Tdt enzyme), $CoCl_2$ (25 mM, supplied with Tdt enzyme), and DNase-free RNase (500 μg/ml, Cat. No. 1119-915) are from Boehringer–Mannheim Biochemicals. Transfer RNA (yeast,

Cat. No. R8759) is from Sigma Chemical Company, and 2′,3′-dideoxyadenosine-5′-[α-³²P]triphosphate (ddATP, 3000 Ci/mmole, Cat. No. PB10233) is from Amersham.

B. *IN SITU* ANALYSIS OF DNA INTEGRITY

2′-Deoxyadenosine-5′-triphosphate coupled to biotin at the 6-position of the purine base via a 14-atom spacer arm (biotin-14-dATP, 0.4 m*M*, Cat. No. 19524-016) is from Gibco-BRL Life Technologies, and 2′-deoxyadenosine-5′-triphosphate (dATP, 100 m*M*, Cat. No. 1051-440) and proteinase K (PK, 20 mg/ml, Cat. No. 1413-783) are from Boehringer–Mannheim. The colorimetric reagents, nitroblue tetrazolium salt (NBT, 75 mg/ml) and 5-bromo-4-chloro-3-indolyl phosphate toluidinium salt (BCIP, 50 mg/ml), and the streptavidin–alkaline phosphatase conjugate (1 mg/ml) are found in the *In Situ* Hybridization and Detection System (Cat. No. 18279-018) from Gibco-BRL Life Technologies.

C. SOLUTIONS

Chemicals can be obtained from local vendors but should be of the highest reagent quality, and all solutions should be prepared with sterile deionized distilled water.

III. Procedures

A. BIOCHEMICAL ANALYSIS OF DNA SAMPLES PREPARED FROM CELLULAR OR TISSUE HOMOGENATES

Total genomic DNA should be extracted, phenol/chloroform purified, resuspended in sterile water, and quantitated by optical density at 260 nm. Although numerous procedures are available for extraction of DNA from tissues or cells, it should be noted that not all methods are capable of effciently retrieving low-molecular-weight (MW) DNA fragments. The reader is therefore referred to a procedure adapted from Gross-Bellard *et al.* (1974) which is a fast and efficient method for preparing high-quality genomic DNA from tissues or cells (Tilly and Hsueh, 1993). Once isolated, the DNA is labeled and analyzed as follows using conditions established in earlier kinetic studies of the 3′-end labeling reaction with DNA obtained from apoptotic cells (Tilly and Hsueh, 1993) (Fig. 1).

Solutions

1. 0.5 *M* EDTA (pH 8.0): Combine 186.1 g EDTA with sterile water to a total volume of 990 ml, pH to 8.0 with 10 *N* NaOH (400 g of sodium hydroxide/liter sterile water), and adjust final volume to 1 liter with sterile water.

2. 25 mg/ml tRNA solution in sterile water.

3. 10 *M* ammonium acetate: Combine 770.8 g ammonium acetate with sterile water to a total volume of 1 liter; filter with 0.45-μm vacuum filtration unit.

4. 1× TAE buffer (40 m*M* Tris–acetate, 1 m*M* EDTA): To prepare a 50× concentrated stock (dilute 1:50 with sterile water for working solution), combine 242 g Tris base, 57.1 ml glacial acetic acid, 100 ml 0.5 *M* EDTA (pH 8.0), and sterile water to a total volume of 1 liter.

5. 1× TE buffer (10 m*M* Tris–HCl, 1 m*M* EDTA, pH 8.0): combine 1.2 g

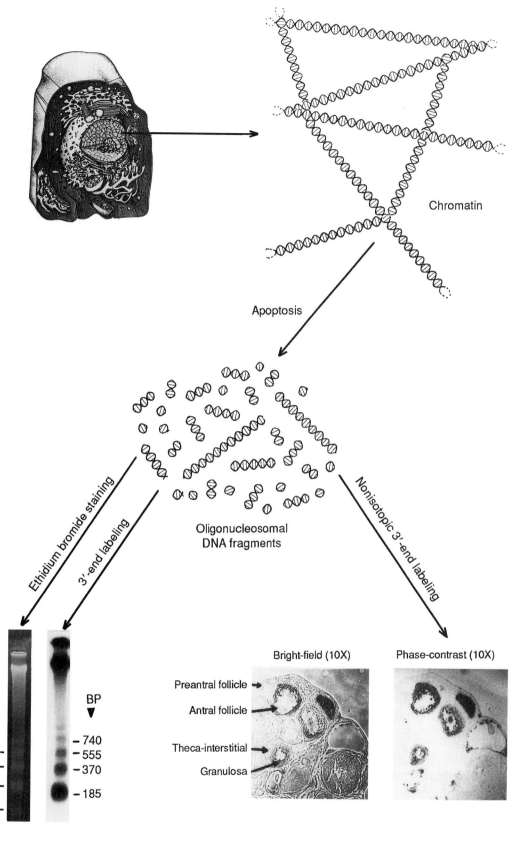

Chromatin

Apoptosis

Oligonucleosomal
DNA fragments

Ethidium bromide staining

3'-end labeling

Nonisotopic 3'-end labeling

BP

▼

— 740
— 555
— 370

— 185

Bright-field (10X)

Phase-contrast (10X)

Preantral follicle

Antral follicle

Theca-interstitial

Granulosa

Biochemical analysis

In situ analysis

Tris base, 372.2 mg EDTA, and sterile water to a total volume of 900 ml, adjust pH to 8.0 with concentrated HCl, and adjust final volume to 1 liter with sterile water.

6. DNA gel loading buffer (30% glycerol, 0.25% bromphenol blue, 0.25% xylene cylanol): dissolve 25 mg bromphenol blue and 25 mg xylene cylanol in 6.67 ml 1× TE buffer (see solution 5 above), combine with 3.33 ml glycerol to a total volume of 10 ml, and aliquot into 1.5-ml tubes (1 ml/tube); store at −20°C.

Steps

1. To a 1.5-ml microcentrifuge tube, add 250 ng of DNA and bring the total volume to 29 μl with sterile water (the amount of DNA used can be changed but should be equivalent for all samples).

2. To each tube containing DNA, add the following reagents: 10 μl 5× Tdt enzyme reaction buffer (1× final), 5 μl $CoCl_2$ solution (2.5 mM final), 5 μl [α-^{32}P]ddATP (50 μCi, 17 pmole), and 1 μl Tdt enzyme (25 units).

3. Vortex and microcentrifuge briefly. Incubate at 37°C for 60 min, and terminate the reaction with 5 μl 0.5 M EDTA.

4. Add 2 μl tRNA solution (50 μg) as carrier and precipitate the DNA with 0.2 vol (12 μl) 10 M ammonium acetate and 3 vol (180 μl) ice-cold absolute ethanol followed by incubation at −70°C for 60 min (mix well before incubation at −70°C).

5. Microcentrifuge the samples at 14,000 g for 20 min at 4°C to pellet the DNA. Discard supernatant (radioactive) and resuspend pellet with 60 μl 1× TE.

6. Repeat the precipitation (see step 4) by adding 12 μl 10 M ammonium acetate and 180 μl ice-cold absolute ethanol followed by incubation at −70°C for 60 min.

7. Microcentrifuge the samples at 14,000 g for 20 min at 4°C to pellet the DNA, discard the supernatant (radioactive), and air-dry the pellet by inverting the tube over a paper towel for 15–20 min at room temperature.

8. Resuspend the DNA with 40 μl 1× TE buffer and store in acrylic shields at −20°C overnight.

9. The following day, prepare a 2% agarose/1× TAE gel (w/v).

10. Thaw the labeled DNA samples and add 5 μl of DNA gel loading buffer. Vortex well and microcentrifuge briefly.

11. Load one-half of the sample (e.g., 22 μl) onto the gel and resolve by

FIGURE 1 Biochemical and *in situ* analysis of apoptosis. During the initiation of apoptosis in a cell (upper left), a specific endonuclease(s) cleaves the nuclear chromatin at internucleosomal sites, generating oligonucleosomal DNA fragments in size multiples of approximately 185 bp. Apoptotic DNA breakdown can be detected biochemically (by 3′-end labeling of extracted DNA, gel electrophoresis, and autoradiography) and histologically (by nonisotopic 3′-end labeling of DNA in fixed tissue sections; darkly stained cells in the phase-contrast photomicrograph indicate extensive DNA labeling/breakdown) as described in the text. Note that radiolabeling of extracted DNA on 3′-ends prior to gel electrophoresis (100 ng radiolabeled DNA loaded onto the gel) markedly improves the sensitivity of detection over that obtained with ethidium bromide staining (10 μg DNA loaded onto the gel; note that tics on the left side correspond to the first four oligonucleosomal DNA fragments as indicated for the 3′-end labeling analysis). Additionally, the *in situ* localization of DNA breakdown allows identification of specific cell populations undergoing apoptosis in tissues with heterogenous cell types (a rat ovary with healthy and atretic follicles is pictured here; see Tilly, 1993).

electrophoresis (6.5 V/cm) for approximately 3 hr using 1× TAE as running buffer.

12. Following electrophoresis, remove the gel and dry in slab-gel dryer (*without* heat) for 2 hr. Wrap the dried gel in plastic wrap and expose to X-ray film at −70°C (exposure time is dependent on the amount of DNA labeled and the extent of DNA fragmentation present).

13. Once the appropriate autoradiographic exposure has been obtained, the radiolabeled low-molecular-weight DNA fragments can be excised from the gel with a scalpel, mixed with 3 ml of scintillation fluid (Scintiverse BD, Fisher Scientific), and counted in a beta counter to obtain quantitative estimates of the degree of DNA labeling (which reflects the number of 3′-ends available for labeling and, hence, the extent of DNA cleavage) among samples (see Tilly and Hsueh, 1993).

B. *IN SITU* ANALYSIS OF DNA INTEGRITY IN FIXED TISSUE SECTIONS

Tissues should be fixed in 4% paraformaldehyde (40 g paraformaldehyde/liter 1× Dulbecco's phosphate-buffered saline, filtered with 0.45-μm vacuum filtration unit) for 24 hr (optimum length of fixation may vary with different tissues and should be determined empirically in preliminary studies to establish a time that maintains morphological characteristics of the tissue of interest). Fixed tissues should be embedded in parafin, sectioned at 5-μm thickness, mounted unstained to microscope slides, and processed as follows. (*Note:* all procedures with Coplin jars should be performed on a rocker platform.)

Solutions

1. 100 mM NaCl: Combine 5.844 g sodium chloride and sterile water to 1-liter final volume.

2. 200 mM NaCl: Combine 11.688 g sodium chloride with sterile water to 1-liter final volume.

3. Proteinase K (PK) reaction buffer (2 mM CaCl$_2$, 20 mM Tris–HCl/pH 7.5): First prepare 1 M Tris–HCl by combining 121.1 g Tris base and sterile water to a total volume of 900 ml, pH to 7.5 with concentrated hydrochloric acid, adjust final volume to 1 liter with sterile water, dilute 1:50 with sterile water for 20 mM Tris–HCl working solution (readjust pH if necessary). For PK reaction buffer, combine 294 g calcium chloride and 20 mM Tris–HCl to a total volume of 1 liter; filter with 0.45-μm vacuum filtration unit.

4. 10 mM dATP: Dilute 100 mM dATP stock 1:10 in 10 mM Tris–HCl (see solution 3 above for preparation of Tris–HCl).

5. *In situ* buffer 1 (150 mM NaCl, 100 mM Tris–HCl, pH 7.5): Combine 8.77 g sodium chloride, 12.11 Tris base, and sterile water to a total volume of 950 ml, pH to 7.5 with concentrated hydrochloric acid, adjust final volume to 1 liter with sterile water, and filter with 0.45-μm vacuum filtration unit.

6. *In situ* buffer 2 (3% BSA): Dissolve 30 mg bovine serum albumin in 1 ml of *in situ* buffer 1 (see solution 5 above); prepare fresh each time.

7. Streptavidin–alkaline phosphatase dilution buffer (0.1 M Tris–HCl, pH 7.5, 0.15 M MgCl$_2$, 1% BSA): Combine 1 ml 1 M Tris–HCl, pH 7.5 (see solution 3 above), 305 mg magnesium chloride, 100 mg bovine serum albumin, and sterile water to a total volume of 10 ml. Store at 4°C; discard unused portion after 1 month.

8. *In situ* buffer 3 (100 mM NaCl, 100 mM Tris–HCl, 50 mM $MgCl_2$, pH 9.5): Combine 5.844 g sodium chloride, 12.11 g Tris base, and sterile water to a total volume of 950 ml, pH to 9.5 with concentrated hydrochloric acid, add 10.17 g magnesium chloride, adjust final volume to 1 liter with sterile water, and filter with 0.45-μm vacuum filtration unit.

9. Stop solution (10 mM Tris–HCl, 1 mM EDTA): Combine 1.21 g Tris base, 372 mg ethylenediaminetetraacetic acid disodium salt, and sterile water to a total volume of 950 ml, pH to 8.0 with concentrated hydrochloric acid, and adjust final volume to 1 liter with sterile water.

Steps

1. Deparafinize the tissues by incubating the slides on a slide warmer for 30 min at 60°C followed by two 5-min washes in xylene at room temperature (RT) using Coplin jars.

2. Rehydrate the tissues through a graded ethanol series as follows (using Coplin jars): absolute ethanol, 2 × 5 min; 90% ethanol, 1 × 3 min; 80% ethanol, 1 × 3 min; 70% ethanol, 1 × 3 min; sterile water, 1 × 3 min.

3. Blot away excess liquid and add 10 μg/ml proteinase K solution (diluted in PK reaction buffer) to each tissue section. Although the amount added depends on the size of the section, enough solution should be added to completely cover the tissue.

4. Incubate the slides with proteinase K at 37°C for 30 min in a humidifying chamber containing 100 mM NaCl.

5. Wash the slides 2 × 5 min with sterile water in Coplin jars at RT to remove the proteinase K, and blot away excess liquid.

6. Preequilibrate the tissues with Tdt reaction buffer and $CoCl_2$ (mix 100 μl 5× Tdt reaction buffer, 100 μl $CoCl_2$, and 300 μl sterile water) for 10 min at RT (add enough solution to fully cover the tissue section).

7. Blot away preequilibration reaction buffer and add the following solution to each section (enough to fully cover): 37.5 μl sterile water, 20 μl 5× Tdt reaction buffer (1× final), 20 μl $CoCl_2$ (5 mM final), 12.5 μl biotin–dATP (50 μM final), 5 μl 10 mM dATP (500 μM final), and 5 μl Tdt enzyme (125 units).

8. Incubate slides at 37°C for 15 min in a humidifying chamber containing 200 mM NaCl (3′-end labeling reaction).

9. Wash slides 3 × 10 min in *in situ* buffer 1 at RT in Coplin jars to remove the Tdt reaction components.

10. Blot away excess liquid and block for nonspecific streptavidin binding by incubating the sections with *in situ* buffer 2 for 60 min at RT (add enough solution to cover the section).

11. Blot away blocking solution, add streptavidin conjugated to alkaline phosphatase (diluted 1:50 in streptavidin–alkaline phosphatase dilution buffer) to each section, and incubate at RT for 15 min in a humidifying chamber containing 200 mM NaCl.

12. Dip slides in a Coplin jar containing *in situ* buffer 1 to rinse away alkaline phosphatase solution and wash slides 3 × 10 min in *in situ* buffer 3 at RT in Coplin jars.

13. Blot away excess liquid and perform the colorimetric reaction to detect

localization of biotin–dATP/streptavidin–alkaline phosphatase complexes by adding the following solution to each section (add enough to fully cover the tissue section): 4 μl (300 μg) NBT and 3.3 μl (247.5 μg) BCIP in 1 ml of *in situ* buffer 3. Note that NBT and BCIP are light sensitive, and therefore this reaction should be performed under low light to prevent a nonspecific colorimetric reaction.

14. Incubate the slides at RT for 10–120 min under low or no light in a humidifying chamber containing 200 mM NaCl.

15. Periodically monitor the progression of the reaction by light microscopy and terminate when desired by placing the slides in a Coplin jar containing the stop solution.

16. Dehydrate the sections (reverse of step 2), seal with coverslips using Permount (Fisher Scientific, Cat. No. SP15-100) or other histological adhesive, and assess DNA breakdown (blue reaction product) by conventional light microscopy. In some cases, light counterstaining of tissues with eosin prior to sealing with coverslips may be required to allow visualization of tissue or cell morphology by light microscopy.

IV. Comments

The procedures described herein should facilitate the study of qualitative and quantitative changes in internucleosomal DNA fragmentation in minute amounts of biological starting material, as well as identify, *in situ,* specific cell populations that exhibit increased DNA breakdown associated with apoptosis. For additional information on these techniques, the reader is referred to Tilly and Hsueh (1993: biochemical analysis of apoptosis), Gavrieli *et al.* (1992: *in situ* analysis of apoptosis), and the Protocol Books from Gibco-BRL Life Technologies for the *In Situ* Hybridization and Detection System (Cat. No. 18250-019) and the BluGENE Nonradioactive Nucleic Acid Detection System (Cat. No. 18279-018).

V. Pitfalls

The *in situ* analysis of DNA fragmentation, although a potentially powerful tool that can identify specific cell populations undergoing cell death in any given tissue, does not discriminate between DNA breakdown associated with apoptosis (internucleosomal) and necrosis (random cleavage). Therefore, it must be emphasized that the *in situ* analysis of DNA integrity should be confirmed by biochemical analysis of DNA extracted from the tissue to ensure that the DNA breakdown detected *in situ* is a result of cells dying via apoptosis.

Depending on the tissue examined by the *in situ* analysis, the concentration of proteinase K used for digestion (1–100 μg/ml) as well as the length of proteinase K digestion (15–60 min) can be changed and should be determined empirically in preliminary studies. Additionally, the dilution of streptavidin–alkaline phosphatase may be altered (between 1:5 and 1:500) to overcome a low incidence of 3'-ends available for labeling or background labeling problems.

Additionally, treatment of tissues with levamisole (Sigma Chemical Company, Cat. No. L-9756) may be required in some instances to inactivate endogenous alkaline phosphatases which would cause high background labeling.

REFERENCES

Gavrieli, Y., Sherman, Y., and Ben-Sasson, S. A. (1992) Identification of programmed cell death *in situ* via specific labeling of nuclear DNA fragmentation. *J. Cell Biol.* **119,** 493–501.

Gross-Bellard, M., Oudet, P., and Chambon, P. (1973) Isolation of high-molecular-weight DNA from mammalian cells. *Eur. J. Biochem.* **36,** 32–38.

Hughes, F. M., Jr., and Gorospe, W. C. (1991) Biochemical identification of apoptosis (programmed cell death) in granulosa cells: Evidence for a potential mechanism underlying follicular atresia. *Endocrinology* **129,** 2415–2422.

Kerr, J. F. R., Wyllie, A. H., and Currie, A. R. (1972) Apoptosis: A basic biological phenomenon with wide-ranging implications in tissue kinetics. *Br. J. Cancer* **26,** 239–257.

Schwartz, L. M., Smith, S. W., Jones, M. E. E., and Osborne, B. A. (1993) Do all programmed cell deaths occur via apoptosis? *Proc. Natl. Acad. Sci. USA* **90,** 980–984.

Tapanainen, J. S., Tilly, J. L., Vihko, K. K., and Hsueh, A. J. W. (1993) Hormonal control of apoptotic cell death in the testis: Gonadotropins and androgens as testicular cell survival factors. *Mol. Endocrinol.* **7,** 643–650.

Tilly, J. L. (1993) Ovarian follicular atresia: A model to study the mechanisms of physiological cell death. *Endocrine J.* **1,** 67–72.

Tilly, J. L., and Hsueh, A. J. W. (1993) Microscale autoradiographic method for the qualitative and quantitative analysis of apoptotic DNA fragmentation. *J. Cell. Physiol.* **154,** 519–526.

Tilly, J. L., Kowalski, K. I., Johnson, A. L., and Hsueh, A. J. W. (1991) Involvement of apoptosis in ovarian follicular atresia and postovulatory regression. *Endocrinology* **131,** 2799–2801.

Ucker, D. S., Obermiller, P. S., Eckhart, W., Apgar, J. R., Berger, N. A., and Meyers, J. (1992) Genome digestion is a dispensable consequence of physiological cell death mediated by cytotoxic T lymphocytes. *Mol. Cell. Biol.* **12,** 3060–3069.

Wyllie, A. H. (1980) Glucocorticoid-induced thymocyte apoptosis is associated with endogenous endonuclease activation. *Nature* **284,** 555–556.

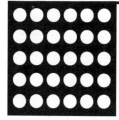

Growth and Induction of Metastasis of Mammary Epithelial Cells

Barry R. Davies and Philip S. Rudland

I. Introduction

Clonal mammary epithelial cell lines derived from inbred animals represent a valuable model system in which to assay candidate genes for metastatic potential using DNA transfection techniques. Stably diploid epithelial cell lines derived from appropriate tissues are greatly to be preferred to well-established, aneuploid, fibroblastic cell lines as recipients for transfection, because the majority of life-threatening tumors in humans are solid carcinomas (Fidler, 1992), and certain cell lines may acquire metastatic potential spontaneously or as a result of the process of DNA transfection per se (Kerbel *et al.,* 1987; Verelle *et al.,* 1987; Cassingena *et al.,* 1992). The experimental details presented in this article describe the establishment of a benign, non-metastasising mammary epithelial cell line from an inbred rat strain, a protocol for the transfection of these cells with potentially metastatic DNA and an *in vivo* assay for metastatic potential.

II. Materials

Dulbecco's modified Eagle's medium (DMEM; Cat. No. 041-01965M), Ham's F12 medium (Cat. No. 041-01765M), fetal calf serum (FCS; Cat. No. 011-06290M), EDTA (Cat. No. 043-05040H), trypsin (Cat. No. 043-05090H), Geneticin (G418 sulfate; Cat. No. 066-1811), 200 mM L-glutamine (Cat. No. 043-05030H), 7.5% (w/v) sodium bicarbonate (Cat. No. 043-05080H), and 1000 IU/ml penicillin plus 1000 μg/ml streptomycin (Cat. No. 043-05140H) are purchased from Gibco Bio-Cult. Tissue culture plates, bacteriological-grade Petri dishes, and multiwell plates are obtained from Nunc. Insulin (Cat. No. I-5500), hydrocortisone (Cat. No. H-4001), epidermal growth factor (EGF; Cat. No. E-4127), collagenase type I (Cat. No. C-0130), hyaluronidase type I (Cat. No. H-3506), crystalline bovine serum albumin (BSA; A-9647), mitomycin C (M-0503), and dimethyl sulfoxide (DMSO; Cat. No. D-5879) are obtained from Sigma. Dimethylbenzanthracene (DMBA; Cat. No. D-3254) and pronase grade B (Cat. No. 537088) are from Calbiochem, and silicone grease for cloning (Cat. No. 555-083) is from RS Components Ltd. Methanol, acetic acid, calcium chloride, sodium hydrogen phosphate, sodium chloride, and Hepes (all analar grade) are obtained from BDH. Inbred Furth–Wistar rats (Ludwig–Wistar strain DLA) are obtained from Harlan Olac Ltd.

III. Procedures

A. ISOLATION AND PROPAGATION OF MAMMARY EPITHELIAL CELLS

Solutions

1. *7,12-Dimethylbenzanthracene solution:* 100 mg dissolved in 10 ml corn oil.

2. *Digest solution:* RM containing 150 U/ml collagenase and 230 U/ml hyaluronidase.

3. *PBS:* Phosphate-buffered isotonic saline, Ca^{2+} and Mg^{2+}-free. To make 1 liter weigh out 10 g NaCl, 0.25 g KCl 1.44 g Na_2HPO_4, 0.25 g KH_2PO_4, dissolve in distilled water and sterilize by autoclaving.

4. *RM:* To make 1 liter, add 900 ml DMEM, 25 ml sodium bicarbonate, 7.5% (w/v), 50 ml FCS, 5 ml of 5 μg/ml insulin stock solution, 5 ml of 5 μg/ml hydrocortisone stock solution, 5 ml of penicillin/streptomycin stock solution, and 10 ml 200 mM L-glutamine under sterile conditions.

5. *CM:* To make 100 ml, add 95 ml of Ham's F12 medium to 5 ml FCS, expose for 24 hr to confluent cultures of the Rama 29 myoepithelial-like cell line, and then sterilize by filtration.

6. *Cloning medium:* To make 100 ml, add 50 ml CM, 40 ml DMEM, 10 ml FCS, 1 ml of insulin and hydrocortisone stock solutions, and 0.2 ml of EGF stock solution.

7. *Insulin stock solution:* To make 100 ml, dissolve 500 μg insulin in 1 ml 0.1 M HCl; then dilute in 100 ml of PBS containing 100 μg/ml BSA and sterilize by filtration.

8. *Hydrocortisone stock solution:* To make 4 ml, dissolve 20 μg in 1 ml of ethanol and dilute with 3 ml PBS.

9. *EGF stock solution:* To make 10 ml, dissolve 50 μg of EGF in 10 ml PBS containing 100 μg/ml BSA and sterilize by filtration.

10. *DMEM–EDTA:* To make 100 ml, weigh out 2 mg EDTA, dissolve in 100 ml DMEM, Ca^{2+} and Mg^{2+}-free, adjust to pH 7.0, and sterilize by filtration.

11. *Trypsin–EDTA:* To make 100 ml, weigh out 2 mg EDTA, dissolve in 98 ml PBS, add 2 ml trypsin solution, and sterilize by filtration.

12. *Pronase solution:* To make 1 liter of PBS containing 30 μM Ca^{2+}, 15 μM Mg^{2+}, weigh out 2.2 g $CaCl_2 \cdot H_2O$ and 6.0 g $MgCl_2 \cdot H_2O$ and dissolve in 1 liter of PBS. To make 10 ml of pronase solution dissolve 1 mg in 10 ml and sterilize by filtration.

Steps

1. Inbred Furth–Wistar rats are fed 1 ml of 7,12-dimethylbenzanthracene solution by stomach tube when 50 days old (Huggins *et al.*, 1961).

2. After about 2 months, a small tumor is selected, chopped into 150-mm cubes, and digested with 2 to 4 ml digest solution at 37°C for 2 hr; this yields a mixture of cell clumps or organoids (predominantly epithelial cells) and single cells (mostly stromal cells) which are collected by centrifugation at 800 rpm for 5 min.

3. The mixture is suspended in cloning medium. The single cells adhere most rapidly to the dishes. To select for epithelial cells, the unattached cells are transferred to new dishes after 90 min and again after 180 min, and finally the

epithelial cells are plated out in cloning medium and grown overnight at 37°C in a 90% air, 10% CO_2 moist atmosphere.

4. The attached epithelial cells are rinsed twice in PBS and once in warm DMEM–EDTA solution. After 3 min incubation, an upper layer of small epithelioid cells becomes partly detached from a basal cell layer, and these are replated and grown in cloning medium together with mitomycin C-treated Rama 29 feeder cells.

5. Stromal cells are removed by incubating PBS-washed cultures with pronase solution for 1 min at 37°C and replaced by mitomycin C-treated Rama 29 feeder cells.

6. Epithelial cell cultures are transferred at a ratio of 1:1 by treatment with DMEM–EDTA solution and replated and grown in cloning medium.

7. Repeat steps 5 and 6 until visibly growing cultures arise due to spontaneous immortalization.

8. To prepare cells for single-cell cloning, cells are detached with DMEM–EDTA solution and the cell suspension is diluted greatly in cloning medium to give a density of 10^2 to 10^3 cells/cm^2 in a bacteriological-grade Petri dish. Single cells are located using an inverted microscope and picked with a drawn-out pasteur pipette and plugged mouth tube. Each cell is transferred to a 6-mm culture well containing 100 μl of cloning medium and 5×10^4 mitomycin C-treated Rama 29 feeder cells. These feeder cells are produced by incubating near-confluent Rama 29 cells in RM with 0.5 μg/ml mitomycin C for 14 to 16 hr and detached with trypsin–EDTA solution. After 4–8 days of incubation, selected cell colonies are passaged by washing with PBS, incubating with trypsin–EDTA solution for 3–5 min at 37°C, and transferred to 16-mm wells.

9. Representative cuboidal epithelial cells are subjected to two further successive single-cell cloning procedures at passage 10 in cloning medium without the use of feeders, to rule out the possibility that elongated cells had been introduced into the epithelial cell cultures by incomplete inactivation of the feeders by mitomycin C.

10. The cells are subsequently cultured in RM and passaged subconfluently by trypsin–EDTA treatment with a 1:8 split ratio.

11. The clonal cuboidal epithelial cells may be karyotyped (Dunnington *et al.*, 1983) and characterized serologically with various antisera (Rudland, 1987). Mammary epithelial cells should stain with antisera to milk fat globule membrane (MFGM), epithelial membrane antigen (EMA), and MAb PKK3 to Keratin 18.

B. INDUCTION OF METASTASIS IN MAMMARY EPITHELIAL CELLS

The experimental procedure employed to investigate the ability of DNA to confer directly metastatic potential on a representative cuboidal epithelial mammary cell line is outlined in Fig. 1 and described in detail below.

C. TRANSFECTION OF MAMMARY EPITHELIAL CELLS IN CULTURE

Solutions

1. *HBS:* 280 mM NaCl, 50 mM Hepes, 1.5 mM Na$_2$HPO$_4$·12H$_2$O. To make 1 liter, weigh out 16.38 g NaCl, 11.9 g Hepes, 0.53 g Na$_2$HPO$_4$·2H$_2$O; dissolve in 1 liter of distilled water making the pH 7.1 ± 0.05 and sterilize by filtration.

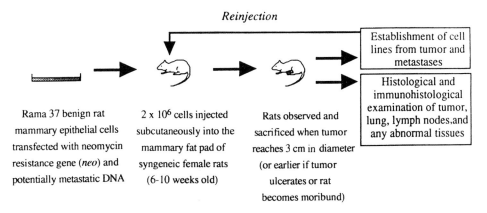

Reinjection

Rama 37 benign rat mammary epithelial cells transfected with neomycin resistance gene (*neo*) and potentially metastatic DNA → 2 x 10⁶ cells injected subcutaneously into the mammary fat pad of syngeneic female rats (6-10 weeks old) → Rats observed and sacrificed when tumor reaches 3 cm in diameter (or earlier if tumor ulcerates or rat becomes moribund) → Establishment of cell lines from tumor and metastases / Histological and immunohistological examination of tumor, lung, lymph nodes,and any abnormal tissues

FIGURE 1   Rat mammary model system to assay DNA for metastatic potential.

2. *1 M CaCl₂:* For 100 ml, dissolve 14.7 g of CaCl₂·2H₂O in sterile distilled water and adjust to a total volume of 100 ml. Autoclave and store at 4°C.

3. *SM:* RM plus 1 mg/ml Geneticin (G418 sulfate). Sterilize by filtration.

4. *pSV2neoDNA:* For 1 ml, dissolve 10 μg in 1 ml of distilled water and sterilize by filtration.

Steps

1. Four 9-cm-diameter culture dishes are seeded with approximately 0.7×10^6 cells/dish and grown overnight at 37°C in RM.

2. The next morning, the medium is changed and the cells are incubated at 37°C for 4 hr in 10 ml RM.

3. For each transfection, two siliconized Eppendorf vials are required. To the first Eppendorf vial, add 500 μl of 2× HBS. To the second, add 125 μl of 1 *M* CaCl₂, 2 μg or 100 μl of pSV2*neo*DNA (Southern and Berg, 1982), 18 μg of the DNA of interest, and make up the volume to 500 μl with sterile, double-distilled water. The calcium phosphate–DNA precipitate is formed by adding the contents of the second Eppendorf vial to the first in a dropwise manner, while bubbling air through the mixture using sterile, siliconized Pasteur pipettes. Include as controls a transfection experiment with pSV2*neo* alone and a negative control with no DNA present. Leave the vials to stand for 30 min at room temperature.

4. The vials are inverted to mix, and the calcium phosphate–DNA precipitates are added directly to individual dishes of cells. The cells on the fourth dish are counted to determine the transfection frequency.

5. The cultures are incubated at 37°C for 4 hr to allow the calcium phosphate–DNA precipitate to settle on the cells.

6. The medium is removed and replaced with RM containing 10% (v/v) DMSO. Incubate at room temperature for 90 sec.

7. Remove the medium, wash the cells with RM, and then add 10 ml RM and incubate for 24 hr at 37°C.

8. Passage cells 1:10 into SM. Change the medium every 3–4 days thereafter. Colonies of transfected cells should appear after 10–14 days. After 3 weeks the colonies may be pooled and the cells expanded in SM, or alternatively individual colonies may be ring-cloned to obtain a homogenous population of cells derived from a single transfectant.

9. To ring clone, cloning rings are made by slicing 5-mm lengths off the wide end

of 200-μl Gilson pipette tips using a hot scalpel blade. The cloning rings are approximately 5 mm in diameter and may be autoclaved and stored in a universal until required. Selected colonies are marked on the underside of the culture dish by viewing under an inverted microscope. The cells are washed twice with PBS and allowed to dry. A sterile cloning ring is dipped in sterile cloning grease and placed over a colony; the position is checked under an inverted microscope. Colonies are then detached with trypsin–EDTA solution and transferred to 1-cm-diameter culture wells containing SM, and the colonies grown and expanded.

D. BIOASSAY FOR METASTATIC POTENTIAL IN SYNGENEIC RATS

Steps

1. Harvest cells with trypsin–EDTA solution and resuspend in PBS containing 10% FCS (v/v) at 4°C.

2. Centrifuge cells at 800 rpm for 5 min at room temperature. Resuspend cells in 20 ml PBS at 4°C and repeat the centrifugation step.

3. Resuspend cells in PBS at 4°C to give a concentration of 10^7 cells/ml.

4. Inject syngeneic Furth–Wistar female rats of 6–10 weeks of age subcutaneously into the left or right inguinal mammary fat pad with 0.2 ml of cell suspension.

5. Observe the rats at 3- to 4-day intervals throughout the postinjection period. When the primary tumor reaches 3 cm in diameter (or earlier if the tumor ulcerates or the rat suffers serious morbidity), the animal is sacrificed and a full autopsy carried out. Samples of the primary tumor, lungs, lymph nodes, and any other tissues of abnormal appearance are fixed in Methacarn (methanol:Inhibisol: acetic acid in the ratio 6:3:1 v/v) and processed for histological examination.

IV. Selected Example and Comments

The Rama 37 cuboidal epithelial cell line was established by the above protocol (Bennett *et al.,* 1978) and single-cell cloned three times at passage 10 in cloning medium, without the use of feeder cells, to rule out the possibility that elongated cells had been introduced into the culture by incomplete inactivation of the feeder cells by mitomycin C (Dunnington *et al.,* 1983). The resulting cell line Rama 37 CL-A3 represents a diploid, epithelial cell population which retains its karyology and epithelial staining characteristics, even after up to 40 passages *in vitro.* When reintroduced into the mammary tissue of the same inbred rat strain from which it was derived, this cell line produces benign, glandular, adenomatous tumors that fail to metastasize (Fig. 2A) (Dunnington *et al.,* 1983).

Rama 37 cells convert to more elongated, spindle cells at low frequency in culture, and the proportion of elongated variants appears to be increased at high cell densities. Some of the more elongated cells have been characterized as myoepithelial-like cells (Rudland, 1987). Elongated cells can also arise as a result of the transfection process. Hence the majority of transfected cell tumors consist entirely of spindle cells (Fig. 2B).

Transfection of plasmid constructs containing the *neo* gene or cotransfection of pSV2*neo* and unlinked genes/DNA fragments yields drug-resistant colonies with a frequency of 10^{-5} to 10^{-4} in this system. Transfected DNA remains stably incorporated into the genome of Rama 37 cells even after passage *in vivo.* The metastatic potential of the transfected cell lines is retained when cells are reestablished in culture from tumors and metastatic lesions and reinjected into fresh animals.

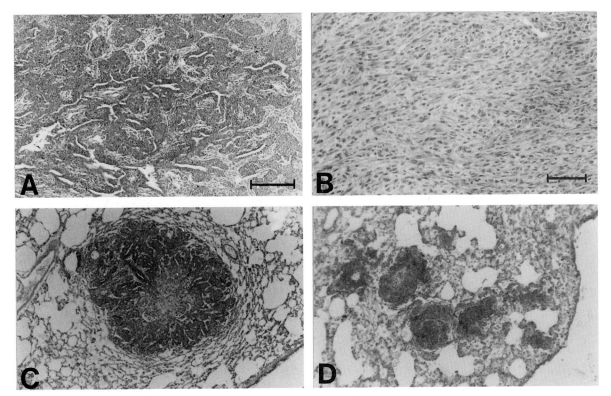

FIGURE 2 Tumors produced by Rama 37 cells and transfected cells. (A) Glandular, benign, adenomatous tumor produced by untransfected Rama 37 mammary epithelial cells. (B) Primary tumor produced by Rama 37 cells cotransfected with pSV2*neo* and DNA fragments from the human malignant breast carcinoma cell line Ca2-83, consisting of undifferentiated spindle cells. (C) A large "canonball" metastasis in the lungs of a rat injected with Rama 37 cells transfected with a plasmid construct containing the p9Ka gene (pSV2*neo*p9Ka). (D) Multiple micrometastatic lesions in the lung tissue of a rat injected with Rama 37 cells cotransfected with pSV2*neo* and DNA fragments from the malignant human cell line MCF-7. Magnification for A, B, D: ×58, bar = 200 μm. Magnification for C: ×230, bar = 50 μm.

Using the protocol described in this article, we have investigated the ability of a battery of known genes that have been correlated with metastatic breast disease in rodents and in humans to confer directly metastatic potential. Transfection of the p9Ka gene, which codes for a small, acidic, rat calcium-binding protein, is able to confer metastatic potential on Rama 37 cells (Davies *et al.*, 1993a). In addition, gene-length DNA fragments from metastatic rat and human breast cancer cell lines can induce the metastatic phenotype (Jamieson *et al.*, 1990a; Davies *et al.*, 1993b). The most common sites of metastasis are the lungs and axillary lymph nodes (Figs. 2C,D). The H-*ras*, polyoma large-T antigen, and bFGF genes and the drug resistance plasmid pSV2*neo* alone fail to confer metastatic properties (Jamieson *et al.*, 1990b; Davies *et al.*, 1993a,b). This indicates that induction of metastatic ability is a specific property of the transfected DNA/gene of interest.

V. Pitfalls

1. To obtain clonal cell lines from the primary epithelial cell cultures it is essential that these cultures are passaged at least five or six times and are actively growing in cloning medium; this ensures that a population of cells has become immortalized (Bennett *et al.*, 1978).

2. It is essential that a fine calcium phosphate–DNA precipitate is formed if the transfection procedure is to be successful. Coarse or lumpy precipitates lead to low transfection frequencies. It is recommended that the 2× HBS is prepared freshly for each transfection experiment and not stored.

3. Some ring-cloned transfected cells appear to undergo sudden crisis and die. This may reflect unstable integration of the drug resistance plasmid into the genome of the recipient cells.

4. Small micrometastatic lesions may fail to be detected by histological techniques unless many serial sections are examined. Therefore, we recommend that samples of lung, axillary lymph node, and any abnormal-looking tissues are cultured by digesting with type I collagenase and replated in RM (Davies *et al.*, 1993b). Only tumor cells will form permanently growing cell lines; fibroblasts and other contaminating host cells die after several passages *in vitro*. This provides a reliable second screen for metastatic colonies.

5. It is possible that accidental damage to blood vessels/lymphatics at the site of injection will lead to artificial metastases. To confirm the metastatic potential of transfected cells, we recommend that cells reestablished in culture from possible metastatic lesions are reassayed for metastatic potential in larger groups of animals.

REFERENCES

Bennett, D. C., Peachey, L. A., Durbin, H., and Rudland, P. S. (1978) A possible mammary stem cell line. *Cell* **15**, 283–298.

Cassingena, R., Lafarge-Frayssinet, C., Frayssinet, C., Nardeux, P., Estrade, S., Viegas-Pequignot, E., and Dutrillaux, B. (1992) Spontaneous metastatic potential of rat hepatocarcinoma cells after cell fusion or DNA transfection. *Int. J. Cancer* **50**, 238–245.

Davies, B. R., Davies, M. P. A., Gibbs, F. E. M., Barraclough, R., and Rudland, P. S. (1993a) Induction of the metastatic phenotype by transfection of a benign rat mammary epithelial cell line with the gene for p9Ka, a rat calcium-binding protein, but not with the oncogene EJ-*ras*-1. *Oncogene* **8**, 999–1008.

Davies, B. R., Barraclough, R., Davies, M. P. A., and Rudland, P. S. (1993b) Production of the metastatic phenotype by DNA transfection in a rat mammary model. *Cell Biol. Int.*, in press.

Dunnington, D. J., Hughes, C. M., Monaghan, P., and Rudland, P. S. (1983) Phenotypic instability of rat mammary tumour epithelial cells. *J. Natl. Cancer Inst.* **71**, 1227–1240.

Huggins, C., Grand, L. C., and Brillantes, F. P. (1961) Mammary cancer induced by a single feeding of polynuclear hydrocarbons and its suppression. *Nature* **189**, 204–207.

Jamieson, S., Barraclough, R., and Rudland, P. S. (1990a) Generation of metastatic variants by transfection of a non-metastatic rat mammary epithelial cell line with DNA from a metastatic rat mammary cell line. *Pathobiology* **58**, 329–342.

Jamieson, S., Barraclough, R., and Rudland, P. S. (1990b) Transfection of a non-metastatic diploid rat mammary epithelial cell line with the oncogenes for EJ-*ras*-1 and polyoma large-T antigen. *Int. J. Cancer* **46**, 1071–1080.

Kerbel, R. S., Waghorne, C., Man, H. S., Elliot, B., and Breitman, M. L. (1987) Alterations of the tumorigenic and metastatic properties of neoplastic cells is associated with the process of calcium phosphate-mediated DNA transfection. *Proc. Natl. Acad. Sci. USA* **84**, 1263–1267.

Rudland, P. S. (1987) Stem cells in mammary development and cancer. *In* "Cellular and Molecular Biology of Mammary Cancer" (D. Medina, W. Kidwell, G. Heppner, and E. Anderson, eds.), pp. 9–27, Plenum, New York.

Southern, P. J., and Berg, P. (1982) Transformation of mammalian cells to antibiotic resistance with a bacterial gene under the control of the SV40 early region promotor. *J. Mol. Appl. Genet.* **1**, 327–341.

Verelle, P., Lescaut, V., Poupon, M. F., and Hillova, J. (1987) DNA transfection affects the metastatic capacity of tumour cells. *Anticancer Res.* **7**, 181–186.

Measurement of Cell–Cell and Cell–Extracellular Matrix Interactions: A Quantitative Cell Attachment Assay

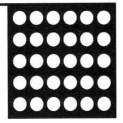

Thomas E. Lallier

I. Introduction

The accurate measurement of cell adhesion, either to another cell or to the extracellular matrix, is a requirement of many researchers investigating the metastatic properties of cells, as well as cells undergoing morphogenetic movements and migration. The measurement of the attachment of cells that are rare or difficult to isolate was first described by McClay and colleagues (1981). Their technique, which was first used to measure the attachment properties of sea urchin micromeres, has recently been used to study the adhesive characteristics of avian neural crest cells (Lallier and Bronner-Fraser, 1991, 1992, 1993) and human macrophages (Shaw *et al.*, 1990).

II. Materials and Instrumentation

Polyvinyl chloride (PVC, Cat. No. 3912) and polystyrene 96-well plates (Cat. No. 3915) were obtained from Falcon. Double-sided carpet tape was obtained from 3M (Cat. No. 140). Minimal essential medium (MEM) was obtained from Gibco (Cat. No. 410-100EB). L-[^{3}H]leucine and L-[^{14}C]leucine (sterile in 2% ethanol) were obtained from ICN (Cat. Nos. 20032E and 10088E). Bovine serum albumin (BSA, Cat. No. A-2153), ovalbumin (Cat. No. A-5398), sodium phosphate (monobasic, Cat. No. S-0751), sodium phosphate (dibasic, Cat. No. S-0876), sodium chloride (Cat. No. S-9888), sodium bicarbonate (Cat. No. S-6014), phenol red (Cat. No. P-0290), calcium chloride (Cat. No. C-4901), EDTA (Cat. No. EDS), magnesium chloride (Cat. No. M-8266), EHS laminin (Cat. No. L-2020), human plasma fibronectin (Cat. No. F-2006), rat collagen type I (Cat. No. C-7661), and collagen type IV (Cat. No. C-0543) were obtained from Sigma Chemical Company.

Required common equipment includes a table-top centrifuge with swinging buckets for 96-well plates; a metal vise with a 8 × 4-cm minimum area; a liquid scintillation counter; scintillation vials; an 18-gauge needle; scissors; a cork bore 7 mm in diameter; a dry ice/methanol bath; and forceps.

Special equipment includes modified dog nail clippers (Figs. 1A and 2B) and stainless-steel "chuck" for microassay plates (Figs. 1C and 2A).

III. Procedures

A. RADIOLABELING OF CELLS

Solutions

1. *Tissue culture medium:* MEM with 10% fetal calf serum, or the preferred medium for your cells.

2. *L-[^{3}H]Leucine:* Dilute with sterile distilled H_2O to 1 mCi/ml.

3. *L-[^{14}C]Leucine:* Dilute with sterile distilled H_2O to 1 mCi/ml.

Steps

1. Grow the population of cells to be tested to a nonconfluent state in a 35-mm tissue culture dish. If these cells are abundant, 10^4 to 10^5 cells per assay plate will give best results. For rare cells, as few as 10^3 cells per assay plate can be measured reliably. Label these cells by adding 10–100 μCi of L-[^{3}H]leucine to 1 ml of tissue culture medium, and incubate this with the cells overnight. Serum in the medium does not appreciably affect the incorporation of the isotope. Cells should be grown on fibronectin substrata (coated 25 μg/ml in a 35-mm tissue culture dish) to facilitate cell removal.

2. If cell–cell interactions are to be assayed, label a second group of cells (greater than 10^7 cells) overnight with 10–100 μCi L-[^{14}C]leucine.

B. PREPARATION OF ADHESION ASSAY PLATES

Solutions

1. *Substratum coating solution:* 10 mM sodium bicarbonate, pH 7.4, 100 mM sodium chloride containing extracellular matrix molecules (i.e., laminin or fibronectin) at a final concentration of 10–100 μg/ml. Dilute collagen type I in ice-cold buffer to prevent premature gelling. Store at 4°C.

2. *Substratum blocking solution (SBS):* 1× MEM, pH 7.4, with 1 mg/ml heat inactivated BSA or ovalbumin. BSA or ovalbumin can be heat inactivated in a 10 mg/ml stock solution by heating to 60°C for 1 hr. In this solution, 1× MEM can be replaced with whichever serum-free medium best supports the cells to be tested or phosphate-buffered saline (PBS). Store at 4°C.

3. *Phosphate-buffered saline (PBS):* To make 1 liter, dissolve 8.2 g NaCl, 1.15 g Na_2HPO_4, and 0.2 g NaH_2PO_4 in distilled H_2O; adjust pH to 7.4. Store at room temperature.

4. *500 mM EDTA stock:* To make 100 ml, dissolve 14.6 g of EDTA in distilled H_2O, and neutralize to pH 7.0–8.0 with 10 M NaOH. Store at room temperature.

5. *Nitrocellulose solution:* To make 100 ml, dissolve 2.5 cm^2 of nitrocellulose in 100% methanol. Store at room temperature.

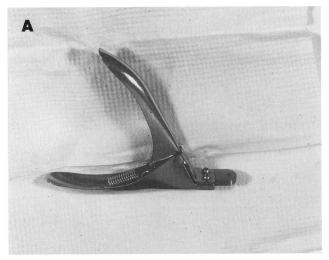

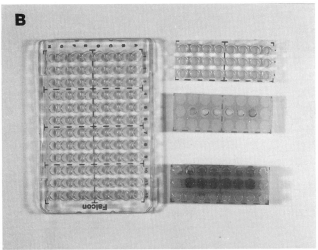

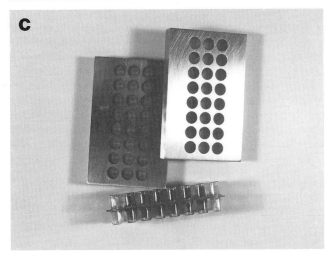

FIGURE 1 Special equipment. (A) Modified dog nail clippers used to remove the ends of assay wells. (B) Polyvinyl chloride 96-well plate (left), 24-well assay chamber cover (top right), substratum plate with tape and holes for central six wells (center right), and a filled and sealed assay chamber (bottom right). (C) Two stainless-steel "chucks" for clamping assay plates together (top) and a filled and sealed assay chamber (side view, bottom).

A

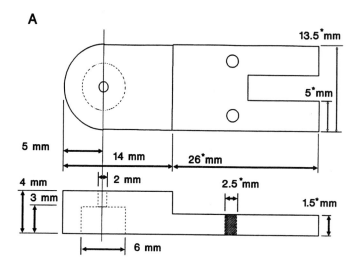

B

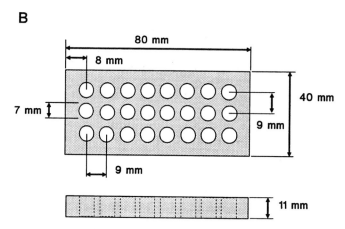

FIGURE 2 Custom equipment (schematics). (A) Modified head for dog nail clippers. Large commercially available dog nail clippers can be purchased at most pet shops. The stationary top ring, designed to hold the dog nail during cutting, should be removed and replaced with a solid brass (or stainless-steel) fitting, milled to the specifications in the diagram. The measurements with asterisks will vary depending on the exact configuration of the clippers purchased. The 2.5*-mm-diameter hole is threaded for a screw and should match the specifications of the "host" clippers. The 6-mm hole (only partially through the head) allows for ease in reproducibly cutting the same volume of fluid and cells. The small 2-mm hole allows one to easily eject the bottom of the clipped well with a blunted 18-gauge needle. (B) Steel "chuck" for clamping assay plates together. This can be made of either stainless steel or brass. The measurements for the holes and their placement are critical. Note that the holes go entirely through the block.

Steps

1. Cut the edges off PVC 96-well plates, and cut into quarters so that there are four plates of 8 × 3 wells. A typical experiment would use 24 plates, 12 substratum plates, and 12 covers (see Fig. 1B).

2. Cover half of the plates with double-sided carpet tape (with the backing retained). Trim off excess tape. These are the bottom assay plates. Rub plate, tape side down, on a flat surface to achieve even adherence of the tape to the plate.

3. Label the bottom of the central six wells with a black sharpie (other colors are soluble in methanol). Remove backing to the tape. Heat a 7-mm cork bore

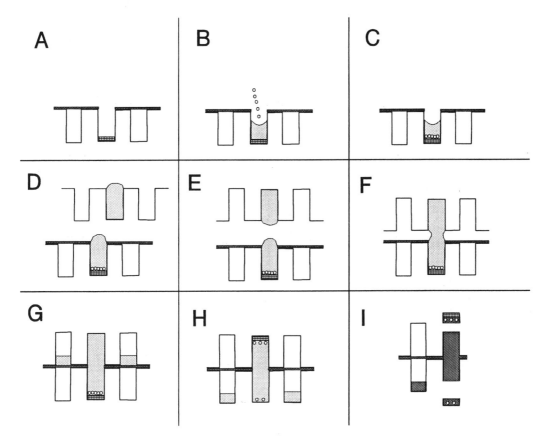

FIGURE 3 Schematic of procedural steps. (A) Side view of an assay plate (cutaway). Tape has to be placed over all the wells, and the edges trimmed. A hole has been burnt through the tape covering the center six wells, and a substratum molecule has been coated in the bottom of these wells. (B) The central wells have been partially filled with SBS and labeled cells have been added. (C) The cells have been brought into contact with the substratum by centrifugal force. (D) The central wells have been further filled with SBS, until the menisci bulge. A second plate (the cover) has had its central six wells filled with SBS, until the menisci also bulge (but only slightly). (E) The cover plate is inverted over the substratum plate, so that the central six wells now align. (F) The cover plate is lowered into proximity with the substrata plate, so that the menisci meet. (G) The cover plate is brought into contact with the substratum plate, to be sealed by the metal vise. Note that the excess solution tends to fill the empty wells in the cover plate. (H) The chamber is inverted, and subjected to a centrifugal force. Note that some of the cells are now attached to the substratum, whereas others are adjacent to the cover. (I) The chamber is "quick"-frozen, and one row of wells is cut off. The ends of the assay wells, both substratum and cover, are clipped off using modified dog nail clippers and placed into scintillation vials for counting.

with a Bunsen burner, and gently touch heated metal to the center six wells (see Fig. 1B). This burns holes through the tape. Be careful not to let the metal touch the sides of the PVC wells, or it will burn a hole through them as well. This will lead to the wells leaking fluid and unusable wells (Fig. 3A).

4. Place assay plates into polystyrene 96-well plates, three plates per 96-well plate so that the sticky edges of adjacent plates do not touch. Coat wells with extracellular matrix (ECM) or cells of substrate of interest. *For ECM molecules,* dilute protein to desired concentration with substratum coating buffer. Fifty microliters of coating solution per well is generally sufficient. Label plates by writing directly onto the tape with a black sharpie. Place in humid chambers to prevent evaporation of coating solution. Overnight coating at 4°C works best, but incubating for as little as 2 hr at room temperature will result in comparable

results for solutions at greater than 10 μg/ml ECM molecule concentration. *For cell–cell interactions,* a confluent monolayer of cells must be plated into each well. Pretreat the wells first with the nitrocellulose solution by adding 25 μl of this solution to each of the center six wells. Allow this solution to evaporate (about 15–30 min) at room temperature in a tissue culture hood. Then rinse the wells five times with PBS. Remove cells from their 35-mm dish as described below in Section C. Then aliquot 10^7 cells into each of the center six wells of the assay plate, and allow the cells to adhere for 1 hr at 37°C.

5. Rinse wells five times with PBS to remove nonadherent protein or cells. If cells were plated, visually inspect them to determine if they are confluent.

6. Block substrata by incubation with SBS for 2 hr at 37°C.

C. PREPARATION OF RADIOLABELLED CELLS

Steps

1. Rinse labeled cells five times with SBS. Remove cells from substrate. This can be done by incubating the cells in 5–10 mM EDTA in SBS for 5–20 min (depending on the cell type). The cells should become rounded and be easily removed by gentle trituration. This has the advantage of not destroying the cell's surface receptors. Alternatively, cells can be removed from the substrate by incubation with 0.25% trypsin for 5–20 min.

2. Transfer cells to a sterile polypropylene test tube. Gentle trituration of the cells with a Pasteur pipette will yield a suspension of single cells.

D. CENTRIFUGAL CELL ADHESION ASSAY

Solution

1. *Test solution:* This solution varies with each experiment. It should contain about 1 mg/ml protein to reduce nonspecific adhesion to plastic and to other cells. It may contain MEM or PBS, antibodies, enzymes, or competitive inhibitors for adhesion.

Steps

1. Have standing by scintillation vials—12 vials per plate of 6 wells will be needed, 6 for adherent cells (substratum side) and 6 for nonadherent cells—and a methanol/dry ice bath. The bath should contain at least a liter of methanol and several pounds of dry ice. Add dry ice to methanol until the dry ice fails to produce bubbles. This quickly freezes water. This bath can be reused several (20 or more) times, so do not discard after your experiment.

2. Rinse wells of substratum-coated plates twice with SBS, and fill with 200 μl/well test solution. Place three assay plates into a polystyrene 96-well plate so that their taped edges do not touch (Fig. 3A).

3. Lay out top assay plates and fill the central six wells with test solution. The top assay plates should be filled so that each well has a small positive meniscus (i.e., the solution should bulge up slightly in the well).

4. Load cells into plates by placing an aliquot of the cells (50 μl) into each of the central 6 wells on the bottom assay plate (Fig. 3B).

5. Bring cells into contact with the substrate. We commonly do this by

placing the open bottom assay plates in their polystyrene 96-well plates into a bench-top centrifuge and subjecting them to a centrifugal force of 150 g for 5 min (Fig. 3C).

6. Seal micro-assay plates.

  a. Place the bottom assay plate into one of a pair of stainless-steel chucks.

  b. Fill the central 6 wells with the test solution so that there is a bulging positive meniscus (Fig. 3D).

  c. Invert the top assay plate, and lower it so that the central 6 wells of the two plates align (Fig. 3E).

  d. Bring the two plates together so that the menisci touch (Fig. 3F). Continue lowering the cover plate so that 6 fluid-filled chambers are formed. Excess test solution should flow into the empty wells on the top assay plate (Fig. 3G).

  e. Place the second steel chuck over the top assay plate.

  f. Place this unit into the sheet metal vise, and press together firmly.

  g. Remove joined assay plates and incubate at desired temperature for desired time. This varies with the experiment. We have found that significant adherence occurs within 5 min, but have standardized our experiments to 15 min to simplify the manipulations. Incubations at 37°C or room temperature to allow for receptor clustering and cytoskeletal interaction. Incubations at 4°C allow for measurements of receptor–ligand interaction.

7. Remove nonadherent cells. Invert assay unit so that the labeled wells are now visible. Place in centrifuge, and spin for 5 min (Fig. 3H). The removal force used will vary from cell to cell. For avian neural crest cells, we remove cells by subjecting them to a force of 50 g. This parameter can also be varied within an experiment to compare the strength of attachment between substrata or cell types.

8. After spinning cells off of the substrata, note which wells have air bubbles. Air bubbles destroy the reliability of those wells in two ways. Large air bubbles tend to lyse cells during the spinoff process, releasing their labeled contents to the medium. Small air bubbles tend to buoy up cells, giving them an apparent high adhesion to the substrate.

9. Quick-freeze cells by placing them rapidly into a methanol/dry ice bath. (Use black sharpies, as this ink is more stable in methanol than blue or red.)

10. Clip plate tops and bottoms.

  a. Remove one row of 8 wells from the side of the now-frozen assay plate (Fig. 3I).

  b. Using the modified dog nail clippers, clip off the bottoms of the 6 central wells from the bottom and top assay plates (Fig. 3I). Be careful to match bottoms and tops for later analysis. A blunted 18-gauge needle is useful for pushing well bottoms out of the nail clippers. Forceps are also useful for retrieving misplaced well bottoms.

  c. Place the clipped well bottoms into scintillation vials. Fill vials with scintillation fluid and measure radioactivity using a scintillation counter.

11. Analyze the data. Each well is a separate assay chamber, so that if the tops

---

Measurement of Cell–Cell and Cell–Extracellular Matrix Interactions

and bottoms can be matched, the percentage of cells bound can be calculated accurately:

$$\% \text{cells bound} = \frac{\text{cpm}_{\text{bottom}}}{\text{cpm}_{\text{bottom}} + \text{cpm}_{\text{top}}} \times 100$$

IV. Comments

This cell attachment assay can be used to measure the cell attachment of any cell, no matter how rare (within reason), to either other cells or extracellular matrix molecules. Some cells, especially large embryonic cells, lyse under moderate centrifugal forces (25 g). The first experiment to be performed for any cell should be to test the cell's resilience to centrifugation. Cells should be allowed to adhere under increasing g forces, starting with settling under 1 g on a bench top, followed by a long (1-hr) 1 g removal force. Once the force used to bring cells into contact with their substratum is established, the removal force should be varied, to establish the best parameters under which to measure cell attachment later. We generally use attachment and removal forces that allow between 70 and 90% of the cells to remain attached in the absence of adhesion inhibitory agents.

V. Pitfalls

1. Burning through the well walls when cutting holes in double-sided tape results in leaky chambers.

2. Air bubbles in assay chambers eliminate the reliability of the results.

3. Adherent cell wells can be mismatched with appropriate unbound cells.

4. Centrifuging cells too forcefully results in lysed cells.

5. Poor blocking of substrata can result in attachment that is not inhibitable.

6. Allowing tape to become wet destroys its ability to stick to plastic.

REFERENCES

Lallier, T., and Bronner-Fraser, M. (1991) Avian neural crest cell adhesion to laminin: Involvement of divalent cation dependent and independent integrins. *Development* **113**, 1069–1084.

Lallier, T., and Bronner-Fraser, M. (1992) $\alpha_1\beta_1$ integrin on neural crest cells recognizes some laminin substrates in a Ca^{2+}-independent manner. *J. Cell Biol.* **119**, 1335–1346.

Lallier, T., and Bronner-Fraser, M. (1993) Inhibition of neural crest cell attachment by integrin antisense oligonucleotides. *Science* **259**, 692–695.

McClay, D. R., Wessel, G. M., and Marchase, R. B. (1981) Intercellular recognition: Quantitation of initial binding events. *Proc. Natl. Acad. Sci. USA* **78**, 4975–4979.

Shaw, L. M., Messier, J. M., and Mercurio, A. M. (1990) The activation dependent adhesion of macrophages to laminin involves cytoskeletal anchoring and phosphorylation of the $\alpha_6\beta_1$ integrin. *J. Cell Biol.* **110**, 2167–2174.

SECTION J

Electrophysiological Methods

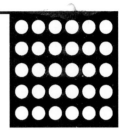

Patch-Clamp Recording

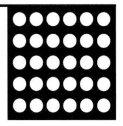

James L. Rae and Richard A. Levis

I. Introduction

Patch-clamp recording has become the method of choice for making high-resolution functional measurements from ionic channels in the membranes of cells. Only small modifications of the basic approach allow either recordings of the currents flowing through single ionic channels or those flowing through all of the channels in a single cell. Many review articles and book chapters about patch-clamp methodology have been published previously (Hamill *et al.*, 1981; Levis and Rae, 1992; Rae and Levis, 1984, 1992a,b; Sherman-Gold, 1993; Rudy and Iverson, 1992; Standen *et al.*, 1987; Sakmann and Neher, 1983).

II. Materials and Instrumentation

Patch-clamping requires the use of an electrode puller, a dissecting microscope for use in electrode elastomer coating, an electrode tip firepolisher, a microscope with a high-quality micromanipulator, a patch-clamp amplifier with an electrode holder designed for use with the amplifier, an anti-aliasing filter, and a computer. Each of these items is obtainable from a commercial supplier. Patch-clamp amplifiers come with resistive and/or capacitive feedback elements, the capacitive feedback amplifiers having much lower noise for single-channel recording.

III. Procedures

A. PULLING ELECTRODES

1. Electrodes can be constructed from a wide variety of glass tubing. Corning 7052, available from Garner Glass, is good for single-channel recordings, whereas Kimble KG-12 from Friedrich and Dimmock is particularly useful for whole-cell recordings. Quartz tubing is best for low-noise single-channel recording but requires a P2000 laser puller from Sutter Instruments.

2. Tubing with an outside diameter of 1.65 mm and an inside diameter of 1.15 mm or so is particularly convenient. In general, the thicker the wall, the lower the noise in single-channel recordings, whereas thin walls are best for whole-cell recording.

3. The glass to be pulled should be clamped in the puller so the resulting two electrodes are the same length. Tubing to be pulled should not exceed 2.7–3.0 in. in length.

4. Long heating filaments or coils are good for making long, slowly tapering tips, whereas short filaments or coils most easily make blunt tips.

5. Whole-cell electrodes should be blunt and low resistance ($2-3$ μm in tip diameter), whereas single-channel electrodes can be sharper with tips as small as $0.2-0.5$ μm.

6. Pulled electrodes should not be touched near their tips with bare fingers and should be placed in closed containers to keep dust from the tips which are often statically charged.

B. ELECTRODE COATING

1. Using either a bright-field or a dark-field dissecting microscope, coat the electrode with a hydrophobic elastomer such as Sylgard No. 184 (Dow Corning) or General Electric RTV615 obtainable from Newark Electronics.

2. The painting can be done with the tapered end of a piece of glass tubing, $1.5-2.0$ mm in diameter, which has been pulled in two in a Bunsen burner. Any kind of glass will do.

3. Use elastomers that have been made up according to the manufacturer's instructions, aliquoted into 1.5-ml microcentrifuge tubes and stored at $-20°C$. Elastomers made this way are useful for several weeks.

4. Remove a single 1.5-ml tube from the freezer but do not open it until it has reached room temperature. This keeps H_2O from condensing into the elastomer and altering its electrical properties.

5. Using the tapered glass from step 2, carefully paint the elastomer on the electrode whose tip is angled upward while observing it under the dissecting microscope. Be sure not to cover the tip with elastomer. With practice it should easily be possible to get it to within 100 μm of the tip without actually covering the tip. For single-channel recordings, background noise will fall progressively as you paint closer to the tip. In whole-cell recording, the coating allows easier cancellation of the fast capacity transient but has little effect on total background noise.

6. The elastomer can be cured by placing it, electrode tip upward, into the hot air stream of a heat gun such as a Master Model 10008, available from Newark Electronics. Five to ten seconds is required to fully cure many elastomers.

C. FIREPOLISHING ELECTRODES

1. This should be done after elastomer coating either with a commercially available microforge or with a custom constructed apparatus.

2. Either an inverted or an upright microscope works well; however, metallurgical microscopes with superlong-working-distance objectives (such as the Nikon SLWD100X) are ideal. With 15× eyepieces and a 100× objective, there is enough magnification to allow direct observation of changes in the electrode tip as it is heated even for a final tip diameter less than 1 μm.

3. The polishing (heating) is done with a filament of 0.003-in. platinum–iridium (AM Systems) bent into a fine hairpin loop. The loop is coated with electrode glass to prevent the platinum from vaporizing onto the tip of the electrode being polished. The glass coating can be done by substantially overheating the platinum loop and then moving the tip of a pulled patch electrode directly against the platinum wire. The tip melts and begins to coat the

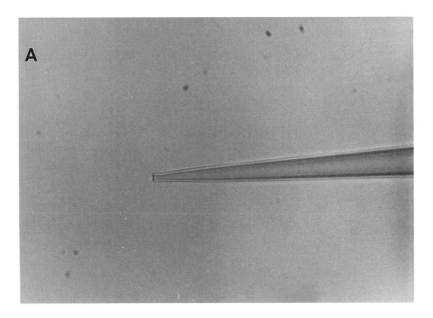

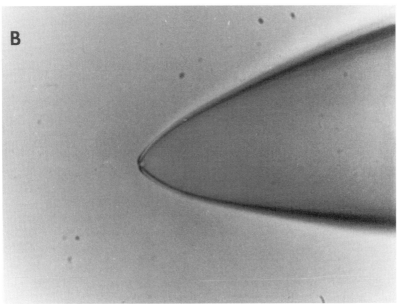

FIGURE 1   Photomicrographs showing the tip shape for (A) patch electrodes and (B) whole-cell electrodes.

wire and the electrode glass is then withdrawn while the wire is still hot. Three or four electrode tips may be required to fully coat this wire loop and to make a ball of glass encompassing it.

4. In firepolishing, the glass-coated wire is heated and brought close to the electrode tip so that the tip becomes rounded and smooth with an opening of 2–3 μm for whole-cell recording and 0.2–1 μm for single-channel measurements (Fig. 1).

D. ELECTRODE FILLING

1. Fill the electrode tip by simply dipping it into the desired filling solution. Alternatively, a suction apparatus made of a 10-ml syringe and a piece of tubing can be used to draw up enough solution to fill most of the electrode shank. One to thirty seconds of suction is required depending on the size of the tip.

2. Insert a hypodermic needle of the right gauge and about $1\frac{1}{2}$ in. long into the back of the electrode and inject filling solution to the desired level (usually enough so it will just contact the tip of the reference electrode which will be placed into it later).

3. A bubble will remain behind the filled tip and in front of the back-filled fluid. Remove this by gently tapping against the electrode just above its shank. Verify by direct observation that all the bubbles are gone.

4. Using a hypodermic needle connected to a suction line, carefully remove any excess fluid from the pipette and vacuum any droplets away from the back of the electrode.

5. Place the electrode into the holder and verify that the reference electrode tip contacts the filling solution.

E. NOISE TESTING (PRIMARILY FOR SINGLE-CHANNEL RECORDING)

1. Using the manipulator, place the filled electrode in its holder just above the chamber in which the cells and their bathing solution are located.

2. Most modern patch-clamps contain an RMS noise meter. Read the value of the meter and be sure it is not more than 30% higher than the value of the headstage alone without its holder.

3. If it is, put in the holder alone. The noise increment should not be greater than 10–20% above that of the headstage alone. Greater increments usually mean that the holder is either dirty or wet. Dry it by blowing clean air or nitrogen through the holder suction line. If noise is still elevated, dismantle the holder and sonicate it first in distilled H_2O and then in ethanol. Dry for at least 3 hr at 60°C.

4. If noise is okay, proceed.

F. MAKING A SEAL

1. With the patch-clamp amplifier in voltage-clamp mode, immerse the electrode tip in the bath.

2. Adjust the pipette offset so that the current is zeroed.

3. Apply a 5-mV or so rectangular pulse and observe the resulting current pulse.

4. Lower the electrode gently against the cell until the current pulse falls to about 50% of its original value.

5. Using a 10-ml syringe with the barrel already pulled back to 7 ml, gently apply suction. Moving the barrel to the 8- to 9-ml position will usually provide enough suction for seal formation (Fig. 2).

6. If the seal does not form, remove the syringe, push the barrel all the way in, reconnect it, and then move the barrel back ever so gently. Often the seal will form with this reapplication of suction. You now have a cell-attached patch.

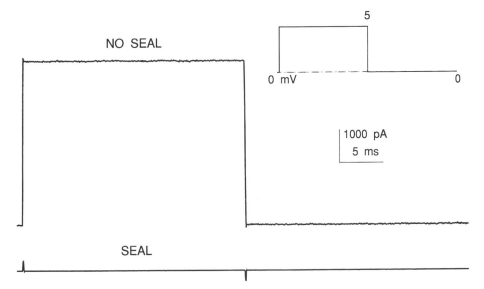

NO SEAL

5

0 mV   0

1000 pA
5 ms

SEAL

FIGURE 2   Current recordings before and after seal formation.

G. RECORDING CONFIGURATIONS (see Hamill, *et al.,* 1981)

1. Cell-Attached Patch

If there is a channel in the patch, you can go ahead and record in this cell-attached patch configuration. Realize, however, that the inside of the membrane is at the cell's resting potential and you can control only the potential in the pipette. Therefore, the transmembrane potential of the patch is usually unknown.

2. Inside-Out Patch

1. After sealing, rapidly move the electrode back from the cell surface. Usually a patch of membrane will be torn from the cell and remain adherent to the pipette tip.

2. Often a complete vesicle forms rather than just a patch. Single-channel currents in the vesicle are low in amplitude, may have rounded edges, or may droop in amplitude rather than being rectangular current pulses.

3. One side of the vesicle may often be disrupted by lifting the electrode tip into the air for 1–20 sec and then reimmersing it in the bath. Vesicles form less often and are broken more easily if a low-calcium bathing solution is used. An inside-out patch is so named because the inside surface of the membrane faces the bathing solution.

3. Standard Whole Cell

1. Shortly after seal formation while still applying the rectangular pulse, remove the suction syringe, push the barrel all the way in, reattach the suction line, and begin to gently withdraw the syringe barrel. Usually before you get to 1 ml, the patch of membrane will rupture and connect your pipette filling solution

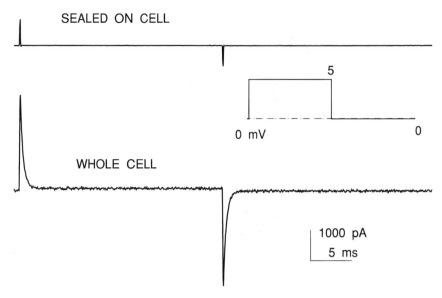

SEALED ON CELL

5

0 mV   0

WHOLE CELL

1000 pA
5 ms

FIGURE 3 Current recordings before and after going whole cell.

to the cell interior. The current response to the voltage pulse changes as the whole-cell configuration is achieved, as shown in Fig. 3.

2. In some cells, it is very hard to disrupt the patch and a 20- or 50-ml syringe used as described above may be required.

4. Outside-Out Patch

After going whole cell by disrupting the membrane patch, slowly remove the pipette from the cell. Usually a stalk of membrane can be seen stretching between the pipette tip and the cell. When this stalk ruptures, an outside-out patch often forms. This configuration is so named because the outside surface of the membrane patch faces the bathing solution.

5. Perforated Patch Whole-Cell Recording (see Rae *et al.*, 1991)

1. Preweigh 3 mg of amphotericin B (Sigma A-4888) or Nystatin (Sigma N-3503) in 1.5-ml centrifuge tubes and store in the freezer.

2. At time of use, dissolve the antibiotic in 50 μl of DMSO and mix by pipetting in and out several times and then mix with a Vortex mixer.

3. Add 10 μl of this solution to 3 ml of the desired filling solution in a 15-ml screw-capped centrifuge tube. Shake vigorously and then vortex.

4. Draw 1 ml of the solution into a 1-ml syringe to use for back-filling electrodes.

5. Dip the tip of the electrode into the same filling solution without antibiotic and allow the tip to fill no more than 300–400 μl, then back-fill with the antibiotic solution in the usual way.

6. Following seal formation, the antibiotic will slowly diffuse to the tip and partition into the membrane patch. Partitioning forms channels permeable to Na, K, and Cl but not Ca^{2+}, Mg^{2+}, or glucose.

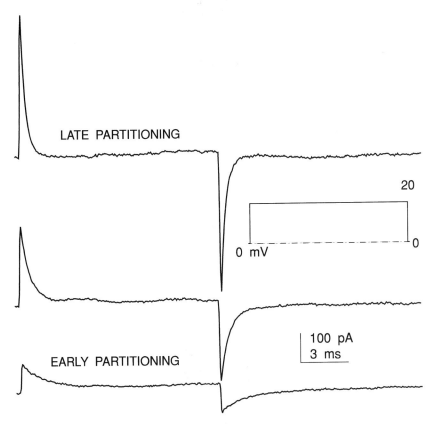

LATE PARTITIONING

20

0 mV   0

100 pA
3 ms

EARLY PARTITIONING

FIGURE 4   Current records of going whole cell with amphotericin perforation.

7. As partitioning occurs, the current response to a rectangular voltage pulse changes as shown in Fig. 4.

6. Perforated Outside-Out Vesicle (see Levitan and Kramer, 1990)

1. Once the antibiotic has produced an access resistance of less than 100 MΩ, simply remove the pipette from the cell.

2. This often results in a tiny vesicle at the tip whose pipette side is perforated with antibiotic. This is the functional equivalent of an outside-out patch but may also contain trapped cytoplasm and cell organelles. It can be used for reasonable signal-to-noise single-channel recordings.

H. RECORDING

1. Use one of the IBM-compatible or Macintosh computer systems and software which are commercially available. Alternatively, use a digital video tape recorder.

2. Be sure that the current output of the patch-clamp is filtered through a four- or eight-pole Bessel filter before going to either the computer or the tape recorder.

3. Verify that the digital sampling is at least three to five times the −3-dB bandwidth of the filter setting (Levis and Rae, 1992).

IV. Comments

For the highest-quality whole-cell recordings, the electrode resistance should be as low as possible (1–3 MΩ). For low-noise single-channel recordings, low-noise pipette glass and optimal elastomer coating must be used in combination with capacitive feedback electronics. Perforated patch whole-cell recordings are more physiological than standard whole-cell recordings and may prevent channel rundown.

V. Pitfalls

1. Proteins such as serum in the bathing medium often prevent seal formation.

2. Low-calcium filling solutions may make seal formation more difficult.

3. In perforated whole-cell recordings, the filling solution must contain the correct permeant anion concentration or the cell will be unable to control its volume (Rae *et al.*, 1991).

4. Improperly filtered and sampled current data can add unnecessary noise and obscure results.

5. Compounds that alter channel behavior may leach out of the electrode glass being used.

6. Recording of single channels in membrane patches may alter both channel kinetics and density.

7. It is very easy to record from membrane vesicles when you believe you are recording from membrane patches.

8. In standard whole-cell configuration, access resistance changes often occur during the recordings.

9. In perforated patch whole-cell recordings, many compounds placed in the electrode filling solution are unable to get into the cell.

REFERENCES

Hamill, O. P., Marty, A., Neher, E., Sakmann, B., and Sigworth, F. J. (1981) Improved patch-clamp techniques for high-resolution current recording from cells and cell-free membrane patches. *Pfluegers Arch.* **391**, 85–100.

Levis, R. A., and Rae, J. L. (1992) Constructing a patch clamp setup. *In* "Methods in Enzymology" (B. Rudy and L. E. Iverson, eds.), Vol. 207, pp. 18–66. Academic Press, San Diego.

Levitan, E. S., and Kramer, R. H. (1990) Neuropeptide modulation of single calcium and potassium channels detected with a new patch clamp configuration. *Nature (London)* **348**, 545–547.

Rae, J. L., Cooper, K., Gates, P., and Watsky, M. (1991) Low access resistance perforated patch recordings using amphotericin B. *J. Neurosci. Methods* **37**, 15–26.

Rae, J. L., and Levis, R. A. (1984) Patch voltage clamp of lens epithelial cells: Theory and practice. *Mol. Physiol.* **6**, 115–162.

Rae, J. L., and Levis, R. A. (1992a) A method for exceptionally low noise single channel recordings. *Pfluegers Arch.* **420**, 618–620.

Rae, J. L., and Levis, R. A. (1992b) Glass technology for patch electrodes. *In* "Methods in Enzymology" (B. Rudy and L. E. Iverson, eds.), Vol. 207, pp. 18–66. Academic Press, San Diego.

Rudy, B., and Iverson, L. E. (eds.) (1992) "Methods in Enzymology," Vol. 27. Academic Press, San Diego.

Sakmann, B., and Neher, E. (eds.) (1983) "Single-Channel Recording." Plenum Press, New York.

Sherman-Gold, R. (ed.) (1993) "The Axon Guide for Electrophysiology and Biophysics Laboratory Techniques." Axon Instruments, Foster City, CA.

Standen, N. D., Gray, P. T. A., and Whitaker, M. J. (eds.) (1987) "Microelectrode Techniques." The Plymouth Workshop, The Company of Biologists Limited, Cambridge.

SECTION K

Histocultures

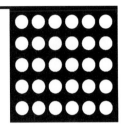

Three-Dimensional Sponge-Gel Matrix Histoculture: Methods and Applications

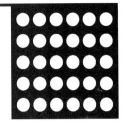

Robert M. Hoffman

I. Introduction

By 1951, monolayer cell cultures, in which cells grow as "sheets" on the surfaces of glass or plastic, had become the predominant culture technique and paradigm. Such monolayer cultures had rather limited use in histological studies or for pathological diagnosis, however, and in view of this, Leighton (1951) returned to Carrel's (1912) original idea of three-dimensional culture. Leighton improved the earlier system by using a tissue support consisting of cellulose sponges surrounded by plasma clots, contained within glass tubes. He also tested natural and gelatin sponges for their ability to support the organized aggregations of cells.

Because of its architectural resemblance to native tissue (Color Plate 6), three-dimensional histoculture represents a unique and *in vivo*-like model for investigating crucial events in tumor biology such as drug response, tumor cell migration, invasion, metastasis, and antigen expression (Leighton *et al.*, 1962; Miller *et al.*, 1984, 1985; Hoffman, 1991; Guadagni *et al.*, 1992; Kobayashi *et al.*, 1993).

II. Materials and Instrumentation

A. MATERIALS

Fetal bovine serum (Gemini Bio Products, Lot No. A6528G), Gelfoam sponge (UpJohn, Cat. No. 0342-01), gentamicin sulfate (Gemini Bio Products, Cat. No. 400-107), media (Sigma, MEM Earle), six-well plates (Fisher Scientific, Cat. No. 087721B), tissue culture plate 100 (Fisher Scientific, Cat. No. 08772-E), Hanks' balanced salt solution (Sigma, Cat. No. 9269), penicillin G (Sigma, Cat. No. P-3032), streptomycin (Sigma, Cat. No. S-9137), Fungizone (Irvine Scientific, Cat. No. 9352), tetracycline (Sigma, Cat. No. T-7660), amikacin (Sigma, Cat. No. A-1774), chloramphenicol (Sigma, Cat. No. C-1919), NaCl (Fisher Scientific, Cat. No. P330-3), KCl (Fisher Scientific, Cat. No. S271-3), Na_2HPO_4 (Fisher Scientific, Cat. No. S374-500), KH_2PO_4 (Fisher Scientific, Cat. No. P284-500), phenol red solution (Fisher Scientific, Cat. No. P-391), 3-(4,5-dimethylthiazol-2-yl)-2,5-diphenyl-2*H*-tetrazolium bromide (MTT, Sigma, Cat. No. M-2128), 0.45-μm membrane filter (Millipore), BCECF (Molecular Probes, Cat. No. B-1170), dimethylsulfoxide (Sigma, D-8779), propidium iodide (Sigma, Cat. No. 4170), Tissue Tek OCT compound (Baxter, Cat. No. M7148-4), Isotype Matched Antibody (Becton Dickinson), 0.2-μm membrane filter (Millipore), collagenase type I (Sigma, Cat. No. C-0130), HK20

Assay Kit (Sigma, Cat. No. 16-20), chloroform (Aldrich Chemical Co., Cat. No. 28,830-6), methanol (Sigma, Cat. No. M-1770), butanol (Sigma, Cat. No. 27,067-9), toluene (Sigma, Cat. No. 27,037-7), fluorescein isothiocyanate (Sigma), sodium bicarbonate (Sigma, Cat. No. S-8875), 99% formic acid (Sigma, Cat. No. F-4636), ethyl acetate (Sigma, Cat. No. 27,052-0), n-hexane (Sigma, Cat. No. 9379), 70% $HClO_4$ (Aldrich, Cat. No. 31,142-1), 60% HNO_3 (Aldrich, Cat. No. 22,571-1), HCl (Sigma, Cat. No. H-7020), acetonitrile (Fisher Scientific, Cat. No. A996-4), silica gel (Kanto Kagaku, Cat. Nos. 60-80 and 80-100 mesh), reversed-phase column (Toyo Sotatsu, TSK gel ODS-120A), acetone (Fisher Scientific, Cat. No. A929-4), Develosil 60-3 silica gel column (Nomura Kagaku), mitomycin-C (Sigma, Cat. No. M-0503), doxorubicin (Sigma, Cat. No. D-1515), 5-fluorouracil (Sigma, Cat. No. F-6627), cisplatin (Sigma, Cat. No. P-4394), 3-t-butyl-4-hydroxyanisole (Sigma, Cat. No. B-1253), t-butyl hydroxytoluene (Sigma, Cat. No. B-1378), Sephadex G-25 (Sigma, Cat. No. G-25-150), nonessential amino acids (Sigma, Cat. No. M-7145), sodium hypochlorite (Sigma, Cat. No. S-1898).

B. INSTRUMENTATION

Various instruments include a Coulter cell counter with microprocessor controls; Sorvall preparative centrifuge and SS-34 Sorvall rotor; Forma −70°C and −20°C freezers; Nu-aire Laminar Flow Biological Safety Cabinet, Model NU-408FM.300; Hot-Pack incubator with microprocessor-regulated CO_2, temperature, and humidity controls; Beckman pH meter; Fisher shaking water bath; Fisher Vortex Genie 2; Nanopure water deionizer; Leitz rotary microtome; and Leitz Cryostat, Model 1720. The confocal microscopy system consists of a MRC-600 Confocal Imaging System (Bio-Rad) mounted on a Nikon photomicroscope with a Nikon Optiphot microscope lighting system. A 10× Plan Apo objective is used. The fluorescence filter is a Nikon DM-S10 B-2A. The automated image analysis system consists of a Nikon photomicroscope with a Nikon Optophot microscope lighting system using an IGS filter cube (Nikon) and a DM 580 G-2A filter cuber (Nikon) connected to a RCA TC-1501 video camera, Hitachi monitor, and IBM personal computer. Other microscope equipment includes an Olympus inverted phase-contrast microscope and an Olympus IM T200 inverted research microscope with automatic photoapparatus and fluorescence attachment. Software includes Sigmaplot (Jandel Scientific), Image Scanner, Conway filter and Bright Pixel Planimeter (DS-88 Digisector Video (The Microworks), and Confil (The Microworks, Version 1.0).

III. Procedures

A. ESTABLISHMENT OF HUMAN TUMOR EXPLANTS IN CULTURE

Solutions

1. *Culture medium:* To 500 ml of minimal essential Medium (MEM) with Earle's salts add 50 ml of fetal bovine serum (FBS), 5 ml of gentamicin sulfate (10 mg/ml), and 5 ml of nonessential amino acids 100× (NEAA).

2. *Transport medium:* To 500 ml of Hanks' balanced salt solution (HBSS), add 50 ml of FBS, 10 ml of gentamicin sulfate (10 mg/ml), and 5 ml of NEAA.

3. *Antibiotic washes:* To 500 ml of MEM with Earle's salts, add 70 ml FBS, 75.2 mg of penicillin G, 125 mg of streptomycin, 10 ml of Fungizone, 5 mg of tetracycline, 50 mg of amikacin, 75 mg of chloramphenicol, and 5 ml of gentamicin sulfate (10 μg/ml).

Steps

1. To prepare the collagen gel, remove the dehydrated squares from their sterile packages and place them in 60-mm plastic tissue culture dishes containing culture medium. Soak the gels in this medium with at least one fluid change before use.

2. Immediately after surgery or biopsy, tumor sections in transport medium are brought to the laboratory.

3. Rigorously wash colon, stomach, and head and neck tumor specimens with antibiotic. A minimum of two washes are done (Freeman and Hoffman, 1986; Vescio *et al.*, 1987; Hoffman *et al.*, 1989).

4. Cut necrotic tissue away, and mince the remaining healthy tumor with scissors into 1-mm^3 bits.

5. Excise six pieces of tissue from different areas of the original specimen and then place these (six pieces per gel) on top of previously hydrated flexible sponge gels derived from the extracellular matrix of pigskin.

6. Add culture medium to culture dishes such that the upper part of the gel is not covered.

7. Incubate the cultures at 37°C in a humidified sterile atmosphere, containing 95% air/5% CO_2, for various periods.

B. SPECTROPHOTOMETRIC MEASUREMENT OF 3-(4,5-dimethylthiazol-2-yl)-2,5-diphenyl-2*H*-tetrazolium bromide (MTT) ENDPOINT TO DETERMINE *IN VITRO* DRUG RESPONSE

This method allows for *in vivo*-like culture of human tumors with fast results for chemotherapy drug response testing (Furukawa *et al.*, 1992).

Solutions

1. *HBSS with collagenase:* To 500-ml bottle of HBSS add 300 mg of collagenase.

2. *Phosphate-buffered saline (PBS):* To 2.5 liters of distilled water, add the following ingredients in the order listed: 24 g of NaCl, 0.6 g of KCl, 3.45 g Na_2HPO_4, 0.6 g KH_2PO_4 (all anhydrous), and 0.18 ml of phenol red solution. Once all ingredients have dissolved, add distilled water to bring the volume to 3 liters.

3. *MTT stock solution:* MTT needs to be made fresh each time it is to be used and it is light sensitive. Calculate the total number of wells to be assayed. Multiply the total number of wells by 100 μl (the amount of MTT needed per well). This is the volume of PBS needed. Stock concentration of MTT is 8 mg/ml; therefore multiply total volume calculated above by 8, weigh out MTT, and add to the calculated volume of PBS. Vortex the MTT solution for approximately 5 min. The MTT will not go completely into solution. Therefore, filter it through a 0.45-μm membrane filter.

Steps

1. Establish histoculture of tumors as in Section A.

2. The chemotherapy drugs to be tested for efficacy are tested in dose–response measurements on the histocultured human tumors for 24 hr.

3. Remove medium containing chemotherapy drugs, and add new medium before adding anything further to each well.

4. Add HBSS with collagenase and MTT stock solution to each well and incubate the plates for an additional 8 hr. The collagen gels are dissolved within the first 30 min and the tumor pieces, which by then are floating in the medium, turn violet.

5. Aspirate the medium completely from each well by carefully using micropipettes.

6. Add 1 ml DMSO per well to dissolve the MTT–formazan product.

7. After 2 hr transfer the solutions to 96-well microplates (100 μl per well) and read the absorbance of the solutions in each well at 540 nm.

8. Calculate the absorbance per gram of each tumor from the mean absorbance from four wells and initial tumor weight, which is estimated prior to culture. Calculate the inhibition rate at each concentration as follows: inhibition rate (%) = [1 − (mean absorbance/g tumor of the treated wells)/(mean absorbance/g tumor of the control wells)] × 100.

C. MEASUREMENT OF MTT IMAGE ANALYSIS ENDPOINT TO DETERMINE *IN VITRO* DRUG RESPONSE

The histoculture method with the MTT endpoint measured by pixel analysis allows the simultaneous observation of the histology and this endpoint of human tumor specimens *in vitro* (Colangelo *et al.*, 1992). This offers the possibility of detecting rare drug-resistant clones in the histocultured tumors. Data are available in as few as 2 days after the culture of the specimen is initiated, which means widespread application of this method for cancer patients is possible.

Solution

1. *Propidium iodide solution (PI):* To 500 ml of distilled water add 725 μg of propidium iodide (1.25 μg/ml stock concentration).

Steps

1. Establish histocultures of tumors as in Section A.

2. The chemotherapy drugs to be tested for efficacy are tested in dose–response measurements on the histocultured human tumors for 24 hr.

3. Transfer the sponge-gel-supported tumor pieces to drug-free culture media (see Section A) and incubate for 1.3 hr with 2 ml of MTT solution (see Section B) in each well.

4. At the end of this reaction, remove the gels from the incubation medium containing MTT and place in 2 ml of cold phosphate-buffered saline (see Section B).

5. Keep the specimens at 4°C until 4-μm frozen sections are made. Water-soluble embedding media, Tissue Tek OCT Compound (Baxter), and a Leitz Cryostat 1720 are used to make frozen sections.

6. Dip the slides in PI solution for 30 sec and then dry.

7. They are now ready for the pixel image analysis of formazan crystals formed by the enzymatic reduction of MTT (PIAFC) and pixel analysis measurement of the fluorescent dye propidium iodide (PIAPI). Analyze the slides microscopically under a mercury lamp using an IGS filter for polarized light and a DM 580 G-2A filter, composed of EX 510-560 excitation and BA590 emission filters, for fluorescent light. The objective magnification is 200× and the image is digitized by a digitizer board. The areas of brightness, corresponding to the amount of formazan crystals, which reflect polarized light, or red nuclei due to fluorescence of propidium iodide, are calculated as the ratio of the area of enhanced pixels to total pixels by the Image Scanner, Conway Filter, and Bright Pixel Planimeter.

8. The PIAFC and the PIAPI are measured in the non-drug-treated control twice, once at the beginning of the experiment and once at the end, within 5–6 hr of the beginning. During this time no statistically significant changes are detected, indicating that the system is stable during the measurement period. By measuring the PIAFC and the PIAPI only in the areas where crystals are present, it is possible, using the formula of inhibition rate = 100 − [(PIAFC treated/PIAPI treated)/(PIAFC control/PIAPI control) × 100], to demonstrate that the tumor is or is not sensitive *in vitro* to a drug.

D. MEASUREMENT OF FLUORESCENT DYE-LABELING ENDPOINT TO DETERMINE DRUG RESPONSE

This method allows the quantitation of live and dead cells in three-dimensional histoculture tissues (Guo *et al.,* 1992).

Solution

1. *BCECF-AM:* Add 50 μg of BCECF-AM to 50 μl DMSO.

Steps

1. Establish histoculture of tumors as in Section A.

2. The chemotherapy drugs to be tested for efficacy are tested in dose–response measurements on the histocultured human tumors for 24 hr.

3. Remove the medium containing chemotherapy drugs, and add new medium before adding anything further to each well.

4. Selectively label viable cells with the dye BCECF-AM, which is activated to fluorescence by nonspecific esterases present only in living cells. Add 15–20 μl BCECF-AM solution to wells with 2 ml culture medium to a final concentration of 10 μg/ml.

5. Label nonviable cells, whose plasma membranes are leaky, with PI (see Section C), a dye that enters only cells with nonintact membranes. As the emission spectra of these dyes are different they can be used simultaneously on the same specimen. Add 10–15 μl PI solution to wells with 2 ml culture medium to a final concentration of 10–25 μg/ml.

6. Analyze the double dye-treated cultures by fluorescence and confocal microscopy after 20 min of staining.

7. Manually, on the screen of a confocal fluorescence scanning laser microscope, count the number of living cells (BCECF-positive cells) with respect to the number of total cells [PI-positive (red) plus BCECF-AM-positive (green) cells] in treated cultures, compared with untreated controls. Use this ratio to determine drug-induced cytotoxicity and express as follows: Percentage of living cells − 100 × $G_a/(G_a + R_a)$, where G_a = number of green cells after treatment

and R_a = number of red cells after treatment. The same ratio is calculated for both the control and the treated specimen at the same time of incubation and their relative ratios determine the degree of chemosensitivity.

E. MEASUREMENT OF GLUCOSE CONSUMPTION ENDPOINT TO DETERMINE DRUG RESISTANCE

The collagen-sponge-gel-supported histoculture system allows the study of histocultured tumors *in vitro* for several months or longer (Slocum *et al.*, 1992), while maintaining tissue architecture present in the original tumor. The histoculture system therefore appears to be useful for monitoring the long-term growth of tumors and is a suitable system for quantitation of drug effects by determination of glucose consumption rates that is nondestructive and may be used over long periods (Chang *et al.*, 1992).

Steps

1. Establish histoculture of tumors as in Section A.

2. The chemotherapy drugs to be tested for efficacy are tested in dose–response measurements on the histocultured human tumors for 24 hr.

3. Remove the medium containing chemotherapy drugs, and add new medium before adding anything further to each well.

4. Take 50 μl of culture medium (see Section A) every 24 hr for determination of glucose content in triplicate using the (HK20) assay kit from Sigma.

5. Make the measurements by monitoring the change in optical density at 340 nm due to reduction of NAD through glucose consumption by hexokinase.

6. Plot the glucose content of the medium as a semilog plot versus time after medium renewal using Sigmaplot from Jandel Scientific.

7. Then fit a simple exponential model of glucose consumption to the data with the program Systat from Systat, Inc.

8. Calculate the half-life of glucose from the slope parameter of this model using the equation $t_{1/2} = 0.693/s$, where s = slope (or *s*-slope) of the best-fit linear regression line of the natural log of the glucose concentration plotted versus time.

9. Measure glucose content of the medium daily for 3 days. Plot the log values over 3 days versus time, and take the slope of best-fit line as the glucose consumption rate during the 3-day period (one period).

F. *IN VITRO* PHARMACOKINETICS

The following section outlines how to determine drug pharmocokinetics *in vitro*, using mitomycin-C, doxorubicin, 5-fluorouracil, and cisplatin as examples (Furukawa *et al.*, 1992).

Solutions

1. *Antioxygenating solution:* Prepare by dissolving 400 mg 3-t-butyl-4-hydroxyanisole and 250 mg t-butyl hydroxytolene in 1 ml of acetonitrile.

2. *1 N Formic acid:* Add 37.73 ml 99% formic acid to 1 liter deionized water.

3. *0.5 M Phosphate buffer (pH 8.0)*: Add 35.49 g Na_2HPO_4 to 500 ml deionized H_2O and use NaOH to bring the pH up to 8.0.

Steps

1. Establish histoculture of tumors as in Section A.

2. The chemotherapy drugs to be tested for efficacy are tested in dose–response measurements on the histocultured human tumors for 24 hr.

3. For determination of drug levels in the culture media and in histocultured tumors, collect media in the culture wells and tumor pieces on collagen gels on days 1, 2, 3, 5, and 7 and store at −80°C (for determination of cisplatin levels, part of the medium sample is centrifuged before being stored). Media from three wells and tumor pieces from at least 20 wells are collected for a single measurement of each drug.

4. Determine the concentrations of drugs in the media and the tumor pieces by high-performance liquid chromatography (HPLC) for mitomycin-C (MMC), doxorubicin (DXR), and 5-fluorouracil (5-FU) and by flameless atomic absorption spectrophotometry (FAAS) for cisplatin (DDP). As free DDP cannot be isolated for measurement in the tumor pieces, only total DDP is measured in this case.

5. In the case of quantitation of MMC:

   a. Add 6 ml of ethyl acetate to 500 liters of the serum or the medium sample.

   b. Shake the mixture for 5 min and then centrifuge at 450 g for 10 min.

   c. For the tumor samples, homogenize 200 μg of the sample in 3 ml chilled acetonitrile and 100 mg silica gel (60–80 mesh).

   d. Centrifuge the homogenate after the homogenizer is washed with 2 ml acetonitrile.

   e. Add 50 μl of antioxygenating solution.

   f. Evaporate the organic layer in the case of the medium sample, or the supernatant for the tumor sample, under vacuum at 40°C.

   g. Dissolve the residues in 1 ml of a chloroform and methanol (98:2) mixture.

   h. Inject the resulting solutions onto a silica gel column and elute with a mobile phase consisting of chloroform, methanol, and water (90:10:0.15).

   i. Monitor the eluate at 360 nm.

6. In the case of quantitation of DXR:

   a. Homogenize 100 μg of the tumor sample in 2 ml of 0.1 M Kolthoff buffer (pH 8.0) saturated with NaCl.

   b. Add 8 ml of a mixture of butanol and toluene (1:1), in each case, and shake the mixture for 15 min followed by centrifugation at 450 g for 10 min.

   c. Evaporate 6 ml of the organic layer under vacuum, and dissolve the residue in 1 ml of a mixture of phosphate buffer and methanol.

   d. Inject the supernatant onto a reversed-phase column and elute with a mixture of 1 N formic acid and methanol (55:45). Monitor the fluorescence signal at 470 and 585 nm.

7. In the case of quantitation of 5-FU:

   a. Add 25 μl 0.5 M phosphate buffer (pH 8.0) and 6 ml ethyl acetate to 100 μl of the serum or the medium sample, and shake the mixture for 5 min followed by centrifugation at 450 g for 10 min.

   b. For the tumor samples, homogenize 200 μg of the sample in 3 ml chilled acetonitrile and 100 mg silica gel (60–80 mesh), and centrifuge the homogenate after the homogenizer is washed with 2 ml acetonitrile.

   c. After centrifugation, evaporate the organic layer for the serum and the medium sample, or the supernatant for the tumor sample, under vacuum.

   d. Purify the residue from the tumor sample using column chromatography, prepared by packing 500 mg of silica gel (80–100 mesh) into a disposable syringe and washed with acetone before use.

   e. Dissolve the residue in each case in a mixture of mobile phase for HPLC, consisting of ethyl acetate and n-hexane (3:2).

   f. Analyze the solution by HPLC using a silica gel column, and monitor the mobile phase with the eluate at 264 nm.

8. In the case of quantitation of DDP:

   a. Directly apply the serum or the medium sample to flameless atomic absorption spectrophotometry (FAAS).

   b. Weigh, freeze-dry, and triturate the sample to yield a homogeneous sample.

   c. Liquefy and digest the sample by heating with the addition of approximately 20 ml per gram of tissue of a mixture of 70% $HClO_4$ and 60% HNO_3 (3:2).

   d. When the digest is almost dry, take up the residue in 10% HCl, evaporate, and resolubilize in a known volume of the HCl.

   e. Apply the solution to FAAS.

9. Calculate the drug concentration in each sample from the calibration curves for which linearity has been established. Pharmacokinetic data in nude mice are analyzed by computer-assisted fitting of the data to a most adapted one- or two-compartment model. Peak drug concentrations (C_{max}) and the area under the curve (AUC) of each drug are calculated as the index.

G. MONOCLONAL ANTIBODY TARGETING TO LIVING HUMAN TUMORS IN HISTOCULTURE

The use of live three-dimensional tissues for targeting seems to be more *in vivo*-like than binding studies on fixed tissues on slides. Histoculture and confocal microscopy are well suited for such determinations. The system is suitable for *in vitro* studies to determine if individual patient tumors can bind potentially diagnostic and/or therapeutic antibodies specific for tumor-associated antigens (Guadagni *et al.*, 1992).

Solutions

1. *0.1 M Sodium bicarbonate buffer, pH 5*: Add 4.2 g $NaHCO_3$ to 500 ml deionized H_2O; adjust to pH 5.0.

Steps

A prototype monoclonal antibody is the mouse monoclonal antibody W6/32 specific for the constant region of the class 1 histocompatibility antigen HLA-ABC (Cappel, Inc.). The antibody is labeled as follows:

1. Incubate the purified antibody for 1 hr at 37°C with a 40-fold excess of fluorescein isothiocyanate.

2. Remove the unbound fluorescein by gel filtration with Sephadex G-25 (10-ml column) using a 0.1 M sodium bicarbonate buffer, pH 5.

3. Test the immunoreactivity of the antibody in a flow cytometric assay, against normal human lymphocytes. For a control, obtain an isotype-matched antibody from Becton Dickinson.

4. Histoculture of tissues are established as in Section A.

5. After 24 hr of histoculture, add 4 μg/ml fluorescein-labeled antibody for 1 hr at 37°C followed by five washes with culture medium (see Section A).

6. Analyze the antibody treated samples with a Bio-Rad MRC 600 scanning laser confocal microscope equipped with an argon laser.

H. IN VITRO SKIN HISTOCULTURE TOXICITY ASSAY

This method allows for the testing of toxicity in vitro on intact skin that contains hair follicle cells (Color Plate 7), which are probably the most sensitive cells in the body (Li et al., 1991).

Steps

1. Establish histocultures of tissues as in Section A, using pieces of intact mouse or human scalp skin ($\approx 2 \times 5$ mm^2 and 2.0 mm thick), which are scissor-cut under a dissecting microscope.

2. For in vitro skin toxicity, the toxicities of ethanol, doxorubicin, and sodium hypochlorite can be used as model systems for toxicity testing in dose–response measurements on histocultured mouse skin:

   a. After 2 days of incubation, stain the histocultured skin with BCECF-AM and PI (as described above) before treatment to obtain the untreated self control.

   b. After the initial observation, expose the skin preparations to various concentrations of ethanol for 5 min, to doxorubicin for 24 hr, and to sodium hypochlorite for 2 hr.

   c. After treatment, remove the culture medium and replace it with fresh medium; restain the culture with BCECF-AM and PI.

   d. After treatment, observe the same area examined before treatment. Observe the cell types (epidermal, dermal, and follicle cells) within the intact skin cultures for toxicity. Measure the fraction of killed cells (PI-positive cells) with respect to total cells [PI-positive (red) and BCECF-AM-positive (green) cells] in treated cultures, compared with untreated controls, by confocal fluorescence scanning laser microscopy to determine cytotoxicity.

   e. Calculate the percentage of killed cells from the following formula:
   Percentage of killed cells $= (R_a - R_b)/[$total cells $(G_a + R_a)]$, where $R_a =$

number of red cells after treatment, R_b = number of red cells before treatment, and G_a = number of green cells after treatment (Li *et al.*, 1991).

3. To determine cytostatic effects, inhibit [³H]thymidine incorporation by histological autoradiography after treatment with a potential toxic agent for 24 hr. The percentage cell proliferation relative to control is calculated with a Nikon or Olympus photomicroscope fitted with an epi-illumination polarization lighting system to determine cytostatic effects of substances.

I. *IN VITRO HAIR GROWTH*

Histocultured skin also allows for the measurement of hair growth *in vitro* (Color Plate 8) and the testing of drugs for their effect on the hair cycle. It should be noted that all procedures can be used to histoculture mouse skin as well as human skin (Li *et al.*, 1992a–c).

Steps

1. Prepare human scalp skin for histoculture:

a. Prewash human scalp skin tissue taken from autopsy or facelift surgery with the antibiotic wash described in Section A for 30 min.

b. Clean the top surface of the scalp skin with 70% alcohol after shaving the outgrowing hair shafts.

c. Cut intact scalp skin (2×2 cm²) with a 2-mm Acu-punch or surgical blade along the direction of hair growth.

d. Remove the additional subcutaneous fat carefully with a scalpel without injuring the hair follicle bulbs (Li *et al.*, 1992c).

2. Histoculture human scalp tissue:

a. Explant small pieces of intact human scalp tissue with the epidermis up at the air–liquid interphase and dermis down on $1 \times 1 \times 1$-cm pieces of collagen-containing sponge gels that had been prehydrated for at least 4 hr with culture medium (see Section A).

b. Maintain the cultures at 37°C in a gassed incubator with a mixture of 95% air/5% CO_2 (Li *et al.*, 1992a–c).

3. To measure hair growth *in vitro*, measure the length of hair shafts in dissection microscope photomicrographs with a ruler.

IV. Comments

Why use histoculture or other three-dimensional culture systems? Heppner and her co-workers performed experiments that demonstrated that three-dimensional structure itself rather than just simple inaccessibility to nutrients accounts for increased drug resistance over cultures in two dimensions (Lawler *et al.*, 1983; Miller *et al.*, 1984, 1985). Heppner and colleagues embedded cell clusters or fragments in collagen gels, exposed the culture to various cytotoxic drugs, and compared the drug responses of the same cells in monolayers. They found that the increased resistance in the three-dimensional cultures could be up to 1000-fold greater than in monolayer cultures, for example, with melphalan. In three-dimensional bolus cultures in collagen, the cells grew even in the presence of drug concentrations that reduced survival in monolayers to less than 0.1% of controls. Heppner and colleagues observed that if the cells from the collagen gels were replated as monolayers they became sensitive again. Their key experiment demonstrated that the tissue architecture itself is critical in determining sensitivity. They treated the monolayer cultures with melphalan and 5-fluorouracil and subsequently transferred the cultures to collagen gels; the cells became highly resistant to these drugs. The cells were exposed to the drugs as monolayers, where the drugs can access the cells readily and diffusion is not limiting; however, once the cells were transferred after drug exposure to a three-dimensional structure, the structure seemed to confer high resistance to the drugs.

In this light, an illustrative set of experiments is described comparing drug resistance in tumors grown in animals with the drug resistance of the tumors in monolayer versus three-dimensional culture. The EMT-6 tumor in mice was treated with cisplatin, cyclophosphamide, and thiotepa over a 6-month period with a total of 10 passages. This treatment induced highly-resistant tumors *in vivo*. When these tumors were grown as monolayer cultures, however, they were as drug sensitive as the parental cells. The authors concluded (Teicher *et al.*, 1990) that certain types of drug sensitivity may only be expressed *in vivo*. However, Kobayashi *et al.* (1993) grew these same *in vivo* drug-resistant tumor cell lines as spheroids in three-dimensional cultures, and observed resistance up to almost 5000 times that of the parent with certain drugs, for example, 4-hydroperoxycyclophosphamide (4-HO_2-CTX), the active form of cyclophosphamide used *in vitro*. High resistance was also observed to cisplatin and thiotepa. This resistance was not observed in monolayer culture, even when the monolayers were cultured on laminin or matrigel. Kobayashi and colleagues (1993) observed that while the parental nonresistant tumor lines formed spheroids that were loose and grapelike multicellular aggregates that were ellipsoidal in shape, every resistant tumor subline formed a very highly compact spheroid. It should also be noted that *in vitro* exposure of the parental EMT-6 cells to 4-HO_2-CTX induced the formation of compact spheroids just as the *in vivo* exposure did as described above. Thus, the experiments by Kobayashi *et al.* reconfirm that cells in a three-dimensional configuration can be much more resistant than monolayers of the same cells *in vitro*, and for the first time demonstrate that three-dimensional cellular configurations may become resistant to suprapharmacological doses of drugs by forming compact structures. The compact nature of the spheroids may confer a "tissue-based" resistance to drugs (Kobayashi *et al.*, 1993), as opposed to cellular resistance indicated by membrane pumps which reduce drug concentration.

In the 1950s, Leighton (1959) observed that tumors grew as aggregates in histocultures and suggested that these aggregates were the units of metastasis rather than single cells on the basis of their migration in sponge-gel matrices. In this light, Kobayashi *et al.* (1993) have observed that the EMT-6 cells selected to be highly resistant *in vivo* are highly metastatic. These results have deep implications: If drug resistance generated *in vivo* is mediated by formation of tight aggregates, drug resistance may promote metastasis. Thus, the generation of drug resistance could greatly enhance the malignancy of tumors. Therefore, failure of drug treatment of patients may have a double ramification: Not only will the tumor still remain viable despite drug treatment, but, indeed, the tumor could become more highly malignant because of the formation of highly aggregated emboli.

V. Pitfalls

As with any *in vitro* model, three-dimensional histoculture has certain limitations that must be considered when interpreting data. One drawback is the inherent heterogeneity of tumors as opposed to cloned cell lines. Another is the quantification of specific subpopulations of cells, which is technically more difficult in histocultures than in monolayer cultures.

REFERENCES

Carrel, A. (1912) On the permanent life of tissues outside the organism. *J. Exp. Med.* **15**, 516–528.

Chang, S. G., Slocum, H., Toth, K., Hoffman, R. M., Perrapato, S. D., Huben, R. P., and Rustum, Y. M. (1992) Glucose consumption end point in primary histoculture indicates recovery of human tumors from drug treatment. *In Vitro Cell. Dev. Biol.* **28A**, 585–587.

Colangelo, D., Guo, H-Y, Silvestro, L., and Hoffman, R. M. (1992) Noncolorimetric measurement of cell activity in three-dimensional histoculture using the tetrazolium dye 3-(4,5-dimethylthiazol-2-yl)-2,5-diphenyltetrazolium bromide: The pixel image analysis of formazan crystals. *Anal. Biochem.* **205**, 8–13.

Freeman, A. E., and Hoffman, R. M. (1986) *In vivo*-like growth of human tumors *in vitro*. *Proc. Natl. Acad. Sci. USA* **83**, 2694–2698.

Furukawa, T., Kubota, T., Watanabe, M., Takahara, T., Yamaguchi, H., Takeuchi, T., Kase, S., Kodaira, S., Ishibiki, K., Kitajima, M., and Hoffman, R. M. (1992) High *in vitro–in vivo* correlation of drug response using sponge-gel-supported three-dimensional histoculture and the MTT end point. *Int. J. Cancer* **51**, 489–498.

Guadagni, F., Li, L., and Hoffman, R. M. (1992) Targeting antibodies to live tumor tissue in 3-D histoculture. *In Vitro Cell. Dev. Biol.* **28A**, 297–299.

Guo, Y. H., Guo, H. Y., Colangelo, D., Li, L., Connors, K. M., Kubota, T. and Hoffman, R. M. (1992) *In vitro* histoculture of human tumors with fluorescent dye endpoints measured by confocal microscopy: High correlation of *in vitro* and *in vivo* chemosensitivity. *Anticancer Res.* **12**, 1055–1061.

Hoffman, R. M. (1991) *In vitro* sensitivity assays in cancer: A review, analysis and prognosis. *J. Clin. Lab. Anal.* **5**, 133–143.

Hoffman, R. M., Connors, K. M., Meerson-Monosov, A. Z., Herrera, H., and Price, J. H. (1989) A general native-state method for determination of proliferation capacity of human normal and tumor tissues in vitro. *Proc. Natl. Acad. Sci. USA* **86**, 2013–2017.

Kobayashi, H. I., Man, S., Grahm, C., Kapitain, S., Teicher, B., and Kerbel, R. S. (1993) Acquired multicellular mediated resistance to alkylating agents in cancer. *Proc. Natl. Acad. Sci. USA*, **90**, 3294–3298.

Lawler, E. M., Miller, F. R., and Heppner, G. H. (1983) Significance of three-dimensional growth patterns of mammary tissues in collagen gels. *In Vitro* **19**, 600–610.

Leighton, J. (1951) A sponge matrix method for tissue culture. Formation of organized aggregates of cells *in vitro*. *J. Natl. Cancer Inst.* **12**, 545–561.

Leighton, J. (1959) Aggregate replication, a factor in the growth of cancer. *Science* **129**, 466–467.

Leighton, J., Siar, J. W., and Mahoney, M. J. (1962) Examination of invasion by manipulating stroma and parenchyma of carcinomas *in vitro* and *in vivo*. In "Biological Interactions in Normal and Neoplastic Growth: A Contribution to the Host–Tumor Problem" (M. J. Brennan and E. L. Simpson, eds.), pp. 681–702. Little, Brown, Boston.

Li, L., Margolis, L. B., and Hoffman, R. M. (1991) Skin toxicity determined *in vitro* by three-dimensional, native-state histoculture. *Proc. Natl. Acad. Sci. USA* **88**, 1908–1912.

Li, L., Paus, R., Margolis, L. B., and Hoffman, R. M. (1992a) Hair growth *in vitro* from histocultured mouse skin. *In Vitro Cell. Dev. Biol.* **28A**, 479–481.

Li, L., Paus, R., Slominski, A., and Hoffman, R. M. (1992b) Skin histoculture assay for studying the hair cycle. *In Vitro Cell. Dev. Biol.* **28A**, 695–698.

Li, L., Paus, R., Margolis, L. B., and Hoffman, R. M. (1992c) Hair shaft elongation, follicle growth and spontaneous regression in long-term, sponge-gel supported histoculture of human scalp skin. *Proc. Natl. Acad. Sci. USA* **89**, 8764–8768.

Miller, B. E., Miller, F. R., and Heppner, G. H. (1984) Assessing tumor drug sensitivity by a new *in vitro* assay which preserves tumor heterogeneity and subpopulation interactions. *J. Cell. Physiol. Suppl.* **3**, 105–116.

Miller, B. E., Miller, F. R., and Heppner, G. H. (1985) Factors affecting growth and drug sensitivity of mouse mammary tumor lines in collagen gel cultures. *Cancer Res.* **45,** 4200–4205.

Slocum, H. K., Hoffman, R. M., Chang, S-G., Li, L., Toth, K., and Rustum, Y. M. (1992) Long-term passage of human tissues *in vivo* as three-dimensional histolines. *In Vitro Cell. Dev. Biol.* **28A,** 573–577.

Teicher, B. A., Herman, T. S., Holden, S., Wang, S., Pfeffer, M. R., and Crawford, J. W. (1990) Tumor resistance to alkylating agents conferred by mechanisms operative only *in vivo. Science* **247,** 1457–1461.

Vescio, R. A., Redfern, C. H., Nelson, T. J., Ugoretz, S., Stern, P. H., and Hoffman, R. M. (1987) *In vivo*-like drug response of human tumors growing in three-dimensional, gel-supported, primary culture. *Proc. Natl. Acad. Sci. USA* **84,** 5029–5033.

Vescio, R. A., Connors, K. M., Youngkin, T., Bordin, G. M., Robb, J. A., Umbreit, J. N., and Hoffman, R. M. (1990a) Cancer biology for individualized therapy: Correlation of growth fraction index in native-state histoculture with tumor grade and stage. *Proc. Natl. Acad. Sci. USA* **87,** 691–695.

Vescio, R. A., Connors, K. M., Bordin, G. M., Robb, J. A., Youngkin, T., Umbreit, J. N., and Hoffman, R. M. (1990b) The distinction of small cell and non-small cell cancer by growth in native-state histoculture. *Cancer Res.* **50,** 6095–6099.

Vescio, R. A., Connors, K. M., Kubota, T., and Hoffman, R. M. (1991) Correlation of histology and drug response of human tumors grown in native-state three-dimensional histoculture and in nude mice. *Proc. Natl. Acad. Sci. USA* **88,** 5163–5166.

SECTION L

Other Cell Types

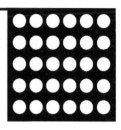

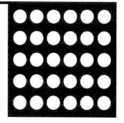

Primary Culture of *Drosophila* Embryo Cells

Paul M. Salvaterra and Izumi Hayashi

I. Introduction

Primary cultures of *Drosophila* embryonic cells offer a unique system to study the transitions of undifferentiated cells into a variety of cell types. Coupled with the power of *Drosophila* classical and molecular genetics, the analyses that are possible *in vitro* using differentiating embryo cells will continue to contribute to a deeper understanding of development. Preparation of primary embryo cell cultures was developed independently in the laboratories of Seecof and his colleagues (Seecof and Unanue, 1968) and Shields and Sang (1970). The procedures for preparing cultures are technically undemanding and can be adapted to solve a wide range of biological problems. Important variations include the culture of single embryos (Cross and Sang, 1978), as well as the development of techniques for isolating the precursors of different cell types such as neurons and muscle cells (Furst and Mahowald, 1985). Figure 1 shows an egg collection plate and population cage, and Fig. 2 illustrates a typical setup we use for preparing primary embryo cultures.

Cultures are initiated from embryos in early gastrula stage, making it possible to observe cell development from committed precursor to final differentiated cell type. The types of cells that differentiate in culture are primarily neurons (Seecof *et al.*, 1973a) and multinucleate myotubes (Seecof *et al.*, 1973b), but other epidermal and mesodermal derivatives are also present (Shields *et al.*, 1975). Cultures form a variety of neurons with highly differentiated phenotypes, including neurotransmitter systems (Salvaterra *et al.*, 1987), ion channels (Germeraad *et al.*, 1992), axonal specializations, and even functional neuromuscular junctions (Seecof *et al.*, 1972). Medium conditioned by embryo cells has also been shown to contain a variety of activities which can modulate the growth and differentiation properties of neurons (Salvaterra *et al.*, 1987; Hayashi *et al.*, 1992). Figure 3 shows some of the cell types observed in a differentiated *Drosophila* primary embryo culture.

II. Materials and Instrumentation

Penicillin and streptomycin are obtained from Calbiochem (Cat. Nos. 5161 and 5711). Insulin is from Sigma (Cat. No. I-5500). Schneider's powdered *Drosophila* medium is obtained from Irvine Scientific (Cat. No. 9553). Fetal calf serum is from Gibco (Cat. No. 200-6140AJ).

Cells are usually cultured in 35-mm plastic dishes from Corning (Cat. No. T4150-1). For finer morphological observations cells are plated directly onto round glass

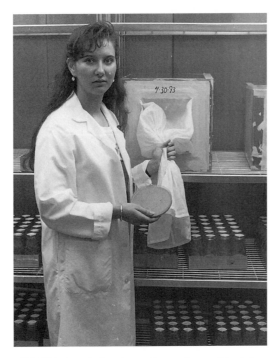

FIGURE 1   Collecting embryos from a Plexiglas population cage. The large petri plate will be inserted into the population cage through the nylon mesh sleeve.

coverslips placed in the bottom of a 35-mm plate (five per culture dish, Bellco Glass, Cat. No. 1943-00012. Coverslips are presterilized using standard gas or autoclave procedures.

We dissociate dechorionated embryos in 15-ml Dounce glass–glass homogenizers from Baxter Diagnostics(Cat. No. T4018-15). Nylon mesh (25-100 μm pore size) can be obtained from most fabric stores. All other equipment is of a type commonly used for general laboratory work or tissue culture and can be obtained from any scientific supply company.

III. Procedures

A. EGG COLLECTION AND AGING TO EARLY GASTRULA STAGE

Solution

1. *Yeast-water paste:* Dissolve live yeast in water and stir to make a semi-solid paste.

Steps

1. Collect eggs from large Plexiglas population cages (50 × 35 cm) in a 25°C humidified fly room. For convenience maintain the room on a reverse light–dark cycle so collections can be done in the investigators' morning (i.e., the flies' dusk).

2. Apply a small amount of semisolid live yeast–water paste on a small piece of filter paper and place it in the center of a large (14-cm) food plate to attract females to lay eggs.

3. Put three plates in each cage and collect eggs for 1 or 2 hr.

4. If better developmental timing is desired, do a 30-min to 1-hr precollection,

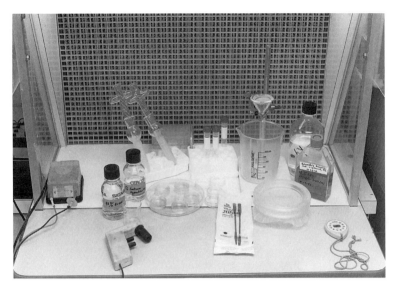

FIGURE 2 Typical apparatus, set up in a small laminar flow hood, used to prepare mass cultures of *Drosophila* gastrula-stage embryo cells. See the text for a more complete description.

as described above, and discard plates. This may be necessary to induce females to lay eggs they have been storing for longer times.

5. Remove egg collection plates from the population cage, cover, and allow embryos to develop to early gastrula stage at 25°C for 3.5 hr.

B. HARVESTING OF EMBRYOS

Solutions

1. *Deionized water:* Prepare 2 to 3 liters of deionized water.

Steps

1. Embryos should be harvested 5–10 min before the 3.5-hr aging period so the cultures can be initiated immediately at 3.5 hr.
2. Discard filter papers with yeast mixture.
3. Transfer plates to sink and rinse extensively and gently with deionized water to remove adult flies and other debris.
4. Pour water on the plates and gently loosen embryos with a camel's hair paint brush.
5. Pour suspended embryos into a nylon mesh filter to allow further washing and collection from other food plates.
6. Continue washing and remove large food particles and other debris with forceps if necessary.
7. Transfer nylon mesh with eggs to sterile tissue culture hood.

C. PREPARATION OF EMBRYONIC CULTURES

Solutions

1. *Penicillin–streptomycin stock solution:* Dissolve penicillin in distilled H_2O to a final concentration of 200,000 units/ml. Dissolve streptomycin in H_2O to

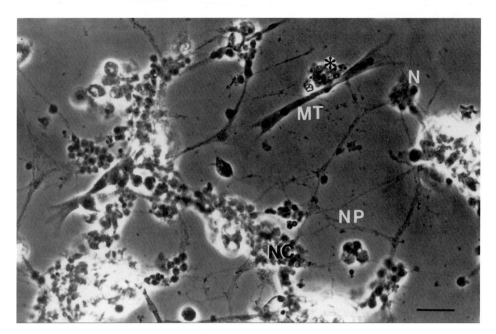

FIGURE 3   Differentiated *Drosophila* embryo cell culture showing neuronal clusters (NC), more isolated neurons (N), multinucleate myotubes (MT), and neuronal cell processes (NP). The cells have been cultured for 24 hr. Note also the presence of other unidentified cell types (*).

final concentration of 200 mg/ml. Mix equal parts of penicillin and streptomycin and store at −20°C. Use 1 ml per liter of medium (i.e., final concentration of 100 units/ml penicillin, 100 μg/ml streptomycin).

2. *Insulin stock solution:* Dissolve insulin in 0.05 N HCl at a final concentration of 2 mg/ml. Filter-sterilize (0.2 μm) and store at 4°C (stock is stable for 1 year). Use at a final concentration of 0.2 μg/ml of medium.

3. *Schneider's medium with glutamine and 5% fetal calf serum:* Weigh out enough Schneider's powdered *Drosophila* medium for 1 liter of medium and 1.8 g of L-glutamine. Add 948 ml distilled H_2O and mix well. Adjust pH to 6.6 using 1M KOH. Add 1 ml penicillin–streptomycin stock solution (see above) and filter-sterilize (prefilter through Whatman No. 4 and 0.45-μm filters if necessary) using a 0.2-μm filter. Before use, add 50 ml of fetal calf serum (final serum concentration = 5%) and 1 ml of insulin stock solution (see above).

4. *Sodium hypochlorite–ethanol:* In a small beaker mix 10 ml of 95% ethanol and 10 ml of 3% sodium hypochlorite. This solution will dechorionate the embryos and sterilize them.

5. *Deionized water:* Prepare about 1 liter of sterile deionized water.

Steps

1. Preclean the laminar flow hood with ethanol using normal tissue culture procedures. All further operations are carried out under sterile conditions in the hood.

2. Transfer embryos to the beaker of sodium hypochlorite–ethanol using a sterile spatula and swirl gently for 1 to 2 min. The time may vary slightly but do not exceed 3 min. Timing depends on the freshness of the hypochlorite and the compromises you are willing to make with respect to yield and sterility. Shorter

times tend toward better yields and longer times are necessary if you wish to totally eliminate yeast contamination.

3. Pour dechorionated embryos onto a small nylon mesh filter funnel and wash extensively with about 500 ml sterile distilled water.

4. Transfer to a 15-ml Dounce homogenizer that contains about 6 ml of culture medium and dissociate cells by gently homogenizing with three rotary up-and-down strokes.

5. Filter dissociated cells through a 25 to 100-μm nylon mesh filter (the mesh is taped loosely over a 5-cm-diameter glass funnel or fitted into a 3.5-cm metal ring which is placed into the funnel) to remove undissociated clumps and other large debris.

6. Collect filtrate in a 15-ml centrifuge tube and pellet cells by centrifugation at 1400 rpm for 4 min. Wash cells one time in 6 ml of culture medium and centrifuge as above, followed by a final suspension in 10 ml of culture medium.

7. Place a small aliquot in a hemocytometer and count the round, intact, medium-sized cells and cell clusters to determine cell number.

8. Calculate the concentration of cells, add sufficient medium to obtain a final density of 8×10^5 cells/ml, and plate approximately 1.6×10^6 cells in a 35-mm culture dish (i.e., 2 ml of cell suspension per dish).

9. Culture cells in a humidified 25°C incubator (CO_2 is not necessary). Cells begin to differentiate in a few hours and are substantially developed after about 24 hr. Cells can be cultured for several days before replacing the medium. It is possible to keep cultures for more than 1 year.

IV. Comments

We usually grow cells in 35-mm dishes but it is also possible to plate directly onto coverslips (see above) and even to grow cells in the raised condensation rings found on the lids of many 96-well microtiter plates. This is especially convenient when screening monoclonal antibodies, as each embryo culture can be isolated and matched with the corresponding position for a hybridoma clone growing in a 96-well culture dish. Furst and Mahowald (1984) have described a method of treating the lids with H_2SO_4 that results in a significant improvement in the attachment and differentiation of *Drosophila* embryo cells.

The yield of cells depends on how vigorously the cells are dissociated and how long the embryos are exposed to the ethanol–hypochlorite mixture. Using the above procedures, with a 2-hr egg collection, we can routinely obtain more than 10^7 cells for plating. A 2-hr egg collection from a population cage stocked with about 10^5 adults (1–4 weeks old) yields on the order of 0.5 g of eggs. The procedure can easily be scaled up or down by at least a factor of 10, depending on the needs of a particular experiment.

V. Pitfalls

1. In the past we have used up to 20% fetal calf serum, however, such high concentrations are not necessary to support optimal growth and differentiation. It is especially important to use prescreened lots of fetal calf serum that are suitable for *Drosophila* embryo cultures. Some lots of fetal calf serum do not support differentiation and even appear to be toxic to *Drosophila* embryonic cells. We have had good success with serum from Gibco and Gemini Products.

2. The surface coating of tissue culture plasticware from different manufacturers varies. We have found that some types of 35-mm plastic dishes, such as those from Falcon, are not optimal for *Drosophila* cultures.

ACKNOWLEDGMENTS

Work in the authors' laboratories has been supported by the NIH-NINDS (P.M.S.) and the Council for Tobacco Research (I.H.). We thank our past and current laboratory colleagues for many helpful suggestions and ideas about *Drosophila* primary embryo cultures, in particular Dr. K. Ikeda, Dr. N. Bournias-Vardiabasis, and Ms. M. Perez.

REFERENCES

Cross, D. P., and Sang, J. H. (1978) Cell culture of individual *Drosophila* embryos. I. Development of wild-type cultures. *J. Embryol. Exp. Morphol.* **45**, 161–172.

Furst, A., and Mahowald, A. P. (1984) Rapid immunofluorescent screening procedure using primary cell cultures or tissue sections. *J. Immunol. Methods.* **70**, 101–109.

Furst, A., and Mahowald, A. P. (1985) Differentiation of primary embryonic neuroblasts in purified neural cell cultures from *Drosophila. Dev. Biol.* **109**, 184–192.

Germeraad, S., O'Dowd, D., and Aldrich, R. W. (1992) Functional assay of a putative *Drosophila* sodium channel gene in homozygous deficiency neurons. *J. Neurogenet.* **8**, 1–16.

Hayashi, I., Perez-Magallanes, M., and Rossi, J. M. (1992) Neurotrophic factor-like activity in *Drosophila. Biochem. Biophys. Res. Commun.* **184**, 73–79.

Salvaterra, P. M., Bournias-Vardiabasis, N., Nair, T., Hou, G., and Lieu, C. (1987) *In vitro* neuronal differentiation of *Drosophila* embryo cells. *J. Neurosci.* **7**, 10–22.

Seecof, R. L., Donady, J. J., and Teplitz, R. L. (1973a) Differentiation of *Drosophila* neuroblasts to form ganglion-like clusters of neurons *in vitro. Cell Diff.* **2**, 143–149.

Seecof, R. L., Gerson, I., Donady, J. J., and Teplitz, R. L. (1973b) *Drosophila* myogenesis *in vitro*: The genesis of "small" myocytes and myotubes. *Dev. Biol.* **35**, 250–261.

Seecof, R. L., Teplitz, R. L., Gerson, I., Ikeda, K., and Donady, J. J. (1972) Differentiation of neuromuscular junctions in cultures of embryonic *Drosophila* cells. *Proc. Natl. Acad. Sci. USA* **69**, 566–570.

Seecof, R. L., and Unanue, R. L. (1968) Differentiation of embryonic *Drosophila* cells *in vitro. Exp. Cell Res.* **50**, 654–660.

Shields, G., Dubendorfer, A., and Sang, J. H. (1975) Differentiation *in vitro* of larval cell types from early embryonic cells of *Drosophila* melanogaster. *J. Embryol. Exp. Morphol.* **33**, 159–175.

Shields, G., and Sang, J. H. (1970) Characteristics of five cell types appearing during *in vitro* culture of embryonic material from *Drosophila melanogaster. J. Embryol. Exp. Morphol.* **23**, 53–69.

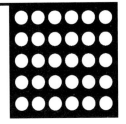

Laboratory Cultivation of *Caenorhabditis elegans* and Other Free-Living Nematodes

Ian M. Caldicott, Pamela L. Larsen, and Donald L. Riddle

I. Introduction

Nematodes have been cultured continuously in the laboratory since 1944 when Margaret Briggs Gochnauer isolated and cultured the free-living hermaphroditic species *Caenorhabditis briggsae*. Work with *C. briggsae* and other rhabditid nematodes, *C. elegans*, *Rhabditis anomala*, and *R. pellio*, demonstrated the relative ease with which they could be cultured (Dougherty, 1960; Vanfleteren, 1980). The culturing techniques described here were developed for *C. elegans*, but are generally suitable (to varying degrees) for other free-living nematodes. Whereas much of the early work involved axenic culturing, most of these techniques are no longer in common use and are not included here.

In the 1970s *C. elegans* became the predominant research model due to work by Brenner and co-workers on the genetics and development of this species (Brenner, 1974). An adult *C. elegans* is about 1.5 mm long, and under optimal laboratory conditions has a life cycle of approximately 3 days. There are two sexes, males and self-fertile hermaphrodites (Fig. 1), that are readily distinguishable as adults. The animals are transparent throughout the life cycle, permitting observation of cell divisions in living animals using differential interference microscopy. The complete cell lineage and neural circuitry have been determined and a large collection of behavioral and anatomical mutants has been isolated (Wood, 1988). *C. elegans* has six developmental stages: egg, four larval stages (L1–L4), and adult. Under starvation conditions or specific manipulations of the culture conditions a developmentally arrested dispersal stage, the dauer larva, can be formed as an alternative third larval stage (Golden and Riddle, 1984).

Many of the protocols included here and other experimental protocols have been summarized in "The Nematode *Caenorhabditis elegans*" (Wood, 1988). We also include a previously unpublished method for long-term chemostat cultures of *C. elegans*. General laboratory culture conditions for nematode parasites of animals have been described (Hansen and Hansen, 1978), but none of these nematodes can be cultured in the laboratory through more than one life cycle. Marine nematodes and some plant parasites have been cultured xenically or with fungi (Nicholas, 1975). Laboratory cultivation of several plant parasites on *Arabidopsis thaliana* seedlings in agar petri plates has also been reported (Sijmons *et al.*, 1991).

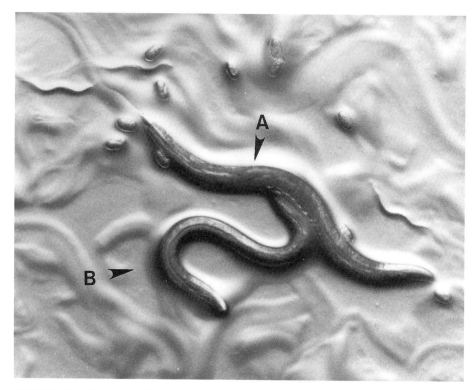

FIGURE 1 *Caenorhabditis elegans* hermaphrodite (**A**) and male (**B**) copulating. Also visible are several eggs and young larvae.

II. Materials and Instrumentation

C. elegans strains, as well as strains of other free-living nematodes, and bacterial food sources for them are available from the Caenorhabditis Genetics Center (250 Biological Sciences Center, University of Minnesota, 1445 Gourtner Ave, St. Paul, MN, 55108). Most chemicals are obtained from general laboratory supply companies such as Fisher Scientific and Sigma; catalog numbers are for Fisher except where noted. Three sizes of polystyrene petri dishes are used in culturing nematodes: 35 × 10 mm (Cat. No. 8-757-100-A), 60 × 15 mm (Cat. No. 8-757-13-A), and 100 × 15 mm (Cat. No. 8-757-13). Triple-baffled Fernbach flasks (250 ml, 1 liter, and 2.8 liter, Cat. No. 2554) for liquid culture are from Bellco. The programmable dispensing pump (Model DP-200) used when making plates and the chemostat (Bioflo I) are from New Brunswick Scientific Company. An IEC clinical centrifuge (Cat. No. 05-101-5) with rotor 221 and metal shields 303 at setting 4 (RCF approx 750) for 30 sec is used for pelleting nematodes.

Tools for manipulating individual nematodes on plates are made by anchoring a 1.5-cm piece of 32-gauge platinum wire (Cat. No. 13-766-10-B) in a 6-in. inoculating loop holder or in a Pasteur pipette (by breaking off the pipette at the point where it narrows and holding in a flame with the wire to seal the end). For best results the end of the wire used for manipulation should be flattened and, if necessary, rounded to remove sharp edges. Observation of nematodes on plates is performed through a dissecting microscope with a magnification range of approximately 6 to 50×, fitted with a variable-angle transmitted light source. The microscopes in most common use for research are the Wild M3, M5, and M8 (Leica Inc.).

III. Procedures

A. PREPARATION OF PLATES

The procedure for preparation of plates is modified from that of Brenner (1974).

Solutions

1. *Cholesterol stock (5 mg/ml):* Dissolve 0.5 g cholesterol (Cat. No. C314) in a final volume of 100 ml of 95% ethanol.

2. *1 M CaCl₂:* Dissolve 14.7 g of $CaCl_2 \cdot 2H_2O$ (Cat. No. C79) in a final volume of 100 ml of distilled water and autoclave.

3. *1 M MgSO₄:* Dissolve 24.65 g of $MgSO_4 \cdot 7H_2O$ (Cat. No. M63) in a final volume of 100 ml of distilled water and autoclave.

4. *KH₂PO₄ stock (1 M):* Dissolve 68.04 g of KH_2PO_4 (Cat. No. P285) in approximately 425 ml of distilled water. Add KOH (Cat. No. P250) pellets while monitoring the pH until pH is 6.0. Bring the volume to 500 ml; autoclave in 100-ml aliquots.

5. *B broth:* Add 1.0 g of tryptone and 0.5 g of NaCl (Cat. No. S640) to 100 ml of distilled water in a 250-ml screw-cap flask and autoclave.

6. *OP50 stock:* Inoculate 100 ml of B broth (in screw-cap flask) with *Escherichia coli* strain OP50, a uracil auxotroph, and shake overnight at 37°C. Store the stationary-phase culture at 4°C for up to 60 days.

7. *NG agar:* Add 3 g of NaCl, 17 g of Difco agar (Cat. No. DF0140-01-0), 2.5 g of peptone (Cat. No. DF0118-15-2), and 975 ml of distilled water to a 2-liter erlenmeyer flask. Autoclave; then place the flask in a 50°C water bath to prevent solidification while dispensing medium into plates. Allow the flask to cool to approximately 65°C and add the following, using sterile technique and swirling the flask after adding each ingredient: 1 ml cholesterol stock, 1 ml 1 *M* CaCl₂, 1 ml 1 *M* MgSO₄, and 25 ml KH₂PO₄ stock.

Steps

1. Accurate dispensing of medium is most easily accomplished with the aid of a programmable dispensing pump. Fill 60 × 15-mm plates with 13 ml of agar, 100 × 15-mm plates with 30 ml, and 35 × 10-mm plates with 4 ml. The plates should be bubble free; flame the surface to remove bubbles.

2. Allow the plates to cool overnight; then put plates at 37°C for 24 hr. Allow the plates to return to room temperature; store at 4°C.

3. Seed the plates (Fig. 2) with OP50 stock by spreading approximately 0.05 ml on the surface using a 1-ml pipette, and incubate overnight at 37°C or for 24–48 hr at room temperature. Plates should be at room temperature before placing worms on them.

B. LIQUID CULTURE

The procedure is modified from that of Sulston and Brenner (1974).

Solutions

1. *M9 buffer:* Dissolve 3 g of KH_2PO_4, 6 g of Na_2HPO_4 (Cat. No. S393), and 5 g of NaCl in distilled water; then add 1 ml of 1 *M* MgSO₄. Bring the volume to 1 liter with distilled water and autoclave in 100-ml aliquots.

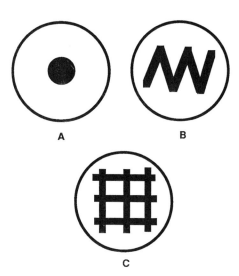

FIGURE 2 Examples of seeded plates. (**A**) Spot plate, used for matings with single males or with mutant animals that do not mate well. (**B**) Zigzag plate, used for routine strain maintenance and crosses. (**C**) Grid plate, used for mutant screens, strain maintenance, or crosses in which progeny are counted.

2. *S basal:* Add 5.84 g of NaCl, 50 ml KH_2PO_4 stock, and 1 ml cholesterol stock to 950 ml of distilled water; autoclave in 100-ml aliquots.

3. *Potassium citrate stock (1 M):* Add 105.07 g of citric acid monohydrate (Cat. No. A104) to 250 ml of distilled water. Add KOH pellets while monitoring the pH until pH is 6.0. Bring the volume to 500 ml and autoclave in 100-ml aliquots.

4. *100× trace metals:* Dissolve 0.69 g of $FeSO_4 \cdot H_2O$ (Cat. No. I467), 1.86 g of Na_2EDTA (Cat. No. O2793), 0.197 g of $MnCl_2 \cdot 4H_2O$ (Sigma, Cat. No. M-3634), 0.287 g of $ZnSO_4 \cdot 7H_2O$ (Cat. No. Z76), and 0.025 g of $CuSO_4 \cdot 5H_2O$ (Cat. No. C493) in 1 liter of distilled water. Autoclave in 100-ml aliquots; store in foil-wrapped bottles.

5. *50% glucose:* Add 50 g of glucose (Cat. No. D16) to 50 ml of distilled water and autoclave.

6. *60% sucrose:* Add 120 g of sucrose (Cat. No. S5) to 80 ml distilled water and autoclave. Store at 4°C.

7. *S medium:* Add in the order indicated, using sterile technique, 1 ml potassium citrate stock, 1 ml 100× trace metals, 0.3 ml 1 M $CaCl_2$, and 0.3 ml 1 M $MgSO_4$ to 100 ml of S basal.

8. *X1666 medium:* Add 20 g of $Na_2HPO_4 \cdot 7H_2O$ (Cat. No. S373), 4.5 g of KH_2PO_4, 1.2 g of NH_4Cl (Cat. No. A661), 16 g of tryptone (Cat. No. DF0123-15-5), and 4 g of yeast extract (Cat. No. DF0127-15-1) to 980 ml distilled water in a 2.8-liter baffled flask. Mix, autoclave, allow to cool, and add 20 ml of 50% glucose and 8 ml of 1 M $MgSO_4$.

9. *X1666 stock:* Inoculate X1666 medium with X1666, a nalidixic acid-resistant, prototrophic, plasmid-free strain of *E. coli*. Shake at 37°C for overnight. Transfer to preweighed sterile centrifuge bottles/tubes and centrifuge at 4000 RCF for 10 min. Remove supernatant and determine weight of bacteria. Resuspend in S medium to 5% (w/w). Store at 4°C.

Steps

1. With 2 ml of M9 buffer per plate wash worms off five 60 × 15-mm plates that have just cleared of bacteria. Pellet nematodes. Remove supernatant and wash twice with fresh M9.

2. Add the washed worms to 250 ml X1666 stock in a 1-liter sterile baffled flask and place on shaker at 20°C. When the medium is cleared of bacteria centrifuge at 750 RCF for 5 min.

3. Remove supernatant and resuspend in 15 ml of M9 buffer, divide between two 15-ml tubes, and place on ice. When cold add 7.5 ml of cold 60% sucrose to each tube. Mix by inversion and centrifuge immediately at 1500 RCF for 5 min.

4. Remove nematodes from top of tube immediately and wash twice with 15 ml of M9 buffer. Place at 20°C on shaker for 30 min to allow digestion of bacteria in nematode intestines.

5. Wash twice with M9 buffer and use immediately or freeze at −70°C.

C. CHEMOSTAT CULTURE

Solution

1. *OP50 concentrate:* Make in same manner as X1666 stock except use *E. coli* strain OP50 and resuspend the pellet in M9 buffer (1/20th volume, or less, of the overnight culture).

Steps

Figure 3 is a diagram of the chemostat assembly.

1. Fill nutrient reservoir with 10 liters of $\frac{1}{5}\times$ S basal [substitute

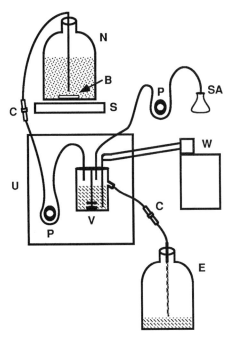

FIGURE 3 Chemostat assembly. **N**, nutrient reservoir; **V**, culture vessel; **E**, effluent tank; **S**, large stir plate; **B**, large stir bar (in reservoir to keep bacteria evenly suspended); **W**, refrigerated circulating water bath (set at 12°C) connected to cold finger of chemostat culture vessel; **U**, Bioflo I control unit; **P**, peristaltic pump; **SA**, selective agent; **C**, compression fitting (Swagelok Co.) used in the line for easy reservoir replacement (see Section IIIC, step 12). Sterility is critical for maintenance of long-term cultures.

polyoxyethanyl-cholesteryl sebacate (Sigma, Cat. No. C-1145) for cholesterol]
and add large stir bar.

2. Fill culture vessel with 0.2 vol water. Attach autoclavable 0.2-μm filters to
the vents and air entry tubing. Autoclave connected nutrient reservoir, culture
vessel, and effluent tank.

3. When cool add the other stock solutions, as to complete $\frac{1}{5}\times$ S medium (see
Section B), to the nutrient reservoir.

4. Add the concentrate from 12 liters of overnight OP50 cultures to the
nutrient reservoir (final $OD_{600nm} = \sim3.7$).

5. Install culture vessel in chemostat control unit and make connections.

6. Start air flow and stir the culture vessel impeller at 220 rpm. Set the heat
regulator to 20°C.

7. Run the feeding pump until culture vessel is full; then turn it off.

8. Inoculate culture vessel with sterile L1 larvae prepared as described in
Section E, steps 10 and 11.

9. Add OP50 concentrate from a 1-liter overnight culture to culture vessel.
Add approximately 1 ml sterile Antifoam A (Sigma, Cat. No. A-5758) as
necessary to minimize foam.

10. Monitor the culture every 2 days by removing a sample and counting
replicate aliquots spotted on plates (see Section A). Continue to add sterile
Antifoam A to culture vessel as needed. When the culture reaches ~50 animals
per 100 μl, turn on the feeding pump (setting 9).

11. Monitor population density and adjust the speed of the feeding pump as
necessary to maintain a reproducing culture. A dense population (~125 animals/
10 μl) that is mostly L1 and L2 larvae and roughly one-fourth dauer larvae can
be maintained.

12. Prepare a replacement nutrient reservoir for use when the first one is
depleted. The effluent tank should be changed at the same time.

D. FREEZING STRAINS FOR LONG-TERM STORAGE

The procedure is modified from that of Brenner (1974).

Solutions

1. *1 M NaCl:* Dissolve 29.22 g of NaCl in a final volume of 500 ml distilled
water and autoclave.

2. *S + glycerol:* Add 20 ml of 1 *M* NaCl, 10 ml of KH_2PO_4 stock, and 60 ml
of glycerol (Cat. No. G33) to 110 ml distilled water and autoclave.

Steps

1. Take three contaminant-free 60 × 15-mm plates 1 day after food is depleted
and wash worms off plates with 2 ml M9 buffer.

2. Add equal volume of S + glycerol and mix by brief vortexing. Transfer in
0.5-ml aliquots to 2-ml cryovials (Vangard International, Cat. No. MS4502).
Place vials in a styrofoam freezing box (a styrofoam block with holes the size of

cryovials and a styrofoam lid) and immediately put at −70°C (cool at approximately 1°C/min).

3. After 6 hr the vials can be transferred to liquid nitrogen or to standard −70°C freezer boxes.

4. One vial should be thawed to check for viability, strain accuracy, and microbial contamination. Thaw vial by warming between hands until liquid; then pour contents onto seeded plate. Transfer young healthy worms to fresh plates the next day.

E. ISOLATION OF STAGED ANIMALS

Solutions

1. *Dauer-inducing pheromone stock* (modified from Golden and Riddle, 1984): Take 1 liter of starved liquid culture. Reduce volume 75% by evaporation under a stream of air at 100°C. Centrifuge at 10,000 RCF for 10 min. Dry the supernatant completely at 60°C. Extract four to six times with 50 ml of 95% ethanol until the extract is only slightly colored. Combine the extracts and dry under a stream of air at 60°C. Back-extract the resulting oily residue with 10 ml distilled water. Filter through Whatman 3MM paper and store at 4°C.

2. *OP50 strep:* Transfer OP50 stock (see Section A) to preweighed sterile centrifuge bottles/tubes and centrifuge at 4000 RCF for 10 min. Remove supernatant and determine weight of bacteria. Resuspend in S medium to 5% (w/w). Add streptomycin (Sigma, Cat. No. S-6501) to 50 μg/ml final concentration. Store at 4°C for a maximum of 2 days.

Steps

Eggs

1. Wash the worms off approximately five 60 × 15-mm plates containing a large number of gravid adults with approximately 2 ml M9 buffer per plate.

2. Combine in a 15-ml Corning polystyrene conical centrifuge tube and pellet nematodes. Remove all but 8 ml of the liquid.

3. Mix together 0.5 ml 5 N KOH and 1.2 ml 20% NaOCl (Cat. No. SS290) in a separate tube; then combine with M9 and worms and vortex briefly.

4. Remove a small aliquot and monitor under a dissecting scope while gently agitating the remaining sample. When 50 to 75% of the adults in the sample have broken open, pellet nematodes.

5. Remove the supernatant, add 8 ml of fresh M9 buffer, and pellet. Repeat two more times leaving 0.5-ml volume after last wash.

6. Resuspend the eggs and pipet onto plates. This method will generally leave some carcass parts.

Dauer Larvae
(This procedure should give greater than 80% dauers.)

1. Make NG agar without peptone (see Section A). Add approximately 25 μl/ml dauer-inducing pheromone stock just before pouring (make only as much as will be used immediately). Pour 2 ml per 35 × 10-mm plate.

2. After plates solidify, spot with 10 μl OP50 strep solution and allow to dry.

3. Add approximately 100 eggs; or allow adults to lay 100 eggs; then remove the adults and incubate at 25°C for 48–60 hr.

Other Stages

1. Follow the egg isolation procedure through step 5.

2. Bring volume to 10 ml with fresh M9 buffer; incubate on a rocker for 12 hr or overnight.

3. Feed synchronized L1 larvae from the previous step. At 20°C mid-L1 larvae can be harvested after approximately 8 hr, mid-L2 larvae at 18 hr, mid-L3 larvae at 25 hr, and L4 larvae at 37 hr (Byerly *et al.*, 1976).

IV. Comments

For genetic analysis and maintenance of strains in active use, the nematodes should be grown on 60 × 15-mm petri plates. When large numbers of worms are needed 100 × 15-mm plates are used. When special additives are being used that are expensive or in limited supply 35 × 10-mm plates are used. Long-term storage of all strains and those not in active use is best accomplished by freezing in liquid nitrogen. For biochemical purposes the nematodes should be grown in liquid culture. Chemostat culturing enables selection on a continuously reproducing population whose density is held constant (Dykhuizen and Hartl, 1983). Most commonly, selection is for an altered growth rate, whether due to induced or spontaneous mutations. Liquid or gaseous selective agents are compatible with the system described.

More precise synchronization for L4 larvae and adults can be accomplished by synchronizing through the dauer stage. If large numbers of dauers are needed they can be obtained by slightly modifying the liquid culturing procedure. The culture should be allowed to continue for 2–3 days after clearing. After sucrose flotation, treat with a sterile solution of 1% sodium dodecyl sulfate (SDS) for 1 hr [resuspend in 22.5 ml of M9 and add 2.5 ml of 10% SDS (dissolve 10 g of SDS, Cat. No. S529, in a final volume of 100 ml distilled water)]. Wash twice with M9 buffer and then repeat liquid culture protocol starting with step 3.

REFERENCES

Brenner, S. (1974) The genetics of *Caenorhabditis elegans*. *Genetics* **77**, 71–94.

Byerly, L., Cassada, R. C., and Russell, R. L. (1976) The life cycle of the nematode *Caenorhabditis elegans*. I. Wild type growth and reproduction. *Dev. Biol.* **51**, 23–33.

Dougherty, E. C. (1960) Cultivation of Aschelminths, especially Rhabditid nematodes. *In* "Nematology" (J. N. Sasser and W. R. Jenkins, eds.), pp. 297–318. Univ. of North Carolina Press, Chapel Hill.

Dykhuizen, D. E., and Hartl, D. L. (1983) Selection in chemostats. *Microbiol. Rev.* **47**(2), 150–168.

Golden, J. W., and Riddle, D. L. (1984) The *Caenorhabditis elegans* dauer larva: Developmental effects of pheromone, food, and temperature. *Dev. Biol.* **102**, 368–378.

Hansen, E. L., and Hansen, J. W. (1978) *In vitro* cultivation of nematodes parasitic on animals and plants *In* "Methods of Cultivating Parasites *in Vitro*" (A. E. R. Taylor and J. R. Baker, eds.), pp. 227–278. Academic Press, London.

Nicholas, W. L. (1975) "The Biology of Free-Living Nematodes," pp. 74–91. Clarendon Press, Oxford.

Sijmons, P. C., Grundler, F. M. W., von Mende, N., Burrows, P. R., and Wyss, U. (1991) *Arabidopsis thaliana* as a new model host for plant-parasitic nematodes. *Plant J.* **1**, 245–254.

Sulston, J. E., and Brenner, S. (1974) The DNA of *Caenorhabditis elegans*. *Genetics* 77, 95–104.

Vanfleteren, J. R. (1980) Nematodes as nutritional models. *In* "Nematodes as Biological Models" (B. M. Zuckerman, ed.), Vol. 2, pp. 47–79. Academic Press, New York.

Wood, W. B. (1988) "The Nematode *Caenorhabditis elegans*" (W. B. Wood, ed.), pp. 1–16. Cold Spring Harbor Laboratory Press, Cold Spring Harbor, NY.

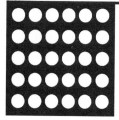

Cultivation of *Tetrahymena* Cells

Yoshio Watanabe, Osamu Numata, Yasuhiro Kurasawa, and Mariko Katoh

I. Introduction

The ciliated protozoan *Tetrahymena* is one of the most convenient experimental materials for studying the molecular bases of various cellular functions and phenomena in animal cells. *Tetrahymena* was the first animal cell to be cultivated under sterile conditions (Lwoff, 1923) and in a chemically defined synthetic medium (Kidder and Dewey, 1951), and was the first animal cell to exhibit temperature-induced synchronous division (Scherbaum and Zeuthen, 1954). In addition, useful techniques for isolating mutants (Orias and Bruns, 1976; Frankel *et al.,* 1976) were developed using inbred strains. This article describes the methods for stock culture, ordinary experimental culture, and synchronous culture of *Tetrahymena* cells.

II. Materials and Instrumentation

A. ORGANISMS

Representative *Tetrahymena* cells used in the fields of cell and molecular biology are *Tetrahymena pyriformis* W, *Tetrahymena pyriformis* GL (amicronucleated strains), and *Tetrahymena thermophila* (micronucleated species). In the last organism, inbred strains with a coded nomenclature are often used, for example, *Tetrahymena thermophila* (B1868-III), where *B* is the name of one of the inbred strains, *18* is the number of the sister–brother mating, *68* represents the year the strain was established (1968), and *III* represents the mating type. *Tetrahymena* strains or species can be requested from authors of recent *Tetrahymena* papers or from the American Type Culture Collection (ATCC, Rockville, MD).

B. CULTURE MEDIA

1. Conventional Culture Medium

For the conventional sterile culture, so-called PYD medium is used (Watanabe, 1963). The PYD medium consists of proteose–peptone No. 3 (Difco Laboratories, Cat. No. 0122-01), yeast extract (Difco, Cat. No. 0127-01-7), and dextrose (Sigma Chemical Co., Cat. No. G-7528). For other proteose–peptone media, see Scherbaum and Zeuthen (1955).

2. Chemically Defined Synthetic Medium

We have used modified synthetic medium (Watanabe, 1963), designated as basal medium 2A, basically established by Kidder and Dewey (1951). Ingredients of basal medium 2A are purchased from Sigma Chemical Company: DL-alanine (Cat. No. A-7377), L-arginine (Cat. No. A-3784), L-aspartic acid (Cat. No. A-4534), glycine (Cat. No. G-6388), L-glutamic acid (Cat. No. G-5889), L-histidine (Cat. No. H-9386), DL-isoleucine (Cat. No. I-7258), L-leucine (Cat. No. L-1512), L-lysine (Cat. No. L-1262), DL-methionine (Cat. No. M-2768), L-phenylalanine (Cat. No. P-5030), L-proline (Cat. No. P-4655), DL-serine (Cat. No. S-5386), DL-threonine (Cat. No. T-1520), L-tryptophan (Cat. No. T-0271), DL-valine (Cat. No. V-6379), uracil (Cat. No. U-1128), adenylic acid (Cat. No. A-9540), cytidylic acid (Cat. No. C-9782), guanylic acid (Cat. No. G-8002), calcium pantothenate (Cat. No. P-5155), nicotinamide (Cat. No. N-3376), pyridoxine-HCl (Cat. No. P-6280), pyridoxal-HCl (Cat. No. P-6155), pyridoxamine-HCl (Cat. No. P-9158), riboflavin (Cat. No. R-9504), thiamine-HCl (Cat. No. T-1270), biotin (Cat. No. B-4639), choline chloride (Cat. No. C-7527), pteroylglutamic acid (Cat. No. F-8758), DL-thioctic acid (Cat. No. T-1395), $MgSO_4 \cdot 7H_2O$ (Cat. No. M-7774), $Fe(NH_4)(SO_4)_2 \cdot 12H_2O$ (Cat. No. F-3629), $MnCl_2 \cdot 4H_2O$ (Cat. No. M-3634), $ZnCl_2$ (Cat. No. Z-0152), $CaCl_2 \cdot 2H_2O$ (Cat. No. C-7902), $CuCl_2 \cdot 2H_2O$ (Cat. No. C-6917), $FeCl_3 \cdot 6H_2O$ (Cat. No. F-2877), K_2HPO_4 (Cat. No. P-8281), KH_2PO_4 (Cat. No. P-5655), Tween 80 (Cat. No. P-4675), dextrose (Cat. No. G-7528), and sodium acetate (Cat. No. S-5636).

3. Inorganic Solutions

Inorganic solutions are sometimes used for washing the cells when they are transferred from PYD medium to synthetic medium; before isolating a certain organelle or cellular molecule; in labeling; or for inducing the conjugation of *T. thermophila*. One of the inorganic solutions, designated NKC solution, contains 34 mM NaCl (Sigma, Cat. No. S-5886), 1 mM KCl (Sigma, Cat. No. P-5405), and 1 mM $CaCl_2$ (Sigma, Cat. No. C-7902) in deionized, distilled water (Watanabe, 1963). For other inorganic solutions, see Hamburger and Zeuthen (1957).

C. CULTURE VESSELS AND SHAKING DEVICES

Middle-sized test tubes (10.5–14 cm long and 12–14 mm in internal diameter), 50-ml Erlenmeyer flasks, 300-ml Erlenmeyer flasks, 3-liter French flasks, and rubber or silicon double-cap stoppers can be purchased from a scientific instrument company. The conventional shaking bath is from Taiyo Bussan Company Ltd. (type, Taiyo Monosin-IIA). The large-scale culture is carried out with a special shaking device (custom-made by Hayashi Rikagaku Co. Ltd.). For inducing synchronous culture, a custom-made fully automatic instrument (Ohtake Works Co. Ltd.) is available.

III. Procedures

A. PREPARATION OF CONVENTIONAL CULTURE MEDIUM

Solution

To prepare conventional culture medium (PYD medium), 1 or 2% (w/v) proteose–peptone No. 3, 0.5% (w/v) yeast extract, and 0.87% (w/v) dextrose are dissolved in deionized water (distilled water that has been passed through an ion-exchange column).

TABLE I Basal Medium 2A (Concentrations in μg/ml)

A		B	
DL-Alanine	220	Calcium pantothenate	0.20
L-Arginine	420	Nicotinamide	0.20
L-Aspartic acid	240	Pyridoxine-HCl	2.00
Glycine	20	Pyridoxal-HCl	0.20
L-Glutamic acid	460	Pyridoxamine-HCl	0.20
L-Histidine	180	Riboflavin	0.20
DL-Isoleucine	560	Thiamine-HCl	2.00
L-Leucine	680	Biotin	0.001
L-Lysine	540	Choline chloride	2.00
DL-Methionine	500	Pteroylglutamic acid	0.20
L-Phenylalanine	320	DL-Thioctic acid	8.00
L-Proline	500		
DL-Serine	780	**D**	
DL-Threonine	660	$MgSO_4 \cdot 7H_2O$	140.0
L-Tryptophan	140	$Fe(NH_4)(SO_4)_2 \cdot 12H_2O$	60.0
DL-Valine	320	$MnCl_2 \cdot 4H_2O$	1.0
		$ZnCl_2$	0.1
C		$CaCl_2 \cdot 2H_2O$	30.0
Uracil	20	$CuCl_2 \cdot 2H_2O$	3.0
Adenylic acid	50	$FeCl_3 \cdot 6H_2O$	1.0
Cytidylic acid	50	K_2HPO_4	1000.0
Guanylic acid	150	KH_2PO_4	1000.0
Tween 80	10000	Dextrose	
Sodium acetate	100		5000.0

Steps

1. Filter the medium with coarse filter paper (Toyo Roshi Kaisha, filter No. 1).

2. Pour aliquots of the filtered medium into culture vessels.

3. Cap the test tubes and flasks for culture with rubber or silicon double-cap stoppers or with cotton stoppers. In the former case, injection needles (1/3 gauge) closed with small cotton plugs are inserted into each tube through the double-cap stoppers.

4. Sterilize culture vessels containing appropriate amounts of medium with an autoclave at 15 psi pressure (120°C) for 20 min. After autoclaving, injection needles of the test tubes are pulled up from the double-cap stoppers.

B. PREPARATION OF CHEMICALLY DEFINED SYNTHETIC MEDIUM

Solutions

1. *Basal medium 2A:* See Table I.

2. *Stock solutions:* Tenfold concentrated stock solutions of solution A (amino acids), solution B (vitamins), solution C (nucleotides), and solution D (inorganic chemicals) are prepared with reference to the concentrations shown in Table I and stored at −20°C.

Steps

1. Prepare basal medium 2A by using 1/10th volumes of the stock solutions A, B, C, and D, and then adding Tween 80, dextrose, and sodium acetate at the final concentrations indicated in Table I.

FIGURE 1   Culture vessels for *Tetrahymena* cultivation.

2. Adjust the final pH of the medium to 6.6 with 1 *N* NaOH.

3. Transfer aliquots of the medium to culture vessels and cap with cotton stoppers or silicon double-cap stoppers.

4. Autoclave the culture vessels containing the synthetic medium at 10 psi pressure (110°C) for 10 min.

5. Immediately after autoclaving, gently shake the culture vessels by hand until Tween 80 is completely resuspended, as Tween 80 tends to sink to the bottom of the culture vessels.

6. Sterilized synthetic medium is best used within a week.

IV. Comments

The middle-sized test tube containing 10 ml culture medium (Fig. 1, left) can be used for keeping cells alive for more than 1 year at 18–20°C. When many cells are needed for experiments, 300-ml cotton-plugged Erlenmeyer flasks containing 50 ml culture medium are used. From such a stock culture kept at 26°C, living cells should be transplanted into new flasks every 1–2 weeks.

For ordinary experimental culture, various sized culture vessels can be used. As an example, representative vessels are shown in Fig. 1: 10-ml cultures (50-ml Erlenmeyer flask), 50-ml cultures (300-ml Erlenmeyer flask), and 500-ml cultures (3-liter French flask) are usually used. The former two cultures are immersed in a water bath adjusted at an optimum temperature with gentle shaking (a 2.5-cm amplitude, 40–60 strokes/min) in a shaking bath (Taiyo Monosin-IIA) (Fig. 2). The large-scale culture is carried out with a shaking device (a 4-cm amplitude, 60 strokes/min) in a culture room adjusted to the optimum temperature (Fig. 3). In these shaking cultures, one generation time of the cell is 115–210 min, and a final population density of approximately $1–2 \times 10^6$ cells/ml can be obtained. Using the method described here, it is possible to collect a cell mass of up to 100 g dry weight from 18 liters culture.

Synchronous culture can be induced by exposing cells growing exponentially in 10-, 50-, or 500-ml cultures to a cyclic temperature treatment. In the case of *T. pyriformis* W (optimum temperature = 26°C), eight alternate half-hour exposures to $34 \pm 0.2°C$ and $26 \pm 0.2°C$ can induce approximately 85% synchronous division at 75 min after the end of the last heat treatment (Watanabe, 1963) (Fig. 4). In *T.*

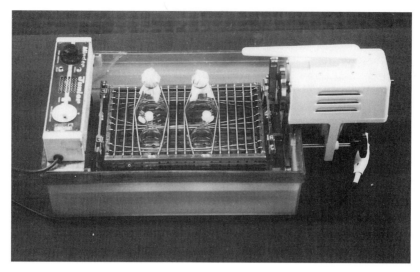

FIGURE 2 Water bath with the shaking device for *Tetrahymena* cultivation.

pyriformis GL (optimum temperature = 29°C), about 85% synchronous division can be induced by eight alternate half-hour exposures to 34 ± 0.2°C and 29 ± 0.4°C (Scherbaum and Zeuthen, 1954). In the case of *T. thermophila* (optimum temperature = 34°C), 40–60% synchronous division can be induced by five to seven alternate half-hour exposures to 42.8 ± 0.2°C and 35 ± 0.4°C (Holz *et al.*, 1957) or 42.2°C and 34°C (Ohba *et al.*, 1986) or by five alternate exposures to 16°C for 90 min and 30°C for 30 min (Ohba *et al.*, 1986). Peaks of synchronous division appear at 55–60 and 65 min after the ends of the last heat and cold treatments, respectively. For inducing synchronous culture, a custom-made automatic instrument (Ohtake Works) is available (Fig. 5).

The stock culture in the upright test tube was renewed every year by transfer of about 0.1 ml inoculum (50–100 cells) with a sterilized tuberculin syringe to fresh medium. In an experimental culture, exponentially growing cells are inoculated into fresh PYD medium or synthetic medium to give a concentration of 10^3–10^4 cells/ml under sterile conditions in a clean bench (Hitachi Ltd., type PC H). For cell growth estimation, 0.4-ml samples are withdrawn at intervals by inserting a sterilized

FIGURE 3 Shaking device for large-scale *Tetrahymena* culture.

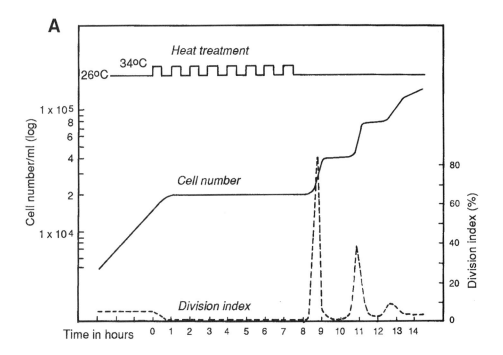

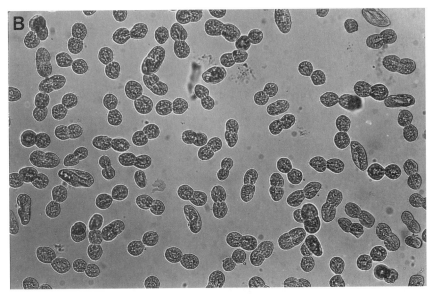

FIGURE 4 Temperature-induced synchronous divisions in *Tetrahymena pyriformis* W. (A) The controlled temperature cycle is shown in the upper part. The continuous and broken curves represent cell number and division index, respectively. (B) The photograph shows synchronous cell division 75 min after the heat treatment.

pipette into the culture flask. Each sample is immediately fixed with an equal volume of brilliant green fixative (5% formol containing 0.001% brilliant green). For counting the total numbers of cells and dividing cells per milliliter, a Fuchs–Rosenthal counting chamber is used.

V. Pitfalls

1. Do not shake the test tube stock culture. Keep upright at 18–20°C.
2. Do not forget the final pH adjustment for the chemically defined synthetic medium.

FIGURE 5   A fully automatic instrument for inducing synchronous culture in *Tetrahymena*.

3. Use deionized, distilled water for preparing culture media.
4. Ensure that all glassware is rinsed with deionized water before drying.

REFERENCES

Frankel, J., Jenkins, L. M., Doerder, F. P., and Nelsen, E. M. (1976) Mutations affecting cell division in *Tetrahymena pyriformis*. I. Selection and genetic analysis. *Genetics* **83**, 489–506.

Hamburger, K., and Zeuthen, E. (1957) Synchronous divisions in *Tetrahymena pyriformis* as studied in an inorganic medium. *Exp. Cell Res.* **13**, 443–453.

Holz, G. G., Scherbaum, O. H., and Williams, N. (1957) The arrest of mitosis and stomatogenesis during temperature-induction of synchronous division in *Tetrahymena pyriformis*, mating type 1, variety 1. *Exp. Cell Res.* **13**, 618–621.

Kidder, G. W., and Dewey, V. C. (1951) The biochemistry of ciliates in pure culture. *In* "Biochemistry and Physiology of Protozoa" (A. Lwoff, ed.), Vol. 1, pp. 323–400. Academic Press, New York.

Lwoff, A. (1923) Sur la nutrition des infusoires. *C. R. Acad. Sci. Paris* **176**, 928–930.

Ohba, H., Ohmori, I., Numata, O., and Watanabe, Y. (1986) Purification and immunofluorescence localization of the mutant gene product of a *Tetrahymena cdaA1* mutant affecting cell division. *J. Biochem.* **100**, 797–808.

Orias, E., and Bruns, P. J. (1976) Induction and isolation of mutants in *Tetrahymena*. *In* "Methods of Cell Biology" (D. M. Prescott, ed.), Vol. 13, pp. 247–282. Academic Press, New York/London.

Scherbaum, O., and Zeuthen, E. (1954) Induction of synchronous cell division in mass cultures of *Tetrahymena pyriformis*. *Exp. Cell Res.* **6**, 221–227.

Scherbaum, O., and Zeuthen, E. (1955) Temperature-induced synchronous divisions in the ciliate protozoon *Tetrahymena pyriformis* growing in synthetic and proteose–peptone media. *Exp. Cell Res.*, Suppl. **3**, 312–325.

Watanabe, Y. (1963) Some factors necessary to produce division conditions in *Tetrahymena pyriformis*. *Jpn. J. Med. Sci. Biol.* **16**, 107–124.

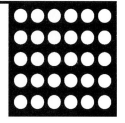

Acanthamoeba castellanii: A Model System for Correlative Biochemical and Cell Biological Studies

Ivan C. Baines and Edward D. Korn

I. Introduction

Acanthamoeba castellanii provides an excellent model system for combining bio-chemical and cell biological methodologies to elucidate the function of cytoskeletal proteins for two principal reasons: (1) single cells exhibit almost all forms of cellular and intracellular motility, for example, pseudopod extension and retraction, phago-cytosis, pinocytosis, intracellular organelle translocation and motility associated with the contractile vacuole; (2) cells can be grown in axenic suspension culture to provide greater than 1 kg of starting material for biochemical purifications, allowing the isolation and characterization of pure proteins *in vitro*. Therefore, information obtained from studies on living cells by techniques such as video microscopy and information from studies performed on intact preserved cells by techniques such as electron microscopy and immunofluorescence microscopy can be correlated with the known properties of proteins that have been characterized after purification (Fig. 1).

II. Materials and Instrumentation

$CaCl_2 \cdot 2H_2O$ (Cat. No. C79), $FeCl_3$ (Cat. No. I89), $MgSO_4$ (Cat. No. M65), paraformaldehyde (Cat. No. 04042), and $Na_4P_2O_7 \cdot 10H_2O$ (Cat. No. S390) were from Fisher Scientific. Glucose (Cat. No. 4912), KH_2PO_4 (Cat. No. 9100), NaCl (Cat. No. 7581), and KCl (Cat. No. 6858) were from Mallinckrodt. Methionine (Cat. No. M-9500), thiamine (Cat. No. T-4625), soybean trypsin inhibitor (Cat. No. T-9003), Tes (Cat. No. T-0772), and diisopropyl fluorophosphate (DFP, Cat. No. D-0879) were from Sigma Chemical Company. Vitamin B_{12} (Cat. No. 95190), sodium borohydride (Cat. No. 71320), L-lysine (Cat. No. 62840), thimerosal (Cat. No. 71230), imidazole (Cat. No. 56750), and phenylmethanesulfonyl fluoride (PMSF, Cat. No. 78830) were from Fluka. Biotin (Cat. No. 2031), saponin (Cat. No. 558255), and 30% bovine serum albumin (BSA) solution (Cat. No. 126625) were from Calbiochem. Proteose–peptone (Cat. No. 0120–01) was from Difco Laboratories. Lab-Tek tissue culture slides (Cat. No's.: glass one-well, 177372; glass two-well, 177380; glass four-well, 177399, glass eight-well, 177402; plastic eight-well, 177445) were from Nunc. Concentrated (10×) phosphate-buffered saline (PBS, Cat. No. 20–031-LV) was from Mediatech. Glutaraldehyde (8%, Cat. No. 18421)

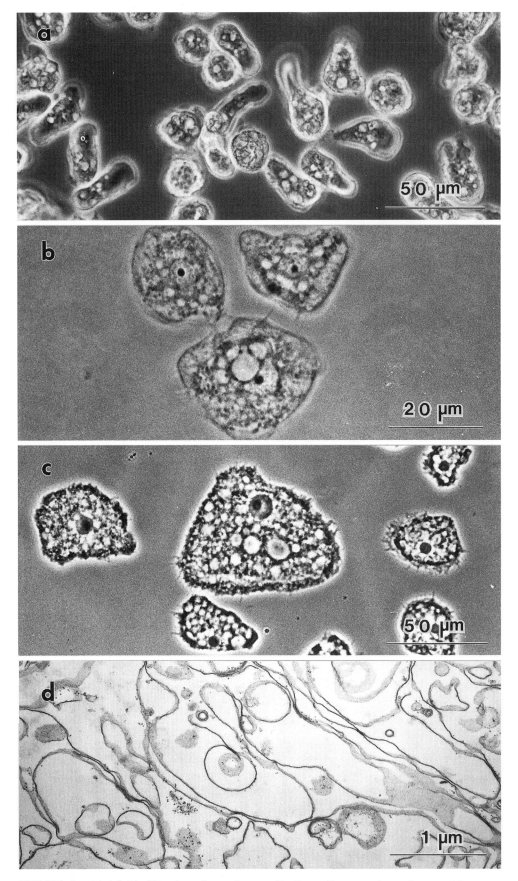

FIGURE 1 (a) A field of live *Acanthamoeba castellanii* crawling on a glass substrate. Many cells have extended long anterior pseudopods. (b) Cells fixed in 1% formalin in methanol. (c) Cells fixed in 4% formalin plus 0.05% glutaraldehyde in PBS, pH 7.2, followed by permeabilization in acetone. (d) Purified *Acanthamoeba* plasma membranes.

was from Ted Pella. Dithiothreitol (DTT, Cat. No. 856126), pepstatin A (Cat. No. 195368), and sucrose (Cat. No. 821721) were from ICN. Leupeptin (Cat. No. 1017101) was from Boehringer-Mannheim.

III. Procedures

A. CELL CULTURE

See Pollard and Korn (1973)

Solutions

1. *Growth medium:* To make 15 liters (1 carboy), add 225 g of proteose–peptone and 250 g glucose to 15 liters of distilled water. Supplement with 120 ml of a mixture of essential salts and vitamins: 37.5 ml methionine (6 g/500 ml), 37.5 ml KH_2PO_4 (80 g/500 ml), 7.5 ml $CaCl_2$ (0.3 g/100 ml), 7.5 ml $FeCl_3$ (32 mg/100 ml), 7.5 ml $MgSO_4$ (2.4 g/100 ml), 7.5 ml thiamine (0.2 g/100 ml), 7.5 ml biotin (40 mg/100 ml), 7.5 ml vitamin B_{12} (2 mg/100 ml). Growth medium must be autoclaved, after which it may be stored for up to 1 year at room temperature.

Steps

Suspension Culture
Cells can be grown conveniently in 1-liter flasks, which are continuously shaken to retain the cells in suspension, or in 15-liter carboys, which are aerated under pressure with sterile or filtered air and stirred to keep the cells in suspension.

1. Autoclave 1-liter flasks containing fresh growth medium for 30 min, and 15-liter carboys containing fresh growth medium for 1 hr.

2. Allow flasks or carboys to equilibrate in a 30°C UV-irradiated culture room for at least 24 hr.

3. Inoculate 1-liter flasks with 1 ml of cells at about 1×10^7 cells/ml and grow at 30°C for 3–4 days. Inoculate 15-liter carboys with a single 1-liter flask of cells at about 1×10^6 cells/ml and grow at 30°C for 3–4 days. A propane torch can be used to sterilize the necks of flasks and carboys during inoculation and care should be taken at all times to maintain sterile conditions. Stock cells (*Acanthamoeba castellanii*: Neff strain) can be conveniently maintained in bubbling culture using an aquarium air pump and passaging the cells about twice weekly.

Substrate Culture
Cells can be conveniently grown on plastic or glass surfaces using Lab-Tek one-, two-, four- or eight-well tissue culture slides.

1. Inoculate tissue culture slides with about 1×10^6 cells/ml and about 0.1 ml of cells for every 1 ml of growth medium in the well. Inoculation should be performed in a sterile hood and the cells grown for 2–3 days in a 30°C incubator.

B. INDIRECT IMMUNOFLUORESCENCE

See Fukui *et al.* (1986).

Solutions

1. *1% Formalin in methanol:* To make 100 ml, first make a stock of 40% formalin in distilled water (add 40 g paraformaldehyde to a total volume of 100 ml with distilled water; heat and add NaOH to dissolve; final pH should be pH 7–8). Then add 2.5 ml of 40% formalin to a total of 100 ml with methanol. This solution is used at −20°C (cool either in freezer or carefully on dry ice) and should be made fresh each time it is used.

2. *4% Formalin, 0.05% glutaraldehyde in PBS, pH 7.2:* Prepare a stock of 40% formalin in distilled water as described above. Then bring 10 ml of 40% formalin and 0.625 ml of 8% glutaraldehyde to a final volume of 100 ml with PBS, pH 7.2. This solution should be made fresh each time it is used.

3. *0.1% saponin in PBS, pH 7.2:* Dissolve 0.1 g of saponin in a total volume of 100 ml PBS, pH 7.2. Use fresh.

4. *Sodium borohydride (1 mg/ml):* Dissolve 100 mg of sodium borohydride to a final volume of 100 ml in PBS, pH 7.2. Prepare immediately before use.

5. *Blocking buffer* (1% BSA, 50 mM L-lysine, 0.01% thimerosal in PBS, pH 7.4): To make 100 ml, dissolve 0.73 g of L-lysine, 0.01 g thimerosal, and 3.33 ml of 30% BSA solution to a final volume of 100 ml in PBS, pH 7.4.

Steps

1. Grow cells on glass Lab-Tek tissue culture slides as described. These slides consist of upper plastic wells connected by a rubber gasket to the glass microscope slide. The plastic wells are useful for antibody incubations and, in most cases, should be removed only just prior to mounting the slide for viewing. If, however, acetone is to be used to permeabilize the cells, the plastic wells (which are not acetone resistant) should be removed first; in this instance the rubber gasket (which is resistant to acetone) can serve to hold minimal volumes for antibody incubations.

2. Two fixation protocols are given. Both should be tested for each antibody and each antigen:

a. Carefully pipet growth medium from the slide, shake off excess liquid, and immerse the slide rapidly and completely in 1% formalin in methanol at −20°C for about 5 min. This protocol works for most antigens (with the notable exception of F-actin) but may result in poor preservation of morphology.

b. Add formalin stock (40% in distilled water) and glutaraldehyde stock (8%) to the growth medium in each well of the culture slide to yield a final concentration of 4% formalin and 0.05% glutaraldehyde. Fix cells for about 15 min; then remove the fixative in growth medium, replace with 4% formalin and 0.05% glutaraldehyde in PBS, pH 7.2, and fix the cells further for 40 min. Wash fixed cells twice in PBS and then permeabilize with either 0.1% saponin in PBS, pH 7.2, for 30 min (good for large proteins but may result in the loss of small membrane-associated proteins) or in 100% acetone at −20°C for 1 min (good for phalloidin staining of F-actin).

3. Wash cells twice in PBS.

4. Reduce cells fixed with 4% formalin and 0.05% glutaraldehyde with sodium borohydride (1 mg/ml). Two 10-min incubations at room temperature are sufficient. Wash cells twice in PBS after reduction.

5. Block nonspecific antibody binding sites by incubating cells in blocking buffer (1% BSA, 50 mM L-lysine, 0.01% thimerosal in PBS, pH 7.4) for 30 min at room temperature.

6. Incubate in primary antibody for 2 hr at room temperature with the antibody diluted appropriately in blocking buffer.

7. Wash cells five times for 5 min each wash in PBS.

8. Incubate cells in the fluorophore-coupled secondary antibody as for the primary antibody.

9. Wash cells five times for 5 min each wash in PBS.

10. Remove any remaining plastic culture wells or rubber gaskets from the slide, and mount the cells in PBS:glycerol (1:1 v/v) containing an antifade compound or in mounting medium (e.g., Cat. No. 71-00-16, Kirkegaard & Perry).

C. PREPARATION OF A HIGH SPEED SUPERNATANT FOR PROTEIN PURIFICATION

See Lynch et al. (1991).

Solutions

1. *Wash buffer (100 mM NaCl, 10 mM imidazole-HCl, pH 7.5)*: To make 1 liter, dissolve 5.8 g NaCl and 0.7 g imidazole in distilled water, and bring to pH 7.5 with HCl and to a final volume of 1 liter with distilled water. All solutions for protein purification should be made fresh and cooled to 4°C.

2. *Extraction buffer (30 mM imidazole-HCl, pH 7.5, 75 mM KCl, 12 mM $Na_4P_2O_7$, 5 mM DTT, 0.5 mM PMSF, 2 mg/liter leupeptin, 20 mg/liter soybean trypsin inhibitor, 10 mg liter pepstatin A)*: To make 1 liter, dissolve 2 g of imidazole, 5.6 g KCl, and 5.4 g $Na_4P_2O_7 \cdot 10 H_2O$ in about 900 ml of distilled water, and bring to pH 7.5 with HCl and to a final volume of 1 liter with distilled water. Prepare a stock of leupeptin, soybean trypsin inhibitor, and pepstatin (×1000: 2 mg/ml leupeptin, 20 mg/ml soybean trypsin inhibitor, and 10 mg/ml pepstatin; forms a suspension in water) and add 1 ml for each liter of extraction buffer. Add 0.8 g of DTT and 2 ml of PMSF (from a 250 mM stock in ethanol) 1 hr before use. Cool extraction buffer to 4°C.

Steps

1. Harvest cells from 15-liter carboy cultures by centrifugation at 1000 g for 5 min, e.g., with an IEC CRU-5000 centrifuge at 2400 rpm. All the following steps are at 4°C.

2. Wash cells twice in wash buffer (about 3 vol buffer per volume of cells for each wash) by resuspension and pelleting at 1000 g for 10 min.

3. Homogenize cells in 2 vol of extraction buffer per volume of cells in 100-ml Dounce homogenizers by 14 strokes with a type B pestle.

4. Centrifuge the homogenate for 1 hr at 23,000 g (e.g., at 12,000 rpm in a Sorvall GSA rotor) and discard both the pellets and lipid floats.

5. Add DFP to the supernatant to a final concentration of 0.5 mM.

6. Centrifuge the supernatant for 3.5 hr at >100,000 g (e.g., in a Beckman type 30 rotor). For larger volumes, an initial for 3 hr at 19,000 g (in a Beckman type 19 rotor) followed by recentrifugation of the lower turbid regions and pellets from each tube at high speed works satisfactorily.

7. The resultant high-speed supernatant is an appropriate starting point for protein purification by conventional column chromatography.

D. PREPARATION OF A CRUDE MEMBRANE PELLET

See Clarke *et al.* (1988).

Solutions

1. *10 mM Tes, pH 7.4:* To make 1 liter, dissolve 2.3 g Tes in distilled water and bring to pH 7.4 with HCl and a final total volume of 1 liter with distilled water. Cool the buffer to 4°C.

2. *10 mM Tes, pH 6.9:* Prepare exactly as above but adjust pH to 6.9.

3. *2 M sucrose in 10 mM Tes, pH 7.4:* To make 500 ml, dissolve 342.3 g sucrose to a final volume of 500 ml in 10 mM Tes, pH 7.4.

4. *Protease inhibitor stock:* To make a ×1000 concentrated stock, prepare 1 mg/ml leupeptin and 10 mg/ml pepstatin as a suspension in distilled water.

5. *PMSF stock (250 mM in ethanol):* To make 100 ml, dissolve 4.4 g PMSF in 100 ml ethanol.

Steps

1. Perform all steps at 4°C with each buffer precooled. Add protease inhibitors (1 ml added per liter of buffer) and PMSF (2 ml added per liter of buffer) to every buffer.

2. Harvest cells as for protein purification (see above) and wash twice (by pelleting at 1000 g for 10 min and resuspending) in 10 mM Tes, pH 7.4.

3. Resuspend cells in 10 mM Tes, pH 7.4, supplemented with 3 mM NaI, and allow cells to swell in this hypotonic buffer for 1 hr.

4. Bring the cell suspension to a final concentration of 0.35 M sucrose by addition of 2 M sucrose in 10 mM Tes, pH 7.4.

5. Homogenize cells with 14 strokes in a 40-ml Dounce homogenizer with tight-fitting pestle.

6. Centrifuge the homogenate for 10 min at 250 g (e.g., 1400 rpm in a Sorvall SS-34 rotor) and discard the pellet, which contains mainly unbroken cells and nuclei.

7. Bring the supernatant to 0.3 M sucrose by dilution with 10 mM Tes, pH 6.9, and centrifuge for 20 min at 590 g (e.g., 2200 rpm in a Sorvall SS-34 rotor).

8. Resuspend the pellet in 0.25 M sucrose in Tes, pH 6.9, and centrifuge for 20 min at 590 g (e.g., 2200 rpm in a Sorvall SS-34 rotor).

9. The crude plasma membrane pellet obtained from this centrifugation can be further purified by density gradient centrifugation on Percoll (see Clarke *et al.*, 1988).

IV. Comments

We have attempted in this brief article to provide methodologies for setting up *Acanthamoeba castellanii* as a model system for correlative biochemical and cell biological studies. For indirect immunofluorescence, only two protocols have been given, whereas the literature contains hundreds of possible variations. It should be emphasized that the protocols described have been found to be the most widely applicable and optimal for most uses but do not exclude the possibility that other procedures may be better for particular antibodies or antigens. The protocol for fixation in 4% formalin and 0.05% glutaraldehyde followed by permeabilization with 0.1% saponin has also been used successfully for immunogold cytochemistry (see Baines *et al.,* 1992). The protocol for preparation of a high-speed supernatant for protein purification is a good starting point but readers are also referred to Lynch *et al.* (1991) and Bubb and Korn (1991). A procedure for facilitating the entry of bioreactive probes into live cells has recently been reported for *Acanthamoeba* (Doberstein *et al.,* 1993).

V. Pitfalls

1. Contamination of *Acanthamoeba* cultures by bacteria may occur during passaging of cells or inoculation. Contamination by mold can be caused by spores in the growth medium and may be prevented by increasing time in the autoclave.

2. Cells may adhere only poorly to Lab-Tek tissue culture slides and may be lost during processing for immunofluorescence. This appears to be related to the cleanliness of the slides and varies from lot to lot. If poor adherence is experienced it is worth trying a different lot of slides.

3. Extensive proteolysis in the high-speed supernatant may be due to overhomogenization of cells, resulting in lysosomal breakdown and consequent release of lysosomal enzymes. Reducing the number of strokes in the homogenizer should help. Use of too few strokes in the homogenizer results in incomplete cell breakage and poor protein yields.

REFERENCES

Baines, I. C., Brzeska, H., and Korn, E. D. (1992) Differential localization of *Acanthamoeba* myosin I isoforms. *J. Cell Biol.* **119,** 1193–1203.
Bubb, M. R., and Korn, E. D. (1991) Purification of actobindin from *Acanthamoeba castellanii. In* "Methods in Enzymology" (R. B. Vallee, ed.), Vol. 196, pp. 119–125. Academic Press, San Diego.
Clarke, B. J., Hohman, T. C., and Bowers, B. (1988) Purification of plasma membrane from *Acanthamoeba castellanii. J. Protozool.* **35,** 408–413.
Doberstein, S. K., Baines, I. C., Wiegand, G., Korn, E. D., and Pollard, T. D. (1993) Inhibition of contractile vacuole function *in vivo* by myosin-I antibodies. *Nature (London)* **365,** 841–843.
Fukui, Y, Yumura, S, Yumura, T. K., and Mori, H. (1986) Agar overlay method: High-resolution immunofluorescence for the study of the contractile apparatus. *In* "Methods in Enzymology" (R. B. Vallee, ed.), Vol. 134, pp. 573–580. Academic Press, San Diego.
Lynch, T. J., Brzeska, H., Baines, I. C., and Korn, E. D. (1991) Purification of myosin I and myosin I heavy chain kinase from *Acanthamoeba castellanii. In* "Methods in Enzymology" (R. B. Vallee, ed.), Vol. 196, pp. 12–23. Academic Press, San Diego.
Pollard, T. D., and Korn, E. D. (1973) *Acanthamoeba* myosin. Isolation from *Acanthamoeba castellanii* of an enzyme similar to muscle myosin. *J. Biol. Chem.* **248,** 4682–4690.

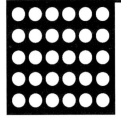

Cell Biological, Molecular Genetic, and Biochemical Methods to Examine *Dictyostelium*

Sandra K. O. Mann, Peter N. Devreotes, Susannah Eliott,
Keith Jermyn, Adam Kuspa, Marcus Fechheimer,
Ruth Furukawa, Carole A. Parent, Jeffrey Segall,
Gad Shaulsky, Philip H. Vardy, Jeffrey Williams,
Keith L. Williams, and Richard A. Firtel

I. Overview

Dictyostelium discoideum has proven to be an excellent experimental system in which to examine problems in cellular differentiation, signal transduction, chemotaxis, cell motility, cytoskeletal structure, and gene regulation. Much of this progress has required the development of appropriate cell biological and molecular genetic methods.

Dictyostelium grows vegetatively as single-celled amoebae. The multicellular program is initiated in response to starvation. Within a few hours, cells within the population begin to emit nanomolar pulses of cAMP, which binds to cell surface receptors. Cells respond by (1) chemotaxing toward the signal, (2) relaying the signal through a G-protein-activated adenylyl cyclase, and (3) activating genes essential for multicellular development. By 8 hr, the initial aggregate is formed. Prestalk and prespore cells differentiate within the aggregate and cellular morphogenesis ensues. The pathways regulating these processes and cell-type differentiation are described in the following reviews: Kimmel and Firtel (1991), van Haastert (1992), Williams and Jermyn (1991).

This article describes a number of methods for studying cell–cell interactions in this organism, concentrating on more recently developed approaches. A number of essential, basic methods in cellular and molecular biology (including methods of RNA and DNA extraction, DNA-mediated transformation, and basic cell biology) have been described previously and, for the most part, these methods are generally applicable (Spudich, 1987). In addition, major advances in understanding developmental processes in this system and basic cellular processes common to all eukaryotes have resulted from the ability to create gene disruptions and gene replacements via homologous recombination (De Lozanne and Spudich, 1987). Presently, two auxotrophic markers are available, Pyr5–6 (uracil) and Thy1 (thymidine). In addition, negative selection against uracil prototrophs using 5-fluoroorotic acid (5FOA) enables one to perform multiple, sequential selections. Use of these markers for homologous recombination has been described previously (Kalpaxis *et al.*, 1990; Kumagai *et al.*, 1991; Sun and Devreotes, 1991).

II. Expression of *Dictyostelium* and Heterologous Proteins during Growth and Multicellular Development

A. INTRODUCTION

The understanding of the function of individual genes has been significantly enhanced by the ability to express the encoded proteins at various times during *Dictyostelium* development and in specific cell types. Such approaches can also be extended to include various gene products from other systems such as reporter constructs [e.g., the *Escherichia coli lacZ* and *uidA* gene products encoding β-galactosidase and β-glucuronidase (GUS), respectively] and selectable markers (e.g., the gene encoding neomyosin resistance used for G418 selection). The use of β-gal and GUS reporter constructs is described in the following section.

By using particular promoters, gene products can be expressed in all cells during growth and development using actin promoters such as Actin 6 or 15 (*Act6, Act15*) or in individual cell types using cell-type-specific promoters such as *SP60/cotC* (prespore), *ecmA* (prestalk A/0), *ecmB* (prestalk AB), and *rasD* (prestalk-enriched). Use of promoters such as *csA*, which is not expressed during vegetative growth, allows expression in all cell types during the aggregation stage in response to cAMP pulses.

This versatile approach enables one to examine the function of a particular gene at a specific time in development or in a specific cell type. For example, cell-type-specific promoters can be used to express a wild-type protein in a particular cell type in null mutants. This complements the function in only one cell type, allowing one to examine the function of a gene in that cell type and the lack of function in other cells. In addition, one can express a dominant negative or constitutively active allele in one cell type, allowing the examination of the loss or gain of function in that cell type.

The use of discoidin promoters provides a depressible gene system that allows the conditional expression of genes during the growth phase (Blusch *et al.*, 1992). Discoidin promoters are expressed during vegetative growth when cells are at higher cell densities ($>5 \times 10^5$/ml) and during early development. Expression of this promoter during the growth phase is repressible by folate. This allows one to examine the phenotype caused by a particular wild-type or mutant protein by using a discoidin promoter fusion transformed into cells that are grown in the presence of 1 m*M* folate, conditions under which the discoidin promoters are repressed. The promoter can be derepressed by replacing the folate-containing medium with normal HL5 growth medium (the very low concentration of folate in HL5 that is required for growth has no effect on discoidin expression), leading to expression of the downstream gene. This approach is also useful for determining whether a particular gene is required for growth by using an antisense construct downstream from the discoidin promoter. Such an antisense construct expressed from an actin promoter would be lethal.

1. Expression Vectors

Figure 1 shows two reporter constructs for quantitatively examining promoter function, using *lacZ* (see below) or the firefly luciferase gene (Haberstroh and Firtel, 1990). Either of these vectors can be used as a backbone for switching promoters and protein coding regions. The vectors contain a putative polyadenylation signal/terminator from the *SP70/cotB* gene (designated 2H3) and a cassette allowing G418 selection in *Dictyostelium*. Increasing the G418 concentration allows one to select for higher-copy-number insertions that provide higher levels of expression. For

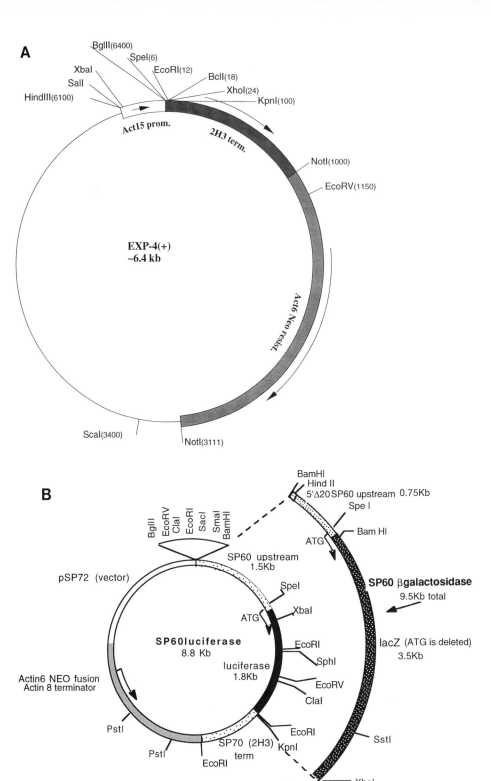

FIGURE 1 *SP60* luciferase and *lacZ* expression vectors. These vectors carry G418 resistance and have a cassette construction that allows easy switching of promoters (sites upstream of the *SP60* promoter shown as an example) or protein coding regions (Haberstroh and Firtel, 1990). These vectors are constructed to allow proteins to be expressed from their own ATG translation initiation codon. Vectors derived from those shown here allow expression from the *ecmA*, *ecmB*, *Act15*, *rasD*, *csA*, and *discoidin* promoters.

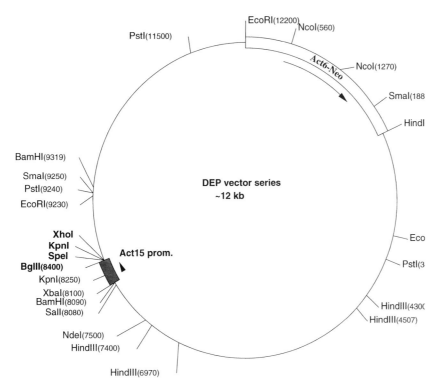

FIGURE 2 **DEP vectors (12 kb).** These vectors are based on pATANB43 (Dynes and Firtel, 1989) and contain the origin of replication from the endogenous plasmid Ddp1 (see text). They carry G418 resistance, transform at very high efficiency, and have the same copy number in all transformed cells.

directed expression, cassettes have been made for a number of promoters, including *Act15, SP60/cotC, ecmA, ecmB, csA,* discoidin, and *rasD.* These have an *Spe*I site in the untranslated region and, at the 5' end of the cassette, one or more sites present in the indicated polylinker. In general, to insert a gene of interest, an *Spe*I linker is added in the 5' untranslated region of a cDNA either by ligation, by *in vitro* site-directed mutagenesis, or by polymerase chain reaction (PCR). An *Xho*I or *Kpn*I linker is added at the 3' end. These sites were also chosen to allow ready cloning from λZap cDNA libraries.

A series of three vectors based on BS18 (Firtel and Chapman, 1990) that use the *Act15* promoter are available. These carry the *Act15* ATG translation initiation codon and allow insertion of an open reading frame via a GATC 5' overhang. This is provided by a unique *Bgl*II restriction site, present in each of the three reading frames.

In addition to integrating vectors, extrachromosomal expression vectors are available for vegetative growth (Firtel *et al.,* 1985; Leiting and Noegel, 1988). An example of an expression vector using the Ddp1 endogenous plasmid is shown in Fig. 2. These vectors carry the origin of replication from a *Dictyostelium* endogenous plasmid and have the advantage of transforming at relatively high frequencies compared with integrating vectors, producing useful transformed populations in a shorter period with a more uniform copy number. The vectors have a major disadvantage in that they appear not to be as useful for cotransformations, are relatively large, and are less stable in *E. coli;* also, it is more difficult to readily switch promoters. For the expression of a cDNA during growth, however, they are very useful.

2. Expression of Heterologous Proteins

Expression of heterologous genes from other systems can present a problem as translation initiation is inhibited by a high GC content immediately upstream of the ATG and/or a second codon that is a rare codon in *Dictyostelium*. To rectify this, add six A residues immediately upstream of the ATG, preceded by an *Spe*I site, and change the codon for the second amino acid to one that is used at high levels in *Dictyostelium*. These changes can be easily made using an appropriate oligonucleotide primer and PCR. Such expression cassettes can then be readily inserted into the expression vectors described above.

3. Use of the N-End Rule to Change Protein Stability

Proteins have different stabilities in *Dictyostelium* cells. The use of ubiquitin fusions combined with the N-end rule allows the expression of proteins with different levels of stability (Varshavsky, 1992). This is useful to restrict the function of a protein to a particular stage of development, using an unstable protein construct and a stage-specific promoter, or to express a protein ubiquitously using the *Act15* protein and a stable protein construct. This approach was first developed in *Dictyostelium* by H. MacWilliams for *lacZ* constructs (see below) and has been successfully used for a number of proteins.

4. Coexpression

More than one protein or marker can be expressed in *Dictyostelium* by cotransformation using CaPO₄ precipitates (Nellen *et al.*, 1987), which results in a high percentage of transformed cells carrying and expressing both vectors. This is particularly useful in examining the effect of a regulatory protein on cell type differentiation, by cotransforming with a vector expressing a particular regulatory protein and a vector expressing a cell type-specific *lacZ* construct. In such approaches, one only needs the G418 selectable marker for *Dictyostelium* transformation on the first vector; the presence of the second vector can be screened for by staining. If, however, a gene product has a deleterious effect on growth, it is recommended that only the vector containing that gene carry the G418 selectable marker.

B. MATERIALS AND INSTRUMENTATION

Bacteriological peptone (Cat. No. L37) is obtained from Oxoid. Na₂HPO₄ (Mallinckrodt, Cat. No. 7917-500*NY), KH₂PO4 (Mallinckrodt, Cat. No. 7100-500*NY), and sucrose (Mallinckrodt, Cat. No. 8256-2.5*NY) are purchased from Baxter. Vitamin B₁₂ (Cat. No. V-2876) and folic acid (Cat. No. F-7876) are from Sigma. G418 (Geneticin, Cat. No. 11811-031) is purchased from Gibco-BRL. KOH (Cat. No. P251-3) and Difco yeast extract (Cat. No. DF0127-07-1) are purchased from Fisher Scientific.

The Gene Pulser Apparatus (Cat. No. 165-2077) and Gene Pulser Cuvettes (Cat. No. 165-2088) are purchased from Bio-Rad. Petri dishes (100 × 20-mm Falcon 1005 Optilux plates, Cat. No. 08-757-103C) are obtained from Fisher Scientific.

C. PROCEDURES

1. Transformation by Electroporation

Solutions

1. *HL5 medium:* To make 1 liter, solubilize the following in distilled water: 17.8 g peptone, 7.15 g yeast extract, 0.54 g Na₂HPO₄, 0.4 g KH₂PO₄. Add

vitamin B$_{12}$ to 5 μg/liter and folate to 200 μg/liter. Autoclave twice for 20–25 min, cooling completely between cycles. Before use, add 25 ml 50% glucose and 10 ml Fungi-Bact antibiotics. For selection of G418-resistant cells, supplement with G418 to 10–200 μg/ml.

2. *12 mM Na/K phosphate buffer:* 12 mM NaH$_2$PO$_4$, pH to 6.1 with 5 M KOH.

3. *Electroporation buffer:* 10 mM Na/K phosphate buffer, 50 mM sucrose. Filter-sterilize or autoclave for 25 min.

Steps

1. Grow cells to $1-2 \times 10^6$/ml in suspension culture in HL5 axenic medium.

2. Cool flask on ice for 15 min, swirling every few minutes.

3. Harvest the cells by centrifugation at 1500 rpm for 5 min at 4°C.

4. Resuspend in electroporation buffer at 10^7 cells/ml.

5. Add 0.8 ml of cells to 30 mg DNA.

6. Transfer cell/DNA mix to prechilled 0.4-cm electroporation cuvettes on ice, two cuvettes at a time.

7. Electroporate at 3 μF and 1 kV. Pulse twice in rapid succession.

8. Immediately add cells to 12 ml of HL5 in Optilux petri dishes and pulse the next sample.

9. Put cells under selection 24 hr later.

2. Transformation by CaPO$_4$ precipitation

The protocol for transformation by CaPO$_4$ precipitation is provided in Nellen *et al.* (1987).

D. COMMENTS

Transformation frequencies range from a few transformed clones to several hundred per plate.

Some researchers report that electroporation provides higher transformation frequencies and more consistent results in their hands, whereas others report the same for CaPO$_4$ transformations.

Individual clones can be isolated from transformed populations by making a dilution series and plating the *Dictyostelium* cells with 0.5 ml of an overnight culture of *Klebsiella aerogenes* onto SM agar plates (see next section).

E. PITFALLS

For each cell line that is being transformed, always carry out a "no DNA" control. Occasionally, a few cells will appear on this control, or a background "lawn" of cells will appear on this and the experimental plates. This problem is usually resolved by increasing the selection pressure (e.g., by increasing the G418 concentration).

III. Detection of Gene Expression Using Enzymatic Reporter Constructs

A. INTRODUCTION

Fusion constructs containing *E. coli lacZ* (encoding β-galactosidase) or *uidA* (encoding β-glucuronidase) under the control of a eukaryotic promoter have become invaluable tools for measuring eukaryotic gene expression. Both enzymes can easily be assayed spectrophotometrically, but, more importantly, the spatial pattern of their expression can be visualized at a single-cell level and the sensitivity, speed, and ease of detection compare very favorably with immunological methods.

1. β-Galactosidase (GAL)

Many *lacZ* fusion vectors for transformation into *Dictyostelium* are now in common use. Those developed by Harwood and Drury (1990) consist of the *lacZ* gene with the *Dictyostelium* Actin 8 terminator sequence inserted into a vector originally derived from pEMBL18+. This contains a *neo* gene cassette conferring G418 drug resistance. One such vector is pDdGAL-17 (Fig. 3a). In addition, "nuclear-tagged" vectors that direct GAL expression to the *Dictyostelium* nucleus have been constructed. They add to the 5′ end of the *lacZ* gene a synthetic oligonucleotide corresponding to the SV40 T-antigen core nuclear localization signal (Kalderon *et al.*, 1984). A second set of *lacZ* expression vectors that use cassette construction are based on the vector described in Haberstroh and Firtel (1990) and presented in Fig. 1. In these vectors, the fusion point between the promoter and reporter is in the 5′ untranslated region. *lacZ* and *uidA* reporter genes altered to contain a *Dictyostelium* translation initiation region are available.

Cells are transformed with an appropriate vector, and positive clones or pooled populations are identified by staining after selection with G418. Cells are then allowed to develop to the appropriate morphological stage on agar plates or nitrocellulose filters. GAL expression can be analyzed in single cells, in single whole mounts, or in populations stained *in situ* on a nitrocellulose filter. The type of preparation determines the exact staining methods used. It is often important to analyze expression in isolated cells to determine the percentage expressing a particular *lacZ* construct.

2. β-Glucuronidase (GUS)

Because of the success in using *lacZ* as a reporter gene, the *E. coli uidA* gene, encoding β-glucuronidase, was developed as a second enzymatic reporter gene system that works at the single-cell level (Early *et al.*, 1993). By using substrates that give different colored products for each enzyme reaction, the expression of two genes can be concurrently analyzed. β-Galactosidase substrates that yield red or pink precipitates have allowed the establishment of double staining protocols. Using compatible reaction systems, coexpressed genes can be detected within individual cells.

The vectors pDdGUS-17 (Fig. 3b) and pDdNucGUS-17 (Fig. 3c) are, respectively, cytoplasmic and nuclear-tagged GUS expression vectors that contain the *uidA* gene in place of the *lacZ* gene in pDdGal-17 (Harwood and Drury, 1990). Vectors based on the Haberstroh and Firtel (1990) *lacZ* construct have also been made in which the *uidA* gene was modified to contain a *Dictyostelium* 5′ translation initiation region preceded by an *Spe*I site, with an *Xho*I site at the 3′ end to facilitate usage with various promoters (see Fig. 1).

Staining for β-glucuronidase is less sensitive than for *lacZ*. Most promoters and

a)
    XbaI   BamHI   EcoRI   BglII   Asp718   HindIII   *PstI   *SmaI
    T CTA GAC TGG GAT CCA GAA TTC AGA TCT CGG TAC CAA GCT TAC TGC AGG ATG ATC CCG GGC AAT
                                                                                            └─ GAL

b)
    XbaI   BamHI   EcoRI   BglII
    T CTA GAC TGG GAT CCA GAA TTC AGA TCT GTA GAA ACC CCA ACC CGT GAA ATC AAA AAA CTC GAC
                                    └─ GUS

c)
    XbaI   BamHI   EcoRI   BglII   ┌─ GUS
    T CTA GAC TGG GAT CCA GAA TTC AGA TCT CCA AAA AAA AAA AGA AAA GTT GAA GAT CCA GGA TCT
                                         Nuc. loc. signal

MCS

CP1 terminator

uidA

lacZ

neo

Act8 terminator

XhoI

HindIII

Act 6 promoter

Amp

ori

* Not unique site

FIGURE 3 (A) pDdGAL-17 (8.5 kb), which has been described elsewhere (Harwood and Drury, 1990). (B) pDdGUS-17. A section of the GUS promoter sequences was replaced by a synthetic oligonucleotide corresponding to a eukaryotic consensus translation initiation site. A PCR fragment of 1860 bp, containing the *uidA* gene, was ligated into pDdGAL-17 in place of the *lacZ* gene. The new vector is approximately 7.5 kb and lacks a translation initiation codon. (C) pDdNucGUS-17. A synthetic oligonucleotide corresponding to the SV40 T-antigen nuclear localization signal (Kalderon *et al.*, 1984) was inserted into the 5′ end of GUS protein coding region in pDdGUS-17.

constructs require that transformants be kept under selection at 200 μg/ml G418 to maintain a high copy number so that expression remains at detectable levels.

B. MATERIALS AND INSTRUMENTATION

Glucose (dextrose, Cat. No. D16-500), bactopeptone (Difco, Cat. No. DF 0118-07-2), yeast extract (Difco, Cat. No. DF 0127-07-1), agar (Difco, Cat. No. DF 0140-01-0), KCl (Cat. No. P217-500), CaCl$_2$ (Cat. No. C79-500), K$_3$Fe(CN)$_6$ (Cat. No. P232-500), K$_4$Fe(CN)$_6$ (Cat. No. P236-500), glutaraldehyde (Cat. No. G151-1), and dimethyl formamide (Cat. No. D119-1) are obtained from Fisher Scientific. MgSO$_4$ (Cat. No. M-1880), Tween 20 (Cat. No. P-1379), poly-L-lysine (Cat. No. P-2636), and phenylethyl β-D-thiogalactoside (Cat. No. P-4902) are purchased from Sigma. KH$_2$PO$_4$ (Cat. No. 7100-2.5*NY), K$_2$HPO$_4$ (Cat. No. 7088-2.5*NY),

NaH$_2$PO$_4$ (Cat. No. 7892-125*NY), and Na$_2$HPO$_4$ (Cat. No. 7917-125*NY) are from Baxter. X-gal (Cat. No. 15520-018) is from Gibco-BRL. X-glcA CHX (Cat. No. B-1691) is from Molecular Probes. Salmon-β-D-gal is obtained from Biosynth AG. Gelvatol 20/30 is from Monsanto.

Multiwell plates (Falcon 3047 24-well tissue culture plates, Cat. No. 08-772-1) and nylon filters (MSI, Cat. No. NJ4HY08250) are purchased from Fisher Scientific. Nitrocellulose filters (Cat. No. HAWP 025 00) are from Millipore. Multiwell slides (Cat. No. 60-408-05) are obtained from ICN Flow.

C. PROCEDURES

1. Isolation and Screening of GAL Transformants

Solutions

1. *HL5 medium:* See Section IIC1.

2. *SM agar:* For 1 liter of plates, solubilize the following in distilled water: 10 g glucose, 10 g bactopeptone, 1 g yeast extract, 1.9 g KH$_2$PO$_4$, 0.6 g K$_2$HPO$_4$, 4 ml of 1 *M* MgSO$_4$. Add 20 g agar and autoclave 25 min.

3. *Z buffer:* 100 m*M* Na phosphate (60 m*M* Na$_2$HPO$_4$, 40 m*M* NaH$_2$PO$_4$), 10 m*M* KCl, 1 m*M* MgSO$_4$, pH 7.0. [*Note:* A convenient variant of Z buffer that works equally well is based on PBS, a buffer that is frequently in routine laboratory use for cell culture. It comprises 400 ml of PBS (10 m*M* Na$_2$HPO$_4$, 2 m*M* KH$_2$PO$_4$, 3 m*M* KCl, 150 m*M* NaCl, pH 7.2) supplemented with 0.8 ml of 1 *M* MgCl$_2$.]

4. *Z buffer + Tween:* As above, with the addition of 2% Tween 20 (v/v).

5. *GAL fixing solution:* 1% Solution of glutaraldehyde in Z buffer (w/v). Formaldehyde and paraformaldehyde may also be used at a similar concentration.

6. *GAL staining solution:* Z buffer containing 5 m*M* K$_3$Fe(CN)$_6$, 5 m*M* K$_4$Fe(CN)$_6$, 1 m*M* X-gal (5-bromo-4-chloro-3-indolyl-β-D-galactopyranoside), 1 m*M* EGTA (optional). The solution is stable at 4°C. The X-gal is kept as a 2% solution in dimethyl formamide (DMF), at −20°C.

Steps

1. Transform *Dictyostelium* amoebae by electroporation or CaPO$_4$ precipitation as outlined in Section II and select initially at 10–20 μg/ml G418 (Gibco). When the colonies are well established, they can be selected at G418 concentrations up to 200 μg/ml, if desired, to amplify the copy number.

2. Make a dilution series from a suspension of transformed cells, and plate 100 μl from each dilution (between approximately 10^{-2} and 10^{-4}) with 0.5 ml of an overnight culture (grown at 22°C) of *Klebsiella aerogenes* on a 9-cm petri dish containing SM agar. Then incubate at 22°C.

3. Five days later, the *Dictyostelium* clones should be approximately 3 mm wide, with several culminants in the center of most clones.

4. For *in situ* colony assays (Buhl *et al.*, 1993), outline each clone on the base of the plate with a marker and number between 12 and 24 discrete plaques. Pick some of the growing zone from each of these plaques into HL5 medium containing G418 (20 to 200 μg/ml) in multiwell plates.

5. Lay a blotting membrane on top of the agar in the original plate, and gently flatten the filter onto the agar to eliminate air bubbles and to help the culminants stick to the filter. Nitrocellulose filters can be used, but nylon filters, such as MSI

Magnagraph, are more durable. Make orientation marks on the filter and the plate with a waterproof marker pen.

6. Remove the filter and place face up in a fresh petri dish, then fix with 3 ml of GAL fixing solution for 10 min. Wash the filter three to five times with Z buffer + Tween. The more bacteria left on the plate, the more washes are required.

7. Stain the filter with 0.5–3 ml of GAL staining solution and leave at room temperature overnight, or at 37°C for one to several hours.

8. The positive clones can be identified by their blue stain, and will hopefully include the ones you chose. If not, don't despair. There should still be an identifiable growing zone around the other positives from which cells can be cultured. Cells from the corresponding positive wells in the multiwell plate are then further cultivated.

2. Histochemical Assay of GAL in Transformed Cells

Solution

1. *Na/K-PO$_4$-buffered agar:* 12 mM NaH$_2$PO$_4$, 2 mM MgSO$_4$, 0.2 mM CaCl$_2$, pH to 6.1 with 1 M KOH. Add 15 g agar and autoclave for 25 min.

Steps

For individual cells on slides

1. Dissociate aggregates before fixation by trituration through a syringe needle (23- to 25-gauge bore) or by repeated pipetting in 20 mM EDTA, pH 6.5, followed by centrifugation. Repeat this process two or three times.

2. Place a drop of cell suspension onto a multiwell slide coated with poly-L-lysine, and allow the cells to settle for 10 min.

3. Replace the solution above the cells with fix and incubate for 1–10 min.

4. Carefully immerse the whole slide in Z buffer, remove and drain, then repeat in fresh Z buffer, and remove and drain well.

5. Apply 20 μl staining solution per well. Overlay with a coverslip and incubate at 37°C in a closed box with wet tissue to provide a humid atmosphere.

6. Incubate 30 min to several hours.

7. The reaction can, if desired, be stopped with 1 mM phenylethyl β-D-thiogalactoside.

8. Slides are mounted in Gelvatol and a coverslip placed on top. GAL-expressing blue cells in aggregates may be viewed on a dissecting microscope with overhead illumination.

For individual cells in suspension

1. Pellet the cell suspension by centrifugation.

2. Resuspend the cells in fix and incubate for 1–10 min.

3. Pellet the cells by centrifugation, and resuspend in Z buffer. Repeat this step.

4. Pellet the cells by centrifugation, and resuspend in 200 μl staining solution.

5. Incubate at 37°C.

For aggregates on slides

1. Develop cells on Na/K-PO$_4$-buffered agar.

2. Gently overlay agar plates with fix so that the aggregates float up.

3. After 10–15 min, transfer the aggregates onto a multiwell slide by picking them up in a platinum wire loop or in a shortened Gilson pipette tip.

4. Wash and stain as for individual cells on slides (above), except use 50 μl staining solution per well.

For aggregates immobilized on filters

1. Allow aggregates to develop on 2.5-cm Millipore filters placed on Na/K-PO$_4$-buffered agar.

2. At the appropriate stage, transfer the filters onto two layered Whatman 3 filters saturated with fix solution. Several small filters can be placed on one set of 12.5-cm filters in a large petri dish. Keep the petri dish covered to prevent evaporation of the glutaraldehyde.

3. After fixing the filters from below for 10 min, gently add fix solution to cover the aggregates for another 10 min.

4. Blot the filters, then wash by placing in individual 60-mm petri dishes with 8 ml Z buffer.

5. Blot again, then place in individual 35-mm petri dishes with 1 ml stain solution.

6. Cover and place in humid chamber.

7. Incubate at 37°C for 30 min to several hours.

3. Isolation and Screening of GUS Transformants

Solutions

1. *GUS phosphate buffer:* 50 mM NaHPO$_4$ (pH 7.0).

2. *GUS phosphate buffer + Tween:* GUS phosphate buffer containing 0.2% Tween 20 (v/v) (Sigma).

3. *GUS fixing solutions:* (A) GUS phosphate buffer containing 0.05% (w/v) glutaraldehyde. (B) GUS phosphate buffer containing 0.5% (w/v) glutaraldehyde.

4. *GUS staining solution:* GUS phosphate buffer containing 5 mM Fe$_2$(CN)$_4$/Fe$_3$(CN)$_6$ and 2 mM X-glcA CHX (5-bromo-4-chloro-3-indolyl-β-D-glucuronic acid, cyclohexylammonium salt).

Steps

1. Follow steps 1–5 for isolation and screening of GAL transformants (Section IIIC1).

2. Fix the filter with 3 ml of GUS fixing solution A for 10 min.

3. Wash three to five times with GUS phosphate buffer + Tween.

4. Overlay the filter with 0.5–3 ml GUS staining solution.

5. Incubate overnight at room temperature or 37°C. High-level expression can be seen after a few hours.

4. Histochemical Assay of GUS in Transformed Cells

Steps

1. Manipulate the samples as in the GAL protocol (Section IIIC2).

2. Incubate single cells or multicellular structures in GUS fixing solution A for 10 min.

3. Wash twice in GUS phosphate buffer for 2 min each.

4. Stain samples by incubating (usually overnight) at 37°C in GUS staining solution.

5. As an alternative fixation method for multicellular structures, preincubate the samples in GUS phosphate buffer + Tween for 5 min, then incubate for 2 min in GUS fixing solution 2.

5. Double Labeling of Cells That Coexpress *lacZ* and *uidA* Reporters

Solution

1. *Salmon GAL staining solution:* Replace the X-gal in GAL staining solution with salmon-β-D-gal. This gives a pink to red color when hydrolyzed and precipitated.

Steps

1. For consistent colocalization of GUS and GAL staining, it is necessary to have the *uidA* vector nuclear tagged, with the *lacZ* vector remaining cytosolic. Other combinations appear to be susceptible to substrate or product cross-inhibition of the enzyme reactions.

2. Fix and stain the filters (for screening) or samples (for histochemical assays) for GUS, as above.

3. On the following day, remove the GUS staining solution and replace with salmon gal staining solution. Reincubate at room temperature or 37°C as long as necessary.

4. The reaction can be stopped with 1 mM phenylethyl β-D-thiogalactoside.

5. The double positive clones can be identified as those with red and blue, or purple, staining.

D. COMMENTS

By staining multicellular structures on filters, the morphology of the developmental stages is maintained *in situ,* and the white filters present an ideal background for photography. Although specimens cannot immediately be viewed properly at high power, with care they can be detached from the filter for more detailed microscopy.

β-Galactosidase activity is relatively insensitive to glutaradehyde fixation. As an alternative GAL fixation protocol for multicellular structures, aggregates can be permeabilized in Z buffer containing 0.1% Nonidet P-40 (NP40) before fixation.

This makes the initial staining more even, which can be quite useful for visualizing stalk staining, for example. However, the end result remains the same.

For double staining, individual GAL-positive cells stained by this method often show a surrounding pink haze at high magnification. Close inspection shows this to consist of tiny colored "vesicles," which presumably contain the cytosolic β-galactosidase. They seem to leak out during fixation, as the phenomenon seems to be reduced with stronger fixing methods. Unfortunately, these also reduce the β-glucuronidase expression. Thus, with double staining, it becomes a trade-off between strength of the GUS expression and tight outlining of single-cell GAL expression. The authors acknowledge David Traynor for his work on the GUS system.

The sensitivity of enzymatic staining compared with immunohistochemical detection is different for the two reporters. In one of our laboratories (J.W.), staining with β-galactosidase is three to five times more sensitive than detection with the β-2 antibody. This laboratory has also raised a polyclonal antiserum to β-glucuronidase in chicken. Immunodetection with this antiserum has so far been comparable with the enzymatic stain. The principal advantages of the enzymatic staining are its rapidity and simplicity relative to immunohistological techniques.

E. PITFALLS

β-Glucuronidase is very sensitive to glutaraldehyde fixation, and overfixing can lead to misleading staining patterns. The enzyme is also sensitive to cations and to agar, which should be removed from the staining vessel.

For GUS analysis, it is essential to propagate growth-phase cells, rather than spores, as the β-glucuronidase gene is apparently lost during spore formation. (In general, tandem arrays of transformed vector sequences decrease in copy number during sporulation.) In addition, if the cells were selected at very high G418 concentration to ensure a high copy number of the expression vector, there is normally a drop in GUS expression within isolated clones over a period (within a month or so). If a clone is plated out and reassayed by colony lifting, it appears no longer clonal; some cells express GUS more weakly and some have lost expression, although the cells remain resistant to high G418. The solution is to reclone the cells periodically or to renew them from a frozen stock.

The same caution must be exercised with the double transformants as with the single β-glucuronidase expressers. When there is a drop in expression, cells plated out and reassayed by the *in situ* colony assay are seen to be no longer clonal. Cells lose GAL expression besides GUS activity, but at a lower frequency, which may be further masked by the greater sensitivity of β-galactosidase staining. This causes problems when determining whether there are low numbers of coexpressing cells within a population. Again the solution is to reclone periodically or to renew from frozen stock.

IV. Insertional Mutagenesis Using Restriction Enzyme-Mediated Integration

A. INTRODUCTION

Developmental mutants of *Dictyostelium discoideum* can be readily recognized by their altered morphology. Of the genes that control development in *Dictyostelium*, about 300 are essential for development, dispensable for growth, and functionally nonredundant. These are therefore susceptible to mutagenesis and cloning by insertional tagging. As wild-type strains of *Dictyostelium* are haploid, it is possible

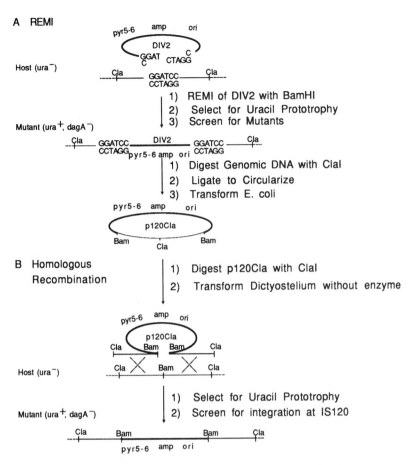

FIGURE 4 Protocol for REMI mutagenesis. See text for details.

to use insertional mutagenesis for screening mutants in these genes after a single step of random mutagenesis. Restriction enzyme-mediated integration (REMI) of vector DNA facilitates this purpose and provides a useful tool for cloning developmental genes in *Dictyostelium*. Insertional mutagenesis in general is based on introduction of foreign DNA segments into the host genome. REMI provides a high frequency of transformation into random loci and allows for rapid isolation of the mutated genes.

In REMI, active restriction endonuclease is added to the electroporated vector DNA solution to mediate integration into the host genome. Addition of an adequate restriction enzyme elevates the transformation frequency up to 60-fold higher than vector DNA alone, yielding frequencies as high as 4×10^{-5}. The ends on the linearized vector must be compatible with the ends that would be generated by the mediating enzyme.

The mutagenic shuttle vector (Fig. 4) consists of the *D. discoideum* *pyr5–6* gene as well as sequences that facilitate replication and ampicillin resistance in *E. coli*. Deficiency in *pyr5–6* leads to uracil auxotrophy without any consequences to development, so DIV transformants of a *pyr5–6* null strain can be selected on minimal essential media for uracil prototrophy (Dingermann *et al.*, 1990; Kuspa and Loomis, 1992). Transformants are then collected and diluted, mixed with *Klebsiella aerogenes* bacteria, and plated on SM plates. Plaques appear in the bacterial lawn 3–4 days later, each of which consists of a clonal population of transformants. As the cells in the plaques begin to starve and develop, mutants with altered morphology are picked and grown for further analysis.

Mutagenesis with REMI results in genetically tagged genes that are easy to clone out (see Fig. 4). The basic method involves digestion of purified mutant genomic DNA with a restriction enzyme that does not cut within the mutagenic vector. The genomic DNA is then ligated under conditions that bias for monomolecular reaction. Some of the circular molecules will consist of the mutagenic vector and two *Dictyostelium* genomic DNA fragments from regions flanking the original insertion site. The ligation reaction is concentrated and transformed into *E. coli,* using ampicillin for selection. DNA from the drug-resistant bacterial colonies is typically analyzed with the cloning restriction endonuclease as well as the mediating REMI enzyme.

An essential step that should precede any further efforts to analyze the tagged gene is to genetically prove that the original insertion site and the cloned-out insertion site are identical and sufficient to regenerate the mutant phenotype. This is accomplished by using the plasmid DNA for "knock-out" mutagenesis of a ura^- strain and checking the resultant morphology. This procedure also allows one to generate strains with complex genotypes, such as the original mutation in combination with various *lacZ* reporter constructs.

In addition to recapitulating the mutation over various genetic backgrounds, the cloned genomic fragment is used as a probe to determine the developmental regulation of the tagged gene as well as the size of the message. Complementary mRNA should be present in wild-type cells and absent in the mutant. Determining the developmental regulation of the gene is important to correlate the pattern of gene expression with the developmental defect. It is important to know the mRNA size before starting to sequence the tagged gene.

B. MATERIALS AND INSTRUMENTATION

K_2HPO_4 (Mallinckrodt, Cat. No. 7088-500*NY) and NaOH (Mallinckrodt, Cat. No. 7708-2.5*NY) are purchased from Baxter. H_3PO_4 (Cat. No. JT0260-2) is from VWR Scientific. LB broth base (Cat. No. 12780-029) and T4 DNA ligase (Cat. No. 15224-025) are obtained from Gibco-BRL. Agar (Difco, Cat. No. DF 0140-01-0) and NaCl (Cat. No. S271-10) are obtained from Fisher Scientific. Penicillin, streptomycin, all amino acids, vitamins, and components of the salts and trace elements stock solutions are purchased from Sigma, and catalog numbers are provided below. $MgSO_4$ (Cat. No. M-1880), vitamin B_1 (Cat. No. T-4625), uracil (Cat. No. U-0750), ampicillin (Cat. No. A-9518), and carbenicillin (Cat. No. C-1389) are also purchased from Sigma. *E. coli* Sure competent cells (Cat. No. 200227) are from Stratagene.

C. PROCEDURES

Solutions

1. *FM medium* (minimal essential medium for ura^+ selection): To make 10 liters, dissolve 50 mM K_2HPO_4 in 9.4 liters deionized water, heat to 50–60°C, and add the amino acids listed below. Occasionally, adjust the pH of the solution to 7.0 to avoid precipitation. Add 100 ml of the vitamin stock solution, 100 ml of the salts and trace elements stock solution, and 100 ml Pen/Strep stock solution (all at 100×, see below). Add 200 ml 50% glucose and adjust the pH to 6.5 with NaOH or H_3PO_4. Adjust final volume to 10 liters. To sterilize, filter through a 0.45-μm filter using cellulose prefilter, or autoclave the medium without glucose and Pen/Strep, cool, and add the omitted ingredients sterilely. All stock solutions, as well as the final medium, are stable for at least 1 year at 4°C.

Arginine (free base, Cat. No. A-5006	5.7 g
Asparagine (A-0884)	3.0 g
Cysteine (C-7755)	2.7 g
Glycine (G-7126)	9.0 g
Glutamic acid (free acid, G-1251)	5.0 g
Histidine (free base, H-8000)	2.2 g
Isoleucine (I-2752)	6.0 g
Leucine (L-8000)	9.0 g
Lysine (monohydrochloride, L-5626)	9.1 g
Methionine (M-9625)	3.0 g
Phenylalanine (P-2126)	5.0 g
Proline (P-0380)	8.0 g
Threonine (T-8625)	5.0 g
Tryptophan (T-0254)	2.0 g
Valine (V-0500)	7.0 g

2. *100× vitamin stock solution:* For 1 liter, solubilize the following in H_2O, and adjust the pH to 7.0.

Biotin (B-4501)	2.0 g
Cyanocobalamin (V-2876)	0.5 g
Folic acid (F-7876)	20.0 g
Lipoic acid (DL-6,8-thioctic acid, T-5625)	40.0 g
Riboflavin (R-4500)	50.0 g
Thiamine·HCl (T-4625)	60.0 g

3. *100× salts and trace elements stock solution:* For 1 liter, solubilize the following in H_2O, and adjust the pH to 7.0.

NaOH (S-0899)	8.0 g
$NaHCO_3$ (S-6014)	1.7 g
NH_4Cl (A-5666)	5.4 g
$CaCl_2·2H_2O$ (C-3881)	0.29 g
$FeCl_3·6H_2O$ (F-2877)	2.70 g
$MgCl_2·6H_2O$ (M-0250)	8.10 g
$Na_2EDTA·2H_2O$ (E-4884)	0.48 g
H_3BO_3 (B-0252)	0.11 g
$CoCl_2·6H_2O$ (C-3169)	0.017 g
$CuSO_4·5H_2O$ (C-7631)	0.015 g
$(NH_4)_6Mo_7O_{24}·4H_2O$ (A-7302)	0.01 g
$MnCl_2·4H_2O$ (M-3634)	0.051 g
$ZnSO_4·7H_2O$ (Z-4750)	0.23 g

4. *100× Pen/Strep stock solution:* Dissolve the following in H_2O and filter-sterilize: 10,000 U/ml penicillin G (Cat. No. P-3032), 10 mg/ml streptomycin sulfate (Cat. No. S-6501).

5. *L agar:* For 1 liter, solubilize 20 g LB broth base in H_2O. Add 10 ml of 1 *M* Tris, pH 7.5, 1 ml of 1% vitamin B_1, 1 ml of 1 *M* $MgSO_4$, and 14 g agar. Autoclave, cool, and pour plates.

6. *HL5 medium:* See Section IIC1.

7. *SM agar:* See Section IIIC1.

Steps

REMI: Transformation and screening of mutants

1. Linearize vector DNA with the restriction enzyme that will be used for REMI or with an enzyme that creates compatible ends. Purify the linearized DNA by standard techniques.

2. Grow *ura⁻* cells in HL5 medium supplemented with 20 mg/ml uracil to a concentration of $1-4 \times 10^6$ cells/ml.

3. Transform the cells by electroporation as described in the preceding section, except add 40 mg linearized vector DNA to each 0.8-ml aliquot of cold washed cells and immediately add 100–200 U of the mediating restriction enzyme. Electroporate within 5 min.

4. Immediately after each electroporation, distribute the cells into four 100-mm petri dishes containing 12 ml of FM medium (2×10^6 cells/plate). Control samples consisting of cells electroporated with no DNA can be distributed to plates containing FM medium as well as plates containing FM with uracil at 20 μg/ml. The no DNA controls test the uracil selection in FM and cell viability in FM with added uracil.

5. Colonies should appear after 6–8 days at 22°C, at a frequency of $1-6 \times 10^5$. At this time replace the medium with fresh FM and incubate for 4–6 more days. By 12 days after the electroporation, the background of untransformed cells will be negligible and the transformed colonies will be about 1–3 mm in diameter, each containing at least 10^4 cells.

6. Collect transformants by pipetting the medium up and down several times. Keep the cells from each plate separate, dilute appropriately, and spread on SM agar plates with 0.3–0.5 ml of a saturated suspension of *Klebsiella aerogenes* (grown in SM liquid medium). As the plating efficiency varies, dilute the cells in a series of four 10-fold dilutions into liquid SM medium and spread 0.1, 0.2, and 0.4 ml of cells from the three greatest dilutions. This ensures that there will be appropriate numbers of clones on one or more plates.

7. After 5 to 6 days plaques should appear, containing multiple structures that can be visually inspected under a dissecting microscope. About 0.3% of the clones display aberrations. Cells from the clones of interest are picked from the edges and streaked on fresh SM plates spread with *K. aerogenes* to test that the aberrations are hereditarily stable. It is unlikely that two independent mutants with the same morphological phenotype will arise from a population of 2×10^6 cells, so only one representative of each distinct phenotype should be picked. The other mutant plaques on the original plate are likely to be sibling transformants, harboring the vector in the same site. The occurrence of several clones that show identical morphological defects provides added assurance that an insertional mutant of this type arose on the original FM plate.

Recovery of the tagged gene

1. Isolate genomic DNA from the mutant strain and purify on CsCl gradients (Nellen *et al.*, 1987).

2. Digest 0.5 mg of purified DNA with a restriction enzyme that does not cut within the integrating vector and will therefore cut in flanking *Dictyostelium* sequences. (As there is an upper limit on the size of plasmids that are stably carried in *E. coli*, it is useful to first determine the map positions of these and other sites. Use radiolabeled vector to probe Southern blots of DNA purified from the mutant strains and cut with various enzymes. Choose an enzyme that will

produce a vector-containing fragment less than 15 kb in size.) Purify the DNA by phenol extraction and ethanol precipitation, and dissolve it in 20 μl sterile water.

3. Bring the DNA solution up to 0.5 ml with ligase buffer, add 5 units of T4 DNA ligase, and incubate at 12–15°C for at least 12 hr. The low concentration of the DNA favors circularization of monomolecular fragments over concatemerization.

4. Precipitate the ligation products by adding 10 μl of 5 N NaCl and 1 ml of ethanol. Mix and centrifuge at 12,500 g for 10 min. Rinse the DNA precipitate twice with 70% ethanol followed by brief centrifugation, removing as much of the wash ethanol as possible at each step. It is necessary to reduce the salt concentration as much as possible for the high-voltage electroporation of bacteria that follows. Dissolve the pellet in 40 ml of sterile water.

5. Add several different volumes of the ligation products, in the range 2–6 μl, to competent E. coli SURE cells on ice. Electroporate with a Gene Pulser or other suitable device, according to the manufacturer's suggested protocol. Note that in most cases, transformation efficiency of the bacteria should be greater than 10^9/μg. Plate out the entire population from each electroporation on several L agar plates containing 75 μg/ml carbenicillin or 40 μg/ml ampicillin and incubate at 37°C. Expect 10–100 bacterial transformants after a 16-hr incubation. A range of DNA concentrations is recommended as 4 μl of the concentrated ligation mixture has about 50 ng of DNA, which is close to the level that is toxic to E. coli cells.

6. Isolate the vector DNA, carrying the genomic fragments, using a standard plasmid prep protocol. CsCl purify this and check with both the cloning enzyme and the enzyme used for REMI.

Regeneration of mutant phenotype

1. Digest the plasmid DNA with the same restriction enzyme used for cloning, thus creating a linear "knock out" construct in which the mutagenic vector is flanked by the Dictyostelium sequences that presumably flanked the insertion site.

2. Electroporate 30 μg linear DNA into a fresh ura$^-$ host strain, as above, but without addition of restriction endonucleases.

3. Select prototrophs on FM medium.

4. Plate transformants on bacteria and monitor morphology as in the first mutagenesis step. At this stage, a large proportion (usually >10%) of the transformants should exhibit a phenotype identical to the original mutant and should have a genomic structure identical to that of the original mutant.

D. COMMENTS

Characterization of mutants begins with physiological and morphological description of the mutant. In Dictyostelium, a combination of morphology and molecular markers provides a canonical 24-hr developmental time course of about 2-hr resolution. Mutants are developed and morphology is monitored for 48 hr; at the same time, samples can be taken for RNA preparation and analysis of developmental gene expression by Northern blot. Probing Northern blots with various developmental genes allows one to determine if the mutation affects development prior to the expression of a specific marker. For example, if a mutant fails to express the prestalk-specific gene ecmA, it is deduced that the mutation was epistatic to that specific differentiation.

Other aspects of *Dictyostelium* development can be further analyzed after the initial characterization. For example, an inability to aggregate could result from defects in recognition of the nutritional status, production of or response to cAMP, motility, and so on. Specific assays can be performed on aggregation-defective mutants to determine the pathways that are affected. For mutants that do aggregate, assays can be carried out to examine the ability of the mutant to produce, respond to, or metabolize the prestalk morphogen DIF. Such assays would be pertinent to the example given above in which expression of the prestalk-specific marker *ecmA* is affected.

Another useful tool that is unique to *Dictyostelium* is the ability to easily generate chimeric organisms in which mutants and wild-type cells can interact during development. A mutant may fail to form spores when developed in a pure population, but when mixed with wild-type cells it may readily do so. This would indicate that the mutant fails to produce an extracellular signaling molecule that is essential for sporulation, but wild-type cells can provide the missing component *in trans* and rescue that aspect of development. Mixing experiments are useful, therefore, to distinguish the cell-autonomous effects of the mutation from the indirect ones. In this type of experiment it is advantageous to "mark" mutants by transformation with a vector in which expression of *E. coli* β-galactosidase is driven by a *Dictyostelium* promoter. The reporter gene can be expressed under a prespore promoter such as *SP70/cotB*, a prestalk promoter such as *ecmA,* or a cell type-nonspecific promoter such as Actin 15. The X-gal staining pattern of a chimeric aggregate will provide information about the physiological and spatial patterning effects of the wild-type cells on the mutant cell type.

E. PITFALLS

As *Dictyostelium* genomic DNA contains a high frequency of AT, rearrangements tend to occur during the cloning process; comparison of the plasmid physical map with the mutant genomic map (see below) is useful in choosing the appropriate plasmid. For plasmid preparation, it is recommended that bacterial clones be grown for a short time (4–5 hr is usually sufficient) or at a low temperature (30°C) to limit the number of bacterial generations to the essential minimum. Although in most cases this technique is efficient in cloning tagged genes, it is worth mentioning that sometimes other means are taken to avoid DNA sequences that are unstable in *E. coli.* The most useful technique is to clone with restriction enzymes that cut within the mutagenic vector. This results in the cloning of genomic DNA at only one side of the insertion site, but with knowledge of the mutagenic vector physical map and careful selection of sites, it is possible to separately clone DNA from either side of the insertion site.

V. Analysis of Signal Transduction

A. INTRODUCTION

Cyclic AMP plays a central role in the early stages of *Dictyostelium* development. Secreted cAMP serves as a chemoattractant for surrounding cells, stimulating them to synthesize and secrete additional cAMP in an oscillatory fashion, thereby relaying the signal outward. Such cAMP oscillations are necessary for gene expression as well as for aggregation. At the resulting multicellular (mound) stage, *Dictyostelium* development continues to be influenced by cAMP; however, constant rather than oscillatory levels of cAMP are responsible for the induction of a second class of cAMP-responsive genes. In this program, therefore, extracellular cAMP functions analogously to a hormone, as it interacts with receptors on the cell surface and elicits several intracellular responses, including stimulation of adenylyl cyclase, guanylyl cyclase, and phospholipase C (see Section I for reviews).

The *Dictyostelium* signal transduction system includes typical G-protein-linked pathways, and several of its molecular components have been identified, including four cAMP receptors (cAR1–cAR4), eight G-protein α subunits, one G-protein β subunit, a phospholipase C, and an adenylyl cyclase. All of these components, except the G-protein β subunit, are developmentally regulated.

A number of molecular approaches combined with biochemical analyses have been used to examine the function of individual components of the signaling pathway. These include the creation by homologous recombination and characterization of null mutants and the overexpression of wild-type and mutant proteins. Several of the null cell lines engineered ($car1^-$, $g\alpha2^-$, $g\beta^-$, aca^-) are aggregation deficient following starvation, but can be "rescued" when transformed with plasmids containing wild-type genes. These cell lines can therefore be used to screen for mutations and overexpressed genes that "complement" the particular signal transduction defect. These may affect the regulation and activity of receptor, G-protein, or effector elements involved in *Dictyostelium* signal transduction.

In the present section, current techniques used to assess the state of activity of receptors, G-proteins, and adenylyl cyclase are described. These techniques can be used on null and overexpresser cell lines to learn more about a given signal transduction pathway.

A novel and rapid cAR1 binding assay is presented that uses ammonium sulfate to stabilize cAMP binding, as in a previously developed technique (Devreotes *et al.*, 1987). This is complemented by an assay for cAR1 phosphorylation, which causes a shift in apparent molecular weight on SDS–PAGE. This shift in receptor size occurs in perfect synchrony with the oscillations in cAMP synthesis observed in early aggregation. Another way to assess receptor function is to assay for loss of ligand binding, as cAR1 occupancy is known to be involved in this phenomenon, in which preexposure of cells to cAMP leads to a rapid and reversible loss of binding sites on the cell surface.

As with many G-protein-coupled receptors, interaction of cAR1 with Gα2 results in high-affinity binding with cAMP (Kumagai *et al.*, 1991). This ligand–receptor interaction is, however, reduced *in vitro* in the presence of GTP, which promotes the uncoupling of the G-protein α subunit from both the receptor and its β and γ subunits. Consequently, cAMP binding to cAR1 in the absence and presence of GTP represents a useful assay for both receptor and G-protein functions.

Several G-protein α subunits, in both mammals and *Dictyostelium*, are known to be sensitive to trypsin digestion. However, it has been shown that binding of GTP (or GTPγS) to the α subunit prevents this trypsin cleavage from occurring, thereby protecting the protein from complete degradation (a cleavage near the N terminus does occur, giving a slightly smaller protein). Consequently, this assay can be used to assess the functional integrity of α-subunit mutants.

The adenylyl cyclase A gene product shares significant sequence and topological homology with its mammalian counterparts (two large hydrophilic domains separated by two sets of six transmembrane spans). ACA is developmentally regulated; transcripts are undetectable by Northern analysis in vegetative cells and reach peak levels at 6 hr. As expected, cells that have no cyclase activity fail to aggregate. A specific antibody made against the C-terminal 15 amino acids is available.

B. MATERIALS AND INSTRUMENTATION

Na_2HPO_4 (Cat. No. 3824-1), NaH_2PO_4 (Cat. No. 3818-5), KH_2PO_4 (Cat. No. 3246-1), $CaCl_2$ (Cat. No. 1332-01), ammonium sulfate (Cat. No. 0792-05), glycerol

(Cat. No. 4043-00), and EDTA (Cat. No. 8991) are purchased from J. T. Baker. $MgSO_4$ (Cat. No. M63-500) is obtained from Fisher Scientific. Cyclic AMP (Cat. No. A-6885), DTT (Cat. No. D-0632), caffeine (Cat. No. C-0750), GTP (Cat. No. G-8877), Tris (Cat. No. T-1503), lubrol PX (Cat. No. L-753), β-mercaptoethanol (Cat. No. M-6250), Hepes (Cat. No. H-7006), TPCK-trypsin (Cat. No. T-8642), soybean trypsin inhibitor (Cat. No. T-9003), $MnSO_4$ (Cat. No. M-7634), bromphenol blue (Cat. No. B-0126), SDS (Cat. No. L-6026), and protein kinase A (Cat. No. P-5511) are from Sigma. [^{3}H]cAMP (Cat. No. NET-275) is purchased from NEN. [^{32}P]cAMP (Cat. No. 37004) is from ICN. GTPγS (Cat. No. 220647) and GDPβS (Cat. No. 528536) are from Boehringer-Mannheim.

Nuclepore filters (Cat. No. 28158-668) are purchased from VWR Scientific. Nitrocellulose filters (Cat. No. HAWP 025 00) are from Millipore.

C. PROCEDURES

1. *Dictyostelium* Development in Shaking Culture

Solutions

1. *HL5 medium:* See Section IIC1.

2. *Development buffer (DB):* 5 mM Na_2HPO_4, 5 mM NaH_2PO_4, 2 mM $MgSO_4$, 200 μM $CaCl_2$, pH 6.1.

Steps

1. Grow axenic cells in shaking culture (200 rpm) to 5×10^6 cells/ml in standard growth medium (HL5).

2. Shake washed cells at a density of 2×10^7 cells/ml in DB at 110 rpm. When working with a cell line that cannot "pulse" itself, pulse the cells with cAMP every 6 min to produce a final concentration of 30–50 nM.

3. At the desired time points, harvest the cells by centrifugation (1–2×10^3 rpm for 3–4 min at 4°C) and process according to the subsequent biochemical assay performed.

2. cAR1 Binding Assays

Solution

1. *Phosphate buffer (PB):* 5 mM Na_2HPO_4, 5 mM KH_2PO_4, pH 6.1.

Steps

1. Harvest cells that have been developed in shaking culture (above) and wash once in PB.

2. Load cells (2×10^5 cells in 100 μl) into each well of a 96-well plate (polyvinylidene difluoride bottom).

3. Remove the buffer by manifold filtration and replace with 50 μl phosphate buffer with 10 mM DTT (to inhibit phosphodiesterase).

4. Add 250 μl of 0.5 nM [^{32}P]cAMP in saturated ammonium sulfate to each well.

5. As a control, determine nonspecific binding in the presence of 0.1 mM cAMP.

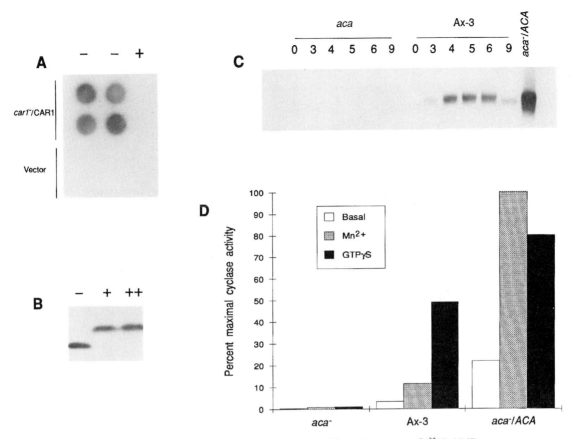

FIGURE 5 Functional assays of cAR1 in *Dictyostelium*. (**A**) Filter plate assay of [^{32}P]cAMP binding to wild-type cAR1-transformed *car1$^-$* cells (*car1$^-$/cAR1*) and vector-transformed control cells (Vector). Cyclic AMP binding at 0.5 n*M* [^{32}P]cAMP is measured in the absence (−, performed in duplicate) or in the presence (+) of 0.1 m*M* cAMP. These data were kindly provided by Michael Caterina. (**B**) Cyclic AMP-induced phosphorylation of wild-type cAR1. Cells were stimulated with 50 n*M* (+) or 0.1 m*M* (++) cAMP for 15 min, or with no treatment (−), loaded on a 10% SDS–polyacrylamide gel, and subjected to Western analysis. Detection is performed by enhanced chemiluminescence (ECL). These data were kindly provided by Michael Caterina. (**C**) ACA expression in *aca$^-$*, Ax-3, and ACA-transformed *aca$^-$* cells (*aca$^-$/ACA*). Ax-3 and *aca$^-$* cells were developed in DB. At the times indicated (in hours), whole cells were solubilized in Laemmli buffer, loaded on a 7% SDS–polyacrylamide gel (2.5 × 10^6 cells per lane), and subjected to Western analysis. Detection was performed by ECL. (**D**) "*In vitro*" adenylyl cyclase assay of *aca$^-$*, Ax-3 and *aca$^-$/ACA* cells. Cells are developed in DB and filter-lysed, and the adenylyl cyclase activity measured in basal (Mg^{2+}), unregulated (Mn^{2+}), or stimulated (GTPγS) conditions as described (Devreotes *et al.*, 1987). See text for additional details regarding these assays.

6. After a 5-min incubation at room temperature, wash the cells three times with 250 μl saturated ammonium sulfate.

7. Subject the dried filters to autoradiography. Figure 5A shows an example. As shown, cAR1-transformed *car1$^-$* cells specifically bind 15- to 20-fold more [^{32}P]cAMP than *car1$^-$* cells.

3. cAR1 Phosphorylation Assay

Solution

1. *5× Laemmli buffer*: 2.5 ml 20% SDS, 1.0 ml 1 *M* Tris, pH 6.8, 0.1 ml β-mercaptoethanol, 2.5 ml glycerol, 3.9 ml H$_2$O, few grains of bromphenol blue.

Steps

1. Harvest cells that have been developed in shaking culture, wash twice in PB, and resuspend at 3×10^7 cells/ml.

2. To convert the receptor to its basal nonphosphorylated form, shake the cells in the presence of 5 mM caffeine, which prevents adenylyl cyclase activation.

3. Add DTT to 10 mM.

4. Initiate phosphorylation (in the presence of caffeine) with the addition of cAMP (see step 8).

5. Stop the reaction at 15 min by lysing the cells and solubilizing in Laemmli buffer: Dilute 200 μl of cells to 250 μl with 5× Laemmli buffer, and load 40 μl (9.6×10^5 cell equivalent) on a 10% SDS–polyacrylamide gel.

6. Perform a Western analysis on the gel.

7. Using this protocol, one can carry out an initial two-dose assay (e.g., 50 nM and 0.1 mM cAMP) (see Fig. 5B). Thereafter, the EC50 of cAR1 phosphorylation can be measured in the most interesting mutants by performing a complete cAMP dose–response curve (e.g., 1 nM to 0.1 mM).

4. Assay for Loss of Ligand Binding

Steps

1. Harvest cells that have been developed in shaking culture, wash once in PB, resuspend to 3×10^7 cells/ml, and shake for 20 min (200 rpm at 22°C) with 10 mM DTT.

2. Add cAMP to 10 μM and continue shaking for 15 min.

3. Dilute the cells 15-fold with ice-cold PB, centrifuge (2000 rpm for 3 min at 4°C), and wash three times with ice-cold PB.

4. Measure binding in PB at 16 nM [^{3}H]cAMP and 10 mM DTT as previously described (van Haastert, 1985). Under these conditions, Ax-3 wild-type cells routinely show 80% loss of ligand binding.

5. GTP-Induced Inhibition of cAMP Binding

Steps

1. To ensure that all of the extracellular cAMP is removed, develop cells for 5 hr in shaking culture, then dilute them to 5×10^6 cells/ml with DB.

2. Shake for 20 min (200 rpm at 22°C).

3. Wash once in PB and resuspend at 4×10^7 cells/ml

4. Shake again for 10 min (200 rpm at 0°C).

5. Lyse the cells by filtration through 5-μm-pore-size Nuclepore filters.

6. Centrifuge the lysate (10,000 rpm for 5 min at 4°C) and remove the supernatent.

7. Resuspend the membranes in PB at 6×10^7 cell equivalent/ml and keep on ice.

8. Carry out binding in PB in the presence and absence of 100 μM GTP, as previously described (van Haastert, 1985).

9. Using this assay, GTP will reduce cAMP binding in wild-type membranes by about 70%.

6. Gα Trypsin Resistance Assay

Solutions

1. *PM buffer:* Prepare development buffer, but omit the $CaCl_2$.

2. *Hepes + lubrol:* 20 mM Hepes, pH 8.0, 10 mM $MgCl_2$, 1 mM EDTA, 2 mM β-mercaptoethenol, 0.64% lubrol PX.

Steps

1. Develop cells in shaking culture for 5 hr, wash, and resuspend in PM buffer.

2. Add Tris, pH 8.0, to 10 mM and $MgSO_4$ to 1 mM.

3. Divide cells. To one sample add GTPγS, to assay for trypsin resistance (see Section VA.). To a second sample add GDPβS, which locks the α subunit in its basal, nonactivated form. A third sample receives no treatment.

4. Quickly lyse the cells by filtration through 5-μm-pore-size Nuclepore filters.

5. Incubate for 30 min on ice.

6. Centrifuge (10,000 rpm for 5 min at 4°C), then wash the pellet in PM buffer and centrifuge again.

7. Resuspend the pellet in Hepes + lubrol at 3×10^7 cell equivalent/ml.

8. Centrifuge at high speed for 15 min at 4°C.

9. Transfer the supernatent, containing the solubilized proteins, to a new tube and treat with 5 μg/ml TPCK-trypsin for 5 min at 30°C.

10. Stop the reaction with soybean trypsin inhibitor at 1 mg/ml.

11. Load the sample on a 10% SDS–polyacrylamide gel.

12. Subject the gel to Western analysis, using an antibody raised against the C-terminal portion of the Gα subunit.

13. In the case of *Dictyostelium* Gα1 protein, GDPβS pretreatment leads to complete degradation of the protein. In the presence of GTPγS, however, Gα1 decreases in size from 40 to 38 kDa, but is protected from total degradation, thereby indicating that it has achieved the correct activated conformation.

7. Screening for Adenylyl Cyclase Mutants

When developing screens to determine enzymatic activities in adenylyl cyclase mutants, it is important to consider the high basal activity of overexpressing cells (see Fig. 5C). The assay presented in Tomchik and Devreotes (1981) relies on the high levels of cAMP these overexpressing cells produce in the basal state and uses a protein binding assay based on the binding of cAMP to the regulatory subunit of protein kinase A.

In this case, ACA overexpressing cells, spiked with a constant concentration of [^{32}P]cAMP, would be incubated with nitrocellulose filters (Millipore, HA type, 0.45 μm) previously saturated with protein kinase A. After incubation, the filters are washed in phosphate buffer, air-dried, and subjected to autoradiography. The clones showing expression of ACA as well as catalytic activity, known to have a high basal activity, would show lower counts. Consequently, this technique can be used to screen hundreds of ACA mutants consecutively, thereby allowing one to further characterize only the mutants that possess catalytic activity, using the previously published methods (Devreotes *et al.*, 1987).

8. Measuring Adenylyl Cyclase Activity

The methods used to measure adenylyl cyclase activity have previously been fully reviewed and are only briefly discussed here (Devreotes *et al.*, 1987). Under normal basal conditions (in the presence of Mg^{2+}), the cyclase activity of wild-type Ax-3 cells developed for 5 hr is about 4 pmole/min/mg protein. By adding 2 to 10 mM $MnSO_4$ in the reaction mix, the "unregulated" or uncoupled activity of adenylyl cyclase can be assessed. The G-protein-stimulated activity can be measured by adding GTPγS (80 μM) prior to cell lysis (rapid uncoupling occurs in the G-protein–effector complex in lysed cell preparations). A 5-min preincubation at 0°C is required to achieve maximal activation of adenylyl cyclase by GTPγS.

As shown in Fig. 5D, the basal activity of *aca*⁻/ACA cells (cells overexpressing ACA from the *Act15* promoter in *aca*⁻ null cells) is ~20-fold greater when compared with developed Ax-3 cells, whereas the GTPγS-mediated activity is only stimulated 3-fold. This discrepancy is presumably due to the limited availability of G-protein in the *aca*⁻/ACA cells.

D. COMMENTS

The information obtained when receptor binding and phosphorylation assays are accomplished in parallel is complementary. Indeed, if no specific binding can be measured, the shifting experiment will provide information on the level of cAR1 expression. If binding is present, the shifting assay will determine whether the receptor is activated and if the interaction with the receptor kinase occurs. Finally, the two-dose shifting results will provide insight regarding ligand–receptor interaction (affinity). Consequently, by performing these two simple assays, one can obtain a very specific profile of receptor function and from there proceed to further analysis on the most intriguing mutants [Scatchard plots, binding of cAMP analogs, loss of ligand binding (see below), photoaffinity labeling (Devreotes *et al.*, 1987), GTP-induced inhibition of binding (see below), calcium influx (Milne and Devreotes, 1993), "*in vivo*" adenylyl cyclase assay (Devreotes *et al.*, 1987)].

VI. Assaying Chemotaxis

A. INTRODUCTION

The motility responses of cells can be divided into two types: taxis and kinesis. Taxis is the oriented movement of a cell in a particular direction, as in the movement of growth-stage *Dictyostelium* amoebas toward folic acid and the movement of aggregation-stage amoebas toward cAMP. Kinesis is a change in cell motility that is not dependent on a directional stimulus; for example, the velocity of neutophils is increased by the tripeptide f-Met–Leu–Phe, even in the absence of a spatial gradient. Assays that have been used to analyze the motility behavior of *Dictyostelium* cells include the cellophane square assay, the small population assay (Konijn and van Haastert, 1987), the micropipette assay, and the flow cell assay (Segall, 1992). This section focuses on two alternative assays: the agar well assay and the Zigmond chamber assay. The agar well assay allows rapid screening of relatively large numbers of colonies, but does not distinguish effectively between chemotactic and chemokinetic responses. It works best as a qualitative assay for folate chemotaxis. The Zigmond chamber assay allows measurement of single-cell parameters, clearly separating chemokinesis from chemotaxis.

B. MATERIALS AND INSTRUMENTATION

KH$_2$PO$_4$ (Cat. No. 7100-2.5*NY), Na$_2$HPO$_4$·7H$_2$O (Cat. No. 7914-2.5*NY), MgCl$_2$ (Cat. No. 5958-500*NY), and NaOH (Cat. No. 7708-2.5*NY) are purchased from Baxter. Folic acid (Cat. No. F-7876) is obtained from Sigma. CaCl$_2$ (Cat. No. C 79-500), HCl (Cat. No. A 14451-212), and Bactoagar (Difco, Cat. No. DF 0140-05-6) are from Fisher Scientific.

Coverslips (22 × 40 mm, Cat. No. 48393-048) are purchased from VWR. The Zigmond chamber is obtained from Neuroprobe. Also required are a compass for inscribing circles, toothpicks, a dissecting microscope, a microscope with video camera and recorder, and image analysis equipment.

C. PROCEDURES

1. Agar Well Assay

Solutions

1. *Sorenson's phosphate buffer:* For a 10× stock solution, dissolve, in 1 liter, 20.6 g KH$_2$PO$_4$ and 5.05 g Na$_2$HPO$_4$·7H$_2$O. The pH of the 1× solution should be 6.0–6.1.

2. *Ca/Mg phosphate buffer:* 1 mM CaCl$_2$, 1 mM MgCl$_2$ in Sorenson's phosphate buffer.

Steps

Several hours or days ahead of time

1. Add Bactoagar to Ca/Mg phosphate buffer to a concentration of 1% (w/v). Dissolve by boiling, then pour into a petri dish to produce a 3- to 4-mm-thick layer of agar.

2. Grow *Dictyostelium* cells axenically or on low nutrient agar plates with *E. coli* B/2.

On the day of the experiment

3. Make a 1 mM solution of folic acid in Sorenson's phosphate buffer. Folic acid requires neutralization; add 2 mM equivalent of NaOH. The solution should become clear yellow after several minutes.

4. Using the compass, inscribe one or several 14-mm-diameter circles on the bottom of the petri dish.

5. Using the large end of a Pasteur pipette, punch a 7-mm-diameter hole in the agar, at the center of each circle. Carefully remove the agar from the hole, creating a well.

6. For cells grown as colonies on low nutrient agar, take cells from the edge of a colony with a toothpick. For cells grown uniformly in suspension or on plates, wash and gently pellet in an Eppendorf tube. Using a toothpick, collect a clump of cells from the pellet.

7. Under the dissecting microscope, carefully deposit a droplet of the cell slurry about 3 mm from the edge of the well. Droplets of several types of cells can be deposited around one well.

8. Fill the well carefully with the folic acid solution, cover with aluminum foil, and incubate in a culture room at about 23°C for 5–8 hr.

9. After 5–8 hr, chemotactic cells will form a ring moving outward from the original site of deposition. A high density of cells at the edge of the ring next to the well indicates that the cells are responding chemotactically.

2. Zigmond Chamber Assay

Steps

Several hours or days before the experiment

1. Place coverslips in 2.7% HCl solution for 10 min, swirling occasionally to ensure that all surfaces are exposed to the acid. Rinse extensively with distilled water and air-dry. Store in a clean, sealed container. It is important that the coverslips be clean and hydrophilic for easy assembly of cells in the chamber.

Day of experiment

2. Starve cells for 6 to 8 hr. For optimal resonse, many strains require pulsing with 50–100 nM cAMP at 6-min intervals for the last 2–4 hr.

3. Form a single-cell suspension. Typically, dilute to 10^6 cells/ml and shear a 400-μl suspension by taking up and expelling 10–20 times with a 200-μl pipetman set to 200 μl. View a drop of the suspension under the microscope to be certain that the cells are single.

4. Dilute to 5×10^4 cells/ml in Ca/Mg phosphate buffer. Place 50 μl in a narrow (2-mm) line across the center of the coverslip, along the short axis. Allow the cells to settle and attach (5–10 min).

5. Carefully flip the coverslip upside down and install on the Zigmond chamber, with the line of cells centered on the bridge of the chamber. Attach the clips to hold the coverslip in place.

6. Place the chamber under the microscope and use the 40× objective to determine the distance between the coverslip and the bridge. The distance should be less than 10 μm. If not, remove the coverslip, clean the chamber, and try again. Too much liquid on the coverslip can result in the distance being more than 10 μm.

7. Fill the troughs with Ca/Mg phosphate buffer.

8. Incubate in humidified chamber for 20 min to allow cells to equilibrate. An inverted petri dish with a wet Kimwipe maintains adequate humidity on an inverted microscope.

9. Flush one trough with 0.1 mM cAMP in Ca/Mg phosphate buffer, the other with unsupplemented Ca/Mg phosphate buffer. Flushing is performed by removing fluid with a Kimwipe on one end while adding fluid with a Pasteur pipette at the other end.

10. Place under the microscope and observe a field in the center of the bridge for 10-min intervals, using a video recorder to provide a copy of the data.

11. Calculate the speed of translocation, direction of movement, and rate of turning for each cell in the field of view.

D. COMMENTS

An important component of the analysis of individual cells moving in spatial gradients or exposed to sudden concentration changes is the use of specialized image analysis and cell tracking programs. These programs use the coordinates of the cell periphery in performing their calculations. Depending on the degree of resolution required, a commercially available program can use bright-field images for automatic detection of the cell edge or a mouse to trace the cell edge in high-resolution Nomarski images. The accurate tracking of individual cells allows the measurement of cell shape changes, cell velocity, and direction.

There are multiple methods for analyzing cell behavior, depending on budget and time constraints. Sophisticated, rapid programs that provide extensive information include DIAS (Solltech) and Expertvision (MotionAnalysis). These systems can provide automatic tracking of cells, provided that the illumination results in a clear light intensity difference between the cell interior and the background. Alternatively, simple image processing programs allow one to trace cell peripheries by hand from single frames and calculate area and centroid. This information can then be collated by hand and used to calculate centroid translocation, turning, and orientation.

The combination of defined stimulus assays together with sophisticated image processing allows a detailed phenotypic comparison of the behavior of mutant cells with wild type. It has been useful for identifying changes that occur when a specific gene is disrupted, leading to partial defects in chemotactic responses. The integration of such phenotypic analyses with detailed molecular biology manipulations will extend our understanding of amoeboid cell motility and chemotaxis.

E. PITFALLS

The agar well assay probably relies on the cells' ability to degrade the chemoattractant. *Dictyostelium* cells secrete folate deaminase and cAMP phosphodiesterase. Degradation of the chemoattractant should steepen the gradient, amplifying the response. The high density of cells used, long times required for a response, and the possible requirement for inactivating enzymes make this assay qualitative in nature.

VII. Loading of Molecules into *Dictyostelium*

A. INTRODUCTION

Exogenous molecules can be introduced into *Dictyostelium* amoebas by five methods: (1) sonication loading, (2) ATP loading, (3) electroporation, (4) passive loading, and (5) syringe loading. Scrape loading and microinjection are not recommended for use with *Dictyostelium* (Fechheimer and Taylor, 1987). The loading of DNA to *Dictyostelium* is considered elsewhere in this article.

There are three issues common to all loading methods: quantitative characterization of the loading of various types of exogenous molecules; viability of the loaded cells; and evaluation of the intracellular compartment to which the exogenous molecules have been introduced. Quantitative characterization of the loading method determines the method of choice to introduce the exogenous molecule. The viability of the cells and the intracellular localization of the exogenous molecule must be determined for each molecule and loading method.

B. MATERIALS AND INSTRUMENTATION

Fluorescent and ester (AM)-conjugated dyes are obtained from Molecular Probes. Probenecid (Cat. No. P-8761), fluorescein isothiocynate dextrans (FD-4, FD-10S,

FD-20, FD-40, FD-70, FD-150, FD-500S, FD-2000S), leucine (Cat. No. L-5652), phenylalanine (Cat. No. P-8324), valine (Cat. No. V-0258), glycine (Cat. No. G-7403), arginine (Cat. No. A-5949), histidine (Cat. No. H-7625), tryptophan (Cat. No. T-0254), threonine (Cat. No. T-8534), lysine (Cat. No. L-5876), methionine (Cat. No. M-6039), isoleucine (Cat. No. I-2752), $CaCl_2$ (Cat. No. C-7902), and sucrose (Cat. No. S-9378) are purchased from Sigma. ATP (Cat. No. 10585) is from U.S. Biochemical Company. $Na_2HPO_4 \cdot 7H_2O$ (Cat. No. 3824-1), KH_2PO_4 (Cat. No. 3246-1), $MgCl_2$ (Cat. No. 2444-01), $CaCl_2 \cdot 2H_2O$ (Cat. No. 1332-01), NaCl (Cat. No. 3624-05), and KCl (Cat. No. 3040-01) are obtained from J. T. Baker.

The Branson sonifier (Model 200) is purchased from Branson Ultrasonics.

C. PROCEDURES

1. Sonication Loading

Solutions

1. *17 mM phosphate buffer, pH 6.1:* Dissolve 0.54 g Na_2HPO_4 and 2.04 g KH_2PO_4 in distilled water. Adjust to a total volume of 1 liter. Store at room temperature.

2. *Supplemented phosphate buffer:* For 1 liter, solubilize the following in H_2O: 0.54 g Na_2HPO_4, 2.04 g KH_2PO_4, 1.8 g glucose, and 5 g each of leucine, phenylalanine, valine, glycine, arginine, histidine, tryptophan, threonine, lysine, methionine, and isoleucine. Adjust the pH to 6.1. Store at 4°C.

Steps

1. Wash NC-4 until free of bacteria (three or four times) or Ax-3 cells until free of HL5 (two or three times) with 17 mM phosphate buffer by centrifugation at 200 g (1000 rpm).
2. Resuspend the cells to a final density of 1×10^6 cells/ml in supplemented phosphate buffer to which has been added the molecule to be loaded.
3. While stirring, sonicate 1 ml in a 13 × 45-mm ($d \times h$) vial in a Branson sonifier Model 200 with microtip. Use power 1 for 2 × 0.5-sec pulses.
4. Dilute immediately to 10 ml with ice-cold supplemented phosphate buffer.
5. Wash amoebas by centrifugation at 200 g (1000 rpm) with ice-cold supplemented phosphate buffer + supplements, until the exogenous molecules are removed from the medium (three to five times).

2. ATP Loading

See Furukawa *et al.* (1990).

Solutions

1. *17 mM phosphate buffer, pH 6.1:* See Section VIIC1.

2. *17 mM phosphate buffer, pH 7.0:* Prepare as solution 1, except adjust the pH to 7.0 with NaOH. Store at room temperature.

3. *100 mM ATP:* Dissolve ATP in 17 mM phosphate buffer at pH 7. Keep frozen as a stock. Prior to use, thaw and keep on ice.

4. *Dye solution:* For 2 ml total, add the following to 17 mM phosphate buffer, pH 7: 100 μl of 0.1 M ATP, 100 μl of 0.1 M probenecid, 8–10 mM dye (weight depends on the dye). Titrate to pH 7.0.

5. *100 mM probenecid:* For 10 ml, dissolve 0.28 g probenecid in 17 mM phosphate buffer. Titrate with 5 M KOH while stirring until the probenecid dissolves (about pH 10–11). Adjust the volume to 10 ml. Make fresh.

6. *17 mM phosphate, 5 mM probenecid at pH 7.0 and 0°C:* Add 1.25 ml of 0.1 M probenecid to 20 ml of 17 mM phosphate buffer, pH 7.0. Titrate to pH 7.0. Adjust the volume with phosphate buffer, pH 7.0, to 25 ml. Place on ice.

7. *17 mM phosphate, 5 mM probenecid at pH 6.1 and 20°C:* Add 1.25 ml of 0.1 M probenecid to 20 ml of 17 mM phosphate buffer, pH 6.1. Titrate to pH 6.1. Adjust the volume with phosphate buffer to 25 ml.

Steps

1. Wash NC-4 cells until free of bacteria (three or four times) or Ax-3 cells until free of medium (two or three times) with 17 mM phosphate buffer, pH 6.1, by centrifugation at 200 g (1000 rpm). Resuspend cells at approximately 10^8 cells/ml.

2. Keep on ice 15 min.

3. Pellet cells and note the volume of the pellet. Remove all of the buffer with a Pasteur pipette.

4. For every 0.1 ml packed cells, add 2 ml of dye solution containing the exogenous molecule to be loaded. Leave on ice 10 min.

5. Pellet cells. Wash cells in 10 ml of phosphate + probenecid, pH 7.0.

6. Repeat step 6 two times.

7. Wash cells twice with 10 ml of phosphate + probenecid, pH 6.1.

8. Cells are ready to use.

3. Electroporation

Solutions

1. *10 mM phosphate buffer, pH 6.5:* For 1 liter, solubilize, in distilled water, 1.06 g KH_2PO_4 and 0.57 g $Na_2HPO_4 \cdot 7H_2O$.

2. *10 mM phosphate buffer + Ca/Mg, pH 6.5:* For 1 liter, solubilize, in distilled water, 1.06 g KH_2PO_4, 0.57 g $Na_2HPO_4 \cdot 7H_2O$, 2 ml of 0.1 M $CaCl_2 \cdot 2H_2O$, and 0.41 g $MgCl_2 \cdot 6H_2O$.

3. *Bonner's salt:* For 1 liter, solubilize, in distilled water, 1.17 g NaCl, 0.75 g KCl, and 0.44 g $CaCl_2 \cdot 2H_2O$.

Steps

Electroporation after Van Haastert et al. *(1989)*

1. Wash cells with 10 mM phosphate buffer, pH 6.5, by centrifugation.

2. Resuspend at 2×10^8 cells/ml in 10 mM phosphate buffer, pH 6.5.

3. Mix 750 μl cells with 250 μl of exogenous molecule.

4. Place in electroporation cell with a 1-cm gap between the electrodes.

5. Pulse two times (210 μsec) at 7 kV at 5-sec intervals.

6. Remove the cells from the electroporation chamber and mix with 10 m*M* phosphate buffer + Ca/Mg, pH 6.5. Immediately place cells on ice for 10 min.

7. Centrifuge 2 min at 200 *g*. Wash twice with 10 m*M* phosphate buffer, pH 6.5.

Electroporation after Abe and Maeda (1989)

1. Wash cells twice with ice-cold Bonner's salt and once with ice-cold 50 m*M* sucrose by centrifugation.

2. Resuspend at 1–2 × 10⁷ cells/ml in ice-cold 50 m*M* sucrose with exogenous molecule.

3. Use 250–300 μl of cell suspension in 2-mm-gap chamber. Electroporate at 700–725 V/cm with a condenser capacitance of 120 μF.

4. Wash cells free of exogenous molecules by differential centrifugation.

4. Passive Loading

Steps

1. Wash cells with 17 m*M* phosphate buffer, pH 6.1, by centrifugation.

2. Resuspend to approximately 1 × 10⁷ cells/ml at 4°C.

3. Incubate with dye.

4. Pellet cells. Wash cells until exogenous molecule is removed.

D. COMMENTS

Passive loading occurs when neutral molecules diffuse through the cell membrane. The concentration of dye and incubation time of the dye with the cells must be established for each compound used. Successful loading can be monitored by fluorescence microscopy.

For sonication loading, modifications of the basic protocol are devised as required. The time and power of sonication and the volume of the solution are critical variables that must be carefully controlled. The fluorescein-labeled dextran is recommended for use as a probe during characterization of the method. To establish the procedure after switching sonicators or cell types, it is necessary to recalibrate the power and time of sonication according to the following strategy. Select a power setting, sonicate for various periods, and measure cell viability using 0.04% trypan blue and a hemocytometer. Curves of viability as a function of time are obtained for each power setting. Loading of fluorescein dextran can then be assessed at a few points on the viability curve. Optimal loading and live cell recovery are obtained at approximately 50–70% viability. The live cell recovery after washing is typically 40%, and the viability is near 100%.

ATP loading works well for anionic molecules with a molecular weight less than 1 kDa. The concentration of the dye molecule to be introduced is a variable. The fluorophore distribution in NC-4 amoebas was assessed by fluorescence microscopy (Furukawa *et al.*, 1990). If variations of the solutions are desired, note that the loading solution should not contain divalent cations, as the ATP should exist as ATP⁴⁻.

For electroporation, modifications of the basic protocol are devised as required. To establish the procedure, it is necessary to calibrate the number of pulses, potential, cell density, and kinetics of uptake with a low-molecular-weight dye, as the percentage of loaded cells varies with the molecular weight of the exogenous molecule.

Syringe loading has been used successfully for other cells (Clarke and McNeil, 1992). This method has great promise but has not been characterized for *Dictyostelium* amoebas, although there has been an initial report of syringe loading (Pham, 1993). The extent of loading depends on the syringe needle gauge, the length of the needle, and the time the cells are dispensed through the syringe needle. Times must be determined empirically. Loading can be monitored by fluorescence microscopy using a fluorescent exogenous molecule such as fluorescein-labeled dextran.

E. PITFALLS

For passive loading, the most widely used application employs fluorescent dyes that are rendered neutral by chemical modification of charged residues with ester groups. These molecules enter the membrane by diffusion. Intracellular esterases cleave the ester groups, releasing the free fluorescent dye and, among other compounds, a proton. Thus, intracellular acidification can accompany loading of all dyes in this class. Some dyes must be dissolved in DMSO and diluted so that the final concentration of DMSO is 1%.

For ATP loading, the addition of probenecid to the buffer helps to prevent the sequestration of organic anions into vesicles and the loss of dye from the amoebas. The concentration of probenecid required varies by lot number. Too little probenecid will not be effective to prevent dye sequestration, while too much probenecid is lethal. Molecules with a molecular weight less than 900 Da are loaded into macrophages by this method, and it is most effective for anionic compounds.

Electroporation requires a custom-built electroporator to deliver a high-voltage discharge with a time constant in the microsecond range, compared with the millisecond range available with commercial instrumentation (van Haastert *et al.*, 1989).

VIII. Using Monoclonal Antibodies to Identify and Locate Molecules in Developing *Dictyostelium*

A. INTRODUCTION

Crude antigens, including whole cells, have been used to obtain monoclonal antibodies to cell surface molecules on both prestalk and prespore cells of the multicellular *Dictyostelium discoideum* slug. For example, the slug forms an extracellular matrix (ECM) around itself through which it migrates, leaving the ECM behind as a collapsed trail. This makes *D. discoideum* very attractive for studies on ECM, as a two-dimensional historical record is left on the agar surface that documents cell/ECM interactions. This ECM serves as a useful source of antigens. Antibodies raised against these antigens have been used to locate specific molecules in the organism, to identify cell-type-specific glycoproteins, and to predict the function of specific molecules in the tissue. Flow cytometry has been used to gain information about cell size and the presence of cell surface molecules, to study and quantitate the surface or intracellular location of particular antigens, and to track the fate of cell surface molecules when cells are asked to redifferentiate.

Monoclonal antibodies are widely used to detect proteins on Western blots, and common techniques can be employed. Monoclonal antibodies have revolutionized the purification of proteins, as they can be used as ligands to separate out the molecule(s) of interest from a complex mixture. This is particularly true of membrane proteins, where affinity columns with bound monoclonal antibodies are rou-

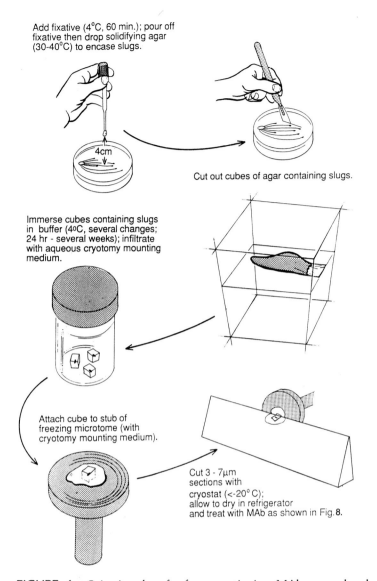

Add fixative (4°C, 60 min.); pour off fixative then drop solidifying agar (30-40°C) to encase slugs.

4cm

Cut out cubes of agar containing slugs.

Immerse cubes containing slugs in buffer (4°C, several changes; 24 hr - several weeks); infiltrate with aqueous cryotomy mounting medium.

Attach cube to stub of freezing microtome (with cryotomy mounting medium).

Cut 3 - 7μm sections with cryostat (<-20° C); allow to dry in refrigerator and treat with MAb as shown in Fig. 8.

FIGURE 6 Orienting slugs for frozen sectioning. MAb, monoclonal antibody.

tinely used to bind detergent-solubilized membranes. An interesting extension of this principle is the use of immunoprecipitation to study protein complexes; this has been done with proteins involved in spore coat deposition (Watson *et al.*, 1993).

This section focuses on manipulations of *Dictyostelium* slugs to facilitate immuno-histochemical studies. Methods for disaggregating slugs for flow cytometry and for studying the ECM are presented, as are methods for sectioning slugs. *D. discoideum* slugs are delicate, so they present some difficulty in sectioning. To preserve them intact and maintain their orientation, it is best to fix them *in situ* and then embed them in agar so that they can be easily manipulated (Fig. 6). A number of different fixatives can be used, depending on what the antibody recognizes (e.g., sugar versus peptide epitope). Two of the most useful are described here.

B. MATERIALS AND INSTRUMENTATION

NaCl (Cat. No. S271-10), KCl (Cat. No. P217-500), CaCl$_2$·2H$_2$O (Cat. No. C79-500), agar (Difco Noble, Cat. No. DF0142-17-0), KOH (Cat. No. P251-3), formalin

(Cat. No. SF98-4), and acetone (Cat. No. A18-1) are purchased from Fisher Scientific. Tris (Cat. No. T-1503), cysteine (Cat. No. C-7755), papain (Cat. No. P-3125), and leupeptin (Cat. No. L-2023) are obtained from Sigma. KH_2PO_4 (Cat. No. 7100-500*NY) is from Baxter.

C. PROCEDURES

1. Disaggregating Slugs for Flow Cytomentry

Solutions

1. *Bonner's salt solution:* For 1 liter, solubilize, in distilled water, 1.17 g NaCl, 0.75 g KCl, and 0.44 g $CaCl_2 \cdot 2H_2O$.

2. *Tris/cysteine solution:* 50 mM Tris buffer, 5 mM cysteine, pH 7.

Steps

1. Grow wild-type *Dictyostelim* cells on *E. coli* or *K. aerogenes* (these can be stored on nutrient agar plates at 4°C for several weeks as a source of bacteria.)

2. Collect spores from a fruiting body, using a toothpick. Make slugs as shown in Fig. 7.

3. Remove four slugs from the water agar by picking up with a wire loop and transferring to an Eppendorf centrifuge tube containing 0.2 ml Bonner's salt solution. If carefully done, this does not disturb the slugs.

4. Centrifuge the slugs and resuspend in Tris/cysteine solution.

5. Disaggregate either by mechanical agitation or using protease treatment.

   a. Protease treatment is simple to perform and for most purposes is the method of choice. Incubate cells in 0.15% (w/v) papain for 10 min at room temperature, with occasional vortexing. The papain is removed by brief centrifugation (4 sec) and the protease reaction is terminated by addition of leupeptin (4 μg per Eppendorf tube).

   b. Mechanical disaggregation is achieved by agitation of the Eppendorf tube against a cross-bar with rubber insert that is mounted on an electric motor shaft. This requires some skill to achieve a clean population of cells, because too little agitation leads to clumps of cells, while too much leads to cell breakage. Mechanical disaggregation is essential if the epitope expressed at the cell surface is protease sensitive.

6. Add together 0.1 ml monoclonal antibody culture supernatent and 0.1 ml second antibody labeled with FITC (or other fluorochrome).

7. Incubate on ice for 1 hr.

8. Analyze the sample by flow cytometry. No washing of the samples is performed as this leads to cell breakage and it is not necessary to remove the unincorporated antibody.

9. It is also possible to examine internal epitopes by flow cytometry, although this is technically more demanding than studying cell surface molecules. This is because the cells must be permeabilized to allow the antibodies to enter; but if cells are too harshly treated they lyse.

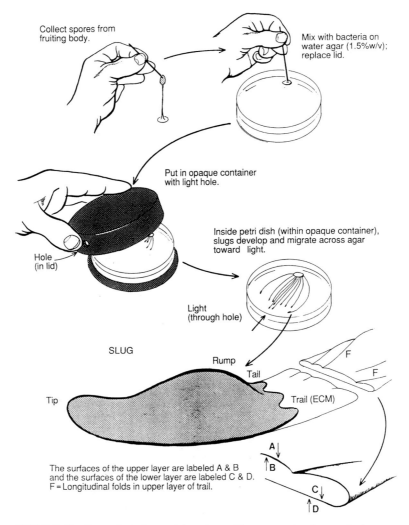

Collect spores from fruiting body.

Mix with bacteria on water agar (1.5%w/v); replace lid.

Put in opaque container with light hole.

Hole (in lid)

Inside petri dish (within opaque container), slugs develop and migrate across agar toward light.

Light (through hole)

SLUG

Tip

Rump

Tail

Trail (ECM)

F

F

A

B

C

D

The surfaces of the upper layer are labeled A & B and the surfaces of the lower layer are labeled C & D. F = Longitudinal folds in upper layer of trail.

FIGURE 7 Procedure for making slugs. Slugs can also be made from axenically grown cells. (In this case cells are washed and placed as a thin line of cells on the agar.) The agar plate is either wrapped individually or placed in a darkened cyclinder containing a thin slit to allow unidirectional light to enter. Slugs migrate toward the light. A short burst of overhead light arrests movement and initiates culmination. ECM, extracellular matrix.

2. Slime Trail (ECM) Studies

Solution

1. *Phosphate-buffered saline (PBS):* 15 mM KH_2PO_4, 0.9% (w/v) NaCl, pH to 7.2 with 5 M KOH.

The steps are presented in Fig. 8, which describes simple experiments that allow study of the ECM using monoclonal antibodies. Tricks for beginners include such simple things as the nature of the agar on which the slugs move: some agars are sticky, whereas other agars allow the ECM and slugs to be removed easily. Difco Agar Noble is preferred (expensive, but especially good for time-lapse filming), although Calbiochem Agar is usually adequate.

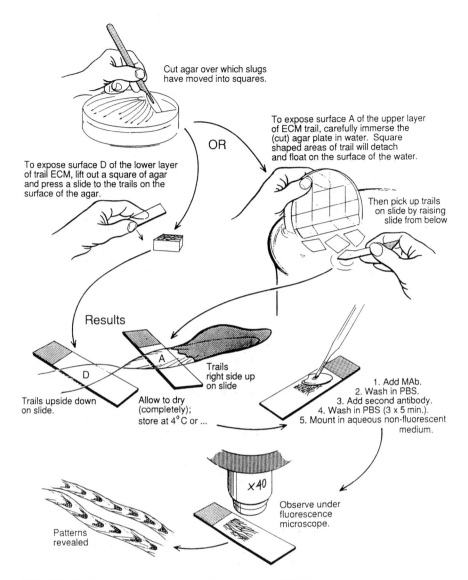

Cut agar over which slugs
have moved into squares.

To expose surface A of the upper layer
of ECM trail, carefully immerse the
(cut) agar plate in water. Square
shaped areas of trail will detach
and float on the surface of the water.

OR

To expose surface D of the lower layer
of trail ECM, lift out a square of agar
and press a slide to the trails on the
surface of the agar.

Then pick up trails
on slide by raising
slide from below

Results

D

A

Trails
right side up
on slide

Trails upside down
on slide.

Allow to dry
(completely);
store at 4°C or ...

1. Add MAb.
2. Wash in PBS.
3. Add second antibody.
4. Wash in PBS (3 x 5 min.).
5. Mount in aqueous non-fluorescent
   medium.

×40

Observe under
fluorescence
microscope.

Patterns
revealed

FIGURE 8 Preparation of extracellular matrix (ECM) for immunofluorescence microscopy.

3. Fixing and Embedding Slugs

Steps

Paraformaldehyde fixation

1. Prepare slugs as shown in Fig. 7.

2. Use 2–4% (w/v) paraformaldehyde in PBS as the fixative.

3. Pour the fixative gently onto the agar as the slugs and ECM float during
this process.

4. Fix for ~4 hr at room temperature.

5. When removing the fixative, it is important to carefully drain off as much of
the fluid as possible so that the slugs rest once again on the agar in their original
orientation. This can be done either using a Pasteur pipette or by gently pouring
off the fixative. Excess fluid is removed using filter paper strips.

Cold formaldehyde/acetone fixation

1. This fixative is particularly good for cytoskeletal components such as actin and myosin. Fukui *et al.* (1987) pioneered this technique for use in studying the cytoskeleton of single amoebas. The same basic technique is useful for studying the multicellular stages, particularly when visualizing cell–cell interactions.

2. Blocks of agar (4 × 4 mm) containing individual migrating slugs are cut from the agar plate and placed on glass coverslips. Approximately three blocks of agar with a single slug on each will fit easily on one coverslip. Do not spend too long cutting the slugs out or they will begin to change shape due to entry into culmination. Desiccation is also a problem so you must work quickly. Select slugs that have migrated 3–4 cm from the source, as younger slugs often have an immature shape.

3. Gently lower each coverslip into a beaker containing 1% (v/v) formalin in acetone at −15 ± 2°C for 15 min. The easiest way to do this is to make a coverslip holder with a folded strip of aluminum foil so that the coverslip remains horizontal as it is lowered into the fixative. Slugs fixed in acetone do not float off the agar. (Alternatively, the coverslip can be plunged into liquid nitrogen prior to fixation to better preserve tissue structure; in this case the frozen material is then brought to −15°C in the fixative by transfer from the liquid nitrogen.) The fixative can be kept at −15°C in ice with salt added or on dry ice with layers of paper towelling between the beaker and the dry ice to prevent the fixative from getting too cold. It is important that the fixative be not colder than −17°C, to avoid ice crystal damage.

Embedding slugs in agar

1. Embed slugs fixed by either of the above techniques in 1.5% (w/v) agar as described in Fig. 6.

2. As an aid to orientation, the agar covering the slug can be colored with a dye such as neutral red.

3. After embedding, trim each block containing a slug with a scalpel so that the cut edges are parallel to the sides of the slug. This helps in orienting the slug for sectioning.

4. Wash blocks as described in Fig. 6 and then infiltrate with an embedding compound (e.g., OCT, Miles Tissue Tek II) on a rotater for 1–2 days at 4°C.

5. Fixed slugs can be stored in OCT for several months at 4°C. Do not freeze them!

4. Cryosectioning Slugs

Steps

1. Slugs are small (only approximately 0.1 × 1 mm). Sectioning them on a freezing microtome can be difficult and frustrating; however, there are a number of tricks to facilitate this.

2. Make sure that the agar blocks are properly infiltrated with the embedding compound before beginning. Failure to do this leads to blocks that shatter on sectioning.

3. Do not place the agar block directly on the stub of the microtome. Instead, squeeze about 3 ml of embedding compound onto the precooled stub, just enough to make a hemisphere about 2 cm in diameter. Once frozen, the

embedding compound can be trimmed to make a flat surface on which the block can be mounted.

4. Position the agar block on a square of filter paper (5 × 5 mm) that has been wetted with embedding compound, noting the orientation carefully. The slug will now be oriented on a flat solid support.

5. Using fine forceps, carefully transfer the paper onto the frozen trimmed hemisphere of embedding compound on the stub.

6. Squeeze a small amount of the embedding compound onto the agar block which contains the slug, to make a small hemisphere, and freeze immediately with freon. The neater the hemisphere, the easier it is to section.

D. COMMENTS

The techniques presented above allow precise studies on sections of slugs that are less than one cell thick (3 μm), so that details pertaining to one cell can be discerned. This is technically demanding and most molecular groups now stain whole mounts of slugs to observe the expression of cloned gene products. This provides a very useful guide to the location of labeled cells, but is of limited precision. If one needs to see which cells are labeled, it is undesirable to observe the labeled cells through 20 unlabeled cells. Orientation is also very difficult in whole mounts; one cannot easily distinguish dorsal from ventral surfaces. For antibody studies, whole mounts present additional problems, as the antibodies do not penetrate the tissue completely. As is always true, the method chosen will depend on the reason for the study. Whole mounts are quite excellent for answering many questions. They are not suitable if a single-cell layer on one side of the slug is to be studied.

The above-mentioned techniques lead to oriented sections, so that it is easy to determine the dorsal and ventral side of the slug. Until recently most sections were not oriented and this did not allow understanding of the importance of peripheral cells. Which orientation should be used? For most purposes, longitudinal sectioning normal to the plane of the agar (i.e., sagittal) or transverse sectioning sausage style (i.e., coronal) is preferred. Longitudinal sectioning reveals cells along the length of the organism, whereas coronal sectioning allows a zone at a particular distance from the tip to be studied.

A recent finding is that there is an epithelium-like layer of cells around the periphery of the slug, which can be clearly discerned only if slugs are freeze-substituted (Fuchs *et al.*, 1993). The rapid freezing and slow infiltration of fixative at low temperature used in this technique lead to excellent preservation of ultrastructure and cell contents. The problem with freeze-substitution is that the tissue prepared by this method has altered antigenicity due to the use of osmium fixative. However, if methanol is used as the fixative, glycoantigens can be well preserved.

E. PITFALLS

Most workers use axenic strains (Ax-2, Ax-3, Ax-4), as these are easy to handle for biochemistry and they are readily transformed. However, they develop less well than wild strains, especially for studies on the multicellular slug, culmination, and fruiting stages. They also tend to be fruity, so any treatment that favors fruiting (e.g., exposure to overhead light) will lead to the cessation of movement. By contrast, a number of wild strains (including V12, WS380B, and WS576) are "sluggy" and will continue to migrate even under conditions that normally trigger fruiting. This makes possible many biological studies on slugs, including extended time-lapse filming. Moreover, axenic strains tend to have some undifferentiated cells in the final fruiting body, especially at the top and bottom of the spore head; in wild strains, essentially all cells differentiate into spores, stalk, or basal disc cells.

REFERENCES

Abe, T., and Maeda, Y. (1989) The prestalk/prespore differentiation and polarized cell movement in *Dictyostelium discoideum* slugs: A possible involvement of the intracellular Ca^{2+} concentration. *Protoplasma* **151**, 175–178.

Blusch, J., Morandini, P., and Nellen, W. (1992) Transcriptional regulation by folate-inducible gene expression in *Dictyostelium* transformants during growth and early development. *Nucleic Acids Res.* **20**, 6235–6238.

Buhl, B., Fischer, K., and MacWilliams, H. K. (1993) Cell sorting within the prespore zone of *Dictyostelium discoideum*. *Dev. Biol.* **156**, 481–489.

Clarke, M. S. F., and McNeil, P. L. (1992) Syringe loading macromolecules into living mammalian cell cytosol. *J. Cell Sci.* **102**, 533–541.

De Lozanne, A., and Spudich, J. A. (1987) Disruption of the *Dictyostelium* myosin heavy chain gene by homologous recombination. *Science* **236**, 1086–1091.

Devreotes, P. N., Fontana, D., Klein, P., Sherring, J., and Theibert, A. (1987) Transmembrane signaling in *Dictyostelium*. *In* "Methods in Cell Biology" (J. A. Spudich, ed.), Vol. 28, pp. 299–331. Academic Press, San Diego.

Dingermann, T., Reindl, N., Brechner, T., Werner, H., and Nerke, K. (1990) Nonsense suppression in *Dictyostelium discoideum*. *Dev. Genet.* **11**, 410–417.

Dynes, J. L., and Firtel, R. A. (1989) Molecular complementation of a genetic marker in *Dictyostelium* using a genomic DNA library. *Proc. Natl. Acad. Sci. USA* **86**, 7966–7970.

Early, A. E., Gaskell, M. J., Traynor, D., and Williams, J. G. (1993) Two distinct populations of prestalk cells within the tip of the migratory *Dictyostelium* slug with differing fates at culmination. *Development* **118**, 353–362.

Fechheimer, M., and Taylor, D. L. (1987) Introduction of exogenous molecules into the cytoplasm of *Dictyostelium discoideum* amoebae by controlled sonication. *In* "Methods in Cell Biology" (J. A. Spudich, ed.), pp. 179–190. Academic Press, New York.

Firtel, R. A., and Chapman, A. L. (1990) Role for cAMP-dependent protein kinase-A in early *Dictyostelium* development. *Genes Dev.* **4**, 18–28.

Firtel, R. A., Silan, C., Ward, T., Howard, P., Metz, B. A., Nellen, W., and Jacobson, A. (1985) Extrachromosomal replication of shuttle vectors in *Dictyostelium discoideum*. *Mol. Cell. Biol.* **5**, 3241–3250.

Fuchs, M., Jones, M. K., and Williams, K. L. (1993) Characterisation of an epithelium-like layer of cells in the multicellular *Dictyostelium discoideum* slug. *J. Cell Sci.* **105**, 243–253.

Fukui, Y., Yumura, S., and Yumura, T. K. (1987) Agar overlay immunofluorescence: High-resolution studies of cytoskeletal components and their changes during chemotaxis. *In* "Methods in Cell Biology" (J. A. Spudich, ed.), Vol. 28, pp. 347–356. Academic Press, San Diego.

Furukawa, R., Wampler, J. E., and Fechheimer, M. (1990) Cytoplasmic pH of *Dictyostelium discoideum* amoebae during early development: Identification of two cell subpopulations before the aggregation stage. *J. Cell Biol.* **110**, 1947–1954.

Haberstroh, L., and Firtel, R. A. (1990) A spatial gradient of expression of a cAMP-regulated prespore cell-type-specific gene in *Dictyostelium*. *Genes Dev.* **4**, 596–612.

Harwood, A. J., and Drury, L. (1990) New vectors for expression of the *E. coli lacZ* gene in *Dictyostelium*. *Nucleic Acids Res.* **18**, 4292.

Kalderon, D., Roberts, B. L., Richardson, W. D., and Smith, A. E. (1984) A short amino acid sequence able to specify nuclear location. *Cell* **39**, 499–509.

Kalpaxis, D., Werner, H., Boy-Marcotte, E., Jacquet, M., and Dingermann, T. (1990) Positive selection for *Dictyostelium* mutants lacking uridine monophosphate synthase activity based on resistance to 5-fluoro-orotic acid. *Dev. Genet.* **11**, 396–402.

Kimmel, A. R., and Firtel, R. A. (1991) Signal transduction pathways regulating development of *Dictyostelium discoideum*. *Curr. Opin. Genet. Dev.* **1**, 383–390.

Konijn, T. M., and van Haastert, P. J. (1987) Measurement of chemotaxis in *Dictyostelium*. *In* "Methods Cell Biology" (J. A. Spudich, ed.), Vol. 28, pp. 283–298. Academic Press, San Diego.

Kumagai, A., Hadwiger, J. A., Pupillo, M., and Firtel, R. A. (1991) Molecular genetic analysis of two Gα protein subunits in *Dictyostelium*. *J. Biol. Chem.* **266,** 1220–1228.

Kuspa, A., and Loomis, W. F. (1992) Tagging developmental genes in *Dictyostelium* by restriction enzyme-mediated integration of plasmid DNA. *Proc. Natl. Acad. Sci. USA* **89,** 8803–8807.

Leiting, B., and Noegel, A. (1988) Construction of an extrachromosomally replicating transformation vector for *Dictyostelium discoideum*. *Plasmid* **20,** 241–248.

Milne, J. L., and Devreotes, P. N. (1993) The surface cyclic AMP receptors, cAR1, cAR2, and cAR3, promote Ca^{2+} influx in *Dictyostelium discoideum* by a Gα2-independent mechanism. *Mol. Biol. Cell* **4,** 283–292.

Nellen, W., Datta, S., Reymond, C., Sivertsen, A., Mann, S., Crowley, T., and Firtel, R. A. (1987) Molecular biology in *Dictyostelium:* Tools and applications. *In "Methods in Cell Biology"* (J. A. Spudich, ed.), Vol. 28, pp. 471–487. Academic Press, New York.

Pham, P. A., Jay, P. Y., Elson, E. L. (1993) Actin filament dynamics in motile *Dictyostelium* cells. *Mol. Biol. Cell* **4,** 54a.

Segall, J. E. (1992) Behavioral responses of streamer F mutants of *Dictyostelium discoideum*: Effects of cyclic GMP on cell motility. *J. Cell Sci.* **101,** 589–597.

Spudich, J. A. (ed.) (1987) *"Methods in Cell Biology,"* Vol. 28. Academic Press, New York.

Sun, T. J., and Devreotes, P. N. (1991) Gene targeting of the aggregation stage cAMP receptor cAR1 in *Dictyostelium*. *Genes Dev.* **5,** 572–582.

Tomchik, K. J., and Devreotes, P. N. (1981) Adenosine 3′,5′-monophosphate waves in *Dictyostelium discoideum*: A demonstration by isotope dilution-fluorography. *Science* **212,** 443–446.

Van Haastert, P. J. M. (1985) The modulation of cell surface cAMP receptors from *Dictyostelium discoideum* by ammonium sulfate. *Biochim. Biophys. Acta* **845,** 254–260.

Van Haastert, P. J. M. (1992) Sensory transduction in *Dictyostelium*. *In "Adenine Nucleotides in Cellular Energy Transfer and Signal Transduction,"* pp. 379–386. Birkhauser, Boston/New York.

Van Haastert, P. J. M., De Vries, M. J., Penning, L. C., Roovers, F., van der Kaay, J., Erneux, C., and van Lookeren Campagne, M. M. (1989) Chemoattractant and guanosine 5′-[γ-thio]triphosphate induce the accumulation of inositol 1,4,5-triphosphate in *Dictyostelium* cells that are labelled with [^{3}H]inositol by electroporation. *Biochem. J.* **258,** 577–586.

Varshavsky, A. (1992) The N-end rule. *Cell* **69,** 725–735.

Watson, N., Williams, K. L., and Alexander, S. (1993) A developmentally regulated glycoprotein complex from *Dictyostelium discoideum*. *J. Biol. Chem.* **268,** in press.

Williams, J. G., and Jermyn, K. A. (1991) Cell sorting and positional differentiation during *Dictyostelium* morphogenesis. *In "Cell–Cell Interactions in Early Development,"* pp. 261–272. Wiley–Liss, New York.

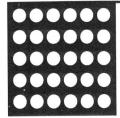

Large-Scale Culture of *Physarum:* A Simple Method for Growing Several Hundred Grams of Plasmodia

Kazuhiro Kohama, Ryoki Ishikawa, and Mitsuo Ishigami

I. Introduction

Plasmodia of *Physarum polycephalum* are multinuclear cells in which vigorous cytoplasmic streaming is apparent, and, for this reason, they have attracted the attention of scientists engaged in studies of cell motility. Culture of plasmodia holds marked advantages for biochemical studies of eukaryotic cells in that ordinary laboratory equipment can be used to generate 200–300 g of cells within a week. Such cultures of large quantities of cells have facilitated biochemical studies on the actomyosin system (Hatano, 1973) and the regulation of this system by Ca^{2+} ions (Kohama, 1990).

Here we describe the nonsterile surface-culture method of Camp (1936) as modified by Hatano and Oosawa (1966). The reader should, however, note that a method for axenic culture of plasmodia in liquid medium was developed by Daniel and Rush (1961). This latter method, although not suitable for preparation of hundreds of grams, allows plasmodia to be transferred to and cultured on conventional agar plates, facilitating genetic analysis and studies of the cell cycle (Sauer, 1982).

The life cycle of *P. polycephalum* is characterized by plasmodia, spores, and amoebae. Efforts to culture amoebae in large quantities (Kohama *et al.*, 1986) and in liquid medium (Dee *et al.*, 1989) have been reported, although the yields are far behind those from surface culture of plasmodia. Sporulation from plasmodia is described in Section V. Induction of the sclerotium, a dormant form of the plasmodium, is also described, in Section IIIB. We start our plasmodial culture with sclerotia (see Section IIIA), a technique that allows us to generate synchronously developed plasmodia, which can then be harvested at once.

II. Materials and Instrumentation

Rolled oats from the Quaker Oats Company, paper towels from Kimberly–Clark Corporation (23×22 cm², Cat. No. F950), plastic buckets with lids (15–13 liters), and a spray bottle can generally be purchased in local shops. Transparent plastic boxes with lids (35 cm long × 25.5 cm wide × 6.2 cm high, Cat. No. 2320 BF) and Falcon plastic dishes (100 mm in diameter, Cat. No. 1001) can be purchased from Sanplastec (Tel. No. +81-6-353-5975) and Becton Dickinson Overseas Inc. (Tel. No. +81-3-3403-5008), respectively.

Culture of plasmodia requires a dark room equipped with a conventional air-conditioning system to keep the room at 23–25°C. We use a prefabricated chamber (180 cm long × 180 cm wide × 210 cm high) equipped with an air conditioner.

III. Procedures

A. SURFACE CULTURE

Steps

1. Remove lids from plastic dishes, and place six dishes upside down in a plastic box, as shown in Color Plate 9A.

2. Fill the box to a level of about 1 cm with tap water.

3. Place paper towels over the dishes (Color Plate 9B) such that the edges of the paper towels are immersed in the water.

4. Place three to four pieces of a desiccated yellow preparation of sclerotia (each about 5 cm square, see Section B) on each towel (Color Plate 9C).

5. Scatter oat flakes on the sclerotia and towels (Color Plate 9D), spray with water to moisten them, and place the lids on the boxes.

6. Incubate each box in a dark room for 1 day at 23–25°C so that plasmodia emerge from the sclerotia.

7. Place rolled oats on the towels so as to cover the plasmodia, and incubate the plasmodial culture under the same conditions as in step 6 for a couple of days until the oats are covered with proliferating plasmodia (Color Plate 9E).

8. Repeat step 7 (Color Plate 9F).

9. Cut the plasmodial culture into two or three pieces when the oats became covered with proliferating plasmodia again, and place one piece on the bottom of each bucket. (Note that no oats are placed on plasmodial cultures in buckets.)

10. Incubate the buckets with the plasmodial cultures in the dark at 23–25°C until plasmodia climb up the inner walls of the buckets, as shown in Color Plate 9G. (Note that each bucket must be kept covered with a lid during the incubation.)

B. PREPARATION OF SCLEROTIA

Steps

1. Repeat steps 1–8 in Section A to the point that the plasmodial culture is ready for transfer to buckets.

2. Moisten fresh paper towels by spraying with water, and allow them to adhere to the inner walls of the buckets.

3. Place one piece of plasmodial culture on the bottom of each bucket, and incubate the cultures until plasmodia climb up onto the towels as described in step 10 in Section A (Color Plate 9H).

4. Remove the towels on which plasmodia have grown, and transfer them to dry plastic boxes (Color Plate 9I).

5. Leave the boxes open and allow plasmodia to dry out in a dark room at 23–25°C. (Note that good sclerotia are obtained by drying plasmodia for about 48 hr under the conditions described. If the drying is too rapid, spray towels with water after step 4.)

6. Cut out sclerotia on the dry paper towels (see Color Plate 9C), and store them in a desiccator in a cool, dark place.

IV. Comments

We routinely start plasmodial cultures with six boxes for activation of sclerotia and transfer the resultant cultures to 15 buckets. Surface culture in such quantities for about 8 days yields 200–300 g of packed fresh cells. Harvesting for maximum yield should be performed before the bucket is overgrown with plasmodia (see Color Plate 9G), as judged by observing the yellow color of healthy plasmodia. A reddish color is a sign of overgrowth. Harvesting is performed by scraping plasmodia off the walls with a large, flat spatula.

In theory, the paper towels on which the plasmodia have grown as described in Section IIIB, step 4 (see Color Plate 9I), can be subjected to the procedure described in Section IIIA, step 3, and then steps 7 to 10 in Section IIIA can be repeated. Healthy plasmodia can be obtained in this way; however, it is difficult to synchronize such cultures, and the yield of plasmodia is poor. It is thus advisable to start by activating dried sclerotia, as described in Section III.

V. Pitfalls

We often find that the plasmodia of *P. polycephalum* that have proliferated repeatedly on rolled oats suddenly show a decrease in growth activity as a result of aging. In such cases, we have to produce new plasmodia from spores at 23–25°C as follows.

1. Place a sample of sclerotia (about 1 cm square) on one edge of a 2% (w/v) agar plate (100 mm in diameter) prepared with tap water. Incubate the plate in the dark room as described in Section III for about 24 hr to allow the sclerotia to develop into plasmodia. Then place the plate under a white fluorescent light (3000–4000 lux). Within 2–3 days, numerous sporangia should be produced from the plasmodia. Collect the sporangia, and store them in a desiccator.

2. Gently grind 40–50 sporangia in a small mortar, and suspend the spores from the sporangia in 1 ml of 0.1 M sterile phosphate buffer (pH 6.5). Spread a few drops of the suspension of spores on 2% agar plates (100 mm in diameter) prepared in 0.1 M phosphate (pH 6.5). Incubate the plates in the dark room. The spores should germinate into amoebae within a couple of days (Fig. 1A).

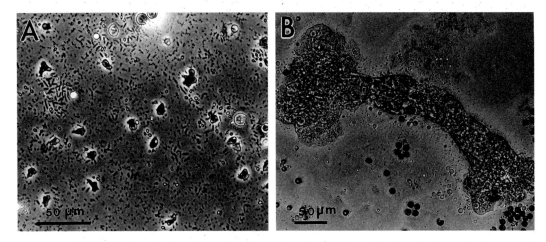

FIGURE 1 (A) Amoebae of *Physarum polycephalum* germinated from the inoculated spores. (B) A young plasmodium seen under the light microscope. Scale bars denote 50 μm.

Amoebae feed on surrounding bacteria. At this time, the addition of *Escherichia coli* cells in suspension may facilitate the growth of amoebae. Zygote formation takes place within several days. The zygotes grow up and become plasmodia, which become evident under the microscope within 7–10 days of placing the spore suspension on the plates (Fig. 1B). At this time, place a small amount of rolled oats on the plate. The plasmodia should grow during the subsequent week and become visible to the naked eye. At this point, we select plasmodia that grow actively on the oats. Transfer the selected plasmodia onto wet paper towels (see step 3 in Section IIIA), and allow them to grow on the rolled oats (see steps 7 and 8 in Section IIIA). The grown plasmodia can be subjected to the preparation of sclerotia as described in Section IIIB, steps 2 to 6.

REFERENCES

Camp, W. G. (1936) A method of cultivating myxomycete plasmodia. *Bull. Torrey Bot. Club* **63**, 205–210.

Daniel, J. W., and Rush, H. P. (1961) The pure culture of *Physarum polycephalum* on a partially defined soluble media. *J. Gen. Microbiol.* **25**, 47–59.

Dee, J., Foxon, J. L., and Anderson, G. W. (1989) Growth, development and genetic characterization of *Physarum polycephalum* amoebae able to grow in liquid, axenic medium. *J. Gen. Microbiol.* **135**, 1567–1588.

Hatano, S. (1973) Contractile proteins from the myxomycete plasmodium. *Adv. Biophys.* **5**, 143–176.

Hatano, S., and Oosawa, F. (1966) Isolation and characterization of plasmodium actin. *Biochim. Biophys. Acta* **127**, 488–598.

Kohama, K. (1990) Inhibitory mode for Ca^{2+} regulation. *Trends Pharmacol. Sci.* **11**, 433–435.

Kohama, K., Takano-Ohmuro, H., Tanaka, T., Yamaguchi, Y., and Kohama, K. (1986) Isolation and characterization of myosin from amoebae of *Physarum polycephalum*. *J. Biol. Chem.* **261**, 8022–8027.

Sauer, H. W. (1982) "Developmental Biology of *Physarum*." Cambridge University Press, Cambridge.

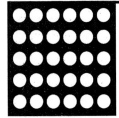

Induction of Regeneration-Competent Monocot Callus

Roberta H. Smith and Shyamala Bhaskaran

I. Introduction

Research using plant cell, tissue, and/or organ culture techniques covers a very broad spectrum of applied and basic activities. Figure 1 outlines some of the more common applications of plant cell culture methods. Unfortunately there is no general method to achieve these various endpoints. For instance, a procedure developed to obtain somatic embryos for cotton, *Gossypium hirsutum* (L.) cv Coker 215, will not be successful for most other *G. hirsutum* cultivars, let alone *Gossypium* species in general. A procedural outline to obtain somatic embryos in carrot, *Daucus carota* (L.) which is a classic model system, will not work for tobacco, cotton, soybean, and other plants, and indeed not for all carrot cultivars. Research focused on transformation of cereals has been limited by the lack of general methods to initiate regenerative callus (Kyozuka and Shimamoto, 1993). As many applied studies rely on ultimately regenerating plants, this article focuses on callus induction and regeneration of two important cereals, sorghum, *Sorghum bicolor* (L.) Moench (Bhaskaran and Smith, 1988, 1989; Bhaskaran *et al.,* 1992; Smith *et al.,* 1983), and rice, *Oryza sativa* (L.) (Peterson and Smith, 1991).

Historically it has been very simple to initiate callus from most dicotyledonous plant material and more recently monocotyledons. The challenge, however, is to be able to initiate callus that can differentiate into plants. There are four major components to consider in callus induction: the explant (piece of plant tissue placed in culture), the genotype or cultivar, the culture medium formulation, and the culture environment. The best source of information on a specific cultivar is the literature. This article presents protocols for the induction of competent callus from sorghum and rice. The general approach is useful with modifications for other cereal species (Bhaskaran and Smith, 1990).

II. Materials and Instrumentation

Seed can be obtained from major agricultural seed companies and/or farm supply companies (Pioneer Hi Bred Intl., Inc., Bioseed Genetics, Garrett Seed Co., Cox–Nelson Seed Co.). The inorganic salts, vitamins, carbohydrate, plant growth regulators, and agar can be obtained from most scientific supply companies such as Sigma, Gibco-BRL, Fisher Scientific, Calbiochem Behring, and Flow Laboratories. Sigma chemicals and their catalog numbers are amonium nitrate (A-3795), potassium

Tissue Explant

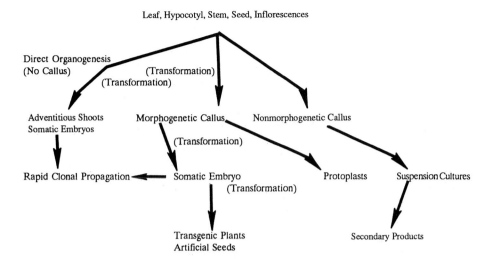

FIGURE 1   Outline of some applications of plant cell culture. (Transformation) indicates steps in the procedure where genetic transformation protocols have been used.

nitrate (P-8291), magnesium sulfate (M-7774), zinc sulfate (Z-1001), cupric sulfate (C-3036), calcium chloride (C-2661), potassium iodide (P-8166), cobalt chloride (C-2911), potassium phosphate (P-8416), boric acid (B-9645), sodium molybdate (M-1651), ferrous sulfate (F-8263), ethylenediaminetetraacetic acid, disodium salt (E-6635), nicotinic acid (N-0765), pyridoxine-HCl (P-8666), thiamine-HCl (T-3902), D-pantothenic acid (P-6045), biotin (B-3399), 2,4-dichlorophenoxyacetic acid (D-8407), naphthaleneacetic acid (N-1145), kinetin (K-0753), 6-benzylamino-purine (B-9395), myo-inositol (I-3011), sucrose (S-5390), Sigma type I agarose (A-6013), abscisic acid (A-1049), and glycine (G-6143). Gelrite (4900-1890) is purchased from Scott Laboratories, Inc. Manganous sulfate (M-113-75757) is purchased from Fisher Scientific.

Glassware and petri dishes for plant cell culture can be purchased from Sigma, Carolina Biological Supply Company, and Fisher Scientific. Petri dishes (100 × 20 mm, polystyrene, Cat. No. 08-772-32) are purchased from Fisher.

Shelving for cultures is commonly constructed of perforated wire which allows for air flow and permits lighting from the bottom and top of cultures. Generally the light source is white fluorescent lamps 4 feet long, mounted 8 in. above the culture shelf and 12 in. apart (Smith, 1992). The temperature range is 25–27°C under a 16:8 hr light:dark photoperiod.

III. Procedures

A. CALLUS INDUCTION AND PLANT REGENERATION FROM RICE

See Peterson and Smith (1991).

Solutions

1. *MS salts* (Murashige and Skoog, 1962)

   a. To make 1 liter of the nitrate stock, solubilize 165.0 g of NH_4NO_3, and 190.0 g of KNO_3 in deionized water and adjust to a total volume of 1 liter. Store at 4°C. The nitrate stock solution may need slight warming with stirring to facilitate dissolution before each use.

   b. To make 1 liter of the sulfate stock, solubilize 37.0 g of $MgSO_4 \cdot 7H_2O$, 1.69 g $MnSO_4 \cdot H_2O$, 0.86 g $ZnSO_4 \cdot 7H_2O$, and 0.0025 g $CuSO_4 \cdot 5H_2O$ in deionized water and adjust to a total volume of 1 liter. Store at 4°C.

   c. To make 1 liter of the halide stock, solubilize 44.0 g $CaCl_2 \cdot 2H_2O$, 0.083 g KI, and 0.0025 g $CoCl_2 \cdot 6H_2O$ in deionized water and adjust to a total volume of 1 liter. Store at 4°C.

   d. To make 1 liter of the PBMo stock, solubilize 17.0 g KH_2PO_4, 0.620 g H_3BO_3, and 0.025 g $Na_2MoO_4 \cdot 2H_2O$ in deionized water and adjust to a total volume of 1 liter. Store at 4°C.

   e. To make 1 liter of the iron stock, solubilize 2.784 g $FeSO_2 \cdot 7H_2O$ and 3.724 g Na_2EDTA in deionized water and adjust to a total volume of 1 liter. Store at 4°C in an amber-colored bottle to keep light out.

2. *Vitamins*

   a. To make 1 liter of the nicotinic acid and pyridoxine-HCl stock, solubilize 50 mg each in deionized water and adjust to a total volume of 1 liter. Ten-milliliter aliquots are stored frozen in individual vials. Use one vial per liter of medium.

   b. To make 1 liter of thiamine-HCl, solubilize 40 mg in 1 liter of deionized water and adjust to a total volume of 1 liter. Store at 4°C.

3. *2,4-Dichlorophenoxyacetic acid* (2,4-D), or *naphthaleneacetic acid (NAA):* Dissolve 10 mg of the auxin in a few drops of 1 N NaOH to dissolve the crystals; make up volume to 100 ml with deionized water. Store at 4°C.

4. *Kinetin or benzyladenine (BA):* Dissolve 10 mg of the cytokinin in a few drops of 1 N HCl with mild warming; make up volume to 100 ml with deionized water. Store at 4°C.

Steps

1. To approximately 800 ml of deionized water add 10 ml each of the five Murashige and Skoog inorganic salt stocks.

2. Add 10 ml of the pyridoxine-HCl, nicotinic acid stock.

3. Add 10 ml of the thiamine-HCl stock.

4. Add 100 mg of myo-inositol.

5. Add 35 ml of the 2,4-D stock.

6. Add 30 g sucrose, and dissolve.

7. Dilute to 1 liter, and adjust the pH to 5.7 with 1.0 or 0.1 N NaOH or HCl.

8. Add 4 g Sigma type I agarose.

9. Autoclave 15 min at 121°C, 15 psi.

10. When medium is cool, mix and dispense 25 ml per sterile, plastic petri dish in a transfer hood.

11. To prepare the explant, dehusk rice, *Oryza sativa* L. cvs 'Lemont,' 'Rico,' 'Skybonnet,' 'Rexmont,' or 'Taipei 309" seeds. Surface-disinfect in 70% ethanol for 1 min followed by 3% (v/v) Clorox bleach with 2 drops Tween 20 per 100 ml bleach solution for 30 min and rinse five times in sterile water.

12. Aseptically culture seeds on rice callus induction medium. Culture in the dark at 27–30°C.

13. In 2–3 weeks separate the embryogenic callus (smooth, white, and knobby in appearance, Color Plate 10A) from nonembryogenic callus (yellow-to-translucent, wet, crystalline-appearing, Color Plate 10B) using a dissection microscope in the culture hood.

14. Follow steps 1, 2, 3, 4, and 6 in preparation of the subculture medium.

15. Add 22 ml of the 2,4-D stock solution.

16. Add 26 mg abscisic acid.

17. Follow steps 7 through 10.

18. The callus in step 13 is subcultured onto the subculture medium and cultured in the dark at 27°C. Embryogenic callus should be subcultured every 2 to 3 weeks either on the same subculture medium or on to the plant regeneration medium below.

19. Follow steps 1, 2, 3, 4, and 6 in preparation of the plant regeneration medium.

20. Add 5 ml of the BA stock.

21. Add 0.5 ml of the NAA stock.

22. Subculture 10-mg pieces of callus on the plant regeneration medium and place cultures in the dark for 1 week; then transfer to light:dark photoperiod shelves. Plants will be ready to transfer to soil in about 4 weeks.

B. CALLUS INDUCTION AND PLANT REGENERATION FROM SORGHUM

(See Bhaskaran and Smith, (1988, 1989) and Bhaskaran *et al.*, (1992).

Solutions

To prepare the five-vitamin stock solution for sorghum regeneration medium prepare the following solutions:

1. *Solution A:* 13 mg nicotinic acid in 100 ml deionized water.

2. *Solution B:* 25 mg each of pyridoxine-HCl, calcium pantothenate, and thiamine-HCl in 100 ml deionized water.

3. *Solution C:* 1 mg biotin in 25 ml deionized water.

Store 10 ml of solution A, 1 ml of solution B, and 0.1 ml of solution C mixed together in individual vials in freezer. Use one vial per liter of medium.

Steps

1. To approximately 800 ml of deionized water, add 10 ml each of the five Murashige and Skoog inorganic salt stocks.

2. Add 2.5 ml of the thiamine-HCl stock.

3. Add 10 ml of the nicotinic acid and pyrodoxine-HCl stock.

4. Add 25 ml of the 2,4-D stock (for cv RTx 430 use 1 ml).

5. Add 0.5 ml of kinetin stock.

6. Add 100 mg of myo-inositol.

7. Add 2 mg glycine.

8. Add 20 g sucrose, and dissolve.

9. Dilute to 1 liter, and adjust the pH to 5.7 with 1.0 or 0.1 N NaOH or HCl.

10. Add 1.5 g Gelrite.

11. Autoclave 15 min at 121°C, 15 psi.

12. When medium is cool, mix and dispense 25 ml per sterile, plastic petri dish in a transfer hood.

13. To prepare the explant, surface-sterilize *Sorghum bicolor* (L.) Moench cvs. IS3620C, RTx 430, or BTx 3197 seeds are in 20% (v/v) Clorox bleach with 2 drops Tween 20 per 100 ml bleach solution for 20 min and rinse three times in sterile water. Surface-sterilized seeds are aseptically germinated on water-moistened filter paper in petri dishes. Dissect shoot tips out of 2- to 3-day-old seedlings using a dissection microscope. The shoot tip explant is approximately 1 mm.

14. To induce callus, place five to ten shoot tips on the callus induction medium. Incubate cultures at room temperature with a photoperiod of 16 hr at a light intensity of 28 μE m^{-2} sec^{-1}. Subculture at 4-week intervals for two or three passages on the same medium as in steps 1–12.

15. Follow step 1 in preparation of the plant regeneration medium.

16. Add 7.7 mg glycine.

17. Add 50 mg myo-inositol.

18. Add one vial of the five-vitamin stock solution.

19. Add 15 g sucrose and dissolve.

20. Dilute to 1 liter and adjust the pH to 5.7 with 1.0 or 0.1 N NaOH or HCl.

21. Add 1.5 g Gelrite.

22. Autoclave 15 min at 121°C, 15 psi.

23. When medium is cool, mix and dispense 25 ml per sterile, plastic petri dish in a transfer hood.

24. Transfer callus to plant regeneration medium.

IV. Comments

Using the protocols described in this article, it is possible to obtain embryogenic callus from several cultivars of rice and sorghum. It may also be possible to obtain embryogenic callus from other cultivars.

V. Pitfalls

1. Some seed batches may be so contaminated that it is difficult to obtain clean cultures. Increase the surface sterilization time in the Clorox and the concentration of Clorox for optimum germination and minimum contamination. Seeds harvested from greenhouse grown plants are often much easier to surface-disinfect.

2. The frequency of plant regeneration will decrease progressively during prolonged passage and culture.

3. Always use glass-distilled water for preparation of media and stock solutions.

4. Store stock solutions in the refrigerator. Be sure to heat and dissolve the crystals in the MS nitrate stock before removing the desired portion for preparation of media. If a stock solution becomes cloudy, discard.

5. Wrap all petri dishes and culture tubes with Parafilm to prevent insect contamination and desiccation of the medium.

6. Approximately 50% of the rice seeds from any one cultivar will initiate embryogenic callus. Visual examination under a dissection microscope is important.

REFERENCES

Bhaskaran, S., Rigoldi, M., and Smith, R. H. (1992) Developmental potential of sorghum shoot apices in culture. *J. Plant Physiol.* **140,** 481–484.

Bhaskaran, S., and Smith, R. H. (1988) Enhanced somatic embryogenesis in *Sorghum bicolor* from shoot tip culture. *In Vitro Cell Dev. Biol.* **24,** 65–70.

Bhaskaran, S., and Smith, R. H. (1989) Control of morphogenesis in sorghum by 2,4-dichloro-phenoxyacetic acid and cytokinins. *Ann. Bot.* **64,** 217–224.

Bhaskaran, S., and Smith, R. H. (1990) Regeneration in cereal tissue culture: A review. *Crop Sci.* **30,** 1328–1337.

Kyozuka, J., and Shimamoto, K. (1993) Transgenic rice plants: Tools for studies in gene regulation and crop improvement. *In* "Transgenic Plants, Fundamentals and Applications" (A. Hiatt, ed.), pp. 173–194. Marcel Dekker, New York.

Murashige, T., and Skoog, F. (1962) A revised medium for rapid growth and bioassays with tobacco tissue cultures. *Physiol. Plant.* **15,** 473–497.

Peterson, G., and Smith, R. (1991) Effect of abscisic acid and callus size on regeneration of American and international rice varieties. *Plant Cell Rep.* **10,** 35–38.

Smith, R. H. (1992) "Plant Tissue Culture, Techniques and Experiments," pp. 1–27. Academic Press, San Diego.

Smith, R. H., Bhaskaran, S., and Schertz, K. (1983) Sorghum plant regeneration from aluminum selection media. *Plant Cell Rep.* **2,** 129–132.

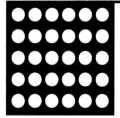

Isolation, Culture, and Plant Regeneration from Protoplasts

German Spangenberg and Ingo Potrykus

I. Introduction

Plant protoplasts are cells deprived of their walls. Enzymatically isolated protoplasts represent an ideal system to demonstrate totipotency of single plant cells, as plant regeneration from cultured protoplasts is possible. In addition, protoplasts are target cells for performing genetic manipulations *in vitro,* such as direct gene transfer for transient expression assays or for stable transformations to generate transgenic plants, and protoplast fusion for the production of somatic hybrid/cybrid plants. An example of the isolation, culture, and regeneration of plants is given for leaf protoplasts obtained from axenic shoot cultures of *Nicotiana tabacum* L. cv. Petit Havana SR1 (Maliga *et al.,* 1973), a widely used tobacco genotype with model character. The protoplasts are isolated following a modified protocol of Nagy and Maliga (1976) and grown in bead-type culture (Shillito *et al.,* 1983).

Plant regeneration from protoplasts is according to Potrykus and Shillito (1986) with modifications.

II. Materials and Instrumentation

A source for the standard components of the culture media required is given in Table I. Agar (Merck), agarose (type I, Sigma), and low-melting-temperature Sea Plaque agarose (FMC BioProducts) are used as gelling agents. Cellulase "Onozuka" R10 and Macerozyme R10 were from Yakult Pharmaceutical Ind. Co., Ltd.

Other chemicals (Tween 80, KOH, NH$_4$OH, NaCl, KCl, and CaCl$_2$) were purchased from Merck; Ca(OCl)$_2$ (~65%) was from Roth GmbH & Company. Parafilm "M" (ABS, Cat. No. 46 002 00, Auer Bittmann Soulie AG) was used as sealing tape. Sterile disposable bottle-top filters (Zapcap S, 0.2 μm, Cat. No. 67250) and disposable filter holders (FP 030/3, 0.2 μm, Cat. No. 462200) were filter-sterilization units from Schleicher & Schuell. Also used were sterile disposable pipettes: 1 ml (Falcon, Cat. No. 7521, Becton Dickinson), 2-ml Stripette (Costar, Cat. No. 4021), and 10 ml (Falcon, Cat. No. 7551); sterile plastic centrifuge tubes with screw caps (14 ml, Greiner, Cat. No. 163160, Greiner GmbH); sterile plastic culture dishes (9-cm Sterilin dish, Cat. No. 101R20, Bibby Sterilin Ltd.), 6-cm Easy Grip dish (Falcon, Cat. No. 3004); and sterile plastic culture vessels (9 cm diameter, 305 ml, Greiner, Cat. No. 972161). Culture glass jars (400-ml glass jars, ABS, Cat. No. 9025204, and 765-ml glass jars, ABS, Cat. No. 9025205) with twist-off metallic caps, perforated with one 8-mm- or 10-mm-diameter hole, respectively, and closed with a Ceapren plug (22 mm, Greiner, Cat. No. 323070, and 26 mm, Greiner, Cat. No. 330070,

TABLE I   Compositions of the Media Used

Media component		A	H	K3	MS	MS morpho
Macro elements (mg/l final concentration):						
KNO₃	[Merck]	1010	1900	2500	1900	1900
NH₄NO₃	[Merck]	800	600	250	1650	1650
CaCl₂ x 2H₂O	[Merck]	440	600	900	440	730
MgSO₄ x 7H₂O	[Merck]	740	300	250	370	370
(NH₄)₂SO₄	[Merck]			250		
KH₂PO₄	[Merck]	136	170		170	170
NaH₂PO₄ x H₂O	[Merck]			150		
(NH₄) Succinate	[ICN]	50				
CaHPO₄	[Sigma]			50		
Micro elements (mg/l final concentration):						
Na₂EDTA	[Fluka]	37.3	37.3	37.3	37.3	37.3
FeSO₄ x 7H₂O	[Merck]	27.8	27.8	27.8	27.8	27.8
H₃BO₃	[Merck]	3.0	3.0	3.0	6.2	6.2
KI	[Merck]	0.75	0.75	0.75	0.83	0.83
MnSO₄ x H₂O	[Merck]	10.0	10.0	10.0	16.9	16.9
ZnSO₄ x 7H₂O	[Merck]	2.0	2.0	2.0	8.6	8.6
CuSO₄ x 5H₂O	[Merck]	0.025	0.025	0.025	0.025	0.025
Na₂MoO₄ x 2H₂O	[Merck]	0.25	0.25	0.25	0.25	0.25
CoCl₂ x 6H₂O	[Merck]	0.025	0.025	0.025	0.025	0.025
Carbohydrates (g/l final concentration):						
D(+) Sucrose	[Roth]	30	0.125	102.69	10	30
D(+) Glucose x 1H₂O	[Sigma]		68.40			
D- Mannitol	[Sigma]	50	0.125			
D- Sorbitol	[Merck]		0.125			
D- Cellobiose	[Serva]		0.125			
D(-) Fructose	[Sigma]		0.125			
D(+) Mannose	[Merck]		0.125			
L(+) Rhamnose	[Fluka]		0.125			
D(-) Ribose	[Fluka]		0.125			
D(+) Xylose	[Fluka]		0.125	0.25		
myo-Inositol	[Merck]	0.1	0.1	0.1	0.1	0.1
Hormones (mg/l final concentration):						
2,4-D (2,4-Dichlorophenoxyacetic acid)	[Serva]		0.1	0.1		
NAA (1-naphthylacetic acid)	[Sigma]	0.1	1.0	1.0		0.1
BAP (6-benzylaminopurine)	[Sigma]	1.0	0.2	0.2		1.0
Vitamins (mg/l final concentration):						
Pyridoxine HCl	[Merck]	1.0	1.0	1.0	0.5	0.1
Thiamine HCl	[Merck]	10.0	10.0	10.0	0.1	0.1
Nicotinamide	[BRL]		1.0			
Nicotinic acid	[Merck]	1.0		1.0	0.5	0.1
Folic acid	[Merck]		0.2			
D- Ca-Pantothenate	[Merck]		0.5			1.0
p-Aminobenzoic acid	[Sigma]		0.01			
Choline chloride	[Sigma]		0.5			
Riboflavin	[Sigma]		0.1			
L(+) Ascorbic acid	[Merck]		1.0			
Vitamin A	[Serva]		0.005			
Vitamin D₃	[Serva]		0.005			
Vitamin B₁₂	[Merck]		0.01			
D- Biotin	[Sigma]		0.005			
Organic acids (mg/l final concentration):						
Sodium pyruvate	[Sigma]		5			
Citric acid	[Sigma]		10			
Malic acid	[Sigma]		10			
Fumaric acid	[Fluka]		10			
Other organics (mg/l final concentration):						
Glycine	[Serva]				2.0	
Casein hydrolysate	[Fluka]		250			

respectively), provided optimal gas exchange conditions for growth of shoot cultures.

A laminar flow hood with horizontal flow (type CHR400, Concept GmbH), a rotary shaker (Infors type RC-406, Infors AG) a bench centrifuge with swing-out rotor (Hettich Universal with 8 × 15-g swing-out rotor, Hettich AG), a water bath (Haake F3, Haake Messtechnik GmbH), a 100-μm stainless-steel mesh sieve (Saulas), a hemocytometer (Fuchs-Rosenthal 0.2-mm depth or Jessen 0.4-mm depth), long forceps (16 cm, bent tip, Gerald, Cat. No. 06.60.91, Medicon), and scalpel (type 5, Cat. No. 2982, Swann-Morton Ltd.) with sterile surgical blades (type 10, Cat. No. 0223, Swann-Morton Ltd.) were used.

Six-week-old sterile shoot cultures of *N. tabacum* cv. Petit Havana SR1 are required as plant material.

III. Procedures

A. ISOLATION AND CULTURE OF MESOPHYLL PROTOPLASTS FROM TOBACCO SHOOT CULTURES

This procedure is modified from those of Nagy and Maliga (1976) and Shillito *et al.* (1983).

Solutions

1. *Enzyme solution:* Dissolve 1.2% (w/v) cellulase "Onozuka" R10 and 0.6% (w/v) Macerozyme R10 in K4 medium [medium K3 (Table 1) with 0.4 M instead of 0.3 M sucrose]. Spin down (Sorvall centrifuge, DuPont Co. SS-34 rotor, at 7000 rpm for 10 min) to pellet starch contaminating the enzyme preparations. Adjust to pH 5.6 with KOH and filter-sterilize (0.2-μm pore size). Store at 4°C for no longer than 3–4 weeks.

2. *Washing solution W5* (Menczel *et al.*, 1981): Dissolve 154 mM NaCl, 125 mM CaCl$_2$, 5 mM KCl, and 5 mM glucose in distilled water, adjust to pH 5.8 with KOH, and autoclave. Store at room temperature.

3. *Media:* The compositions of the media used at the final concentrations of their individual ingredients is given in Table I:

Medium A	Modified from Caboche (1980)
Medium H	Modified from Potrykus and Shillito (1986); modified Kao medium 5p from Kao and Michayluk (1975)
Medium K3	Modified from Nagy and Maliga (1976)
Medium MS	Murashige and Skoog (1962)
Medium MS morpho	Spangenberg *et al.* (1990)

4. *Stock solutions for preparation of media:* For all culture media used, prepare macroelements as 10-fold concentrated stocks. Microelements, vitamins, and organic acid stock solutions are 100-fold concentrated in all cases. For preparation of 1000 ml microelement stock, dissolve first Na$_2$EDTA (3.73 g) and FeSO$_4 \cdot$7H$_2$O (2.78 g) separately in 400 ml distilled water each. Mix dissolved solutions and heat at ca. 60°C. After cooling down, add remaining stock ingredients dissolved in distilled water and complete to 1000 ml. Adjust to pH 5.5 with concentrated NH$_4$OH in stock solution of organic acids for medium H (see Table I) only. Stock solutions of carbohydrates are 10-fold concentrated and without glucose for medium H, 100-fold concentrated and without sucrose for media K3, MS, and MS morpho, and 100-fold concentrated but without sucrose and mannitol for medium A (see Table I). Those carbohydrates required at higher concentrations, and thus not included in the concentrated stocks, are weighed and directly added while preparing media at their final concentrations. Prepare all stock solutions in glass-distilled water and keep at −20°C. Dissolve hormones (BAP, NAA, and 2,4-D) in 1 M KOH and dilute with distilled water to prepare 100 mg/liter concentrated stocks. Filter-sterilize stock solutions of hormones and keep at 4°C.

5. *Medium preparation:* Prepare the culture media using stock solutions (as indicated above) and dilute them with glass-distilled water. Adjust to pH 5.7 with KOH for media A and K3 and autoclave (121°C, 1 bar, 15 min). Filter-sterilize medium H (0.2-μm pore size). Keep sterile liquid media A, H, and K3 in autoclaved glass bottles (500 and 250 ml, respectively) at 4°C. Medium K4 is prepared as medium K3 but contains 0.4 M sucrose final concentration (136.91 g/liter sucrose instead of 102.69 g/liter; see Table I).

Prepare a 1:1 mixture of media K3 and H solidified with 0.6% (w/v) low-gelling-temperature Sea Plaque agarose. Autoclave dry agarose first, add sterile K3 medium, melt in a microwave oven, and after cooling to 45°C, add filter-sterilized medium H.

Adjust to pH 5.8 with KOH for medium MS, add 0.8% (w/v) agar, and autoclave. Pour 100-ml fractions of melted medium in autoclaved culture glass jars (400 and 765 ml) and store at room temperature.

To prepare medium MS morpho solidified with 0.6% (w/v) agarose (agarose type I, Sigma), first autoclave the agarose in three-fourths of the required volume of distilled water. Separately, dilute corresponding stock solutions and other medium ingredients to complete remaining fourth of final volume with distilled water, and after filter-sterilization, add it to the autoclaved, melted agarose to yield the final medium. Pour 80- to 100-ml fractions of melted MS morpho medium in 9-cm sterile plastic culture vessels and in autoclaved culture glass jars (400 ml) and store at room temperature.

Steps

1. Take two to four fully expanded leaves of a 6-week-old shoot culture (Color Plate 11A) under sterile conditions (work in laminar flow hood, use sterilized forceps, scalpel, and blades) and place them in a 9-cm plastic culture dish. Wet the leaves thoroughly with enzyme solution and remove the midribs (Color Plate 11B).

2. Cut the leaf halves into pieces (8–12 mm^2) and transfer leaf pieces bottom side down into a 9-cm dish containing 12 ml enzyme solution (Color Plate 11B). Seal the dish with Parafilm and incubate overnight (14–18 hr) at 25°C in the dark without shaking.

3. Gently agitate the digest. Release of protoplasts from leaf debris is aided by smoothly pumping once the suspension up and down a 10-ml pipette with a wide opening (plastic pipette with broken off tip) (Color Plate 11C). Take up the protoplast suspension with a 10-ml pipette and pour through a 100-μm stainless steel mesh sieve on a 100-ml glass beaker (Color Plate 11C). Add 6–8 ml of K4 medium to the dish and disrupt remaining tissue by carefully pumping it up and down the pipette. Sieve this suspension too. Collect both fractions (18–20 ml) in the glass beaker.

4. Mix the protoplast suspension gently and distribute into two 14-ml sterile plastic centrifuge tubes. Carefully overlay the suspension with 1 ml W5 solution (Color Plate 11D). Spin for 7–10 min at 80 g (Hettich Universal bench centrifuge, swing-out rotor, 35% speed). Protoplasts will float at the interphase (Color Plate 11D).

5. Remove the protoplasts at the interphase with a 2-ml pipette, taking as little as possible of the lower phase. Transfer the protoplasts to one new 14-ml centrifuge tube, combining the protoplasts from two interphases.

6. Gradually add 8–10 ml W5 solution, close the tube, and resuspend the protoplasts by gentle tilting the capped tube. Pellet the protoplasts [spin 70 g

(Hettich Universal bench centrifuge, 30% speed) for 5 min]. Remove the supernatant. Repeat this step.

7. Resuspend protoplast pellet in 5–10 ml W5 solution. To determine protoplast yield, with a 1-ml pipette take up a 100-μl aliquot of the protoplast suspension, add 900 μl W5 solution to it, and count the protoplasts in a hemocytometer.

8. Pellet the protoplasts [spin 70 g (Hettich Universal bench centrifuge, 30% speed) for 5 min]. Remove the supernatant and resuspend protoplast pellet in medium K3 (containing 0.3 M sucrose) to yield a suspension with a cell density of 1×10^6 protoplasts/ml.

9. Place 0.5 ml of the protoplast suspension (ca. 5×10^5 protoplasts) in a 6-cm Falcon petri dish. Add 4.5 ml prewarmed (melt in a microwave oven and keep in a water bath at 40–45°C) 1:1 mixture of media K3 and H containing 0.6% Sea Plaque agarose. Mix gently and allow to set.

10. When medium is solidified (after 20–30 min), seal the dishes with Parafilm and culture the protoplasts for 24 hr in the dark at 24°C (Color Plate 11E), followed by 6 days in continuous dim light (5 μE m^{-2} sec^{-1}, Osram L36 W/21 Lumilux white tubes), where first and multiple cell divisions occur (Color Plate 11F).

11. Cut the agarose containing the dividing protoplasts (Color Plate 11G) into quadrants and place these in 50 ml of medium A (Table I) in a 9-cm plastic culture vessel (Color Plate 11H). Incubate at 24°C in continuous dim light on a rotary shaker at 80 rpm.

12. After 1–2 weeks a lawn of protoplast-derived colonies is formed within the agarose sectors floating in liquid medium A (Color Plates 11I and J) in bead-type culture (Shillito *et al.*, 1983) under continuous shaking and the same culture conditions.

B. REGENERATION OF PLANTS FROM COLONIES OBTAINED FROM TOBACCO MESOPHYLL PROTOPLASTS

This procedure is modified from the one of Potrykus and Shillito (1986).

Steps

1. Microcalli growing within the agarose quadrants (Color Plate 12A) 3–4 weeks after plating of protoplasts become visible, and many are released from the disintegrating agarose beads (Color Plate 12B) 4–5 weeks after the start of the experiment.

2. After a total of 5–6 weeks, transfer protoplast-derived colonies (when 2–3 mm in diameter) onto medium MS morpho solidified with 0.6% (w/v) agarose in 9-cm culture vessels and keep for the following 1–2 weeks at 24°C in continuous dim light (5 μE m^{-2} sec^{-1}, Osram L36 W/21 Lumilux white tubes), where calli proliferate and grow to 8–10 mm in diameter (Color Plate 12C).

3. Subculture protoplast-derived calli (when 1–2 cm in diameter) onto medium MS morpho in culture glass jars (Color Plate 12D), and within the next 1–2 weeks, multiple shoots are induced on the regenerating calli (Color Plate 12E).

4. Normal-looking outgrowing shoots from the protoplast-derived calli (Color Plate 12F) are formed in the next 1–2 weeks, when kept on medium MS morpho in the same glass jars at 24°C in 16 hr/day light (20 μE m^{-2} sec^{-1}, Osram L36 W/21 Lumilux white tubes).

5. When shoots grow to 3–4 cm (Color Plate 12F), they can be cut off and transferred onto 0.8% (w/v) agar-solidified medium MS in culture glass jars. When kept under same culture conditions, roots will form in 1–3 weeks (Color Plate 12G).

6. Treat plantlets with an established root system (Color Plate 12G) as shoot cultures (see Section A). Alternatively, well-rooted shoots are transferred to potting soil, after carefully removing agar rests from the roots, and kept in a humid atmosphere for the first week. Potted plants are hardened off for a further 1–3 weeks (Color Plate 12H) and grown under greenhouse conditions [with 28°C (light period)/16°C (dark period) temperature regime; 14 hr/day light (145 μE m^{-2} sec^{-1}, daylight supplemented with Phillips HPL N400W mercury lamps) and 60–95% relative humidity], where they flower 2–3 months later (Color Plate 12I).

IV. Comments

Using the protocol described here, it is possible to isolate $3–4 \times 10^6$ protoplasts from one dish (see Section IIIA, step 2). Plating efficiencies (number of colonies/number of plated protoplasts) higher than 80% are usual (Color Plate 11). Every protoplast-derived colony plated on MS morpho should regenerate shoots that can be rooted (Color Plate 12). Rooted shoots can already be obtained 3 months after protoplast plating.

V. Pitfalls

1. Perform all manipulations under sterile conditions (in a horizontal laminar flow hood) and use sterile materials.

2. Use new blades for cutting sectors of leaves from shoot cultures. Avoid excessive injury to leaf tissue.

3. Throughout the protocol, treat protoplast suspension gently, pipet smoothly, and avoid strong shaking of tubes. For all centrifugation steps, be sure that the speed builds up slowly.

4. Plate protoplasts at the correct cell density $(1–2 \times 10^5/\text{ml})$.

5. After plating of protoplasts in melted agarose-containing culture medium, do not move the culture dish until the medium is solidified (see Section IIIA, steps 9 and 10).

REFERENCES

Caboche, M. (1980) Nutritional requirements of protoplast derived haploid tobacco cells grown at low densities in liquid medium. *Planta* **149**, 7–18.

Kao, K. N., and Michayluk, M. R. (1975) Nutritional requirements for growth of *Vicia hajastana* cells at very low population density in liquid medium. *Planta* **126**, 105–110.

Maliga, P., Breznovitz, A., and Marton, L. (1973) Streptomycin resistant plants from callus cultures of tobacco. *Nature New Biol.* **244**, 29–30.

Menczel, L., Nagy, F., Kiss, Z., and Maliga, P. (1981) Streptomycin resistant and sensitive somatic hybrids of *N. tabacum* + *N. knigthiana*: Correlation of resistance to *N. tabacum* plastids. *Theor. Appl. Genet.* **59**, 191–195.

Murashige, T., and Skoog, F. (1962) A revised medium for rapid growth and bioassays with tobacco tissue cultures. *Physiol. Plant.* **15**, 473–497.

Nagy, J. I., and Maliga, P. (1976). Callus induction and plant regeneration from mesophyll protoplasts of *N. sylvestris*. *Z. Pflanzenphysiol.* 78, 453–455.

Potrykus, I., and Shillito, R. D. (1986). Protoplasts: Isolation, culture, plant regeneration. *In* "Methods in Enzymology" (A. Weissbach and H. Weissbach, eds.), Vol. 118, pp. 549–578. Academic Press, San Diego.

Shillito, R. D., Paszkowski, J., and Potrykus, I. (1983) Agarose plating and a bead-type culture technique enable and stimulate development of protoplast-derived colonies in a number of plant species. *Plant Cell Rep.* 2, 244–247.

Spangenberg, G., Osusky, M., Oliveira, M. M., Freydl, E., Nagel, J., Pais, M. S., and Potrykus, I. (1990) Somatic hybridization by microfusion of defined protoplast pairs in *Nicotiana*: Morphological, genetic, and molecular characterization. *Theor. Appl. Genet.* 80, 577–587.

PART 2

VIRUSES

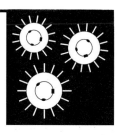

Propagation and Purification of Polyoma and Simian Virus 40

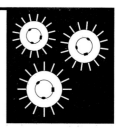

Roland Sahli and Peter Beard

I. Introduction

Murine polyoma and simian virus 40 (SV40) are members of the polyomaviruses, which also include the human BK and JC viruses. They constitute with the papillomaviruses the family Papovaviridae. Polyoma and SV40 have the ability to induce tumors in animals and to transform cells in culture (Tooze, 1981). This oncogenic property of the polyomaviruses has attracted much interest and research. Polyomaviruses have also provided useful models to study the regulation of gene expression, DNA replication, and chromatin structure. The genetic information of the polyomaviruses is carried by a circular double-stranded DNA molecule of approximately 5200 base pairs. In lytically infected cells, two sets of viral proteins are expressed in a temporally regulated fashion: the tumor (T) antigens in the early phase of the viral life cycle and the coat proteins late in infection. Tumor formation results from the expression of the T antigens in nonproductively infected cells. The viral DNA molecule is associated with cellular histones and this minichromosome is encapsidated to form a virion about 45 nm in diameter. The structure of the SV40 capsid (and by extension that of polyoma) has been determined at 3.8-Å resolution (Liddington et al., 1991), using crystals of highly purified virions prepared by the method we describe here. The capsid has icosahedral symmetry. It is made up of 360 copies of VP1, the major coat protein, arranged into 72 pentamers. The two minor coat proteins, VP2 and VP3, are internal to the virion and may form a bridge between the minichromosome and the VP1 shell (Liddington et al., 1991; Griffith et al., 1992). An electron micrograph of purified SV40 virions and the gel electrophoretic profile of the virion proteins are shown in Figs. 1B and C, respectively.

II. Materials and Instrumentation

CsCl (Cat. No. 757306) is from Boehringer–Mannheim. Leupeptin (Cat. No. L-2884), phenylmethylsulfonyl fluoride (PMSF, Cat. No. P-7626), neutral red (Cat. No. N-6634), and sucrose (Cat. No. M-168.4) are from Sigma. NaCl (Cat. No. 6404), $MgCl_2 \cdot 6H_2O$ (Cat. No. 5833), KCl (Cat. No. 4936), $CaCl_2 \cdot 2H_2O$ (Cat. No. 2382), and sodium azide (Cat. No. 6688) are from Merck. N-[2-Hydroxyethyl]-piperazine-N'-[2-ethanesulfonic acid] (Hepes, Cat. No. 391338) is from Calbiochem. Falcon petri dishes of 9-cm (Cat. No. 3003) and 3.5-cm (Cat. No. 3001) diameter are from Becton Dickinson. Seaplaque agarose (Cat. No. 50103) is from FMC. Tenfold concentrated Dulbecco's minimal essential medium (10× DMEM, Cat. No. F0455), fetal calf serum (Cat. No. S0115), 7.5% sodium bicarbonate (Cat.

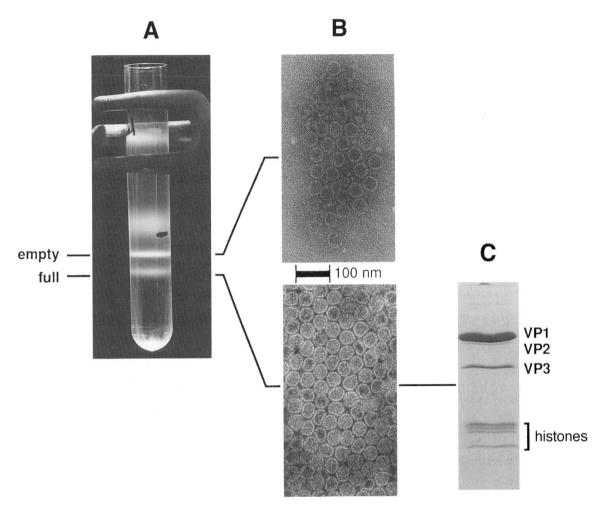

FIGURE 1 Purification of polyomaviruses. (A) Step gradient illuminated from the top showing the two bands of empty and full particles. The other bands correspond to cellular material. (B) Electron micrographs of dialyzed particles from the bands shown in panel A. Particles were negatively stained with sodium phosphotungstate. At this stage of the purification, it is difcult to avoid contamination of each kind of particles by the other (notice the presence of full virus in the empty capsid preparation and vice versa). (C) Electrophoretic profile in a 15% polyacrylamide gel of proteins from purified SV40 virions. The positions of the three viral proteins (VP1, VP2, and VP3) and of histones are indicated.

No. L1713), 200 mM L-glutamine (Cat. No. K0282), 100 mM sodium butyrate (Cat. No. L0473), and penicillin–streptomycin (10,000 units/ml and 10,000 μg/ml, respectively, Cat. No. A2212) are from Biochrom. Neuraminidase (Cat. No. RDE 30-899D) is from Microbiological Associates. Dialysis tubing with a 3500 molecular weight cutoff (Spectra/Por 3, Cat. No. 132720) is from Spectrum. Ultracentrifuge tubes (for rotors SW-28, Cat. No. 344058; SW-40 Ti, Cat. No. 344060; SW-60 Ti, Cat. No. 344062, 70.1 Ti, Cat. No. 344085) are from Beckman.

The ultracentrifuge (L8-70) and rotors (SW-28, SW-40 Ti, SW-60 Ti, and 70.1 Ti) are from Beckman, and the table-top centrifuge (Technospin with swing-out rotor) is from Sorvall. The ultrasonifier (Soniprep 150 with a 3-mm probe) and 20-ml glass tubes (Cat. No. 34411-8163) with sealing caps (Cat. No. 34411-4094) are from MSE.

III. Procedures

A. CELL CULTURE TECHNIQUES

While polyoma and SV40 are best propagated in primary kidney cell cultures of murine or monkey origin, respectively, a simpler alternative that gives reasonably good yields of viruses is to infect permanent cell lines: NIH3T6 cells for polyoma, and CV1 cells for SV40. Titers of up to 10^9 plaque-forming units per milliliter (PFU/ml) can be achieved with these cell lines (Beard and Türler, 1985). Best yields of virions are obtained when the infection is done at low multiplicity (less than 0.1 PFU/cell). Estimation of the viral titer and genetic purification of the virus is done by plaque assay on Swiss 3T3 cells for polyoma and CV1 cells for SV40.

Solutions

Only double-distilled or Milli-Q water is used to prepare all solutions.

1. *1× DMEM:* To prepare 500 ml, add 50 ml of 10× DMEM to 410 ml of sterile water; then add 5 ml of penicillin–streptomycin, 25 ml of sodium bicarbonate, 5 ml of L-glutamine, and 5 ml of sodium butyrate.

2. *2× DMEM:* To prepare 500 ml, add 100 ml of 10× DMEM to 400 ml of sterile water.

3. *2.5% Seaplaque agarose:* Add 2.5 g of Seaplaque agarose to 100 ml of water. Sterilize by autoclaving.

4. *Overlay medium:* Equilibrate 2× DMEM, fetal calf serum, and additives at 45°C. Melt 2.5% Seaplaque agarose in a microwave oven and cool to 45°C. To prepare 100 ml, mix 50 ml of 2× DMEM, 10 ml (3T3 cells) or 2 ml (CV1 cells) of FCS, and 40 ml of agarose. Then add 1 ml of penicillin–streptomycin, 4 ml of sodium bicarbonate, 1 ml of sodium butyrate, and 1 ml of L-glutamine. Keep at 45°C.

5. *Neutral red:* Dissolve 1 g of neutral red in 100 ml of water. Sterilize by autoclaving.

6. *Staining solution:* Mix 1 ml of 1% neutral red and 2 ml of FCS in 100 ml of 1× DMEM.

1. Cell Lines

All the cell lines mentioned here can be cultured in DMEM supplemented with FCS, 10% for 3T3 cells and 5% for 3T6 and CV1 cells. They are cultured at 37°C in a humidified atmosphere of 5% CO_2. They should be passaged just before they reach confluence once a week and fed with fresh medium twice a week.

2. Plaque Assay of Polyoma

Steps

1. Trypsinize subconfluent 3T3 monolayers from 9-cm petri dishes (5×10^6 cells per dish) and resuspend the cells in a small volume of 1× DMEM supplemented with 10% FCS. Count the cells in a hemocytometer. Adjust the cell concentration to 75,000 cells/ml. One 9-cm dish provides enough cells for 30 assays.

2. Distribute evenly 2 ml of suspension (150,000 cells) in 3.5-cm dishes. It is

important that the cells be homogeneously distributed in the dish. Include two dishes for the uninfected controls. Return the cells to the 37°C incubator.

3. Prepare the virus stock for infection. For this, sonicate briefly 5 ml of the lysate in a 20-ml MSE tube equipped with a sealing cap. Warm the suspension at 45°C for 15 min, and discard debris by centrifugation (800 g, 10 min).

4. Prepare 20-fold serial dilutions of the virus stock in 1× DMEM to obtain final dilutions of 400, 8000, 160,000, and 3,200,000.

5. Aspirate medium from four dishes at a time, and infect cells in duplicate with 0.2 ml of each dilution.

6. Return the cells to the 37°C incubator for 90 min. Rock the dishes every 15 min.

7. During the adsorption period prepare the overlay medium, 2.5 ml per dish.

8. At the end of the adsorption period aspirate the inoculum, four dishes at a time, and immediately add 2.5 ml overlay. Place the dishes at room temperature until the overlay solidifies. Return the dishes to the 37°C incubator.

9. Starting at day 6 postinfection, count the plaques by observing the dishes against a black background. The plaques appear as white spots when the dishes are lit from the side. The number of plaques increases with time and is stable after 8 days. The plaques are confirmed by phase-contrast microscopic examination. They consist of local necrotic areas often surrounded by vacuolated cells.

3. Plaque Assay of SV40

The procedure is similar to the polyoma assay with some modifications.

Steps

1–8. Confluent monolayers of CV1 cells are used for infection, four dishes per dilution (two sets of duplicates). Check the color of the medium 4 to 5 days after infection. If yellow, add another 1 ml overlay.

9. After 6 days, stain one set of cells with 2.5 ml staining solution. Leave overnight in the incubator. Repeat this procedure with the other set of cells after 8 days.

10. Remove the staining solution and put the dishes back in the incubator for 1–2 hr; then count the plaques. These appear as white areas in a red background of living cells. Count the plaques after 1 or 2 more days. The number of plaques should be stable after 10 days.

4. Propagation of Polyoma

The following procedure is for 20 petri dishes of 9-cm diameter (which yields about 220 ml of infected cell lysate).

Steps

1. Split 3T6 cells from a confluent monolayer into 21 petri dishes.

2. When the plates are 30% confluent (there are about 3×10^6 cells on a 30% confluent 9-cm dish), aspirate the medium and inoculate 20 cultures with 0.5 ml of a dilution of a virus stock suspension giving a multiplicity of infection (m.o.i.) of 0.01–0.05 (about $3–5 \times 10^4$ PFU). Incubate the dishes at 37°C in a CO$_2$

incubator for 90 min. Rock the dishes every 15 min. After the adsorption period, feed the cells with 8 ml of prewarmed DMEM containing 5% FCS and return the cultures to the incubator. Inoculate one culture with medium only as a control.

3. Add 4 ml fresh medium 4 days after infection. Compare the infected cell monolayer with the control under the microscope every day thereafter. Cell lysis in the infected dishes is complete 6 to 10 days postinfection.

5. Propagation of SV40

Steps

1. Split CV1 cells from two confluent 9-cm petri dishes into 21 dishes.

2/3. When the cells form a confluent monolayer (there are about 5×10^6 to 10^7 cells on a 9-cm dish), aspirate the medium, and inoculate 20 cultures with 0.5 ml of a dilution of a virus stock suspension giving a m.o.i. of 0.01–0.05 (about 10^5 PFU). Continue as above for polyoma. Cell lysis in the infected dishes is complete 8 to 10 days postinfection.

B. PURIFICATION OF VIRIONS

The following procedure is for 20 petri dishes of 9-cm diameter (220 ml lysate).

Solutions

Unless stated otherwise, solutions are sterilized by autoclaving.

1. *0.5 M Hepes, pH 5.4:* dissolve 11.9 g Hepes in water. Adjust the volume to 100 ml.

2. *1 M Hepes, pH 7.9:* Dissolve 23.8 g Hepes in water up to 70 ml. Adjust the pH to 7.9 with 5 N NaOH. Make to 100 ml with water.

3. *1 M CaCl$_2$:* Dissolve 14.7 g CaCl$_2 \cdot 2$ H$_2$O in water up to 100 ml. Filter-sterilize.

4. *1 M KCl:* Dissolve 7.5 g of KCl in water up to 100 ml. Filter-sterilize.

5. *1 M MgCl$_2$:* Dissolve 20.3 g of MgCl$_2 \cdot 6$ H$_2$O in water up to 100 ml. Filter-sterilize.

6. *1.33 g/ml CsCl:* Dissolve 33.5 g of CsCl in 67 ml of 10 mM Hepes, pH 7.9 (10 ml of 1 mM Hepes, pH 7.9, added to 90 ml of sterile water). Adjust the refractive index of the solution to 1.365 with 10 mM Hepes or CsCl as required. Do not sterilize.

7. *10× Buffer A (100 mM Hepes 7.9, 10 mM CaCl$_2$, 10 mM MgCl$_2$, 50 mM KCl):* To 39.5 ml water, add 5 ml 1 M Hepes, pH 7.9, 0.5 ml 1 M CaCl$_2$, 0.5 ml 1 M MgCl$_2$, and 2.5 ml 1 M KCl. Filter-sterilize.

8. *Buffer A:* For 100 ml, add 10 ml 10× buffer A to 90 ml of sterile water.

9. *25 mM Leupeptin:* Dissolve 12 mg leupeptin in water up to 1 ml. Store in aliquots at −20°C.

10. *5 M NaCl:* Dissolve 146 g of NaCl in water up to 500 ml.

11. *Neuraminidase:* Resuspend 10,000 units in 10 ml of sterile water. Store in aliquots at −20°C.

12. *100 mM PMSF:* Dissolve 174 mg of PMSF in 10 ml isopropanol. Store in aliquots at −20°C.

13. *10% sodium azide:* Dissolve 1 g sodium azide in water to a final volume of 10 ml.

14. *15% sucrose:* To make 50 ml, mix 7.5 g sucrose to 5 ml 10× buffer A and 10 ml 5 *M* NaCl and adjust to 50 ml with water. Filter sterilize.

15. *Virion buffer (10 mM Hepes 7.9, 150 mM NaCl, 1 mM CaCl₂):* To 960 ml of sterile water, add 10 ml 1 *M* Hepes, pH 7.9, 30 ml 5 *M* NaCl, and 1 ml 1 *M* CaCl₂.

C. PURIFICATION OF POLYOMA

Polyoma is not easy to purify as it tends to remain associated with cell debris. Neuraminidase treatment is necessary to free the virions from cell debris.

Steps

1. Adjust the pH of the lysate to pH 6–6.5 with a few milliliters of 0.5 *M* Hepes, pH 5.4 (the lysate should turn yellow). Cool the lysate to 4°C and pellet the cell debris and the associated virus by centrifugation at 800 *g* for 25 min at 4°C. Discard the supernant which should not contain more than 10% of virus material. Resuspend the pellet in 3 ml buffer A.

2. Transfer the suspension into a 20-ml MSE tube, and sonicate as in step 3 of the polyoma plaque assay to dissociate the aggregates.

3. Add to the suspension 50 μl of 0.5 *M* Hepes, pH 5.4, 15 μl of 100 m*M* PMSF, 3 μl of 25 m*M* leupeptin, and 300 μl of neuraminidase (300 units) (Garcea and Benjamin, 1983). Incubate at room temperature for 3 hr with occasional shaking.

4. Adjust the pH of the suspension to 7.9 with 150 μl of 1 *M* Hepes, pH 7.9. Incubate the suspension at 37°C for 30 min with occasional mixing. Remove the cell debris by centrifugation at 800 *g* for 10 min.

5. Add ¼ vol (about 0.9 ml) of 5 *M* NaCl to the supernatant (1 *M* final). NaCl is added to dissociate unstable viral intermediates and viral aggregates (Garcea and Benjamin, 1983).

6. Prepare two sucrose/CsCl step gradients as follows (Schaffhausen and Benjamin, 1976). Dispense 5–6 ml of a 1.33 g/ml CsCl solution into two SW-40 ultraclear tubes. Then add gently on top of the CsCl layer an equal volume of 15% sucrose. Avoid perturbing the interface between the sucrose and the CsCl solutions.

7. Layer one-half of the virus-containing supernatant per tube, and ultracentrifuge at 30,000 rpm in the SW-40 rotor for 2 hr 30 min at 20°C.

8. Observe the tubes against a black background with incident light. There should be two bands of viral material in the CsCl layer (Fig. 1A). The lower, sharp, bluish band contains full particles. The upper band contains empty capsids (Fig. 1B).

9. Collect the material from the bottom of the tube, for example, as described by Crawford (1969). For this, place the centrifuge tube vertically on a stand and discard half of the sucrose layer with a Pasteur pipette. Insert into the top of the tube a pierced rubber stopper equipped with tubing. Put a little silicon grease on the bottom of the tube and pierce a hole with a 25-gauge needle while holding the tubing closed. Release the flow of liquid by opening the tubing. Collect fractions when the lower band containing the full particles reaches the bottom of the tube.

10. To further purify empty and full particles, transfer the collected upper and lower bands, each into one 70.1 Ti ultraclear tube. Fill the tubes to an equal weight with CsCl at 1.33 g/ml (total volume of 13.5 ml). Seal the tubes by heating.

11. Ultracentrifuge to equilibrium at 55,000 rpm in the 70.1 Ti rotor for 22 hr at 20°C (or 36,000 rpm for at least 36 hr).

12. Observe the gradients as above and collect the appropriate band from the side using a 3-ml syringe fitted with a 25-gauge needle. Before collecting the material, pierce a hole at the top of the tube with a needle. To avoid spilling of CsCl, the needle is first inserted through a Kimwipe.

13. Transfer the collected material (1–2 ml) into a Spectra/Por 3 dialysis membrane (3500 molecular weight cutoff), and dialyze the virus two to three times each against 500 ml of virion buffer at 4°C.

14. Concentrate the virus by centrifugation for at least 45 min in the SW-60 Ti rotor at 50,000 rpm at room temperature. A glassy pellet should be obtained.

15. Resuspend the virus overnight at 4°C in 100 μl of virion buffer.

16. Transfer into a microtube. Rinse the SW-60 tube with a small volume of virion buffer and pool.

17. Store the virus preparation at 4°C. For long-term storage, add sodium azide to 0.05% final concentration.

D. Purification of SV40

Unlike polyoma, SV40 is not associated with cell debris. Thus, neuraminidase treatment of cell debris can be omitted; however, SV40 must be initially concentrated by ultracentrifugation of the infected cell lysate.

Steps

1. Freeze–thaw the infected cell lysate and pellet the cell debris at 800 g for 25 min at room temperature. Save the supernatant and resuspend the pellet in 10 ml of supernatant.

2. Freeze–thaw or sonicate the resuspended cell debris two times and incubate at 37°C for 30 min. Remove the cell debris by centrifugation as above (step 1).

3. Transfer both supernatants into six ultracentrifuge tubes (SW-28, 38 ml). Fill each tube to the same weight with PBS.

4. Pellet the viruses at 28,000 rpm in an ultracentrifuge for at least 1 hr 30 min at 4°C. Discard the supernatant carefully.

5. Resuspend the pellets in 0.4 ml of buffer A per tube. Transfer the virus suspension into a 20-ml MSE tube. Rinse the bottom of the SW-28 tubes two times with a total of 0.4 ml of buffer A and pool. Sonicate briefly and incubate the suspension at 37°C for 15 min. Discard insoluble material by centrifugation at 800 g for 10 min.

6. Continue as above for polyoma from step 5.

IV. Comments

These viruses are classified biohazard level 2. Therefore contaminated material should be handled according to this hazard level. Biosafety cabinets should be used to manipulate the cultures, and all contaminated material must be sterilized before disposal. This is achieved by soaking the contaminated glassware in Clorox or 5% hypochlorite. Disposable glassware and plastic are autoclaved.

Expect 1–3 μg of viral proteins per milliliter of lysate for the full particles.

3T3 cells from long-term passages have the tendency to form foci. These may be confused with polyomavirus plaques, which interferes with reading of the plaque assays. Also, early passages of 3T6 cells may be more permissive than late passages. It is therefore a good practice to use 3T3 or 3T6 cells that have been kept in culture for no more than a few weeks.

Polyoma strains forming large plaques may be purified according to the method given for SV40 as they do not bind to cell debris as strongly as those forming small plaques.

To concentrate virions (see Section IIIB, steps 14 and 15), centrifugation of the dialysate in a Centricon 100 microconcentrator can be performed. This is done at 1000 g in the Sorvall SS-34 rotor until the desired degree of concentration is obtained.

V. Pitfalls

1. Both polyoma and SV40 particles can be lost by nonspecific binding to various substrates. Collodion bags are not suitable to dialyze/concentrate these viruses.

2. Freezing and thawing of the purified virus preparation should be avoided as it may lead to precipitation of the virus.

REFERENCES

Beard, P., and Türler, H. (1985) *In* "Virology: a Practical Approach" (B. W. Mahy, ed.), pp. 169–192. IRL Press.

Crawford, L. (1969) *In* "Fundamental Techniques in Virology" (K. Habel and N. Salzman, eds.), pp. 79–80. Academic Press, New York/London.

Garcea, R., and Benjamin, T. (1983) Isolation and characterization of polyoma nucleoprotein complexes. *Virology* **130**, 65–75.

Griffith, J., Griffith, D., Rayment, I., Murakami, W., and Caspar, D. (1992) Inside polyomavirus at 25-Å resolution. *Nature* **355**, 652–654.

Liddington, R., Yan, Y., Moulai, J., Sahli, R., Benjamin, T., and Harrison, S. (1991) Structure of simian virus 40 at 3.8-Å resolution. *Nature* **354**, 278–284.

Schaffhausen, B., and Benjamin, T. (1976) Defficiency in histone acetylation in nontransforming host range mutants of polyoma virus. *Proc. Natl. Acad. Sci. USA* **73**, 1092–1096.

Tooze, J. (ed.) (1981) "DNA Tumor Viruses," 2nd ed. Cold Spring Harbor Laboratory, Press, Cold Spring Harbor, NY.

Construction and Propagation of Human Adenovirus Vectors

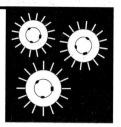

Mary Hitt, Andrew J. Bett, Ludvik Prevec, and Frank L. Graham

I. Introduction

Adenoviruses (Ads), which have been used extensively as a model system for molecular studies of mammalian cell DNA replication, transcription, and RNA processing, are now being increasingly investigated as potential mammalian expression vectors for gene therapy and for recombinant vaccines (Berkner, 1988). There are many reasons for this renewed popularity of Ad vectors: the 36,000-bp double-stranded DNA genome of Ad is relatively easy to manipulate by recombinant DNA techniques; the genome does not undergo rearrangement at a high rate; the viral particle is relatively stable; and the virus replicates efficiently in permissive cells, producing up to 10,000 plaque-forming units (PFU) per infected cell, thus enabling the production of high-titer viral stocks. Late in infection, most of the infected cell protein is virally encoded, potentiating the use of replication-proficient recombinant Ads as short-term high-level expression vectors. In nondividing, nonpermissive cells the viral genome may persist as an episome and continue to express for long periods. Finally, a variety of different cell types can be transformed by integration of Ad DNA into the host cell genome. If the efficiency of this can be increased, Ad recombinants may also be useful for gene transfer into mammalian cell chromosomes.

In this article, we describe methods for inserting foreign genes into the Ad genome and for purifying, growing, and titrating the recombinant viruses. Our vectors are based on the human Ad5 genome, the structure of which is shown in Fig. 1. In a normal infection, early genes (E1a, E1b, E2, E3, and E4) are expressed prior to DNA replication, and late gene expression, driven predominantly by the major late promoter at 16 map units (mu), occurs after DNA replication. Both the E1 and E3 regions can accept insertions or substitutions to generate helper-independent recombinant viruses. By deleting nonessential Ad sequences in each of these two regions, we have developed vector systems for inserting foreign genes up to 5.2 kb in length in E1 or up to 4.7 kb in E3. Both systems rely on *in vivo* recombination between shuttle plasmids containing the gene of interest flanked by Ad E1 or E3 sequences and a second plasmid containing essentially the entire Ad genome in a circular form (Fig. 2). For E1 insertions, the second plasmid, pJM17 (McGrory *et al.*, 1988), consists of a complete Ad5 genome with an E1 insert of pBR322 DNA which exceeds the packaging constraints of Ad, resulting in infectious progeny only by internal rearrangement (which is relatively rare) or by recombination with the shuttle plasmid containing the foreign gene. Because E1 is essential for Ad replication, it should be noted that these progeny can be rescued and propagated only in 293 cells (Graham *et al.*, 1977), a transformed human cell line

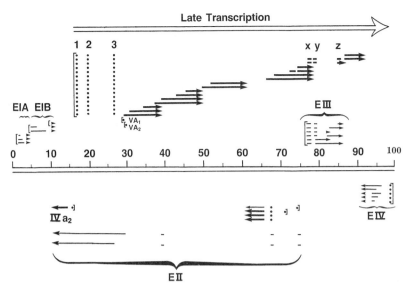

FIGURE 1 Structure of the Ad5 genome. Messages from the early regions are indicated as light lines and late messages are indicated in bold. Late transcription originating from the major late promoter at 16 map units and terminating near the right end of the genome is indicated by the open arrow. This transcript is processed into five families of late mRNAs spliced to a common tripartite leader (1, 2, and 3 at map units 16.5, 19.5, and 26.5, respectively) although some mRNA species contain additional leaders. (For more details, see Ginsberg, 1984.)

that constitutively expresses Ad5 E1 proteins. In the E3 insertion system, the second plasmid, pFG173 (Mittal *et al.*, 1993), carries a lethal deletion spanning E3, giving rise to infectious progeny only by recombination with the plasmid containing the foreign gene.

By the use of standard recombinant DNA techniques (not described here), foreign genes, including their own or heterologous promoters, can be inserted into the shuttle plasmids in an orientation either parallel or antiparallel to the E1 or E3 transcription unit. In general, higher expression levels have been obtained with inserts in the parallel orientation in either E1 or E3 (unpublished results); however, the sequence of the insert itself can affect expression levels, particularly for E3 insertions. Once the desired plasmids have been constructed, the following protocols are used to produce and purify the recombinant Ads.

II. Materials and Instrumentation

All tissue culture reagents [including minimal essential medium (MEM) F11, Cat. No. 61100, and Joklik's modified MEM, Cat. No. 22300], tissue culture dishes, and buffer-saturated phenol can be obtained from Gibco-BRL. All sera are inactivated prior to use by heating to 56°C for 30 min. Becton Dickinson BBL LB broth base (Cat. No. B99301) and sterile petri dishes can be obtained from Fisher Scientific. Pronase and salmon sperm DNA can be purchased from Boehringer-Mannheim, and orcein from Sigma Chemical Company. Spinner flasks can be obtained from Bellco and Spectra/por dialysis tubing (MW cutoff 12–14 kDa) from Spectrum. The SDT Tissumizer with SDT100 probe can be purchased from Tekmar. Beckman 50 Ti (vertical or fixed-angle) and SW 50.1 rotors are also required. Reagents for plasmid DNA isolation, as well as restriction enzymes, and reagents and apparatus for horizontal slab gel electrophoresis are described in a number of cloning manuals.

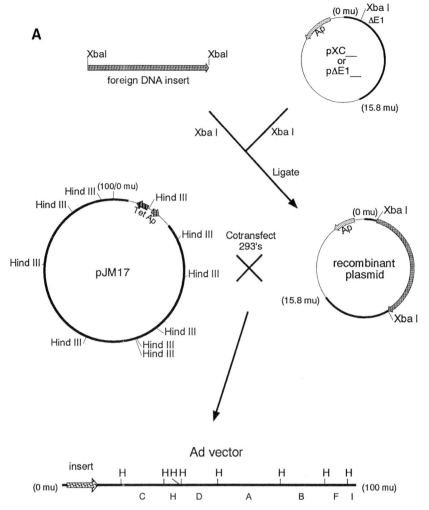

FIGURE 2A Ad E1 insertion vector system. The general strategy used to introduce foreign DNA inserts into the E1 region for rescue into virus is illustrated. The foreign DNA insert is first isolated with appropriate flanking restriction enzyme sites (*Xba*I in the example shown) for insertion into the E1 deletion of one of the pXC or pΔE1 series of plasmids, generating a recombinant plasmid with the insert in the E1 parallel or antiparallel orientation as desired. The recombinant plasmid is then cotransfected with pJM17 into 293 cells and infectious virus is generated by *in vivo* recombination. The pXC and pΔE1 plasmids differ in the E1 deletion they contain. The pXC series of plasmids contain an E1 deletion of 2.88 kb (452–3328 bp), whereas the pΔE1 plasmids contain a deletion of 3.19 kb (339–3533 bp). The plasmids also differ in the cloning sites present in the position of the E1 deletion: pXCX2 (Spessot *et al.*, 1989) contains *Xba*I; pXCJL1 (F. L. Graham and J. Lu, unpublished data) contains *Xba*I, *Bam*HI, *Xho*I, *Sal*I, and *Cla*I; pXCJL2 (F. L. Graham and J. Lu, unpublished data) contains these same sites in the reverse orientation; pΔE1sp1A (A. J. Bett *et al.*, submitted for publication) contains *Cla*I, *Bam*HI, *Xho*I, *Xba*I, *Eco*RV, *Eco*RI, *Hin*dIII, *Sal*I, and *Bgl*II; and pΔE1sp1B (A. J. Bett *et al.*, submitted for publication) contains these same sites in the reverse order. Map units (mu) refer to Ad5 sequences; solid bars represent Ad5 sequences and hatched bars represent the ampicillin resistance gene (Ap), tetracyclin resistance gene (Tet) or foreign DNA insert as indicated.

III. Procedures

A. PREPARATION OF PLASMID DNA FOR COTRANSFECTIONS

To minimize the amount of rearranged DNA which is occasionally observed in preparations of very large plasmids such as pJM17 and pFG173, we have adopted the following protocol for bacterial growth prior to plasmid DNA isolation.

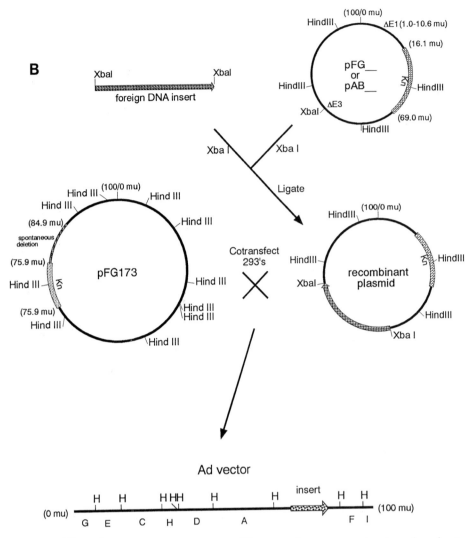

FIGURE 2B Ad E3 insertion vector system. The general strategy used to introduce foreign DNA inserts into the E3 region for rescue into virus is illustrated. The foreign DNA insert is first isolated with appropriate flanking restriction enzyme sites (*Xba*I in the example shown) for insertion into the E3 deletion of one of the pFG or pAB series of plasmids, generating a recombinant plasmid with the insert in the E3 parallel or antiparallel orientation as desired. The recombinant plasmid is then cotransfected with pFG173 into 293 cells and infectious virus is generated by *in vivo* recombination. The pFG and pAB plasmids differ in the E3 deletion they contain. The pFG series of plasmids contain an E3 deletion of 1.88 kb (28,592–30,470 bp), whereas the pAB plasmids contain a deletion of 2.69 kb (28,133–30,818 bp). The plasmids also differ in the cloning sites present in the position of the E3 deletion: pFG144K3 contains *Xba*I, pAB14 contains *Xba*I, pAB26 contains *Xba*I, *Bam*HI, *Sca*I, *Xho*I, *Sal*I, and *Cla*I, and pAB27 contains these same sites in the reverse orientation (Bett *et al.*, 1993). Map units (mu) refer to Ad5 sequences; solid bars represent Ad5 sequences and hatched bars represent the kanamycin resistance gene (Kn), spontaneous deletion, or foreign DNA insert as indicated.

Solutions

1. *Luria broth (LB):* Dissolve 20 g BBL LB broth base (dehydrated) and 1 g glucose in 1 liter H$_2$O. Sterilize by autoclaving.

2. *LB–agar plates:* Add 10 g agar to 500 ml LB. Sterilize by autoclaving. Cool

LB–agar to about 50°C, add antibiotics as required, and pour 25 ml into each of 20 sterile petri dishes. Store at 4°C.

3. *Reagents for isolating plasmid DNA on CsCl gradients:* Not described here.

Steps

1. Streak plasmid-bearing bacteria on an LB–agar plate containing appropriate antibiotics, and grow overnight at 37°C.

2. Pick two or more colonies off the plate, resuspend each in 5 ml LB plus antibiotics, and incubate at 37°C on a shaker for several hours.

3. Add each 5 ml culture to 500 ml LB plus antibiotics and continue incubating overnight.

4. Purify the plasmid DNA by alkaline lysis of the bacteria and CsCl banding as described in standard cloning manuals. Plasmid DNA that has not undergone any detectable rearrangement is suitable for use in cotransfections.

B. DNA TRANSFECTION FOR RESCUE OF RECOMBINANT ADENOVIRUS VECTORS: CALCIUM PHOSPHATE COPRECIPITATION

Solutions

1. *Complete MEMF11 (or Joklik's modified MEM):* Add 5 ml 0.2 M L-glutamine, 5 ml penicillin–streptomycin (10,000 U/ml and 10 mg/ml, respectively), and 5 ml 0.25 mg/ml Fungizone to 500 ml MEMF11 (or Joklik's modified MEM). Store at 4°C for up to 2 weeks. Add 55 ml heat-inactivated newborn bovine serum (NBS) or fetal bovine serum (FBS) prior to use in cell culture.

2. *10× citric saline:* Dissolve 50 g KCl and 22 g sodium citrate in H_2O to a final volume of 500 ml. Sterilize by autoclaving, and store at 4°C. Dilute 1:10 in sterile H_2O to prepare 1× citric saline.

3. *Hepes-buffered saline (HEBS):* Dissolve 5 g Hepes, 8 g NaCl, 0.37 g KCl, 0.125 g $Na_2HPO_4 \cdot 2H_2O$, and 1 g glucose in 900 ml H_2O. Adjust pH to 7.1. Adjust volume to 1 liter with H_2O. Aliquot into small glass bottles, sterilize by autoclaving, and store at 4°C.

4. *10× SSC:* Dissolve 8.7 g NaCl and 4.4 g sodium citrate dihydrate in H_2O to a final volume of 100 ml. Adjust pH to 7.0. Autoclave. Prepare 0.1× SSC by diluting 10× SSC and then autoclaving.

5. *2 mg/ml carrier DNA:* Dissolve 100 mg salmon sperm DNA in 50 ml sterile 0.1× SSC by stirring overnight at room temperature. Determine concentration by reading the OD at 260 nm (one OD unit = 50 μg/ml). Store in small aliquots at −20°C.

6. *2.5 M $CaCl_2$:* Add H_2O to 36.8 g $CaCl_2 \cdot 2H_2O$ to a final volume of 100 ml. Sterilize by filtration and store in small plastic tubes at 4°C.

7. *MEMF11–agarose overlay:* To make approximately 200 ml, add 10 ml horse serum (HS) and 2 ml each of L-glutamine, penicillin–streptomycin, Fungizone (at above concentrations), and autoclaved 5% yeast extract (w/v in H_2O) to 100 ml 2× MEMF11. Autoclave 1 g agarose in 100 ml H_2O. Bring the 2× medium and agarose to 44°C before mixing, and use within an hour.

Steps

1. Monolayer cultures of 293 cells are grown in 150-mm dishes in complete MEMF11 medium plus 10% FBS (or NBS). At 90% confluence, remove medium, wash each dish twice with 10 ml 1× citric saline, and then incubate for a maximum of 15 min at room temperature in 3 ml 1× citric saline to detach cells. Resuspend cells in medium and divide between two or three 150-mm dishes. 293 cells should be refed with fresh medium every 3 days if not ready to passage.

2. Set up low-passage (<p40) 293 cells in 60-mm dishes to be about 70–80% confluent at the time of use. As a rule of thumb, one 150-mm dish of nearly confluent 293 cells can be split into eight 60-mm dishes each containing 5 ml complete MEMF11 + 10% FBS, which will be ready for transfection in 1–2 days.

3. Add 0.005 vol 2 mg/ml carrier DNA to 1× HEBS, and shear by vortexing for 1 min.

4. For each virus to be rescued, aliquot 2 ml HEBS + carrier DNA (enough for four dishes) into each of three sterile clear plastic tubes.

5. To these tubes add plasmid DNA containing the foreign gene insert and the plasmid with which it will recombine (e.g., pJM17) in the following amounts, respectively: 20 μg plus 20 μg, 20 μg plus 40 μg, and 40 μg plus 40 μg. If a negative control is desired, set up similar coprecipitations omitting the first plasmid. A useful positive control is the infectious plasmid pFG140.

6. Gently mix by shaking, then slowly add 100 μl of 2.5 M CaCl$_2$ to each tube.

7. Gently mix and let stand at room temperature for 15–30 min. (A fine precipitate should form within a few minutes). Without removing the growth medium, add 0.5 ml DNA suspension to each dish of cells, then incubate at 37°C in a CO$_2$ incubator for 4–5 hr or overnight.

8. Remove the medium and add to each dish 10 ml MEMF11–agarose overlay previously equilibrated to 44°C. After the agarose solidifies, incubate at 37°C. Plaques should appear after about 5–10 days. When dishes are examined by eye, plaques appear turbid as a consequence of light scattering by dead cells in an otherwise smooth cell monolayer. Microscopic examination reveals plaques as zones of dead or lysed cells surrounded by rounded infected cells.

C. SCREENING ADENOVIRUS PLAQUE ISOLATES

The following protocol describes the expansion of plaque isolates by growth in monolayer cultures of 293 cells. The conditioned medium containing released virus can be stored for further purification; the cell monolayer, with which most of the virus remains, is harvested for analysis of viral DNA.

Solutions

1. *Phosphate buffered saline^{++} (PBS^{++})*: Prepared as follows: To make solution A, dissolve 80 g NaCl, 11.5 g Na$_2$HPO$_4$, 2 g KCl, and 2 g KH$_2$PO$_4$ in H$_2$O to a final volume of 1 liter. To make solution B, add 1 g CaCl$_2 \cdot$2H$_2$O to 100 ml H$_2$O. To make solution C, add 1 g MgCl$_2 \cdot$6H$_2$O to 100 ml H$_2$O. Sterilize solutions separately by autoclaving. For 100 ml PBS^{++}, mix 88 ml sterile H$_2$O with 10 ml solution A and 1 ml each of solutions B and C.

2. *PBS^{++} + 10% glycerol:* Add 10 ml sterile glycerol to 90 ml PBS^{++}.

3. *Pronase stock solution:* Dissolve 0.5 g pronase in 100 ml 10 mM Tris-HCl, pH 7.5; heat at 56°C for 15 min, then incubate at 37°C for 1 h. Aliquot and store at −20°C. Thaw stock solution just before use and add 1 ml to 10 ml 10 mM Tris-HCl, pH 7.5; 10 mM EDTA; 0.5% (w/v) SDS.

4 *Complete MEMF11 + 5% HS:* Add 25 ml HS to 475 ml complete MEMF11.

5. *0.1× SSC:* See Section B, solution 4. *Buffer-saturated phenol:* Purchased from Gibco-BRL.

6. *Reagents for restriction analysis of viral DNA* (not described here).

Steps

1. Pick well-isolated plaques from transfected cultures (see above) by punching out agar plugs using a sterile Pasteur pipette, and transfer agar to 0.5 ml sterile PBS^{++} + 10% glycerol in sterile vials. Store at −70°C until use.

2. Set up 60-mm dishes of 293 cells to be 80–90% confluent at time of infection. The denser and older the cell monolayer, the longer it takes for cytopathic effect (cpe) to reach completion.

3. Remove medium from 293 dishes and add 0.2 ml virus (agar plug suspension). Rock dishes once and adsorb at room temperature for 30 min. Add 5 ml complete MEMF11 + 5% HS and incubate at 37°C.

4. Cytopathic effect should be visible within 1–2 days. Harvest virus and extract infected cell DNA (as below) when all cells are rounded and most have detached from the dish (usually 3–4 days).

5. To partially separate released virus from the infected cells, leave dishes undisturbed in the tissue culture hood for 30 min. Gently remove 4 ml medium with a pipette and add to a sterile vial containing 0.5 ml sterile glycerol. Store these candidate viruses at −70°C. Aspirate any remaining medium from the plate. If this is done carefully, the majority of cells will remain in the dish.

6. To extract DNA from the infected cells, add 0.5 ml Pronase solution to the cells remaining in each dish and incubate at 37°C for 4–18 hr.

7. Transfer the viscous lysate to a 1.5-ml microfuge tube, and extract once with buffer-saturated phenol. Spin 10 min. Collect the aqueous phase (top) and transfer to a fresh tube.

8. Add 1 ml 96% ethanol to precipitate the DNA. Mix by inverting tube several times—a fibrous precipitate should be easily visible. Spin 10 min at 14,000 rpm. Wash pellet twice with 96% ethanol, and air-dry.

9. Dissolve DNA pellet in 50 μl 0.1× SSC (complete solubilization may take several hours) and digest 5 μl with *Hin*dIII (1 unit overnight is usually sufficient for complete digestion).

10. Run on a 1% agarose gel with appropriate markers (a *Hin*dIII digest of wild-type Ad5 being one convenient marker) and identify the candidate recombinants. If the cytopathic effect was complete, viral DNA bands should be easily visible above a background smear of cellular DNA. Note that in *Hin*dIII digests of human DNA there will be a band of cellular repetitive DNA at 1.8 kb. Figure 3 shows restriction digests from a typical screening of plaques obtained by cotransfection to rescue an E1 insertion plasmid with pJM17 and an E3 insert with pFG173.

11. Verify candidate recombinants using other diagnostic restriction enzymes. Correct recombinants should be further purified by at least one round of plaque

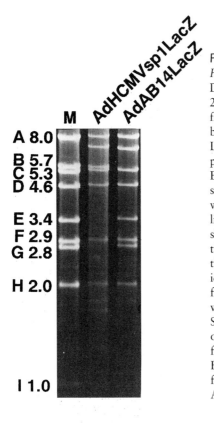

FIGURE 3 *Hin*dIII restriction digests of recombinant adenoviruses. The *Hin*dIII digestion patterns for recombinant Ad vectors containing foreign DNA inserts in E1 (AdHCMVsp1LacZ) or E3 (AdAB14LacZ) are shown. 293 cells were infected with AdHCMVsp1LacZ (Morsy *et al.*, 1993), obtained from the cotransfection of pJM17 and pHCMVsp1lacZ (LacZ gene driven by the HCMV promoter combined with the 3.19-kb E1 deletion) or AdAB14-LacZ (Bett *et al.*, 1993), obtained from the cotransfection of pFG173 and pAB14LacZ (LacZ gene plus the SV40 promoter combined with the 2.69-kb E3 deletion), and infected cell DNA was extracted, digested with *Hin*dIII, and separated by electrophoresis on a 1% agarose gel. The gel was then stained with ethidium bromide and the DNA fragments were visualized under UV light. Lane 1 contains wild-type Ad5 DNA digested with *Hin*dIII. Fragment sizes are indicated to the left in kilo-base pairs (kb). Lanes 2 and 3 contain the HindIII digest of AdHCMVsp1LacZ and AdAB14LacZ respectively. In the *Hin*dIII digest of AdHCMVsp1LacZ, fragments A, C, D, F, H, and I are identical to wild-type, and fragments E and G are replaced by a diagnostic fragment of 6.7 kb containing the insert. Fragment B is slightly smaller than wild-type fragment B because pJM17 was derived from dl309 (Jones and Shenk, 1979), an Ad5 variant that contains a small deletion and substitution of foreign DNA in the E3 region. In the *Hin*dIII digest of AdAB14LacZ, fragments A, C, D, E, F, G, H, and I are identical to wild type, and fragment B is replaced by a diagnostic fragment of 6.8 kb containing the insert. The faint bands seen under fragment H in the digest of AdHCMVsp1LacZ and AdAB14LacZ are repetitive cellular DNA.

purification, as described below, and screening, prior to preparation of high-titer stocks.

D. PLAQUE ASSAYS FOR PURIFICATION AND TITRATION OF ADENOVIRUS

Solutions

1. *PBS^{++} and MEMF11–agarose overlay (at 44°C):* See Section C.

Steps

1. Set up 60-mm dishes of 293 cells to be confluent at time of infection.

2. Remove medium from dishes. Add 0.2 ml virus (dilution of agar plug suspension in PBS^{++} if you wish to plaque purify or dilution of stock for titration). We typically assay dilutions ranging from 10^{-3} to 10^{-6} for plaque purification or 10^{-3} to 10^{-9} for virus titration. Adsorb the virus for 30–60 min at room temperature, occasionally rocking the dishes. Add 10 ml MEMF11–agarose overlay, cool, and then incubate at 37°C.

3. Plaques should be visible within 4–5 days and should be counted for titration at 7 days and again at 10 days. For plaque purification proceed as for isolation of plaques following transfections.

E. PREPARATION OF HIGH-TITER VIRAL STOCKS (CRUDE LYSATES) FROM CELLS IN MONOLAYER

Because most of the virus remains associated with the infected cells until very late in infection, high-titer stocks can be prepared easily by concentrating infected 293 cells as described here.

Solutions

PBS++, PBS++ + 10% glycerol, and complete MEMF11 + 5% HS; See Section C.

Steps

1. Set up 150-mm dishes of 293 cells to be 80–90% confluent at time of infection. We generally use eight or more dishes for each virus.

2. To prepare high-titer stocks, remove medium from the 293 cells and infect at a multiplicity of infection of 1–10 PFU per cell (1 ml virus suspension per 150-mm dish). For the initial stock preparation, we dilute virus (from the untitered 4-ml sample stored at −70°C after the last round of viral screening) 1:8 with PBS++. To minimize the probability of rearrangement of the recombinant virus, prepare subsequent high-titer stocks from the same viral screening sample.

3. Adsorb for 30–60 min, then refeed with complete MEMF11 + 5% HS. Incubate at 37°C, and examine daily for signs of cytopathic effect.

4. When cytopathic effect is nearly complete, i.e., most cells rounded but not yet detached, harvest by scraping the cells off the dish, combining the cells plus spent medium, and centrifuging at 800 *g* for 15 min. Aspirate the medium, and resuspend the cell pellet in 2 ml PBS++ + 10% glycerol per 150-mm dish. Freeze (−70°C) and thaw (37°C) the crude virus stock three times prior to titration. Store aliquots at −70°C.

F. PREPARATION OF HIGH-TITER VIRAL STOCKS (PURIFIED) FROM CELLS IN SUSPENSION

Recombinant Ads can be purified from crude lysates of either monolayer or suspension cultures. Because of the higher cell density obtained in suspension culture, however, this source is preferable for the preparation of purified high-titer viral stocks, as described here.

Solutions

1. *Complete Joklik's modified MEM + 10% HS (or 10% NBS):* Add 50 ml HS (or NBS) to 450 ml complete Joklik's modified MEM (described in Section B). Store at 4°C.

2. *1% Sodium citrate:* Dissolve 1 g sodium citrate dihydrate in H_2O to a final volume of 100 ml.

3. *Carnoy's fixative:* Add 25 ml glacial acetic acid to 75 ml methanol.

4. *Orcein:* Add 1 g orcein dye to 25 ml glacial acetic acid plus 25 ml H_2O. Filter through Whatman No. 1 paper.

5. *0.1 M Tris–HCl, pH 8.0:* Add 1.2 g Tris base to 80 ml H_2O. Adjust pH to 8.0 with HCl. Adjust volume to 100 ml and autoclave.

6. *5% Na deoxycholate:* Add 5 g Na deoxycholate to 100 ml H_2O.

7. *Saturated CsCl solution:* At room temperature, add sufficient CsCl to 10 m*M* Tris–HCl, pH 8.0, 1 m*M* EDTA to saturate the buffer. Store at 4°C, but bring to room temperature before use.

8. *PBS++ + 10% glycerol:* See Section C.

Steps

1. For infection with replication-defective viruses (E1 insertion recombinants) grow 293N3S cells in spinner culture to a density of $2-4 \times 10^5$ cells/ml in 4 liters complete Joklik's modified MEM + 10% HS. For infection with replication-proficient viruses (E3 insertion recombinants), grow 4 liters KB cells to a density of $5-6 \times 10^5$ cells/ml in complete Joklik's modified MEM + 10% NBS. Centrifuge cell suspension at 750 g for 20 min, saving 50% of the conditioned medium. Resuspend the cell pellet in 0.1 vol fresh medium.

2. Add virus at a multiplicity of infection of 10–20 PFU/cell and stir gently at 37°C for 1 hr. Bring to the original volume using 50% conditioned medium and 50% fresh medium, and continue stirring at 37°C.

3. Monitor infection twice daily by inclusion body staining as follows:

    a. Remove a 5-ml aliquot from the infected spinner culture. Spin for 10 min at 750 g and resuspend the cell pellet in 0.5 ml of 1% sodium citrate.

    b. Incubate at room temperature for 10 min; then add 0.5 ml Carnoy's fixative and fix for 10 min at room temperature.

    c. Add 1 ml 1% sodium citrate, spin, and resuspend the pellet in a few drops of 1% sodium citrate. Add one drop of fixed cells to a slide and let air-dry for at least 1 hr; then add one drop orcein and a coverslip and examine in the microscope. Inclusion bodies appear as densely staining nuclear structures resulting from accumulation of large amounts of virus and viral products at late times in infection. A negative control should be included in initial tests.

4. When inclusion bodies are visible in 80–90% of the cells ($1\frac{1}{2}$ to 2 days), harvest by centrifugation at 750 g for 20 min in sterile 1-liter bottles. Combine pellets in a small volume of medium, and spin again. Resuspend pellet in 20 ml 0.1 M Tris–HCl, pH 8.0. Store at −70°C until use.

5. Thaw the frozen crude stock and add 0.1 vol 5% Na deoxycholate. Mix well and incubate on ice for 30 min. This disrupts cells without disrupting virions, resulting in a relatively clear, highly viscous suspension.

6. Shear the cellular DNA using a probe-type homogenizer. To avoid exposure to aerosols of recombinant virus generated by homogenization, the sample must be completely contained in an enclosed vessel. We homogenize on ice for three 10-sec bursts at a setting of 50 on a Tekmar SDT Tissumizer, then at 60 for one or two 5-sec bursts. Viscosity should be reduced so that, when the suspension is pipetted dropwise, there is still some noticeable viscosity, but only slightly more than that of water.

7. Add 1.8 ml saturated CsCl solution for each 3.1 ml virus suspension. Be sure that the saturated CsCl solution is equilibrated to room temperature, as this affects the concentration.

8. Transfer virus to Beckman 50 Ti quickseal (or similar) tubes and spin in a Beckman 50 Ti angle (or vertical) rotor for 16–20 hr at 4°C and 35,000 rpm.

9. Collect the viral bands and pool. (For tubes other than nitrocellulose, one can collect by puncturing the top of the tube with a hot needle and then puncturing the bottom, controlling the flow of solution out the bottom with a gloved finger over the top hole.)

10. Centrifuge pooled virus in a Beckman SW 50.1 rotor at 35,000 rpm, 4°C, for 16–20 hr.

11. Collect the virus band in the smallest volume possible and dialyze at 4°C against two changes of 100 vol PBS^{++} + 10% glycerol for at least 4 h total.

IV. Comments

Once the desired recombinant Ad is obtained, the ability to express the foreign gene must be tested. The most suitable procedure for detecting expression would depend on the particular properties of the foreign protein. If antibodies to the protein are available, then ELISA, Western blotting analysis, or immunoprecipitation of infected cell extracts may be the simplest method to quantitate protein expression. If possible, the biological activity of the recombinant protein should also be tested to ensure that the expressed protein is functional. (See Graham and Prevec, 1991, for additional details.)

It is important to use caution when handling recombinant Ads. Adenoviruses with inserts in E3 are infectious in humans and other permissive species. Experimentation with these vectors should be carried out in accordance with relevant regulations. If inadvertantly exposed, individuals without previous immunity to Ad5 may seroconvert not only against Ad5, but also against the foreign gene product expressed. This should be avoided, especially if the development of antibody may confuse diagnosis of a particular disease. Finally, no known toxic or potentially toxic gene product should be expressed from nondefective Ad vectors.

V. Pitfalls

1. There can be a number of different causes for failure to obtain the proper recombinant virus following cotransfection. First, the transfection efficiency may be low (a suitable control would be transfection of wild-type viral DNA or infectious plasmid DNA such as pFG140). The 293 cells used in transfections must be at low passage, growing slowly, and slightly subconfluent. In addition, the plasmid DNA must be of high quality; we routinely use CsCl-banded DNA in cotransfections. Finally, although infrequently, the desired recombinant might not be obtained because the foreign gene insert is toxic to the cells or virus, in which case it would not be possible to rescue a high-expression-level recombinant Ad.

2. The level of expression in E1 insertion vectors depends mainly on the strength of the promoter immediately upstream of the coding sequence for the foreign gene. In E3 insertion vectors, this is not necessarily true; even some promoterless constructs express relatively high levels of recombinant proteins. In these cases the major late or E3 promoter is presumably driving expression of the foreign gene insert. It is not, at this time, possible to predict which E3 constructs will use an inserted promoter; consequently care must be taken in analyzing E3 insertion recombinants for appropriate expression, in particular, for example, when tissue-specific promoters are required.

REFERENCES

Berkner, K. L. (1988) Development of adenovirus vectors for expression of heterologous genes. *Biotechniques* **6**, 616–629.
Bett, A. J., Prevec, L., and Graham, F. L. (1993) Packaging capacity and stability of human adenovirus type 5 vectors. *J. Virol.* **67**, 5911–5921.
Ginsberg, H. S. (1984) "The Adenoviruses." Plenum, New York.
Graham, F. L., and Prevec, L. (1991) Manipulation of adenovirus vectors. *In* "Methods in

Molecular Biology," Vol. 7 "Gene Transfer and Expression Protocols" (E. J. Murray, ed.), pp. 109–128. Humana Press, Clifton, NJ.

Graham, F. L., Smiley, J., Russell, W. C., and Nairn, R. (1977) Characteristics of a human cell line transformed by DNA from human adenovirus type 5. *J. Gen. Virol.* **36,** 59–72.

Jones, N., and Shenk, T. (1979) Isolation of adenovirus type 5 host range deletion mutants defective for transformation of rat embryo cells. *Cell* **17,** 683–689.

McGrory, J., Bautista, D., and Graham, F. L. (1988) A simple technique for the rescue of early region I mutations into infectious human adenovirus type 5. *Virology* **163,** 614–617.

Mittal, S. K., McDermott, M. R., Johnson, D. C., Prevec, L., and Graham, F. L. (1993) Monitoring foreign gene expression by a human adenovirus based vector using the firefly luciferase as a reporter gene. *Virus Res.* **28,** 67–90.

Morsy, M. A., Alford, E. L., Bett, A., Graham, F. L., and Caskey, C. T. (1993) Efficient adenoviral-mediated ornithine transcarbamylase expression in deficient mouse and human hepatocytes. *J. Clin. Invest.* **92,** 1580–1586.

Sambrook, J., Fritsch, E. F., and Maniatis, T. (1989) "Molecular Cloning: A Laboratory Manual." Cold Spring Harbor Laboratory Press, Cold Spring Harbor, NY.

Spessot, R., Inchley, K., Hupel, T. M., and Bacchetti, S. (1989) Cloning of the herpes simplex virus ICP4 gene in an adenovirus vector: Effects on adenovirus gene expression and replication. *Virology* **168,** 378–387.

Tissue Culture Techniques for the Study of Human Papillomaviruses in Stratified Epithelia

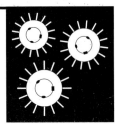

Craig Meyers, Mark G. Frattini, and Laimonis A. Laimins

I. Introduction

The life cycle of human papillomaviruses (HPVs) is closely linked to the differentiation of squamous epithelial cells. Human papillomaviruses infect stratified squamous epithelial and establish their genomes as episomes in the basal cells. Viral DNA is stably maintained at approximately 50–100 copies within the basal cells. Vegetative replication and virion assembly occur only in the differentiated suprabasal cells. To study these processes in the laboratory, extensive use has been made of organotypic cultures, which are also referred to as collagen rafts (Asselineau and Prunieras, 1984; Asselineau et al., 1986; McCance et al., 1988; Rader et al., 1990). The use of this methodology for studying the HPV life cycle first involves obtaining HPV DNA containing cell lines derived from biopsies or generated by transfection of keratinocytes with HPV sequences. Many aspects of the viral life cycle can be duplicated in organotypic (raft) cultures using cell lines that maintain viral episomes. (Bedell et al., 1991; Meyers et al., 1992). Use of raft culture systems should allow for a detailed analysis of the mechanisms that control viral transcription, replication, and virion morphogenesis.

II. Materials

Dulbecco's modified Eagle's medium (DMEM, Cat. No. 430-2100EF), Hams F-12 (Cat. No. 430-1700EF), trypsin–EDTA (Cat. No. 610-5300AG) and penicillin–streptomycin (Cat. No. 600-5140AG) were obtained from Gibco-BRL. Epidermal growth factor (Cat. No. 40001) and rat tail collagen (Cat. No. 40236) were obtained from Collaborative Research. Bovine serum albumin (BSA, Cat No 12657) and Hepes buffer (Cat. No. 391338) were obtained from Calbiochem–Novabiochem Corporation. Hydrocortisone (Cat. No. H-088), adenine (Cat. No. A-2786), insulin (Cat. No. I-6634), transferrin (Cat. No. T-1147), 3,3′,5-triiodo-L-thyronine (Cat. No. T-6397), and BES (Cat. No. B-6266) were obtained from Sigma. Defined fetal bovine serum was obtained from Hyclone Laboratories. Mitomycin C (Cat. No. 107409) was obtained from Boehringer-Mannheim. Cholera toxin (Cat. No. 856011) was obtained from Schwarz–Mann Biotech/ICN. Gene Pulser (Cat. No. 1652075) was purchased from Bio-Rad Laboratories.

Cell Biology: A Laboratory Handbook Copyright © 1994 by Academic Press, Inc. All rights of reproduction in any form reserved.

III. Procedures

A. GROWTH OF KERATINOCYTES

Solutions

Keratinocyte Growth Medium or E Medium
See Wu *et al.* (1982).

1. Use a Nalgene 8-liter carboy and add 6.5 liters of distilled, deionized water.

2. Add 6 (1-liter) packets of DMEM. (Rinse out packets.)

3. Add 2 (1-liter) packets of Hams F-12. (Rinse out packets.)

4. Add 24.55 g tissue culture-grade $NaHCO_3$.

5. Add 80 ml 100× cocktail.

6. Add 80 ml penicillin–streptomycin.

7. Add 8 ml 1000× hydrocortisone.

8. Add 8 ml 1000× cholera toxin.

9. Shake briefly to mix.

10. Add 2.5 ml concentrated HCl, shake, and remove a small quantity to check that the pH is approximately 7.1.

11. For 5% FBS, add 400 ml FBS. For 10% FBS, add 800 ml FBS. Bring total volume to 8 liters using doubly distilled water.

12. Filter-sterilize using a low-protein-binding 0.2-μm filter and aliquot aseptically. Wrap neck with Parafilm and store at 4°C in the dark.

Supplements

1. *Epidermal growth factor (200×):* 100 μg EGF dissolved in 10 ml dH_2O and 100 mg BSA dissolved in 10 ml dH_2O, and 80 ml dH_2O. Filter-sterilize, aliquot, and store at −20°C.

2. *Hepes buffer:* A 1 M stock solution is made by dissolving 23.83 g into 75 ml distilled water. Use 10 N NaOH to adjust the pH to 7.0. Bring volume to 100 ml and filter-sterilize.

3. *Hydrocortisone:* Weigh 25 mg and dissolve in 5 ml 100% EtOH to make a 5 mg/ml stock. To make 60 ml of a 1000× (0.4 μg/ml) stock, take 4.8 ml of 5 mg/ml stock and add 55.2 ml Hepes buffer. Aliquot and store at −20°C.

4. *Cholera toxin:* Add 1 ml sterile distilled water to the 1-mg vial to make a 1×10^{-5} M stock solution. A 1000× solution is made by diluting the stock solution 1:100 in sterile distilled water. Store at 4°C in the dark.

5. *Defined fetal bovine serum:* Lots should be tested for the ability to induce adequate differentiation in raft cultures before purchasing. FBS is stored at −20°C.

6. *100× Cocktail:* Combine 20 ml 1.8×10^{-1} M adenine, 20 ml 5 mg/ml insulin, 20 ml 5 mg/ml transferrin, 20 ml 5 mg/ml T_3, and 120 ml PBS in a plastic beaker; mix well and filter-sterilize. Store in 40-ml aliquots at −20°C.

   a. *Adenine:* Weigh 486 mg and add to 15 ml sterile distilled water. Add

5–6 drops 10 N HCl until dissolved. Bring volume to 20 ml using sterile distilled water.

b. *Insulin:* Weigh 100 mg insulin and dissolve in 20 ml of 0.1 N HCl.

c. *Transferrin:* Weigh 100 mg transferrin and dissolve in 20 ml sterile PBS.

d. *3,3',5-Triiodo-L-thyronine (T$_3$, Sigma Cat. No. T-6397):* Weigh out 13.6 mg of T$_3$ and dissolve in 100 ml 0.02 N NaOH (2×10^{-4} M T$_3$). Take 0.1 ml of 2×10^{-4} M T$_3$ and add to 9.9 ml sterile PBS (2×10^{-6} M T$_3$). Take 1.0 ml of 2×10^{-6} M T$_3$ and add to 99 ml sterile PBS (2×10^{-8} M T$_3$). Aliquot into 5- to 20-ml tubes and store at $-20°$C.

Other Tissue Culture Supplements

1. J2 3T3 fibroblasts are maintained in monolayer culture with DMEM and 10% calf serum.

2. Mitomycin C is extremely toxic and should be handled with gloves and care. The 2 mg is resuspended in 5 ml sterile PBS (0.4 mg/ml) and filter-sterilized with a low-protein-binding 0.2-μm filter. Store in 15-ml tubes wrapped in aluminum foil at 4°C for 1 week.

Steps

Passaging of Keratinocyte and J2 3T3 Cell Lines

1. Keratinocyte cell lines containing HPV sequences are maintained as monolayers in E medium in the presence of mitomycin C-treated J23T3 fibroblast feeders. Cells are grown in a 37°C 5% CO$_2$ humidified incubator and passaged when they reach 80–90% confluence. (Do not allow keratinocyte cell lines to reach 100% confluence.)

2. Aspirate medium and wash plate with PBS (10 ml for 100-mm plate).

3. Aspirate PBS and add 1.5 ml trypsin–EDTA per 100-mm dish. Allow trypsin to completely cover surface and place plate in 37°C incubator for 3–6 min (varies for different cell lines).

4. Periodically check plate to see if cells have been released from the surface. Plate can be rocked and even tapped on the sides to assist in releasing cells.

5. When the majority of cells have been released (>80%), add at least 1 vol medium containing serum to each dish to inactivate the trypsin. Mix carefully and rinse the surface of the dish to release any additional cells.

6. Dispense aliquots of the cell suspension into dishes containing fresh medium. J2 3T3 cells are usually passaged 1:5 or 1:10 but can be split up to 1:20 if desired. Keratinocytes should usually be passaged 1:5 or 1:10 but this depends on the cell line. Also, keratinocytes should be passaged onto plates containing mitomycin C-treated J2 3T3 cells (outlined below).

7. Return the plates to the incubator overnight and change the medium the following day.

8. Refeed cells as desired until the next passage.

Treatment of J2 3T3 Feeder Cells

1. J2 3T3 fibroblasts can be used until spontaneously transformed foci are observed. Add 200 μl of 0.4 mg/ml mitomycin C solution to 10 ml medium on a

FIGURE 1   Collagen–fibroblast gel in 35-mm six-well dish.

confluent plate of J2-3T3 cells, swirl gently, and incubate for 2–4 hr at 37°C in 5% CO_2 incubator.

2. Aspirate off medium containing mitomycin C and wash three times with PBS.

3. If cells are to be used right away, continue by trypsinizing cells from dish. One confluent dish will feed four to six 100-mm dishes of epithelial cells.

4. If cells are to be stored for later use, add 10 ml DMEM with 10% calf serum. Cells may be stored for 1 week if refed every 2–3 days with fresh medium.

Versene Treatments

1. If the primary epithelial cell line is contaminated with fibroblasts, Versene may help to remove fibroblasts. Versene selectively removes fibroblasts, leaving epithelial cells attached.

2. Versene is prepared by adding 0.5 ml sterile 0.5 M EDTA, pH 8.0, to a 500-ml bottle of sterile PBS. This may be stored at room temperature.

3. Remove fibroblasts by aspirating off medium from the dish, rinsing with 5 ml sterile PBS, aspirating off PBS, and then adding 3 ml Versene. After 1 min, use a 5-ml pipette to spray the dish vigorously with the Versene.

4. Check under microscope to see that most fibroblasts have been removed and repeat procedure if necessary. (*Warning:* Repetition can select for fibroblasts that cannot be removed by Versene treatment.)

B. ELECTROPORATION OF KERATINOCYTES

Solutions

See Section A.

Steps

1. Cells should not be more than 75–80% confluent.

2. Approximately 3 hr before transfection, change medium.

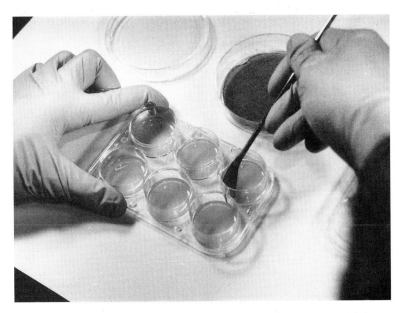

FIGURE 2   Releasing the collagen–fibroblast gel from the side of the 35-mm dish.

3. You want 5×10^6 cells per electroporation, so trypsinize the number of plates accordingly.

4. After trypsinization, count the cells using a hemocytometer and trypan blue.

5. Spin out the cells and then wash the pellet in 10 ml PBS.

6. Resuspend the pellet in E medium containing 10% FBS and 5 mM BES, pH 7.2, at a concentration of 20×10^6 cells/ml.

7. Mix 250 μl (5 million) cells with your DNA (usually a total of 50 μg with sonicated salmon sperm DNA being used as carrier) in a 1.5-ml tube.

8. Incubate 10 min at room temperature.

9. Transfer cell/DNA suspension into an electroporation cuvette.

10. Electroporate using a Bio-Rad Gene Pulser at 960-μF capacitance and 140–280 V, depending on cell type.

11. Incubate 10 min at room temperature.

12. Layer cuvette contents onto the top of 10 ml E medium containing 10% FBS and spin the tubes at 250 rpm for about 10 min.

13. Aspirate supernatant and resuspend the cells in 4–6 ml E medium (10% FBS). Seed cells onto plates containing mitomycin C-treated J2 3T3 feeders.

14. Next day, change the medium (10 ml E medium with 10% FBS plus EGF if desired). Forty-eight hours posttransfection, begin selection protocol; at this point you can switch to E medium with 5% FBS, if desired.

C. FREEZING KERATINOCYTE CELL LINES

Solution

1. *Freezing medium:* For 100 ml, mix 80 ml E medium with 15% FBS and add 20 ml sterile glycerol. Mix thoroughly and filter-sterilize. Store at 4°C for 4–6 weeks.

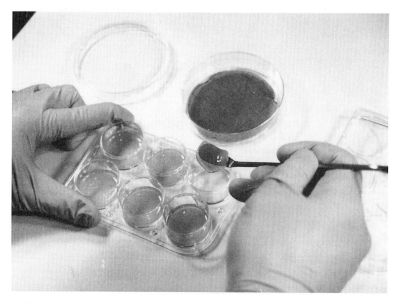

FIGURE 3 Transfer of collagen fibroblast gel to metal grid.

Steps

1. Trypsinize exponentially growing cells and spin down cells. Resuspend in freezing medium, and slow-cool using freezing chamber in −80°C freezer overnight prior to transfer to liquid nitrogen.

2. To thaw cells frozen in glycerol, thaw cryovial of cells in 37°C water bath. Remove cells from cryovial into 10 ml fresh medium in 15-ml tube. Gently centrifuge cells, and aspirate off medium. Resuspend cells with fresh medium and plate onto one 100-mm dish containing feeders.

D. MAKING COLLAGEN–FIBROBLAST RAFTS FOR AIR–LIQUID INTERFACE CULTURES OF EPIDERMAL CELLS

Solutions:

1. *Collagen mix:* Combine 8 parts rat tail collagen type I, 1 part 10× reconstitution butter, 1 part 10× DMEM, and 1.5×10^5 J2 3T3 cells/ml.

2. *Reconstitution buffer (10×):* Combine 2.2 g NaHCO$_3$ and 4.77 g Hepes. Dissolve in 100 ml 0.05 N NaOH. Filter-sterilize aliquot, and store at −20°C.

3. *10× DMEM medium, without NaHCO$_3$ and serum:* Filter-sterilize (*note:* precipitate will form) and store at −20°C.

Steps

1. For each raft, you will need 3 ml sterile collagen mix (below) and at least 4.5×10^5 live (not mitomycin C-treated) J2 3T3 fibroblasts. Make enough mix to pour at least two extra plates. To prepare the mix, place a 50-ml sterile tube on ice. Collagen will gel at room temperature.

2. Trypsinize and pellet the J2 3T3 cells that you will need. Aspirate the medium and resuspend in the 10× reconstitution buffer and 10× DMEM. Transfer to 50-ml tube, add collagen, and mix thoroughly.

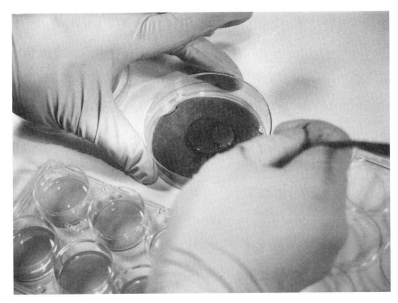

FIGURE 4   Spreading collagen–fibroblast gel on metal grid. Care must be taken to avoid trapping air bubbles under the gel.

3. Place 3 ml collagen–fibroblast mixture into each 35-mm plate. Be careful not to form too many bubbles while pipetting.

4. Gently move the dishes into the 37°C incubator and allow the collagen mix to solidify. It should take approximately 30 min.

5. After the gel has formed, add 2–3 ml of E medium to each dish and return to the incubator for at least 1 day before using.

6. Add $0.5–1 \times 10^6$ epithelial cells to each plate.

7. Allow the cells to grow to confluency.

8. Feed by replacing the medium just like a monolayer culture. (*Note:* Care must be taken not to aspirate the collagen gel.)

9. When the cells have grown to confluency, transfer to the air–liquid interface, as outlined below. (*Note:* **No** EGF is added to the media for the raft system once the cells have been lifted to the air–liquid interface.)

E. TRANSFERRING THE RAFT TO THE AIR–LIQUID INTERFACE

See Figs. 1–5.

Steps

1. Prepare, beforehand, stainless-steel grids (sterile) bent at three equidistant places on the edge to raise the grid above the plate surface; sterile metal spatulas; and 100-mm plates.

2. Place the grid in the 100-mm plate, using sterile forceps.

   a. Remove medium from the collagen gel to be transferred to the air–liquid interface. Using a spatula, release the collagen gel from the side of the dish by gently sliding the spatula around the perimeter of the gel (Fig. 2). Then, tilting the plate slightly, carefully slip the spatula under the collagen gel and carry it to the metal grid (Fig. 3). Gently spread the

FIGURE 5   Overhead view of raft culture. Note that the grid is bent at three positions to raise it above the surface of the dish.

collagen gel out on the metal grid, without allowing bubbles to be trapped under the collagen (Fig. 4).

b. More than one gel can be placed on a grid in a 100-mm plate.

c. Add medium until the grid holds medium under all its surface. When feeding, make sure no bubbles are trapped under the grid and that medium is not covering any part of the raft.

d. Using sterile forceps, scalpels, and scissors, remove gel sections for histology. The raft can also be used for radiolabeling and/or protein extractions.

F. TPA TREATMENT FOR HPV VIRION PRODUCTION

Epithelial cells used for virion production must contain episomal copies of HPV genomes and still retain the ability to differentiate in raft cultures (Meyers *et al.*, 1992).

Steps

1. Prepare rafts as explained above.

2. Grow raft cultures for 16 days at the air–liquid interface to obtain sufficient differentiation and virion production. (The exact number of days may vary depending on the cell line used.)

3. On days 1, 5, 9, and 13, feed the raft cultures with E medium containing 16 nM phorbol-12-myristate 13-acetate (PMA or TPA). After 16–20 hr remove the E medium with 16 nM TPA and feed with E medium only.

4. On day 16, harvest raft cultures.

   a. Rafts or sections of the rafts can be fixed and prepared by standard histological techniques.

   b. Rafts can be used for radiolabeling and/or protein extractions.

   c. Virion can also be purified by isopycnic gradient centrifugation.

IV. Pitfalls

1. Ensure that sufficient numbers of feeders are maintained on keratinocyte monolayers in order to retain the ability to differentiate in raft cultures.

2. Poor differentiation in rafts can be due to too low a density of keratinocytes on collagen–fibroblast gel, improper raft construction, or failure to change medium every other day.

REFERENCES

Asselineau, D., Bernard, B. A., Bailly, C., Darmon, D., Prunieras, M. (1986) Human epidermis reconstructed by culture: Is it normal? *Soc. Invest. Dermatol.* **86**, 181–186.

Asselineau, D., and Prunieras, M. (1984) Reconstruction of 'simplified' control of fabrication. *Br. J. Dermatol. Suppl.* **111**, 219–221.

Bedell, M. A., Hudson, J. B., Golub, T. R., Turyk, M. E., Hosken, M., Wilbanks, G. D., and Laimins, L. A. (1991) Amplification of human papillomavirus genomes in vitro is dependent on epithelial differentiation. *J. Virol.* **65**, 2254–2260.

McCance, D., Kopan, R., Fuchs, E., and Laimins, L. A. (1988) Human papillomavirus type 16 alters human epithelial cell differentiation in vitro. *Proc. Natl. Acad. Sci. USA* **85**: 7169–7173.

Meyers, C., Frattini, M., Hudson, J., and Laimins, L. A. (1992) Biosynthesis of human papillomavirus from a continuous cell line upon epithelial differentiation. *Science* **257**, 971–973.

Rader, J., Golub, T., Hudson, J., Patel, D., Bedell, M., and Laimins, L. A. (1990) In vitro differentiation of epithelial cells from cervical neoplasias resembles in vivo lesions. *Oncogene* **5**, 571–576.

Wu, Y-J., Parker, M., Binder, N. E., Beckett, M. A., Sinard, J. H., Griffiths, C. T., and Rheinwald, J. G. (1982) The mesothelial keratins—A new family of cytoskeletal proteins identified in cultured mesothelial cells and non-keratinizing epithelia. *Cell* **31**, 693–703.

Growth and Purification of Murine Leukemia Virus

Jette Lovmand, Anders H. Lund, and Finn Skou Pedersen

I. Introduction

Murine leukemia viruses play important roles in studies of virus–host interactions during retroviral replication and pathogenesis as well as in vector systems for transfer of heterologous genes (Varmus, 1989). The virus particle contains the single-stranded RNA genome (two copies) and the viral enzymes reverse transcriptase, integrase, and protease. After infection, the reverse transcriptase copies the RNA genome into double-stranded DNA, which then stably integrates as a provirus into a host cell chromosome. Transcription and translation of the murine leukemia virus genes (*gag, pol,* and *env*) as well as production of the new viral RNA genome depend on the host cell machinery (Fig. 1). A productively infected cell is generally refractory to superinfection due to saturation of the membrane receptors with the viral surface protein (Rein and Schultz, 1984).

Cells carrying a stably integrated provirus may be used as a source for continuous production of virus over many cell generations; however, the best yields and the purest virus preparations are usually obtained by use of freshly infected cells. Pure virus strains are now most conveniently kept as recombinant DNA clones of complete, replication-competent proviruses. Infectious virus may then be generated by transfection of such DNA into permissive cells, where the infection will spread until all cells have been infected. We here provide protocols for generation of virus-producing fibroblasts either by transfection of recombinant proviral DNA (protocol A, modified from Graham and van der Eb, 1973) or by infection with a virus stock (protocol B). For the infection of cells in suspension culture that may be less efficiently transfected, cocultivation with a virus-producing fibroblastic line may be preferable (protocol C, Paludan *et al.,* 1989). Virus production is most conveniently monitored by measurement of virion-associated reverse transcriptase activity on exogenous templates (protocol D, Jørgensen *et al.,* 1992, adapted from Goff *et al.,* 1981). The Final protocol (E) describes the purification of murine leukemia virus particles for biochemical studies.

II. Materials and Instrumentation

NaCl (Cat. No. 6404), KCl (Cat. No. 4936), $NaH_2PO_4 \cdot 2H_2O$ (Cat. No. 6345), glucose (Cat. No. 8342), NaOH (Cat. No. 6498), $CaCl_2 \cdot 2H_2O$ (Cat. No. 2382), $MnCl_2$ (Cat. No. 5927), EDTA (disodium salt, Cat. No. 8418) are from Merck. Hepes (Cat. No. H-3375), polybrene (Cat. No. H-9268), Tris (Cat. No. T-1503), and dithiothreitol (DTT, Cat. No. D-0632) are from Sigma. Nonidet P-40 (NP-40,

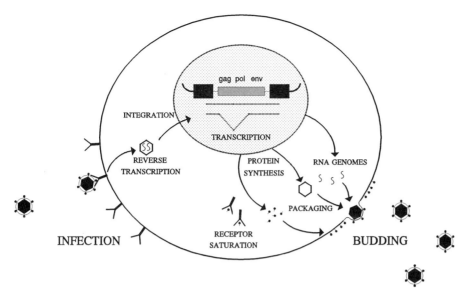

FIGURE 1 Schematic overview of the murine leukemia virus life cycle.

Cat. No. 74385) is from Fluka. Sucrose (Cat. No. 10274) is from BDH. Poly(A)·(dT)$_{15}$ (Cat. No. 108677) and dTTP (Cat. No. 1051482) are from Boehringer–Mannheim. [^{3}H]dTTP [specific activity, 1.11 TBq/mmole (30 Ci/mmole); radioactive concentration, 37 MBq/ml (1 mCi/ml), Cat. No. TRK.354] is from Amersham. Dulbecco's modified Eagle's medium (DMEM, Cat. No. 041-31965 M), RPMI-1640 (Cat. No. 041-31870M), newborn calf serum (Cat. No. 021-06010 M), and penicillin–streptomycin (10,000 units/ml and 10,000 μg/ml, Cat. No. 600-5140 AG) are from Gibco.

DEAE paper (Cat. No. NA45) and filters (0.2 μm, Cat. No. FP030/3) are from Schleicher & Schuell. T-80 tissue culture flask (Cat. No. 153732), T-25 tissue culture flask (Cat. No. 163371), and 50-ml tubes (Cat. No. 339497) are from Nunc. Roller bottle (850 cm^2, Cat. No. 25240) is from J. Bibby Science Products. Ultra-Clear tubes (Cat. No. 344059) and 250-ml bottles (Cat. No. 334205) are from Beckman. Microtubes (1.5 ml, Cat. No. 72690) are from Sarstedt. Speed Vac Concentrator (Model No. SVC 200 H) is from Savant. Biofuge 13 is from Heraeus. Centra 3C centrifuge is from International Equipment Company.

NIH 3T3 cells are available from the American Type Culture Collection as CCL 1658. L691 cells are a non-retrovirus-producing T-lymphoid cell line derived from a radiation-induced thymoma of a C57L mouse (McGrath *et al.*, 1980). Murine leukemia virus molecular clones are available from the American Type Culture Collection Animal Virus Collection.

III. Procedures

A. TRANSFECTION OF NIH 3T3 CELLS

Solutions

1. *Growth medium for NIH 3T3 cells:* Combine 500 ml DMEM, 55 ml newborn calf serum, and 5.5 ml penicillin–streptomycin.

2. *2× Hepes-buffered saline (HBS), 1 liter:* Solubilize 10 g Hepes, 16 g NaCl, 0.74 g KCl, 0.25 g Na$_2$HPO$_4$·2H$_2$O, and 2 g glucose in distilled water, adjust pH

to 7.05 with NaOH, and bring to a total volume of 1 liter. Sterilize the solution by filtration (0.2-μm filter) and store in aliquots at $-20°$C.

3. *2.5 M CaCl$_2$, 100 ml:* Solubilize 36.75 g of CaCl$_2 \cdot 2H_2O$ in distilled water and adjust to a total volume of 100 ml. Sterilize by filtration (0.2-μm filter) and store in aliquots at $-20°$C.

Steps

1. The day before transfection replate cells at a density of 10^4 cells/cm^2 in 20 ml growth medium in a T-80 culture flask.

2. One hour prior to transfection replace the medium with 10 ml of growth medium.

3. Prepare a calcium phosphate–DNA precipitate using stock solutions warmed to room temperature: Into a sterile 1.5-ml microtube add 10 μg virus DNA, 10 μg carrier DNA, 50 μl 2.5 M CaCl$_2$, and double-distilled H$_2$O to a final volume of 500 μl. Add the DNA solution *dropwise* to a 10-ml tube containing 500 μl 2× HBS bufier.

4. Add the precipitate onto the cells and immediately put the cells back into the incubator (37°C, 5% CO$_2$, 90% humidity).

5. The day after transfection replace the medium.

B. INFECTION OF NIH 3T3 CELLS

Solutions

1. *8 mg/ml polybrene, 100 ml:* Solubilize 800 mg polybrene in distilled water and adjust volume to 100 ml. Sterilize by filtration (0.2-μm filter) and store in aliquots at $-20°$C.

2. *Growth medium for NIH 3T3 cells:* Combine 500 ml DMEM, 55 ml newborn calf serum, and 5.5 ml penicillin–streptomycin.

Steps

1. The day before infection change the medium of the donor strain (i.e., the virus-producing cell line).

2. Seed recipient cells in 2.5 ml growth medium to a density of 3×10^3 cells/cm^2 in a T-80 culture fiask.

3. Incubate for 6 hr (37°C, 5% CO$_2$, 90% humidity) (or until cells are adherent).

4. Add 2–3 ml virus suspension containing medium from the donor strain and 8 μg/ml polybrene, filtrated (0.2-μm filter).

5. Incubate for 1 hr (37°C, 5% CO$_2$, 90% humidity).

6. Add fresh medium or filtrated medium from the donor strain up to 10 ml.

7. Incubate overnight (37°C, 5% CO$_2$, 90% humidity).

8. Repeat steps 4, 5, and 6.

C. COCULTIVATION OF L691 CELLS AND VIRUS-PRODUCING NIH 3T3 CELLS

Solutions

1. *Growth medium for NIH 3T3 cells:* Combine 500 ml DMEM, 55 ml newborn calf serum, and 5.5 ml penicillin–streptomycin.

2. *Growth medium for L691 cells:* Combine 500 ml RPMI, 55 ml newborn calf serum, and 5.5 ml penicillin–streptomycin.

3. *8 mg/ml polybrene, 100 ml:* Solubilize 800 mg polybrene in distilled water and adjust volume to 100 ml. Sterilize by filtration (0.2-μm filter) and store in aliquots at $-20°C$.

Steps

1. Replate the donor strain (*in casu* infected NIH 3T3 cells) at a density of 10^4 cells/cm^2 in a T-25 culture flask (i.e., 2.5×10^5 cells).

2. On the following day add 2.5×10^5 L691 cells and polybrene to a final concentration of 8 μg/ml.

3. After 3 days of cocultivation, transfer the now infected L691 cells to a new culture flask. (The NIH 3T3 cells are adherent and the L691 cells will be in the medium.)

D. REVERSE TRANSCRIPTASE ASSAY

Solutions

1. *1 M Tris–HCl, pH 7.8, 1 liter:* Solubilize 121.1 g Tris in distilled water, adjust the pH to 7.8 with HCl, and bring the volume to 1 liter.

2. *0.02 M MnCl$_2$, 100 ml:* Solubilize 39 mg MnCl$_2$ in distilled water and adjust the volume to 100 ml.

3. *1 M NaCl, 1 liter:* Solubilize 58.44 g NaCl in distilled water and adjust the volume to 1 liter.

4. *1% NP-40, 100 ml:* Mix 1 ml NP-40 and 99 ml distilled water.

5. *Solution A, 2 ml:* Mix 0.25 ml 1 M Tris–HCl, pH 7.8 (125 mM Tris–HCl), 0.05 ml 0.02 M MnCl$_2$ (0.5 mM MnCl$_2$), 0.30 ml 1 M NaCl (150 mM NaCl), 0.25 ml 1% NP-40 (0.125% NP-40), and 1.15 ml double-distilled H$_2$O.

6. *Solution B, 2 ml:* Solubilize poly (A)$\cdot$(dT)$_{15}$ (5 A_{260} units) in 2 ml double-distilled H$_2$O.

7. *Solution C, 20 ml:* 0.5 M DTT. Solubilize 1.55 g of DTT in distilled water and adjust volume to 20 ml.

8. *Solution D, 5 ml:* 200 μM dTTP. Mix 10 μl 100 mM dTTP and 4.99 ml double-distilled H$_2$O. Store stock solutions A–D in aliquots at $-20°C$.

9. *Solution E, 75 μl:* Transfer 75 μl[^{3}H]dTTP (2.8 MBq or 75 μCi [^{3}H]dTTP) to a 1.5-ml microtube and lyophilize in a Speed Vac Concentrator.

10. *Reverse transcriptase assay mix (for 40 assays):* Add 400 μl A, 400 μl B, 40 μl C, 60 μl D, and 100 μl double-distilled H$_2$O to the lyophilized [^{3}H]dTTP in tube E.

11. *1 M NaH$_2$PO$_4$, 1 liter:* Solubilize 156.01 g NaH$_2$PO$_4\cdot$2H$_2$O in distilled water and adjust volume to 1 liter.

Steps

1. Replace the medium the day before samples are taken for the assay.

2. Transfer 0.5 ml cell culture medium to an 1.5-ml micro tube and centrifuge at 2000 rpm in a Heraeus centrifuge (or Eppendorf centrifuge) for 10 min to sediment cells and cell debris.

3. Transfer the supernatant to a fresh microtube (can be stored at $-80°C$).

4. Centrifuge at 13,000 rpm in a Heraeus centrifuge for 1 hr at $4°C$ to sediment virus particles.

5. Carefully remove the supernatant without disturbing the pellet and place the tubes on ice.

6. Resuspend the pellet in 25 μl double-distilled H_2O and 25 μl assay mix (freshly made).

7. Vortex briefly and centrifuge shortly (15–30 sec).

8. Incubate for 30 min at $37°C$ and place the tubes on ice.

9. Spot the mixture onto DEAE paper (approx 1.5×1.5 cm) and dry thoroughly (e.g., under infrared light).

10. Wash the DEAE paper for 3×10 min in 1 M NaH_2PO_4 and once in 96% ethanol.

11. Dry the paper under infrared light or in a vacuum oven.

12. Place the DEAE paper in a scintillation vial and add 5 ml scintillation fluid. Count the ^3H activity in a scintillation counter.

E. PURIFICATION OF VIRUS PARTICLES FROM NIH 3T3 CELLS

Solutions

1. *1 M Tris–HCl, pH 7.5, 1 liter:* Solubilize 121.1 g Tris in distilled water, adjust pH to 7.5 with HCl, and bring the volume to 1 liter.

2. *1 M NaCl:* Solubilize 58.44 g NaCl in distilled water and adjust the volume to 1 liter.

3. *250 mM EDTA, 200 ml:* Solubilize 18.6 g EDTA in distilled water. To help dissolve the EDTA, adjust the pH to 8 using NaOH (~2 g NaOH pellets) and adjust volume to 200 ml.

4. *TNE buffer, 100 ml:* Combine 5 ml 1 M Tris–HCl, pH 7.5 (50 mM Tris–HCl, pH 7.5), 10 ml 1 M NaCl (100 mM NaCl), and 400 μl 250 mM EDTA (1 mM EDTA).

5. *25% sucrose in TNE, 20 ml:* Solubilize 5 g sucrose in TNE and adjust the volume to 20 ml.

6. *45% sucrose in TNE, 20 ml:* Solubilize 9 g sucrose in TNE and adjust the volume to 20 ml.

Steps

1. Infected NIH 3T3 cells are grown in 850-cm^2 roller bottles containing approximately 50 ml medium each.

2. Change the medium the day before starting harvesting virus.

3. Collect the medium in 50-ml tubes and centrifuge the medium at 2000 rpm for 10 min in a Centra 3C centrifuge to sediment cells and cell debris.

4. Transfer the supernatant to a Beckman 250-ml centrifuge tube and centrifuge in a type 19 rotor for 3 hr at 19,000 rpm, 4°C. Locate the pellet and gently pour off supernatant. Place the bottles upside down on paper cloth to remove the remaining liquid.

5. Place the tubes on ice and resuspend the pellet in 1 ml TNE per tube by gentle shaking, or gentle aspiration, if necessary.

6. Make a 25–45% linear sucrose gradient in an Ultra-Clear ultracentrifuge tube for a SW-41 rotor at 4°C and add the resuspended virus pellets. Add extra TNE buffer to fill the tube if necessary.

7. Centrifuge in a SW-41 rotor overnight at 35,000 rpm at 4°C (equilibrium centrifugation).

8. Identify the virus band around the middle of the gradient (~35% sucrose) by visual inspection. Collect the virus band by aspiration into a narrow pipette gently submerged through the gradient to the proper position and dilute with 3 vol of TNE.

9. Transfer the virus suspension to an SW-41 tube and centrifuge at 40,000 rpm for 3 hr at 4°C.

10. Dissolve the pellet in a small volume of TNE or in a buffer appropriate for further steps. Steps 6 through 9 may be repeated if further purification is desired.

IV. Comments

For use of protocols A, B, and C it must be kept in mind that only actively dividing cells are susceptible to murine leukemia virus infection (Miller *et al.*, 1990). In the choice of viruses and murine cell lines the NB-tropism of the virus and the *Fv-1* genotype of the cell should be compatible (Boone *et al.*, 1988). NIH 3T3 cells are $Fv-1^{n/n}$ and allow replication of N-tropic viruses, such as Akv MLV, or NB-tropic viruses, such as Moloney MLV.

In interpretation of results of reverse transcriptase assays the following figures may serve as guidance. For noninfected cultures we usually obtain values below 1000 cpm and good producers should result in values above 500,000 cpm. Alternative techniques for virus detection and quantitation employ immunostaining (Nexø, 1977) or plaque assays (Rowe *et al.*, 1970).

For mass production of virus (protocol E), supernatant may be collected with regular intervals from the same roller bottles over a period of 1 week or longer. Supernatants should be immediately clarified from cell debris (step 3), but may be kept refrigerated and pooled for further processing. Infected suspension cells (protocol B) may also be used for mass culture if more convenient. If no virus band is clearly visible after equilibrium centrifugation the gradient may be collected in fractions and virus-positive fractions identified by assay of reverse transcriptase activity.

Protocol E is not well suited for purification of infectious virus particles. Protocols for concentration of infectious MLV particles are available, but their yields are not uniformly high (Cepko, 1992).

REFERENCES

Boone, L. R., Glover, P. L., Innes, C. L., Niver, L. A., Bondurant, M. C., and Yang, W. K. (1988) *Fv-1* N- and B-tropism-specific sequences in murine leukemia virus and related endogenous proviral genomes. *J. Virol.* **62**, 2644–2650.

Cepko, C. (1992) Unit 9.12. *In* "Current Protocols in Molecular Biology" (F. M. Ausubel *et al.*, eds.). Greene Publishing Associates/John Wiley & Sons, New York, NY.

Goff, S., Traktman, P., and Baltimore, D. (1981) Isolation and properties of Moloney murine leukemia virus mutants: Use of a rapid assay for release of virion reverse transcriptase. *J. Virol.* **38**, 239–248.

Graham, F. L., and van der Eb, A. J. (1973) A new technique for the assay of infectivity of human adenovirus 5 DNA. *Virology* **52**, 456–467.

Jørgensen, E. C. B., Pedersen, F. S., and Jørgensen, P. (1992) Matrix protein of Akv murine leukemia virus: Genetic mapping of regions essential for particle formation. *J. Virol.* **66**, 4479–4487.

McGrath, M. S., Pillemer, E., Kooistra, D., and Weissmann, I. L. (1980) The role of MuLV receptors on T-lymphoma cells in lymphoma cell proliferation. *In* "Contemporary Topics in Immunobiology" (N. L. Warner, ed.), pp. 157–184. Plenum, New York.

Miller, D. G., Adam, M. A., and Miller, A. D. (1990) Gene transfer by retrovirus vectors occurs only in cells that are actively replicating at the time of infection. *Mol. Cell. Biol.* **10**, 4239–4242.

Nexø, B. A. (1977) A plaque assay for murine leukemia virus using enzyme coupled antibodies. *Virology* **77**, 849–852.

Paludan, K., Dai, H. Y., Duch, M., Jørgensen, P., Kjeldgaard, N. O., and Pedersen F. S. (1989) Different relative expression from two murine leukemia virus long terminal repeats in unintegrated transfected DNA and in integrated retroviral vector proviruses. *J. Virol.* **63**, 5201–5207.

Rein, A., and Schultz, A. (1984) Different recombinant murine leukemia viruses use different cell surface receptors. *Virology* **136**, 144–152.

Rowe, W. P., Pugh, W. E., and Hartley, J. W. (1970) Plaque assay techniques for murine leukemia viruses. *Virology* **42**, 1136–1139.

Varmus, H. (1989) Retroviruses. *Science* **240**, 1427–1435.

PART 3

ORGANELLES, CELLULAR STRUCTURES, MACROMOLECULES, AND FUNCTIONAL ASSAYS

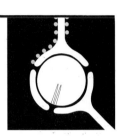

Purification of Rat Liver Golgi Stacks

Paul Slusarewicz, Norman Hui, and Graham Warren

I. Introduction

The study of intracellular organelles has been greatly facilitated by their purification from cellular homogenates. Such protocols yield an abundant source of material for both structural and functional studies. Here we describe a simple protocol, derived from several earlier methods (Leelavathi *et al.*, 1970; Fleischer and Fleischer, 1970; Hino *et al.*, 1978), for obtaining a highly purified preparation of stacked Golgi apparatus from rat liver and for determining their relative purity over the liver homogenate.

II. Materials and Instrumentation

Centrifugation was carried out using an L8-70M preparative ultracentrifuge and SW-28 rotor (Cat. No. 342207) containing Ultra-Clear tubes (Cat. No. 344058) from Beckman Instruments Inc. A 150-μm-mesh steel laboratory test sieve (Cat. No. 200 SBW.150) was obtained from Endecotts Ltd., and a 0–50% Delta refractometer (Cat. No. 2-70) from Bellingham and Stanley Ltd. Dipotassium hydrogen orthophosphate (Cat. No. 10436), potassium dihydrogen orthophosphate (Cat. No. 10203), sucrose (Cat. No. 10274), magnesium chloride (Cat. No. 10149), sodium cacodylate (Cat. No. 30118), and manganese chloride (Cat. No. 10152) were obtained from BDH Laboratory Supplies. Triton X-100 (Cat. No. T-6878), ovomucoid (Cat. No. T-2011), UDP-galactose (Cat. No. U-4500), and ATP (Cat. No. A-5394) were obtained from Sigma Chemical Company, Ltd. [3H]UDP-galactose with a specific activity of 30–50 Ci/mmole (Cat. No. NET758) was obtained from NEN Research Products. β-mercaptoethanol (Cat. No. 161-0710), Tris (Cat. No. 161-0719), and SDS (Cat. No. 161-0302) were obtained from Bio-Rad Laboratories Ltd. Ninety-five percent ethanol (Cat. No. SIN 1170) was obtained from Hayman Ltd. Concentrated hydrochloric acid (Cat. No. H/1200/PB17) was obtained from Fisons Scientific Equipment. The BCA Protein Assay Reagent (Cat. No. 23225) was obtained from Pierce Chemicals. All reagents were of analytical grade and the water used was double distilled and filtered.

III. Procedures

A. PURIFICATION OF RAT LIVER GOLGI STACKS

Solutions

1. *0.5 M potassium phosphate, pH 6.7:* Make up 500-ml solutions of 0.5 *M* anhydrous K_2HPO_4 (43.6 g) and 0.5 *M* anhydrous KH_2PO_4 (34 g). To 400 ml of the latter, gradually add the former until the pH reaches 6.7. Store at 4°C.

2. *2 M Sucrose:* Dissolve 342.3 g in water by stirring at 50°C. Make up to a final volume of 500 ml and store at 4°C.

3. *2 M MgCl₂:* Dissolve 40.7 g of $MgCl_2 \cdot 6H_2O$ in water to a final volume of 100 ml. Store at room temperature.

4. *Gradient buffers:* Buffers A–E can be made up from the preceding three stock solutions and cold water as shown in the following table. The water should be cooled to 4°C overnight to ensure that all the buffers are ice cold.

Buffer	A	B	C	D	E
Sucrose concentration	0 *M*	0.25 *M*	0.5 *M*	0.86 *M*	1.3 *M*
0.5 *M* potassium phosphate pH 6.7	20 ml	40 ml	80 ml	20 ml	12 ml
2 *M* sucrose	—	25 ml	100 ml	43 ml	39 ml
2 *M* MgCl₂	0.25 ml	0.5 ml	1 ml	0.25 ml	0.15 ml
Water	79.8 ml	135 ml	219 ml	36.8 ml	8.9 ml

Steps

1. Starve six female Sprague–Dawley or Wistar rats for 24 h.

2. Before killing the rats, pour six discontinuous gradients consisting of 13 ml of buffer D underlaid with 7.5 ml of buffer E into SW-28 rotor tubes and keep them on ice. Underlaying of buffer E can be performed with a 10-ml syringe connected to a plastic tube.

3. After killing the rats, rapidly remove the livers and place into 200 ml of buffer C. Swirl and squeeze the livers occasionally to expel blood and to speed cooling.

4. Weigh out 48 g of liver into 100 ml of fresh buffer C; cut the liver into several pieces to release as much blood as possible. Pour off excess buffer, leaving a volume of less than 80 ml, and then mince into small pieces (approximately 4–5 mm in diameter) with a clean pair of scissors.

5. Homogenize the tissue by gently pressing it through a 150-μm-mesh steel sieve with the bottom of a conical flask and collect the homogenate in a plastic tray. Pour the homogenate into a 100-ml measuring cylinder, add buffer C to a final volume of 80 ml, and mix well.

6. Overlay 13 ml of the homogenate onto each of the gradients, top up the tubes with buffer B, and centrifuge in an SW-28 rotor at 28,000 rpm for 1 hr at 4°C. Keep the remaining homogenate on ice for later assay.

7. Aspirate away the lipid layer on the surface of the gradient and collect the Golgi fraction from the interface between buffers C and D using a Pasteur pipette as depicted in Fig. 1. Collect approximately 2–3 ml from each gradient.

8. Dilute the pooled Golgi fractions to 0.25 *M* sucrose using buffer A. Check the concentration using a refractometer (0.25 *M* reads as approximately 9.5%) and measure the exact volume of this sample.

9. Aliquot the diluted samples into two fresh centrifuge tubes and keep 100 μl on ice for enzyme assay. Top up the tubes with buffer B and slowly add 100 μl of buffer E to each, to form a sucrose cushion, by dribbling it down the side of the tube. Centrifuge at 7000 rpm for 30 min at 4°C in the SW-28 rotor.

10. Aspirate and discard the supernatant, resuspend each of the two pellets in 2 ml of buffer B, and pool the suspensions. Make up to 38 ml with buffer B,

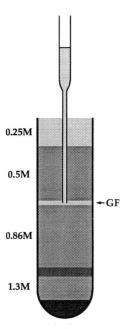

0.25M

0.5M

←GF

0.86M

1.3M

FIGURE 1 Collection of the Golgi fraction from a discontinuous sucrose gradient. The Golgi stacks form a thin band (GF) at the 0.5/0.86 *M* interface and can be collected using a Pasteur pipette.

place into a fresh centrifuge tube, and add 100 μl of buffer E to form another cushion. Balance with a tube containing buffer A alone and spin as in step 9.

11. Aspirate and discard the supernatant and resuspend the final pellet in 4.5 ml of buffer B. Measure the exact volume, aliquot appropriately, flash-freeze in liquid nitrogen, and store at −80°C. Samples can be thawed and refrozen at least twice without significant loss of enzymatic activity or loss of morphology.

B. DETERMINATION OF β-1,4-GALACTOSYLTRANSFERASE ACTIVITY

The relative purification of the Golgi stacks can be assessed by measuring the increase in specific activity of a *trans*-Golgi enzyme, β-1,4-galactosyltransferase (GalT), over that of the whole cell homogenate. The enzyme assay used is that of Bretz and Staubli (1977), where the addition of tritiated galactose onto the oligosaccharides of an acceptor protein, ovomucoid, is measured.

Solutions

1. *0.4 M sodium cacodylate, pH 6.6:* Dissolve 17.1 g in 150 ml of water and adjust the pH to 6.6 with HCl. Make up to 200 ml and store at room temperature.

2. *175 mg/ml Ovomucoid:* Dissolve 1 g in water and make up to a final volume of 5.7 ml. Filter through a 0.45-μm nitrocellulose filter, aliquot, and store at −20°C.

3. *10 mM UDP-galactose:* Dissolve 25 mg in a final volume of 4.4 ml of water. Aliquot and store at −20°C.

4. *10% (w/v) Triton X-100:* Dissolve 10 g in 80 ml of water and make up to a final volume of 100 ml. Store at 4°C.

5. *0.2 M ATP:* Dissolve 605 mg in 3 ml of water. Adjust the pH to 6.5–7.0

with 1 M NaOH and make up to a final volume of 5 ml with water. Aliquot and store at −20°C.

6. *2 M MnCl₂:* Dissolve 9.9 g of $MnCl_2 \cdot 4H_2O$ in 15 ml of water and make up to 25 ml. Store at room temperature.

7. *1% Phosphotungstic acid/0.5 M HCl (PTA/HCl):* Dissolve 5 g of phosphotungstic acid in 400 ml of water. Add 22 ml of concentrated HCl and make up to 500 ml with water. Store at 4°C.

8. *5% (w/v) SDS:* Dissolve 5 g of SDS in 80 ml of water and make up to 100 ml. Store at room temperature.

9. *2 M Tris:* Dissolve 24.2 g of Tris in 70-ml of water and make up to 100 ml. Store at room temperature.

10. *Assay mixture:* Make up a fresh batch of the assay mixture from the above stocks as follows: 200 μl sodium cacodylate, 200 μl ovomucoid, 6 μl β-mercaptoethanol, 40 μl UDP-galactose, 40 μl Triton X-100, 20 μl ATP, 40 μl MnCl₂, 10 μl [³H]UDP-galactose, and 1040 μl of water.

Steps

1. Once the Golgi preparation has been completed, make 1:20 dilutions of the homogenate, intermediate, and Golgi fractions with water.

2. Add 80 μl of assay mixture to screw-capped Eppendorf tubes containing duplicate 20-μl aliquots of the diluted samples and of water (blanks). Vortex and incubate at 37°C for exactly 30 min.

3. Stop the reaction by adding 1 ml of ice-cold PTA/HCl and spin at 14,000 rpm on a benchtop centrifuge for 7 sec.

4. Aspirate and discard the supernatants, and add 1 ml of PTA/HCl. Resuspend the pellets by vortexing or scraping and spin as in step 3.

5. Aspirate and discard the supernatant, add 1 ml of ice-cold 95% ethanol, and resuspend the pellets.

6. Spin as in step 3 and remove the supernatant. Add 50 μl of 2 M Tris followed by 200 μl of 5% SDS and shake or vortex until dissolved. Add 10 μl of assay mixture, 40 μl of water, and 200 μl of 5% SDS to a fresh tube to allow determination of the [³H]UDP-galactose specific activity in the mixture.

7. Add 1 ml of scintillation fluid to each sample. Vortex and count in a scintillation counter using the tritium channel.

C. DETERMINATION OF PROTEIN CONCENTRATION

Steps

1. While the GalT assays are incubating, make up the following dilutions of the three samples in water: 1:100 for the homogenate, 1:20 for the intermediate fraction, and 1:5 for the Golgi preparation.

2. Prepare a standard curve by aliquoting 50, 45, 40, 35, and 30 μl of water in duplicate and adding 0, 5, 10, 15, and 20 μl of 2 mg/ml BSA. This gives protein standards containing 0, 10, 20, 30, and 40 μg of BSA.

3. Aliquot 50 μl of each of the samples in duplicate and 50 μl of water as a blank.

TABLE I Purification Table Showing the Enrichment of a *trans*-Golgi Marker, β-1,4-Galactosyltransferase (GalT), over the Homogenate in both the Intermediate Fraction (0.5/0.86 *M* Interface) and the Golgi Preparation[a]

Fraction	Volume	[Protein] (mg/ml)	[GalT] (nmol/hr/ml)	Specific activity	Yield (%)	Purification (-fold)
Homogenate	78.0	82.8 ± 3.6	760.0 ± 57.4	9.4 ± 0.6	100.0	1.0
0.5/0.86 *M*						
Interface	65.7 ± 4.0	5.7 ± 0.4	236.8 ± 16.3	45.0 ± 3.2	25.6 ± 1.4	5.0 ± 0.4
Golgi	4.5 ± 0.1	2.8 ± 0.2	2060.0 ± 228.7	749.0 ± 70.0	15.5 ± 1.5	81.8 ± 6.9

[a] This table was compiled using the results from 24 separate purifications, presented as the mean ± SEM for each parameter. Note that the specific activity, yield, and purification fold are not, therefore, arithmetically related to the GalT and protein concentrations.

4. Add 1 ml of the Pierce protein assay mixture to the standards and the samples, allow to develop, and measure absorbance as described in the manual.

D. CALCULATION OF PURIFICATION TABLES

Steps

1. Construct a protein standard curve by plotting the absorbance of each standard against the amount of BSA it contains. Calculate the slope (m) and the intercept at the ordinate axis (c). Calculate the protein concentrations of the samples as follows:

$$\text{Protein concentration (mg/ml)} = \frac{(\text{sample absorbance} - c) \times \text{dilution}}{m \times 50}$$

2. Calculate the specific activity (SA) of [³H]UDP-galactose in the assay mixture as follows:

$$\text{SA [}^3\text{H]UDP-galactose (dpm/nmole)} = \frac{(\text{dpm of standard} - \text{blank})}{2.5}$$

3. Calculate the concentration of galactosyltransferase in each sample as follows:

$$\text{Concentration GalT (nmole/hr/ml)} = \frac{(\text{average dpm} - \text{blank}) \times 2000}{\text{SA [}^3\text{H]UDP-galactose}}$$

4. Calculate the SA of GalT by dividing its concentration by the protein concentration of the same sample to give SA in nmole/hr/mg.

5. The yields of Golgi membranes can be calculated from the ratio between the total GalT in the intermediate and Golgi fractions and that of the homogenate.

6. The purification fold is the factor by which the GalT specific activity increases in the intermediate and Golgi fractions over the homogenate.

IV. Comments

This protocol typically yields Golgi membranes which are purified 70- to 90-fold over the homogenate, as depicted in Table I. Purification folds are usually higher when β-1,2-*N*-acetylglucosaminyltransferase I (NAGT I) is used as the marker, as shown in Table II. This enzyme can be assayed as described by Vischer and Hughes (1981), though this assay is more time consuming than that for GalT. This difference

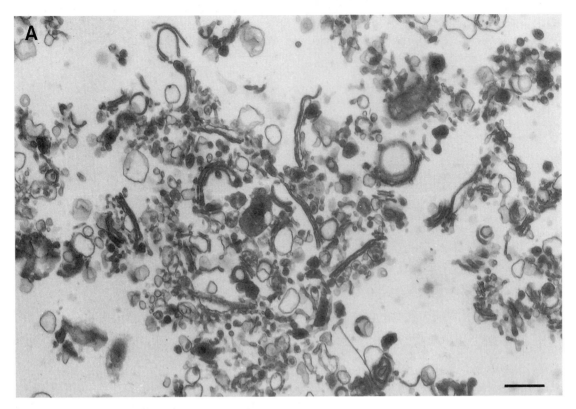

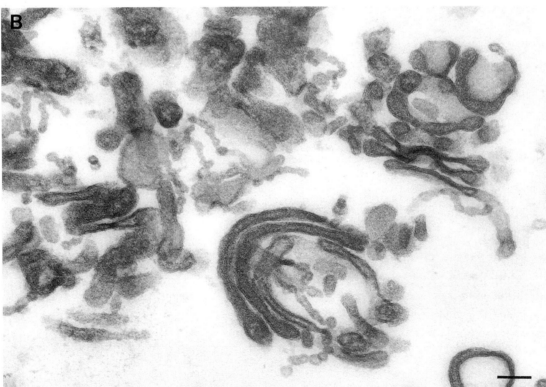

FIGURE 2 Representative micrographs of a typical rat liver Golgi apparatus preparation showing stacked Golgi membranes (arrows) at low (A) and high (B) magnification. Magnification: (A) 22,250 (bar = 0.5 μm) and (B) 97,500 (bar = 0.1 μm).

TABLE II Purification Table Showing Relative Purification of a Medial-Golgi Marker, β-1,2-N-acetylglucosaminyltransferase I (NAGT I), over the Homogenate[a]

Fraction	Volume	[Protein] (mg/ml)	[NAGT I] (nmol/hr/ml)	Specific activity	Yield (%)	Purification (-fold)
Homogenate	78	78.9	45.2	0.6	100	1
0.5/0.86 M Interface	74.8	5.2	49.6	9.6	88.3	16.6
Golgi	4.9	2.7	370	144	51.0	192

[a] This table shows the average value obtained from two experiments.

is probably due to some loss of the *trans*-Golgi network during purification because this organelle contains a significant amount of GalT but no NAGT I (see Nilsson *et al.*, 1993).

The Golgi preparations contain very little lysosomal or endoplasmic reticulum contamination as assessed by assay of β-N-acetylhexosaminidase (Landegren, 1984) and rotenone-insensitive NADH–cytochrome c reductase (Sottocasa *et al.*, 1967).

The stacked nature of these Golgi membranes can be confirmed by examination of preparations by electron microscopy (Fig. 2). Samples are fixed in suspension by the method described by Pypaert *et al.* (1991).

V. Pitfalls

1. Like many organelle purification procedures, it is vital to keep all solutions at 4°C during the whole protocol to prevent excessive protease digestion. If possible, steps 3–6 should be performed in a cold room.

2. All steps should be carried out as quickly as possible and the entire procedure, from the killing of rats to the freezing of final samples, should take approximately 3–3.5 hr.

3. Gradients should not be overloaded by increasing the concentration of the homogenate, as this increases the amount of mitochondrial contamination of the preparation.

4. The final Golgi pellet should be white. A brown pellet indicates the presence of contaminating mitochondria. Such contamination can be reduced by lowering the concentration of the homogenate.

5. The 150-μm sieve will become clogged with connective tissue after excessive use. This can be removed by soaking the sieve in 4 M NaOH overnight followed by washing with copious amounts of water.

REFERENCES

Bretz, R., and Staubli, W. (1977) Detergent influence on rat-liver galactosyltransferase activities towards different acceptors. *Eur. J. Biochem.* 77, 181–192.

Fleischer, B., and Fleischer, S. (1970) Preparation and characterisation of Golgi membranes from rat liver. *Biochim. Biophys. Acta* 219, 301–319.

Hino, Y., Asano, A., Sato, R., and Shimizu, S. (1978) Biochemical studies of rat liver Golgi apparatus. I. Isolation and preliminary characterization. *J. Biochem. Tokyo* 83, 909–923.

Landegren, U. (1984) Measurement of cell numbers by means of the endogenous enzyme hexosaminidase. Applications to the detection of lymphokines and cell surface antigens. *J. Immunol. Methods* 67, 379–388.

Leelavathi, D. E., Estes, L. W., Feingold, D. S., and Lombardi, B. (1970) Isolation of a Golgi-rich fraction from rat liver. *Biochim. Biophys. Acta* **211**, 124–138.

Nilsson, T., Pypaert, M., Hoe, M. H., Slusarewicz, P., Berger, E., and Warren, G. (1993) Overlapping distribution of two glycosyltransferases in the Golgi apparatus of Hela cells. *J. Cell Biol.* **120**, 5–13.

Pypaert, M., Mundy, D., Souter, E., Labbe, J.-C., and Warren, G. (1991) Mitotic cytosol inhibits invagination of coated pits in broken mitotic cells. *J. Cell Biol.* **114**, 1159–1166.

Sottocasa, G. L., Kuylenstierna, B., Ernster, L., and Bergstrand, A. (1967) An electron-transport system associated with the outer membrane of liver mitochondria. *J. Cell Biol.* **32**, 415–438.

Vischer, P., and Hughes, C. R. (1981) Glycosyl transferases of baby-hampster-kidney (BHK) cells and ricin-resistant mutants. *Eur. J. Biochem.* **117**, 275–284.

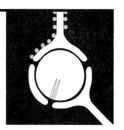

Preparation and Purification of Post-Golgi Transport Vesicles from Perforated Madin-Darby Canine Kidney Cells

Lukas A. Huber and Kai Simons

I. Introduction

An *in vitro* system is described that allows the isolation of transport vesicles derived from the *trans*-Golgi network (TGN) with the aim of identifying the molecular machinery involved in protein sorting and vesicle targeting in polarized epithelia (Bennett *et al.*, 1988). Madin–Darby canine kidney cells (MDCK strain II cells) are grown on permeable filter supports allowing them to attach tightly to the substrate and to form a fully polarized monolayer. The cells are then infected for short times with influenza or vesicular stomatitis virus (VSV) and incubated at 20°C, causing the transport markers to accumulate in the TGN (Griffiths *et al.*, 1985; Matlin *et al.*, 1983; Hughson *et al.*, 1988). Subsequently, the cells are mechanically perforated with the aid of a nitrocellulose filter. This introduces holes in the plasma membranes but leaves the cells attached to the filter support with their subcellular organization intact (Simons and Virta, 1987). Using this system, we demonstrated previously that HA and VSV G-protein, accumulated in the TGN before perforation, were released from the perforated cells in sealed membrane vesicles (Bennett *et al.*, 1988). The vesicles had the topology expected for authentic transport vesicles and required ATP for their formation and release. The release of membranes from such perforated cells was quite specific: only low levels of resident Golgi markers, endocytic markers, or endoplasmic reticulum (ER)-derived vesicles were recovered in the incubation medium (Bennett *et al.*, 1988). The TGN-derived transport vesicles have been resolved into apical and basolateral fractions and further characterized (Wandinger-Ness *et al.*, 1990; Kurzchalia *et al.*, 1992; Huber *et al.*, 1993).

II. Materials and Instrumentation

Media and reagents for cell culture are purchased from Gibco Biocult and Biochrom. Growth medium for MDCK strain II cells consisted of MEM with Earle's salts (E-MEM) supplemented with 10 mM Hepes, pH 7.3, 10% FCS, 100 U/ml penicillin, and 100 μg/ml streptomycin. MDCK II cells are grown and passaged as described previously (see article by Hilkka Virta and Kai Simons). For large-scale isolation of vesicles, cells from a 75-cm² flask were seeded on a single 100-mm-diameter, 0.4-μm-pore-size Transwell filter (24 × 10⁶ cells) as described (see article by Virta and Simons in this volume).

ATP was from Sigma (Cat. No. 5394); creatine phosphate (Cat. No. 621714, disodium salt) and creatine kinase (CK, Cat. No. 127566, rabbit muscle) from Boehringer-Mannheim; NC filters (HATF 02500 0.45-μm filter type HA, Triton free) from Millipore; No. 1 filters from Whatman Scientific Limited; and cell filters (0.4-μm pore size; No. 3412, ϕ 24 mm; No. 3419, ϕ 100 mm Transwell) from Costar.

III. Procedures

A. GENERATION AND PERMEABILIZATION OF MDCK CELLS

Solutions

1. *10× KOAc transport buffer:* To make 200 ml, combine 250 m*M* Hepes–KOH, pH 7.4, (11.92 g, 1150 m*M* potassium); acetate (22.58 g); and 25 m*M* MgCl$_2$ (1.02 g).

2. *10× GGA buffer (transport buffer):* To make 50 ml, prepare three solutions: (a) 1150 m*M* L-glutamate (MW 185.2, 10.65 g); (b) 1150 m*M* L-aspartate (MW 171.2, 9.84 g); (c) 1150 m*M* potassium gluconate (MW 234.2, 13.47 g). To each solution a–c, add 250 m*M* Hepes–KOH, pH 7.4, and 25 m*M* MgCl$_2$·6H$_2$O. Filter-sterilize the solutions. Mix solutions a–c 1:1:1. Dilute 10× (add 1 m*M* DTT and 2 m*M* EGTA). Adjust to pH 7.4 just before use.

3. *ATP regenerating system (ATP mix), 100× stocks, prepare three solutions (10ml each):*

a. 100 mM ATP (disodium salt, pH 6–7, neutralized with 2 M NaOH; 0.605g/ 10 ml)

b. 800 mM creatine phosphate (disodium salt, 2,620 g/10 ml)

c. 800 U/mg (at 37°C) creatine kinase (0.5 mg/10 ml in 50% glycerol)

Store stocks in aliquots at −20°C. Mix solutions a–c 1:1:1 just before use.

Steps

The basic procedure for the generation of perforated cells is quite simple. A monolayer of cells grown on a solid substrate is overlain with a nitrocellulose filter. The filter is allowed to bind under controlled conditions for a specified period and is then peeled away from the cells. The cells remain attached to the substrate but now have holes in their plasma membrane. These holes allow manipulation of the cytoplasmic composition in cells whose overall morphology and organellar organization remain intact.

A number of factors are important in establishing an efficient and reproducible system for the perforation of cells using the nitrocellulose filter procedures. Perhaps the most important consideration is the strength of the cell attachment to the substrate on which they are grown. This will determine the amount of binding between the cells and the nitrocellulose filter that can be allowed to occur. If the cells are weakly adherent, the entire cell layer, instead of small fragments of the plasma membrane, will be removed by the nitrocellulose filter. A second consideration is the method of binding the nitrocellulose filter to the cell layer, in this case, the amount of binding: with insufficient drying, the cells will not be perforated; with excessive drying, the cells will become detached. It is therefore important to establish conditions that allow for reproducible and even drying. A number of variables

FIGURE 1

including the time, temperature, humidity, and air circulation should be controlled to obtain the most reproducible results.

The following manipulations are performed in a cold room (4°C) with cold buffers.

MDCK cells grown for 3 days on Transwell filters (3412 or 3419)

1. Wash filter cells twice with PBS(+) [dip twice in beaker with PBS(+)]. Aspirate excess liquid carefully so as not to destroy filter.

2. Incubate filters for 45–60 min at 20°C (TGN block).

Perforation (in Cold Room!)

3. Presoak NC filters in KOAc transport buffer

4. Wash cell filter (Transwell 3412 or 3419) twice in KOAc transport buffer (glass beaker). Cut out cell filter with a sharp scalpel (**Fig. 1a**). Place cell filter in KOAc transport buffer, cell side up.

5. Place predrained NC filter on Whatman No. 1 paper, put another Whatman paper on it, and drain a bit with an L-form Pasteur pipette.

6. Time: 0 sec.

7. Time: 30 sec. Place cell filter in 20°C water bath (on petri dish), cell side up.

8. Time: 60 sec. Place NC filter exactly on cell filter (Fig. 1b) and immediately place a Whatman paper on it; drain it a bit by using an L-form Pasteur pipette (this should take 15 sec) and drain again with a new Whatman paper (Fig. 1c).

9. Time: 75 sec. During a time course of 90 sec (starting after the first draining) the cells become attached to the NC filter at 20°C.

10. Time: 165 sec (90 sec after the first draining). Add 200 μl of KOAc transport buffer on the cell filter–NC filter sandwich. Aspirate excess moisture (Fig. 1d) and take the petri dish out of the water bath. Flip the filter sandwich around (cell filter–NC filter on top) (Fig. 1e). Peel off the cell filter carefully (still on the petri dish) (Fig. 1f)

11. Place cell filter in 1× GGA buffer + ATP-regenerating system (for Transwell 3412: 1 ml in 3.5-cm dish and 30 μl ATP mix; for Transwell 3419, 10 ml in 10-cm dish and 300 μl ATP mix).

12. Discard NC filter or use it for nuclear control stain (Hoechst). No more than 10% of the cells should be on the NC filter.

13. Incubate cell filter at 37°C for 1 hr in a water bath in the presence of GGA buffer and ATP-generating system (place wet Whatman paper inside the lid to collect condensed water).

B. PREPARATION OF EXOCYTIC VESICLES FROM PERFORATED MDCK CELLS

Solutions

1. 0.25 M sucrose (8.5 g/100 ml) in 10 mM Hepes (0.238 g/100 ml), 2 mM EGTA (0.076 g/100 ml), 1 mM DTT (0.015 g/100 ml).

2. 1.5 M sucrose (51.3 g/100 ml) in 10 mM Hepes, 2 mM EGTA, 1 mM DTT.

3. 1.2 M sucrose (41.04 g/100 ml) in 10 mM Hepes, 2 mM EGTA, 1 mM DTT.

4. 0.8 M sucrose (27.36 g/100 ml) in 10 mM Hepes, 2 mM EGTA, 1 mM DTT (filter-sterilize).

Steps

Pelleting vesicles through sucrose cushion

1. Collect GGA buffer with ATP-generating system with pipette (may be kept on ice for up to 30 min). Centrifugation: 1500 rpm, 10 min, 4°C (Falcon 15-ml tube/cell debris in pellet).

2. First ultracentrifugation through the sucrose cushion: SW 40, 36,000–40,000 rpm; 3 hr; 4°C. Overlay 6 ml vesicle solution (from six Transwell 3412 filters), on to 6 ml sucrose solution (0.25 M), or for 10 ml vesicle solution (from one Transwell 3419 filter), overlay on to 2 ml sucrose (0.25 M).

3. Aspirate supernatant carefully with a drawn-out Pasteur pipette (pellet is hardly detectable).

4. Resuspend pellet in 100 μl sucrose solution (1.5 M).

Floating of vesicles in discontinous sucrose gradient

1. Bottom: vesicles from the sucrose cushion, resuspended in 1.5 M sucrose in 10 mM Hepes, 2 mM EGTA, 1 mM DTT: 0.4 ml per tube of vesicles from up to 36 ϕ24-mm filters or up to 6 ϕ100-mm filters. Overlay with 1.2 M sucrose in 10 mM Hepes, 2 mM EGTA, 1 mM DTT: 1.7 ml; overlay with 0.8 M sucrose in 10 mM Hepes, 2 mM EGTA, 1 mM DTT: 1.5 ml.

2. Centrifugation: 14 hr, 35,000 rpm, 4°C, SW 60 (no brake).

3. Fractionate gradient into 0.3-ml aliquots from the top to the bottom.

4. Recover the peak fractions containing vesicles at the 0.8/1.2 M sucrose interface and pool for further analysis (immunoisolation).

C. IMMUNOISOLATION OF APICAL AND BASOLATERAL VESICLE FRACTIONS

Solutions

1. Cellulose fibers coupled with sheep affinity-purified anti Fc antibodies.

2. Mouse monoclonal antibodies directed against the cytoplasmic domains of VSV-G protein (Kreis, 1986) and influenza PR8 (Hughson *et al.*, 1988) are used in the form of concentrated hybridoma culture supernatants.

3. Antiprotease mix (CLAP): 10 mg/ml DMSO of each: chymostatin, leupeptin, antipain, pepstatin; use 1:1000. Store stock at −20°C.

Steps

Immunoisolation can be used as the final vesicle purification step, allowing for the separation of transport vesicles destined for either the apical or the basolateral plasma membrane domains (Wandinger-Ness *et al.*, 1990). MDCK cells were grown and infected with VSV (for basolateral vesicles) or influenza virus (WSN ts61 influenza strain for apical vesicles) as described previously (Pfeiffer *et al.*, 1985; Wandinger-Ness *et al.*, 1990). We use antibodies directed against the cytoplasmic domains of either VSV G-protein or influenza HA for these studies, but antibodies directed against other markers with cytoplasmically exposed epitopes (e.g., mannose 6-phosphate receptor, clathrin, synaptophysin) could be used to isolate different types of vesicles. The following immunoisolation methods represent a modification of previously published procedures.

1. Divide the vesicle pool from the flotation gradient into three equal aliquots (usually 300 μl each).

2. Dilute the first aliquot fourfold with 10 mM Hepes–KOH, pH 7.4, 1 mM EGTA (to reduce the sucrose concentration to 0.25 M) and centrifuge at 55,000 rpm (200,000 g) in a TLS55 rotor in a Beckman TL-100 centrifuge. One resulting

pellet serves as a control for the total particulate material in the starting vesicle fraction. Two remaining pellets are used for immunoisolation using either specific or control monoclonal antibodies. Antibody P5D4 directed against the cytoplasmic domain of VSV G-protein serves as the specific antibody for vesicles obtained from VSV-infected cells and as the control antibody for vesicles obtained from WSN-infected cells (Wandinger-Ness *et al.*, 1990). Antibody 2D1 directed against the cytoplasmic domain of WSN HA serves as the specific antibody for vesicles obtained from WSN-infected cells and as the control antibody for vesicles obtained from VSV-infected cells (Wandinger-Ness *et al.*, 1990).

3. Add 0.5 vol (150 μl) of PBS containing 0.1% (w/v) gelatin and a protease inhibitor cocktail (10 μg/ml each of chymostatin, leupeptin, antipain, and pepstatin) to each aliquot.

4. Add monoclonal antibody (20 μl of a 10-fold concentrated hybridoma culture supernatant) and incubate the sample at 4°C with rotation either for 3 hr for VSV samples or overnight for WSN samples. Cellulose fibers to which an affinity-purified sheep antibody generated against the Fc domain of mouse IgG is covalently coupled are used as the solid support to recover the antibody–vesicle complexes.

5. Add 1 mg of the cellulose fibers (500 μl of 2 mg/ml fibers in PBS containing 0.1% w/v gelatin) to each sample and continue the incubation for 1.5 hr at 4°C with rotation.

6. Pellet the fibers in the microfuge at 1500 rpm for 10 min and wash three times with PBS containing 0.1% (w/v) gelatin and once with PBS. Under these conditions greater than 50% of the viral glycoproteins are recovered on the specific fibers, whereas less than 10% are recovered on the control fibers.

The immunoisolation conditions used are optimized to obtain maximal specific recovery of the desired marker with minimal nonspecific binding. One factor important for maximal recovery is to carry out antibody binding in solution (i.e., in the absence of the solid support) to increase the possibility of antibody–antigen interaction. The HA-containing vesicles proved to be more difficult to recover quantitatively than the VSV G-containing vesicles, perhaps because of the short cytoplasmic domain of WSN HA (only 11 amino acids) or because of differences in antibody affinity for the respective antigens. Two modifications of the VSV G protocol were used that increased the recovery of HA-containing vesicles. The first was to increase the antibody binding time from 3 hr to overnight. The second was the use of a temperature-sensitive mutant of WSN (ts 61). The mutant HA fails to be transported out of the ER at the nonpermissive temperature and therefore accumulates in the ER when the infection is carried out at 39°C. When the cells are subsequently shifted to 20°C the HA is transported out of the ER and accumulates in the TGN at higher concentrations than would be obtained with wild-type virus. This presumably results in a higher concentration of the antigen in the transport vesicles; therefore, a more efficient recovery by immunoisolation is achieved.

Nonspecific binding can be a serious problem when dealing with small amounts of material and with the mild washing conditions required to maintain membrane integrity. The minimization of nonspecific binding required screening of a number of different solid supports (cellulose fibers, magnetic beads, fixed *Staphylococcus aureus* cells) and the use of gelatin as a blocking reagent. In our experience the cellulose fibers gave the lowest nonspecific binding.

Steps

1. Pool vesicle fractions from flotation gradient.

Sample	Volume (µl)	Antibody (20 µl)	Temp/time	PBS/0.1% gelatin (CLAP) 1:1000	Cellulose fibers/anti-Fc
VSV	200	Anti-G	4°C/3 hr	150 µl	500 µl
Influenza	300	Anti-HA	4°C/12 hr	150 µl	500 µl
Influenza	300	Anti-G	4°C/12 hr	150 µl	500 µl

2. Incubate sample (flotation gradient pool from influenza virus) on VSV-infected MDCK cells (perforated, etc.) with appropriate antibody and PBS/0.1% gelatin (CLAP) for the indicated time. Incubate in Eppendorf tube under rotation in cold room.

3. Add 1 mg (500 µl) of cellulose fibers containing anti-Fc antibodies, prewashed. To wash fibers, place them in a Falcon tube and fill tube with PBS/0.1% gelatin. Centrifuge at 2000 rpm for 10 min. Aspirate supernatant and repeat. Resuspend fibers into original volume with PBS/0.1% gelatin).

4. Incubate 1.5–2 hr at 4°C under rotation.

5. Wash fibers three times in 1 ml PBS/0.1% gelatin and once in 1 ml PBS (Biofuge at 2500 rpm and 4°C for 8–10 min).

6. After the last wash, aspirate supernatant and centrifuge 30 sec in a microfuge to remove all excess liquid. Add 50 µl two-dimensional gel lysis buffer and a few grains of solid urea. Mix well and store −20°C until loading.

7. Control vesicle samples (sucrose concentration <0.3 M) that have not been immunoisolated are concentrated in small polyallomer tubes (rotor TLS 55) for 3 hr at 5500 rpm in Beckman table-top ultracentrifuge. Take off supernatant with drawn-out Pasteur pipette and process for further analysis (SDS–PAGE, etc.).

IV. Comments and Pitfalls

The vesicles become sticky and adsorb to the walls of nonpolyallomer tubes. When we used large polyallomer tubes for concentration, we lost vesicles as well.

REFERENCES

Bennett, M. K., Wandinger-Ness, A., and Simons, K. (1988) Release of putative exocytic transport vesicles from perforated MDCK cells. *EMBO J.* 7, 4075–4085.

Griffiths, G., Pfeiffer, S., Simons, K., and Matlin, K. (1985) Exit of newly synthesized membrane proteins from the trans cisternae of the Golgi complex to the plasma membrane. *J. Biol. Chem.* 101, 949–964.

Huber, L. A., Pimplikar, S. W., Virta, H., Parton, R. G., Zerial, M., and Simons, K. (1993) rab8, a small GTPase involved in vesicular traffic between the TGN and the basolateral plasma membrane. *J. Cell Biol.* 123, 35–45.

Hughson, E., Wandinger-Ness, A., Gausepohl, H., Griffiths, G., and Simons, K. (1988) The cell biology of enveloped virus infection of epithelial tissues. *In* "The Molecular Biology of Infectious Diseases. Centenary Symposium of the Pasteur Institute" (M. Schwartz, ed.), pp. 75–89. Elsevier, Paris.

Kreis, T. E. (1986) Microinjected antibodies against the cytoplasmic domain of vesicular stomatitis virus glycoprotein block its transport to the cell surface. *EMBO J.* 5, 931–941.

Kurzchalia, T. V., Dupree, P., Parton, R. G., Kellner, R., Virta, H., Lehnert, M., and Simons, K. (1992) VIP21, a 21-kD membrane protein, is an integral component of *trans*-Golgi-network-derived transport vesicles. *J. Cell Biol.* 118, 1003–1014.

Matlin, K., Bainton, D. F., Pesonen, M., Louvard, D., Genty, N., and Simons, K. (1983) Transepithelial transport of a viral membrane glycoprotein implanted into the apical plasma membrane of Madin–Darby canine kidney cells. I. Morphological evidence. *J. Cell Biol.* 97, 627–637.

Pfeiffer, S., Fuller, S. D., and Simons, K. (1985) Intracellular sorting and basolateral appearance of the G protein of vesicular stomatitis virus in MDCK cells. *J. Cell Biol.* **101**, 470–476.

Simons, K., and Virta, H. (1987). Perforated MDCK cells support intracellular transport. *EMBO J.* **6**, 2241–2247.

Wandinger-Ness, A., Bennett, M. K., Antony, C., and Simons, K. (1990) Distinct transport vesicles mediate the delivery of plasma membrane proteins to the apical and basolateral domains of MDCK cells. *J. Cell Biol.* **111**, 987–1000.

Purification of Clathrin-Coated Vesicles from Bovine Brain, Liver, and Adrenal Gland

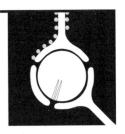

Robert Lindner

I. Introduction

Clathrin-coated vesicles are intermediates in selective membrane transport processes in eukaryotic cells (Smythe and Warren, 1991). Since the first report on the purification of these organelles a variety of protocols have been published (for review see Pearse, 1989). In this article I describe a differential centrifugation protocol that has been adapted from Campbell *et al.* (1984) for bovine brain tissue as a source. It rapidly provides crude clathrin-coated vesicles which are ideally suited for the preparation of various coat proteins (see Keen *et al.*, 1979; Ahle *et al.*, 1988; Ahle and Ungewickell, 1990; Lindner and Ungewickell, 1991). Because of the existence of tissue-specific isoforms of several coat components, remarks on modifications in the procedure for other bovine organs (adrenal gland, liver) are included.

II. Materials and Instrumentation

Ficoll 400 (Cat. No. 17-0400-02) was obtained from Pharmacia LKB Biotechnology AB. Sucrose (Cat. No. BP 220-1) was purchased from Fisher Scientific. EGTA (Cat. No. E-3889), MES (Cat. No. M-3023), and PMSF (Cat. No. P-7626) were from Sigma. All other reagents were analytical grade.

The biological material was obtained from a local abattoir within 1 hr of slaughter and was kept on ice until further processing (usually 1 hr). Fresh and cleaned material can be frozen in liquid nitrogen and stored at −80°C for several months; however, freezing and thawing often reduce yield and purity of the following preparation, probably because of an increased tendency of membrane vesicles toward aggregation and/or a liberation of proteolytic activities. It is therefore crucial to cut the tissue into small pieces before freezing. This supports a rapid drop of temperature in the tissue and thus minimizes ice crystal formation, which can cause the above-mentioned negative effects.

For homogenization of the organs a Waring commercial blender (VWR International, Cat. No. 58977-169) was used. Membrane pellets were resuspended with Potter–Elvehjem homogenizers of various sizes (10–55 ml) obtained from Fisher Scientific (Cat. Nos. 08414-14 A to D). It is advisable to attach the metal shaft of the larger homogenizers to a variable-speed overhead drive so that the pestle can be rotated. This increases the efficiency and eases the homogenization. Low-speed centrifugations are done in a Sorvall centrifuge using GS-3, GSA, or SS-34 heads.

High-speed centrifugations are performed with Beckman Ti 45 or Ti 35 rotors in conventional ultracentrifuges.

III. Procedures

A. PREPARATION OF THE ORGANS

Solution

1. *PBS*: 137 mM NaCl, 2.7 mM KCl, 8.2 mM Na_2HPO_4, 1.9 mM KH_2PO_4, 0.02% NaN_3, pH 7.0. The buffer should be cooled to 4°C prior to use. Approximately 2–3 liters is needed per kilogram of tissue.

Steps

1. Separate the cerebellum and the lower part of the brain from the cortex.

2. Take one hemisphere of the cortex, place it in an ice bucket covered with Saran wrap, and remove the meninges along with the blood vessels contained therein using forceps.

3. Collect the stripped cortex hemispheres in a preweighed beaker on ice and weigh again to estimate the amount of homogenization buffer needed for the second step (approximately 1 liter/kg tissue).

4. To remove the remaining blood, wash the cortex hemispheres with cold PBS in a beaker several times. It is helpful to use a standard household sieve to pour off the PBS after each wash. Repeat the washes until the blood is removed.

5. If you want to store the brain tissue for later processing cut it into small pieces after the washing step and freeze it in liquid nitrogen. Keep frozen material at −80°C. Otherwise continue with Section B.

B. HOMOGENIZATION

Solutions

1. *Buffer A*: 0.1 M MES, 0.5 mM $MgCl_2$, 1.0 mM EGTA, 0.02% NaN_3, pH 6.5. Cool the buffer to 4°C and supplement with 0.1 mM PMSF prior to use. Prepare about 3 liters/kg tissue.

2. *Protease inhibitors* (PMSF stock solution, 1000×): Dissolve PMSF at 0.1 M in pure methanol. PMSF is not very well soluble in H_2O and will hydrolyze therein. Methanol solutions can be stored at 4°C for prolonged times.

Steps

1. Fill the cup of a Waring commercial blender with 300–400 g of washed tissue and an equivalent amount of buffer A containing 0.1 mM freshly added PMSF. Do not fill the cup to the top, but leave space below the rim.

2. Homogenize the tissue with three to six bursts of 10–15 sec duration with the setting on maximum speed. The number of bursts required to give a good homogenization varies: for brain, usually three bursts are sufficient; other organs, especially the adrenal glands, require more. Do not increase the length of the bursts, only their number, to prevent heating of the homogenate.

C. DIFFERENTIAL CENTRIFUGATIONS

1. Preparation of a Postmitochondrial Supernatant

Steps

1. Pour the homogenate into the buckets of a Sorvall GS-3 or GSA rotor, balance the buckets, and centrifuge them in the precooled rotor at 7000 rpm (about 8000 g in both types of rotors) for 50 min at 4°C.

2. Pour the supernatants through a funnel with several layers of gauze to separate floating lipids from the supernatant.

3. The bulky pellets (up to a third of the total volume) should be resuspended with an at least equivalent volume of homogenization buffer and recentrifuged under the above conditions.

4. Discard the pellets after the second centrifugation and keep the combined supernatants on ice.

2. Preparation of Microsomal Pellets

Steps

1. Pour the postmitochondrial supernatant into the tubes of a Beckman Ti 35 or Ti 45 rotor, balance the tubes, and ultracentrifuge them at 32,000 rpm and 4°C for 1.6 hr (Ti 35 rotor) or at 40,000 rpm for 1 hr (Ti 45 rotor).

2. After the centrifugation discard the clear supernatant and either refill the tubes with postmitochondrial supernatant for the next spin (leave the first pellet in the tube without resuspending it to save time) or carefully remove the microsomal pellets when all the postmitochondrial supernatant has been centrifuged or pellets from three or four ultracentrifugations have been collected in one tube.

3. Resuspend the pellets with 1–2 vol of buffer A by pipetting them up and down a 10-ml glass pipette which is used in the reverse orientation (the wide top end down) and then thoroughly homogenize with 10–15 strokes in a Potter–Elvehjem device.

3. Purification of Coated Vesicles from Microsomal Pellets

Solution

1. *Ficoll solution:* Dissolve Sucrose and Ficoll 400, both at a final concentration of 12.5% in buffer A, pH 6.5, and stir overnight in the cold room. Ficoll 400 dissolves only slowly. Keep at 4°C.

Steps

1. Mix the well-homogenized microsomes with the same volume of Ficoll–sucrose solution and pour into open tubes suitable for an SS-34 Sorvall rotor. Centrifuge the tubes at 43,000 g (19,000 rpm) and 4°C for 40 min in a precooled rotor.

2. After centrifugation, pour the supernatants containing clathrin-coated vesicles through a funnel filled with gauze to remove floating lipids. The compact sediment (about a fifth of the total volume) will remain in the tube and can be discarded.

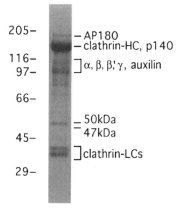

205— — AP180
        — clathrin-HC, p140
116—
        ] α, β, β,' γ, auxilin
97—

66—

        _ 50kDa
        ‾ 47kDa
45—
        ] clathrin-LCs

29—

FIGURE 1   Coat proteins obtained by Tris extraction of a clathrin-coated vesicle preparation from bovine brain. Coated vesicles were incubated in 0.5 M Tris, pH 7.0, to liberate the peripheral membrane proteins and ultracentrifuged to remove membranes from the released proteins. Approximately 12 μg Tris extract was electrophoresed in a low bis-SDS–polyacrylamide gel (for details, see Lindner and Ungewickell, 1992). Note that in this gel system the brain-specific clathrin-associated protein AP180 is well resolved from the clathrin heavy chain. Both AP180 and another clathrin-associated protein, auxilin, are not detectable in coated vesicles from adrenal gland and liver (data not shown).

3. Dilute the combined supernatants with 3–4 vol of cold buffer A containing 0.1 mM PMSF.

4. Concentration of Coated Vesicles by Pelleting

Steps

1. Subject the coated vesicles in the diluted Ficoll–sucrose solution to ultracentrifugation as described in Section C2. The pellets obtained in this step are considerably smaller than the microsomal pellets. The color usually varies from yellowish white to brown and is most likely due to contaminating ferritin (Kedersha and Rome, 1986).

2. Pour off the supernatants and carefully remove the pellets from the tubes with a spatula. Use a small volume of buffer A + PMSF to wash off material still attached to the walls of the tube.

3. Homogenize the combined pellets in approximately the same volume of buffer A + PMSF using a suitable Potter–Elvjehem homogenizer (5–15 ml volume, 10 strokes).

4. The material obtained after this step can either be directly used for extraction of the coat proteins (for a typical electrophoresis pattern of a Tris extract of bovine brain clathrin-coated vesicles, see Fig. 1) or be frozen in liquid nitrogen and stored at −80°C.

IV. Comments

Following this protocol (for summary, see Fig. 2), 80–90% pure clathrin-coated vesicles are obtained from bovine brain. Major contaminants are smooth vesicles, ferritin, and some filamentous material (Pearse, 1989). The yields usually range from 100 to 150 mg clathrin-coated vesicles per kilogram of brain cortex.

This basic protocol can be also used with other organs rich in clathrin-coated membranes, like adrenal glands, liver, and placenta. For adrenal glands a more

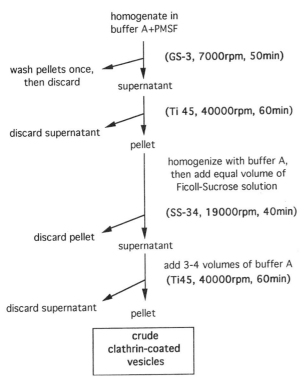

FIGURE 2   Purification scheme for crude clathrin-coated vesicles.

thorough homogenization (usually six or more 10-sec bursts in a Waring commercial blender) is required to break up the very resistant capsule material.

Clathrin-coated vesicle preparations from liver usually contain a considerable amount of ribonucleoprotein complexes termed *vaults* (Kedersha and Rome, 1986). It is advisable to remove these structures by velocity centrifugation on 5–40% sucrose gradients as an additional step after the procedure described above (see also Kedersha and Rome, 1986). Vaults are at least partially dissociated by the conventional extraction methods for clathrin-coated vesicles and thus contribute to impurities in coat protein extracts.

Although the main intention of the protocol described above is to provide rapid access to sources for various coat proteins, it might serve as a basis for the further purification of clathrin-coated vesicles as well (see Morris *et al.*, 1988, and the references therein). Recently a more elaborate protocol for the isolation of fusion-competent clathrin-coated vesicles from tissue culture cells has been described (Woodman and Warren, 1992).

V. Pitfalls

1. Do not mix Ficoll–sucrose solution with microsomal pellets obtained in Section C3 before homogenization of the pellets. The high viscosity of the Ficoll–sucrose solution prevents proper homogenization.

2. To quantitatively pellet the clathrin-coated vesicles from the supernatant after the centrifugation in Ficoll–sucrose, dilute with a *minimum* of 3 vol of buffer A + PMSF to decrease both the density and the viscosity of the supernatant.

REFERENCES

Ahle, S., Mann, A., Eichelsbacher, U., and Ungewickell, E. (1988) Structural relationships between clathrin assembly proteins from the Golgi and the plasma membrane. *EMBO J.* **7**, 919–929.

Ahle, S., and Ungewickell, E. (1990) Auxilin, a newly identified clathrin-associated protein in coated vesicles from bovine brain. *J. Cell Biol.* **111**, 19–29.

Campbell, C., Squicciarini, J., Shia, M., Pilch, P. F., and Fine, R. E. (1984) Identification of a protein kinase as an intrinsic component of rat liver coated vesicles. *Biochemistry* **23**, 4420–4426.

Kedersha, N. L., and Rome, L. H. (1986) Isolation and characterization of a novel ribonucleoprotein particle: Large structures contain a single species of small RNA. *J. Cell Biol.* **103**, 699–709.

Keen, J. H., Willingham, M. C., and Pastan, I. H. (1979) Clathrin-coated vesicles: Isolation, dissociation and factor-dependent reassociation of clathrin baskets. *Cell* **16**, 303–312.

Lindner, R., and Ungewickell, E. (1991) Light-chain-independent binding of adaptors, AP180 and auxilin, to clathrin. *Biochemistry* **30**, 9097–9101.

Lindner, R., and Ungewickell, E. (1992) Clathrin-associated proteins from bovine brain coated vesicles. An analysis of their number and assembly-promoting activity. *J. Biol. Chem.* **267**, 16567–16573.

Morris, S. A., Hannig, K., and Ungewickell, E. (1988) Rapid purification of clathrin-coated vesicles by free-flow electrophoresis. *Eur. J. Cell Biol.* **47**, 251–258.

Pearse, B. M. F. (1989) Characterization of coated-vesicle adaptors: Their reassembly with clathrin and with recycling receptors. *Methods Cell Biol.* **31**, 229–243.

Smythe, E., and Warren, G. (1991) The mechanism of receptor-mediated endocytosis. *Eur. J. Biochem.* **202**, 689–699.

Woodman, P. G., and Warren, G. (1992) Isolation and characterization of functional clathrin-coated vesicles. *In* "Methods in Enzymology" (J. E. Rothman, ed.), Vol. 219, pp. 251–260. Academic Press, San Diego.

Functional Identification of Membranes Derived from the Rough Endoplasmic Reticulum of Yeast

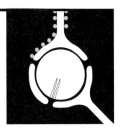

Christopher M. Sanderson and David I. Meyer

I. Introduction

In eukaryotic cells, nascent proteins enter the secretory pathway by their translocation into the endoplasmic reticulum (ER). Structurally, the endoplasmic reticulum is divided into two contiguous domains which are distinguished by the presence (rough ER) or absence (smooth ER) of membrane-bound ribosomes. Only the rough ER-derived membranes are capable of translocating proteins (Sanderson *et al.*, 1990; Sanderson and Meyer, 1991), but components of the translocation apparatus are also found in smooth (translocationally inactive) membranes (Sanderson *et al.*, 1990; Sanderson and Meyer, 1991). As such, translocationally competent membranes cannot be identified simply by protein composition alone. For this reason we have adopted a functional assay that facilitates identification and purification of rough endoplasmic reticulum (RER)-derived membranes following yeast cell fractionation. In this assay we measure the relative ability of membrane fractions to translocate and glycosylate the yeast mating factor (prepro-α-factor) using an *in vitro* translocation assay developed by Rothblatt and Meyer (1986).

II. Materials and Instrumentation

Sodium salts of ATP (Cat. No. A-5394), UTP (Cat. No. U-8128), and CTP (Cat. No. C-1381) were obtained from Sigma as were spermidine (Cat. No. S-2876), BSA (Cat. No. A-2153), sorbitol (Cat. No. S-1876), Ficoll 400 (Cat. No. F-4375), PMSF (Cat. No. P-7626), and EGTA (Cat. No. E-4378). DTT (Cat. No. 100-032), Hepes (Cat. No. 242 608), Creatine phosphate (Cat. No. 127-574), creatine phosphokinase (Cat. No. 127-566), tRNA (Cat. No. 109-495), EDTA (Cat. No. 808-270), micrococcal nuclease (Cat. No. 107-921), and SDS (Cat. No. 100-155) were obtained from Boehringer-Mannheim. Sephadex G-25 (medium grade) was obtained from Pharmacia LKB. Oxalyticase (Cat. No. O-105) was obtained from Enzogenetics. Translation-grade [^{35}S]methionine was obtained from NEN Research Products, Dupont. GTP (Cat. No. 16800) was obtained from United States Biochemical Corporation.

III. Procedures

A. PREPARATION OF TRANSLOCATION-COMPETENT YEAST MEMBRANES

Solutions

1. *Tris sulfate solution:* To prepare 100 ml, combine 5 ml of 2 M Tris sulfate (pH 9.4) and 154 mg of DTT and then make up to a final volume of 100 ml with double-distilled (dd) H_2O.

2. *Sorbitol buffer:* To prepare 100 ml, dissolve 21.86 g of sorbitol in 50 ml of ddH_2O, then add 2 ml of 1 M KP_i (pH 7.4) and 77 mg of DTT. Stir until the sorbitol is dissolved, and make up the volume to 100 ml with ddH_2O.

3. *Spheroplasting medium:* To prepare 100 ml, dissolve 21.86 g of sorbitol and 77 mg of DTT in 50 ml of YPD. After all sorbitol is dissolved, make up the final volume to 100 ml with YPD.

4. *Sucrose–Ficoll solution:* To prepare 100 ml, combine 32 ml of 2.5 M sucrose with 2 ml of 1 M Hepes (pH 7.4) and 1.5 g of Ficoll 400. Add approximately 80 ml of ddH_2O, stir until all Ficoll is dissolved, and make up to 100 ml with ddH_2O. *This solution should be prepared in advance as the Ficoll 400 may take some time to dissolve.*

5. *Lysis buffer:* To prepare 100 ml, combine 2 ml of 1 M Hepes (pH 7.4), 0.2 ml of DTT (500 mM), 0.4 ml of EDTA (500 mM), and 2.5 ml of 2 M KOAc, and make the final volume 100 ml with ddH_2O.

6. *0.5 M sucrose solution:* To prepare 100 ml, combine 20 ml of 2.5 M sucrose, 2.5 ml of 2 M KOAc, 0.4 ml of 500 mM EDTA, 0.2 ml of 500 mM DTT, and 2 ml of 1 M Hepes (pH 7.4). After mixing, make the total volume 100 ml with ddH_2O.

7. *1 M Sucrose solution:* To prepare 100 ml, combine 40 ml of 2.5 M sucrose, 2.5 ml of 2 M KOAc, 0.2 ml of 500 mM DTT, and 2 ml of 1 M Hepes (pH 7.4), and make the final volume 100 ml with ddH_2O.

8. *Membrane buffer:* To prepare 100 ml, combine 10 ml of 2.5 M sucrose, 2.5 ml of 2 M KOAc, 0.2 ml of 500 mM DTT, and 2 ml of 1 M Hepes (pH 7.4), and make the final volume 100 ml with ddH_2O.

Steps

1. Prepare 100 ml of each solution listed above.

2. Harvest cells at 1.5 A_{600} units/ml by centrifugation for 5 min at 5000 rpm in a Sorvall GS3 rotor.

3. Wash cells twice with sterile water and note the wet weight of the cells.

4. Resuspend cells at 0.5 g/ml in Tris sulfate solution pH 9.4 and incubate at 30°C, shaking gently for 30–45 min.

5. Harvest cells by centrifugation for 5 min at 5000 rpm in a Sorvall GSA rotor.

6. Wash once with sorbitol buffer and harvest as in step 5 above.

7. Resuspend cells at 0.2 g/ml in spheroplasting medium containing 400 μl oxalyticase solution (approximately 0.5 mg oxalyticase) and incubate at 30°C for 45–60 min. Spheroplast formation can be monitored by observing the yeast under the light microscope. The treatment is complete when all yeast become spherical.

8. Transfer spheroplast suspension to 30-ml Corex tubes and underlay approximately 10 ml of 0.8 M sucrose solution.

9. Centrifuge at 5000 rpm for 15 min at 4°C in a Sorvall HB-4 rotor.

10. Resuspend spheroplasts at 0.5 g/ml in lysis buffer on ice and add PMSF (0.2 mg/ml). Transfer to a large Dounce homogenizer (B pestle). After 5 min on ice homogenize with 10–15 passes and check for cell breakage under the light microscope.

11. Add an equal volume of 0.5 M sucrose solution again containing PMSF, mix, and transfer homogenate to 30-ml Corex tubes. Underlay with 10 ml of 1 M sucrose solution and centrifuge at 8000 rpm for 15 min at 4°C in the Sorvall HB-4 rotor.

B. CELL FRACTIONATION

The method of cell fractionation and gradient selection is determined by the requirements of individual investigators; however, we have found that sucrose gradients containing low-salt buffer (50 mM Tris–HCl, pH 7.5, 25 mM KCl, 5 mM MgCl$_2$) are suitable for maintaining translocation competence of RER-derived membranes.

C. FUNCTIONAL IDENTIFICATION OF RER-DERIVED MEMBRANES

Two experimental strategies have been successfully used to identify translocation-competent membranes following cell fractionation. Crude microsomal membranes can be prepared as described above and then preloaded with glycosylated pro-α-factor *in vitro* before further fractionation. Or, membranes can be fractionated by gradient centrifugation and then analyzed for translocation using a postgradient translocation assay.

D. PREGRADIENT LABELING OF TRANSLOCATIONALLY COMPETENT MEMBRANES

Steps

1. Prepare crude 8K supernatants as described above and centrifuge at 15,000 rpm for 15 min at 4°C in a Beckman Ti 45 rotor.

2. Resuspend pellets in membrane buffer by homogenization and dilute to 40 A_{280} units/ml. Absorbance readings should be determined in 2% SDS.

3. This crude microsomal membrane population can then be used as the membrane component of an *in vitro* translocation assay described below. As a result, translocation-competent membranes will be selectively loaded with glycosylated pro-α-factor which will then serve as a marker for RER-derived membranes during subsequent gradient centrifugation.

E. POSTGRADIENT ANALYSES OF RER DISTRIBUTION

Steps

1. A crude postnuclear supernatant should be prepared as described above and then centrifuged through the gradient of choice.

2. After centrifugation, fractions should be diluted three- to fivefold with low-salt buffer and then centrifuged at 100,000 g for 45 min to pellet all membranes.

3. Membranes should be resuspended in membrane buffer to 40 A_{280} units/ml.

4. Each membrane fraction can then be used in the *in vitro* translocation assay described below.

An example of results obtained by post- and pregradient analyses of RER distribution are shown in Figs. 1B and C, respectively.

F. PREPARATION OF YEAST LYSATE FOR USE IN *IN VITRO* TRANSLOCATION ASSAYS

Solution

1. *Lysate buffer:* 100 mM KOAc, 2 mM Mg(OAc)$_2$, 2 mM DTT, 20% glycerol, 20 mM Hepes, pH 7.5, 0.2 mg/ml PMSF.

Steps

1. Harvest cells at approximately 5 A_{600} units/ml.

2. Wash cells twice with sterile water and note wet weight.

3. Resuspend cells in lysate buffer at 2 g of cells per milliliter and add PMSF to a final concentration of 0.2 mg/ml. (*Note:* PMSF should be dissolved in isopropanol.)

4. Load cell suspension into French pressure cell and freeze to −80°C for 1 hr.

5. Place the pressure cell in the hydraulic press and pressurize to 20,000 psi for about 5 min to allow partial thawing, then open valve slowly until frozen "ribbon" of lysate emerges slowly. Collect into a 250-ml flask and allow to thaw on ice for 30 min. PMSF should be added to a final concentration of 0.2 mg/ml.

6. Transfer lysate to 30-ml Corex tubes and centrifuge at 8000 rpm for 15 min at 4°C in a Sorvall HB-4 rotor.

7. Remove the resulting supernatant and measure the final volume.

8. Add 0.01 vol of 200 mM CaCl$_2$ and 0.02 vol 30,000 U/ml micrococcal nuclease.

9. Incubate 25 min at room temperature and then inactivate nuclease with 1/50th vol of 200 mM EGTA.

10. Transfer the lysate to polycarbonate ultracentrifuge tubes and centrifuge at 40,000 rpm for 30 min in a Beckman Ti 80 rotor.

11. While centrifuging, equilibrate Sephadex G-25 column with lysis buffer.

12. Collect the supernatant from the centrifugation, avoiding the upper lipid layer and the fluffy sediment.

13. Load supernatant onto Sephadex G-25 column (16 × 2.5 cm) and collect fractions until turbid fractions appear. *Keep all fractions on ice.*

14. Add 10 μl of each fraction to 990 μl of 2% SDS and measure the absorbance at 260 nm. Pool aliquots that are greater than 40 units/ml and store in 1-ml aliquots at −80°C.

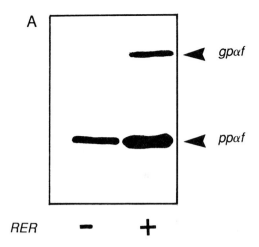

A

RER   —   +

gpαf

ppαf

B

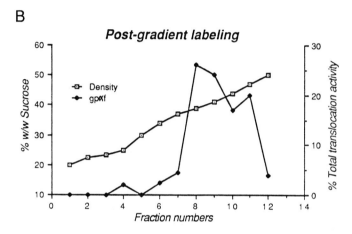

Post-gradient labeling

□ Density
◆ gpαf

% w/w Sucrose

% Total translocation activity

Fraction numbers

C

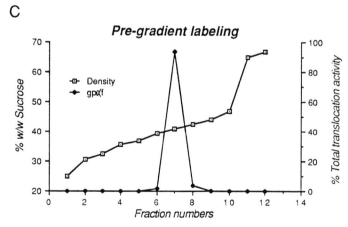

Pre-gradient labeling

□ Density
◆ gpαf

% w/w Sucrose

% Total translocation activity

Fraction numbers

FIGURE 1 Results of a cotranslational translocation assay performed in the presence (+) and absence (−) of RER-derived membranes (A) and the relative distribution of RER-derived membranes following cell fractionation as determined by either pregradient (B) or postgradient (C) labeling of translocation-competent membranes. gpαf, glycosylated pro-α-factor; ppαf, prepro-α-factor.

G. PREPARATION OF MESSENGER RNA TRANSCRIPT FOR USE IN TRANSLOCATION ASSAYS

Solutions

1. *6× Concentrated salt mix:* To prepare 1 ml of sixfold concentrated salt mix, combine 400 μl of 1 M Hepes (pH 7.5), 60 μl of 1 M Mg(OAc)$_2$, 100 μl of 200 mM spermidine (50.8 mg/ml), and 440 μl of diethylpyrocarbonate (DEPC)-treated water.

2. *Transcription premix:* To prepare a 6-ml stock of transcription premix, combine 1 ml of 6× transcription salt mix, 100 μl of 10 mg/ml BSA, 100 μl of 500 mM DTT, 100 μl of 50 mM ATP, 100 μl of 50 mM UTP, 100 μl of 50 mM CTP, 20 μl of 50 mM GTP, and 4.48 ml of DEPC-treated water. Sterilize by filtration through a 0.2-μm filter, aliquot into 65-μl fractions, freeze in liquid nitrogen, and store at $-80°$C.

Steps

1. cDNA encoding prepro-α factor should be cloned into a suitable expression vector downstream of an SP6 or T7 promoter sequence. In our case we routinely use pGEM vectors (Promega, Biotech).

2. Linearize the 10 μg of DNA with a suitable restriction enzyme that cuts downstream of the required coding sequence. The total reaction volume should be 10 μl.

3. To the total restriction digest mixture, add 60 μl of transcription premix, 2.5 μl of RNasin, 5 μl of 7-methyl-G-ppG (5 A_{250} units dissolved in 60 μl 20 mM Hepes–KOH), and 3 μl of SP6 polymerase (20 U/μl), and make up to 10 μl with DEPC-treated water.

4. Incubate for 10 min at 40°C.

5. Add 1 μl of 40 mM GTP.

6. Incubate for 10 min at 40°C, and then remove tubes to ice.

7. Analyze 2 μl of the reaction on a 0.8% agarose gel; a clear RNA band should be visible below the linearized DNA. *This is the transcript to be used for* in vitro *translation and translocation assays. It should be aliquoted and stored at $-80°$C. Aliquots may be thawed and refrozen.*

IV. *Standard* in Vitro **Cotranslational Translocation Assay**

Solution

1. *Translation premix:* To prepare 4 ml of stock translation premix, combine 1.48 ml of combined amino acids (−) methionine (1 mM concentration of each), 1.48 ml of 1 M Hepes–KOH (pH 7.5), 100 μl of 1 M DTT, 10 mg of tRNA (lyophilized), 33.3 μl of 150 mM GTP, 100 μl of 500 mM ATP, 667 μl of 1.5 M creatine phosphate, 100 μl of 40 mg/ml creatine phosphokinase (in 59% glycerol), and 40 μl of 20 mM Hepes–KOH (pH 7.5). Sterilize by filtration through a 0.2-μl filter and aliquot into 500-μl fractions. Freeze in N$_2$ and store at $-80°$C.

Steps

1. Per assay, combine 2 μl translation premix, 2 μl [^{35}S]methionine, 1 μl 3 M KOAc 1 μl 100 mM Mg(OAc)$_2$ 6 μl H$_2$O (DEPC), 1 μl mRNA (transcript), 8 μl lysate, and 1 μl membranes.

2. Mix and incubate at 22°C for 30 min.

3. Add an equal volume of sample buffer and heat at 95°C for 5 min.

4. Analyze samples by polyacrylamide gel electrophoresis.

An example of results obtained by the cotranslational translocation assay described above are shown in Fig. 1A.

V. Comments

Each of the methods used to identify translocation-competent membranes—the pregradient assay and the postfractionation assay—has advantages and disadvantages.

In the pregradient assay membranes are "fresh" and highly competent at the time of translocation and therefore provide a high level of glycosylated translocation product. The drawback with this system is that membranes are first pelleted prior to translocation and this can lead to organelle aggregation if membranes are not thoroughly resuspended by homogenization following centrifugation.

In the postfractionation assay, a crude postnuclear supernatant is used as the starting material, thereby reducing organelle aggregation; however, membranes are maintained at 4°C for extended periods during centrifugation, and this may result in a decrease in translocation competence.

REFERENCES

Rothblatt, J. A., and Meyer, D. I. (1986) Secretion in yeast: Reconstitution of the translocation and glycosylation of α-factor and invertase in a homologous cell-free system. *Cell* **44,** 619–628.

Sanderson, C. M., Crowe, J. S., and Meyer, D. I. (1990) Protein retention in the yeast rough endoplasmic reticulum: Expression and assembly of human ribophorin I. *J. Cell Biol.* **111,** 2861–2870.

Sanderson, C. M., and Meyer, D. I. (1991) Purification and functional characterization of membranes derived from the rough endoplasmic reticulum of *Saccharomyces cerevisiae*. *J. Biol. Chem.* **266,** 13423–13430.

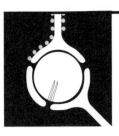

Isolation of Yeast Mitochondria and Study of Mitochondrial Protein Translation

Johannes M. Herrmann, Heike Fölsch, Walter Neupert, and Rosemary A. Stuart

I. Introduction

The formation of mitochondria is a detailed process that involves the precise cooperation of two separate genetic systems, one in the mitochondria the other in the nucleus. Studies on the biogenesis of mitochondria address the synthesis and translocation of these proteins across or into the mitochondrial membranes and finally their assembly, often into multimeric subunit complexes. Unlike most organisms, *Saccharomyces cerevisiae* can survive with defective respiratory chain and oxidative phosphorylation because it can use fermentable carbon sources for energy production. This ability to grow anaerobically, together with the ease of genetic manipulation of this yeast, has enabled the identification of many mutants defective in aerobic growth. Such mutants have led to the identification and cloning of genes that encode proteins essential for mitochondrial function (for reviews see Grivell, 1989; Tzagoloff and Dieckmann, 1990; Bolotin-Fukuhara and Grivell, 1992).

Approximately 5% of the mitochondrial proteins are encoded by the mitochondrial genome and here we describe how one can study the synthesis of these proteins in isolated mitochondria. The vast majority of mitochondrial proteins, however, are encoded by the cell nucleus and are synthesized in the cell cytosol as precursor proteins. These precursors are imported into mitochondria in a posttranslational manner. Our knowledge of mitochondrial protein import has increased over the past years due to a number of detailed *in vitro* studies using mainly *S. cerevisiae* and *Neurospora crassa* as model systems (for reviews, see Hartl and Neupert, 1990; Baker and Schatz, 1991). These *in vitro* import systems employ radiolabeled precursor proteins which have been cloned, transcribed *in vitro,* and then translated in a lysate (usually rabbit reticulocyte) in the presence of a radiolabeled amino acid (e.g., [35S]methionine) and which are incubated with isolated mitochondria. Here we describe a procedure for the growth of *S. cerevisiae* and subsequent isolation of mitochondria that is an adaptation of an earlier protocol from Daum *et al.* (1982). The resulting isolated mitochondria are suitable for use in both *in organello* translation studies, a protocol for which is outlined here (as previously described by McKee and Poyton, 1984), and *in vitro* studies of import of the nuclear-encoded proteins, which has been described in detail elsewhere (Wienhues *et al.*, 1992; Glick, 1991).

II. Materials and Instrumentation

Yeast extract (Cat. No. 0127-05-3) was purchased from Difco, agar (Cat. No. 1614), glucose monohydrate (Cat. No. 4074), KH_2PO_4 (Cat. No. 4873), K_2HPO_4

(Cat. No. 5104), NH_4Cl (Cat. No. 1145), $CaCl_2 \cdot 2H_2O$ (Cat. No. 2382), NaCl (Cat. No. 6404), KCl (Cat. No. 4936), $MgSO_4 \cdot 7H_2O$ (Cat. No. 5886), $FeCl_3 \cdot 4H_2O$ (Cat. No. 5886), lactate (Cat. No. 366), trishydroxymethylaminomethane (Tris, Cat. No. 8382), sorbitol (Cat. No. 7758), sucrose (Cat. No. 7651), and EDTA (Titriplex, Cat. No. 8418) were all obtained from Merck. Fatty acid-free BSA (Cat. No. A-6003), PMSF (Cat. No. P-7626), Mops (Cat. No. M-1254), β-mercaptoethanol (Cat. No. 6250), LiDS (Cat. No. 4632), SDS (Cat. No. 20760), glycerol (Cat. No. G-7757), and bromophenol blue (Cat. No. 15375) were purchased from Serva. ATP (Cat. No. 635316), GTP (Cat. No. 414581), α-ketoglutarate (Cat. No. 127205), phosphoenolpyruvate (Cat. No. 182112), pyruvate kinase (Cat. No. 127418), and dithiothreitol (DTT, Cat. No. 708992) were all obtained from Boehringer-Mannheim. [^{35}S]Methionine (10 mCi/ml, 1142 Ci/mmole) was obtained from ICN, acrylamide (Cat. No. 10675) and N,N'-methylenebisacrylamide (Cat. No. 289195), N,N,N',N'-tetramethylenediamine (Cat. No. 35925) were obtained from Serva, and ammonium persulfate (Cat. No. 1201) was obtained from Merck. Zymolyase (20,000 U/g) was obtained from Seikagaku (Cat. No. 120491), and the protein assay from Bio-Rad (Bio-Rad Protein Assay Kit I, Cat. No. 500-0001). *S. cerevisiae* strain, D273-10B can be obtained from the American Tissue Culture Collection (ATCC No. 24657).

III. Procedures

A. GROWTH OF *Saccharomyces cerevisiae*

Solutions

1. *YPEG agar plates:* To make 600 ml, solubilize 6 g yeast extract, 12 g Bacto-peptone, and 12 g agar in distilled water, adjust the pH to 5 with concentrated HCl, and bring to a final volume of 570 ml. Autoclave 20 min at 120°C. Prior to preparation of the agar plates mix 18 ml sterile 87% glycerol and 12 ml ethanol to the hot solution. Store the solid plates at 4°C.

2. *Lactate medium:* To make 1 liter, solubilize 3 g yeast extract, 1 g glucose monohydrate, 1 g KH_2PO_4, 1 g NH_4Cl, 0.5 g $CaCl_2 \cdot 2H_2O$, 0.5 g NaCl, and 1.1 g $MgSO_4 \cdot 7H_2O$ in ± 700 ml distilled water. Add 0.3 ml of a 1% $FeCl_3$ solution and 22 ml 90% lactate. Adjust the pH to 5.5 with 10 M KOH and bring to a total volume of 1 liter. Autoclave 20 min at 120°C. Store at room temperature.

Steps

1. Streak out the yeast strain D273-10B onto a YPEG agar plate and grow for 2–3 days at 30°C.

2. Inoculate 20 ml of lactate medium in a 100-ml Erlenmeyer flask with a loop full of the culture. Grow overnight at 30°C and shaking at 120 rpm.

3. Use the overnight culture to inoculate fresh lactate medium (100 ml in an 500-ml Erlenmeyer flask). The initial OD_{578} should be 0.5–1.0. Grow the culture overnight as described in step 2.

4. Repeat step 3 at three or four times.

5. For the main culture inoculate 1.5 liters of lactate medium into a 5-liter Erlenmeyer flask with the preculture to an initial OD_{578} of 0.05. Grow the culture for 14–15 hr at 30°C and 120 rpm.

6. Measure the OD_{578} of the culture, which should be 1.0–1.5.

B. ISOLATION OF YEAST MITOCHONDRIA

Solutions

1. *100 mM Tris–SO$_4$, pH 9.4:* To make 1 liter, solubilize 12.11 g of Tris in distilled water, adjust pH to 9.4 with H$_2$SO$_4$, and adjust to a total volume of 1 liter. Store at 4°C.

2. *100 mM Tris–HCl, pH 7.4:* To make 1 liter, solubilize 12.11 g Tris in distilled water, adjust pH to 7.4 with HCl, and adjust to a total volume of 1 liter. Store at 4°C.

3. *1 M KPi buffer, pH 7.2:* First make 100 ml of a 1 M K$_2$HPO$_4$ solution (17.4 g) and 100 ml of a 1 M KH$_2$PO$_4$ solution (13.6 g). To 50 ml of the K$_2$HPO$_4$ add the KH$_2$PO$_4$ solution until a pH of 7.2 is achieved. Store at 4°C.

4. *1 M DTT:* To make 1 ml solubilize 154.3 mg DTT in 1 ml distilled water. This solution should be prepared freshly each time.

5. *0.2 M PMSF:* To make 1 ml, solubilize 34.5 mg PMSF in 1 ml ethanol. Prepare fresh each time.

6. *2.4 M Sorbitol:* To make 500 ml, solubilize 218.6 g sorbitol in distilled water and adjust to a total volume of 500 ml. Store at 4°C.

7. Zymolyase buffer: To make 500 ml, mix 250 ml 2.4 M sorbitol with 10 ml 1 M KP$_i$ buffer, pH 7.2, and adjust to a total volume of 500 ml. Store at 4°C.

8. Homogenization buffer: To make 500 ml, mix 125 ml 2.4 M sorbitol and 50 ml 100 mM Tris–HCl, pH 7.4, add 100 mg fatty acid-free BSA, and adjust to a total volume of 497.5 ml. Finally add 2.5 ml 0.2 M PMSF.

9. *SEM buffer:* To make 1 liter, solubilize 85.58 g sucrose, 2.1 g Mops, and 0.37 g EDTA in distilled water, adjust pH to 7.2 with KOH, and bring to a total volume of 1 liter. Store at 4°C.

Steps

1. Collect cells of the main culture by centrifugation at 3000 rpm (Beckman JA2-21, rotor JA10) for 5 min at 4°C.

2. Decant supernatant and resuspend the cells in a total of 100 ml of distilled H$_2$O.

3. Spin as described in step 1 in a preweighed centrifuge bottle.

4. Decant supernatant and determine the weight of the pellet.

5. Resuspend the cells in 100 mM Tris-SO$_4$, pH 9.4, using 2 ml/g of cells.

6. Transfer the cells with a pipette into an Erlenmeyer flask and determine the volume of the suspension which ideally should be one-tenth of the volume of the flask. Add DTT from a 1 M stock to a final concentration of 10 mM.

7. Incubate the cells for 10 min at 30°C in a shaking water bath.

8. Spin down the cells at 4000 rpm (Beckman JA2-21, rotor JA20) for 5 min at 4°C.

9. Resuspend cells in 1.2 M sorbitol using 2 ml/g cells.

10. Repeat step 8.

11. Resuspend the pellet in zymolyase buffer to a final concentration of 0.15 g/ml, and add 2–3 mg zymolyase per gram wet weight. Remove a small aliquot prior to the addition of zymolyase to use as a control for the spheroplast test (see step 13).

12. Incubate the cells for 20–40 min at 30°C in a shaking water bath.

13. Check for efficient spheroplast formation by adding 50 μl sample to 2 ml H_2O and measuring the $OD_{600\,nm}$. Incubation should be continued until the $OD_{600\,nm}$ is in the range 10–20% of the value measured prior to the addition of zymolyase.

The sample should be kept cold at all times throughout the following steps. **NOTE**

---

14. Spin the spheroplasts at 4000 rpm (Beckman rotor JA20) for 5 min at 4°C.

15. Resuspend the spheroplasts in 100 ml 1.2 M sorbitol and spin them again at 4000 rpm (Beckman rotor JA20) for 5 min at 4°C.

16. Decant the supernatant carefully and resuspend the spheroplasts in the "homogenization buffer" at a concentration of 0.15 g/ml.

17. Transfer the spheroplast suspension to a glass douncer and dounce for 10–15 times, avoiding foaming of the sample.

18. Spin at 3000 rpm for 5 min (Beckman rotor JA20) at 4°C.

19. Decant the supernatant into fresh tubes and centrifuge again at 4000 rpm (Beckman rotor JA20) for 5 min at 4°C.

20. Decant the supernatant again into fresh tubes and spin at 10,000 rpm for 12 min at 4°C (Beckman rotor JA20).

21. Discard the supernatant and resuspend the pellet carefully in approximately 25 ml of SEM buffer.

22. Spin at 4000 rpm for 5 min (Beckman rotor JA20) at 4°C.

23. Decant the supernatant again into fresh tubes and spin at 10,000 rpm for 12 min at 4°C (Beckman rotor JA20).

24. Resuspend the mitochondrial pellet in 300 μl of SEM buffer and determine the protein concentration using the Bio-Rad assay method and then adjust the protein concentration to 10 mg protein/ml.

25. Freeze aliquots (50 μl) of the mitochondrial suspension in liquid nitrogen and store at −70°C.

C. TRANSLATION OF MITOCHONDRIA-ENCODED PROTEINS IN ISOLATED YEAST MITOCHONDRIA

Solutions

1. *1 M KCl:* To make 100 ml, solubilize 7.5 g KCl in distilled water and adjust to a total volume of 100 ml. Store at 4°C.

2. *1 M MgSO₄:* To make 100 ml, solubilize 24.6 g $MgSO_4 \cdot 7H_2O$ in distilled water and adjust to a total volume of 100 ml. Store at 4°C.

3. *1 M Tris–HCl, pH 7.2:* To make 100 ml, solubilize 12.1 g Tris in 70 ml distilled water, adjust the pH to 7.2 with 5 M HCl, and add water to a total volume of 100 ml. Store at 4°C.

4. *200 mM ATP:* Dissolve 13 mg ATP in 100 μl distilled water and adjust with 10 M KOH to a pH around 7. Make fresh each time.

---

5. *50 mM GTP:* Dissolve 2.8 mg GTP in 100 μl distilled water. Make fresh each time.

6. *Amino acid stock solution:* Solubilize 20 mg each of the amino acids alanine, arginine, aspartic acid, asparagine, glutamic acid, glutamine, glycine, histidine, isoleucine, leucine, lysine, phenylalanine, proline, serine, threonine, tryptophan, and valine in 10 ml distilled water. Aliquot in 100-μl portions and keep at $-20°C$.

7. *10 mM Cysteine:* Solubilize 1.2 mg of cysteine in 1 ml of distilled water. Aliquot in 20 μl and store at $-20°C$.

8. *1 mg/ml Tyrosine:* Solubilize 1 mg of tyrosine in 900 μl of distilled water, adjust to pH 7 with KOH, and add water to a total volume of 1 ml. Aliquot in 20 μl and keep at $-20°C$.

9. *200 mM Methionine:* Solubilize 30 mg of methionine in 1 ml of distilled water. Make fresh each time.

10. *BSA stock solution:* Solubilize 1 g of fatty acid-free BSA in 10 ml of distilled water. Aliquot in 100-μl portions and store at $-20°C$.

11. *1.5× Translation buffer:* To make 1 ml of the buffer, add 375 μl 2.4 M sorbitol, 225 μl 1 M KCl, 22.5 μl 1 M KP$_i$ buffer, pH 7.2, 30 μl 1 M Tris–HCl, pH 7.2, 19 μl 1 M MgSO$_4$, 45 μl BSA stock solution, 30 μl 200 mM ATP, 15 μl 50 mM GTP, 1.7 mg α-ketoglutarate, 3.5 mg phosphoenolpyruvate, 9.1 μl amino acid stock solution, 10 μl 10 mM cysteine, and 18.2 μl 1 mg/ml tyrosine. Adjust to 1 ml with distilled H$_2$O.

12. *500 mM EDTA:* Dissolve 18.6 g EDTA in distilled water. To help dissolve EDTA, adjust pH to 7.2 with NaOH and stir at room temperature. Adjust total volume to 100 ml.

13. *Washing buffer:* Mix 1.25 ml 2.4 M sorbitol, 10 μl 500 mM EDTA, and 125 μl 200 mM methionine, and adjust to 5 ml with distilled water.

14. *LiDS sample buffer:* To make 50 ml of the solution solubilize 1 g LiDS, 5 ml glycerol, and 0.36 g Tris in 40 ml of distilled water. Adjust with HCl to a pH of 6.8, add 5 mg bromophenol blue 1.25 ml β-mercaptoethanol and adjust total volume to 50 ml. Store at room temperature.

Steps

1. Heat the thermoblock to 30°C.

2. Thaw mitochondria immediately before you start the experiment.

3. Mix 20 μl 1.5× buffer, 1.5 μl pyruvate kinase (0.5 mg/ml), 5.5 μl distilled water, and 2 μl mitochondria in SEM (10 mg protein/ml). Incubate the mixture for 2 min at 30°C.

4. Add 1 μl [^{35}S]methionine and incubate for 20 min at 30°C.

5. Add 30 μl 0.2 M methionine to the reaction mix and centrifuge at room temperature for 5 min at 14000 rpm in an Eppendorf centrifuge.

6. Remove the supernatant and wash the mitochondrial pellet carefully with 200 μl washing buffer.

7. Centrifuge again as in step 5 and remove the supernatant again.

8. Add 25 μl LiDS sample buffer and shake for 45 min in an Eppendorf mixer at 4°C to achieve good solubilization of the proteins.

9. Resolve the mitochondrial proteins by SDS–polyacrylamide gel electrophoresis and the radiolabeled proteins can be visualized by fluorography of

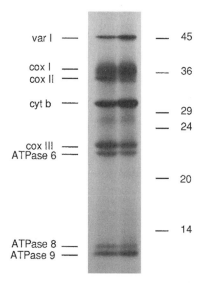

FIGURE 1   Products of translation in isolated yeast mitochondria. Proteins were translated for 10 min (lane 1) or 30 minutes (lane 2) as described, and labeling was stopped following the addition of cold methionine. After a 5-min chase, mitochondria were reisolated by centrifugation, washed, and resuspended in sample buffer. Labeled proteins were separated by SDS–PAGE and visualized by fluorography. Translation products are indicated. var I, a protein of the small ribosomal subunit; cox I–III, subunits I–III of the cytochrome c oxidase complex; cyt b, cytochrome b of the bc_1 complex; ATPase 6, 8, and 9, subunits 6, 8, and 9 of the ATP synthase. The positions marked by 45, 36, 29, 24, 20, and 14 indicate the mobility of the protein standards used and the numbers refer to their molecular weight (in kDa).

the resulting gel (Fig. 1) (Laemmli, 1970; see also article by Julio E. Celis and Eyδfinnur Olsen). For gel analysis we recommend using a gel whose final concentrations of acrylamide and bisacrylamide are 16 and 0.1% (w/v), respectively.

IV. Comments

The mitochondria prepared using the protocol described in Section IIIB are stable for several months if stored at $-70°C$. It is essential though that they are frozen and thawed only once as they are not suited to refreezing. The isolated mitochondria can be used for *in vitro* experiments to study the import of various mitochondrial preproteins as described by Hartl and Neupert (1990), Koll *et al.* (1992), and Glick *et al.* (1992). The mitochondria isolated according to this protocol are also suitable for *in vitro* analysis of mitochondrial protein translation, as was described in Section IIIC. In addition, one can use the isolated mitochondria for submitochondrial localization of proteins, for example, using hypotonic swelling of mitochondria to rupture specifically the outer membrane and leave the inner membrane intact (Glick, 1991). For the latter purpose we observed that best results are achieved if one isolates mitochondria from yeast cells harvested prior to reaching an OD of 1. The normal yield of mitochondria is between 2 and 5 mg per gram of yeast cells.

V. Pitfalls

1. Sometimes the zymolyase treatment does not work efficiently within a 30- to 45-min period; this usually happens if the yeast cultures were grown too long

and the cells are harvested at an OD of 2 or higher. If this occurs, the same amount of zymolyase should be added again and incubated for a further 15–30 min.

2. Take care that the zymolyase treatment does not occur too long after the spheroplast formation is complete because the zymolyase is often contaminated with other proteases, whose activities may affect the quality of your mitochondria preparation, i.e., degradation of mitochondrial surface receptors required for preprotein import.

3. The douncing step is critical: douncing with too much force will result in broken mitochondria, whereas insufficient douncing often results in a high level of intact spheroplasts, thereby decreasing the yield of mitochondria.

REFERENCES

Baker, K., and Schatz, G. (1991) Mitochondrial proteins essential for viability mediate protein import into yeast mitochondria. *Nature* **349**, 205–208.

Bolotin-Fukuhara, M., and Grivell, L. A. (1992) Genetic approaches to the study of mitochondrial biogenesis in yeast. *Antonie van Leeuwenhoek* **62**, 131–153.

Daum, G., Böhni, P. C., and Schatz, G. (1982) Import of proteins into mitochondria: Cytochrome b_2 and cytochrome c peroxidase are located in the intermembrane space of yeast mitochondria. *J. Biol. Chem.* **257**, 13028–13033.

Glick, B. S. (1991) Protein import into isolated yeast mitochondria. *In* "Methods in Cell Biology," Vol. 34, pp. 389–399. Academic Press, San Diego.

Glick, B. S., Brandt, A., Cunningham, K., Müller, S., Hallberg, R. L., and Schatz, G. (1992) Cytochromes c_1 and b_2 are sorted to the intermembrane space of yeast mitochondria by a stop-transfer mechanism. *Cell* **69**, 809–822.

Grivell, L. A. (1989) Nucleo-mitochondrial interactions in yeast mitochondrial biogenesis. *Eur. J. Biochem.* **182**, 477–493.

Hartl, F.-U., and Neupert, W. (1990) Protein sorting to mitochondria: Evolutionary conservations of folding and assembly. *Science* **247**, 930–938.

Koll, H., Guiard, B., Rassow, J., Ostermann, J., Horwich, A. L., Neupert, W., and Hartl, F.-U. (1992) Antifolding activity of hsp60 couples protein import into the mitochondrial matrix with export to the intermembrane space. *Cell* **68**, 1163–1175.

Laemmli, U. K. (1970) Cleavage of structural proteins during the assembly of the head of bacteriophage T4. *Nature* **227**, 680–685.

McKee, E. E., and Poyton, R. O. (1984) Mitochondrial gene expression in *Saccharomyces cerevisiae*. I. Optimal conditions for protein synthesis in isolated mitochondria. *J. Biol. Chem.* **259**, 9320–9338.

Tzagoloff, A., and Dieckmann, C. L. (1990) PET genes of *Saccharomyces cerevisiae*. *Microbiol. Rev.* **54**, 211–225.

Wienhues, U., Koll, H., Becker, K., Guiard, B., and Hartl, F.-U. (1992) Protein targeting to mitochondria. *In* "A Practical Approach to Protein Targeting." IRL (Oxford University Press), London.

Inclusion of Proteins into Isolated Mitochondrial Outer Membrane Vesicles

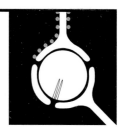

Andreas Mayer, Arnold Driessen, Walter Neupert, and Roland Lill

I. Introduction

The translocation of proteins into and across biological membranes requires the coordinated action of multiple components (for a review, see articles in Neupert and Lill, 1992). In addition to a membrane-embedded translocation machinery, further components on both the *cis* and the *trans* sides of the membrane are needed to achieve translocation. While it is experimentally easy to manipulate factors on the *cis* side of a membrane, it is a considerable problem to gain access to proteins on the *trans* side, thus precluding the investigation of the functional role of such components. So far, soluble proteinaceous factors of the *trans* side of a biological membrane can be varied either by entrapping the proteins into the lumen of proteoliposomes reconstituted from detergent-solubilized vesicles or by alkaline treatment of the membranes in the presence of the protein to be entrapped. Whereas the first procedure is difficult, sometimes yields low efficiencies, and has been developed only for *Escherichia coli* inner membranes and microsomal membranes (Driessen and Wickner, 1990; Nicchitta *et al.*, 1991; Brodsky *et al.*, 1993), the second procedure involves extreme pH shifts, restricting its applicability to alkali-stable proteins (Bulleid and Freedman, 1988).

Here we describe a simple method to introduce soluble proteins into the lumen of membrane vesicles using a freeze–thaw technique developed by adapting a procedure originally described for the reconstitution of membrane proteins (Driessen and Konings, 1993). As a model system, we use vesicles derived from purified outer membranes of *Neurospora crassa* mitochondria (Mayer *et al.*, 1993). The lumen of these vesicles corresponds to the intermembrane space of intact mitochondria. Thus, enclosing soluble proteins from this submitochondrial compartment may help to elucidate the role of these components in protein translocation across the outer membrane. The procedure may be used in an analogous way for inclusion of soluble proteins into vesicles derived from any other isolated cellular membrane, rendering it possible to identify and characterize luminal proteins involved in protein translocation. Moreover, the role of luminal proteins in other membrane-related processes, e.g., signal transduction, may be investigated.

II. Materials and Instrumentation

PMSF (Cat. No. P-7626), Mops (Cat. No. M-1254), and fatty acid-free BSA (Cat. No. A-6003) were obtained from Sigma. K_2HPO_4 (Cat. No. 5104), KH_2PO_4 (Cat.

No. 4873), KCl (Cat. No. 4936), KOH (Cat. No. 5033), and EDTA (Cat. No. 8418) were obtained from Merck. Sucrose (Cat. No. 4621) was purchased from Roth. Protein concentrations were determined by using the Bio-Rad protein assay method (Bio-Rad, Cat. No. 500-0006). Mitochondria were prepared according to Mayer *et al.* (1993) and were centrifuged at 17,000 *g* in a Beckman JA20 rotor for 12 min at 2°C to give a mitochondrial pellet.

The glass–Teflon homogenizer was from Braun. Centrifugations were done in Beckman L8/50 ME and TL-100 ultracentrifuges. The refractometer was from Leitz.

III. Procedures

A. ISOLATION OF MITOCHONDRIAL OUTER MEMBRANE VESICLES

Solutions

1. *200 mM PMSF:* To make 1 ml, dissolve 34.5 mg PMSF in 1 ml ethanol. Prepare fresh each time.

2. *Swelling buffer:* 5 mM potassium phosphate, pH 7.2, 5 mM EDTA, 1 mM PMSF. To make 500 ml, dissolve 0.435 g K_2HPO_4 and 0.340 g KH_2PO_4 in 250 ml each in H_2O, and adjust the pH of the KH_2PO_4 solution by adding the K_2HPO_4 solution to pH 7.2. Dissolve 0.931 g EDTA in 250 ml of this solution, adjust to 497.5 ml, and store at 4°C. Before use add 2.5 ml 0.2 *M* PMSF.

3. *2 M sucrose:* To prepare 100 ml, dissolve 68.4 g sucrose in H_2O and bring to 100 ml.

4. *EM buffer:* 2.5 mM EDTA, 10 mM Mops–KOH, pH 7.2. To make 100 ml, dissolve 93 mg EDTA and 0.21 g Mops in H_2O, adjust pH to 7.2 with 5 *M* KOH, and bring to 100 ml with H_2O.

5. *EMP buffer containing various amounts of sucrose:* To make 100 ml, dissolve 93 mg EDTA, 0.21 g Mops in H_2O, adjust pH to 7.2 with 5 *M* KOH, and bring to 50 ml with H_2O. To make EMP buffer containing (i) 0 *M*, (ii) 0.25 *M*, (iii) 0.72 *M*, and (iv) 0.9 *M* sucrose, add (i) 0 ml, (ii) 12.5 ml, (iii) 36 ml, and (iv) 45 ml of 2 *M* sucrose. Adjust the volume of each solution to 99.5 ml and add 0.5 ml 0.2 *M* PMSF just before use.

Steps

Samples should be kept on ice throughout the procedure.

1. Resuspend the mitochondrial pellet (550 mg protein) at a protein concentration of 6 mg/ml in EMP buffer and incubate for 10 min on ice to promote swelling of the mitochondria.

2. Transfer the suspension into a glass–Teflon homogenizer and homogenize (20 strokes) to dislodge the mitochondrial outer membrane from the remaining mitoplasts and intact mitochondria.

3. Prepare six sucrose step gradients by loading 12 ml of 0.9 *M* sucrose in EMP buffer into tubes for a Beckman SW 28 ultracentrifugation rotor (Fig. 1A). Carefully overlay with 9 ml of 0.25 *M* sucrose in EMP buffer using a glass pipette with a wide opening to avoid mixing of the two layers.

4. Load 15 ml of the homogenate from step 2 on top of each gradient by using the same glass pipette. Avoid mixing of the load and the top sucrose solution.

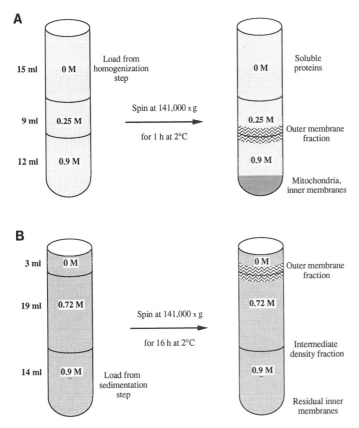

FIGURE 1 Purification of outer membrane vesicles from *Neurospora crassa* mitochondria by sucrose step gradient centrifugation. Sucrose step gradients for (**A**) sedimentation centrifugation and (**B**) flotation centrifugation are formed in tubes for a Beckman SW 28 ultracentrifugation rotor using the indicated molarities of sucrose in EMP buffer (left side). The positions of the various fractions after centrifugation are shown on the right side of the figure.

5. Spin for 1 hr at 141,000 *g* and 2°C in a Beckman SW 28 rotor (sedimentation centrifugation).

6. The outer membrane fraction is visible as a light-orange band (cf. Fig. 1A). Harvest the outer membrane fraction from the 0.25 and 0.9 *M* sucrose interface after removing most of the top layer by aspiration. The total volume of the harvested outer membrane fraction is usually about 25 ml.

7. Determine the sucrose concentration of the outer membrane fraction using a refractometer. If a refractometer is not available, it suffices to assume the sucrose concentration to be 0.55 *M*. Adjust the sucrose concentration to 0.9 *M* by adding sucrose from a 2 *M* stock solution.

8. Load 14 ml each of this solution into tubes for a Beckman SW 28 ultracentrifugation rotor. Carefully overlay the outer membrane suspension with 19 ml of 0.72 *M* sucrose in EMP buffer and 3 ml EMP buffer. Avoid mixing of the layers (see step 3, Fig. 1B).

9. Spin for 10 hr at 141,000 *g* and 2°C in a Beckman SW 28 rotor (flotation centrifugation).

10. Harvest the purified outer membrane fraction from the 0 and 0.72 *M* sucrose interface (see Fig. 1B).

11. Dilute the sample fivefold with EM buffer and concentrate the membrane vesicles by centrifugation for another 3 hr at 141,000 *g* and 2°C in a Beckman SW 28 rotor.

12. Resuspend the pellet in 0.5 ml EM buffer and determine the protein concentration using the Bio-Rad protein assay method. Adjust the protein concentration to 0.5 mg/ml. The typical yield is 1–2.5 mg outer membrane protein per gram of mitochondrial protein.

13. Freeze 100-μl aliquots in liquid nitrogen and store at $-70°C$ until use.

B. INCLUSION OF PROTEINS INTO THE LUMEN OF ISOLATED MITOCHONDRIAL OUTER MEMBRANE VESICLES

Solutions

1. *Inclusion buffer:* 10 mM Mops–KOH, pH 6.5, and 5 mg/ml BSA. To make 10 ml, dissolve 21 mg Mops and 50 mg fatty acid-free BSA in H_2O, titrate pH to 6.5 with 1 M KOH, and adjust the volume to 10 ml.

2. *Wash buffer A:* EM buffer containing 0.25 M sucrose and 100 mM KCl. To make 100 ml, dissolve 8 g sucrose, 93 mg EDTA and 0.21 g Mops, and 0.75 g KCl, adjust pH to 7.2 with 5 M KOH, and bring to 100 ml with H_2O.

3. *Wash buffer B:* EM buffer containing 0.43 M sucrose and 100 mM KCl. To make 100 ml, dissolve 15 g sucrose, 93 mg EDTA, 0.21 g Mops, and 0.75 g KCl, adjust pH to 7.2 with 5 M KOH, and bring to 100 ml with H_2O.

4. *100 mM Mops, pH 7.2:* To make 10 ml, dissolve 0.21 g Mops in H_2O, adjust pH to 7.2 with 5 M KOH, and bring to 10 ml.

Steps

Samples and buffers should always be kept at 0–4°C if not stated otherwise.

1. Quickly thaw 50 μg isolated outer membrane vesicles at 25°C and transfer to an ice bath. Reisolate the vesicles by ultracentrifugation (260,000 g for 15 min at 2°C in a Beckman TLA 100 rotor).

2. Resuspend the vesicles in 12.5 μl inclusion buffer by gently pipetting up and down through a yellow pipette tip. Transfer to a 1.5-ml Eppendorf tube.

3. Add the protein to be included (e.g., cytochrome c as a model protein) to a final protein concentration of up to 30 mg/ml. We routinely use a final concentration of 3 mg/ml. Adjust the total volume of the sample to 20 μl with inclusion buffer.

4. Snap-freeze the solution in liquid nitrogen. Place the tube in an ice water bath and let the sample thaw slowly, which may take up to 1 hr.

5. Add 4 μl of 100 mM Mops–KOH, pH 7.2, and incubate for 5 min at 25°C. Dilute with wash buffer A to a final volume of 80 μl.

6. Pipette 100 μl wash buffer B into a tube for a Beckman TLA 100 rotor and carefully overlay with the vesicle suspension.

7. Spin for 15 min at 260,000 g at 2°C in a TLA 100 rotor.

8. Aspirate 150 μl of the supernatant using an injection needle connected to a suction hose. Spin again for 2 min at 260,000 g and aspirate the remaining supernatant. Carefully resuspend the pellet in EM buffer containing 0.25 M sucrose.

9. The vesicles may now be used for further biochemical analyses (e.g., protein translocation).

IV. Comments

The vesicles produced by the isolation procedure described in Section IIIA are relatively large (average diameter approximately 300 μm) and should be handled with care. Extensive passages through narrow pipette tips can cause a transient opening of the membrane and release of the contents into the medium. Therefore, we routinely cut off 5 mm of the yellow pipette tips before use for pipetting the loaded vesicles.

Repeated freeze–thaw steps do not increase the efficiency of inclusion and rather diminish the competence of the vesicles for protein translocation.

The inclusion of proteins can be checked by immunoblotting. A very convenient alternative used successfully for establishing the procedure is FITC–dextran (average molecular weight 70,000, Sigma Cat. No. FD-70S) as a model substrate. Its inclusion can be traced fast and easily by measuring the fluorophore retained by the vesicles.

After the inclusion of proteins the vesicles cannot be frozen before use in further experiments.

V. Pitfalls

1. To obtain an outer membrane preparation that is free of contaminants such as endoplasmic reticulum and mitochondrial inner membranes, it is essential to keep all equipment as clean as possible. It is necessary to use double-distilled water for all solutions.

2. The inclusion procedure should be performed in the pH range 6.0 to 7.2. Higher pH will decrease the efficiency of inclusion, whereas lower pH may cause aggregation of the vesicles.

3. It is crucial to freeze the vesicles very rapidly and leave them undisturbed during the (slow) thawing period.

4. The buffer containing the protein to be included should be of low ionic strength and must not contain any cryopreservatives, e.g., glycerol, as these chemicals interfere with the inclusion.

REFERENCES

Brodsky, J., Hamamoto, S., Feldheim, D., and Schekman, R. (1993) Reconstitution of protein translocation from solubilized yeast membranes reveals topologically distinct roles for BiP and cytosolic Hsc70. *J. Cell Biol.* **120,** 95–102.

Bulleid, N. J., and Freedman, R. B. (1988) Defective co-translational formation of disulphide bonds in protein disulphide-isomerase-deficient microsomes. *Nature* **335,** 649–651.

Driessen, A. J. M., and Konings, W. N. (1993) Insertion of lipids and proteins into bacterial membranes by fusion with liposomes. *In* "Methods in Enzymology," Vol. 221, pp. 394–408. Academic Press, San Diego.

Driessen, A. J. M., and Wickner, W. (1990) Solubilization and functional reconstitution of protein-translocation enzymes of *Escherichia coli. Proc. Acad. Natl. Sci. USA* **87,** 3107–3111.

Mayer, A., Lill, R., and Neupert, W. (1993) Translocation and insertion of precursor proteins into isolated outer membranes of mitochondria. *J. Cell Biol.* **121,** 1233–1243.

Neupert, W., and Lill, R. (eds.). (1992) Membrane biogenesis and protein targeting. *In* "New Comprehensive Biochemistry," Vol. 22 (A. Neuberger and L. L. M. Van Deenen, series eds.). Elsevier Science, Amsterdam.

Nicchitta, C. V., Migliaccio, G., and Blobel, G. (1991) Biochemical fractionation and assembly of the membrane components that mediate nascent chain targeting and translocation. *Cell* **65,** 587–598.

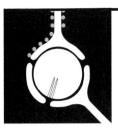

Isolation of Peroxisomes

Alfred Völkl and H. Dariush Fahimi

I. Introduction

The investigation of unique functional and structural aspects of peroxisomes requires the preparation of highly purified fractions of this organelle. This is, however, hampered by two serious problems: first, the relative paucity of peroxisomes (2% of total liver protein), and second, their considerable fragility. Thus, mild homogenization conditions minimizing mechanical, hydrostatic, and osmotic stress have to be sustained. In general, the isolation of peroxisomes is accomplished in three steps: (1) homogenization of the tissue or disruption of the cells; (2) subfractionation of the homogenate by differential centrifugation, usually according to the classic scheme of de Duve *et al.* (1955); and (3) isolation of purified peroxisomes by density gradient centrifugation of the so-called light mitochondrial (λ) fraction.

The homogenization is carried out in an isotonic medium (e.g., see Section IIIA, solution 1). High salt concentrations should be avoided as they cause aggregation. On the other hand the addition of a chelator (e.g., EDTA) is feasible because it prevents the aggregation of microsomes which may contaminate peroxisomes. For purification of peroxisomes by density gradient centrifugation three approaches have been developed. In the classic procedure (Leighton *et al.*, 1968) sucrose gradients and the specialized-type Beaufay rotor are employed. A self-generating Percoll gradient in conjunction with a vertical rotor is used for the isolation of peroxisomes under isotonic conditions (Neat *et al.*, 1980). The most straightforward approach to obtain highly purified peroxisomes makes use of iodinated gradient media such as Metrizamide and Nycodenz in conjunction with a vertical rotor (Völkl and Fahimi, 1985; Hartl *et al.*, 1985).

Peroxisomes band because of their permeability to low-molecular-weight compounds (van Veldhoven *et al.*, 1983), at the high density of 1.24 g/cm³, well separated from lysosomes as well as from mitochondria and microsomes. The method described in this article is a modification of an approach developed for isolation of highly purified (>98%) peroxisomes from normal rat liver (Völkl and Fahimi, 1985). In the meantime it has been applied to the livers of several other mammalian species (Fahimi *et al.*, 1993) as well as to the isolation of renal peroxisomes (Zaar, 1992).

II. Instrumentation and Materials

A. INSTRUMENTATION

1. Perfusion device (self-made)
2. Potter–Elvehjem tissue grinder (30 ml, Cat. No. 9.124250) with loose-

fitting pestle (Cat. No. 9.124290, clearance 0.10–0.15 mm) and a motor-driven homogenizer (Cat. No. 9.651000) obtained from Bender and Hobein

3. Refrigerated low- and high-speed centrifuges (e.g., Beckman TJ-6 and J2-21) and ultracentrifuge (e.g., Beckman L90) with corresponding rotors (e.g., Beckman JA-20 and VTi 50)

4. Refractometer

B. CHEMICALS

Mops (Cat. No. 29-836), PMSF (Cat. No. 32-395), and DTT (Cat. No. 20-710) were obtained from Serva. Ethanol (Cat. No. 8006) and NaCl (Cat. No. 0277) were from J. T. Baker. EDTA (Cat. No. E2628-2) was purchased from Max Keller, ϵ-aminocaproic acid (Cat. No. 62 075) from Riedel-de Haen, sucrose (Cat. No. 4621) from Roth, and Metrizamide (Cat. No. 222010) from Nycomed.

C. ANIMALS

Female rats of 220–250 g body weight, starved overnight, were used.

III. Procedures

A. PERFUSION AND HOMOGENIZATION

Solutions

1. *Homogenization medium (HM):* To make 1 liter, dissolve 85.55 g of sucrose, 1.406 g of Mops, 0.292 g of EDTA and 1 ml of ethanol in distilled water, adjust pH to 7.2 with NaOH, and add water up to 1 liter. Store at 4°C. Prior to use add, per 100 ml, 0.2 ml of 0.1 M PMSF, 0.1 ml of 1 M ϵ-aminocaproic acid, and 20 μl of 1 M DTT.

2. *0.9% Saline:* To make 1 liter, dissolve 9 g of NaCl in distilled water and adjust to a total volume of 1 liter.

Steps

1. Anesthetize the animal (e.g., by intraperitoneal injection of chloral hydrate).

2. Weigh the animal, open the abdominal cavity, and perfuse liver with 0.9% saline via the portal vein until all blood is drained away.

3. Remove liver, dissect connective tissue, weigh and cut liver into small pieces in a Potter–Elvehjem tissue grinder held in an ice bath and containing 3 ml/g (wet liver weight) of ice-cold HM.

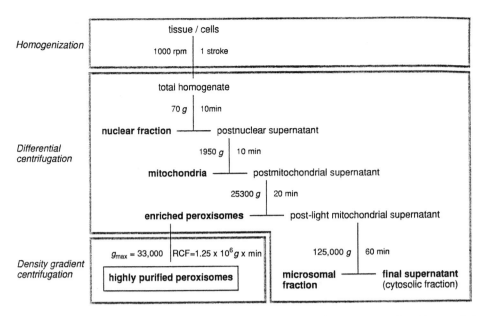

FIGURE 1 Diagrammatic representation of the procedure for isolation of highly purified (>98%) peroxisomes from rat liver.

4. Homogenize tissue with a single up and down stroke using a loose-fitting pestle rotating at 1000 rpm (Fig. 1).

5. Pour homogenate into a 50-ml centrifuge tube.

B. SUBCELLULAR FRACTIONATION

Steps

1. To remove debris, unbroken hepatocytes, blood cells, and, concomitantly, most of the nuclei, centrifuge the total homogenate at 70 g for 10 min in a refrigerated low-speed centrifuge.

2. Carefully pour off the supernatant (loose pellet), resuspend pellet in 2 ml/g ice-cold HM, rehomogenize, and spin again under the same conditions.

3. Pour off the second supernatant and combine it with the first one (postnuclear supernatant) (see Fig. 1).

4. Centrifuge the postnuclear supernatant at 1950 g for 10 min in a refrigerated high-speed centrifuge.

5. Decant supernatant (firm pellet), resuspend pellet manually in 1 ml/g ice-cold HM using an appropriate pestle, and spin again at 1950 g. The final pellet contains the majority of *mitochondria,* large microsomal sheets, and some remaining nuclei. The combined supernatants represent the postmitochondrial supernatant.

6. Subject the latter to 25,300 g for 20 min. Remove the supernatant including the reddish fluffy layer by suction. Resuspend the pellet in about 10 ml of ice-cold HM using a glass-rod and recentrifuge at 25,300 g for 15 min. Resuspend the final pellet in 5 ml of ice-cold HM by means of a glass rod; this constitutes the *enriched peroxisome* (light mitochondrial) fraction. The corresponding supernatant contains the microsomes and soluble proteins (mostly of cytosolic origin).

TABLE I Properties of Purified Peroxisomal Fractions from Normal Rat Liver.

Enzyme	mU/mg homogenate (mg/g liver)	Rate of recovery (%)	Relative specific activity
Protein	256.36 ± 82.94^a	0.28 ± 0.08	—
Catalase	203 ± 42.7	9.96 ± 1.92	37.67 ± 4.28
Hydroxy acid	3.3 ± 0.7	9.46 ± 1.06	40.25 ± 5.83
Fatty acid β-oxidation	3.6 ± 0.96	11.18 ± 3.25	36.32 ± 5.09
β-Glucuronidase	38 ± 5.88	0.01 ± 0.01	0.07 ± 0.06
Acid phosphatase	31	0.15	0.07
Esterase	1229 ± 246.7	0.01 ± 0.01	0.09 ± 0.07
NADPH–Cc reductase[b]	18 ± 4.60	0.18	0.702
Cc oxidase	127 ± 35.6	0.02 ± 0.02	0.09 ± 0.05
L-G1DH	57 ± 16.5	0.08 ± 0.02	0.679

[a] Values given are means $\pm$ standard deviations.
[b] Cc, cytochrome C; L-G1DH, L-glutamate dehydrogenase

C. METRIZAMIDE DENSITY GRADIENT CENTRIFUGATION

Solutions

1. *Gradient buffer (GB):* To make 1 liter, dissolve 1.426 g of Mops, 0.292 g of EDTA, and 1 ml of ethanol in distilled water, adjust pH to 7.2 with NaOH, and add water up to 1 liter. Store at 4°C. Prior to use add, per 100 ml, 0.2 ml of 0.1 M PMSF, 0.1 ml of 1 M ϵ-aminocaproic acid, and 20 μl of 1 M DTT.

2. Metrizamide stock solution, 60% (w/v): Dissolve 60 g of Metrizamide in GB by stirring. Add GB up to 100 ml. Store at 4°C.

3. Metrizamide gradient solution: To prepare one gradient, take 3.78, 3.38, 3.53, 2.06, and 3.2 ml of 60% stock solution. To adjust densities to 1.12, 1.155, 1.19, 1.225, and 1.26 g/ml, add GB up to 10, 7, 6, 3, and 4 ml, respectively.

Steps

Preparation of a Metrizamide gradient

1. Layer sequentially 4, 3, 6, 7, and 10 ml of Metrizamide gradient solution (1.26–1.12 g/ml) in a 40-ml centrifuge tube (e.g., Quick-Seal polyallomer, Beckman) to form a discontinuous gradient.

2. Immediately freeze the gradient in liquid nitrogen and store it at -20°C.

3. Thaw the gradient quickly at room temperature using a metallic stand, thus transforming the step gradient into one with an exponential profile.

Gradient centrifugation

1. Layer 5 ml of the enriched peroxisomal fraction (corresponding to one liver of approximately 5–6 g) on top of the thawed gradient and seal it.

2. Centrifuge gradients in a vertical-type rotor (e.g., Beckman VTi 50) at an integrated force of 1.256×10^6 $g \times$ min ($g_{max} = 33,000$) using slow acceleration/ deceleration. Under the conditions employed *highly purified peroxisomes* band at 1.23–1.24 g/ml.

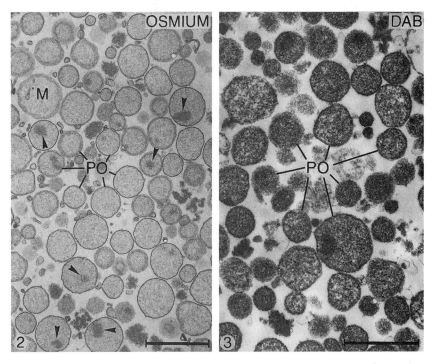

FIGURE 2 Electron microscopic appearance of isolated peroxisomes after fixation in glutaraldehyde and osmium. The fraction consists almost exclusively of peroxisomes (PO) with only a rare mitochondrion (M). Many peroxisomes contain urate oxidase cores (arrowheads). Bar = 1 μm.

FIGURE 3 A preparation comparable to that in Fig. 2 but incubated in the alkaline 3,3'-diaminobenzidine (DAB) for localization of catalase (Fahimi, 1969). Note the electron-dense reaction product of catalase over the matrix of most peroxisomes. This illustrates the absence of catalase leakage, confirming their integrity.

3. Recover the peroxisomal fraction by means of a fraction collector or by puncturing the gradient tube and aspirating with a syringe. Store fractions at −80°C.

4. To remove Metrizamide, which interferes with the determination of some peroxisomal enzymes (e.g., urate oxidase) or of protein (Lowry method), dilute the peroxisome fraction about 10-fold with HM followed by centrifugation (25,000 g, 20 min) to pellet the organelles.

IV. Comments

The properties of the peroxisomal fraction are listed in Table I. By comparison with specific peroxisomal reference enzymes, it shows a purification rate of about 38-fold over that of the original homogenate. More than 95% of the total protein content of this fraction is contributed by peroxisomes (Völkl and Fahimi, 1985), with mitochondria and microsomes accounting for about 2% each and lysosomes for less than 1%. This distribution is confirmed by electron microscopy which shows that peroxisomes make up 98–99% of the fraction (Figs. 2 and 3). Many peroxisomes contain the typical inclusions of urate oxidase in matrix, but some extruded free cores are also found in between. The electron-dense cytochemical reaction product of catalase after incubation of filter preparations in the alkaline 3,3'-diaminobenzidine medium (Fahimi, 1969) is seen over the matrix of the major-

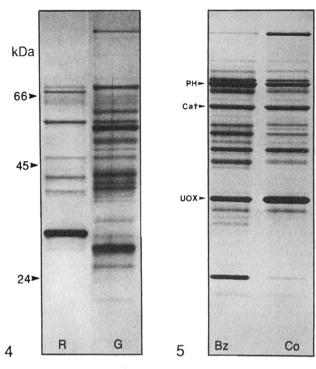

FIGURE 4 SDS–PAGE of highly purified peroxisomes from rat (R) and guinea pig (G) liver. A 10–12.5% resolving gel was used and the amounts of protein loaded per lane were (R) 2.4 μg and (G) 5.4 μg. Silver staining of polypeptide bands. Molecular weight standards: BSA, 66 kDa; ovalbumin 45 kDa; trypsinogen, 24 kDa. Note the distinct differences in the polypeptide patterns between rat and guinea pig peroxisomes.

FIGURE 5 SDS–PAGE of highly purified peroxisomes from control (Co) and bezafibrate-treated (Bz) rat liver. A 10–15% resolving gel was used and 5.0 μg of protein was loaded per lane. Silver staining of bands. Peroxisomal polypeptides indicated by arrowheads are trifunctional protein (PH), catalase (Cat), and urate oxidase (UOX). Note the induction of PH and the concomitant reduction of Cat and UOX in peroxisomes of the Bz-treated rat.

ity of peroxisomes, demonstrating their integrity and the absence of leakage of catalase.

The polypeptide pattern (SDS–PAGE) of rat liver peroxisomes is shown in Fig. 4, confirming their high degree of purity because of the paucity of bands typical for mitochondria and microsomes. Figure 4 also shows the distinct differences in the protein compositions of hepatic peroxisomes of rat and guinea pig. The selective induction of specific peroxisomal proteins, such as the trifunctional protein, with concomitant reductions of catalase and urate oxidase, in rats treated with hypolipidemic fibrates is shown in Fig. 5.

Recently we have extended the procedure outlined above by introducing an additional differential centrifugation step, and have succeeded in isolating two peroxisome subpopulations from normal and regenerating rat liver that differ in density, size, shape, and enzymatic composition (Lüers et al., 1993). Those observations are consistent with the concept of heterogeneity of peroxisomes in rat liver and may have some bearing on the biogenesis of this organelle.

ACKNOWLEDGMENTS

The original work in the laboratory of the authors was supported by grants of the Deutsche Forschungsgemeinschaft, Bonn, Germany (Fa 146/1-3, Vo 317/3-1, SFB 352, and Vo 317/4-1) and Landesforschungsschwerpunkt-Programm of the State of Baden-Württemberg, Germany.

REFERENCES

De Duve, C., Pressman, B. C., Gianetto, R., Wattiaux, R., and Appelmans, F. (1955) 6. Intracellular distribution patterns of enzymes in rat liver tissue. *Biochem. J.* **60**, 604–617.

Fahimi, H. D. (1969) Cytochemical localization of peroxidatic activity of catalase in rat hepatic microbodies (peroxisomes). *J. Cell Biol.* **43**, 275–288.

Fahimi, H. D., Baumgart, E., Beier, K., Pill, J., Hartig, F., and Völkl, A. (1993) Ultrastructural and biochemical aspects of peroxisome proliferation and biogenesis in different mammalian species. *In* "Peroxisomes: Biology and Importance in Toxicology and Medicine" (G. G. Gibson and B. Lake, eds.), pp. 395–424. Taylor & Francis, London.

Hartl, F. U., Just, W. W., Köster, A., and Schimassek, H. (1985) Improved isolation and purification of rat liver peroxisomes by combined rate zonal and equilibrium density centrifugation. *Arch. Biochem. Biophys.* **237**, 124–134.

Leighton, F., Poole, B., Beaufay, H., Baudhuin, P., Coffey, J. W., Fowler, S., and de Duve, C. (1968) The large-scale preparation of peroxisomes, mitochondria and lysosomes from the livers of rats injected with Triton WR-1339. *J. Cell Biol.* **37**, 482–513.

Lüers, G., Hashimoto, T., Fahimi, H. D., and Völkl, A. (1993) Biogenesis of peroxisomes: Isolation and characterization of two distinct peroxisomal populations from normal and regenerating rat liver. *J. Cell Biol.* **121**, 1271–1280.

Neat, C. E., Thomassen, M. S., and Osmundsen, H. (1980) Induction of peroxisomal β-oxidation in rat liver by high-fat diets. *Biochem. J.* **186**, 369–371.

Van Veldhoven, P., Debeer, L. J., and Mannaerts, G. P. (1983) Water- and solute-accessible spaces of purified peroxisomes. *Biochem. J.* **210**, 685–693.

Völkl, A., and Fahimi, H. D. (1985) Isolation and characterization of peroxisomes from the liver of normal untreated rats. *Eur. J. Biochem.* **149**, 257–265.

Zaar, K. (1992) Structure and function of peroxisomes in the mammalian kidney. *Eur. J. Cell Biol.* **59**, 233–254.

Purification of Secretory Granules from PC12 Cells

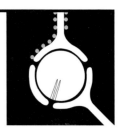

Jane C. Stinchcombe and Wieland B. Huttner

I. Introduction

Specialized cells that secrete certain proteins in response to external signals store these secretory products in specific organelles called *secretory granules* (Burgess and Kelly, 1987). The ability to purify secretory granules is an important prerequisite for their molecular characterization, which in turn is required for a full understanding of their function. Most studies dealing with the purification and characterization of secretory granules have been performed with endocrine (e.g., adrenal medulla; reviewed by Winkler *et al.,* 1986) or exocrine (reviewed by Castle *et al.,* 1987) tissue rather than secretory granule-containing cell lines. This is because secretory granules are denser and more abundant in tissue than in cells in culture and, thus, much more easily purified from the former. On the other hand, cell lines with secretory granules offer many advantages over tissue as model systems for investigating functional aspects of the secretory process. Ideally, one would therefore want to purify and characterize secretory granules from such cell lines.

The neuroendocrine cell line PC12, derived from a rat pheochromocytoma (Greene and Tischler, 1976), has extensively been used as a model system to study various aspects of secretory granule function (see references in Bauerfeind and Huttner, 1993; Kelly, 1993; Tooze *et al.,* 1993). Several procedures for the preparation of secretory granules from PC12 cells have been reported, which vary in the degree of purity of the final material obtained (Roda *et al.,* 1980; Wagner, 1985; Cutler and Cramer, 1990). Here we describe the method developed in our laboratory which yields PC12 cell secretory granules of near-morphological purity (see also Stinchcombe, 1992; Stinchcombe and Huttner, manuscript in preparation). To determine the purification factor and yield, we have used the tyrosine-sulfated secretory granule-specific proteins chromogranin B (CgB, secretogranin I) and secretogranin II (SgII) (Huttner *et al.,* 1991a,b) as markers. CgB and SgII are easily detected either by long-term [35S]sulfate labeling followed by SDS–PAGE (Rosa *et al.,* 1985) or by SDS–PAGE followed by immunoblotting using, in the case of CgB, a commercially available monoclonal antibody (Rosa *et al.,* 1989) (Boehringer-Mannheim, Cat. No. 1112-490).

II. Materials and Instrumentation

Besides standard chemicals and instruments, the following materials are required. Trizma base (Cat. No. T-1503) and leupeptin (Cat. No. L-2884) can be bought from Sigma Chemicals, aprotinin (Cat. No. 236624) from Boehringer–Mannheim,

PMSF (Cat. No. A-32395) from Serva, and Hepes (Cat. No. 9105) and EDTA (Cat. No. 8043) from Roth. Carrier-free [^{35}S]sulfate (25–40 Ci/mg, Cat. No. SJS 1) is obtained from Amersham Buchler. Dulbecco's modified Eagle's medium powder (DMEM, Cat. No. 07401600N) and horse serum (HS, Cat. No. 03406050M) are from Gibco Laboratories, and fetal calf serum (FCS, Cat. No. S0115) from Seromed (Berlin).

Cell culture plates (24 × 24 cm, Cat. No. 166508) are obtained from Nunc, and disposable plastic pipettes and 15-ml tubes (Cat. No. 2095) from Falcon Labware. Ultraclear centrifuge tubes (14 × 95 mm, for SW 40 rotor) are obtained from Beckman (Cat. No. 344060), a 20-ml linear gradient mixing chamber (Cat. No. 42020) from Hoelzel, and an Auto Densi-flow IIC gradient maker from Buchler Instruments. The cell cracker is that described by Balch *et al.* (1984) (prepared by the EMBL workshop, Heidelberg), and is used with a ball with an 18-μm clearance. Plastic reaction tubes (1.5 ml, Cat. No. 3810) are from Eppendorf. These should be prepared for collecting 1.1-ml gradient fractions by marking the 1.1-ml level by comparison with a standard obtained by filling one tube with 1.1 ml of distilled H$_2$O. Twelve or thirteen Eppendorf tubes are required for each gradient used (48–52 tubes per secretory granule preparation).

In addition, the following equipment is required: 22-gauge needles, 1-ml plastic syringes, 15-ml Corex tubes, and a cell scraper, which can be prepared from a slice of a silicone stopper (approximately 2 cm in diameter) attached to a plastic pipette.

III. Procedure

A. CELL CULTURE

For one secretory granule preparation, six to eight plates (24 × 24 cm) of subconfluent PC12 cells (clone 251) (Heumann *et al.*, 1983; see also article by Kenneth K. Teng and Lloyd A. Greene in this volume) are required.

Solutions

1. *Growth medium:* DMEM supplemented with 5% FCS and 10% HS.

Steps

1. Culture cells in growth medium at 37°C in 10% CO$_2$.
2. Passage cells at dilutions of 1:5 or 1:6 and plate them 5–6 days in advance of the experiment.

B. LONG-TERM [^{35}S]SULFATE LABELING OF PC12 CELLS

For monitoring the distribution of the secretory granules during the purification, at least one dish of cells should be incubated with [^{35}S]sulfate to label the sulfated secretory granule content proteins, CgB and SgII.

Solutions

1. *Labeling medium:* Supplement DMEM that lacks cysteine and methionine and in which MgSO$_4$ is replaced with MgCl$_2$, with 1% of the normal DMEM concentration of cysteine, 1% of the normal DMEM concentration of

methionine, 0.05% FCS, 0.1% HS. The FCS and HS should both be dialyzed against phosphate-buffered saline (PBS).

Steps

1. Remove growth medium from the cells and replace with 20 ml per plate of labeling medium.
2. Add 0.15–0.25 mCi/ml carrier-free $[^{35}S]$sulfate to each plate.
3. Incubate at 37°C, 10% CO_2 for 12–16 hr.

C. GRADIENT PREPARATION

Gradients are prepared immediately before cell homogenization and stored at 4°C until used. Four first gradients (three for samples, one as balance) and two second gradients (one for the sample, one as a balance) are required for one secretory granule preparation.

Solutions

1. *2.0 M sucrose stock solution:* Dissolve 68.46 g of sucrose in a small amount of double-distilled (dd) H_2O, then adjust to a final volume of 100 ml. The solution can be aliquoted and stored at −20°C. The molarity of the sucrose solution can be verified by refractometry.

2. *Sucrose solutions for density gradients:* 0.3, 1.1, 1.2, and 2.0 M sucrose solutions, containing 1 μg/ml each of aprotinin and leupeptin, and 0.5 mM PMSF:

	2.0 M sucrose	Distilled H_2O	1 mg/ml aprotinin/leupeptin	250 mM PMSF
First gradient				
0.3 M sucrose	6 ml	34 ml	40 μl	80 μl
1.2 M sucrose	24 ml	16 ml	40 μl	80 μl
Second gradient				
1.1 M sucrose	11 ml	9 ml	20 μl	40 μl
2.0 M sucrose	20 ml	0 ml	20 μl	40 μl

Solutions are made fresh.

Steps

First (0.3–1.2 M continuous sucrose) gradient

1. Connect a Buchler Auto Densi-flow gradient maker II C to a 20-ml gradient mixing chamber containing a stirring bar in the output chamber and placed on a magnetic stirrer.

2. Place an SW 40 tube in the gradient maker, lower the probe to the bottom of the tube, and put the probe in the "up" setting. Set the pump of the gradient maker to "4".

3. Place 6.0 ml of 1.2 M sucrose in the output chamber and 5.5 ml of 0.3 M sucrose in the other chamber, then switch on the stirrer for gentle mixing.

4. Switch the gradient maker to "deposit." Allow the 1.2 M sucrose to exit for

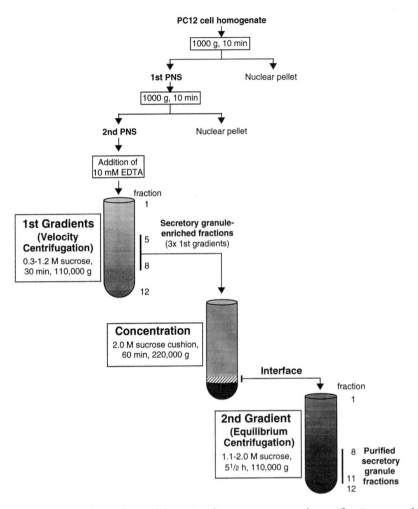

FIGURE 1 Flow scheme illustrating the secretory granule purification procedure.

about 5–10 sec, then open the channel connecting the two chambers of the gradient mixer, allowing the 0.3 M sucrose to enter the output chamber.

5. Check that the sucrose solutions are mixing evenly while being deposited into the tube, until all the sucrose has been used.

Second (1.1–2.0 M continuous sucrose) gradient

1. Prepare two continuous sucrose second gradients as described above, using 5.5 ml of 1.1 M and 5.0 ml of 2.0 M sucrose.

D. PREPARATION OF THE POSTNUCLEAR SUPERNATANT

See also Fig. 1. All subsequent steps should be performed at 4°C and all solutions, centrifuge tubes, and the cell cracker should be precooled to 0°C.

Solutions

1. *Tris-buffered saline (TBS)*: 25 mM Tris–HCl, pH 7.4, 137 mM KCl, 0.6 mM Na_2HPO_4: For 1 liter, dissolve 0.4 g KCl, 3.0 g Trizma base, 8.0 g NaCl, and 0.1 g Na_2HPO_4 in ≈900 ml ddH_2O, adjust the pH to 7.4 with 1 N and then

Organelles, Cellular Structures, Macromolecules, and Functional Assays

0.1 N HCl, and adjust the volume to 1 liter with ddH$_2$O. The solution can be aliquoted and stored at −20°C.

2. *Homogenization buffer (HB):* 0.25 M sucrose, 10 mM Hepes, pH 7.4, 1 mM EDTA, containing 1 μg/ml each of aprotinin and leupeptin, and 0.5 mM PMSF. Mix 6.25 ml 2.0 M sucrose stock solution, 0.5 ml 1.0 M Hepes–KOH, pH 7.4, 0.5 ml 100 mM EDTA–NaOH, pH 7.4, and 42.75 ml ddH$_2$O. To the final solution, add 50 μl 1 mg/ml aprotinin and 1 mg/ml leupeptin (in ddH$_2$O) and 100 μl 250 mM PMSF (in 100% ethanol). The buffer is made fresh.

Steps

1. Place the plates on ice, remove the growth or labeling medium, and wash each plate three times with 15–20 ml of TBS.

2. Remove the cells in 10 ml TBS per plate, using the cell scraper. Place the cell suspension from one plate into one 15-ml Falcon tube and pellet the cells by centrifuging for 5 min at 700 g (800 rpm in a Heraeus Minifuge RF).

3. Resuspend each pellet in 1 ml of HB, divide the total suspension between three preweighed (see below) 15-ml Falcon tubes, and adjust each volume to 6 ml. Centrifuge for 5 min at 1700 g (1800 rpm in a Heraeus Minifuge RF).

4. Remove the supernatant. Weigh the tube with the pellet and determine the weight of the pellet by subtracting the weight of the empty tube (see above). Resuspend each pellet in 1.5–2 vol of HB. Pool the resuspended pellets. Typically, this yields ≈6.0 ml of total cell suspension when starting with six to eight subconfluent 24 × 24-cm plates of PC12 cells.

5. Pass the cell suspension, in 1-ml aliquots, six times through a 22-gauge needle attached to a disposable 1-ml plastic syringe, to disperse cell clumps. Homogenize the cells by passing 1-ml aliquots through the cell cracker until the maximum number of cells is disrupted and the minimum number of nuclei is destroyed. This is typically the case after four to six single passes, and should be determined by phase-contrast microscopy of a small aliquot of the homogenate after staining with trypan blue. After homogenization of each 1-ml aliquot, remove any material remaining within the cell cracker by suction with a syringe and add to the homogenate. In addition, wash out the cell cracker with a minimal volume of HB (about 0.5–0.8 ml) between every two to three 1-ml aliquots, and add the wash to the homogenate.

6. Place the final homogenate (typically 7.0–7.5 ml) in one 15-ml Corex centrifuge tube and centrifuge for 10 min at 1000 g (3000 rpm in a precooled Sorvall SS 34 rotor).

7. The resulting postnuclear supernatant (PNS) should be carefully removed from the nuclear pellet, transferred into one fresh 15-ml Corex tube, and recentrifuged for 10 min at 1000 g. The second PNS (≈4 ml, ≈14 mg/ml protein) should again be carefully removed and placed in a 15-ml Falcon tube.

8. To prevent contamination of the final secretory granule preparation with rough endoplasmic reticulum (RER) (see Section IV), raise the EDTA concentration of the second PNS to 11 mM EDTA by adding, per milliliter of PNS, 20 μl of 500 mM EDTA–NaOH, pH 7.4, to the side of the tube, then gently mixing the sample by inversion. Count a 10- to 30-μl aliquot to determine the total amount of [^{35}S]sulfate-labeled material, and take a 1- to 5-μl aliquot for protein analysis by SDS–PAGE.

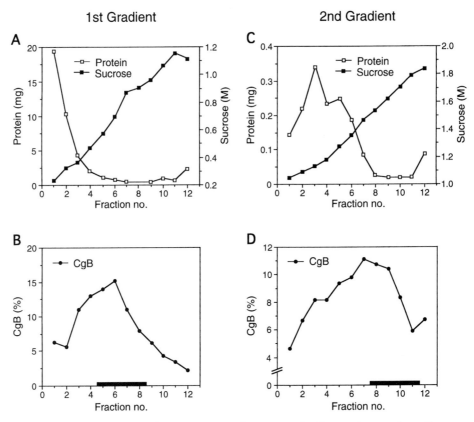

1st Gradient

A

2nd Gradient

C

B

D

FIGURE 2 Distribution of secretory granules across the first and second gradients, as indicated by CgB quantitated after immunoblotting (Stinchcombe and Huttner, in preparation). The amount of CgB in each fraction (1 = top) is expressed as a percentage of total per gradient. The bar in B indicates the fractions typically taken for further purification; the bar in D indicates the purified secretory granule fractions.

E. FIRST GRADIENT (VELOCITY CENTRIFUGATION)

See also Fig. 1.

Steps

1. Divide the EDTA-treated PNS into three 1.2- to 1.4-ml aliquots, and load each onto the top of a first (0.3–1.2 M sucrose) gradient.

2. Centrifuge the gradients at 110,000 g_{max} (25,000 rpm for the Beckman SW 40 rotor), with the centrifuge set at maximum acceleration and with the brake on, for 30 min timed from when the rotor reaches full speed.

3. Collect 1.1-ml aliquots from the top of the gradient into premarked Eppendorf tubes using the Buchler Auto Densi-flow set at "4–6." Use the most dense fraction (No. 12) to resuspend the pellet. Count an aliquot (50–150 μl) of each fraction to identify the fractions containing [^{35}S]sulfate-labeled CgB and SgII, i.e., secretory granules. The secretory granule peak is typically found in fractions 3–7, corresponding to a sucrose concentration of 0.4–0.9 M (Figs. 2A and B). Remove a 5- to 10-μl aliquot from each fraction for SDS–PAGE minigel analysis of the protein distribution across the gradient.

F. CONCENTRATION OF SECRETORY GRANULES FOR THE SECOND GRADIENT

See also Fig. 1.

Solutions

1. *0.7 M sucrose solution:* For 10 ml of 0.7 M sucrose solution, dilute 3.5 ml of 2.0 M sucrose stock with 6.5 ml of ddH$_2$O.

Steps

1. From the three first gradients, pool fractions 5–8, which are relatively enriched in secretory granules [compare the total protein (Fig. 2A) with CgB (Fig. 2B). Gently mix the pooled fractions ($\approx$13 ml, $\approx$0.7 M sucrose average).

2. Load the pooled material onto a single 700-μl cushion of 2.0 M sucrose at the bottom of an SW 40 centrifuge tube.

3. Centrifuge for 60 min at 220,000 g_{max} (36,000 rpm for the Beckman SW 40 rotor). After this a thick band should be visible at the cushion interface.

4. Remove most of the material above the interface band, leaving $\approx$0.5 ml of fluid above the interface band. Carefully collect the interface band plus the residual fluid above it, but minimize the amount of 2.0 M sucrose cushion collected.

5. Check that the density of the collected material is less than 1.1 M sucrose by placing a drop of the material onto the top of the second (1.1–2.0 M sucrose) gradient. If the material enters the gradient, carefully reduce the density of the sample by adding small aliquots of fresh 0.7 M sucrose until the sample no longer sinks into the second gradient.

G. SECOND GRADIENT (EQUILIBRIUM CENTRIFUGATION)

See also Fig. 1.

Steps

1. Load the sample onto the top of the second (1.1–2.0 M sucrose) gradient. Centrifuge the gradient for $5\frac{1}{2}$ hr at 110,000 g_{max} (25,000 rpm for the Beckman SW 40 rotor), with the centrifuge set at maximum acceleration and with the brake on.

2. Collect 1.1-ml aliquots into premarked Eppendorf tubes as before. Take 5- to 30-μl aliquots of each gradient fraction for SDS–PAGE analysis of the distribution and purity of secretory granules (see Section IV). Store the remainder of the fractions at 4°C or frozen, as appropriate.

3. Analyze the gradient fractions by SDS–PAGE using minigels. After electrophoresis, the gel can be (i) stained with silver (Heukeshoven and Dernick, 1988) (CgB and SgII appear blue, other proteins brown) or Coomassie blue to analyze the protein profile including CgB and SgII; (ii) subjected to fluorography to detect [^{35}S]sulfate-labeled CgB and SgII; or (iii) processed for Western blotting to detect CgB and SgII immunologically. The purest secretory granule material is typically found in fractions 8–11, corresponding to a sucrose concentration of 1.55–1.8 M (Figs. 2C and D).

TABLE I Recovery and Enrichment of CgB in the Purified Granule Preparation

	Protein		CgB			
	Total (mg)	%	Total (arbitrary units)	%	CgB/protein (arbitrary units/mg)	Purification (-fold)
PNS	46.500	100.0	139,793	100.0	3,006	1
First gradient						
Total	42.670	91.8	134,390	96.1	3,150	1
Fractions 5–8	2.770	6.0	64,490	46.1	23,282	8
Interface	1.490	3.2	52,715	37.7	35,379	12
Second gradient						
Total	1.613	3.5	47,868	34.2	29,676	10
Fractions 8–11	0.084	0.2	16,933	12.1	201,583	67

IV. Comments

The characteristics of the secretory granule preparation obtained by the procedure described above are shown in Table I and Fig. 3. The purified secretory granule preparation has a protein concentration of $\approx$20 μg/ml. Using CgB as marker, $\approx$12% of the secretory granules present in the EDTA-treated PNS are recovered in the purified secretory granule preparation (Table I). The purification factor, calculated from the ratio of CgB to total protein, is $\approx$70-fold as compared with the EDTA-treated PNS (Table I). By electron microscopy, at least 90% of the structures are indistinguishable from dense-cored secretory granules of intact PC12 cells (Fig. 3), and thus the secretory granule preparation approaches morphological homogeneity by this criterion. The yield of secretory granules can be increased, although at the expense of purity, by taking the entire secretory granule peak from the first and second gradients (see Fig. 2).

Raising the EDTA concentration in the PNS before velocity centrifugation is crucial. This treatment reduces the buoyant density of the RER by dissociating the membrane-bound polysomes. Without this treatment, significant amounts of RER

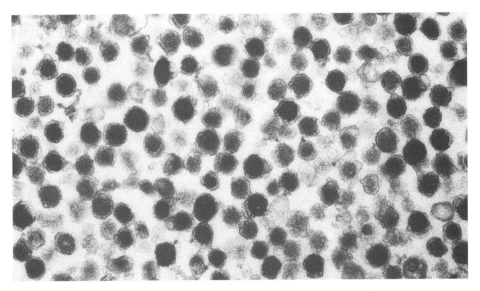

FIGURE 3 Electron micrograph showing the appearance of the purified secretory granule preparation. The diameter of the dense cores is $\approx$80–120 nm.

are recovered in the secretory granule preparation (Stinchcombe, 1992). EDTA treatment cannot be carried out with the homogenate as nuclei will lyse and the released DNA will aggregate organelles.

The procedure described above has been developed for PC12 cells. The principles of the procedure should, however, be applicable to the purification of secretory granules from other cell lines if the specific parameters are adjusted to the cell and secretory granule type under study.

V. Pitfalls

1. Too stringent homogenization of the cells will result in lysis of nuclei, release of DNA, and aggregation of membranes.

2. Sudden reduction of the sucrose concentration by dilution, and freezing and thawing, may result in lysis of secretory granules.

REFERENCES

Balch, W. E., Dunphy, W. G., Braell, W. A., and Rothman, J. E. (1984) Reconstitution of the transport of protein between successive compartments of the Golgi measured by the coupled incorporation of N-acetylglucosamine. *Cell* **39**, 405–416.

Bauerfeind, R., and Huttner, W. B. (1993) Biogenesis of constitutive secretory vesicles, secretory granules, and synaptic vesicles. *Curr. Opin. Cell Biol.* **5**, 628–635.

Burgess, T. L., and Kelly, R. B. (1987) Constitutive and regulated secretion of proteins. *Annu. Rev. Cell Biol.* **3**, 243–293.

Castle, J. D., Cameron, R. S., Arvan, P., von Zastrow, M., and Rudnick, G. (1987) Similarities and differences among neuroendocrine, exocrine and endocytic vesicles. *Ann. N.Y. Acad. Sci.* **493**, 448–459.

Cutler, D. F., and Cramer, L. P. (1990) Sorting during transport to the surface of PC12 cells: Divergence of synaptic vesicle and secretory granule proteins. *J. Cell Biol.* **110**, 721–730.

Greene, L. A., and Tischler, A. S. (1976) Establishment of a noradrenergic clonal line of rat adrenal pheochromocytoma cells which respond to nerve growth factor. *Proc. Natl. Acad. Sci. USA* **73**, 2424–2428.

Heukeshoven, J., and Dernick, R. (1988) Improved silver staining procedure for fast staining in Phast System Development Unit. I. Staining of sodium dodecyl sulfate gels. *Electrophoresis* **9**, 28–32.

Heumann, R., Kachel, V., and Thoenen, H. (1983) Relationship between NGF-mediated volume increase and "priming effect" in fast and slow reacting clones of PC12 pheochromocytoma cells. *Exp. Cell Res.* **145**, 179–190.

Huttner, W. B., Gerdes, H.-H., and Rosa, P. (1991a) Chromogranins/secretogranins—Widespread constituents of the secretory granule matrix in endocrine cells and neurons. *In* "Markers for Neural and Endocrine Cells. Molecular and Cell Biology, Diagnostic applications" (M. Gratzl and K. Langley, eds.), pp. 93–131. VCH, Weinheim.

Huttner, W. B., Gerdes, H.-H., and Rosa, P. (1991b) The granin (chromogranin/secretogranin) family. *Trends Biochem. Sci.* **16**, 27–30.

Kelly, R. B. (1993) Storage and release of neurotransmitters. *Cell* **72**(Suppl.), 43–53.

Roda, L. G., Nolan, J. A., Kim, S. V., and Hogue-Angeletti, R. A. (1980) Isolation and characterisation of chromaffin granules from a pheochromocytoma (PC12) cell line. *Exp. Cell. Res.* **128**, 103–109.

Rosa, P., Hille, A., Lee, R. W. H., Zanini, A., De Camilli, P., and Huttner, W. B. (1985) Secretogranins I and II: Two tyrosine-sulfated secretory proteins common to a variety of cells secreting peptides by the regulated pathway. *J. Cell Biol.* **101**, 1999–2011.

Rosa, P., Weiss, U., Pepperkok, R., Ansorge, W., Niehrs, C., Stelzer, E. H. K., and Huttner, W. B. (1989) An antibody against secretogranin I (chromogranin B) is packaged into secretory granules. *J. Cell Biol.* **109**, 17–34.

Stinchcombe, J. C. (1992) "The Purification and Characterisation of Secretory Storage Granules from PC12 Cells." Ph.D. thesis, Council of National Academic Awards (U.K.).

Tooze, S. A., Chanat, E., Tooze, J., and Huttner, W. B. (1993) Secretory granule formation. *In* "Mechanisms of Intracellular Trafficking and Processing of Proproteins" (Y. Peng Loh, ed.), pp. 157–177. CRC Press, Boca Raton, FL.

Wagner, J. A. (1985) Structure of catecholamine secretory vesicles from PC12 cells. *J. Neurochem.* **45,** 1244–1253.

Winkler, H., Apps, D. K., and Fischer-Colbrie, R. (1986) The molecular function of adrenal chromaffin granules: Established facts and unresolved topics. *Neuroscience* **18,** 261–290.

Preparation of Synaptic Vesicles from Mammalian Brain

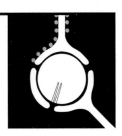

Johannes W. Hell and Reinhard Jahn

I. Introduction

Synaptic vesicles are secretory organelles that store neurotransmitter in presynaptic nerve endings. When an action potential arrives in the nerve terminal, the plasma membrane is depolarized, leading to the opening of voltage-gated Ca^{2+} channels. The rise in intracellular Ca^{2+} concentration leads to exocytosis of synaptic vesicles within a time interval that can be as short as 200 μsec (reviewed by Augustine *et al.,* 1987).

Synaptic vesicles possess several remarkable properties that distinguish them from most other organelles involved in membrane traffic. First, they are very abundant in brain tissue. Model calculations show that an average neuron contains approximately 10^6 synaptic vesicles, with a total of around 10^{17} in the human central nervous system (CNS) (Jahn and Südhof, 1993). Approximately 5% of the protein of CNS tissue is contributed by synaptic vesicles. This means that synaptic vesicles need to be purified only about 20-fold from homogenate to obtain a pure preparation. Second, synaptic vesicles are very homogenous in size and shape as judged by electron microscopy. In addition, they are smaller than most other organelles, only 50 nm in diameter. This allows the application of size fractionation techniques for the isolation of synaptic vesicles. In fact, theoretical considerations show that a phospholipid vesicle contains no more than approximately 10,000 phospholipid molecules and a limited number of membrane proteins. Third, synaptic vesicles do not contain a matrix of soluble proteins (Jahn and Südhof, 1993) as they recycle many times in the nerve terminal and thus can only be reloaded with nonpeptide transmitters by means of specific transport systems.

Study of synaptic vesicles is facilitated by the recent advances in understanding their protein composition. To date, more than half a dozen protein families have been shown to be localized specifically on the membrane of synaptic vesicles. With exception of some variation due to isoforms, most of these proteins are residents of all synaptic vesicles irrespective of their neurotransmitter content or of the location of the neuron. These include the synapsins, synaptophysins, synaptotagmins, synaptobrevins, rab's, and subunits of the vacuolar proton pump (for recent reviews see Trimble *et al.,* 1991, Jahn and Südhof, 1994). Antibodies against synaptophysin are commercially available and may be used as probes to assess synaptic vesicle purity.

Purification protocols for synaptic vesicles can be divided into two major groups. The first group involves the preparation of isolated nerve terminals (synaptosomes) by differential centrifugation which are subsequently lysed to release the synaptic vesicles. This has the advantage that small membrane fragments generated during homogenization are removed prior to vesicle extraction, as synaptosomes sediment at low *g* forces. The first protocol described here belongs in this category. These protocols are usually laborious and result in relatively low yields but the resulting synaptic vesicle preparations are of exceptionally high purity. In the second group of protocols, synaptic vesicles are directly purified from homogenate, without prior isolation of synaptosomes. To obtain high yields, initial homogenization is harsh to break up as many nerve terminals as possible, e.g., by freeze-powder homogenization as described in the second procedure. In both cases, a combination of differential centrifugation, rate-zonal density gradient centrifugation or isopycnic density gradient centrifugation, and size exclusion chromatography is employed for purification. It should be noted that analytical amounts of synaptic vesicles can also be obtained by immunoisolation using antibodies specific for synaptic vesicle proteins (see, e.g., Burger *et al.*, 1989).

II. Materials and Instrumentation

The following chemicals are used: Hepes (American Bioanalytical, Cat. No. AB892), sucrose (J. T. Baker, Cat. No. 4072-05), glycine (Bio-Rad, Cat. No. 161-0718), PMSF (Pierce, Cat. No. 36978), pepstatin (ICN, Cat. No. 0219536805), DMSO (American Type Culture Collection, Cat. No. 442608), controlled-pore glass beads (see Section V). Note that the standard reagents can also be obtained from other sources.

The following instrumentation is required: loose-fitting motor-driven glass–Teflon homogenizer (Braun), cooled centrifuge [Sorvall RC5 (DuPont) or comparable, SS 34 rotor], ultracentrifuge with fixed-angle and swing-out rotors [Beckman L80 (Beckman Instruments) or comparable, Ti 70 or Ti 50.2 rotor, SW 28 rotor, Ti 45 rotor] and corresponding tubes, equipment for column chromatography (peristaltic pump, UV monitor, fraction collector), gradient mixer for forming continuous sucrose gradients, filtration device for the filtration of buffers using 0.45-μm membranes (Millipore), glass columns (see Section V).

III. Procedures

A. PREPARATION OF SYNAPTIC VESICLES FROM SYNAPTOSOMES

In this protocol, a crude synaptosomal fraction (P2) is first isolated by differential centrifugation (Nagy *et al.*, 1976; Huttner *et al.*, 1983). The synaptosomes are then lysed by osmotic shock and synaptic vesicles are released into the medium. After removal of synaptosomal fragments and large membranes, synaptic vesicles are sedimented by high-speed centrifugation. The resulting pellet, already five- to sixfold enriched in synaptic vesicles, is then further purified by sucrose velocity-density gradient centrifugation and size exclusion chromatography on controlled-pore glass beads (CPG Inc.). This procedure is the standard method for obtaining synaptic vesicles of the highest purity, with less than 5% contamination as judged by electron microscopy and biochemical analysis. This preparation does contain, however, decoated coated vesicles that lost their clathrin but retained adaptors and endosomes derived from nerve terminals. The degree of this contamination is probably minor but cannot be easily quantified.

Solutions

1. *Homogenization buffer:* 320 mM sucrose, 4 mM Hepes–NaOH, pH 7.3 (optional, we found no difference when the buffer is omitted).

2. *1 M Hepes–NaOH, pH 7.4.*

3. *40 mM sucrose.*

4. *50 mM sucrose.*

5. *800 mM sucrose.*

6. *Glycine buffer:* 300 mM glycine, 5 mM Hepes–KOH, pH 7.4, degassed and filtered through 0.45-μm filter.

7. *Protease inhibitors:* 1 mg/ml pepstatin A in DMSO, 200 mM PMSF in dry ethanol. Keep stocks at room temperature. Add 0.001 vol where indicated. Note that PMSF is unstable in aqueous solutions and should not be added to buffers prior to use.

Steps

After collecting the brains, all steps are carried out on ice or at 4°C.

1. Decapitate 20 rats (180–200 g), remove the brains avoiding myelin-rich areas such as corpus callosum or medulla oblongata, place into 180 ml ice-cold homogenization buffer, and homogenize in several aliquots with a loose-fitting glass–Teflon homogenizer (nine strokes, 900 rpm). Add protease inhibitors.

2. Centrifuge the homogenate for 10 min at 1000 g_{max} (2700 rpm in a Sorval SS 34 rotor); discard the resulting pellet P1 containing large cell fragments and nuclei, and collect the supernatant S1.

3. Centrifuge S1 for 15 min at 12,000 g_{max} (SS 34 rotor, 10,000 rpm); remove the supernatant S2 containing small cell fragments like microsomes or small myelin fragments and soluble proteins. Wash the pellet P2 by carefully resuspending it in 120 ml homogenization buffer (pipette, avoiding the dark brown bottom part of the pellet that consists mainly of mitochondria) and recentrifuging at 11,000 rpm (SS 34 rotor, 13,000 g_{max}); discard the supernatant S2′. The resulting pellet P2′ represents a crude synaptosomal fraction.

4. To release synaptic vesicles from the synaptosomes, resuspend P2′ homogenization buffer to yield a final volume of 12 ml, transfer this fraction into a glass–Teflon homogenizer, add 9 vol (108 ml) ice-cold water, and perform three up-and-down strokes at 2000 rpm. Add 1 ml of 1 M Hepes–NaOH, pH 7.4, and protease inhibitors.

5. Centrifuge the suspension for 20 min at 33,000 g_{max} (16,500 rpm, SS 34 rotor) to yield the lysate pellet LP1 and the lysate supernatant LS1. Carefully remove LS1 immediately after the end of the run without disturbing LP1 using an electric pipetter. It is crucial that LS1 does not get contaminated even with traces of membrane fragments from LP1 which otherwise significantly affects the purity of the final vesicle fraction.

6. Centrifuge LS1 for 2 hr at 260,000 g_{max} (50,000 rpm in a Beckman 60 Ti or comparable rotor). Discard the supernatant LS2 and resuspend the pellet LP2 in 6 ml of 40 mM sucrose using a small, tight-fitting glass–Teflon homogenizer, followed by, consecutively, a 23-gauge and a 27-gauge hypodermic needle attached to a 10-ml syringe.

7. Layer the suspension (3 ml each) on top of two linear sucrose gradients, formed from 18.5 ml of 800 mM sucrose and 18.5 ml of 50 mM sucrose, and centrifuge for 4 hr at 25,000 rpm in a Beckman SW 28 rotor (65,000 g_{av}). After the run a turbid (white–opaque) zone is visible in the middle of the gradient (in the range 200 to 400 mM sucrose). These bands are collected with the aid of a glass capillary connected to a peristaltic pump, yielding a combined volume of

25–30 ml. This fraction represents synaptic vesicles that are 8- to 10-fold enriched over the homogenate (Jahn et al., 1985). Note that synaptic vesicles do not reach isopycnic equilibrium during centrifugation (velocity gradient centrifugation); changes in angular velocity or in the run time will therefore affect the result.

8. Equilibrate a CPG-3000 column (180 × 2 cm, see Section V) with 10 column volumes of glycine buffer (optimally done overnight before the preparation). Apply the sample on top of the resin and overlay it carefully with glycine buffer without diluting the sample. Elute the column with glycine buffer at a flow rate of 40 ml/hr, collecting 6- to 8-ml fractions. Monitor protein efflux at 280 nm. The first peak contains plasma membranes and some microsomes and is usually smaller than the second peak containing synaptic vesicles. Pool fractions of the second peak and centrifuge for 90 min at 260,000 g_{max} (50,000 rpm, Beckman 60 Ti rotor). Resuspend the synaptic vesicle pellet in the desired buffer as in step 6. Freeze the suspension rapidly (e.g., in liquid nitrogen) and store at −70°C.

Size exclusion chromatography on glyceryl-coated controlled-pore glass beads or on Sephacryl S-1000 is omitted in many protocols and, if applied, is usually the last step of the procedure. Both resins have a relatively low capacity, do not tolerate overloading, and require some experience in their use. Sephacryl S-1000 has higher separation capacity than CPG per gel volume, but the columns have low flow rates, do not tolerate increased pressure and have a tendency to adsorb proteins and membrane particles, in particular during the first few separation runs in the life of the column. CPG columns are more difficult to set up and tolerate less material; however, glass beads are noncompressible and allow high flow rates, substantially shortening separation times. The experimenter who does not shy away from the effort to set up a large CPG column is rewarded with highly reliable results for many runs and exceptionally clean synaptic vesicle preparations. In our laboratory, we used a CPG-3000 column (3 × 180 cm) consecutively for 5 years for more than 100 synaptic vesicle preparations without repacking. Column profiles and synaptic vesicle purity were highly reproducible.

B. PREPARATION OF SYNAPTIC VESICLES FROM FROZEN BRAIN

This procedure starts with a harsh homogenization of frozen brains to efficiently break up the nerve terminals, thus releasing synaptic vesicles (Hell et al., 1988). Frozen brains are ground in a precooled mortar to yield a fine powder. This treatment does not affect the function or integrity of the small synaptic vesicles, but larger membrane structures are ruptured. After resuspending the tissue powder in sucrose solution, most of the cell fragments are removed by centrifugation with low and intermediate angular velocities, leaving synaptic vesicles in the supernatant. Synaptic vesicles are then sedimented at a high speed through a cushion of 0.7 M sucrose, removing soluble proteins and membrane contaminants of lower bouyant density (mostly myelin). Synaptic vesicles are five- to sixfold enriched in the pellet and can be purified further by CPG chromatography.

The enrichment factor for synaptic vesicles purified by this protocol is 15–20 (Hell et al., 1988), somewhat lower than in the previous method; however, there are several advantages: First, the tissue can be collected before the experiment and can be stored in liquid nitrogen for more than 1 year, allowing more efficient use of experimental animals. Second, the yield is severalfold higher under optimal conditions than the yield of the preparation from synaptosomes. Third, the procedure is faster, requiring only 12 hr for completion.

Solutions

1. *Homogenization buffer:* 320 mM sucrose, degassed.

2. *700 mM sucrose:* 700 mM sucrose, 10 mM Hepes–KOH, pH 7.3.

3. *Resuspension buffer:* 320 mM sucrose, 10 mM Hepes–KOH, pH 7.3.

4. *Glycine buffer:* 300 mM glycine, 5 mM Hepes–KOH, pH 7.3, degassed.

5. *Protease inhibitors:* 1 mg/ml pepstatin A dissolved in DMSO, 200 mM PMSF in dry ethanol. Add 0.001 vol where indicated.

Steps

After powderizing the frozen brains, all steps are carried out on ice or at 4°C.

1. Decapitate 40 rats (180–200 g), remove the brains avoiding myelin-rich areas such as corpus callosum or medulla oblongata, and freeze immediately in liquid nitrogen. Immediate shock freezing is essential. According to our experience, frozen brains available from commercial sources are usually not satisfactory for this reason.

2. To create a tissue powder, place the frozen brains into a porcelain mortar precooled with liquid nitrogen, cover them with cheesecloth, and break them carefully using a porcelain pestle. Then grind to a fine powder. This step is crucial for obtaining high yields. After evaporation of the liquid N_2, suspend the powder in 320 ml ice-cold homogenization buffer (magnetic stirrer) and homogenize with a glass–Teflon homogenizer (eight strokes, 1000 rpm).

3. Centrifuge the homogenate for 10 min at 47,000 g_{max} (20,000 rpm in a Sorval SS 34 rotor). Collect the supernatant S1. The pellet P1 contains large cell fragments and nuclei, but also some entrapped synaptic vesicles. To increase the yield, the pellet may therefore be reextracted with 160 ml homogenization buffer by means of one slow stroke in the glass–Teflon homogenizer followed by centrifugation as above. Combine the resulting supernatant S1′ with S1.

4. Centrifuge S1 for 40 min at 120,000 g_{max} (32,000 rpm in a Beckman 45 Ti rotor). Collect the supernatant S2 carefully without disturbing P2 by using an electric pipetter. It is crucial that S2 is not contaminated with membrane fragments from the soft pellet P2. S2 should be clear with a reddish color. If it is turbid, it should be recentrifuged using the same conditions to remove contaminating membrane fragments.

5. To sediment synaptic vesicles through a sucrose cushion, fill 25-ml centrifuge tubes fitting into a Beckman 60 Ti rotor with 20 ml S2. The sucrose cushion is formed by pumping 5.5 ml of 700 mM sucrose underneath S2 using a peristaltic pump and a glass capillary. Centrifuge for 2 hr at 260,000 g_{max} (50,000 rpm, Beckman 60 Ti rotor). Remove the supernatant S3 and resuspend the pellet P3 in 6–10 ml resuspension buffer. This sample represents a crude synaptic vesicle fraction. Clear the suspension with a short spin (17,000 rpm for 10 min, SS 34, 35,000 g_{max}) before loading it onto the CPG column.

6. Equilibrate a CPG column (see Section V) with 10 column volumes of glycine buffer. Load the sample on top of the resin and overlay carefully with glycine buffer without disturbing the sample. An 85 × 1.6-cm column has a maximal capacity of 15 mg of protein, requiring several consecutive runs if all material is to be chromatographed. Elute the column with glycine buffer at a flow rate of 80 ml/hr, collecting 2-ml fractions. Follow the elution of protein with a UV detector at 280 nm. The first peak, containing plasma membranes and microsomes, is usually larger than the second peak containing synaptic vesicles.

The two peaks are not completely separated. The shoulder frequently observed at the end of the second peak represents soluble protein. Pool and centrifuge the fractions of the second peak for 2 hr at 260,000 g_{max} (60 Ti rotor, 50,000 rpm), and resuspend the synaptic vesicle pellet in the desired buffer.

IV. Comments

Contamination by other subcellular compartments can be conveniently monitored by assaying for marker enzymes, in particular for plasma membranes, mitochondria, or endoplasmic reticulum (Hell *et al.*, 1988). In parallel with a decrease of these marker enzymes, proteins specific for synaptic vesicles, namely, synaptophysin (p38), for which antibodies are commercially available, (e.g., from Boehringer-Mannheim), should be enriched about 20- to 25-fold over homogenate (Jahn *et al.*, 1985). In addition, the protein profile of the synaptic vesicle preparation as observed after sodium dodecyl sulfate–polyacrylamide gel electrophoresis exhibits a characteristic pattern (Huttner *et al.*, 1983; Hell *et al.*, 1988), with the prominent membrane proteins synaptobrevin (VAMP), synaptophysin (p38), synaptotagmin (p65), and synapsin I being clearly visible. Synaptic vesicle preparations contain various amounts of soluble proteins with affinity for membranes such as glyceraldehyde phosphate dehydrogenase, aldolase, actin, and tubulin. These proteins may be partially removed by a salt wash (resuspend synaptic vesicles in 160 mM KCl, 10 mM Hepes–KOH, pH 7.4, and centrifuge them for 2 hr at 50,000 rpm 260,000 g_{max}); however, this treatment also removes the synaptic vesicle protein synapsin I.

The morphology of the synaptic vesicle fraction can be studied by electron microscopy. Membranes can be easily visualized, e.g., by negative staining (Fig. 1) (Hell *et al.*, 1988). Synaptic vesicle membranes are identified by their very uniform appearance (small vesicular profiles of approximately 50-nm diameter). Confirmation can also be obtained by immunogold labeling for the vesicle protein synaptophysin, which can be carried out conveniently on a single day when combined with negative staining (Jahn and Maycox, 1988).

V. Appendix: Preparation and Maintenance of Controlled-Pore Glass Bead Columns

Controlled-pore glass beads (CPG-3000, glycerol coated) are obtained from CPG Inc. Column dimensions may vary, but the diameter:length ratio should be at least 1:20 to 1:50. Use sturdy, tension-free glass columns that withstand mechanical stress during packing.

Steps

1. Resuspend CPG beads in distilled water and degas thoroughly.

2. Connect the column to a vibration device (e.g., an immobilized Vortex apparatus) using a stiff, nonbreakable connection (e.g., a plastic cylinder). Attach the column with several clamps to a strong support such as a heavy stand or wall-mounted rack, with uneven spacing between the clamps to avoid the generation of waves with large amplitudes.

3. Fill in CPG bead slurry. Vibrate column at a high speed of the Vortex apparatus. Keep adding slurry. Avoid the generation of settled zones between the additions. After filling, keep vibrating until resin does not settle anymore for at least 30 min. Packing of a small column (85 × 1.6 cm) requires around 4 hr, of a large column (180 × 2 cm), approximately 10 hr.

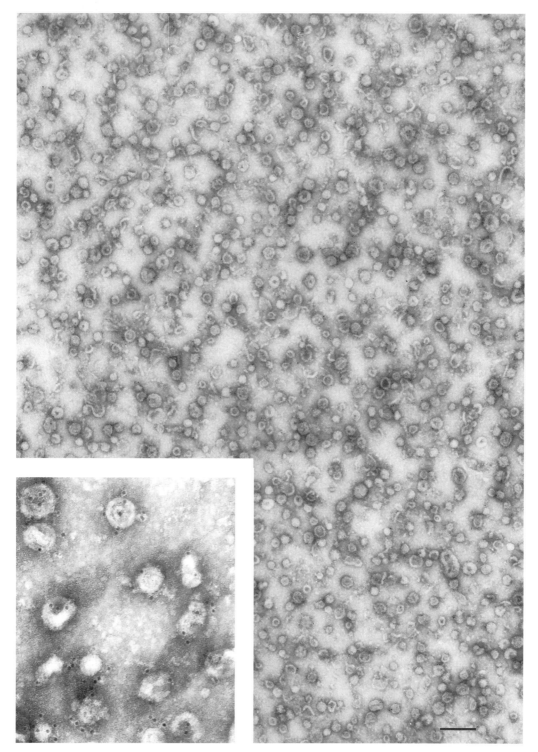

FIGURE 1 Electron micrograph showing a synaptic vesicle fraction purified by the procedure described in Section IIIB (negative staining). The inset shows a magnification of a field following immunogold labeling for the synaptic vesicle protein synaptophysin. For methods see Jahn and Maycox (1988). Bar-200 nm. (Courtesy of Dr. Peter R. Maycox, La Jolla, California.)

4. Equilibrate the column with 10 column volumes of column buffer.

5. For maintenance, the column should be stored in buffer containing 0.02% sodium azide to prevent microbial growth. To avoid accumulation of debris, all samples loaded should be cleared by a short centrifugation and all buffers filtered by ultrafiltration. The column should not be allowed to run dry. If this occurs, the air may be removed by pumping large amounts of extensively degassed and temperature-equilibrated column buffer from the bottom through the column; however, if air bubbles remain, repacking is unavoidable. If contaminants accumulate (after 10–20 runs), the column can be cleaned by washing with 1–2 bed volumes of 4 *M* urea, buffered to pH 7.0, followed by extensive washing. The first run after urea cleaning results in lower yields.

REFERENCES

Augustine, G. J., Charlton, M. P., and Smith, S. J. (1987) Calcium action in synaptic transmitter release. *Annu. Rev. Neurosci.* **10**, 633–693.

Burger, P. M., Mehl, E., Cameron, P., Maycox, P. R., Baumert, M., Lottspeich, F., De Camilli, P., and Jahn, R. (1989) Synaptic vesicles immunoisolated from rat cerebral cortex contain high levels of glutamate. *Neuron* **3**, 715–720.

Hell, J. W., Maycox, P. R., Stadler, H., and Jahn, R. (1988) Uptake of GABA by rat brain synaptic vesicles isolated by a new procedure. *EMBO J.* **7**, 3023–3029.

Huttner, W. B., Schiebler, W., Greengard, P., and De Camilli, P. (1983) Synapsin I (protein I), a nerve terminal-specific phosphoprotein. III. Its association with synaptic vesicles studied in a highly purified synaptic vesicle preparation. *J. Cell Biol.* **96**, 1374–1388.

Jahn, R., and Maycox, P. R. (1988) Protein components and neurotransmitter uptake in brain synaptic vesicles. *In* "Molecular Mechanisms in Secretion" (N. A. Thorn, M. Treiman, and O. H. Peterson, eds.), pp. 411–424. Munksgaard, Copenhagen.

Jahn, R., Schiebler, W., Ouimet, C., and Greengard, P. (1985) A 38,000 dalton membrane protein (p38) present in synaptic vesicles. *Proc. Natl. Acad. Sci. USA* **82**, 4137–4141.

Jahn, R., and Südhof, T. C. (1993) Synaptic vesicle traffic: Rush hour in the nerve terminal. *J. Neurochem.* **61**, 12–21.

Jahn, R., and Südhof, T. C. (1994) Synaptic vesicles and exocytosis. *Annu. Rev. Neurosci.* **17**, 219–246.

Nagy, A., Baker, R. R., Morris, S. J., and Whittaker, V. P. (1976) The preparation and characterization of synaptic vesicles of high purity. *Brain Res.* **109**, 285–309.

Trimble, W. S., Linial, M., and Scheller, R. H. (1991) Cellular and molecular biology of the presynaptic nerve terminal. *Annu. Rev. Neurosci.* **14**, 93–122.

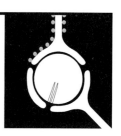

Purification and Reconstitution of the Ca²⁺-ATPase of Red Blood Cells

Paolo Gazzotti and Ernesto Carafoli

I. Introduction

The concentration of Ca^{2+} in red blood cells is about 100 nM, whereas that in the surrounding plasma medium is in the millimolar range. The plasma membrane has limited Ca^{2+} permeability, but some Ca^{2+} continuously penetrates into the cell through it. Because Ca^{2+} has to fulfill important messenger functions inside the cell, efficient transport systems are required to maintain the Ca^{2+} gradient across the membrane. One Ca^{2+}-transporting system, which is found in all plasma membranes, is Ca^{2+}-ATPase. This enzyme, which is commonly called the Ca^{2+} pump, is responsible for the pumping of Ca^{2+} out of the cell against its gradient (Carafoli, 1992). It is modulated by a number of agents, chief among them calmodulin, the intracellular Ca^{2+}-binding protein involved in the regulation of many Ca^{2+}-dependent activities (Jarret and Penniston, 1977; Gopinath and Vincenzi, 1977). The direct interaction of calmodulin with the Ca^{2+} pump has permitted its purification by affinity chromatography (Niggli *et al.*, 1979). The Ca^{2+}-ATPase of erythrocytes is also activated by acidic phospholipid and fatty acids, by a controlled proteolytic treatment, and by kinase-promoted phosphorylation.

ATPase can be solubilized from erythrocyte plasma membrane (ghosts) using the nonionic detergent Triton X-100. After solubilization, the activity of the enzyme can be stabilized by the addition of glycerol and phosphatidylcholine. The enzyme is then purified by applying the extract to a calmodulin affinity column in the presence of Ca^{2+}. After an exhaustive wash of the column with a Ca^{2+}-containing buffer, ATPase is eluted from the column with EGTA. The transport activity of the purified enzyme can be studied in reconstituted vesicles.

II. Materials and Instrumentation

Outdated human erythrocyte concentrate (1 to 2 weeks old) can be obtained from a blood bank. The following reagents are purchased from Sigma Chemical Company: Tris (Trizma Base, Cat. No. T-1503); Hepes (Cat. No. H-3375); Triton X-100 (Cat. No. X-100); phosphatidylcholine from soy beans, type IIS (Cat. No. P-5638); N-hydroxyethylethylenediaminetriacetic acid (HEDTA, Cat. No. H-8126); $CaCl_2 \cdot 2H_2O$ (Cat. No. C-3881); Lasalocid (X-537A, Cat. No. L-1021); malachite green–HCl (Cat. No. M-9636). The following reagents can be purchased from Fluka Chemie AG: $MgCl_2 \cdot 6H_2O$ (Cat. No. 63064); KCl (Cat. No. 60130); NaCl (Cat. No. 71379); EDTA (free acid, Cat. No. 03609); glycerol (Cat. No. 49782); cholic acid sodium salt (Cat. No. 27028); ammonium molybdate (Cat. No. 09880).

The reagents for the coupled enzyme assay are purchased from Boehringer-Mannheim: pyruvate kinase from rabbit muscle (Cat. No. 128155); Na-phospho-enolpyruvate (Cat. No. 127370); NADH, grade I (Cat. No. 107727); lactate dehydrogenase from rabbit muscle (Cat. No. 127230); ATP (Cat. No. 127523); ADP (Cat. No. 236675). Egg phosphatidylcholine and bovine phosphatidylserine (both grade I) are obtained from Lipid Products. DTT (Cat. No. 80-1128-79) and CNBr-activated Sepharose 4B (Cat. No. 17-0430-01) can be purchased from Pharmacia Biotech. Brain calmodulin is purified as described by Watterson *et al.* (1976). All other reagents mentioned can be purchased elsewhere.

Visking dialysis tubing (6-mm diameter, Cat. No. 44104) is purchased from Serva. The polyacrylamide gel electrophoresis setup Mini-Protean II (Cat. No. 165-2940) can be purchased from Bio-Rad Laboratories Inc. The Ca^{2+}-sensitive membranes (containing ionophore ETH 129) are purchased from W. Möller, Glas and Elektroden, and the electrodes are assembled as described by Affolter and Sigel (1979). Spectrophotometric measurements are carried out using a Shimadzu dual-wavelength, double-beam spectrophotometer UV 3000 (Shimadzu Corporation).

III. Procedures

A. PREPARATION OF CALMODULIN-DEFICIENT ERYTHROCYTE PLASMA MEMBRANES (GHOSTS)

Solutions

1. *Washing solution:* 130 mM KCl, 10 mM Tris–Cl, pH 7.0. To prepare 10 liters of solution, add 96.93 g of KCl and 12.11 g of Trizma base. Dissolve in 5 liters of double-distilled water, take the solution to pH 7.0 with HCl, and add double-distilled water to a final volume of 10 liters. Store at 4°C.

2. *Lysis solution I:* 1 mM EDTA, 10 mM Tris–Cl, pH 7.0. To prepare 10 liters of solution, add 2.92 g of EDTA (free acid) and 12.11 g of Trizma base. Dissolve in 5 liters of double-distilled water, take the solution to pH 7.0 with HCl, and add double-distilled water to a final volume of 10 liters. Store at 4°C.

3. *Lysis solution II:* 10 mM Hepes, pH 7.0. To prepare 5 liters of solution, dissolve 11.9 g of Hepes in 3 liters of double-distilled water, take to pH 7.0 with KOH, and add double-distilled water to a final volume of 5 liters. Store at 4°C.

4. *Ghost storage solution:* 130 mM KCl, 10 mM Hepes, 0.5 mM $MgCl_2$, and 0.05 mM $CaCl_2$. To prepare 2 liters of solution, add 4.76 g of Hepes, 19.39 g of KCl, 1 ml of a 100 mM stock solution of $CaCl_2$, and 10 ml of a 100 mM stock solution of $MgCl_2$. Dissolve in 1 liter of double-distilled water, take the solution to pH 7.4 with KOH, and add double-distilled water to a final volume of 2 liters. Store at 4°C.

Steps

All steps are carried out at 4°C, either in a cold room or on ice.

1. Dilute 1.5 liters (six bags) of erythrocyte concentrate with 3 liters of cold washing buffer. Pour the diluted blood into six centrifuge bottles and centrifuge at 4000 g for 15 min. Remove the supernatant with an aspirator water pump. Remove the white cells floating on the top of the erythrocyte pellets. Wash the erythrocytes twice by diluting them with 4 liters of washing solution and centrifuging at 4000 g for 15 min.

2. Resuspend the washed erythrocytes with three liters of cold lysis solution I

and centrifuge at 11,000 g for 45 min. Remove the red supernatant with an aspirator water pump. Wash the erythrocyte ghosts five times with 3 liters of lysis solution I and twice with 2 liters of lysis solution II (washing with the EDTA-containing lysis solution I is also necessary to remove the endogenous calmodulin bound to the ghosts).

3. Resuspend the erythrocyte ghosts in 1 liter of storage solution and centrifuge at 11,000 g for 30 min. Remove the supernatant and wash the pellet once with 1 liter of storage solution. Resuspend the calmodulin-deficient erythrocyte ghosts with 40 ml of storage solution. Determine the protein concentration of the suspension and freeze the ghosts at $-72°C$.

B. PREPARATION OF CALMODULIN–SEPHAROSE 4B FOR AFFINITY CHROMATOGRAPHY

Solutions

1. *Coupling solution:* 100 mM Na-borate, 400 mM NaCl, 0.05 mM CaCl$_2$, final pH 8.2. To prepare 100 ml of the solution, add 618 mg of boric acid, 2.34 g of NaCl, and 50 μl of a 100 mM stock solution of CaCl$_2$. Add 80 ml of double-distilled water, take to pH 8.2 with NaOH, and add double-distilled water to 100 ml. Store at 4°C.

2. *Blocking solution:* 500 mM ethanolamine in coupling solution. To prepare 30 ml of the solution, add 0.9 ml of 99% ethanolamine to 29.1 ml of coupling solution.

3. *Washing solution:* 300 mM NaCl, 20 mM Tris–Cl, pH 8.0. To make 200 ml of the solution, add 3.5 g of NaCl, 484 mg of Trizma base. Dissolve in 150 ml of water, take to pH 7.8 with HCl, and add double-distilled water to 200 ml. Store at 4°C.

4. *Storage solution:* 300 mM NaCl, 20 mM Tris–Cl, pH 7.8, 1 mM CaCl$_2$, 1 mM NaN$_3$. To prepare 20 ml of solution, add 350 mg of NaCl, 48.4 mg of Trizma base, 200 μl of a 100 mM stock solution of CaCl$_2$, and 20 μl of a 1 M stock solution of NaN$_3$. Add 10 ml of double-distilled water and take to pH 7.8 with HCl. Add double-distilled water up to 20 ml. Store at 4°C.

Steps

1. Swell 4 g (1 g resin = 3.5 ml gel) of CNBr-activated Sepharose 4B in 100 ml 1 mM HCl for 15 min.

2. Remove HCl by filtration through a sintered glass filter (11 G3) and wash the swollen gel with 700 ml of 1 mM HCl added in aliquots.

3. Quickly wash with 20 ml of coupling solution and *immediately* after (reactive groups hydrolyze at high pH) transfer the wet resin in 25 ml of coupling solution containing 22 mg of calmodulin.

4. Mix the suspension for 2 hr at room temperature using a rotation apparate (do not use a magnetic stirrer).

5. Wash the resin with 50 ml of coupling solution.

6. Block the remaining active groups of the resin by resuspending the resin in 30 ml of blocking solution. Incubate 16 hr at 4°C with gentle mixing in a rotation apparate.

7. Wash the resin four times by filtration through a sintered glass filter, by

alternating cold distilled water and washing solution. Store the resin as a 1:2 (resin:storage solution) slurry at 4°C.

C. SOLUBILIZATION AND PURIFICATION OF THE CA^{2+}-ATPASE

Solutions

1. *Phospholipid suspension:* The phospholipids are suspended in water at a concentration of 10 mg/ml. To prepare 20 ml, add 200 mg phospholipids in chloroform to a 50-ml round-bottom flask. Evaporate the chloroform, under vacuum, with a rotary evaporator. Resuspend the dry lipids in 20 ml of water using two small glass balls to displace the dry lipid from the wall of the flask. Transfer the suspension to a small beaker and then sonicate to clarity, at 4°C, under N_2, using a Branson sonifier (Branson Ultrasonic Corporation). To prepare the suspension of soy bean phosphatidylcholine weight out 200 mg, dissolve in 20 ml of water, and sonicate to clarity.

2. *Working solution:* 260 mM NaCl, 40 mM Hepes, pH 7.2, 2 mM MgCl$_2$. To prepare 200 ml, add 3.04 g of NaCl, 1.9 g of Hepes, and 4 ml of a 100 mM stock solution of MgCl$_2$. Add 150 ml of double-distilled water and take to pH 7.2 with NaOH. Add double-distilled water to a final volume of 200 ml.

3. *Equilibration solution for the calmodulin affinity column:* 130 mM NaCl, 20 mM Hepes pH 7.2, 1 mM MgCl$_2$, 0.1 mM CaCl$_2$, 15% glycerol, 0.4% Triton X-100, 0.3 mg/ml *soy bean* phosphatidylcholine. To prepare 100 ml, add 50 ml of working solution, 100 μl of a 100 mM stock solution of CaCl$_2$, 17 ml of 87% glycerol, 2 ml of a 20% (w/v) solution of Triton X-100, and 3 ml of 10 mg/ml *soy bean* phosphatidylcholine suspension. Add water to a final volume of 100 ml. Store at 4°C.

4. *Washing solution:* 130 mM NaCl, 20 mM Hepes, pH 7.2, 1 mM MgCl$_2$, 0.1 mM CaCl$_2$, 15% glycerol, 0.05% Triton X-100, 0.5 mg/ml *egg* phosphatidylcholine. To prepare 50 ml, add 25 ml of working solution, 50 μl of a 100 mM stock solution of CaCl$_2$, 8.6 ml of 87% glycerol, 125 μl of a 20% (w/v) solution of Triton X-100, and 2.5 ml of 10 mg/ml *egg* phosphatidylcholine suspension. Add water to a final volume of 50 ml. Store at 4°C.

5. *Eluting solution:* 130 mM NaCl, 20 mM Hepes, 1 mM MgCl$_2$, 2 mM EDTA, 15% glycerol, 0.05% Triton X-100, 0.5 mg/ml *egg* phosphatidylcholine. To prepare 20 ml, add 10 ml of working solution, 0.4 ml of a 100 mM stock solution of Na-EDTA, 3.45 ml of 87% glycerol, 50 μl of a 20% (w/v) solution of Triton X-100, and 1 ml of 10 mg/ml *egg* phosphatidylcholine suspension. Add water to a final volume of 20 ml. Store at 4°C.

6. *Storage solution:* 130 mM NaCl, 20 mM Hepes, pH 7.2, 0.1 mM CaCl$_2$, 5 mM NaN$_3$. To prepare 100 ml, add 50 ml of working solution, 100 μl of a 100 mM stock solution of CaCl$_2$, and 500 μl of a 1 M stock solution of NaN$_3$. Add double-distilled water, and take to pH 7.2 with NaOH. Store at 4°C.

7. *Cleaning solution:* 2 M Guanidine hydrochloride, 1 mM Na-EDTA, 0.5% Triton X-100, final pH 7.2. To prepare 100 ml, add 19.1 g of guanidine hydrochloride, 37.2 mg of Na-EDTA, and 2.5 ml of a 20% stock solution of Triton X-100.

Steps

All steps are carried out at 4°C, either in a cold room or on ice.

1. Dilute 300 mg of calmodulin-deficient ghosts with ghost storage solution to

have a final concentration of 5 mg protein/ml (total volume 60 ml). Before diluting to the final volume add 10 ml of 87% glycerol (15% final concentration).

2. Place the ghosts in a glass beaker immersed in an ice bath. Stir the suspension with a magnetic stirrer. Add dropwise 1.35 ml of a 20% (w/v) Triton X-100 solution. Incubate 10 min and centrifuge the solubilized membranes at 100,000 g for 35 min. Collect the supernatant, add 30 mg of DTT, 50 μM $CaCl_2$, and enough *soy bean* phosphatidylcholine (10 mg/ml in water) to a final concentration of 0.3 mg/ml.

3. Load the supernatant containing the solubilized ghost proteins onto the calmodulin–Sepharose 4B column (3-ml bed volume, flow rate 10 ml/hr) previously washed with 15 ml of equilibrating solution. Wash the column with 25 ml of equilibrating solution and at least 50 ml of washing solution (flow rate 10 ml/hr).

4. Elute the ATPase with eluting solution (flow rate 7 ml/hr). Collect 0.6-ml fractions and measure the ATPase activity in the presence of calmodulin (10 μl of each fraction should be sufficient). The activity should appear after seven or eight fractions (to obtain full activation, preincubate the 10-μl sample with 1 μl of 10 mg/ml phosphatidylserine for 5 min at 37°C). Add 6 μl of 100 mM $MgCl_2$ and 5 μl of 10 mM $CaCl_2$ to the fractions containing activity. Divide the purified ATPase into small aliquots and store at −72°C.

5. Wash the column with 20 ml of storage solution. After four preparations wash the column with 12 ml of cleaning solution and then equilibrate it with storage solution.

D. MEASUREMENT OF Ca²⁺-ATPASE ACTIVITY

Solutions

1. *Coupled enzyme assay solution:* 120 mM KCl, 30 mM Hepes, 2.5 mM $MgCl_2$, 0.6 mM $CaCl_2$, 0.5 mM K-EGTA, 0.5 mM HEDTA, 1 IU/ml pyruvate kinase, 1 IU/ml lactic dehydrogenase, 120 μg/ml phosphoenolpyruvate, 150 μg/ml NADH (the ratios of $CaCl_2$ and Ca^{2+} chelators have been calculated to yield 10 μM free Ca^{2+} in the solution). To prepare 60 ml of the solution, add 536 mg of KCl, 428 mg of Hepes, 30.4 mg of $MgCl_2$, 720 μl of 50 mM $CaCl_2$, 600 μl of 50 mM K-EGTA, and 600 μl of 50 mM HEDTA. Add 40 ml of bidistilled water and adjust the pH to 7.4 with KOH. Place the solution on ice and add 9 mg of NADH, 7.2 mg of phosphoenolpyruvate, 40 μl of pyruvate kinase, and 12 μl of lactic dehydrogenase. Add double-distilled water to a final volume of 60 ml.

2. *Malachite green solution:* Mix 300 ml of 0.045% malachite green hydrochloride with 100 ml of 4.2% ammonium molybdate in 4 N HCl. Filter through Whatman No. 5 filter paper and add 2 ml of 10% Triton X-100.

3. *Lanzetta assay solution:* 120 mM KCl, 1 mM $MgCl_2$, 30 mM Hepes, pH 7.2, 10 μM $CaCl_2$. To prepare 100 ml, add 894 mg of KCl, 714 mg of Hepes, 1 ml of a 100 mM stock solution of $MgCl_2$, and 10 μl of a 100 mM stock solution of $CaCl_2$. Add double-distilled water and take to pH 7.2. Store at 4°C.

Steps

Coupled enzyme assay (Scharschmidt et al., 1979)

1. Add 1 ml of coupled enzyme assay solution and 10 μl of 100 mM Na-ATP to a 1-ml cuvette. Place the cuvette in the double-wavelength spectrophotometer

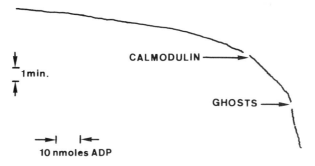

FIGURE 1 Measurement of Ca^{2+}-ATPase activity using the coupled enzyme assay. The experiment was carried out at 37°C in a Shimadzu dual-wavelength, double-beam spectrophotometer UV-3000 (Mono 1, 366 nm; Mono 2, 550 nm). Ghost protein (500 μg) and calmodulin (5 μg) were added. More detailed information is given in the text.

chamber thermoregulated at 37°C (measure the difference in absorbance between 366 and 550 nm, setting a full-scale absorbance of 0.1 and the recorder range at 50 mV).

2. After 5 min add either 40 μl of ghosts or 10 μl of the purified ATPase. Stir with a small disposable plastic rod and measure the activity.

3. After 5 min add 5 μl of 1 mg/ml calmodulin in water and measure the enzyme activity until the stimulation becomes maximal.

4. Calibrate with 10 μl of 1 mM ADP solution.

A typical trace is shown in Fig. 1. The stimulation factor by calmodulin may vary from preparation to preparation, but should never be lower than 3.0.

Phosphate assay according to Lanzetta et al. (1979)

1. Add 0.1 ml of assay solution to an Eppendorf tube. Place at 37°C.

2. Add 1 μl 100 mM ATP, 5 μl of sample, and 1 μl 1 mg/ml calmodulin, stir with a Vortex, and incubate 5 min at 37°C. Carry out a parallel test in the presence of 2 mM EGTA (2 μl of a 100 mM stock solution).

4. Transfer the whole mixture to a test tube containing 1.6 ml of malachite green solution. After 1 min add 200 μl of 34% citrate.

5. After 30 min read the optical absorption at 660 nm in a spectrophotometer. A blank must be prepared with 100 μl of assay solution, malachite green solution, and citrate. A standards curve (2–10 nmole P_i) is prepared by adding aliquots of a 1 mM K-phosphate solution to 1.6 ml of the malachite green solution.

E. PUMPING ACTIVITY OF THE PURIFIED Ca^{2+}-ATPASE RECONSTITUTED IN PHOSPHOLIPID VESICLES

Solutions

1. *Reconstitution solution:* 120 mM KCl, 20 mM Hepes, pH 7.2, 1 mM $MgCl_2$, 0.06 mM $CaCl_2$. To prepare 100 ml, add 894 mg of KCl, 476 mg of Hepes, 1 ml of a 100 mM $MgCl_2$ solution, and 60 μl of a 100 mM $CaCl_2$ solution. Add double-distilled water and take to pH 7.2 with KOH. Store at 4°C.

2. *Cholate–phospholipid solution:* 120 mM KCl, 20 mM Hepes, pH 7.2, 1 mM MgCl$_2$, 0.06 mM CaCl$_2$, 50 mg/ml soy bean phosphatidylcholine, and 100 mM of Na-cholate. To prepare 1 ml add 50 mg of soy bean phosphatidylcholine and 750 μl of reconstitution solution to an Eppendorf centrifuge tube and vortex until a homogenous suspension is obtained. Add 250 μl of 400 mM Na-cholate in reconstitution solution. Vortex until all phospholipids have been solubilized.

3. *Dialysis solution:* 120 mM KCl, 20 mM Hepes, pH 7.2, 0.05 mM MgCl$_2$, 1 mM DTT. To prepare 3 liters, add 26.82 g of KCl, 14.28 g of Hepes, and 609 mg of MgCl$_2$. Add double-distilled water and take to pH 7.2 with KOH. Before using it, add 154 mg DTT/liter.

4. *Ca^{2+} ionophore:* Lasalocid (X-537A), 3 mM in DMSO.

5. *Ca^{2+}-uptake solution:* 120 mM KCl, 2 mM Hepes, pH 7.4, 0.5 mM MgCl$_2$. To prepare 100 ml, add 894 mg of KCl, 47.6 mg of Hepes, and 0.5 ml of a 100 mM MgCl$_2$ solution. Add double-distilled water and take to pH 7.4 with KOH. Store at 4°C.

Steps

Reconstitution

1. Add 350 μl (approximately 50 μg of protein) of the isolated Ca^{2+}-ATPase to 100 μl of the cholate–phospholipid solution. Mix gently with Vortex.

2. Transfer the solution to a dialysis tube (10,000 MW cutoff), and dialyze about 16 hr at 4°C against 1 liter of dialysis solution. Change the dialysis solution twice: after 2 hr and after 6 hr.

3. The reconstituted vesicles can be kept on ice for a day or two; otherwise they can be stored at −72°C in the presence of 15% glycerol without significant loss of activity.

Test of Ca^{2+} pumping activity

The Ca^{2+} pumping activity of the ATPase in the reconstituted vesicles can be measured indirectly by measuring the ATPase activity in the presence and absence of the Ca^{2+} ionophore or directly by using a Ca^{2+}-sensitive electrode (alternatively, a spectrophotometric method based on specific metallochromic indicators, e.g., Arsenazo III, can be used). For the measurement of ATPase activity, the previously mentioned coupled enzyme assay is used (Scharschmidt *et al.*, 1979).

1. Add 1 ml of coupled enzyme assay solution and 10 μl of 100 mM Na-ATP to a 1-ml cuvette. Place the cuvette in the spectrophotometer chamber thermoregulated at 37°C.

2. After 5 min add 50 μl of reconstituted vesicles. Stir with a small disposable plastic rod and measure the activity for a couple of minutes. Add 5 μl of a 3 mM solution of the Ca^{2+} ionophore in DMSO. Record the increase in the rate of ATPase activity; the stimulation factor may vary with the experiment but should exceed 4.0.

Direct measurement of Ca^{2+} uptake using a Ca^{2+}-sensitive electrode (Crompton and Carafoli, 1979)

1. Add 1 ml of Ca^{2+} uptake medium to the Ca^{2+} electrode chamber thermoregulated at 25°C. When the trace is stable add 3 μl of a 50 mM Na-ATP solution.

2. Add 1 μl of a 1 mM CaCl$_2$ solution. Wait until the trace is stable.

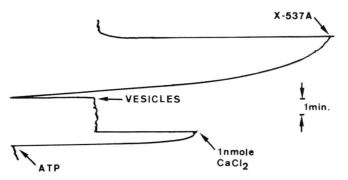

FIGURE 2 Measurement of Ca^{2+} uptake by reconstituted Ca^{2+}-ATPase vesicles using a Ca^{2+}-sensitive electrode. The experiment was carried out at 25°C in the presence of 150 μM ATP and 30 μl reconstituted vesicles. The Ca^{2+} ionophore X-537A was added to a final concentration of 9 μM.

3. Add 30 μl of reconstituted vesicles. The accumulated Ca^{2+} can be released by the addition of 3 μl of a 3 mM solution of the Ca^{2+} ionophore X-537A (higher concentration of the ionophore might affect the Ca^{2+} electrode).

A representative experiment is shown in Fig. 2.

IV. Comments

Preparation of calmodulin-deficient erythrocyte plasma membranes (ghosts) requires about 10 hr. The yield is about 1.2 g of ghost protein per liter of erythrocyte concentrate. The ghosts can be stored for up to 6 months at −72°C without appreciable loss of Ca^{2+}-ATPase activity. The specific activity of the ghost-associated ATPase, if measured in the presence of calmodulin is about 5 μmole/ATP hydrolyzed/hr. The protocol described here allows the purification of calmodulin-activated Ca^{2+}-ATPase; however, small changes in the protocol permit the purification of a Ca^{2+} pump having different properties. For instance, the omission of phosphatidylcholine during the calmodulin affinity chromatographic procedure allows the isolation of lipid-free Ca^{2+}-ATPase (0.1% Triton X-100 should be present in the washing and eluting solutions). On the other hand, when soy bean phosphatidylcholine, which contains about 10% acidic phospholipids, is used instead of egg phosphatidylcholine, the purified Ca^{2+} pump is fully active in the absence of calmodulin. Other nonionic detergents such as Thesit can be used instead of Triton X-100 to solubilize and purify the Ca^{2+} pump. A large preparation of Ca^{2+}-ATPase can be made by using the calmodulin affinity step in a batch-type procedure.

V. Pitfalls

Preparation of the ghosts and purification of the Ca^{2+} pump should be carried out as fast as possible, working at 4°C to prevent activation of endogenous proteases. The purified Ca^{2+} pump has a molecular mass of about 136 kDa, but in some preparations, as a result of proteolytic digestion, a polypeptide band with a molecular mass of about 124 kDa is found associated with the purified ATPase. The presence of other contaminants might be due to insufficient washing with the Ca^{2+} washing solution. The presence of glycerol throughout the preparation and in the storage solution is essential to preserving the enzyme activity.

REFERENCES

Affolter, H., and Sigel, E. (1979) A simple system for the measurement of ion activities with solvent polymeric membrane electrodes. *Anal. Biochem.* **97,** 315–319.

Carafoli, E. (1992) The Ca^{2+} pump of the plasma membrane. *J. Biol. Chem.* **267,** 2115–2118.

Crompton, M., and Carafoli, E. (1979) The measurement of Ca^{2+} movements in mitochondria. *In* "Methods in Enzymology" (D. B. McCormick and L. D. Wright, eds.), Vol. 66, pp. 338–352. Academic Press, San Diego.

Gopinath, R. M., and Vincenzi, F. F. (1977) Phosphodiesterase protein activator mimics red blood cell cytoplasmatic activator of the Ca^{2+}–Mg^{2+}-ATPase. *Biochem. Biophys. Res. Commun.* **77,** 1203–1209.

Jarret, H. W., and Penniston, J. T. (1977) Partial purification of the Ca^{2+}–Mg^{2+}-ATPase activator from human erythrocytes: Its similarity to the activator of 3′,5′-cyclic nucleotide phosphodiesterase. *Biochem. Biophys. Res. Commun.* **77,** 1210–1216.

Lanzetta, P. A., Alvarez, L. J., Reinach, P. S., and Candia, O. A. (1979) An improved assay for nanomole amounts of inorganic phosphate. *Anal. Biochem.* **100,** 95–97.

Niggli, V., Penniston, J. T., and Carafoli, E. (1979) Purification of the Ca^{2+}–Mg^{2+}-ATPase from human erythrocyte membranes using a calmodulin affinity column. *J. Biol. Chem.* **254,** 9955–9958.

Scharschmidt B. F., Keeffe, E. B., Blankenship, N. M., and Ockner, R. K. (1979) Validation of a recording spectrophotometric method for measurement of membrane-associated Mg- and NaK-ATPase activity. *J. Lab. Clin. Med.* **93,** 790–799.

Watterson, D. M., Harrelson, W. G., Keller, P. M., Sharief, F., and Vanaman, T. C. (1976) Structural similarities between the Ca^{2+}-dependent regulatory proteins of 3′:5′-cyclic nucleotide phosphodiesterase and actomyosin ATPase. *J. Biol. Chem.* **251,** 4501–4513.

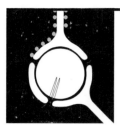

Isolation of Focal Adhesions from Cultured Cells

Markus Niederreiter and Mario Gimona

I. Introduction

Actin filaments of cultured cells are linked to the extracellular substrate via a transmembrane protein bridge recognized in the light microscope as a focal adhesion (Burridge, 1986; Burridge *et al.*, 1988; Geiger and Ginsberg, 1991). Focal adhesions act as key elements in determining cell morphology. They are involved in signal transduction, and are primary targets of cell transforming agents (Burridge, 1986; Burridge *et al.*, 1992; Glenney, 1992; Schwartz, 1992). Their molecular organization has thus been a subject of intense interest. Here we describe procedures for the isolation of focal adhesions that facilitate specific studies on these structures. The method is based on earlier procedures (Avnur and Geiger, 1981; Neyfakh *et al.*, 1983) in which the cell membranes are made fragile (with $ZnCl_2$ or saponin) and the cell bodies washed away with a stream of buffer to leave the adhesion sites attached to the substrate.

II. Materials and Instrumentation

A peristaltic pump was employed to achieve a continuous and definable buffer stream. The pump tubing was connected to a syringe needle with an 0.8-mm inner diameter. Cell culture clusters with 48 wells and lids with condensation rings (Cat. No. 3548) obtained from Costar were used for cell labeling and extraction experiments. Tran[35]S-label (Cat. No. 51006) purchased from ICN was used to label cultured cells with [35S]methionine and [35S]cysteine. Dulbecco's modified Eagle's medium (DMEM, Cat. No. F-0403) and fetal calf serum (FCS, Cat. No. S0115) were obtained from Seromed, saponin (Cat. No. S-2149) and Mes (Cat. No. M-8250) from Sigma, urea (Cat. No. 24524) from Serva and Nonidet P-40 (Cat. No. 74385) from Fluka. All other chemicals were of p.a. grade purchased from Merck.

III. Procedure

A. ISOLATION OF FOCAL ADHESIONS

Solutions

1. *Buffer "C"*: To make 1 liter, solubilize 1.0 g glucose, 0.4 g KCl, 8.0 g NaCl, 0.06 g KH_2PO_4, 0.6 g $Na_2HPO_4 \cdot 2H_2O$, 0.35 g $NaHCO_3$, 0.975 g Mes, 0.4 g $MgCl_2 \cdot 6H_2O$, and 0.074 g $CaCl_2 \cdot 2H_2O$ in distilled water. Adjust pH to

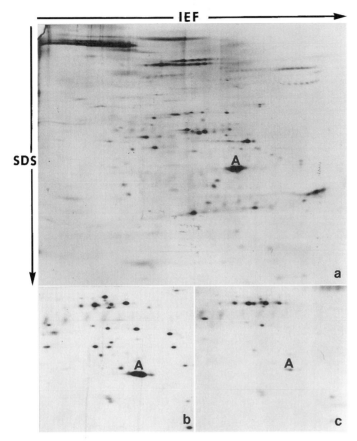

FIGURE 1   Two-dimensional gel analysis of isolated contacts of (a) CEFs and (b,c) AMA cells (transformed human amnion cells). Procedures are described in detail by Julio E. Celis *et al.* and Mario Gimona *et al.* in this volume. Gel b shows a segment of a two-dimensional gel of untreated contacts; gel c shows the corresponding gel segment of contacts treated with the actin capping and severing protein gelsolin, which removes most of the actin (A-actin). Only those proteins whose association with focal adhesions is actin independent remain. IEF, isoelectric focusing.

6.1, bring to a total volume of 1 liter, and filter through a 0.45-μm filter. Store at 4°C.

   2. *Lysis buffer:* To make 100 ml, dissolve 48.85 g urea, 2.0 g Nonidet P-40, 2.0 ml ampholytes 7–9, and 0.77 g dithiothreitol in distilled water, bring to a final volume of 100 ml, and filter through a 0.2-μm filter. Store at −70°C.

Steps

   1. Grow cells in culture medium (DMEM supplemented with 10% FCS) on 10-mm glass coverslips. For radiolabeling the coverslips can be placed inside the condensation rings of the covers of 48-well clusters and incubated overnight in 60–80 μl of methionine-free culture medium containing 0.5 mCi/ml ICN Tran[35]S-label.

   2. Rinse coverslips twice in buffer "C" and place in a petri dish containing a 0.2% solution of saponin in buffer "C". The incubation time can be adjusted according to the purpose and cell type. The optimum time for chick embryo fibroblast (CEF) focal adhesions is 3 min (Figs. 1 and 2). If slight impurities can be accepted the incubation time can be decreased to 2 min, which results in a higher yield of adhesions, but also some residual cell bodies.

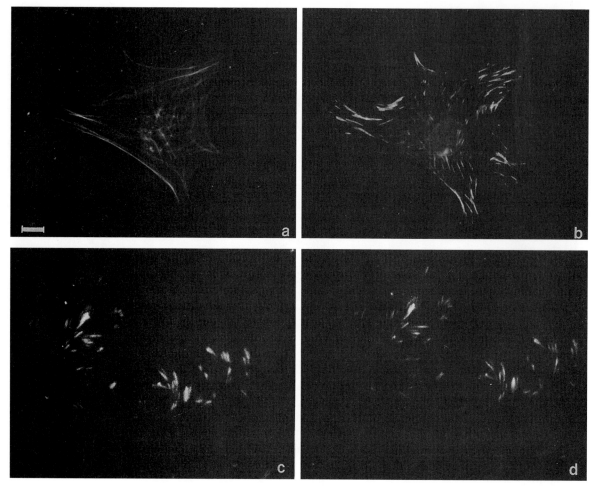

FIGURE 2 Double labeling with FITC–phalloidin against actin (a,c) and a monoclonal antivinculin antibody (b,d) of intact cells (a,b) and isolated focal adhesions (c,d). Vinculin is a marker of focal adhesions. Only the end stubs of the actin bundles remain attached to the focal adhesion sites. Bar = 10 μm.

3. After incubating the cells with saponin, take up the coverslips with a pair of forceps and remove the cell bodies with a constant stream of buffer "C" (Fig. 3) from the syringe needle. Collect the buffer waste in a beaker below the coverslip. Adjust the flow rate to around 0.5–1 ml/sec. The volume of buffer used for one coverslip also should be kept constant. For spraying a coverslip of 1-cm diameter a volume of 50 ml is sufficient.

4. After removal of the cell bodies dry the back sides of the coverslips with a piece of filter paper and place the former, cell side down, on either lysis buffer (for two-dimensional electrophoresis), PBS (for microscopy), or any other buffer according to the experimental design (Fig. 1). If extraction with lysis buffer is desired, it is advisable to use once again the top parts of cell culture clusters. With the coverslips face down on the lysis buffer in the shallow wells of the multiwell lid, very little evaporation and unwanted drying can take place during incubation. After placing coverslips on top of the drops of buffer, it is recommended that the cluster covers be placed in an incubator for 5 min. This dissolves the contacts without precipitating urea from the lysis buffer.

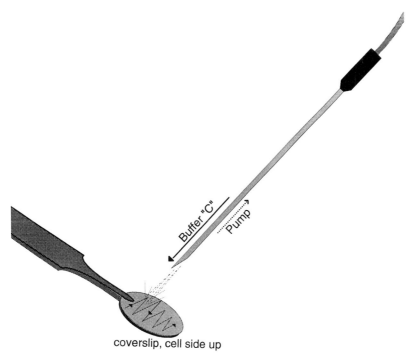

coverslip, cell side up

FIGURE 3 Squirting the coverslips to remove the cell bodies.

IV. Comments

The above procedure is useful for studying focal adhesions in the microscope and by electrophoresis. The isolation process is simple and can easily be adjusted to different needs and cell types. Rapid and efficient control of the purity of the preparations is achieved by observation of the samples in the phase contrast and interference reflection microscopes. The results of these experiments must, however, be interpreted carefully, as impurities caused by remaining membranes and proteins of the cytoskeleton cannot be completely excluded.

V. Pitfalls

1. During the squirting procedure the coverslips must be held firmly in the forceps. It is also important to hold the coverslip close to the edge so as to allow proper spraying of the surface (Fig. 3) and a high overall yield of isolated adhesions.

2. The focal adhesion preparations released from the glass surface with lysis buffer contain matrix proteins. These proteins might affect the electrophoresis in the first dimension (isoelectric focusing). It is thus advisable to load not more than the harvest of one coverslip (CEFs) on first-dimension gels, or the proteins will penetrate the gel poorly.

3. As mentioned in Section IV, the purity of the preparations for electrophoresis is extremely important. Before application of lysis buffer, a precheck of the coverslips by means of phase-contrast microscopy is strongly recommended.

REFERENCES

Avnur, Z., and Geiger, B. (1981) Substrate-attached membranes of cultured cells. *J. Mol. Biol.* **153**, 361–379.

Avnur, Z., Small, J. V., and Geiger, B. (1983) Actin independent association of vinculin with the cytoplasmic aspect of the plasma membrane in cell-contact areas. *J. Cell Biol.* **96**, 1622–1630.

Burridge, K. (1986) Substrate adhesion in normal and transformed fibroblasts. *Cancer Rev.* **4**, 18–78.

Burridge, K., Fath, K., Kelly, T., Nuckolls, G., and Turner, C. (1988) Focal adhesions: Transmembrane junctions between the extracellular matrix and the cytoskeleton. *Annu. Rev. Cell Biol.* **4**, 487–525.

Burridge, K., Petch, L. A., and Romer, L. H. (1992) Signals from focal contacts. *Curr. Biol.* **2**, 537–539.

Geiger, B., and Ginsberg, D. (1991) The cytoplasmic domain of adherens-type junctions. *Cell Motil.* **20**, 1–6.

Glenney, J. R. (1992) Tyrosine phosphorylated proteins: Mediators of signal transduction from tyrosine kinases. *Biochim. Biophys. Acta* **1134**, 113–127.

Neyfakh, A. A., Svitkina, J. R., and Svitkina, T. M. (1983) Isolation of focal contact membrane using saponin. *Exp. Cell Res.* **149**, 582–586.

Schwartz, M. A. (1992) Transmembrane signalling by integrins. *Trends Cell Biol.* **2**, 304–308.

Isolation of Laminins from Tumor Sources and from Normal Tissues

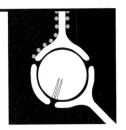

Mats Paulsson and Anders Lindblom

I. Introduction

Members of the laminin protein family influence attachment, motility, differentiation, and gene expression in many types of cells (Paulsson, 1992; Rohrbach and Timpl, 1993). Original studies on laminin were performed on molecules with the subunit composition Ae, B1e, B2e derived from mouse tumor sources such as the Engelbreth–Holm–Swarm (EHS) tumor (Timpl *et al.,* 1979) or the embryonal carcinoma cell line M1536-B3 (Chung *et al.,* 1979). Later work showed that laminins in normal vertebrate tissues form a larger gene family, with the expression being both tissue specific and developmentally regulated (for references and nomenclature, see Paulsson, 1992). Here we describe isolation of laminin by selective EDTA extraction from the transplantable mouse EHS tumor and from normal vertebrate tissues, using bovine heart as an example. While the first protocol yields the "classic" laminin of chain composition Ae, B1e, B2e, the latter procedure may be applied to a variety of basement membrane-containing tissues and will yield a mixture of those laminin isoforms present in the particular tissue. When mild conditions are used the laminin-associated protein nidogen (=entactin) copurifies with laminin in the form of the laminin–nidogen complex. Nidogen may be dissociated by treatment in 2 *M* guanidine–HCl (Paulsson *et al.,* 1987).

II. Materials and Instrumentation

All chemicals used should be of analytical grade but may be from any supplier. Chromatography gels used are Sepharose CL-6B (Cat. No. 17-0160-01), Sepharose CL-4B (Cat. No. 17-150-01), DEAE-Sephacel (Cat. No. 17-0500-01), and DEAE-Sepharose Fast Flow (Cat. No. 17-0709-01), all obtained from Pharmacia LKB Biotechnology. These may be packed in columns from any supplier as long as the columns have the approximate dimensions given below. Gradient elution of ion exchangers is achieved by use of communicating vessels, e.g., the SG 1000 or SG 2000 gradient makers from Hoefer Scientific Instruments. Also needed are a peristaltic pump giving flow rates from 10–250 ml/hr and a fraction collector. Access is needed to a Polytron homogenizer with a PTA 20-S knife (Kinematica), a refrigerated high-speed centrifuge, a magnetic stirrer, and an end-over-end rotation device. Concentration of laminin-containing samples is done by ultrafiltration over Diaflo YM10 ultrafilters in Amicon 400- or 50-ml stirred cells (Amicon). Protein concentration of column effluents is routinely followed by absorbance at 280 nm and final concentrations are determined by the Pierce protein assay (Pierce) using bovine serum albumin as a standard. Purification is followed and final purity assessed by SDS–PAGE with and without reduction, typically in gradient slab gels of 3–10% polyacrylamide.

III. Procedures

A. PURIFICATION OF LAMININ–NIDOGEN COMPLEXES FROM THE MOUSE EHS TUMOR

Solutions

1. *Washing buffer:* 0.15 M NaCl, 50 mM Tris–HCl, pH 7.4, containing 2 mM N-ethylmaleimide (NEM) and 2 mM PMSF as protease inhibitors. The PMSF is added just prior to use from a 100 mM stock solution in ethanol.

2. *Extraction buffer:* 0.15 M NaCl, 10 mM EDTA, 50 mM Tris–HCl, pH 7.4, containing 2 mM NEM and 2 mM PMSF (see above).

3. *Elution buffer for Sepharose CL-6B and CL-4B:* 0.15 M NaCl, 2.5 mM EDTA, 50 mM Tris–HCl, pH 7.4, containing 0.5 mM NEM and 0.5 mM PMSF (see above).

4. *Equilibration buffer for DEAE-Sephacel:* 2.5 mM EDTA, 50 mM Tris–HCl, pH 7.4, containing 0.5 mM NEM and 0.5 mM PMSF (see above). The limiting solution for gradient elution is made in this buffer by addition of solid NaCl to a final concentration of 0.8 M.

Steps

1. Prepare all buffers and columns prior to starting the actual extraction. Cool all buffers to 3–4°C (cold-room temperature) prior to use. Perform all extraction, chromatography, and ultrafiltration steps in the cold room. Laminin–nidogen complexes are sensitive to degradation by tissue proteases, but these are efficiently controlled by making systematic use of protease inhibitors, working at low temperatures, and avoiding interruptions during extraction and purification.

2. Take 60 g of EHS tumor tissue from the freezer. (The tumor is preferably frozen in small pieces and kept at −80°C.) Cut the still frozen tissue into 2- to 3-mm slices with a scalpel. Immerse tumor slices in 1200 ml (20 vol/original tissue weight) of cold washing buffer and homogenize for ca. 30 sec at full speed. Immediately pour the homogenate into centrifuge vessels and centrifuge for 20 min at ca. 15,000 g and 4°C in a fixed-angle rotor. Discard the supernatant.

3. Suspend the pellets in a total of 1200 ml of washing buffer by a brief (ca. 10 sec) homogenization and repeat centrifugation and decanting as above.

4. Transfer the pellets to a beaker with 300 ml (5 vol/original tissue weight) extraction buffer. Suspend by a brief homogenization. Add stirring bar and stir vigorously on a magnetic stirrer for 1 hr in the cold room. Centrifuge for 20 min at 4°C and ca. 15,000 g. Store the supernatant in the cold room and reextract the pellets as described under steps 3 and 4. Pool the two extracts and divide into aliquots of 100 ml. Freeze aliquots that are not immediately used at −30°C.

5. Centrifuge one 100-ml aliquot for 20 min at ca. 48,000 g and 4°C. Apply to a column (5 × 60–70 cm, ca. 1250 ml) of Sepharose CL-6B equilibrated in solution 3. Elute in the same buffer with a flow rate of 50–60 ml/hr and collect fractions of ca. 15 ml. Screen fractions for absorbance at 280 nm. The laminin–nidogen complex elutes as a major peak in or close to the void volume. Its

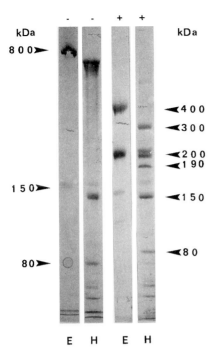

FIGURE 1   SDS–PAGE of laminin from mouse EHS tumor (E) and bovine heart (H). Laminin was purified as described in the protocols above. Approximately 10 μg protein was dissolved in electrophoresis cocktail (Laemmli, 1970), either with (+, right lanes) or without (−, left lanes) 2% (v/v) β-mercaptoethanol, and applied on a gradient (3–10%) polyacrylamide gel. When unreduced, laminin from EHS tumor migrates more slowly than laminin from heart. Unreduced heart laminin often migrates as a doublet which might represent a separation between laminin molecules containing the B1e and the B1s subunits, as these differ in molecular weight (see below). In both laminin preparations nidogen is seen as a band of approximately 150 kDa, both with and without reduction. In addition, heart laminin contains an 80-kDa polypeptide that dissociates from the complex in the presence of SDS. This peptide probably represents the C-terminal part of an Am precursor (Ehrig *et al.*, 1990) which is cleaved at some stage during the maturation of the biosynthetic product. On reduction, EHS laminin gives rise to bands of 400 kDa (Ae chain) and 200 kDa (B1e and B2e). Even though the 200-kDa band contains both kinds of B subunits, these are not resolved in electrophoresis. The reduced heart laminin contains bands with apparent molecular weights of 300 kDa (Am), 210 kDa (B1e), 200 kDa (B2e), and 190 kDa (B1s), in addition to the 150- and 80-kDa components already mentioned.

identity may be confirmed by SDS–PAGE as shown in Fig. 1. Pool laminin-containing fractions.

6. Dilute the laminin pools from up to three runs on the Sepharose CL-6B column with 50% original volume of solution 4 to yield a final NaCl concentration of 0.10 M. Apply the diluted sample to a column (5 × 10 cm) of DEAE-Sephacel equilibrated in solution 4. Loading can be done at a low flow rate overnight. Wash the column with ca. 200 ml of solution 4 and elute with a gradient (500 + 500 ml) of 0–0.8 M NaCl in solution 4. Washing and elution can conveniently be done at a flow rate of up to 250 ml/hr. Collect fractions (15 ml) and screen for absorbance at 280 nm. Laminin containing proteolytically degraded nidogen elutes in the flow-through, whereas intact laminin–nidogen complexes elute as a major peak early in the gradient. The second major peak eluted by the gradient consists mainly of basement membrane proteoglycan and nucleic acids. The identity of the laminin–nidogen complex can be confirmed by

SDS–PAGE, as described above, and the corresponding fractions pooled. The pool is concentrated by ultrafiltration to ca. 2 mg/ml, dialyzed against 0.15 M NaCl, 50 mM Tris–HCl, pH 7.4, and stored frozen in aliquots. A typical yield from 60 g tumor tissue is 200 mg. For a detailed characterization of such preparations see Paulsson *et al.* (1987) and Paulsson (1988).

B. PURIFICATION OF LAMININ–NIDOGEN COMPLEXES FROM NORMAL MAMMALIAN TISSUE

The amount of laminin present in normal tissue is much lower than that in EHS tumor; hence the protocol for laminin-isolation has to be adapted accordingly. With the following method milligram amounts of laminin can be obtained from tissues such as heart, placenta, and kidney (Paulsson and Saladin, 1989; Ehrig *et al.*, 1990; Lindblom *et al.*, 1994). Due to the higher protein complexity in normal tissues, the laminin recovered by our procedure is less pure than that attained with EHS tumor tissue. The protocol we suggest yields a laminin-enriched fraction suitable for some, but not all, cell biological purposes. For homogeneity, further purification steps might have to be employed, depending on the tissue source and the nature of the contaminating proteins.

Solutions

5. *Equilibration buffer for DEAE-Sepharose fast flow:* 0.1 M NaCl, 10 mM EDTA, 10 mM Tris, pH 7.5, containing 0.5 mM NEM and 0.5 mM PMSF.

6. *Elution buffer for DEAE-Sepharose fast flow:* 0.5 M NaCl, 10 mM EDTA, 10 mM Tris, pH 7.5, containing 0.5 mM NEM and 0.5 mM PMSF.

7. *Elution buffer for second Sepharose CL-4B:* 1 M ammonium acetate.

Steps

1. In our experience, the amount of laminin extractable with nondenaturing salts from normal tissues is only approximately 1% of that obtained from EHS tumor; i.e., we can obtain ca. 5–10 mg of purified laminin from 500 g normal tissue. When deciding about the amount of starting material, the volume capacity of rotors for centrifugations after the initial extractions is often the limiting factor. Two hundred grams of tissue as raw material is a practical measure. This implicates a need for 5 liters washing buffer and 2.5 liters extraction buffer for the initial extractions, and these solutions should be prepared beforehand and be precooled at approximately 4°C.

2. Mince the tissue to pieces measuring no more than 0.5×0.5 cm with a kitchen knife. Use 200 g for the extraction. The remainder is preferably flash-frozen (as single pieces) in liquid nitrogen and stored at −80°C for future use. Immerse the 200 g in 2 liters (20 vol/original tissue weight) washing buffer and homogenize for ca. 30 sec at top speed. When big pieces are no longer present, immediately transfer the homogenate into centrifuge tubes (preferred volume: 500 ml) and centrifuge for 20 min at ca. 15,000 g, 4°C. Decant the supernatant, freeze an aliquot (~50 ml, TBS wash 1) for later analyses, and discard the rest.

3. Resuspend the pellet by brief homogenization in washing buffer and repeat centrifugation and decanting as above (save and freeze 50 ml of supernatant as TBS wash 2).

4. When needed repeat step 3 (TBS wash 3). As a rule, extraction with TBS should be continued until the supernatant is macroscopically free from blood

(the color should be gray-pink). Thorough preextraction increases the purity in later steps.

5. Resuspend the pellet by brief homogenization in 1 liter extraction buffer (5 vol/original tissue weight). Transfer the homogenate to a 1.5-liter beaker, add stirring bar, and stir vigorously (the beaker should preferably be plastic to avoid mishaps) on a magnetic stirrer for 1–3 hr in the cold room. Centrifuge as above and store the supernatant (TBS–EDTA 1) overnight at 4°C.

6. Repeat step 5 with stirring overnight finished by centrifugation as above. Collect the supernatant (TBS–EDTA 2). The remaining pellet can be weighed and discarded, or stored at −30°C. Analyze aliquots of the different washing and extraction steps by running a gradient (3–10%) SDS–PAGE. In unreduced samples, laminin can most often be discerned as a high-molecular-weight (~800 kDa) in the two EDTA extracts.

7. Pool the two TBS–EDTA extracts, dilute 2:1 with cold, distilled water, and add 100 ml DEAE-Sepharose Fast Flow (1 ml gel/20 g original tissue). Prior to the addition, the ion exchanger should be equilibrated with solution 5. Incubate overnight at 4°C with end-over-end rotation (e.g., in bottles mounted on a vertical rotating table).

8. Stop the rotation, release the bottles, and allow the DEAE-Sepharose to settle for 1–2 hr. Decant as much as possible of the supernatant without losing any gel, then resuspend and pour the slurry into a column (2.5×25–30 cm). The column should preferably be equipped with an extension vessel to allow pouring of the entire slurry into the column at once. Connect the column outlet to a UV monitor with sensitivity set at 1.0 AU. When the gel has settled, remove the extension vessel and wash extensively (200–500 ml, until UV signal clearly has returned to baseline) with solution 5. After washing, connect the column outlet to a fraction collector (set fraction size to approximately 5 ml) and elute the column with solution 6. Monitor the OD_{280} of the effluent fractions. After the elution, regenerate the gel by washing with 1–2 vol 6 M guanidinium chloride, 10 mM Tris–HCl, pH 7.5, and reequilibrate with solution 5 (200–500 ml).

9. Pool the material eluted with 0.5 M NaCl (maximum volume 100 ml for the next step) and centrifuge at 4°C for 1 hr at 100,000 g to remove particulate material. Then apply the supernatant to a column (5×100 cm) of Sepharose CL-4B equilibrated in solution 3. Connect the outlet to a UV monitor with sensitivity set at 0.1 AU. Elute the column with a flow rate of 50–80 ml/hr and collect 16- to 18-ml fractions. Analyze aliquots (1–2 ml, concentrate by precipitation with 9 vol ethanol overnight at 4°C) of eluted fractions by gradient (3–10%) SDS–PAGE.

10. Pool the laminin-containing fractions from the Sepharose CL-4B chromatogram and dialyze against solution 4 (~10 vol, one or two changes). Apply the material to a column (2.5×10 cm) of DEAE-Sephacel equilibrated in solution 4. Connect the column outlet to a UV monitor with sensitivity set at 0.1 AU. Wash with the equilibration buffer until the OD_{280} of the effluent returns to baseline, and then run a gradient (150 + 150 ml) of 0–0.8 M NaCl in solution 4. Collect 5- to 7-ml fractions and analyze aliquots (~1 ml, concentrate by ethanol precipitation as above) with gradient (3–10%) SDS–PAGE.

11. Pool the laminin-containing fractions from above. Reduce the volume to ca. 20 ml by ultrafiltration at 4°C and dialyze the sample against solution 7 (ca. 50 vol, two changes). Apply the dialyzed sample on a column (2.5×100 cm) of Sepharose CL-4B equilibrated in solution 7. Connect the column outlet to a UV monitor (280 nm) with sensitivity set at 0.1 AU. Elute at 20 ml/min at 4°C and collect 6-ml fractions. Laminin–nidogen complexes elute as a homogenous peak

at K_{av} 0.2–0.3. Precipitate aliquots (~1 ml) of every second fraction and run on a gradient (3–10%) SDS–PAGE. Pool the laminin-containing fractions, and concentrate to 0.5–1 mg/ml with ultrafiltration if desired. Dialyze the laminin pool against solution 3 and freeze in aliquots of 0.5–1 ml at −30°C.

REFERENCES

Chung, A. E., Jaffe, R., Freeman, I. L., Vergnes, J.-P., Braginski, J. E., and Carlin, B. (1979) Properties of a basement membrane-related glycoprotein synthesized in culture by a mouse embryonal carcinoma-derived cell line. *Cell* **16**, 277–287.

Ehrig, K., Leivo, I., Argraves, W. S., Ruoslahti, E., and Engvall, E. (1990) Merosin, a tissue-specific basement membrane protein, is a laminin-like protein. *Proc. Natl. Acad. Sci. USA* **87**, 3264–3268.

Laemmli, U. K. (1970) Cleavage of structural proteins during the assembly of the head of bacteriophage T4. *Nature* **227**, 680–685.

Lindblom, A., Marsh, T., Fauser, C., Engel, J., and Paulsson, M. (1994) Characterization of native laminin from bovine kidney and comparison with other laminin variants. *Eur. J. Biochem.* **219**, 383–392.

Paulsson, M. (1988) The role of Ca^{2+} binding in the self-aggregation of laminin–nidogen complexes. *J. Biol. Chem.* **263**, 5425–5430.

Paulsson, M. (1992) Basement membrane proteins: Structure, assembly, and cellular interactions. *Crit. Rev. Biochem. Mol. Biol.* **27**, 93–127.

Paulsson, M., Aumailley, M., Deutzmann, R., Timpl, R., Beck, K., and Engel, J. (1987) Laminin–nidogen complex. Extraction with chelating agents and structural characterization. *Eur. J. Biochem.* **166**, 11–19.

Paulsson, M., and Saladin, K. (1989) Mouse heart laminin. Purification of the native protein and structural comparison with Engelbreth–Holm–Swarm tumor laminin. *J. Biol. Chem.* **264**, 18726–18732.

Rohrbach, D. H., and Timpl, R. (1993) "Molecular and Cellular Aspects of Basement Membranes." Academic Press, Orlando, FL.

Timpl, R., Rohde, H., Gehron Robey, P., Rennard, S. I., Foidart, J.-M., and Martin, G. R. (1979) Laminin—A glycoprotein from basement membranes. *J. Biol. Chem.* **254**, 9933–9937.

Isolation of Centrosomes from Cultured Animal Cells

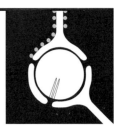

Mohammed Moudjou and Michel Bornens

I. Introduction

The centrosome, a central body playing a key role in the temporal and spatial distribution of the interphasic and mitotic microtubule network, could be considered a major determinant of the cytoplasm's overall organization and of the fidelity of cell division (Bornens, 1992; Kalt and Schliwa, 1993). In animal cells, the centrosome is composed of two centrioles surrounded by the so-called pericentriolar material (PCM) which consists of a complex thin filament network and two sets of appendages (Paintrand *et al.,* 1992). In contrast to the importance given to this organelle in the early days of cell biology, little is known about the molecular mechanisms that govern its main functions: the nucleation of microtubules and the controlled cycle of centrosome duplication, the two duplicated entities functioning as mitotic spindle poles during subsequent cell division. The biochemical and functional identification of centrosomal components has been difficult for several reasons. Genetic approaches were rare and only recently have a few systems been found useful for this strategy (for review see Huang, 1990). Preparative isolation of this organelle was also limited, as the centrosome exists as one copy per interphasic cell and good assays for obtaining enriched fractions of centrosomal proteins were lacking. A number of laboratories have developed protocols for isolation of centrosomes from cultured cells, fungi, or tissues (Mitchison and Kirschner, 1986; Bornens *et al.,* 1987; Rout and Kilmartin, 1990; Komesli *et al.,* 1989). Indirect strategies have also been developed to identify centrosomal components from *Drosophila* embryos (Raff *et al.,* 1993). In this article, we describe a protocol for isolation of centrosomes from cultured human lymphoblastic cells. This method is based largely on an earlier one (Bornens *et al.,* 1987). Several modifications are introduced to refine both quantitative and qualitative aspects of the method.

II. Materials and Instrumentation

Culture medium RPMI-1640 was purchased from Eurobio Laboratories. Fetal calf serum (FCS) was from Jacques Boy. Cytochalasin D (Cat. No. C-8273), Hepes (Cat. No. H-3375), Nonidet P-40 (NP-40, Cat. No. N-3516), Tween 20 (Cat. No. P-5927), PMSF (Cat. No. P-7626), EGTA (Cat. No. E-4378), and Triton X-100 were from Sigma. Nocodazole (Cat. No. 152 405) was from ICN. DNase I (Cat. No. 104 159), Pipes (Cat. No. 1359 045), GTP (Cat. No. 414 581), and protease inhibitors aprotinin (Cat. No. 236 624), leupeptin (Cat. No. 1017 101), and pepstatin (Cat. No. 258 286) were obtained from Boehringer-Mannheim. Sucrose (Cat.

No. 35579) was from Serva. Tris (Cat. No. 8382) and β-mercaptoethanol (Cat. No. 805740) were obtained from Merck. Glutaraldehyde EM-25% (Cat. No. G004) was from TAAB. Glycerol redistilled (RP Normapur 99.5%, Cat. No. 24388.295) and $MgCl_2$ (Cat. No. 25 108 295) were from Prolabo. Bovine serum albumin (Cat. No. 82.045.1, fraction V protease free) was obtained from Miles.

The density gradient fractionator (Model 183) was from Instrumentation Specialities Company (ISCO).

Corex tubes (15 ml) were equipped with a plastic adapter or plug (homemade) to support a 12-mm round glass coverslip for sedimentation of isolated centrosomes (see Evans *et al.*, 1985). Prior to use, coverslips were washed with a mixture of methanol and hydrochloric acid at a ratio of 2:1 for 2 hr, rinsed for 1 hr with distilled water, and finally rinsed with pure ethanol for at least 2 hr. They were transferred one by one to a filter paper to dry and conserved in a closed petri box until use.

The immunofluorescence box was homemade. The monoclonal anti-α tubulin antibody (Cat. No. N356) was purchased from Amersham. Fluorescein (DTAF)-conjugated AffiniPure donkey anti-rabbit IgGs (Cat. No. 711-015-132), and Lissamine Rhodamine (LRSC)-conjugated AffiniPure goat anti-mouse IgGs (Cat. No. 115-085-068) were obtained from Jackson ImmunoResearch Laboratories and were used as secondary antibodies. Mounting solution (Citifluor, Cat. No. AF1) to prevent fading of chromophore-labeled materials was obtained from Citifluor Limited.

III. Procedures

A. CENTROSOME ISOLATION

Solutions

1. *Cytochalasin D at 5 mg/ml:* To make 10 ml, solubilize 10 mg of cytochalasin D in 2 ml of pure DMSO. Store at 4°C.

2. 10^{-3} *M Nocodazole:* To make 10 ml, solubilize 3 mg of nocodazole in 10 ml of pure DMSO. Store as aliquots at −20°C.

3. *DNase I, 1 mg/ml:* To make 10 ml, solubilize 10 mg of DNase I in 10 ml of distilled water. Store as aliquots at 4°C.

4. *TBS buffer:* 10 mM Tris–HCl, pH 7.4, 150 mM NaCl. To make 1 liter, add 1.2 g of Tris and 8.7 g of NaCl to distilled water, adjust pH to 7.4, and complete the volume to 1 liter. Store at 4°C.

5. *TBS 0.1–8% (w/v) sucrose buffer:* To make 1 liter, add 100 ml of TBS buffer, pH 7.4, and 80 g of sucrose to distilled water and bring to a total volume of 1 liter. Prepare fresh or freeze at −20°C.

6. *1 M Hepes stock solution, pH 7.2:* To make 200 ml, add 47.6 g of Hepes to distilled water, adjust pH to 7.2 with 10 N NaOH, and complete the volume to 200 ml. Store at 4°C.

7. *1 M Pipes stock solution, pH 7.2:* To make 200 ml, add 60.5 g of Pipes to distilled water, adjust pH to 7.2 with 10 N KOH, and complete the volume to 200 ml. Store at 4°C.

8. *1 M MgCl₂ stock solution:* To make 100 ml, add 5.84 g of $MgCl_2$ to distilled water. Store at 4°C.

9. *Lysis buffer:* 1 mM Hepes pH 7.2, 0.5% NP-40, 0.5 mM $MgCl_2$, 0.1% β-mercaptoethanol, protease inhibitors (leupeptin, pepstatin, and aprotinin) at 1 μg/ml each, 1 mM of PMSF. To make 1 liter, add 1 ml of 1 M Hepes, pH 7.2, stock

solution, 5 ml of pure NP-40, 0.5 ml of 1 M $MgCl_2$ stock solution, 1 ml of pure β-mercaptoethanol, 1 mg each of aprotinin, leupeptin, and pepstatin, and 174.2 mg of PMSF to distilled water and complete to 1 liter. Prepare fresh or freeze as aliquots at $-20°C$.

10. *Gradient buffer:* 10 mM Pipes, pH 7.2, 0.1% Triton X-100, and 0.1% β-mercaptoethanol. To make 1 liter, add 10 ml of 1 M Pipes, pH 7.2, stock solution, 1 ml of pure Triton X-100, and 1 ml of pure β-mercaptoethanol to distilled water and complete to 1 liter. Store at 4°C.

11. *Sucrose solutions:* To make 200 g of 70% (w/w) sucrose solution, weight 140 g of sucrose and adjust to 200 g with gradient buffer; this gives 150 ml final volume; store at $-20°C$. To make 400 g of 60% (w/w) sucrose solution, weight 120 g of sucrose and adjust to 400 g with gradient buffer; this gives 300 ml final volume; store at $-20°C$. To make 150 g of 50% (w/w) sucrose solution, weigh 75 g of sucrose and adjust to 150 g with gradient buffer; this gives 120 ml final volume; store at $-20°C$. To make 150 g of 40% (w/w) sucrose solution, weigh 60 g of sucrose and adjust to 150 g with gradient buffer; this gives 130 ml final volume; store at $-20°C$.

12. *10 mM Pipes, pH 7.2:* For sedimentation of isolated centrosomes on glass coverslips. To make 500 ml, add 5 ml of 1 M Pipes, pH 7.2, stock solution to distilled water and complete to 500 ml. Store at 4°C.

Steps

1. Culture the human lymphoblastic KE37 cell line in suspension in RPMI-1640 medium supplemented with 10% FCS at 37°C and 5% CO_2. To 1000 ml of cell suspension (8×10^5 to 1×10^6 cells/ml), add 200 μl of 10^{-3} M nocodazole and 200 μl of cytochalasin D at 5 mg/ml, and incubate cells for 1 hr at 37°C. All the following steps are done at 4°C except where indicated.

2. Sediment cells by centrifugation at 280 g (1200 rpm) for 8 min. Wash cells with half of the initial cell suspension volume of TBS by gentle resuspension with a 10-ml pipette. Repeat this step once with TBS 0.1–8% sucrose buffer (half volume of the previous step).

3. Before lysis, resuspend cells in 20 ml of TBS 0.1–8% sucrose buffer, and then add the lysis buffer to obtain a concentration of 1×10^7 cells/ml. Shake cells slowly and resuspend them four to five times with a 10-ml pipette until chromatin aggregates are visible.

4. Remove a 200-μl aliquot to control the quality of the lysis step by immunofluorescence microscopy, and centrifuge down the swollen nuclei, chromatin aggregates, and unlysed cells at 2500 g (3500 rpm) for 10 min.

5. Filter the lysis supernatant through a nylon mesh (Crin Polyamide 125 μm, Fyltis Motte) into a 250-ml Nalgene tube and add concentrated solutions of 1 M Hepes and 1 mg/ml DNase to make final concentrations of 10 mM and 2 units/ml (1 μg/ml), respectively.

6. Let the suspension sit for 30 min, and remove 200-μl aliquot for immunofluorescence observation of the lysis supernatant.

7. Using a 50-ml syringe and a long needle with a flat end, place at the bottom of the Nalgene tube 10 ml of the 60% sucrose solution, and sediment centrosomes onto this cushion by centrifugation at 10,000 g (7500 rpm) for 30 min in a J2-21 M/E Beckman centrifuge equipped with the JS 7.5 rotor.

8. During the centrifugation, prepare a discontinuous sucrose gradient in a 38-ml SW 28 Beckman ultraclear tube, containing from the bottom 5, 3, and 3

ml of 70, 50, and 40% sucrose solutions, respectively. After centrosomes are concentrated on the 60% sucrose cushion by the previous centrifugation (step 7), remove the supernatant until only about 25–30 ml remains in the bottom of the 250-ml Nalgene tube.

9. Vortex vigorously the obtained centrosomal suspension (which is now about 20–25% sucrose) and fill the SW 28 Beckman tube with this sample. Centrifuge the gradient at 40,000 g (25,000 rpm) for 1 hr in the Beckman L8.50B ultracentrifuge equipped with the SW 28 rotor.

10. Place the SW 28 tube on the density gradient fractionator. Optimally, the tube is clamped in the ISCO apparatus, perforated at the bottom with a two-hole needle, and 14 fractions of 0.5 ml each are manually recovered from the bottom into 1.5-ml Eppendorf tubes.

11. Remove 10 μl from each fraction for monitoring the centrosome concentration (see below). Freeze the fractions in liquid nitrogen and store at −80°C.

B. IMMUNOFLUORESCENCE ANALYSIS OF SUCROSE GRADIENT FRACTIONS

Solutions

1. *10 mM Pipes, pH 7.2:* To make 500 ml, add 5 ml of 1 M Pipes stock solution, pH 7.2, to distilled water and complete to 500 ml. Store at 4°C.

2. *PBS 10× stock buffer:* 100 mM Phosphate, 1.5 M NaCl, pH 7.4. Solution A: 0.2 M Na_2HPO_4; to make 500 ml, add 14.2 g of Na_2HPO_4 to distilled water. Solution B: 0.2 M NaH_2PO_4; to make 100 ml, add 2.76 g of Na_2HPO_4 to distilled water. Mix solution A with solution B, add 87.66 g of NaCl, and complete to 1 liter with distilled water by checking the pH. Store at room temperature.

3. *PBS–0.1% Tween 20 buffer:* To make 100 ml, add 10 ml of 10× PBS stock buffer and 100 μl of pure Tween 20 to distilled water and complete to 100 ml. Store at 4°C.

4. *PBS–3% BSA buffer:* To make 50 ml, add 5 ml of 10× PBS stock buffer and 1.5 g of BSA to distilled water. Stir and complete to 50 ml. Store at 4°C.

5. *Secondary labeled antibodies:* Rhodamine-conjugated goat anti-mouse and fluorescein-labeled goat anti-rabbit antibodies are used as secondary antibodies.

Steps

1. Prepare twelve 15-ml Corex tubes containing special adapters and 12-mm round coverslips as described by Evans *et al.* (1985) and fill them with 3 ml of 10 mM Pipes, pH 7.2.

2. Disperse 10 μl each of fractions 4 to 13 in the corresponding tubes and centrifuge them at 20,000 g (10,000 rpm) with JS 13.1 rotor in a Beckman J2-21M/E centrifuge. At the same time, sediment 150-μl aliquots of the lysis step and the lysis supernatant on glass coverslips.

3. After centrifugation, remove the Pipes buffer from the tubes, place the coverslips in a coverslip holder box, and immerse them in methanol at −20°C for 6 min. All the following steps take place at room temperature.

4. Rinse the coverslips three times with PBS–0.1% Tween 20 buffer and place them in a chamber suitable for the immunofluorescence experiments with

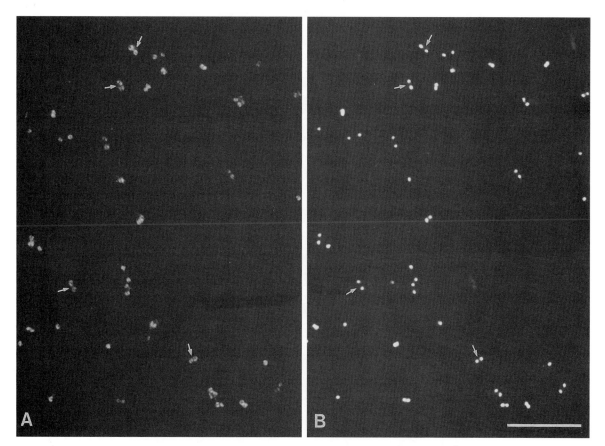

FIGURE 1 Example of double immunofluorescence staining of centrosomes present in fraction 5 of the sucrose gradient. Centrosomes were stained with an anti-pericentriolar material antibody (A) and an anti-α-tubulin antibody that stains centrioles (B). Centrosomes were homogeneously distributed on the glass coverslip. They were recovered mainly as a pair of centrioles, their native configuration (arrows in A and B). Bar = 10 μm.

coverslips. Generally, double immunofluorescence staining with a polyclonal anti-pericentriolar material and a monoclonal anti-α-tubulin antibody (the latter stains centrioles) is performed (an example is shown in Fig. 1). The primary antibodies are diluted in 3% PBS–BSA. Incubate sedimented centrosomes with the primary antibodies for at least 30 min.

5. Rinse the coverslips three times with PBS–0.1% Tween 20 buffer and add mixed fluorescein-labeled anti-rabbit IgGs and rhodamine-conjugated anti-mouse IgGs (both diluted 1/750 in 3% PBS–BSA) as secondary antibodies. Incubate for at least 30 min.

6. Rinse coverslips with PBS–Tween 20 buffer and place them in pure ethanol for 2 min. When coverslips are dry, mount them on a drop of Citifluor placed on microscope slides.

C. QUANTIFICATION OF CENTROSOMES PER SUCROSE GRADIENT FRACTION

Steps

1. Observe the coverslips with an epifluorescence microscope (Leitz Dialux 20), and count centrosomes on a defined field outlined by the camera.

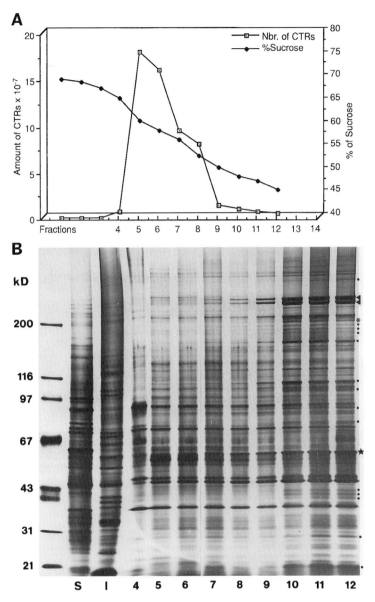

FIGURE 2 (A) Quantification of centrosomes (CTRs) recovered in each fraction of the sucrose gradient used as the late stage of centrosome isolation. The bottom of the gradient is on the left; 3×10^9 cells were used in this preparation. Note that fractions 5 and 6 are more enriched. (B) Electrophoretic analysis of the same fractions represented in (A). A 6–15% SDS–PAGE gradient was used to detect simultaneously the high- and low-molecular-weight polypeptides present in each fraction. The gel was stained by silver nitrate technique. Lanes S and I correspond to Triton X-100-soluble (S) and -insoluble (I) proteins of KE37 lymphoblastic cells from which the centrosomes were isolated. Fractions 5–7 are constant in their protein composition. Many additional bands appear in the top of the sucrose gradient from fractions 8 and 9 and are prominent in fractions 10–12. Among these additional contaminating bands (dots), the major ones has been identified as fodrin (arrowheads), myosin heavy chain (asterisk), and vimentin (star).

2. Measure the area of this field using a slide graduated with a micrometer. Use the ratio to the total area on which centrosomes have been sedimented (i.e., the transverse section of the Corex tube) to calculate the number of centrosomes in the aliquot. From that, obtain the concentration of each fraction (Fig. 2A).

D. BIOCHEMICAL ANALYSIS OF SUCROSE GRADIENT FRACTIONS

Solution

10 mM Pipes, pH 7.2: To make 500 ml, add 5 ml of 1 *M* Pipes stock solution, pH 7.2, to distilled water and complete to 500 ml. Store at 4°C.

Steps

1. Dilute 1 to 2×10^7 centrosomes from each fraction with 1 ml of 10 m*M* Pipes buffer, pH 7.2, and sediment them by centrifugation with a 2-MK Sigma centrifuge at 15,000 rpm for 10 min.

2. Remove all of the supernatant, resuspend the centrosomal pellets in a known volume of Laemmli sample buffer (Laemmli, 1970), and heat each tube for 5 min in boiling water. A short centrifugation is sometimes necessary to remove residual insoluble materials.

3. Analyze the fractions by conventional electrophoresis technique on a 6–15% SDS–PAGE gradient (Fig. 2B).

4. Stain the gel by the classic silver nitrate staining method.

E. FUNCTIONAL ASSAY OF ISOLATED CENTROSOMES

Isolated centrosomes are usually tested for their capacity to promote the nucleation of microtubules. α/β-Tubulin dimers were purified from bovine or porcine brain using temperature-dependent polymerization/depolymerization cycles, followed by a phosphocellulose column.

Solutions

1. *Purified tubulin solution at 2.5 mg/ml.*

2. *1 M Pipes, pH 6.8, stock solution:* To make 200 ml, add 60.5 g of Pipes to distilled water, adjust pH to 6.8 with 10 *N* KOH, and complete the volume to 200 ml. Store at 4°C.

3. *1 M MgCl₂ stock solution:* To make 100 ml, add 5.84 g of $MgCl_2$ to distilled water. Store at 4°C.

4. *0.2 M EGTA stock solution:* To make 200 ml, solubilize 15.2 g of EGTA in distilled water, adjust the pH to 7 with NaOH, and complete the volume to 200 ml.

5. *RG2 buffer:* 80 m*M* Pipes, pH 6.8, 1 m*M* $MgCl_2$, 1 m*M* EGTA. To make 1 liter, add 80 ml of 1 *M* Pipes stock solution, pH 7.2, 1 ml of 1 *M* $MgCl_2$ stock solution, and 5 ml of 0.2 *M* EGTA stock solution to distilled water, check the pH, and adjust the volume to 1 liter. Store at 4°C.

6. *0.2 M GTP stock solution:* Solubilize 1 g of GTP in 9.5 ml of distilled water. Adjust the pH to 7 with NaOH. Store as aliquots at −20°C.

7. *RG1 buffer:* RG2 buffer + 1 m*M* GTP. To make 2 ml, add 10 μl of 0.2 *M* GTP stock solution to 1.990 ml of RG2 buffer. Prepare fresh and maintain at 4°C.

8. *1% (v/v) Glutaraldehyde solution:* To make 1.2 ml, add 48 μl of 25% glutaraldehyde to 1.152 ml of RG1. Prepare fresh and maintain at room temperature.

9. *25% (v/v) Glycerol solution:* To make 40 ml, add 10 ml of pure glycerol solution to 30 ml of RG2 buffer. Prepare fresh and maintain at 4°C.

10. *1% (v/v) Triton X-100 solution:* To make 10 ml, add 0.1 ml of pure Triton X-100 to 9.9 ml of RG2 buffer. Prepare fresh and maintain at 4°C.

Steps

1. Add to an Eppendorf tube 50 μl of tubulin solution, 5 μl of centrosomes (containing 2 to 5 × 10^5 centrosomes), and 10 μl of RG1 buffer. Store the Eppendorf tube at 4°C.

2. Place the mixture at 37°C for 8 min.

3. Add 200 μl of the 1% glutaraldehyde solution, and place the tube at 25°C for 3 min.

4. Place the tube on ice and add 1 ml of RG2 cold buffer.

5. Prepare 15-ml Corex tubes with corresponding adapters and glass coverslips (Evans *et al.*, 1985). Fill them with 5 ml of the glycerol 25% solution. Overlay this solution with the nucleated microtubule sample and sediment the asters at 20,000 g (10,000 rpm) for 10 min with the JS 13.1 rotor in a Beckman J2-21M/E centrifuge at 4°C.

6. Aspirate 1 ml from the top of the Corex tube and replace it with 1 ml of the 1% Triton X-100 solution.

7. Remove all of the 5 ml of glycerol solution leaving just 1 ml of the Triton X-100 solution over the coverslip, and recover the latter from the Corex tube. Classically, a double immunofluorescence experiment (see Section B) is run to detect the centrosomes and microtubule asters (Fig. 3).

IV. Comments

The method described here is based on lysis of cells in very low ionic strength buffer to separate the centrosome from the nucleus after disassembly of microfilament and microtubule cytoskeletal networks. We have eliminated EDTA from all steps of centrosome isolation as we have observed that the structure of centrosomes is affected by this agent (see Paintrand *et al.*, 1992; Moudjou and Bornens, 1992). This method may be modified for each cell type, and preliminary tests of cell lysis in various ionic strength buffers is warranted before undertaking centrosome isolation. As seen in Fig. 1B, the electrophoretic profile of sucrose gradient fractions varies from bottom to top. Some proteins appear specially in the top of the gradient (from fractions 8 and 9). The presence of these proteins correlates with the appearance of centrosome aggregates associated in a large network. The biochemical nature of this network is not understood and could correspond to fodrin aggregates or intermediate or actomyosin filaments. Indeed, vimentin, fodrin, and myosin heavy chain (and other polypeptides) begin to be detected in fractions 8 and 9. Fractions 5, 6, and 7 contain at least 70% of the total centrosomes recovered in the sucrose gradient. Immunofluorescence, ultrastructural, and biochemical analyses have led us to conclude that these fractions are the most representative of isolated centrosomes from KE37 human lymphoblastic cells. Transmission electron microscopic analysis of fractions 5 and 6 showed that their main constituent is centrosomes distributed in a homogenous fashion (see Paintrand *et al.*, 1992). For any stringent biochemical study of a new centrosomal component, it is necessary to work with only these fractions. The isolated centrosomes can be stored at −80°C for many months. They maintain their capacity to nucleate microtubules (Fig. 3) and to pro-

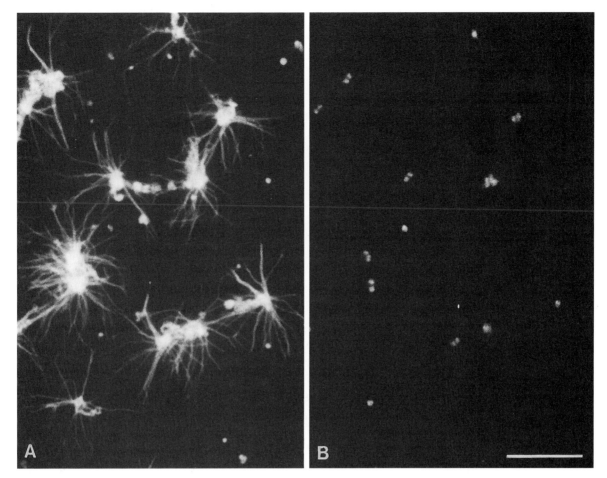

FIGURE 3 Functional assay of isolated centrosomes. Microtubule nucleating activity of isolated centrosomes was tested as described in Section V. After sedimentation on the glass coverslip, aster microtubules were labeled with anti-α-tubulin monoclonal antibody (A) and the centrosomes were detected with an anticentrosome antibody (B). Note that only one centrosome was usually present at the center of each aster. The bright isolated dots in A correspond to tubulin aggregates. Bar = 10 μm.

mote parthenogenetic development after injection into *Xenopus* eggs (Tournier *et al.*, 1991). Finally, convergence between biochemical studies of isolated centrosomes, or related structures, and genetic approaches in appropriate systems will be the key to unraveling the interesting aspects of centrosomal function.

V. Pitfalls

1. The state of cells before centrosome isolation is critical to the quality of centrosomal fractions. Cells must be in the exponential phase of growth (8×10^5 to 1×10^6 cells/ml).

2. To avoid contamination of solution stored at 4°C or at room temperature, 1 mM sodium azide should be added.

3. All solutions must be filtered through a 0.22-μm filter, except for sucrose solutions, which must be sterilized with an autoclave at 105°C.

4. It is important to have a conventional method to recognize the side of the

coverslip on which the material was sedimented for immunofluorescence experiments. Make sure that the coverslips never dry.

ACKNOWLEDGMENTS

We thank Dr. Spencer Brown for checking the English version. The excellent technical assistance of C. Celati is gratefully acknowledged. This work was supported by CNRS, Ligue Nationale de Lutte contre le Cancer, and Fondation pour la Recherche Medicale (FRM). M. Moudjou is the recipient of a postdoctoral fellowship from Association pour la Recherche sur le Cancer (ARC).

REFERENCES

Bornens, M. (1992) Structure and functions of isolated centrosomes. *In* "The Centrosome" (V. I. Kalnins, ed.), pp. 1–43. Academic Press, New York.

Bornens, M., Paintrand, M., Marty, M. C., and Karsenti, E. (1987) Structural and chemical characterization of isolated centrosomes. *Cell Motil. Cytosk.* **8**, 238–249.

Evans, L., Mitchison, T. J., and Kirschner, M. W. (1985) Influence of centrosome on the structure of nucleated microtubules. *J. Cell Biol.* **100**, 1185–1191.

Huang, B. (1990) Genetics and biochemistry of centrosomes and spindle poles. *Curr. Opin. Cell Biol.* **2**, 28–32.

Kalt, A., and Schliwa, M. (1993) Molecular components of the centrosome. *Trends Cell Biol.* **3**, 118–128.

Komesli, S., Tournier, F., Paintrand, M., Margolis, R. L., Job, D., and Bornens, M. (1989) Mass isolation of calf thymus centrosomes: Identification of a specific configuration. *J. Cell Biol.* **109**, 2869–2878.

Laemmli, U. K. (1970) Cleavage of structural proteins during the assembly of the head of bacteriophage T4. *Nature* **227**, 680–685.

Mitchison, T. J., and Kirschner, M. W. (1986) Isolation of mammalian centrosomes. *In* "Methods in Enzymology" (R. B. Vallee, ed.), Vol. 134, pp. 261–268. Academic Press, San Diego.

Moudjou, M., and Bornens, M. (1992) Is the centrosome a dynamic structure? *Compt. Rend. Acad. Sci. (Paris)* **315**, 527–534.

Paintrand, M., Moudjou, M., Delacroix, H., and Bornens, M. (1992) Centrosome organization and centriole architecture: Their sensitivity to divalent cations. *J. Struct. Biol.* **108**, 107–128.

Raff, J. W., Kellogg, D. R., and Alberts, B. A. (1993) Drosophila γ-tubulin is part of a complex containing two previously identified centrosomal MAPs. *J. Cell Biol.* **121**, 823–835.

Rout, M. P., and Kilmartin, J. V. (1990) Components of the yeast spindle and spindle pole body. *J. Cell Biol.* **11**, 1913–1927.

Tournier, F., Komesli, S., Paintrand, M., Job, D., and Bornens, M. (1991) The intercentriolar linkage is critical for the ability of heterologous centrosomes to induce parthenogenesis in *Xenopus*. *J. Cell Biol.* **113**, 1361–1369.

Preparation of Yeast Spindle Pole Bodies

Michael P. Rout and John V. Kilmartin

I. Introduction

Spindle pole bodies (SPBs) are the sole microtubule organizing centers of budding yeast cells. SPBs are embedded in the nuclear envelope, which remains intact during mitosis; thus, spindles are intranuclear (Fig. 1). SPBs can be enriched 600-fold and obtained in high yield from *Saccharomyces uvarum* (Rout and Kilmartin, 1990). The procedure involves preparation of nuclei by a modification of an existing method (Rozijn and Tonino, 1964). The nuclei are then lysed and extracted to free the SPBs from the nuclear envelope, followed by two gradient steps to separate the SPBs from other nuclear components. These SPBs, which are about 10% pure, have been used to prepare monoclonal antibodies and thereby identify components of the SPB and spindle (Rout and Kilmartin, 1990, 1991).

II. Materials and Instrumentation

All catalogue numbers are in parentheses. Anti-foam B (A-5757), sorbitol (S-1876), PVP-40 (PVP-40), pepstatin (P-4265), PMSF (P-7626), digitonin (D-1407), DNase I (DN-EP), RNase A (R-5503), GTP (G-5884), bistris (B-9754), and EGTA (E-4378) were obtained from Sigma. Ficoll 400 (17-0400-01) and Percoll (17-0891-01) were from Pharmacia. Triton X-100 (30632), glucose (10117), and DMSO (10323) were obtained from BDH, and sucrose (5503UA) from Gibco-BRL. Yeast extract (1896) was obtained from Beta Lab, and bactopeptone (0118-08-1) from Difco. Glusulase (NEE-154) was obtained from Du Pont, zymolyase 20T (120491) from Seikagaku, and SP 299 from Novo. (mutanase is no longer commercially available). Liquid malt extract was obtained from a local health food store.

Foam stoppers (FPP6) to seal the neck of the fermenter flasks were from Scientific Instruments. *Saccharomyces uvarum* (NCYC 74) was from The National Collection of Yeast Cultures. Centrifuge tubes (SW 28 Ultraclear, 344058, and 70 Ti, 355654) were obtained from Beckman. The hemocytometer (AC-1) was obtained from Weber Scientific, the continuous-flow centrifuge (KA 1-06-525) from Westfalia, the Polytron (PT 10/35 with PTA 10S probe) from Kinematica, and the refractometer (144974) from Zeiss.

III. Procedures

A. PREPARATION OF NUCLEI FROM *Saccharomyces uvarum*

Solutions

The following solutions are required for processing 36 liters of yeast cells.

1. *Cold distilled water, 5 liters.*

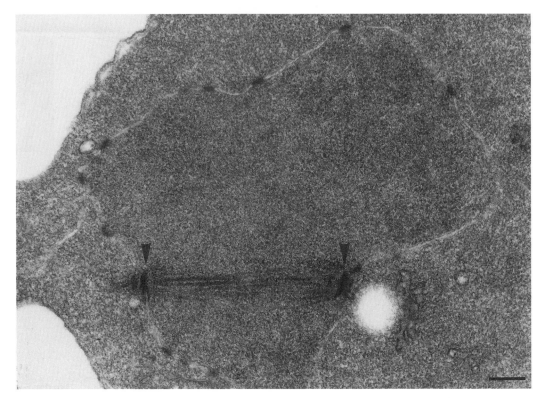

FIGURE 1 Electron micrograph of a thin section of a diploid yeast intranuclear mitotic spindle. Arrowheads show the two SPBs. Bar = 0.2 μm.

2. *1.1 M Sorbitol:* To make 2 liters, dissolve 400 g sorbitol in distilled water and make up to 2 liters. Store at 4°C.

3. *7.5% Ficoll 400 in 1.1 M sorbitol:* To prepare 400 ml, dissolve 30 g Ficoll 400 in 1.1 M sorbitol (it dissolves very slowly), and make up to 400 ml. Store at 4°C.

4. *8% PVP:* To prepare 1 liter, dissolve 80 g PVP-40, 1.57 g KH_2PO_4, 1.46 g K_2HPO_4, and 152 mg $MgCl_2 \cdot 6H_2O$ in distilled water, check the pH and adjust to 6.53 (it usually needs 15 μl of concentrated H_3PO_4), and make up to 1 liter. Store at 4°C. Prepare 1.5 liters if also making up sucrose solutions.

5. *Solution P:* Dissolve 2 mg pepstatin A and 90 mg PMSF in 5 ml absolute ethanol. Store at 4°C and discard after 3 weeks. Note that PMSF is highly poisonous.

6. *20% Triton X-100:* Dissolve 20 g Triton X-100 in distilled water and make up to 100 ml. Store at −20°C; retain a small aliquot at 4°C.

7. *Sucrose solutions for the gradient:* Prepare the sucrose solutions by weighing out sucrose and 8% PVP solution in a beaker and dissolve by stirring the beaker in a large petri dish of hot water. When the sucrose has dissolved, remove it from the hot water and measure the refractive index (RI). Continue stirring and adding 8% PVP until the correct refractive index is obtained (within 0.0003). Store in 50-ml sterile tubes at −20°C. For 2.01 M sucrose, weigh out 183.3 g sucrose and add 8% PVP solution to 338 g in total, then adjust to a final RI of 1.4370. For 2.10 M sucrose, weigh out 193 g sucrose and add 8% PVP to a total of 340 g (final RI 1.4420). For 2.30 M sucrose, weigh out 216 g sucrose and add 8% PVP to a total of 340 g (final RI 1.4540).

8. *Wickerham's medium:* Prepare Wickerman's medium 10× concentrated.

Dissolve 108 g malt extract, 108 g yeast extract, 180 g bactopeptone, and 360 g glucose in 3.6 liters distilled water; remove turbidity by centrifuging 10,000 g for 10 min. Dilute the supernatant 10-fold.

Steps

1. Two days before preparation of the nuclei prepare the concentrated Wickerham's medium to grow the yeast cells. The cells can be grown in a commercial fermenter or using the simple system described below. Dispense 9 liters of diluted medium into four 10-liter glass Pyrex bottles containing a heavy magnetic stirrer. Add 2 ml of Anti-foam B (use a disposable plastic pipette). Prepare a glass aeration tube by attaching a small plastic vial with four or five needle-sized holes in the bottom to one end of the glass tube via a rubber stopper or thick-walled rubber tubing. Attach a glass-fiber filter on the inlet of the aeration tube using rubber tubing. Cut halfway into a foam stopper slightly larger than the diameter of the neck of the flask and use this to position the aeration tube and to seal the flask. Seal the stopper and the filter at the end of the aeration tube with aluminum foil; finally, cover both the aeration tube and the top of the flask with a foil cap. Autoclave for 1 hr and 1 hr exhaust.

2. Set up a starter culture from a single yeast colony in 10–20 ml medium and grow at 25°C in a rotating incubator or small bubbler for up to 24 hr until stationary phase is reached (1.0×10^8 cells/ml). Use a hemocytometer to count the cells; use shearing or sonication to break up any clumps of cells.

3. In the afternoon of the day before preparation of the nuclei set up the 10-liter flasks to grow overnight. Aim for 1×10^7 cells/ml in the morning; it is essential to have mid-log-phase cells to prepare good spheroplasts. To calculate the number of starter cells to add, first work out the number of hours the cells will grow at log phase. If the starter cells are in stationary phase (1×10^8 cells/ml) subtract one doubling time (1.75 hr for *S. uvarum*) to allow for the lag period of growth. Divide the number of hours of log-phase growth by the doubling time to give the number of divisions (d). Then the number of cells needed is the final number of cells divided by 2^d (2^d = antilog $d/3.32$).

4. Transfer these cells by sterile technique to the 10-liter flasks and place in a water bath set at 25°C (the depth of water need be no more than 25 cm). Place magnetic stirrers under the bath to stir the flasks during growth, connect the aeration tube to a compressed air source and water bubbler to humidify the air, and position the aeration tube so that the bubbles of air are blown at the rotating stirring bar and thereby dispersed throughout the flask. The quality of aeration can be checked by growing one culture to stationary phase; it should reach a cell count of 1×10^8 cells/ml.

5. Harvest the cells using a Westfalia continuous-flow centrifuge or in individual centrifuge pots; spin at 3000 g for 5 min (all centrifugation steps are at 4°C).

6. Combine the pellets in one 500-ml centrifuge pot and wash twice with cold distilled water, resuspend the pellet in 1.1 M sorbitol using a thick glass rod, and spin at 5500 g for 5 min. Repeat the resuspension and pelleting in 1.1 M sorbitol and finally resuspend in about one pellet volume of sorbitol for spheroplasting. Dilute this suspension 1:100 and count the cells; then adjust the suspension to 1.5×10^9 cells/ml.

7. Add 50 μl glusulase, 20 μl 1% zymolyase 20T, and 3 μl 5% mutanase or SP 299 per milliliter of suspension. The enzyme solutions should be spun beforehand to remove insoluble material. Incubate at 30°C, leaving the top of the centrifuge pot a little loose as some gas is evolved, and mix carefully from time to

---

time. The digestion, which takes 2–4 hr, can be monitored using the hemocytometer by diluting 10 μl of digesting cells in 0.2 ml of sorbitol to determine the proportion of spheroplasts and another 10 μl in 0.2 ml of water to determine the number of completely intact cells. At 1 hr in sorbitol there should be a few spheroplasts and less than 1% live intact cells in water. At about 1.5 hr the spheroplasts become very clumpy and irregular in shape. After further digestion at 2–3 hr they separate into round spheroplasts with some clumps remaining. In water there should be complete lysis with no undigested cells and less than 5×10^4 black cells or ghosts/ml.

8. While the cells are digesting make up the gradient tubes: 12 Beckman Ultraclear SW 28 tubes or equivalent for a 36-liter prep, *provided not more than 230 ml of cells have been digested;* otherwise increase the gradient tubes in proportion. Add solution P at 1:1000 to the three sucrose solutions and prepare a step gradient in each tube of 8 ml of 2.30 *M*, 8 ml of 2.10 *M*, and 8 ml of 2.01 *M* sucrose–PVP. Leave the tubes in an ice bucket in the cold room covered with foil.

9. While the cells are digesting calculate the approximate amount of 8% PVP needed to lyse the spheroplasts (see below), then prepare the same volume of 0.6 *M* sucrose–PVP (205.2 g/liter 8% PVP) and enough 1.7 *M* sucrose–PVP (581.4 g/liter 8% PVP) to resuspend the crude nuclei for the gradient (about 12 ml per tube); cool these solutions in ice. Also prepare two to four 100-ml Ficoll cushions in 250-ml clear Sorvall pots. Note that the maximum volume that can be conveniently lysed in a 250-ml pot is 150 ml, so have no more than 1.5×10^{11} diploid spheroplasts in each pot.

10. At the end of the digest add an equal volume of 1.1 *M* sorbitol and pellet the spheroplasts in a swinging bucket centrifuge at 5000 *g* for 20 min. Aspirate off the supernatant, then immediately wash the sides of the tube with sorbitol and aspirate off again. Remove as much enzyme as possible as proteases are present. Resuspend the pellet in the same volume of sorbitol. The spheroplasts are *very fragile* so be very careful to avoid lysis: use a thick glass rod to partially resuspend as lumps, then gently shake in ice on a rotating shaker. Use the glass rod occasionally to disperse the lumps.

11. When the cells are resuspended overlay 0.2 ml onto 0.4 ml 7.5% Ficoll in 1.1 *M* sorbitol in a small glass test tube to check that the cells are not too dense to overlay; if the cells fall through the Ficoll dilute them further until they do not. Then overlay the cells onto the 100-ml cushions of 7.5% Ficoll in 1.1 *M* sorbitol in 250-ml clear centrifuge pots. Spin in a swinging bucket centrifuge at 5000 *g* for 20 min.

12. Aspirate the supernatant down to the Ficoll layer, then wash the sides of the pot several times with sorbitol, aspirating each time to remove as much of the enzyme-containing supernatant as possible. Finally, aspirate down through the Ficoll layer to the pellet and wash the sides of the tube with 8% PVP and aspirate that.

13. Add 10 ml 8% PVP, 60 μl solution P, and 12 μl 20% Triton X-100 per 10^{10} spheroplasts. First use the Polytron probe at low speed first to resuspend the pellet. Then increase the speed setting up to 3.5 and Polytron throughout the solution for 1 min, and also drag the probe across the bottom of the pot during this time to try to resuspend as much of the pellet as possible. Place the pot in ice and remove a 5-μl sample to observe by phase-contrast microscopy at a magnification of about 1000×. There should be *complete* cell lysis, plenty of nuclei that look like small perfectly round black balls often with a slightly darker crescent region, and vacuoles that look like white balls the same size as nuclei. The presence of vacuoles is a reassuring sign that the correct quantity of Triton

has been added, i.e., enough to lyse the spheroplasts without disrupting too many other membranes. Unlysed spheroplasts are highly swollen with a prominent vacuole. Check to see what proportion of nuclei are trapped in lysed but undispersed cells. Repeat the Polytron step for a further 1 min. If there is a large proportion of trapped nuclei or unlysed cells then extend the time of the Polytron treatment. In case there is any cell pellet left, decant the lysed cells into clean centrifuge pots or a cold conical and add an equal volume of cold 0.6 M sucrose–PVP, mix carefully, and spin in a 6×250-ml anglehead rotor for 10 min at 10,000 g. Note that the Polytron and spin steps must be completed *as fast as possible,* as after lysis the nuclei slowly clump, trapping cytoplasmic debris and thereby contaminating the gradient.

14. Retain the supernatant from the spin to check that the nuclei have pelleted, resuspend the nuclei in cold 1.7 M sucrose–PVP (12 ml per SW 28 tube) using the Polytron at low speed (try also to resuspend any nuclei that have been daubed up the side of the tube by the spin), and load the gradient tubes with about 15 ml using either a measuring cylinder or a 10-ml pipette. Weigh the tubes and balance by overlaying with 1.0 M sucrose–PVP; spin at 28,000 rpm for 4 hr.

15. The nuclei band mainly at the 2.10/2.30 M layer. Unload by aspirating down from the top, wiping the top part of the tube with tissue as you go down. If the wad of material at the top is particularly thick scoop it out with the end of the Pasteur pipette. Stop at the 2.01/2.10 M interface for the first tube only and remove 5 μl (wipe the sides of the tip to remove sucrose) to check by phase-contrast microscopy if there are significant quantities of nuclei (usually there are a few but they are too contaminated with debris to be of much use), and also check the 2.10 M layer. Aspirate down to just above the nuclear band in the 2.10/2.30 M layer, then quickly wipe the sides of the tube with the rolled up tissue, paying particular attention to that part where the main band was at the sample to 2.01 M interface. Try to get as close to the nuclei as possible as osmiophilic membranes probably from the plasma membrane are concentrated in the 2.10 M layer. Ring the nuclei layer with the sealed off Pasteur pipette to separate it from the walls of the tube, then suck off with a 10-ml pipette, going down partially into the 2.30 M layer to remove as many nuclei as possible. Do not get too close to the pellet containing empty cell walls. Store the nuclei at $-70°C$; they seem to be very stable to storage at this temperature.

B. PREPARATION OF SPINDLE POLE BODIES

Solutions

1. *0.9 M sucrose–PVP:* Dissolve 30.8 g sucrose in 8% PVP and make up to 100 ml. Store at $-20°C$.

2. *0.01 M Bistris–HCl, pH 6.5, 0.1 mM MgCl$_2$ (bt buffer).* Prepare a 0.1 M stock of bistris; dissolve 20.9 g bistris in distilled water, adjust the pH to 6.5 with concentrated HCl, and make up to 100 ml. Store at $-20°C$. To prepare 100 ml bt buffer, add 10 ml 0.1 M bistris, pH 6.5, and 10 μl 1 M MgCl$_2$ (dissolve 0.2 g MgCl$_2$ in a total of 1 ml water) to 90 ml of distilled water.

3. *Sucrose solutions in bt buffer:* Prepare stock 2.50 M sucrose in bt buffer (214 g/250 ml) as described above for the sucrose–PVP solutions; the refractive index should be 1.4533. Prepare 1.75, 2.00, and 2.25 M sucrose–bt solutions by dilution of the stock 2.50 M solution with bt buffer; the final refractive indices should be 1.4174, 1.4295, and 1.4414, respectively. Add a 1:1000 dilution of solution P just before pouring the gradient. Store at $-20°C$.

4. *Nuclear lysis solution:* To prepare 10 ml, add 0.2 g digitonin and 0.15 ml Triton X-100 to 2 ml DMSO and about 1 ml distilled water (wear gloves as digitonin is toxic). Microwave to almost boiling, then stir to dissolve the digitonin. Make up to 10 ml in a measuring cylinder by slowly adding distilled water down the side of the cylinder without mixing; add 1 μl 1 M MgCl$_2$. Place the solution in the cold room and mix immediately before use; it should be a clear solution.

5. *2% DNase I:* Dissolve 5 mg of DNase I in 0.25 ml 0.25 M sucrose, 0.05 M triethanolamine, pH 7.4, 0.25 M KCl, 5 mM MgCl$_2$. Store at $-20°$C.

6. *RNase A:* Dissolve 2 mg RNase A in 1 ml of distilled water.

7. *DMSO buffer:* Prepare this buffer immediately before use. Prepare stocks of 0.1 M GTP (dissolve 55 mg GTP in 1 ml water, store at $-20°$C); 0.1 M EGTA (dissolve 3.8 g EGTA in 100 ml water and adjust the pH to 7.0 with 10 N NaOH); and 1.0 M DTT (dissolve 154 mg DTT in 1 ml water, store at $-20°$C). To prepare 300 ml of DMSO buffer, use 30 ml 0.1 M bistris, pH 6.5, 30 μl 1.0 M MgCl$_2$, 300 μl 0.1 M GTP, 300 μl 0.1 M EGTA, pH 7.0, 30 μl 1.0 M DTT, 300 μl solution P, and 60 ml DMSO, and make up to 300 ml with distilled water. Cool in ice.

8. *bt–DMSO buffer:* To prepare 100 ml, use 10 ml 0.1 M bistris, pH 6.5, 10 μl 1.0 M MgCl$_2$, 100 μl solution P, and 20 ml DMSO, and make up to 100 ml with distilled water. Cool in ice.

Steps

1. Pellet the nuclei by first decreasing the sucrose concentration from about 2.4 to 2.1 M (refractive index 1.434) by addition of 0.9 M sucrose–PVP. Mix very thoroughly by shaking. Calculate the total number of ODs of nuclei by measuring the OD at 260 nm of 10 μl nuclei in 1 ml of 1% SDS (10^{10} nuclei is about 100 OD$_{260\ nm}$). Decant the nuclei into Beckman 70 Ti tubes or equivalent. Six tubes are usually enough for nuclei from 3×10^{11} spheroplasts. Mix the tubes thoroughly again; any unmixed sucrose will prevent proper pelleting of the nuclei. Spin the 70 Ti tubes in a 70 Ti rotor at 40,000 rpm for 1 hr. After spinning, immediately remove the supernatant by aspiration, being careful not to disturb the pellet. These pellets can be stored in the tubes at $-70°$C until needed.

2. Prepare the gradients in Beckman SW 28 Ultraclear tubes. Four tubes are usually enough. Each tube contains 2.5 ml 2.50 M sucrose–bt, 7.5 ml 2.25 M sucrose–bt, 5.0 ml 2.00 M sucrose–bt, and 5.0 ml 1.75 M sucrose–bt. Place tubes in ice.

3. To lyse the nuclei thaw the 70 Ti tubes containing the nuclei pellets (if frozen), aspirate any residual sucrose–PVP, and place in ice. Add 1.0 ml nuclear lysis solution, 10 μl solution P, and 1 μl 2% DNase I for each 100 OD$_{260\ nm}$ in the nuclear pellets, and resuspend at 4°C by whirl-mixing vigorously until about a minute after the last traces of pellet have disappeared. The suspension will froth.

4. After resuspension let the tubes stand for 5 min at room temperature, then add an equal volume of 2.5 M sucrose–bt (at room temperature). Shake well and spin in a 70 Ti rotor at 6000 rpm for 6 min. Do not resuspend any pellet that may form at this stage. Distribute the supernatant equally on top of the SW 28 gradients (check on a balance); each gradient tube should be loaded to within 5 mm of its top and overlayered if necessary with 1.0 M sucrose–bt. Spin tubes in an SW 28 rotor at 28,000 rpm for 6 hr.

5. Remove the gradient layers from the top of the tube using a Pasteur pipette, taking special care when removing material from around the sides of the tubes or

at the gradient interfaces. Take off the top layer (sample layer) to within 5 mm of the first interface (sample/1.75 M), then save each interface fraction separately, taking from 5 mm above one interface through to 5 mm above the next. Resuspend the final interface (2.25/2.50 M) and pellet with a sealed Pasteur pipette and whirl-mix before removing. The SPBs should be mainly (~70%) in the 2.00/2.25 M fraction. Store these fractions at $-20°C$.

6. SPBs can be further enriched on a Percoll gradient. For each SW 28 tube add 20 μl of 2 mg/ml RNase A to 2 ml of the 2.00/2.25 M sucrose SPBs and incubate for 15 min at room temperature. Then add in turn, mixing at each step, 7 ml 2.50 M sucrose–bt, 1 ml Percoll, and 4 ml cold DMSO buffer. Cool to 4°C and place in the SW 28 tube, gently overlaying with cold DMSO buffer. Spin at 28,000 rpm for 6 hr.

7. After the spin the SPBs should be visible as a faint band (viewed against a black background) about 1 cm into the gradient. Mark its position on each tube and then collect the gradient solution above it to within 2–3 mm of this band (~3.5 ml), using a Pasteur pipette. This is fraction 1. Collect the next layer (fraction 2), right through the SPB band to about 17 mm from the bottom of the tube (~4.5 ml). This fraction contains 60–70% of the SPBs originally loaded on the gradient. Collect the next 3.5 ml (fraction 3), then whirl-mix the final 2.0 ml and save (fraction 4). Store the fractions at $-20°C$.

8. To pellet the SPB fractions add 3.5 vol of cold bt–DMSO to each, mix well by shaking, and portion between Beckman 70 Ti tubes (about three-quarters full in each). Centrifuge in a 70 Ti rotor at 40,000 rpm for 1 hr. The SPBs pellet as a faint translucent layer on top of a transparent Percoll pellet, and after 5 min on ice this layer slides off the Percoll pellet to the bottom of the tube. Carefully aspirate off the supernatant and recover the delicate SPB layer in about 0.2 ml of liquid per tube. The presence of SPBs can be assayed by Coomassie staining of SDS gradient gels. Comparison of fractions 1–4 should shows the enrichment of the tubulin (55-kDa) and 110-kDa bands associated with the SPBs in fraction 2. Alternatively, immunoblotting with anti-SPB monoclonal antibodies (Rout and Kilmartin, 1990, 1991) could also be used to detect the presence of SPBs. A fast and quantitative assay for SPBs is that by dark-field microscopy (Rout and Kilmartin, 1990).

IV. Comments

This procedure for spindle pole enrichment has also been applied to *Saccharomyces cerevisiae* strains. The extent of enrichment is not as good because these strains do not spheroplast as well as *S. uvarum*, leading to contamination of the nuclear band with cells. In addition these strains do not appear to disperse their cellular contents during lysis as well as *S. uvarum*, leading to further contamination of the nuclear layer with large aggregated cytoplasmic masses. The lower quality of the nuclei leads to a corresponding decrease in the quality of the SPBs; however, these SPB preparations from *S. cerevisiae* can be very useful for observing the morphology of large numbers of SPBs.

V. Pitfalls

1. The quality of the spheroplast preparation largely determines the quality of the subsequent nuclear preparation. The amount of glusulase added seems to be crucial: the amount given for this protocol is a minimum for reasons of expense;

thus any problems to do with spheroplast quality can probably be cured by addition of more glusulase.

2. The nuclear sucrose gradient is very sensitive to the presence of excess amounts of empty partially digested cell walls. These appear to aggregate at the nuclear band (2.1/2.3 M sucrose–PVP) forming a solid mass, making it impossible to unload the nuclei. It is important to adhere to the loading limits suggested in the protocol for nuclei.

3. The type of digitonin seems to be important in successful nuclear extraction; always use a water-soluble type.

REFERENCES

Rout, M. P., and Kilmartin, J. V. (1990) Components of the yeast spindle and spindle pole body. *J. Cell Biol.* **111**, 1913–1927.
Rout, M. P., and Kilmartin, J. V. (1991) Yeast spindle pole body components. *Cold Spring Harbor Symp. Quant. Biol.* **56**, 687–691.
Rozijn, Th. H., and Tonino, G. J. M. (1964) Studies on the yeast nucleus. I. The isolation of nuclei. *Biochim. Biophys. Acta* **91**, 105–112.

Preparation of Nuclei and Nuclear Envelopes: Identification of an Integral Membrane Protein Unique to the Nuclear Envelope

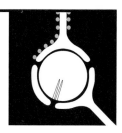

Einar Hallberg

I. Introduction

During interphase the chromatin of eukaryotic cells is surrounded by a nuclear envelope (NE) (Fig. 1). The NE consists of three morphologically and biochemically distinct domains. The outer nuclear membrane (ONM) with its attached ribosomes is continuous with the rough endoplasmic reticulum (RER). The inner nuclear membrane (INM) aligns the inner surface of the nucleoplasm and is attached to a network of intermediate filament proteins called the nuclear lamina. At numerous circumscribed points, referred to as the pore membrane domain (PMD), the ONM and INM are connected to each other, forming circular nuclear pores. The nuclear pores harbor the large multiprotein structures called nuclear pore complexes (NPCs). One of the principal functions of the nuclear envelope is to serve as ports of entry of soluble and integral membrane proteins destined for the nucleoplasm and nuclear membranes, respectively.

Their uniformity in size and density makes it possible to isolate pure intact nuclei at high yields from tissue homogenates by centrifugation through a sucrose cushion (Blobel and Potter, 1966). Nuclei prepared in such a manner can be used as a source for isolation of nuclear components or in various *in vitro* studies of nuclear transport or mitotic disassembly.

NEs can be prepared from isolated nuclei by enzymatic degradation of their nucleic acid content (Dwyer and Blobel, 1976). The resulting NEs are structurally well conserved with attached ribosomes, NPCs, and nuclear lamina. Further fractionation of the NEs has been very useful for the identification and localization of proteins of the NE (Dwyer and Blobel, 1976; Gerace *et al.*, 1982; Davis and Blobel, 1986; Snow *et al.*, 1987; Senior and Gerace, 1988; Hallberg *et al.*, 1993).

II. Materials and Instrumentation

Filters (0.45 μm, Cat. No. HAWP04700) are obtained from Millipore. SW 28 and Ti 100 tubes are obtained from Beckman Instruments. HB-4 tubes (Sorvall) are obtained from the Du Pont Company. Chemicals should be of analytical grade. PMSF (Cat. No. P7626), DNase I (Cat. No. DN-25), and RNase (Cat. No. R4875) are obtained from Sigma Chemical Company. DTT (Cat. No. 709000) is obtained from Boehringer-Mannheim.

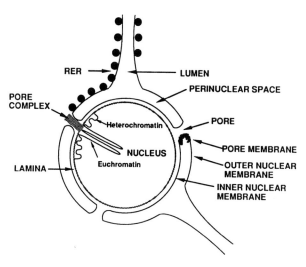

FIGURE 1 Schematic representation of the interface nucleus.

III. Procedures

A. PREPARATION OF NUCLEI FROM RAT LIVER

Solutions

1. *Stock 2.5 M sucrose (85% w/v):* To make 1 liter, dissolve 850 g of sucrose in distilled water and adjust to a total volume of 1 liter. Allow a day for dissolution (at 60°C) and filtration of the sucrose. Store at 4°C.

2. *Stock 2 M KCl:* Filter. To make 1 liter, dissolve 74.5 g of KCl in distilled water and adjust to a total volume of 1 liter. Filter and store at 4°C.

3. *Stock 1 M triethanolamine–HCl, pH 7.5:* Filter. To make 1 liter, dissolve 185 g of triethanolamine–HCl in distilled water, adjust pH with HCl, and dilute to a total volume of 1 liter. Filter and store at 4°C.

4. *Stock 1 M MgCl$_2$:* Filter. To make 1 liter, dissolve 95.2 g of MgCl$_2$ in distilled water and adjust to a total volume of 1 liter. Filter and store at 4°C.

5. *Stock 0.1 M PMSF in ethanol:* Prepare fresh. To make 10 ml, dissolve 174 mg of PMSF in 10 ml of ethanol. Keep on ice 4°C.

6. *Stock 1 M DTT:* Prepare fresh. To make 10 ml, dissolve 1.54 g of DTT in distilled water. Keep on ice. The DTT will form a precipitate, which has to be dissolved by moderate heating just before use.

7. *0.25 M STEAKM (0.25 M sucrose, 25 mM KCl, 50 mM triethanolamine–HCl, pH 7.5, 5 mM MgCl, 0.5 mM PMSF, 1 mM DTT):* To make 1 liter, mix 230 ml of 2.5 M sucrose, 12.5 ml 2 M KCl, 50 ml 1 M triethanolamine–HCl, pH 7.5, 5 ml of 1 M MgCl$_2$, 1 ml 1 M DTT, and 5 ml 0.1 M PMSF. Adjust to 1 liter and keep on ice.

8. *2.3 M STEAKM (2.3 M sucrose, 25 mM KCl, 50 mM triethanolamine–HCl, pH 7.5, 5 mM MgCl, 0.5 mM PMSF, 1 mM DTT).* To make 250 ml, mix 230 ml 2.5 M sucrose, 3.125 ml 2 M KCl, 12.5 ml 1 M triethanolamine–HCl, pH 7.5, 1.25 ml MgCl$_2$, 250 μl 1 M DTT, and 1.25 ml 0.1 M PMSF. Adjust to 1 liter and keep on ice.

Steps

1. Trim fat from livers of six 150- to 200-g starved Sprague–Dawley rats and chop into small (~1–2 mm) pieces using two razor blades.

2. Make a 30% homogenate (15 strokes) in solution 7 using a tight-fitting Potter–Elvehjem homogenizer.

3. Filter the homogenate through four layers of cheesecloth, add 5 μl of solution 6 per milliliter of homogenate, and spin in a HB-4 rotor for 15 min at 2300 rpm (800 g).

4. Remove the supernatant, homogenize the large and loose pellet in a clean Potter–Elvehjem homogenizer, and dilute to 40 ml in solution 7.

5. Add exactly 2 vol (80 ml) of solution 8, mix well, and layer on top of 5 ml solution 8 in SW 28 tubes. Disrupt the interface a little bit with a Pasteur pipette, fill up the tubes completely, and balance. Spin at 27,000 rpm (124,000 g) in an SW 28 rotor for 1 hr at 4°C.

6. Discard the supernatant by inverting the tubes. Cut the tubes right above the pellet, which should appear white. Harvest the pellet with a spatula, resuspend in ~20 ml of solution 7, and homogenize (only a few strokes are necessary).

7. Spin the suspension in an HB-4 rotor at 15 min at 2300 rpm (800 g). Resuspend the nuclei again in ~10 ml of solution 7 and measure the OD at 260 nm (1 $OD_{260\,nm}$ represents 3×10^6 isolated rat liver nuclei). The yield is typically between 200 and 300 $OD_{260\,nm}$ per rat liver. The purified nuclei can be used immediately or be stored at −70°C as a pellet.

B. PREPARATION OF NUCLEAR ENVELOPES FROM RAT LIVER NUCLEI

Solutions

1. *Stock 2.5 M sucrose (85% w/v):* to make 1 liter, dissolve 850 g of sucrose in distilled water and adjust to a total volume of 1 liter. Allow a day for dissolution (at 60°C) and filtration of the sucrose. Store at 4°C.

2. *Stock 1 M MgCl$_2$:* Filter. To make 1 liter, dissolve 95.2 g of MgCl$_2$ in distilled water and adjust to a total volume of 1 liter. Filter and store at 4°C.

3. *Stock 1 M triethanolamine–HCl, pH 7.5:* Filter. To make 1 liter, dissolve 185 g of triethanolamine–HCl in distilled water, adjust pH with HCl, and dilute to a total volume of 1 liter. Filter and store at 4°C.

4. *Stock 1 M triethanolamine–HCl, pH 8.5:* Filter. To make 1 liter, dissolve 185 g of triethanolamine–HCl in distilled water, adjust pH with HCl, and dilute to a total volume of 1 liter. Filter and store at 4°C.

5. *Stock 0.1 M PMSF in ethanol:* Prepare fresh. To make 10 ml, dissolve 174 mg of PMSF in 10 ml of ethanol. Keep on ice 4°C.

6. *Stock 1 M DTT:* Prepare fresh. To make 10 ml, dissolve 1.54 g of DTT in distilled water. Keep on ice. The DTT will form a precipitate, which has to be dissolved by moderate heating just before use.

7. *0.1 mM MgCl$_2$, 1 mM DTT, 0.1 mM PMSF:* To make 100 ml, mix 10 ml 1 M MgCl$_2$, 100 μl 1 M DTT, and 100 μl 0.1 M PMSF, and dilute to 100 ml with distilled water. Keep on ice.

8. *10% sucrose, 20 mM triethanolamine, pH 7.5, 0.1 mM MgCl$_2$, 1 mM DTT, 0.1 mM PMSF:* Make up just prior to use. To make 250 ml, mix 29.4 ml 2.5 M sucrose, 5 ml 1 M triethanolamine–HCl, pH 7.5, 25 μl 1 M MgCl$_2$, 250 μl 1 M DTT, and 250 μl 0.1 M PMSF. Adjust the volume to 250 ml with distilled water.

9. *10% sucrose, 20 mM triethanolamine, pH 8.5, 0.1 mM MgCl$_2$, 1 mM DTT, 0.1 mM PMSF:* Make up just prior to use. To make 250 ml, mix 29.4 ml

2.5 M sucrose, 5 ml 1 M triethanolamine–HCl, pH 8.5, 25 μl 1 M MgCl$_2$, 250 μl 1 M DTT, and 250 μl 0.1 M PMSF. Adjust the volume to 250 ml with distilled water.

10. *30% sucrose, 20 mM triethanolamine, pH 7.5, 0.1 mM MgCl$_2$, 1 mM DTT, 0.1 mM PMSF:* Make up just prior to use. To make 250 ml, mix 88.2 ml 2.5 M sucrose, 5 ml 1 M triethanolamine–HCl, pH 7.5, 25 μl 1 M MgCl$_2$, 250 μl 1 M DTT, and 250 μl 0.1 M PMSF. Adjust the volume to 250 ml with distilled water.

11. *2 mg/ml DNase I:* Dissolve 1 mg DNase I in 500 μl distilled water.

12. *10 μg/ml RNase:* Dissolve 1 mg RNase in 1 ml of distilled water. Dilute 10 μl of this solution to 1 ml.

Steps

1. Suspend 500 OD$_{260\,nm}$ of pelleted rat liver nuclei (Section A) in 5 ml solution 7 by gentle suction up and down in a 10-ml pipette using a pipette aid.

2. Add 20 ml of solution 9 and 25 μl each of solutions 11 and 12. Mix and incubate for 15 min at room temperature.

3. Underlay with 5 ml of solution 10 and spin for 20 min at 10,000 rpm (16,000 g) in an HB-4 rotor at 4°C.

4. Resuspend the pellet in 5 ml solution 8 as in step 1. Add 25 μl each of solutions 11 and 12. Mix and incubate for 15 min at room temperature.

5. Repeat step 3. The pelleted NEs can be suspended or stored frozen as a pellet. One OD$_{260\,nm}$ of rat liver NEs, i.e., the amount of rat liver NEs isolated from 1 OD$_{260\,nm}$ of isolated rat liver nuclei, is equivalent to 10 μg of protein.

C. ANALYSIS OF INTEGRAL AND NONINTEGRAL PROTEINS FROM NUCLEAR ENVELOPES

Solutions

1. *Stock 2.5 M sucrose (85% w/v):* To make 1 liter, dissolve 850 g of sucrose in distilled water and adjust to a total volume of 1 liter. Allow a day for dissolution (at 60°C) and filtration of the sucrose. Store at 4°C.

2. *Stock 1 M triethanolamine–HCl, pH 7.5:* Filter. To make 1 liter, dissolve 185 g of triethanolamine–HCl in distilled water, adjust pH with HCl, and dilute to a total volume of 1 liter. Filter and store at 4°C.

3. *Stock 1 M MgCl$_2$:* Filter. To make 1 liter, dissolve 95.2 g of MgCl$_2$ in distilled water and adjust to a total volume of 1 liter. Filter and store at 4°C.

4. *Stock 8.0 M urea:* Prepare fresh, filter, and keep at room temperature. To make 100 ml, dissolve 480 g urea in distilled water and adjust the volume to 100 ml. Filter and keep at room temperature.

5. *Stock 0.1 M PMSF in ethanol:* Prepare fresh. To make 10 ml, dissolve 174 mg of PMSF in 10 ml of ethanol. Keep on ice 4°C.

6. *Stock 1 M DTT:* Prepare fresh. To make 10 ml, dissolve 1.54 g of DTT in distilled water. Keep on ice. The DTT will form a precipitate, which has to be dissolved by moderate heating just before use.

7. *7 M urea, 20 mM triethanolamine–HCl, pH 7.5, 0.1 mM MgCl$_2$, 0.25 M sucrose, 1 mM DTT, 0.1 mM PMSF:* To make 50 ml, mix 43.75 ml 8 M urea, 1

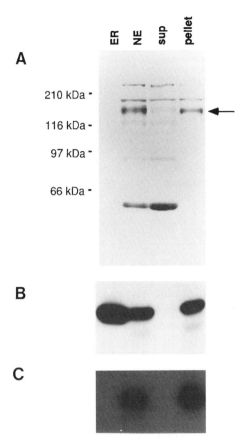

ER **NE** **sup** **pellet**

A

210 kDa -

116 kDa -

97 kDa -

66 kDa -

B

C

FIGURE 2 Identification of p145 as an integral membrane protein that binds to wheat germ agglutinin (WGA) and is unique to the nuclear envelope. A microsomal fraction (ER, 20 μg), a purified nuclear envelope fraction (NE, 20 μg), and equivalent amounts of a 7.0 M urea extract of the NE (sup) and extracted NE (pellet) were subjected to SDS–PAGE. The separated proteins were transferred to nitrocellulose and probed with either (A) WGA, (B) antibodies to the alpha subunit of the signal sequence receptor (SSRa), or (C) monospecific antibodies to p145. p145 is absent from the ER and unique to the NE fraction (A, C). On the other hand, SSRa is present in both the NE and ER fractions, as the ONM of the NE is continuous with the RER (B). Both p145 and SSRa are integral membrane proteins and subsequently remain in the membrane pellet after extraction of the NEs with 7.0 M urea (A–C), whereas the non-membrane-spanning WGA-binding nucleoporins are found in the supernatant (A). Molecular weight standards are indicated on the left. Arrow points to p145. (Reproduced from the Journal of Cell Biology (1993) **122**, 513–521 by permission of the Rockefeller University Press.)

ml 1 M triethanolamine–HCl, pH 7.5, 5 μl 1 M MgCl$_2$, 5 ml 2.5 M sucrose, 50 μl 1 M DTT, and 50 μl 0.1 M PMSF. Adjust to 50 ml and keep at room temperature.

8. *Underlay solution:* To make 10 ml, mix 9 ml solution 7 with 1 ml 2.5 M sucrose. Keep at room temperature.

Steps

1. Pellet 100 OD$_{260\,nm}$ of suspended NEs (see Section B) in a TL-100 tube. Solubilize the pelleted NEs in 1 ml of solution 7 at room temperature by drawing up and down using an automatic pipette. Incubate for 10 min at room temperature.

2. Underlay the extraction with 200 μl of solution 8 and centrifuge at 100,000

rpm (356,000 g) for 20 min at 15°C. The supernatant now contains proteins solubilized by urea, whereas the pellet contains integral membrane proteins of the nuclear envelope (cf. Fig. 2).

IV. Comments

The pellet of isolated nuclei (see Section IIIA) should be completely white and the nuclei should look intact when observed in the phase-contrast microscope. On the ultrastructural level the INM, the pores, the NPCs, and the nuclear lamina appears intact. Holes are produced in the ONM, however, as a result of the tearing off of the RER during homogenization, exposing the perinuclear space to the surrounding medium. Nuclei with intact NEs can be obtained by "sealing" the ONM using *Xenopus* egg extracts.

NEs isolated as described in Section IIIB are freed of chromatin, nucleoplasmic, and nucleolar material but show a well conserved ultrastructure with clearly identifiable ONM, INM, pores, NPCs, and lamina (Dwyer and Blobel, 1976).

Salt extraction of NEs can be used to eliminate less well attached NE proteins, whereas extractions with Triton X-100/high salt produce a structurally well-conserved pore complex lamina fraction free of membranes (Dwyer and Blobel, 1976). Integral and nonintegral membrane proteins can be separated by extractions in 7 *M* urea (see Section IIIC). Figure 2 exemplifies the usefulness of this method in the identification of an integral membrane protein that interacts with wheat germ agglutinin and is unique to the nuclear envelope (Hallberg *et al.*, 1993).

V. Pitfalls

1. To avoid accumulation (via repeated pelleting) of dust particles present in the bulk chemicals it is important to filter the stock solutions through a 0.45-μm Millipore filter.

2. It is necessary to starve the rats for 24 hr before sacrifice to reduce the liver glycogen content.

3. All work, except the extractions with urea, should be performed in the cold room with chilled solutions. The speed of the preparation is essential for the yield.

4. It is absolutely essential for the outcome of the preparation of nuclei (see Section IIIA) that the ratio of solution 8 to the first pellet (suspended in solution 7) is exactly 2:1.

REFERENCES

Blobel, G., and Potter, R. V. (1966) Nuclei from rat liver: Isolation method that combines purity with high yield. *Science* **154**, 1662–1665.

Davis, L. I., and Blobel, G. (1986) Identification and characterization of a nuclear pore complex protein. *Cell* **45**, 699–709.

Dwyer, N., and Blobel, G. (1976) A modified procedure for the isolation of a pore complex-lamina fraction from rat liver nuclei. *J. Cell Biol.* **70**, 581–591.

Gerace, L., Ottaviano, Y., and Kòndor-Koch, C. (1982) Identification of a major polypeptide of the nuclear pore complex. *J. Cell Biol.* **95**, 826–837.

Hallberg, E., Wozniak, R. W., and Blobel, G. (1993) An integral membrane protein of the pore membrane domain of the nuclear envelope contains a nucleoporin-like region. *J. Cell Biol.* **122**, 513–521.

Senior, A., and Gerace, L. (1988) Integral membrane proteins specific to the inner nuclear membrane and associated with the nuclear lamina. *J. Cell Biol.* **107**, 2029–2036.

Snow, C. M., Senior, A., and Gerace, L. (1987) Monoclonal antibodies identify a group of nuclear pore complex glycoproteins. *J. Cell Biol.* **104**, 1143–1156.

Preparation of Cytoplasts and Karyoplasts from HeLa Cell Monolayers

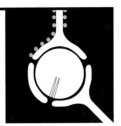

Julio E. Celis and Ariana Celis

I. Introduction

In 1967, Carter observed that one of the effects of cytochalasin B was to cause partial extrusion of the nuclei in a small percentage of the cells. It was not until Prescott *et al.* (1972) discovered that the enucleation frequency could be dramatically increased by applying centrifugal force to cytochalasin B-treated cells that it became possible to perform large-scale enucleation experiments.

The method involves centrifugation of cells, adhering to glass or plastic surfaces, in medium containing cytochalasin B. During centrifugation, the nucleus is drawn out from the cell giving rise to nucleated and enucleated fragments. The enucleated cells (cytoplasts) remain attached to the substrate; the extruded nuclei (karyoplasts) can be recovered from the pellet in the bottom of the tube.

In this article we describe the technique used to prepare cytoplasts and karyoplasts from HeLa cells grown in monolayers.

II. Materials and instrumentation

Cytochalasin B (Cat. No. C-6762) was obtained from Sigma and DMSO (Cat. No. 2950) from Merck. The Sorvall polycarbonate flanged tubes (50/39, Cat. No. 203146) were purchased from Sorvall. The tool to cut the plastic disks as well as the plastic rings were homemade. All other reagents and materials were as described in the article by Ariana Celis and Julio E. Celis in this volume.

Besides general equipment for tissue culture (see article by Ariana Celis and Julio E. Celis in this volume), the protocol requires a Sorvall centrifuge equipped with an SS 34 rotor.

III. Procedures

A. ENUCLEATION OF HeLa CELL MONOLAYERS

This procedure is adapted from that of Prescott *et al.* (1972).

Solutions

1. *Complete Dulbecco's modified Eagle's medium (DMEM):* Prepare as described in the article by Ariana Celis and Julio E. Celis in this volume.

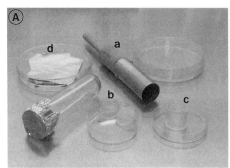

FIGURE 1 (A) Materials needed for enucleation: (a) cutting device, (b) enucleation disks, (c) plastic ring used to secure the enucleation disk in the Sorvall centrifuge tube, (d) sterile pieces of aluminum foil. (B) Sorvall centrifuge tube containing the enucleation disk and the plastic ring.

2. *Cytochalasin B:* To prepare 1 ml, dissolve 1 mg of cytochalasin B in 1 ml of DMSO. Prepare the solution in a glass tube or in a plastic ampoule resistant to DMSO. Keep at −20°C.

3. *Complete DMEM containing 10 μg/ml of cytochalasin B.*

Steps

1. Grow HeLa cell monolayers in complete DMEM (25-cm² tissue culture flask).

2. Cut the enucleation disks (Fig. 1A, b; 23 mm in diameter) from 92-mm tissue culture dishes using the device shown in Fig. 1A, a. Heat the metal end of the device before cutting the plastic in a hood. Mark with a scratch the side of the plastic that has been treated for cell culture. Smooth the edges of the disk with a file, wash in distilled water, and sterilize under ultraviolet light.

3. Trypsinize the HeLa monolayer (see article by Ariana Celis and Julio E. Celis in this volume) and plate in enucleation disks placed in a 58-mm tissue culture dish containing 8 ml of complete DMEM.

4. When the cells have reached nearly confluency, aspirate the medium and wash the cells several times with a stream of medium (pipette up and down) to eliminate loosely attached and dead cells. Aspirate the medium and add 8 ml of complete DMEM containing 10 μg/ml cytochalasin B. Incubate at 37°C for 45 min in a humidified 5% CO_2 incubator. The effect of the cytochalasin B can be easily assessed as the cells show a spiderlike morphology.

5. Add 5 ml of complete DMEM containing 10 μg/ml cytochalasin B to a sterile Sorvall centrifuge (Fig. 1B) and insert the enucleation disk, cell side down, as shown in Fig. 1B. Place a sterile ring (23-mm outside diameter, Fig. 1A, c) on top of the enucleation disk (Fig. 1B). Cover with a piece of sterile aluminum foil (Figs. 1A, d, and B) and centrifuge at 14,500 g for 45 min at 30°C in the SS 34 rotor of the Sorvall centrifuge. Prewarm the centrifuge and the rotor before using. Make sure you clean the inside of the rotor with pieces of tissue paper soaked with alcohol.

6. Remove the enucleation disk with the aid of a sterile Pasteur pipette (bended at the tip) and sterile plastic forceps and place it, cell side up, in a 58-mm tissue culture dish containing complete DMEM. Wash twice with fresh medium and place in the CO_2 incubator. Immediately after enucleation, the

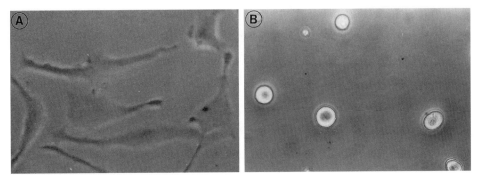

FIGURE 2 HeLa cytoplasts (A) and karyoplasts (B) prepared using the protocol described in this article. For convenience, we have pictured a region of the disk containing few cytoplasts.

enucleated cells (cytoplasts) have a drawn-out, spiderlike morphology. Figure 2A shows HeLa cytoplasts 2 hr after enucleation. Dispose of the DMEM containing cytochalasin B according to the safety procedures enforced in your laboratory.

7. The extruded nuclei are pelleted on the bottom of the centrifuge tube. Aspirate the medium and resuspend the pellet in complete DMEM. Wash two times with the same medium. Resuspend the pellet in 5 ml of complete DMEM and plate in a 58-mm tissue culture dish. After 1 hr, remove the supernatant and observe in the microscope. Karyoplasts (Fig. 2B) do not attach to the culture dish and can be easily separated from loosely attached cells.

IV. Comments

Even though this procedure can be used to enucleate many different monolayer cell types, the cytochalasin B concentration and time of centrifugation may need to be optimized for a given cell type. A procedure for enucleating cells in suspension can be found in Wigler *et al.* (1976).

V. Pitfalls

1. Make sure that you wash the cells with a stream of medium before adding the cytochalasin B. In this way one eliminates loosely attached and dead cells that otherwise will pellet with the karyoplasts.

2. The concentration of cytochalasin B and time of treatment may vary from cell type to cell type.

3. Usually, the enucleation efficiency in the outside of the disk is lower than that in the central parts.

REFERENCES

Carter, S. B. (1967) Effects of cytochalasins on mammalian cells. *Nature* **213**, 261–264.
Prescott, D. M., Myerson, D., and Wallace, J. (1972) A preparative method for obtaining enucleated mammalian cells. *Exp. Cell Res.* **71**, 480–485.
Wigler, M. H., Neugut, A. I., and Weinstein, I. B. (1976) Enucleation of mammalian cells in suspension. *In* "Methods in Cell Biology," Vol. **14**, p. 87. Academic Press, New York.

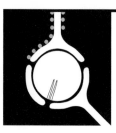

Isolation and Visualization of the Nuclear Matrix, the Nonchromatin Structure of the Nucleus

Jeffrey A. Nickerson, Gabriela Krockmalnic, and Sheldon Penman

I. Introduction

When the light microscope was the only tool available to examine the cell nucleus most of the nuclear interior, except for the nucleolus and a few larger patches of heterochromatin, appeared to be clear. This transparency suggested a structureless space which was called the *nuclear sap* or *karyolymph*. Nuclear metabolism was conceptualized as a soluble process occurring in this nuclear solution.

The electron microscope subsequently showed the nuclear interior to be much more highly structured than previously imagined. What had been termed *sap* was actually highly structured. The architecture of the nuclear interior was composed of two nucleic acid-containing structures: a DNA-containing structure called chromatin and an RNA-containing structure that could be selectively stained (Bernhard, 1969). The RNA-containing structure consisted of granules and fibers and is the only portion of the nuclear matrix that can be seen without first removing chromatin by a suitable extraction protocol.

Beginning with the pioneering efforts of Berezney and Coffey (1974), many procedures have been used to separate the nuclear matrix from the much larger mass of chromatin. The success of these protocols must be judged by how intact they leave the nuclear matrix by both biochemical and morphological criteria. Studies in this laboratory led to development of more gentle nuclear matrix isolation procedures providing greater preservation of nuclear matrix proteins while effectively removing chromatin (Capco *et al.*, 1982; Fey *et al.*, 1986; He *et al.*, 1990).

Development of these procedures required a better electron microscopic technique for visualizing filamentous cell structures. The conventional Epon-embedded thin section can visualize only those filaments that happen to lie in the section surface and therefore attach heavy metal stains. We adopted the method we had previously developed for imaging the filamentous cytoskeleton, i.e., resinless section electron microscopy. Once the embedding resin is removed, it is easy to obtain high-contrast, three-dimensional images of the nuclear filaments (Capco *et al.*, 1984; Nickerson *et al.*, 1990). The resinless section technique combines the image clarity of whole-mount electron microscopy with the ability to section through the nucleus. We present here protocols for both isolating the nuclear matrix and imaging its fine structure.

II. Materials and Instrumentation

A. SEQUENTIAL FRACTIONATION

Vanadyl riboside complex (VRC) is available from 5 Prime to 3 Prime and other suppliers. RNase-free DNase I is purchased from Boehringer-Mannheim. The serine protease inhibitor 4-(2-aminoethyl)benzenesulfonyl fluoride (AEBSF) is available from Boehringer-Mannheim under the trade name Perfabloc SC. Triton X-100, available as a 10% solution, and all other extraction chemicals are also available from Boehringer-Mannheim.

B. RESINLESS SECTION ELECTRON MICROSCOPY

An electron microscope, an ultramicrotome, and an oven are essential. A carbon evaporator, BEEM embedding capsules, and infrared lamp are optional but may be required for certain experiments. Either diamond or fresh glass knives are required. Thermanox coverslips can be purchased from Nunc, Inc. Diethylene glycol distearate (DGD) is available from E. M. Corporation. Either a critical-point drier or hexamethyldisilazane (HMDS), available from Sigma, is required. EM grids with carbon-coated plastic support film, forceps, razor blades, distilled water, Pasteur pipettes, ethanol, butanol, and toluene are also required.

III. Procedures

A. SEQUENTIAL FRACTIONATION

Solutions

1. *Cytoskeletal buffer:* 10 mM Pipes, pH 6.8, 300 mM sucrose, 100 mM NaCl, 3 mM $MgCl_2$, 1 mM EGTA. Freeze in aliquots at $-20°C$. Before use, add Triton X-100 to a final concentration of 0.5% from the 20× stock solution, add VRC to a final concentration of 20 mM from the 100× stock solution, and add AEBSF to a final concentration of 1 mM from the 100× stock solution.

2. *Extraction buffer:* 10 mM Pipes, pH 6.8, 250 mM ammonium sulfate, 300 mM sucrose, 3 mM $MgCl_2$, 1 mM EGTA. Freeze in aliquots at $-20°C$. Before use, add Triton X-100 to a final concentration of 0.5% from the 20× stock solution, add VRC to a final concentration of 20 mM from the 100× stock solution, and add AEBSF to a final concentration of 1 mM from the 100× stock solution.

3. *Digestion buffer:* 10 mM Pipes, pH 6.8, 300 mM sucrose, 50 mM NaCl, 3 mM $MgCl_2$, 1 mM EGTA. Freeze in aliquots at $-20°C$. Before use, add Triton X-100 to a final concentration of 0.5% from the 20× stock solution, add VRC to a final concentration of 20 mM from the 100× stock solution, and add AEBSF to a final concentration of 1 mM from the 100× stock solution.

4. *2 M NaCl buffer:* 10 mM Pipes, pH 6.8, 300 mM sucrose, 50 mM NaCl, 3 mM $MgCl_2$, 1 mM EGTA. Freeze in aliquots at $-20°C$. Before use, add VRC to a final concentration of 20 mM from the 100× stock solution, and add AEBSF to a final concentration of 1 mM from the 100× stock solution.

5. *Triton stock:* 10% (w/v) Triton X-100 frozen in aliquots at $-20°C$. This is a 20× stock solution.

6. *AEBSF stock:* 100 mM 4-(2-aminoethyl)-benzenesulfonyl fluoride, frozen in

aliquots at −20°C. This is a 100× stock solution. Alternatively, phenylmethylsulfonyl fluoride (PMSF) can be used. The PMSF stock solution is 20 mg/ml in isopropanol, stored at room temperature, and is used at a final concentration of 0.2 mg/ml. Other protease inhibitors can be added if proteolysis is suspected, but do not use EDTA as divalent ions are necessary for structural integrity.

Steps

1. Cells are most conveniently processed for biochemical experiments in suspension following trypsinization or scraping. Cells can be extracted in monolayers and grown on glass coverslips for light microscopy and on Thermanox coverslips for electron microscopy. Suspension processing can be done by sequentially resuspending cell pellets in the extraction solutions and centrifuging at 1000 g for 3 min at 4°C between steps. The supernatant fractions can be saved for biochemical analysis. The extracted cell structure at each step is in the pellet. Coverslips are moved between the different extraction solutions when cells are processed in monolayer.

2. Wash cells once with PBS at 4°C. Wash cells to be processed in monolayer on glass or Thermanox by immersing in PBS. Perform subsequent extraction steps by immersing the monolayer in the extraction solution. Centrifuge cells to be processed in suspension at 1000 g for 3 min at 4°C between steps and resuspend in the next wash or extraction solution.

3. Extract cells in cytoskeletal buffer containing 0.5% Triton X-100 at 4°C for 3–5 min. We use about 1 ml for each 10^7 cells until the digestion step and then halve the volume. This step removes soluble proteins—both cytoplasmic and nucleoplasmic.

4. Extract cells with extraction buffer at 4°C for 3–5 min. This step removes histone H1 and strips the cytoskeleton except for the intermediate filaments, which remain tightly anchored to the nuclear lamina.

5. Remove chromatin by digestion with RNase-free DNase I in digestion buffer containing 0.5% Triton X-100. Digestion is with 200–400 units of DNase I for 30–50 min at 32°C. It is important to optimize the removal of chromatin for the cell type selected. This should be done by labeling cell DNA with [^{3}H]thymidine (5 μCi/ml of culture medium) overnight and then quantitating the release of DNA by scintillation counting. This step removes DNA and the remaining histones. What is left with the structure is the complete nuclear matrix.

6. Extract the structure in 2 M NaCl buffer at 4°C for 3–5 min. This step strips some proteins from the nuclear matrix and either uncovers or stabilizes a highly branched network of 10-nm filaments that form the core structure of the nuclear matrix. We believe that this nuclear matrix core filament network is the basic organizing scaffolding of the cell nucleus. It is important to increase the ionic strength gradually or in steps. Nuclear matrix proteins that are not part of the core filament network should be in the supernatant fraction.

B. RESINLESS SECTION MICROSCOPY

Solutions

1. *Digestion buffer:* Prepare as described in Section A.

2. *Cacodylate buffer:* The stock solution is 0.2 M sodium cacodylate, pH 7.2–7.4, and is prepared according to the following method. To make solution A,

combine 42.8 g sodium cacodylate (Na(CH$_3$)$_2$AsO$_2$·3H$_2$O) and 1000.0 ml distilled water. To make solution B (0.2 M HCl), combine 10 ml concentrated HCl (36–38%) and 603 ml distilled water. Then prepare the stock solution of the desired pH by adding solution B as shown below to 50 ml of solution A and diluting to a total volume of 200 ml:

Solution B (ml)	pH of buffer
6.3	7.0
4.2	7.2
2.7	7.4

The 0.2 M sodium cacodylate solution is stable for few months and should be kept at 4°C. The washing buffer is 0.1 M sodium cacodylate and is prepared by mixing together 1:1 (v/v) 0.2 M sodium cacodylate and distilled water.

3. *Glutaraldehyde solution:* 2.5% glutaraldehyde in digestion buffer is used to fix the samples. The glutaraldehyde concentration in the fixative may vary in the range 1–3%. Only EM-grade glutaraldehyde should be used and is available from any electron microscopy supplier. Glutaraldehyde is packaged in 1-ml ampoules of 8 or 25% aqueous solution. The fixative has to be prepared freshly, within 3 hr prior to fixation, and stored at 4°C.

4. *Osmium solution:* A solution of 1% osmium tetroxide in 0.1 M sodium cacodylate, pH 7.2–7.4, is the optional second fixative. Osmium tetroxide can be purchased as a stock solution in distilled water from most electron microscopy suppliers. Prepare the fixative by mixing the osmium stock solution with 0.2 M sodium cacodylate buffer and distilled water. The fixative is stable for 1–2 months at 4°C.

5. *Hematoxylin:* Delafield's hematoxylin was purchased as a solution from Rowley Biochemical Institute.

6. *Eosin:* Saturated solution of eosin Y (Sigma) in 70% ethanol. The solution can be stored at room temperature. The pipetting of the stain should be done with care not to disturb the eosin deposit. Alternatively, a small quantity of stain can be centrifuged before use.

Steps

The following procedures are suitable for cells processed in suspension or preserved as monolayers.

1. *Cell culture and processing.* The cells grown on Thermanox coverslips are fractionated, fixed, and processed through all steps *in situ* while still attached to the coverslip. Suspended cells are harvested, extracted, and fixed as a small pellet. After fixation, the pellet is placed into a BEEM capsule for further processing. The height of the pellet in the BEEM capsule should be less than 2 mm; if larger, then divide the sample or allow more time for individual steps.

2. *Fixation.* The nuclear matrices should be fixed immediately after fractionation. Fix the nuclei in 2.5% glutaraldehyde in digestion buffer for 40 min at 4°C. Wash the fixed nuclei in digestion buffer for 5 min at 4°C.

Optional postfixation. Wash the samples in 0.1 M sodium cacodylate buffer for 5 min at 4°C. Fix the samples in 1–2% osmium tetroxide in 0.1 M sodium cacodylate buffer for 30 min at 4°C. Wash the samples again in 0.1 M sodium cacodylate for 5 min.

The fixed nuclear matrices can be stored overnight, at 4°C in 0.1 *M* sodium cacodylate buffer.

3. *Dehydration.* Dehydration is performed at room temperature. Transfer the samples from digestion buffer (or 0.1 *M* cacodylate buffer) to 50% ethanol for 5 min. Dehydrate the samples in increasing ethanol concentrations ending with three changes of 100% ethanol for 5 min each. The dehydrated matrices can be stored overnight, at 4°C.

4. *Block staining* (optional). The following staining procedure is not necessary for the ultrastructural visualization of the sample, but may facilitate the localization of nuclei in the DGD block prior to sectioning. There are two alternative methods for staining; both are performed at room temperature.

4a. *Staining with eosin Y.* After the first dehydration step transfer the samples to a freshly prepared, saturated solution of eosin Y in 70% ethanol for 20 min. Briefly wash the samples in 70% ethanol and then dehydrate as in step 3.

4b. *Staining with hematoxylin.* Prior to the first dehydration change, incubate in hematoxylin for 20 min. Continue the dehydration as in step 3.

5. *Transition fluid.* Ethanol and DGD are not miscible so a transition fluid, butanol or toluene, is used. Transfer the samples to a 1:1 (v/v) mixture of ethanol:butanol (or toluene) for 5 min, and then through two changes of 100% butanol (or toluene) for 5 min each. Place the samples in a 56–60°C oven.

6. *DGD infiltration.* The infiltration with DGD is performed at 56–60°C. DGD is melted to this temperature in an oven and samples can be handled in the oven or on the lab bench with an infrared lamp. Prepare a mixture of 1:1 (v/v) DGD:butanol (or toluene) and pour it over the samples (use prewarmed transition fluid and molten DGD). Leave the samples in the oven, without a cover, for 30 min to allow the transition solvent to evaporate. Replace the mixture with two changes of pure molten DGD for 30–60 min each to ensure proper infiltration.

7. *Mounting, trimming, and sectioning.* Allow the samples to cool and solidify at room temperature. Peel the Thermanox coverslips from DGD. Cut squares (about 16 mm^2) from the area that contains nuclei and mount them on DGD blocks with a drop of molten DGD. For samples in BEEM capsules, cut away the capsule plastic, and trim with razor blades the remaining block. For thin sections, 0.15 nm or less, trim the block face to as small a size as possible. For thicker sections, up to 1 μm, the block face can be as large as 5 mm^2. The sectioning is done with glass or diamond knives with troughs filled with distilled water. The sections are collected on plastic-covered, carbon-coated grids. The section thickness is estimated by the continuous interference color (Peachy, 1958), which is essentially the same as in Epon sections.

8. *DGD removal.* Immerse the grids in toluene or butanol and incubate them at room temperature. Wax removal is very rapid with toluene; incubation for an hour is sufficient. Butanol effects a slower extraction and samples are best left for a few hours or overnight.

9. *Final sample preparation.* There are two different methods for transferring the samples to air that allow a good preservation of the three-dimensional architecture. Critical-point drying is the standard method. The second method, HMDS drying, although less completely tested, is far simpler and quicker and does not require a special apparatus. The technique uses HMDS, which is a solvent with a very low surface tension. All the following steps are performed at room temperature.

9a. *Critical-point drying.* Transfer the grids with sections to a 1:1 (v/v) mixture of ethanol with the dewaxing solvent (butanol or toluene) for 5 min, and then to three changes of 10 min each of 100% ethanol. Place the samples in 100% ethanol in the critical-point drier and process according to the apparatus instructions.

9b. *HMDS drying.* Transfer the grids to 100% ethanol following the same procedure as in step 9a. After the last change of 100% ethanol is completed, immerse the grids for 5 min in a 1:1 (v/v) mixture of ethanol and HMDS. Then do three changes of pure HMDS, for 10 min each. Place the grids on filter paper to air-dry.

10. *Carbon coating* (optional). When dry, the grids are ready to be placed in the electron microscope; however, many samples are quite delicate and vulnerable to beam damage. Many electron microscopes, especially older ones, require a high minimum beam current for adequate viewing and focusing. The specimens can be stabilized by a light coating with carbon in a standard carbon coating apparatus.

REFERENCES

Berezhey, R., and Coffey, D. S. (1974) Identification of a nuclear protein matrix. *Biochem. Biophys. Res. Commun.* **60**, 1410–1417.

Bernhard, W. (1969) A new procedure for electron microscopical cytology. *J. Ultrastruct. Res.* **27**, 250–265.

Capco, D. G., Krochmalnic, G., and Penman, S. (1984) A new method of preparing embedment-free sections for TEM: Application to the cytoskeletal framework and other three-dimensional networks. *J. Cell Biol.* **98**, 1878–1885.

Capco, D., Wan, K., and Penman, S. (1982) The nuclear matrix: Three-dimensional architecture and protein composition. *Cell* **29**, 847–858.

Fey, E. G., Krochmalnic, G., and Penman, S. (1986) The non-chromatin substructures of the nucleus: The RNP-containing and RNP-depleted matrix analyzed by sequential fractionation and resinless section electron microscopy. *J. Cell Biol.* **102**, 1653–1665.

He, D. C., Nickerson, J., and Penman, S. (1990) RNA containing core filaments of the nuclear matrix. *J. Cell Biol.* **110**, 569–580.

Nickerson, J. A., Krockmalnic, G., He, D., and Penman, S. (1990) Immuno-localization in three dimensions: Immuno-gold staining of cytoskeletal and nuclear matrix proteins in resinless EM sections. *Proc. Natl. Acad. Sci. USA* **87**, 2259–2263.

Peachy, L. D. (1958) Thin sections. I. A study of section thickness and physical distortion produced during microtomy. *J. Biophys. Biochem. Cytol.* **4**, 233–242.

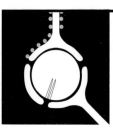

Preparation of U Small Nuclear Ribonucleoprotein Particles

Sven-Erik Behrens, Berthold Kastner,
and Reinhard Lührmann

I. Introduction

Small nuclear ribonucleoprotein particles (snRNPs) occupy a central position in the expression of proteins in eukaryotic cells, as it is their task to remove the introns from newly transcribed messenger RNA. This RNA splicing reaction is reviewed by Green (1991) and Moore *et al.* (1993). In addition, it has been shown that a number of autoimmune diseases are associated with the production of autoantibodies against proteins of the snRNPs (reviewed by Tan, 1989; van Venrooij and Sillekens, 1989). For both of these reasons, snRNPs have come to occupy an increasingly important place in molecular and cell biology, and thus much attention has been paid to questions of their mechanism of action and their biogenesis. A thorough investigation of these issues naturally presupposes the purification of snRNPs in an as nearly as possible native form and their complete characterization, and much effort has been devoted to meeting this challenge.

There are four basic snRNP particles—U1, U2, U5, and U4/U6—that are essential for pre-mRNA splicing. Each contains one or two characteristic RNA molecules and a set of "common" proteins along with a variable number of "specific" proteins. The snRNPs assemble together with additional non-snRNP splicing factors in an ordered pathway onto an intron of the pre-mRNA and form the spliceosome, a 50–60 S RNP complex that facilitates the catalysis of the splicing reaction (Steitz *et al.*, 1988; Moore *et al.*, 1993).

Under conditions of an *in vitro* splicing reaction in Hela cell nuclear extracts (i.e., at about 100 m*M* salt concentration), the spliceosomal snRNPs are organized in three RNP forms: 12 S U1, 17 S U2, and 25 S [U4/U6.U5] tri-snRNP. These snRNP complexes may be considered as functional subunits of the spliceosome. The composition and structures of the snRNPs are reviewed elsewhere (see Lührmann *et al.*, 1990).

The procedures given here for the preparation of snRNPs have been in use in our laboratory for some years. These protocols were developed with a view to obtaining the purest possible snRNPs and snRNP components, a task that has proved very difficult on account of the ease with which the snRNPs lose their proteins, on the one hand, and their higher-order structure, on the other. This has given rise to problems of characterization, and many of the methods described here were developed to overcome these problems. Essential aspects of the methods to be described include the following. (1) The salt concentration must always be exactly right, because the binding of the specific proteins is frequently salt labile, as is the 17 S U2 snRNP and the [U4/U6.U5] tri-snRNP complex. (2) Fortunately, all snRNPs possess a characteristic structural feature, an m₃G group ("cap") at the 5' end of the RNA. This has allowed the development of chromatographic procedures employing immobilized antibodies against the m_3G cap; these bind selectively the snRNPs, which are subsequently eluted by displacement with free m_3G or cross-reacting m^7G. (3) Despite their large size and very similar structures, the snRNPs can be separated from each other by HPLC using the anion exchanger Mono Q.

II. Materials and Instrumentation

S-MEM (Cat. No. 072-01400) and RPMI-1640 (Cat. No. 041-02400) cell media, newborn calf serum, (NCS, Cat. No. 021-06010), and fetal calf serum (FCS, Cat. No. 011-06290) are obtained from Gibco-BRL. All inorganic salts are purchased from Merck AG, as are all organic solvents: acetic acid, 98%, p.a.; methanol, 100%, p.a.; ethanol, 100%, p.a.; acetone, 100%, p.a.; formamide, p.a.; DMSO; glycerol, 87%, p.a.; chloroform, 100%, p.a. Penicillin (Cat. No. 31749) and streptomycin (Cat. No. 35500) are purchased from Serva. Urea (Cat. No. U-5378), N,N,N',N'-tetramethylethylendiamine (TEMED, Cat. No. T-9281), SDS (Cat. No. L-3771), Hepes (Cat. No. H-7523), PMSF (Cat. No. P-7626), dimethyl pimelimidate (DMP, Cat. No. D-8388), dithioerythritol (DTE, Cat. No. D-8255), β-mercaptoethanol (Cat. No. M-3148), Coomassie brilliant blue G and R (Cat. Nos. B-2025 and B-0149), bromophenol blue (Cat. No. B-5525), xylene cyanol blue (Cat. No. X-4126) and N^7-methylguanosine (Cat. No. M-0627) are from Sigma. Gel solutions are obtained from Roth AG, either as Rotiphorese Gel 30 (30% w/v acrylamide, ratio of acrylamide to bisacrylamide = 30:0.8, Cat. No. 3029.1) or as Rotiphorese Gel 40 (40% w/v acrylamide, ratio = 19:1, Cat. No. 3030.1). Phenol (Cat. No. 0038), Tris (Cat. No. 4855), and glycine (Cat. No. 3908) are also from Roth. Antibodies such as the anti-m₃G antibody and H386 were raised in our laboratory (see Bochnig et al., 1987; Reuter and Lührmann, 1986). The anti-mouse IgM antibody used for immunoprecipitation and immunoaffinity purification with H386 is a goat anti-mouse IgM (Cat. No. M-8644) from Sigma. Marker proteins for gel electrophoresis (Cat. No. 161-0303 and 161-0304) are from Bio-Rad. T4 RNA ligase (Cat. No. 1449478) is purchased from Boehringer-Mannheim. [³²P]pCp (Cat. No. PB10208) is obtained from Amersham/Buchler.

Cells are broken with a "douncer" (Cat. No. K-88530) from Kontes Glass. Dialysis tubing with a 3.5-kDa cutoff (Spektrapor 3, Cat. No. 132725) is provided by Spektrum. Protein A–Sepharose CL-4B (Cat. No. 17-0780-01), Protein G–Sepharose (Cat. No. 17-0618-01), and cyanogen bromide-activated Sepharose 4D (Cat. No. 17-0430-01) are from Pharmacia, as is the whole FPLC system (which includes a Mono Q column type HR 5/5. Mini-chromatographic columns (Cat. No. 731-1550) are from Bio-Rad. Glycerol density gradients are poured with the Gradient Master Model 106 from BioComp Instruments. Where necessary, gentle agitation is provided by an end-over-end rotor (type 7637-01, Cole–Parmer). Centrifugation is performed in Heraeus Biofuge A, Heraeus Cryofuge 6000, Sorvall RC-5D centrifuges (rotor types GS3 and SS34), and the Beckman ultracentrifuge type L-60 (rotor types SW 28 and SW 40). Peptides were synthesized on an Applied Biosystems Synthesizer 430A and purified on an PD 10 (G-25) Sephadex column (Cat. No. 17-0851-01) from Pharmacia.

III. Procedures

All buffers are prepared by mixing sterilized (either autoclaved or sterile-filtered) stock solutions and adding autoclaved, doubly distilled water. The following stock solutions were used:

1. *3 M NaCl:* To make 1 liter, add 175.3 g of NaCl to water and bring to a total volume of 1 liter.

2. *1 M K_2HPO_4:* To make 1 liter, add 174.2 g of K_2HPO_4 to water and bring to a total volume of 1 liter.

3. *1 M KH_2PO_4:* To make 1 liter, add 136.1 g of KH_2PO_4 to water and bring to a total volume of 1 liter.

4. *1 M Na_2HPO_4:* To make 1 liter, add 142.0 g of Na_2HPO_4 to water and bring to a total volume of 1 liter.

5. *1 M NaH_2PO_4:* To make 1 liter, add 138.0 g of $NaH_2PO_4 \cdot H_2O$ to water and bring to a total volume of 1 liter.

6. *7.5% (w/v) $NaHCO_3$:* To make 1 liter, add 75 g of $NaHCO_3$ to water and bring to a total volume of 1 liter.

7. *1 M Hepes, pH 8:* To make 1 liter, add 238.3 g of Hepes to water, adjust pH to 8.0 with 5 M KOH, and bring to a total volume of 1 liter.

8. *1 M $MgCl_2$:* To make 1 liter, add 203.3 g of $MgCl_2 \cdot 6H_2O$ to water and bring to a total volume of 1 liter.

9. *5 M $MgCl_2$:* To make 1 liter, add 1016.5 g of $MgCl_2 \cdot 6H_2O$ to water and bring to a total volume of 1 liter.

10. *0.5 M EDTA, pH 8:* To make 1 liter, add 146.1 g of EDTA to water, adjust pH to 8.0 with 5 M NaOH, and bring to a total volume of 1 liter.

11. *3 M KCl:* To make 1 liter, add 223.7 g of KCl to water and bring to a total volume of 1 liter.

12. *1 M Tris, pH 7:* To make 1 liter, add 121.1 g of Tris to water, adjust pH to 7.0 with 1 M HCl, and bring to a total volume of 1 liter.

13. *250 mM DTE:* To make 0.1 liter, add 3.86 g of DTE to water and bring to a total volume of 0.1 liter.

14. *50% (v/v) glycerol:* To make 1 liter, add 575 ml of 87% glycerol to water and bring to a total volume of 1 liter.

15. *20% (w/v) NaN_3:* To make 0.1 liter, add 20.0 g of NaN_3 to water and bring to a total volume of 0.1 liter.

16. *100 mM sodium pyruvate:* To make 1 liter, add 11.0 g of sodium pyruvate to water and bring to a total volume of 1 liter.

17. *100 mM PMSF:* To make 0.1 liter, add 1.74 g of PMSF to ethanol p.a. and bring to a total volume of 0.1 liter with ethanol p.a.

Apart from pyruvate, DTE, and PMSF, which are stored at −20°C, all stock solutions and readymade buffer solutions are kept at 4°C. All steps are carried out at 4°C unless otherwise specified.

A. PREPARATION OF HeLa NUCLEAR EXTRACTS

Solutions

1. *PBS Earle:* 130 mM NaCl, 20 mM K_2HPO_4/KH_2PO_4, pH 7.4. To make 1 liter, add 50 ml of 3 M NaCl and 16.2 ml of 1 M K_2HPO_4, adjust pH to 7.4 with approximately 3.8 ml of 1 M KH_2PO_4, and bring to a total volume of 1 liter.

2. *Buffer A:* 10 mM Hepes–KOH, pH 8, 10 mM KCl, 1.5 mM $MgCl_2$, 0.5

mM DTE. To make 1 liter, add 10 ml of 1 M Hepes, pH 8, 3.3 ml of 3 M KCl, 1.5 ml 1 M MgCl$_2$, and 2 ml of 250 mM DTE, and bring to a total volume of 1 liter.

3. *Buffer C:* 20 mM Hepes–KOH, pH 8, 420 mM NaCl, 1.5 mM MgCl$_2$, 0.5 mM DTE, 0.5 mM PMSF, 0.2 mM EDTA, pH 8, 25% (v/v) glycerol. To make 1 liter, add 20 ml of 1 M Hepes, pH 8, 140 ml of 3 M NaCl, 1.5 ml of 1 M MgCl, 2 ml of 250 mM DTE, 5 ml of 100 mM PMSF (add PMSF very slowly while the solution is stirring), 0.4 ml of of 0.5 M EDTA, and 500 ml of 50% glycerol, and bring to a total volume of 1 liter.

4. *Buffer G:* 20 mM Hepes–KOH, pH 8, 150 mM KCl, 1.5 mM MgCl$_2$, 0.5 mM DTE, 0.5 mM PMSF, 5% (v/v) glycerol. To make 1 liter, add 20 ml of 1 M Hepes, pH 8, 50 ml of 3 M KCl, 1.5 ml of 1 M MgCl$_2$, 2 ml of 250 mM DTE, 5 ml of 100 mM PMSF (see buffer C), and 100 ml of 50% glycerol, and bring to a total volume of 1 liter.

Steps

1. Allow HeLa S3 cells to grow in suspension culture in S-MEM supplemented with 5% (v/v) NCS, 50 μg/ml penicillin, and 100 μg/ml streptomycin at 37°C, keeping the cells at a density between 2.5 and 5×10^5/ml medium at logarithmic growth rate. To harvest sufficient amounts of U snRNPs, the number of cells has to be increased to 5×10^9 (corresponding to about 8–10 liters of medium).

2. Harvest the cells using a Heraeus Cryofuge 6000 with swinging bucket rotor for 10 min at 1000 g.

3. Resuspend cells in PBS–Earle (20 ml/10^9 cells) and pellet again in a Sorvall HB4 rotor for 10 min at 1000 g.

4. Determine the volume of the cell pellet and resuspend in 5 vol of buffer A.

5. Leave the cells to swell for 10 min, pellet again (see step 3), and resuspend in 2 vol of buffer A.

6. Break the cells by 10 strokes in a 40-ml douncer.

7. Remove the cytoplasm by two successive centrifugations in a Sorvall SS 34 rotor for 10 min at 1000 g and then 20 min at 25,000 g.

8. Resuspend the pellet (cell nuclei) in buffer C (3 ml/10^9 cells).

9. Break the nuclei by 10 strokes in a 40-ml douncer.

10. Transfer the resulting suspension into a beaker and stir carefully on ice for 30 min.

11. Remove the nuclear membrane by centrifugation in an SS 34 rotor at 25,000 g for 30 min.

12. The resultant supernatant is the nuclear extract obtained under high-salt conditions (420 mM).

13. To obtain an extract active in splicing, dialyze to a lower salt concentration (150 mM) with 100 vol of buffer G for 4–5 hr. Nuclear extracts prepared in this way are active when they make up ca. 40–60% of the final volume in the usual splicing assay (Krainer *et al.,* 1984); 5×10^9 cells yield about 18 ml of low-salt nuclear extract.

B. GLYCEROL GRADIENT CENTRIFUGATION

Solutions

1. *Buffer C containing 10% (v/v) glycerol:* Make buffer C as described in Section A, but take 200 ml of 50% glycerol.

2. *Buffer C containing 30% (v/v) glycerol:* Make buffer C as described in Section A, but take 600 ml of 50% glycerol.

3. *Buffer G containing 10% (v/v) glycerol:* Make buffer G as described in Section A, but take 200 ml of 50% glycerol.

4. *Buffer G containing 30% (v/v) glycerol:* Make Buffer G as described in Section A, but take 600 ml of 50% glycerol.

Steps

1. Pour 10–30% glycerol gradients either with buffer C ("high-salt gradient") or buffer G ("low-salt gradient") using sterilized SW 28 tubes (see also the manual of the BioComp Gradient Master Model 106). This can be done at room temperature.

2. Store the gradients to even out any irregularities for at least 1 hr (maximum overnight) at 4°C.

3. Load the nuclear extract onto the gradient carefully (use an Eppendorf pipette). It is possible to load up to 8 ml extract onto a 30-ml SW 28 gradient.

4. Start the centrifugation using a low acceleration rate and run it for 17 hr at 27,000 rpm (10^5 g). Stop the centrifugation without the brake.

5. Harvest the gradients manually in 1.5-ml fractions from top to bottom, using an Eppendorf pipette.

6. To analyze the U snRNP content, take one-tenth of each fraction, extract with phenol/chloroform (1/1), and precipitate the RNA of the aqueous phase by adding 0.1 vol sodium acetate (3 M, pH 4.8) and 3 vol ethanol. Check the RNA by gel electrophoresis followed by silver staining using standard procedures (Fig. 1).

C. IMMUNOPRECIPITATION OF U SMALL NUCLEAR RIBONUCLEOPROTEINS

Solutions

1. *PBS:* 130 mM NaCl, 20 mM Na$_2$HPO$_4$/NaH$_2$PO$_4$, pH 8. To make 1 liter, add 50 ml of 3 M NaCl and 18.92 ml of 1 M Na$_2$HPO$_4$, adjust pH to 7.4 with approximately 1.08 ml of 1 M NaH$_2$PO$_4$, and bring to a total volume of 1 liter.

2. *Buffer G:* See Section A.

3. *Antibodies:* Antibodies were used either directly as hybridoma supernatants (RPMI-1640, 10 mM Hepes, 50 μg/ml penicillin, 100 μg/ml streptomycin, 0.2% w/v NaHCO$_3$, 10% v/v FCS, 1 mM sodium pyruvate) or as purified IgG fractions (1 mg/ml, dissolved in buffer G) using a standard procedure that employed protein A–Sepharose (Harlowe and Lane, 1988).

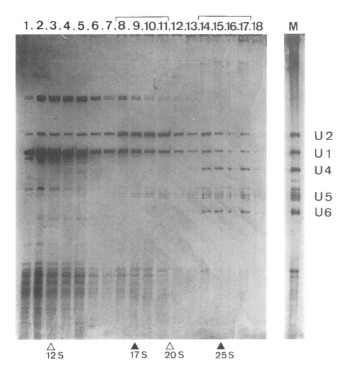

FIGURE 1   Sedimentation of U snRNP particles. HeLa cell nuclear splicing extract was sedimented in a linear, 10–30% glycerol gradient at low salt concentration from left to right. Small nuclear RNAs in each fraction were isolated as described in the text and analyzed on a 10% polyacrylamide–urea gel. Positions of some sedimentation coefficients are indicated. M is a U snRNA marker.

Steps

1. Hydrate protein A–Sepharose CL-4B or protein G–Sepharose overnight in PBS (1 ml per 100 mg Sepharose) using an end-over-end rotor. For long-term storage, add NaN₃ to a final concentration of 0.02% (w/v).

2. Wash the Sepharose twice, each time by adding PBS and then centrifuging (1 min, 10,000 g) in a Sorvall SS 34 tube.

3. Determine the approximate volume of the Sepharose pellet and resuspend it in the same volume of PBS.

4. For analytical immunoprecipitation assays (i.e., to identify or assay the precipitated U snRNP species) use 20 μl; for preparative assays (to determine the protein composition of the precipitated U snRNPs) take 100 μl of the 1/1 (v/v Sepharose/buffer) mixture.

5. For binding of the antibody in an analytical assay, incubate the Sepharose either with 100–200 μl hybridoma supernatant or with 5–10 μg purified antibodies in a total volume of 500 μl PBS overnight at 4°C with end-over-end rotation. For a preparative assay, incubate under the same conditions with 1–2 ml supernatant per 50–100 μg antibody. If the precipitations have to be performed with an IgM antibody, an IgG against the IgM must first be coupled to the Sepharose.

6. Wash the Sepharose pellet four times with 1 ml ice-cold buffer G to remove unbound antibodies. Transfer the pellet with the last wash into a new reaction tube and wash again.

7. As antigenic material use either purified U snRNPs (5–10 μg per analytical

assay, 50–100 μg per preparative assay, prepared as in Section D) or glycerol gradient fractions (200 μl or 2 ml, respectively) of density gradient-fractionated nuclear extract (see Fig. 1). For precipitations with IgM antibody, first preincubate the U snRNPs/gradient fractions with the antibody for at least 2 hr on ice, with occasional shaking.

8. For binding of the antigen, incubate the Sepharose-coupled antibodies with the respective antigen in a total volume of 500 μl buffer G for at least 2 hr at 4°C with end-over-end rotation.

9. Remove the unbound antigen by washing five times with buffer G (see step 2). Again, change the reaction tube between the fourth and fifth wash.

10. For analytical assays, resuspend the Sepharose pellet in 300 μl buffer G, extract the U snRNAs with phenol (without chloroform), precipitate with ethanol (see Section B, step 6), and analyze the precipitate by 3'-end labeling with [^{32}P]pCp using T4 RNA ligase (England and Uhlenbeck, 1978). For preparative assays, resuspend the Sepharose pellet directly in protein sample buffer (Laemmli, 1970), boil for 5 min at 90°C, centrifuge briefly, and analyze the proteins of the supernatant by SDS–PAGE.

D. PURIFICATION OF U SMALL NUCLEAR RIBONUCLEOPROTEINS BY ANTI-m$_3$G IMMUNOAFFINITY CHROMATOGRAPHY

Solutions

1. *Buffer C low:* Same composition as buffer C (see Section A), but only 5% glycerol. Make buffer C as in Section A, but take 100 ml of 50% glycerol.

2. *Buffer F:* Same composition as buffer C low, except that the concentration of NaCl is 250 mM. Make buffer C as in Section A, but take 83.3 ml of 3 M NaCl and 100 ml of 50% glycerol.

Steps

1. Equilibrate an anti-m$_3$G immunoaffinity column (anti-m$_3$G IgG is coupled to CNBr-activated Sepharose by a standard procedure, see Bochnig *et al.,* 1987; Bringmann *et al.,* 1983) by washing with about 5 column volumes of buffer C low. For 15 ml nuclear extract (corresponding to about 5×10^9 HeLa cells), a column with a bed volume of at least 5 ml must be used to achieve sufficient retardation of U snRNPs.

2. Apply nuclear extract prepared under high-salt conditions (see Section B, step 12) to the affinity column at about 1.5 ml/hr.

3. Elute nonspecifically bound components of the extract with about 6 column volumes of buffer C low.

4. Elute the specifically bound U snRNPs using 15 mM m^{7}G nucleoside dissolved either in high-salt buffer (buffer C low) or at more moderate salt concentrations (buffer F). If buffer F is used, the U4, U5, and U6 snRNAs can be eluted as complete [U4/U6.U5] tri-snRNP complexes (see also Section F). From 15 ml nuclear extract, about 4 mg U snRNPs (determined by the method of Bearden, 1978) can be retarded and eluted.

5. Remove the antibody-bound m^{7}G by passing a solution of 6 M urea in buffer C low down the column.

6. Regenerate the affinity column by washing with 20 column volumes of

buffer C low. For long-term storage, add NaN₃ to give a final concentration of
0.2% (v/v).

E. PURIFICATION OF U1 SMALL NUCLEAR RIBONUCLEOPROTEINS BY MONO Q CHROMATOGRAPHY

Solutions

1. *Buffer Q-0:* 20 mM Tris–HCl, pH 7.0, 1.5 mM MgCl$_2$, 0.5 mM DTE, 0.5 mM PMSF. To make 1 liter, add 20 ml of 1 M Tris, pH 7, 1.5 ml of 1 M MgCl$_2$, 2 ml of 250 mM DTE and 5 ml of 100 mM PMSF (see buffer C, procedure A) and bring to a total volume of 1 liter.

2. *Buffer Q-50:* Buffer Q-0 plus 50 mM KCl. Make buffer Q-0 as before, but add also 16.7 ml of 3 M KCl.

3. *Buffer Q-1000:* Buffer Q-0 plus 1000 mM KCl. Make buffer Q-0 as before, but add 333.3 ml of 3 M KCl.

Steps

1. Wash the Pharmacia FPLC System, which includes a 50-ml "superloop" and a Mono Q HR 5/5 column (1-ml bed volume), with a volume of buffer Q-1000 equal to 20 times the total volume of the system.

2. Wash and equilibrate the column with buffer Q-50 (same volume as in step 1). Determine the absorbance at 280 nm. The value obtained is the zero point for subsequent absorbance measurements.

3. Dilute the U snRNPs obtained by anti-m₃G chromatography with buffer Q-0 so as to bring the concentration of univalent ions below 200 mM.

4. Load U snRNPs (1–40 mg) onto the Mono Q column, using the superloop, with a flow rate of 2 ml/min. The pressure should not exceed 3.0 MPa.

5. Wash with buffer Q-50 until the absorbance reaches zero.

6. Elute the snRNPs at a flow rate of 1 ml/min using the following KCl gradient. Start with 50 mM KCl (buffer Q-50). Increase the amount of buffer Q-1000 by 5.4% per minute for 4 min, 1% per minute for 30 min, and then 4.2% per minute for 10 min. Finally, elute the column with pure buffer Q-1000 for 4 min. During the elution, collect 1-ml fractions. The U1 snRNPs elute in the first main peak at 350 to 370 mM KCl.

7. Determine the concentration of U1 snRNPs in the fractions by measurement of their absorbance at 280 nm (1 A_{280} unit is about 0.35 mg/ml) and analyze the RNA and protein content by standard PAGE procedures.

8. Contaminating 20 S U5 snRNPs can be separated from the 12 S U1 snRNPs by glycerol density gradient centrifugation (see Section B) immediately after the Mono Q chromatography (see also Bach *et al.*, 1989).

F. PURIFICATION OF THE [U4/U6.U5] tri-snRNP COMPLEX

NOTE

This procedure employs the antibody H386, which is a monoclonal antibody of the IgM subclass and can be coupled via an anti-IgM antibody to protein A–Sepharose with DMP in a standard procedure. It was originally raised against the U1 snRNP-specific 70K protein (Reuter and Lührmann, 1986), but it also exhibits strong cross-reactivity with a 100-kDa protein that is a component of the [U4/U6.U5] tri-snRNP complex (Behrens and Lührmann, 1991).

Solutions

1. *Buffer G:* See Section A.
2. *Phosphate buffer:* 10 mM phosphate, pH 7.2. To make 1 liter, add 7.2 ml of 1 M Na_2HPO_4, adjust pH to 7.2 with approximately 2.8 ml of 1 M NaH_2PO_4, and bring to a total volume of 1 liter.

Steps

1. Pool the 25 S fractions from a nuclear extract fractionated on a glycerol gradient (see Section B and Fig. 1) and pour slowly (1 ml/min) onto an H386 immunoaffinity column. Up to 7 ml, corresponding to four fractions, containing about 100–150 μg U snRNPs, can be loaded onto a column of 2-ml bed volume.

2. Elute nonspecifically bound components of the extract with about 20 column volumes of buffer G.

3. Elute the specifically bound U snRNPs with 5 column volumes of a 0.01 mM solution in buffer G of a competing 32-mer peptide, which corresponds to the primary epitope of H386 (see Behrens and Lührmann, 1991). Collect in 500-μl fractions and analyze one-tenth of each fraction for RNA and protein content using standard procedures.

4. If necessary, separate minor amounts of coretarded and coeluted 12 S U1 snRNPs (see Fig. 1) from the 25 S [U4/U6.U5] tri-snRNP complexes by glycerol gradient centrifugation (see Section B).

5. Elute the antibody-bound peptide with 5 column volumes of phosphate buffer and then with 5 column volumes of 3.5 M $MgCl_2$ in the same buffer.

6. Regenerate the affinity column by washing with 10 column volumes of buffer G. For long-term storage, add NaN_3 to give a final concentration of 0.2% (w/v).

G. PURIFICATION OF 17 S U2 SMALL NUCLEAR RIBONUCLEOPROTEINS

Solution

Buffer G: See Section A.

Steps

See also Behrens *et al.* (1992).

1. Pool the 17 S fractions from a glycerol gradient-fractionated nuclear extract (see Fig. 1). Remove small quantities of contaminating 12 S U1 snRNPs, U5 snRNPs, and [U4/U6.U5] tri-snRNP complexes by passage over an H386 immunoaffinity column (see Section F).

2. Apply the H386 flow-through, which contains the 17 S U2 snRNPs, to an anti-m_3G immunoaffinity column (see Section D).

NAME	M_R kDa	Presence in snRNP particles		
		12S U1	17S U2	25S U4/U6.U5
G	9	●	●	●
F	11	●	●	●
E	12	●	●	●
D1	16	●	●	●
D2	16,5	●	●	●
D3	18	●	●	●
B	28	●	●	●
B'	29	●	●	●
C	22	○		
A	34	○		
70K	70	○		
B"	28,5		○	
A'	31		○	
	35		○	
	53		○	
	60		○	
	66		○	
	92		○	
	110		○	
	120		○	
	150		○	
	160		○	
	15			○
	40			○
	52			○
	100			○
	102			○
	110			○
	116			○
	200			○
	205			○
	15,5			○
	20			○
	27			○
	60			○○○○
	90			○

FIGURE 2 Protein composition of the 12 S U1 snRNP, the 17 S U2 snRNP, and the 25 S [U4/U6.U5] tri-snRNP complex. The apparent molecular weights of the common proteins (black dots) and the specific proteins (light dots) are indicated.

3. Elute nonspecifically bound components with 20 column volumes of buffer G.

4. Elute the 17 S U2 snRNPs with m^7G and analyze as described in Section A, step 13.

5. Regenerate the affinity columns (see Section F, step 6, or Section D, step 6).

IV. Comments

With these methods it is possible to purify U snRNPs from HeLa nuclear extract under conditions close to those that allow the splicing reaction *in vitro*. Figure 2 shows the various U snRNP species and those of their protein components that have so far been identified by one-dimensional SDS–PAGE.

V. Pitfalls

1. For the preparation of nuclear extracts and the purification of U snRNPs, the following precautions are essential, to keep all solutions and glassware free of RNase contamination and activity:

a. All glassware must be washed thoroughly.

b. Glassware should be rinsed extensively with distilled water.

c. Glassware should be dried thoroughly and then heated for at least 1 hr at 250°C.

d. All buffers and solutions should be autoclaved and then stored, if appropriate, at 4°C.

e. Sterile gloves should be worn during all steps.

f. All steps should be performed at 4°C unless otherwise specified.

2. Immunoaffinity purification protocols are very sensitive to any kind of variations in the pH and salt concentration. For this reason, the pH of all buffers should be monitored very carefully, and buffer solutions should be checked regularly for absence of any precipitate.

3. For reproducible results using immunoaffinity columns, the following precautions should be observed in connection with the bound antibodies. For long-term storage, NaN_3 must be added to the storage buffer. Antibodies must never be incubated with denaturing solutions such as urea or 3.5 M $MgCl_2$ for longer than 4–5 hr; shorter periods are preferable. Affinity columns should always be kept at 4°C.

REFERENCES

Bach, M., Winkelmann, G., and Lührmann, R. (1989) 20 S small nuclear ribonucleoprotein U5 shows a surprisingly complex protein composition. *Proc. Natl. Acad. Sci. USA* **86**, 6038–6042.

Bearden, J. C. (1978) Quantitation of submicrogram quantities of proteins by an improved protein–dye binding assay. *Biochim. Biophys. Acta* **553**, 525–529.

Behrens, S. E., and Lührmann, R. (1991) Immunoaffinity purification of a [U4/U6.U5] tri-snRNP complex from human cells. *Genes Dev.* **5**, 1429–1452.

Behrens, S. E., Tyc, K., Kastner, B., Reichelt, J., and Lührmann, R. (1992) Small nuclear ribonucleoprotein (RNP) U2 contains numerous additional proteins and has a bipartite RNP structure under splicing conditions. *Mol. Cell. Biol.* **13**, 307–309.

Bochnig, P., Reuter, R., Bringmann, P., and Lührmann, R. (1987) A monoclonal antibody against 2,2,7-trimethylguanosine that reacts with intact U snRNPs as well as with 7-methylguanosine capped RNAs. *Eur. J. Biochem.* **168**, 461–467.

Bringmann, P., Rinke, J., Appel, B., Reuter, R., and Lührmann R. (1983) Purification of snRNPs U1, U2, U4, U5 and U6 with 2,2,7-trimethylguanosine-specific antibody and definition of their constituent proteins reacting with anti-Sm and anti-(U1)RNP antisera. *EMBO J.* **2**, 1129–1135.

England, T. E., and Uhlenbeck, O. (1978) 3′-Terminal labelling of RNA with T4 RNA ligase. *Nature* **275**, 560–561.

Green, M. R. (1991) Biochemical mechanisms of constitutive and regulated pre-mRNA splicing. *Annu. Rev. Cell. Biol.* **7**, 559–599.

Harlowe, E., and Lane, D. (1988) "Antibodies: A Laboratory Manual." Cold Spring Harbor Laboratory, Cold Spring Harbor, NY.

Krainer, A. R., Maniatis, T., Ruskin, B., and Green, M. (1984) Normal and mutant human β-globin pre-mRNAs are faithfully and efficiently spliced in vitro. *Cell* **36**, 993–1005.

Laemmli, U. K. (1970) Cleavage of structural proteins during the assembly of the head of bacteriophage T4. *Nature* **227**, 680–685.

Lührmann, R., Kastner, B., and Bach, M. (1990) Structure of spliceosomal snRNPs and their role in pre-mRNA splicing. *Biochim. Biophys. Acta Gene Struct. Expression* **1087**, 265–292.

Moore, M. J., Query, C. C., and Sharp, P. A. (1993) Splicing of precursors to messenger RNAs by the spliceosome. *In* "RNA World" (R. F. Gesteland and J. F. Atkins, eds.), pp. 303–358. Cold Spring Harbor Press, NY.

Reuter, R., and Lührmann, R. (1986) Immunization of mice with purified U1 small nuclear ribonucleoprotein (RNP) induces a pattern of antibody specificities characteristic of the anti-Sm and anti-RNP autoimmune response of patients with lupus erythematosus, as measured by monoclonal antibodies. *Proc. Natl. Acad. Sci. USA* **83**, 8689–8693.

Steitz, J. A., Black, D. L., Gerke, V., Parker, K. A., Krämer, A., Frendeway, D., and Keller, W. (1988) Functions of the abundant U-snRNPs. *In* "Structure and Function of Major and Minor Small Nuclear Ribonucleoprotein Particles" (M. L. Birnstiel, ed.), pp. 115–154. Springer-Verlag, Berlin/New York.

Tan, E. M. (1989) Antinuclear antibodies: Diagnostic markers for autoimmune disease and probes for cell biology. *Adv. Immunol.* **44**, 93–152.

Van Venrooij, W. J., and Sillekens, P. T. G. (1989) Small nuclear RNA associated proteins: Autoantigens in connective tissue disease. *Clin. Exp. Rheumatol.* **7**, 1–11.

Rapid Preparation of hnRNP Core Proteins and Stepwise Assembly of hnRNP Particles *in Vitro*

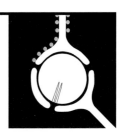

Mei Huang and Wallace M. LeStourgeon

I. Introduction

In mammalian cells pre-mRNA is packaged during transcription into a contiguous array of regular 40 S ribonucleoprotein particles (hnRNP particles) composed of six major proteins (Beyer *et al.*, 1977). These proteins exist as three heterotetramers of $(A1)_3B2$, $(A2)_3B1$, and $(C1)_3C2$, and three copies of each tetramer assemble to package 700-nucleotide (nt) lengths of RNA into each 40 S particle (reviewed in LeStourgeon *et al.*, 1990). Spontaneous assembly of 40 S hnRNP particles occurs *in vitro* through RNA activated protein–protein interactions. The correct *in vitro* assembly of 40 S hnRNP particles depends on the length, rather than the sequence of the RNA transcript (Conway *et al.*, 1988). We have previously described the scheme for the isolation of nuclear ribonucleoprotein particles and for the purification of the core particle proteins (Barnett *et al.*, 1990). Purification of the protein tetramers takes advantage of the large size and strong anionic nature of the $(C1)_3C2$ tetramer and of the ability of $(A2)_3B1$ tetramer to form a fast-sedimenting aggregate on cleavage of the packaged RNA substrate in native monoparticles. With purified native core proteins in hand and with various synthetic pre-mRNAs as assembly substrates, it has been possible to develop an *in vitro* assay to identify the sequence of events leading to 40 S hnRNP particle assembly. These studies demonstrate that the assembly of 40 S hnRNP particles is initiated by the binding of three C protein tetramers to monoparticle lengths of RNA (700 nt) to form a triangular 19 S C protein–RNA complex (Huang *et al.*, 1994). The 19 S C protein–RNA complex then directs the association of three copies of each of the $(A2)_3B1$ and $(A1)_3B2$ tetramers. If the basic A and B group core proteins are allowed to bind RNA first, or in the absence of the C proteins, then 40 S particles fail to form and various artifactual structures are assembled. Described here are refinements in the methods for purification of the native core particle proteins and methods for the assembly and purification of various hnRNP assembly intermediates as well as intact 40 S monoparticles. These methods provide the foundation for further studies on the packaging of pre-mRNA in mammalian cells. The techniques described here generally apply to studies on the assembly of other supramolecular structures composed of protein and nucleic acid.

II. Materials and Instrumentation

HeLa S3 cells (ATCC line CCL2.2) are cultured in minimal essential medium (S-MEM, with L-glutamine, without sodium bicarbonate, Cat. No. 410-1400EH) from

Gibco Laboratories. Pluronic (Cat. No. P-1300), sodium bicarbonate (Cat. No. S-5761), penicillin G (Cat. No. P-7794), streptomycin sulfate (Cat. No. S-9137), Tris (Cat. No. T-6791), and ribonuclease A (5× crystallized, protease free, Cat. No. R-4875) are from Sigma. Bovine calf serum (Cat. No. A-2151-L) is from HyClone Laboratory.

The reagents used in these procedures are obtained as follows. Sodium chloride (Cat. No. S671-3), EDTA (disodium salt, Cat. No. 0311-100), magnesium chloride (Cat. No. M33-500), glycerin (Cat. No. G33-500), and calcium chloride (Cat. No. C79-79197) are from Fisher Scientific. SDS (Cat. No. 1680024), DTT (Cat. No. 1346782), acrylamide (Cat. No. 1812270), and bisacrylamide (Cat. No. 1198373) are from Eastman Kodak Company. Micrococcal nuclease (Nuclease S7, Cat. No. 107-921) is from Boehringer-Mannheim. Triton X-100 (Cat. No. 23472-9) is from Aldrich Chemical Company, and PMSF (Cat. No. 20203) is from U.S. Biochemical Corporation. ATP (Cat. No. 27-1006-01), GTP (Cat. No. 27-2000-02), CTP (Cat. No. 27-1200-02), UTP (Cat. No. 28-0700-01), and Sephadex G-50 (medium, Cat. No. 11-0043-02) are from Pharmacia LKB Biotech Inc.

Equipment used in these procedures include the Sonifier cell disrupter, Model W140, from Heat-Systems Ultrasonics Inc. The Centriprep membrane concentrator (Centriprep-30, Cat. No. 4306) is from Amicon Corporation. The glycerol gradient maker (Cat. No. SG30) is from Hoffer Scientific Instruments. The HP8452 diode array spectrophotometer is from Hewlett–Packard. The Mono Q anion-exchange column (Model HR5/5, Cat. No. 17-0546-01) is from Pharmacia LKB Biotech Inc. Sorvall RC2-B centrifuge, HB4 rotor, and HS-4 rotor are from the Dupont Company. Beckman L3-50 preparative ultracentrifuge, SW 27.1 rotor, and SW 28 rotor are from Beckman. The Model 4451 lyophilizer is from Labconco. The Model SE660-24cm vertical slab gel unit and glass plates for electrophoresis are from Hoffer Scientific Instruments. Dialysis tubing (with molecular weight cutoff of 14,000, Cat. No. 08-667A) is from Spectrum Medical Industries, Inc. The Model 203 fraction collector is from Gilson Medical Electronics, Inc.

III. Procedures

A. HeLa CELL GROWTH, LABELING, NUCLEAR ISOLATION, AND hnRNP EXTRACTION

This procedure is adapted from those of Beyer *et al.* (1977) and Lothstein *et al.* (1985).

Solutions

1. *1.0 M MgCl₂ stock solution:* To make 500 ml of solution, dissolve 101.7 g of $MgCl_2 \cdot 6H_2O$ in distilled water and adjust the volume to 500 ml. Autoclave and store the solution at 4°C.

2. *10% (v/v) Triton X-100 solution:* For a 100-ml stock solution bring 10 ml of Triton X-100 to a final volume of 100 ml with sterile distilled water. Mix well and store the solution at 4°C.

3. *10× HeLa nuclear isolation buffer (HNIB stock solution):* To make 1 liter, dissolve 2.42 g Tris base in about 950 ml distilled water; add 2.0 ml 10% Triton X-100 stock solution and 1.0 ml of 1.0 M MgCl₂ stock solution. Adjust the pH to 7.5 at room temperature with 6 N HCl, then complete to 1000 ml. Autoclave and store the solution at 4°C or freeze 100-ml aliquots and dilute them to 1000 ml of 1× HNIB before use.

4. *1× HeLa nuclear isolation buffer (1× HNIB solution):* Prepare 1 liter of

fresh solution for each nuclear isolation by diluting 100 ml 10× HNIB with distilled water to 1000 ml. Place the solution on ice and readjust the pH of the cold solution to 7.5 before use.

5. *10× Salt–Tris–magnesium buffer (STM), pH 8.0:* To make a liter of 10× stock, dissolve 52.6 g NaCl and 24.21 g Tris base in about 900 ml distilled water. Add 10.0 ml of 1.0 M MgCl$_2$ stock solution and then adjust the pH of the solution to 8.0 with 6 N HCl. Adjust the final volume to 1000 ml. Autoclave and store the solution at 4°C.

6. *1× Salt–Tris–magnesium buffer (STM), pH 7.2:* Make 1000 ml of fresh solution for each nuclear isolation preparation. Dissolve 5.26 g NaCl and 2.42 g Tris base in about 980 ml distilled water. Add 1.0 ml of 1.0 M MgCl$_2$ and then adjust the pH of the solution to 7.2 with 6 N HCl. Adjust the volume to 1000 ml.

7. *15% Glycerol STM solution:* Make the gradient solutions using sterile, DEPC-treated water and sterile glassware. For 500 ml, add 75 ml glycerol and 50 ml of 10× STM (pH 8.0) stock solution to 250 ml of distilled water. Stir the solution aggressively until homogeneous and adjust to 500 ml. Autoclave for 15 min and store at −20°C.

8. *30% Glycerol STM solution:* To make a 500 ml solution, add 150 ml glycerol and 50 ml of 10× STM (pH 8.0) stock solution to 200 ml distilled water. Stir until glycerol dissolves and adjust to 500 ml with DEPC-treated distilled water. Autoclave for 15 min and store at −20°C.

Steps

1. Grow HeLa cells in suspension culture in modified Eagle's minimal essential medium (Eagle's salt base without CaCl$_2$, with 9.61 mM NaH$_2$PO$_4$ and 10 mg/ml phenol red) supplemented with 5% calf serum, 0.09% pluronic acid, streptomycin (6 mg/liter), penicillin (6000 units/liter). Twenty-four hours before labeling, add [^{35}S]methionine to fresh media to a final concentration of 1 μCi/ml.

2. Harvest the cells at a density of 2.0×10^5 to 6.0×10^5 cells/ml and store the cells at −70°C in 50% glycerol.

3. Perform the following nuclear isolation procedures at 0°C on ice using either fresh or frozen cells. Wash the cells twice in hypotonic 1× HNIB buffer. If using large numbers of cells (between 3 and 9 billion), wash the cells with 1× HNIB two more times so that enough hypotonic exposure will lyse the cells. It may be necessary to aid cell lysis with several strokes of a tight-fitting Dounce homogenizer. Wash the nuclei three times with STM buffer (pH 7.2) and resuspend them in STM buffer (pH 8.0) at a final concentration of 1.3×10^9 nuclei/ml.

4. Transfer the tube containing the nuclear pellet to a beaker of ice at 0°C. Disrupt nuclei by sonication at 50–100 W. Apply three to four 15-sec bursts with a 15-sec pause. After sonication examine the mitigated nuclear preparation under a phase-contrast microscope for complete disruption.

5. Incubate the nuclear sonicate at 37°C for 15 min in a water bath with occasional gentle agitation. This step allows the endogenous nuclease to digest the polyparticle complexes into monoparticles.

6. Centrifuge the sonicate at 8000 g (7000 rpm, HB4 rotor, Sorvall RC2B centrifuge) for 10 min at 4°C to remove the chromatin, nucleoli, and nuclear membranes.

7. Load the supernatant containing the RNP complexes on to a 15–30%

(v/v) linear glycerol gradient and centrifuge at 25,000 rpm in a Beckman SW 28 rotor for 16 hr at 4°C.

8. Fractionate the gradients from the bottom by pumping with a peristaltic pump. Monitor the distribution of optical density at 256–266 nm, using the HP8452 diode array spectrophotometer.

9. Collect gradient fractions using a Gilson Model 203 fraction collector. Take 50- to 100-μl aliquots from each fraction for SDS–PAGE in 0.75-mm Laemmli gel (Fig. 1A). Pool 4.0–5.0 ml of peak fractions which correspond to the 40 S zone in glycerol gradients.

10. Estimate the 40 S monoparticle concentration by calculating the product of its optical density at 260 nm and its volume. Under optimal conditions, each 1.0-billion-cell preparation yields 4.0–5.0 ml of 40 S monoparticles with an optical density at 260 nm of 1.5–2.0. Store the sample at −70°C. We have not observed differences between fresh samples and those stored in this condition for months.

B. PURIFICATION OF THE C PROTEIN TETRAMER

This procedure is modified from that of Barnett *et al.* (1988).

Solutions

1. *1.0 M DTT solution:* Dissolve 15.43 g DTT in distilled water to a final volume of 100 ml and divide the solution into 1.0-ml aliquots. Freeze at −20°C.

2. *200 mM Buffer B:* To prepare 1000 ml, dissolve 11.6 g of NaCl, 2.42 g of Tris base, and 0.203 g of $MgCl_2$ in about 900 ml of water, then add 1.0 ml of 1.0 M DTT solution. Adjust the pH to 8.0 and complete the volume to 1000 ml. Filter the solution with a 500-ml 0.22 μM Fisher bottle-top filter.

3. *600 mM Buffer B:* To prepare 1000 ml, dissolve 35.0 g. of NaCl, 2.42 g. of Tris base, and 0.203 g. of $MgCl_2$ in about 900 ml of water, then add 1.0 ml of 1.0 M DTT solution. Adjust the pH to 8.0 and the volume to 1000 ml. Filter the solution with a 500 ml 0.22 μM Fisher bottle top filter.

4. *460 mM Buffer B:* To prepare 1000 ml, mix 350 ml of 200 mM buffer B with 650 ml of 600 mM buffer B. Filter the solution as described above.

Steps

1. Equilibrate the Mono Q HR5/5 anion-exchange column with 200 mM buffer B for 30 min at a flow rate of 0.5 ml/min. Backwash the column (according to Pharmacia protocol) if it has been used repeatedly and/or if the backpressure is greater the 3.0 mPa.

2. Before loading the gradient-isolated 40 S monoparticles (in 22–25% glycerol STM, pH 8.0) onto the strong anion-exchange column remove any particulates by centrifugation at 8000 g (7000 rpm in the HB-4 rotor); centrifuge in a Sorvall RC-2B for 10 min.

3. Load the sample (up to 40 ml or 60 OD) at a flow rate of 0.5 ml/min.

4. Elute the column with a 27.0-ml salt gradient (from 200 to 600 mM NaCl, buffer B) at a flow rate of 0.5 ml/min and monitor the optical density of the column effluent at 214 nm using a Pharmacia UV-M monitor. The C protein tetramer elutes at a salt concentration near 460 mM.

5. Collect and pool the 2.0–3.0 ml of peak C protein fractions. Take a 30-μl

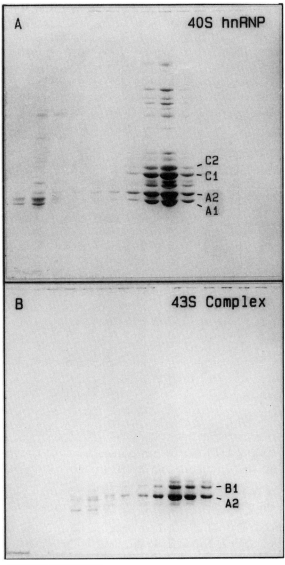

FIGURE 1 (A) Sedimentation and protein composition of intact 40 S hnRNP particles in 15–30% glycerol gradients. These particles spontaneously assemble *in vitro* when monoparticle lengths of RNA are added to crude preparations of RNA-free core particle proteins. These reconstituted particles have the same protein composition and sedimentation properties as native hnRNP particles and they reveal the same pattern of protein–protein crosslinks when exposed to various chemical crosslinking reagents. (B) Sedimentation and protein composition of the artifactual 43 S complex composed of $(A2)_3B1$ tetramers and a 736-nt RNA substrate. The 43 S complex provides rapid access to purified $(A2)_3B1$ tetramers for experimentation.

aliquot for SDS–PAGE and another aliquot for quantitation; freeze the rest of the sample at −70°C.

6. Quantify the C protein by reading absorbance at 214 nm and by the bicinchonic acid (BCA) assay (see Smith, P. K., *et al.*, 1985, *Anal. Biochem.* 150, 76–85) as described below.

7. Dilute the C protein sample 10 times by mixing 50 μl of C protein with 450 μl of 460 mM column elution buffer and estimate the amount of C protein

using a molar extinction coefficient E of 1.6×10^{-6}. This is valid only if the absorbance is below 0.4. If it is above 0.4 then dilute the sample further for the BCA assay below.

8. Prepare the BSA standards with a range of several concentrations which cover the C protein concentration determined from the above assay and perform the BCA assay using the Pharmacia protocol.

9. Read the absorbance of each sample at 562 nm.

10. Plot the BSA standard curve and extrapolate the C protein concentration. Use a correction factor of 0.845 to obtain the true C protein concentration. In such a preparation, the protein concentration ranges from 50 to 400 μg/ml.

C. PURIFICATION OF THE (A2)₃B1 TETRAMERS

This procedure is modified from those of Lothstein *et al.* (1985) and Barnett *et al.* (1991).

Solutions

1. *RNase A stock solution (1 mg/ml):* To make 50 ml solution, weigh out 50 mg RNase A on an analytical balance and add STM (pH 8.0) buffer to make a 1 mg/ml solution. Divide into 1-ml aliquots and boil for 3 min. Cap tightly and store at $-20°C$.

2. *Micrococcal nuclease stock solution (10 units/μl):* Dissolve the lyophilized powder in STM (pH 8) to a concentration of 10 units/μl. Divide the solution into small aliquots and store at $-70°C$.

3. *100 mM DTT:* Dissolve 1.513 g of DTT in 100 ml distilled water, immediately divide the solution into small aliquots, and freeze at $-20°C$.

4. *0.1 M CaCl₂:* Dissolve 14.7 g of CaCl₂·2H₂O in distilled water and adjust the volume to 100 ml. Autoclave the solution.

5. *0.5 M EDTA, pH 8.0:* To make 100 ml, dissolve 18.61 g EDTA to 80 ml water, stir, and adjust the pH to 8.0 with 6 N NaOH. Adjust the volume to 100 ml. Autoclave the solution for 15 min.

Steps

1. Prepare nuclei and nuclear sonic extract as described in Section A (steps 1 through 4). Add RNase A (5 μg/10⁸ nuclei) to crude nuclear sonic extracts. Incubate the preparation at 37°C for 10 to 15 min.

2. Centrifuge this sonicate at 8000 g (7000 rpm, HB4 rotor, Sorvall RC2B centrifuge) for 10 min at 4°C to remove the chromatin, nucleoli, and nuclear membranes.

3. Load the supernatant containing RNP complexes onto a 15–30% linear glycerol gradient and centrifuge at 25,000 rpm in a Beckman SW 28 rotor for 16 hr at 4°C.

4. Fractionate the gradients and collect fractions using the instruments and procedures described in Section A (steps 7 through 9). Analyze the protein composition by taking 50- to 100-μl aliquots from each fraction for SDS–PAGE in 0.75-mm Laemmli gels (Fig. 1B). Pool 3.0–4.0 ml of peak fractions which correspond to the 43 S zone in glycerol gradients.

5. Estimate the 43 S monoparticle concentration by calculating the product of

its optical density at 260 nm and its volume. Under optimal conditions, each 2.0- to 3.0-billion-cell aliquot will yield 3.0–4.0 ml of sample with an optical density at 260 nm of 0.4–0.6.

6. Dialyze the 43 S complex for 4.0 hr against STM (pH 8.0) buffer to remove the glycerol. Change the buffer after 2.0 hr.

7. Add $CaCl_2$ and DTT to a final concentration of 1 mM and add micrococcal nuclease to a concentration of 300 units/ml to digest the endogenous RNA. Perform the digestion for 1 hr at 0°C. After complete digestion of the endogenous RNA, inactivate the enzyme by adding 0.5 M EDTA (pH8.0) to a final concentration of 10 mM. It is very important to keep this preparation at 0°C because insoluble helical fibers spontaneously form through the association of $(A2)_3B1$ tetramers at temperatures above 10°C. Fiber formation can also be slowed with EDTA and DTT.

D. PREPARATION OF TOTAL SOLUBLE hnRNP PROTEINS

This procedure is modified from those of Beyer *et al.* (1977) and Barnett *et al.* (1990). The solutions used are those described in Section C.

Steps

1. Prepare 40 S hnRNP particles according to Section A.

2. Dialyze the sample for at least 4.0 hr against STM (pH 8) at 4°C. Change buffer after 2.0 hr of dialysis to remove sucrose. Clamp the tubing tightly to prevent much dilution of the sample during dialysis.

3. Quantify the sample by measuring the volume of the sample after dialysis and the optical density at 260 nm. For the assembly studies, it is preferable that the optical density of the samples be 1.0–2.0. If it is below 1.0, concentrate the sample with an Amicon Centriprep-30 concentrator by centrifuging at 1500 g (3000 rpm) in a GSA rotor at 4°C for 30 min.

4. Add $CaCl_2$ and DTT to a final concentration of 1 mM. Mix well, then add 1/32nd volume of a micrococcal nuclease solution (10 units/μl) to a final concentration of 300 units/ml.

5. Incubate for 40 min in a water bath at 25°C. After complete digestion of endogenous RNA, inactivate the enzyme by adding 0.5 M EDTA (pH 8.0) to a final concentration of 10 mM.

6. Place the sample on ice. Use freshly prepared material for *in vitro* assembly studies. The core protein stoichiometry may change after thawing samples stored at −20°C (deficient in A1 and B2).

E. *IN VITRO* SYNTHESIS OF RNA

This procedure is adapted from those of Maniatus *et al.* (1982), Conway *et al.* (1988), and Northington (1992).

Solutions

1. *1.0 M Tris, pH 8.0:* For 100 ml, dissolve 12.11 g Tris base in 90 ml distilled water and adjust pH to 8.0. Adjust the volume to 100 ml. Autoclave the solution.

2. *0.5 M EDTA, pH 8.0:* To make 100 ml, dissolve 18.61 g EDTA in 80 ml water, stir, and adjust the pH to 8.0 with 6 N NaOH. Adjust the volume to 100 ml. Autoclave the solution for 15 min.

3. *TE buffer, pH 8.0:* To make 500 ml, add 5.0 ml of 1.0 M Tris (pH 8.0) and 1.0 ml of 0.5 M EDTA (pH 8.0) to distilled water. Adjust the volume to 500 ml. Autoclave the solution for 15 min.

4. *Sephadex G-50 gel filtration medium:* Add 3.5 g of Sephadex G-50 in 100 ml of TE buffer (pH 8.0) and autoclave the slurry for 15 min. Store at 4°C.

Steps

1. Prepare DNA template by digesting 37.0 μg appropriate DNA with desired restriction enzymes in appropriate buffers. Use 2.0 units of enzymes for 1.0 μg of DNA.

2. Incubate at 37°C for 4.0 hr and extract the DNA with an equal volume of phenol/chloroform/isoamyl alcohol (PCI, 50/50/1). Precipitate the sample with 3 vol of ethanol and resuspend in 74.0 μl of distilled water (dH$_2$O).

3. Perform the 400 μl *in vitro* transcription reactions in Eppendorf tubes. Before mixing, thaw out all components except the enzymes and keep them at room temperature before beginning transcription. Add 132 μl dH$_2$O, 80.0 μl 5× transcription buffer, 40.0 μl 100 mM DTT, 8.0 μl RNasin (at 40 units/μl), 16.0 μl 25 mM ATP, GTP, UTP, CTP (25 mM Tris, pH 7.5), 74.0 μl of the DNA template at 0.5 μg/μl, and 2.0 μl T7 RNA polymerase.

4. Incubate the transcription reaction for 1.0–2.0 hr at 37°C. Add 8.0 μl RNasin and 8.0 μl DNase (1 mg/ml) and incubate at 37°C for 10 min.

5. Extract the aqueous phase with phenol/chloroform/isoamyl alcohol (PCI), as described above.

6. Purify the full-length RNA from unincorporated nucleotides by spin column chromatography. Make 5-ml spin columns by adding 4.0–5.0 ml of Sephadex G-50 (in TE buffer) to the barrel of a plastic tuberculin syringe.

7. Load the transcription mix on top of the Sephadex bed and centrifuge the spin column for 2 minutes at one-half maximum speed in a Damon/IEC table top clinical centrifuge. Collect the flow-through containing the high molecular weight RNA.

8. Quantify the RNA from its optical density at 260 nm. Such synthesis usually yield 400 μl of sample at an RNA concentration of 0.5–1.5 μg/μl. To estimate RNA purity, calculate the ratio of the optical density at 260 nm/optical density at 280 nm.

9. Prior to conducting an *in vitro* assembly reaction, examine all transcription products for correct length and absolute homogeneity by electrophoresis of a 2.0 μg aliquot of RNA in an 8 M urea sequencing-type gel.

F. *IN VITRO* ASSEMBLY OF THE 19 S COMPLEX AND OTHER C PROTEIN RNA COMPLEXES

Solutions

1. *10X Salt–Tris–EDTA buffer (STE):* To prepare 1 liter of 10X stock, dissolve 8.00 g of NaOH in about 900 ml of water, then dissolve 37.22 g of disodium dihydrogen edetate dihydrate. Then dissolve 29.22 g of NaCl and 12.12

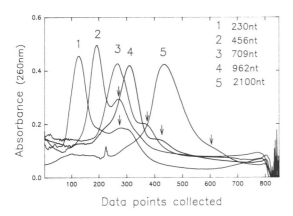

FIGURE 2 Sedimentation of five different C protein–RNA complexes assembled on different lengths of pre-mRNA. The C protein tetramers were purified from 5.0 ml of a 40 S monoparticle preparation with an optical density of 1.0 and were mixed with 50.0 μg RNA (a large RNA molar excess). The C protein–RNA complexes were sedimented in 15–30% glycerol gradients for 18 hr as described in section F. This figure shows the RNA distribution in the gradients (monitored as OD at 256–266 nm), with each data point taken at 1.0-sec intervals on a 100-μl sample window at a flow rate of 16.7 μl/sec. The arrows denote the positions of the protein–RNA complexes assembled on 230,456,709, and 962 nt of *in vitro* synthesized pre-mRNA. Note that in each case the free RNA (the peaks denoted with numbers) sediments more slowly than the corresponding C protein–RNA complexes.

g of Tris base. Add HCl to adjust the pH to 8.0 and adjust the volume to 1000 ml.

2. *1% PMSF in propanol:* Dissolve 1.0 g of PMSF in 100 ml of propanol, divide the solution into small aliquots, and freeze at −20°C.

3. *15% Glycerol STE solution:* Make the gradient solutions using sterile, DEPC-treated water and sterile glassware. For 500 ml, add 75 ml glycerol and 50 ml of 10X STE (pH 8.0) stock solution to 250 ml of distilled water. Stir the solution aggressively until all the glycerol dissolves and adjust to 500 ml. Autoclave for 15 min and store in −20°C freezer.

4. *30% Glycerol STE solution:* To make 500 ml of solution, add 150 ml glycerol and 50 ml of 10X STE (pH 8.0) stock solution to 200 ml distilled water. Stir until glycerol dissolves in solution and adjust to 500 ml with DEPC-treated distilled water. Autoclave for 15 min and store in −20°C freezer.

Steps

1. Prepare the C protein samples for assembly by dialyzing the purified protein 1X STE (pH 8.0) buffer for 4 hr at 4°C in the presence of 0.001% PMSF. Change the buffer after 2.0 hr of dialysis. The C protein concentration ranges from 50 to 400 μg/ml.

2. Prepare the RNA substrates for assembly according to Section E (0.5–1.0 μg/μl in TE buffer). Check each RNA sample on 8% urea denaturing gel for homogeneity.

3. Mix the dialyzed C protein with the *in vitro* synthesized RNA at the specified ratios and concentration. For comparison of sedimentation rates among a series of RNPs assembled on different species of RNA, use the same amount of purified C protein tetramers and RNA in each reaction.

4. Adjust the above reaction mixes to the same volume, in general 1.0–2.0 ml, with STE buffer. The mixture may be allowed to stand for 1 hr on ice.

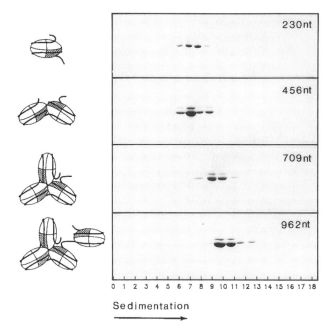

FIGURE 3 Sedimentation and protein composition of four different C protein–RNA complexes. SDS–PAGE shows the distribution of the four C protein–RNA complexes in parallel gradients. These C protein–RNA complexes correspond to the peaks of protein-bound RNA shown in Fig. 2. The number and orientation of the C protein tetramers in each complex are illustrated to the left of each gel. Note that for each RNA length, a single C protein–RNA complex is formed. This occurrence in the presence of excess RNA demonstrates that for the longer lengths of RNA the C proteins bind through a highly self-cooperative binding mode.

5. Prepare 15.0 ml 15–30% glycerol gradients (in STE buffer) for sedimentation analysis using a Hoffer SG30 gradient maker. For comparison of sedimentation of assembled RNP complexes from different experiments, it is important to prepare parallel gradients by carefully controlling the density, volume, and flow rate of the glycerol solutions.

6. For sedimentation analysis, load each sample on the above gradient and centrifuge at 25,000 rpm in a Beckman SW 28 rotor at 4°C. For different separation purposes, sedimentation times may range from 16 to 30 hr, and longer spin times give better resolution.

7. Fractionate the gradients by pumping from the bottom of the gradient tubes at a flow rate of 16.7 μl/sec using a 20-cm-long 23-gauge needle inserted into the bottom of the gradients.

8. Monitor the distribution of optical density at 256–266 and 300–310 nm, and subtract the value at 256–266 nm from that at 300–310 nm. This feature of the HP8452 diode array spectrophotometer automatically corrects for light loss due to scatter in the flow cell. For comparison of RNPs from a series of gradients, it is important to control the pump speed as each collected data point represents a spectroscopic reading monitored at 1.0-sec intervals on a 100-μl sample window (Fig. 2).

9. Collect gradient fractions using a Gilson Model 203 fraction collector. Pool 3.0–4.0 ml of peak fractions which correspond to the RNP complex zone in glycerol gradients.

10. Analyze the assembled RNP products by electrophoresis of the protein and RNA components in each fraction in 7.75% Laemmli gel (Fig. 3).

11. Determine the yield of the various C protein–RNA complexes by calculating the product of each's optical density at 260 nm and its volume. Store the sample at −70°C.

G. *IN VITRO* ASSEMBLY OF THE 43 S (A2)$_3$B1 COMPLEX

The procedure is modified from that of Barnett *et al.* (1991). The solutions used are those described in Section F.

Steps

1. Prepare the (A2)$_3$B1 protein as described in Section C by gradient purifying the 43 S rearrangement complex and by extensively digesting the remaining RNA.

2. Prepare the RNA samples for assembly according to Section E.

3. Mix the RNA with the purified (A2)$_3$B1 tetramers. It has been shown previously that the assembly of (A2)$_3$B1 on RNA is insensitive to protein:RNA ratio (Barnett *et al.*, 1991). In general, mix in a RNA:protein ratio of 3.6 μg RNA:(A2)$_3$B1 protein derived from 1.0 ml of 43 S complex with an optical density of 0.3. Allow the assembly to proceed for 1 hr at 0°C.

4. Analyze the assembled products by sedimentation in a linear 15–30% glycerol gradient (in STE, pH 8.0) for 16 hr at 25,000 rpm in Beckman SW 28 rotor at 4°C.

5. Scan and fractionate the gradients as described in steps 7–9, analyze the protein composition of assembled complex according to step 10. Determine the yield according to step 11 of procedure F.

H. *IN VITRO* ASSEMBLY OF THE (A2)$_3$B1 AND (C1)$_3$C2 TETRAMERS ON RNA SUBSTRATES

The solutions used are those described in Section F.

Steps

1. Prepare the purified C protein tetramers, the (A2)$_3$B1 tetramers, and the purified RNA as described in Sections B, C, and E, respectively. Check the protein samples by electrophoresis in 7.75% Laemmli gel and the RNA in 8% urea gels.

2. Combine the purified C protein and (A2)$_3$B1 tetramers such that the C protein is derived from 5.0 ml of an hnRNP monoparticle preparation with an optical density at 260 nm of 1.0 and the (A2)$_3$B1 is derived from 2.0–2.5 ml of 43 S complex sample with an optical density of 0.3. Add 51.0 μg synthesized RNA to the mixture.

3. Allow the assembly reaction to stand on ice for 1 hr.

4. Analyze the products by sedimentation in a linear 15–30% glycerol gradient (in STE, pH 8.0) for 16 hr at 25,000 rpm in Beckman SW 28 rotor at 4°C.

5. Scan and fractionate the gradients as described in steps 7–9, analyze the protein composition of assembled complex according to step 10, and quantify the yield according to step 11 of Section F.

I. *IN VITRO* ASSEMBLY OF CORE hnRNP PROTEIN TETRAMERS ON PREFORMED RNP COMPLEXES

The *in vitro* assembly experiment described here was performed to determine whether some stable RNP complexes exist as intermediates in the 40 S assembly pathway. We describe here (1) the assembly of (A2)$_3$B1 tetramers on C protein–RNA complex (an obligate first intermediate) in and (2) the assembly of total hnRNP core proteins on preassembled tetramer–RNA complexes. The solutions used are those described in Section F.

1. Assembly of (A2)$_3$B1 Tetramers on Preformed C Protein–RNA Complexes

Steps

1. Prepare the C protein–RNA complexes according to Section F. Dialyze the samples against 1X STE (pH 8.0) buffer for 4 hr at 4°C in the presence of 0.001% PMSF. Change the buffer after 2.0 hr of dialysis.

2. Prepare the (A2)$_3$B1 tetramers according to Section C. Use freshly prepared sample.

3. Add (A2)$_3$B1 samples to C protein–RNA complex at desired rations. To compare the series of assembled RNP products, it is important to adjust the above reaction mixes to the same volume. In general, we adjust the final volume to 1.0 or 2.0 ml by adding STE buffer or concentrating the samples with Amicon Centriprep-30 concentrator by centrifuging at 1500 *g* (3000 rpm) in the GSA rotor at 4°C for 30 min.

4. Incubate the mixture for at least 1 hr on ice.

5. For sedimentation analysis, load each sample on the above gradient and centrifuge at 25,000 rpm in a Beckman SW 28 rotor at 4°C for 16 hr.

6. Fraction the gradients and monitor the distribution of optical density as described in Section F.

7. Analyze the assembled RNP products by taking aliquots from each fraction and electrophorese the protein in each fraction in a 7.75% Laemmli gel (Fig. 4).

8. Collect RNP products by pooling 3.0–4.0 ml of peak fractions which correspond to the RNP complex zone in glycerol gradients. Quantify the yield by calculating the product of its optical density at 260 nm and its volume. Store the sample at −70°C.

2. Assembly of Intact 40 S hnRNP Core Particles on Preassembled C Protein–RNA Complexes

Steps

1. Prepare C protein–RNA complexes, (A2)$_3$B1–RNA complexes, and (A2)$_3$B1–(Cl)$_3$C2–RNA complex samples as described in Sections F, G, and H.

2. Mix the complexes with soluble hnRNP proteins obtained in Section D at desired reactant concentration and ratio. In general, for electrophoresis of sample from each gradient fraction, use soluble hnRNP core proteins corresponding to the protein derived from 1.0 ml hnRNP monoparticles with an optical density of 1.0. Allow the RNP complexes to assemble for 1 hr at 0°C.

3. Analyze assembled products as described Section F, in steps 5–8 (Fig. 5).

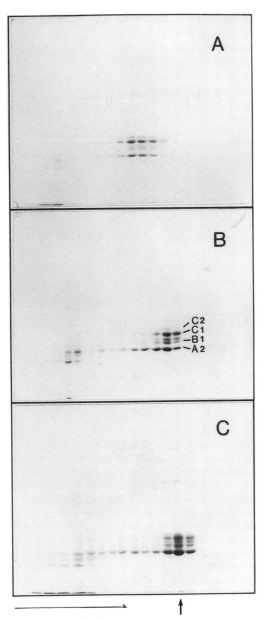

Sedimentation

FIGURE 4 Binding of purified (A2)₃B1 tetramers to preformed 19 S C protein–RNA complexes containing three C protein tetramers. The 19 S C protein–RNA complexes and the (A2)₃B1 tetramers were purified as described in the text. These three SDS–PAGE gels show the protein composition in each successive fraction of three parallel 15–30% glycerol gradients. In each experiment the 19 S complexes were mixed with increasing amounts of purified (A2)₃B1 tetramers. The molar ratios of 19 S complex to (A2)₃B1 were 1:1.5 (A), 1:3 (B), and 1:12 (C). Note the difference in protein composition and the increased sedimentation of the assembled products as additional (A2)₃B1 tetramers bind. Note also in (B) that when three (A2)₃B1 tetramers are allowed to bind the 19 S complex (which contains three C protein tetramers), equal molar amounts of these proteins are present in the assembled RNP intermediate complex. The position of 40 S is indicated with an arrow.

IV. Comments

In the various *in vitro* assembly studies described above, it is important to have no free RNA present in the preformed protein–RNA complexes which are to be

Assembly Substrates   Assembled Products

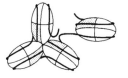

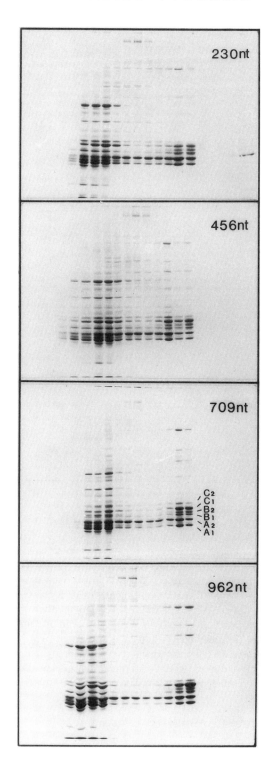

used as assembly substrates. This is because free RNA will nucleate the assembly of soluble hnRNP proteins. For studies using the three-tetramer C protein–RNA complex which assembles on RNAs of 700 nt (i.e., the 19 S complex), we have formed the complexes in two ways. The 19 S complex has been assembled under conditions of protein molar excess (a protein:RNA ratio of 7.46). In this case all the RNA is saturated with protein and no detectable free RNA is present. In other experiments we have purified the protein–RNA complexes following their assembly. The C protein tetramers bind RNA through a highly self-cooperative binding mode and only the 19 S complex (containing three tetramers) forms over a wide range of protein and RNA ratios. In glycerol gradients the 19 S complex exists as a single homogeneous peak sedimenting faster than free RNA and it can easily be collected free of unbound RNA. In the latter case, we suggest extending the sedimentation time to 28 hr and collecting 2.0–3.0 ml RNP peak fractions. Whether assembled under conditions of excess protein or excess RNA the purified 19 S C protein–RNA complexes nucleate the correct assembly of the 40 S hnRNP monoparticle.

V. Pitfalls

1. It is of significant value in the various *in vitro* RNP assembly studies to cosediment the various purified RNAs (used as binding substrates) in parallel gradients. This routine procedure provides a second check (in addition to electrophoresis) for RNA homogeneity, it provides an important standard for quantification following centrifugation, and it allows one to readily distinguish protein-bound from protein-free peaks (especially under assembly conditions where the RNA is in excess).

2. Under conditions of extreme protein excess (20–50 M), about one-third of the purified C in a binding reaction binds RNA to form a fast-sedimenting, artifactual complex (Northington, 1992), which, based on its density in CsCl, is probably composed of two tetramers and eight RNA molecules. This is not inconsistent with the presence of four separate RNA binding sites in each tetramer. It also suggests that tetramer–tetramer interactions may exist at high protein concentrations prior to RNA addition. Under these assembly conditions, the efficiency of the 19 S complex is decreased. Therefore we recommend conducting the protein–RNA binding experiments using RNA excess or slight protein excess. The artifactual complex is either absent or present only in trace amounts when RNA is mixed with protein in a ratio greater than 25 μg:100 μg (molar ratio of 1:7.46).

FIGURE 5 *In vitro* assembly of RNP complexes on preformed C protein–RNA complexes containing one to four tetramers. This series of SDS–PAGE gels shows the protein composition and sedimentation properties of the assembled products. The assembly substrates are diagrammed at the left of each panel and the RNA lengths are shown in the upper right corner of each panel. These structures are illustrated in electron micrographs published elsewhere (Huang *et al.*, 1994). Note that only the RNP complex assembled on the three-tetramer RNA complex (709 nt, third panel from top) has a correct protein stoichiometry of the 40 S hnRNP monoparticles. The complex formed on the one-tetramer RNA complex is rich in (A2)$_3$B1 as expected, as these tetramers can bind short lengths of RNA to form the 43 S artifactual structure. The complexes formed on two-tetramer RNA complex reveal the presence of a two-thirds monoparticle and a faster sedimenting artifactual structure. The complex assembled on the four-tetramer RNA complex is rich in C proteins and sediments slightly faster than native 40 S hnRNP particles.

ACKNOWLEDGMENTS

The work leading to the development of these methods was supported by NSF Grant MCB 8819051 and NIH Grant GM-48567 to W.M.L.

REFERENCES

Barnett, S. F., LeStourgeon, W. M., and Friedman, D. L. (1988) Rapid purification of native C protein from nuclear ribonucleoprotein particles. *J. Biochem. Biophys. Methods* **16**, 87–98.

Barnett, S. F., Northington, S. J., and LeStourgeon, W. M. (1990) "Isolation and In Vitro Assembly of Nuclear Ribonucleoprotein Particles and Purification of Core Particle Proteins" (J. Dahlberg and J. N. Abelson, eds.), Vol. 181, pp. 293–307. Academic Press, New York.

Barnett, S. F., Theiry, T. A., and LeStourgeon, W. M. (1991) The core proteins A2 and B1 exist as (A2)3B1 tetramers in 40 S nuclear ribonucleoprotein particles. *Mol. Cell Biol.* **11**, 864–871.

Beyer, A. L., Christensen, M. E., Walker, B. W., and LeStourgeon, W. M. (1977) Identification and characterization of the packaging proteins of core 40 S hnRNP Particles. *Cell* **11**, 127–138.

Conway, G., Wooley, J., Bibring, T., and LeStourgeon, W. M. (1988) Ribonucleoproteins package 700 nucleotides of pre-mRNA into a repeating array of regular particles. *Mol. Cell Biol.* **8**, 2884–2895.

Huang, M., Rech, J. E., Northington, S. J., Flicker, P., Mayeda, A., Krainer, A. R., and LeStourgeon, W. M. (1994) The C protein tetramer nucleates the assembly of nuclear ribonucleoprotein particles. Submitted for publication.

LeStourgeon, W. M., Barnett, S. F., and Northington, S. J. (1990) Tetramers of the core proteins of 40 S nuclear ribonucleoprotein particles assemble to package nascent transcripts into a repeating array of regular particles. *In* "The Eukaryotic Nucleus: Molecular Biochemistry and Macromolecular Assemblies" (P. R. Strauss and S. H. Wilson, eds.), Vol. 2, pp. 477–502.

Lothstein, L., Arenstorf, H. P., Chung, S., Walker, B. W., Wooley, J. C., and LeStourgeon, W. M. (1985) General organization of protein in HeLa 40 S nuclear ribonucleoprotein particles. *J. Cell Biol.* **100**, 1570–1581.

Maniatus, T., Fritsch, E. F., and Sambrook, J. (1982) "Molecular Cloning: A Laboratory Manual." Cold Spring Harbor Laboratory, Cold Spring Harbor, NY.

Northington, S. J. (1992) "In Vitro Interaction of the C Proteins of Nuclear Ribonucleoprotein Particles with RNA," pp. 1–141. Doctoral thesis, Vanderbilt University.

Preparation of Ribosomes and Ribosomal Proteins from Cultured Cells

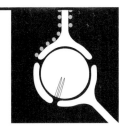

Jean-Jacques Madjar

I. Introduction

For many studies concerning cell metabolism or gene expression, it may be useful to prepare ribosomes and ribosomal proteins from eukaryotic cells in culture. This can be easily achieved by simple and reproducible procedures of cell fractionation that do not require specific equipment. Ribosomes consist of about 80 basic proteins which interact with each other and with four different ribosomal RNAs in the ribosomal particle made up of two subunits (Hill *et al.*, 1990). In an active ribosome, they also interact with many other proteins involved in the complicated process of protein synthesis and with other RNA molecules such as tRNA and mRNA. Preparing a mixture of pure total ribosomal proteins (TP80S) implies getting rid of contaminating nonribosomal proteins and of virtually all RNA molecules. The procedure described below allows us to reach this goal in a way that permits the subsequent separation and analysis of all ribosomal proteins by two-dimensional polyacrylamide gel electrophoresis (Celis, 1992; Kaltschmidt and Wittmann, 1970; Madjar *et al.*, 1979, Sherton and Wool, 1972; see also article by Julio E. Celis, Gitle Ratz, Bodil Basse, Jette B. Lauridsen, and Ariana Celis in this volume).

II. Materials and Instrumentation

Acetic acid (Art. 63), acetone (Art. 14), fuming hydrochloric acid (Art. 317), magnesium acetate tetrahydrate (Art. 5819), magnesium chloride hexahydrate (Art. 5833), potassium chloride (Art. 4936), sodium chloride (Art. 6404), disodium hydrogen phosphate (Art. 6580), and potassium dihydrogen phosphate (Art. 4873) are purchased from Merck. Sucrose (Cat. No. S-0389), guanidine hydrochloride (Cat. No. G-4505), and iodoacetamide (Cat. No. I-6125) are purchased from Sigma. Nonidet P-40 (NP-40, Cat. No. 1332 473), 1,4-dithioerythritol (DTE, Cat. No. 223 662) and Tris (Cat. No. 708 976) are purchased from Boehringer-Mannheim.

Cell tissue culture flasks of 162 cm² are purchased from Costar. Dialysis tubes (1-8/32 in.) are purchased from Medicell International Ltd. Microtubes of 1.5 ml (Cat. No. 3811) are purchased from Eppendorf. Tubes of 15 ml (Corex tube, Cat. No. 03286) are purchased from Sorvall, Du Pont de Nemours. TL-100 table-top ultracentrifuge with TLA-100.3 fixed-angle rotor and thick-wall polycarbonate tubes (Part No. 349622) are from Beckman.

III. Procedures

A. CELL FRACTIONATION FOR PREPARATION OF RIBOSOMES

Solutions

1. *Phosphate-buffered saline (PBS):* To make 2 liters, dissolve 15.3 g of NaCl, 1.45 g of $Na_2HPO_4 \cdot 2H_2O$, and 0.42 g of KH_2PO_4 in distilled water and adjust the volume to 2 liters with distilled water. Store at 4°C.

2. *Potassium chloride stock solution:* 2 M KCl. To make 1 liter, dissolve 149.12 g of KCl in distilled water and adjust the volume to 1 liter with distilled water. Store at 4°C.

3. *Magnesium chloride stock solution:* 1 M $MgCl_2$. To make 100 ml, dissolve 20.33 g of $MgCl_2 \cdot 6H_2O$ in distilled water and adjust the volume to 100 ml with distilled water. Store at 4°C.

4. *Tris–HCl, pH 7.4, stock solution:* 1 M Tris–HCl, pH 7.4. To make 100 ml, dissolve 12.11 g of Tris in 80 ml of distilled water. Adjust the pH to 7.4 with fuming HCl at room temperature. Adjust the volume to 100 ml with distilled water. Store at 4°C.

5. *Buffer A:* 0.25 M sucrose, 25 mM KCl, 5 mM $MgCl_2$, 50 mM Tris–HCl, pH 7.4. To make 100 ml of the buffer, add 8.55 g of sucrose, 1.25 ml of a 2 M stock solution of KCl, 0.5 ml of a 1 M stock solution of $MgCl_2$, and 5 ml of a 1 M stock solution of Tris–HCl, pH 7.4. After dissolving, complete to 100 ml with distilled water. Store at 4°C.

6. *Buffer B:* 0.25 M sucrose, 0.5 M KCl, 5 mM $MgCl_2$, 50 mM Tris–HCl, pH 7.4. To make 100 ml of the buffer, add 8.55 g of sucrose, 25 ml of a 2 M stock solution of KCl, 0.5 ml of a 1 M stock solution of $MgCl_2$, and 5 ml of a 1 M stock solution of Tris–HCl, pH 7.4. After dissolving, complete to 100 ml with distilled water. Store at 4°C.

7. *Buffer C:* 0.25 M sucrose, 2 M KCl, 5 mM $MgCl_2$, 50 mM Tris–HCl, pH 7.4. To make 10 ml of the buffer, add 0.85 g of sucrose, 1.49 g of KCl, 50 μl of a 1 M stock solution of $MgCl_2$, and 0.5 ml of a 1 M stock solution of Tris–HCl, pH 7.4. After dissolving, complete to 10 ml with distilled water. Store at 4°C.

8. *Sucrose cushion:* 1 M sucrose, 0.5 M KCl, 5 mM $MgCl_2$, 50 mM Tris–HCl, pH 7.4. To make 50 ml of the buffer, add 17.1 g of sucrose, 12.5 ml of a 2 M stock solution of KCl, 0.25 ml of a 1 M stock solution of $MgCl_2$, and 2.5 ml of a 1 M stock solution of Tris–HCl, pH 7.4. After dissolving, complete to 50 ml with distilled water. Store at 4°C.

9. *Nonidet P-40 (NP-40):* 20% (w/v) NP-40 in H_2O. To make 10 ml of the solution, weigh 2 g of NP-40 and complete to 10 ml with distilled water. Store at room temperature.

Steps

1. Wash the cells in the 162-cm² flask (about 15×10^6 HeLa cells) three times with cold PBS kept at 4°C. Scrape the cells off the flask with a cell lifter in 10 ml of PBS and pour into a 50-ml conical polypropylene tube kept on ice. Rinse the flask twice with 5 ml of PBS, and add the buffer containing the residual cells to the same conical tube.

2. Centrifuge cell suspension at 500 g for 5 min at 4°C. Remove the supernatant and resuspend the cells in 0.3 ml of cold buffer A (about three times the volume of the cell pellet). Transfer the cell suspension to a 1.5-ml Eppendorf microtube.

3. Stir slowly with a Vortex while adding 14 μl of the 20% NP-40 solution to make it 0.7% and keep on ice for 10 min.

4. Centrifuge the cell lysate at 750 g for 10 min at 4°C to spin down the nuclei. Remove carefully the postnuclear supernatant and put it in another Eppendorf microtube. If necessary save the pellet for other studies.

5. Centrifuge the postnuclear supernatant at 12,500 g for 10 min at 4°C to spin down the mitochondria. Decant carefully the postmitochondrial supernatant into another Eppendorf microtube. If necessary save the pellet for other studies.

6. Measure precisely the volume (which should be about 0.4 ml) and add 0.32 vol of buffer C (128 μl for 0.4 ml) to adjust the final concentration of KCl to 0.5 M.

7. Layer the postmitochondrial supernatant on top of 1 ml of the 1 M sucrose cushion in a thick-wall polycarbonate centrifuge tube. Equilibrate the tubes precisely by adding a few drops of buffer B. Place the tubes in the TLA-100.3 fixed-angle rotor. It is not necessary to fill the tubes.

8. After centrifugation in the TL-100 table-top Beckman ultracentrifuge for 2 hr at 75,000 rpm (245,000 g) at 4°C, with the brake on for maximum deceleration rate, remove the supernatant on top of the translucent pellet of ribosomes. If necessary save the supernatant for other studies. Quickly rinse the pellet twice with distilled water.

9. Resuspend the ribosome pellet in 100 μl of buffer A. Wash the tube twice with 100 μl of buffer A and pool the 300 μl in an Eppendorf microtube.

10. Measure the optical density at 260 nm. Estimate the amount of ribosomes assuming that 14 A_{260} units correspond roughly to 1 mg of ribosomes and to about 0.5 mg of total ribosomal proteins. By this procedure, 15×10^6 HeLa cells (grown in one 162-cm^2 flask) give about 2.8 A_{260} units, i.e., about 200 μg of ribosomes and about 100 μg of total ribosomal proteins (TP80S).

B. EXTRACTION, ALKYLATION, AND LYOPHILIZATION OF RIBOSOMAL PROTEINS

Solutions

1. *Magnesium acetate:* 1 M magnesium acetate. To make 100 ml of the solution, weigh 21.45 g of magnesium acetate. After dissolving in distilled water, complete to 100 ml with distilled water. Store at 4°C.

2. *Acetic acid:* 1 M acetic acid. To make 1 liter of the solution, measure 57 ml of glacial acetic acid and complete to 1 liter with distilled water. Store at 4°C.

3. *Tris base:* 1 M Tris base. To make 100 ml of the solution, weigh 12.14 g of Tris base. After dissolving in distilled water, complete to 100 ml with distilled water. Do not adjust the pH. Store at 4°C.

4. *1,4-Dithioerythritol:* 0.5 M DTE. To make 10 ml of the solution, weigh 0.77 g of DTE. After dissolving in distilled water, complete to 10 ml with distilled water. Make 0.5-ml aliquots in Eppendorf microtubes and store at −20°C.

5. *Guanidine hydrochloride–Tris buffer:* 6 M guanidine hydrochloride, 0.5 M Tris–HCl, pH 8.5. To make 10 ml, dissolve 5.7 g of guanidine hydrochloride in 5 ml of the 1 M Tris base solution. Adjust the pH to 8.5 with fuming HCl

(37%). The final volume should then be 10 ml. Prepare just before use and filter if necessary.

6. *Reducing buffer:* 6 M guanidine hydrochloride, 0.5 M Tris–HCl, pH 8.5, 10 mM dithioerythritol. Add 82 μl of the 0.5 M DTE solution to 4 ml of guanidine hydrochloride–Tris buffer. Prepare just before use.

7. *Alkylating buffer:* 6 M guanidine hydrochloride, 0.5 M Tris–HCl, pH 8.5, 40 mM iodoacetamide. Weigh about 200 mg of iodoacetamide and dissolve in the guanidine hydrochloride–Tris buffer at the rate of 92.5 mg/ml. Prepare just before use.

Steps

1. Adjust the magnesium acetate concentration to 0.2 M by adding to the ribosome suspension one-fourth of its volume of the 1 M magnesium acetate solution.

2. Then add 2 vol of glacial acetic acid, i.e., 2.5 vol of the initial ribosome solution. Stir with a Vortex and keep on ice for 1 hr.

3. Centrifuge at 12,000 rpm for 10 min at 4°C to pellet the RNA which appears as white. Remove the supernatant containing the ribosomal proteins and transfer it in a 15-ml Corex tube.

4. Reextract the ribosomal proteins from the RNA pellet by resuspending the pellet in 200 μl of 0.1 M magnesium acetate (20 μl of 1 M magnesium acetate plus 180 μl of distilled water) and 400 μl of glacial acetic acid. Stir with a Vortex and keep on ice for 10 min. Centrifuge again at 12,000 rpm for 10 min at 4°C. Remove the supernatant containing the residual ribosomal proteins and pool with the first ribosomal protein extract in the 15-ml Corex tube.

5. Precipitate the ribosomal proteins by adding at least 5 vol of cold acetone. Let the proteins precipitate at −80°C for 2 hr or at 4°C overnight.

6. Centrifuge at 10,000 rpm. Remove the liquid carefully and dry the pellet in a SpeedVac Savant concentrator.

7. For reducing the proteins, solubilize the dried TP80S in the reducing buffer (1 to 10 mg/ml or less) in the Corex tube. Let stand at room temperature under nitrogen for 30 min. For this, flow nitrogen over the reducing buffer containing the solubilized TP80S and close the tube with a piece of Parafilm.

8. For alkylating the proteins, add 8.7 μl of alkylating buffer per 100 μl of solubilized proteins. Let stand at room temperature under nitrogen for 1.5 hr, as above.

9. Transfer the protein solution to a dialysis tube and rinse the Corex tube with the 1 M acetic acid solution. Dialyze at least three times against 100 vol of 1 M acetic acid, at 4°C.

10. After dialysis, TP80S can be stored in 1 M acetic acid at −20°C for years. For analysis by two-dimensional gel electrophoresis (2D PAGE), TP80S are first lyophilized in an Eppendorf microtube in a SpeedVac concentrator.

IV. Comments

By using the protocol described here, it is possible to prepare crude ribosomes from cell tissue culture with a good yield. They are salt washed by 0.5 M KCl and are prepared from a mixture of both free and membrane-bound ribosomes after lysis of the cell membranes with Nonidet P-40; however, this treatment does not disrupt the inner nuclear membrane, allowing easy disposition of the nuclei during the cell fractionation procedure. TP80S can be isotopically labeled. TP80S extracted by the acetic acid procedure are extremely stable in 1 M acetic acid, in which they can be stored frozen at $-20°C$ or less. The alkylation step by iodoacetamide after reduction by dithioerythritol allows the blocking of all the SH groups without change of the net charge of the protein (Madjar and Traut, 1980). Rinsing the tube with 1 M acetic acid and dialyzing against the same solution permit lowering the pH to stop the alkylation reaction. After lyophilization TP80S are free of contaminating salts and very easily solubilized in the sample buffer containing at least 8 M urea. Under these conditions, TP80S can be separated by 2D PAGE, according to charge in the presence of at least 8 M urea in the first dimension and according to mass in the second dimension, in either the presence of SDS or urea in a highly reticulated polyacrylamide gel. As most ribosomal proteins are very basic, they are separated by electrophoresis by migration from the anode to the cathode (except if the second dimension is run in the presence of SDS). Under these conditions, alkylation of the proteins avoids possible reoxidation of the proteins which are overflowed by the ammonium persulfate migrating in the opposite direction. Moreover, alkylation of the SH groups does not prevent microsequencing of the proteins (Diaz *et al.*, 1993).

V. Pitfalls

1. To avoid breaking the cells do not spin them down at more than 500 *g*.

2. To obtain the postmitochondrial supernatant first spin down the nuclei after the cell lysis. The risks involved in omitting this step are disruption of the nuclei during centrifugation of the mitochondria at 12,500 *g* and contamination (with fragments of DNA and nucleosomes) of ribosomes obtained through the 1 M sucrose cushion. This contamination can be visualized by the presence of histones among ribosomal proteins after separation by 2D PAGE.

3. The ribosome pellet must be resuspended very carefully, to avoid the loss of ribosomes, to measure the optical density with precision, and to obtain a good yield of protein extracted by the acetic acid procedure.

REFERENCES

Celis, J. E. (ed.) (1992) Two-dimensional gel protein databases. *Electrophoresis* **13**.
Diaz, J.-J., Simonin, D., Massé, T., Deviller, P., Kindbeiter, K., Denoroy, L., and Madjar, J-J. (1993) The herpes simplex virus type 1 US11 gene product is a phosphorylated protein found to be nonspecifically associated with both ribosomal subunits. *J. Gen. Virol.* **74**, 397–406.
Hill, W. E., Dahlberg, A., Garrett, R. A., Moore, P. B., Schlessinger, D., and Warner, J. R. (eds.) (1990) "The Ribosome, Structure, Function, & Evolution." American Society for Microbiology, Washington, DC.
Kaltschmidt, E., and Wittmann, H. G. (1970) Two-dimensional polyacrylamide gel electrophoresis for fingerprinting of ribosomal proteins. *Anal. Biochem.* **36**, 401–412.
Madjar, J-J., Arpin, M., Buisson, M., and Reboud, J. P. (1979) Spot position of rat liver ribosomal proteins by four different two-dimensional electrophoreses in polyacrylamide gel. *Mol. Gen. Genet.* **171**, 121–134.
Madjar, J-J., and Traut, R. R. (1980) Differences in electrophoretic behaviour of eight ribosomal proteins from rat and rabbit tissues and evidence for proteolytic action on liver proteins. *Mol. Gen. Genet.* **179**, 89–101.
Sherton, C. C., and Wool, I. G. (1972) Determination of the number of proteins in liver ribosomes and ribosomal subunits by two-dimensional polyacrylamide gel electrophoresis. *J. Biol. Chem.* **247**, 4460–4467.

Preparation of Proteasomes

Keiji Tanaka and Akira Ichihara

I. Introduction

The proteasome catalyzes the nonlysosomal proteolytic pathway responsible for selective removal of proteins with aberrant structures and naturally occurring short-lived proteins, as well as class I MHC-restricted antigen processing (Goldberg and Rock, 1992). Recently, two types of proteasomes with apparent sedimentation coefficients of 20 S and 26 S were shown to be present in various cells. The 20 S proteasome (also named a multicatalytic proteinase complex) is responsible for endoproteolytic cleavage of peptide bonds on the carboxyl side of basic, neutral, and acidic amino acid residues of proteins (Rivett, 1993). The 26 S proteasome, which consists of one 20 S proteasome and associated components that probably have regulatory roles (Tanaka et al., 1992), catalyzes ATP-dependent degradation of proteins with covalently attached ubiquitin as a signal for their selective breakdown (Goldberg and Rock, 1992). It is also involved in ATP-dependent breakdown of short-lived proteins without ubiquitination (Murakami et al., 1992).

We have reported procedures for purification of 20 S proteasomes from various eukaryotes (Tanaka et al., 1988a) and studied their protein and gene structures (for review, see Tanaka et al., 1992). We have also developed a new method for purification of 26 S proteasomes (Kanayama et al., 1992; Ugai et al., 1993) and examined their physicochemical properties (Yoshimura et al., 1993). In this article, we briefly review procedures for isolating 20 S and 26 S proteasomes from mammalian tissues.

II. Materials and Instrumentation

Q-Sepharose (Cat. No. 17-1014-03) and heparin–Sepharose CL-6B (Cat. No. 17-0467-09) can be purchased from Pharmacia LKB Biotechnology. Bio-Gel A-1.5 m (Cat. No. 151-0449), Bio-Gel A-5m (Cat. No. 151-0730), and hydroxyapatite Bio-Gel HTP (Cat. No. 130-0420) are from Bio-Rad. Polyethylene glycol 6000 (Cat. No. P-2139), succinyl-Leu–Leu–Val–Tyr-4-methyl-coumaryl-7-amide (Suc-LLVY-MCA, Cat. No. S-6510), and ubiquitin (Ub, Cat. No. U-6253) are from Sigma. Amicon PM-10 membranes (Cat. No. 13132) can be obtained from Amicon.

III. Procedures

A. PREPARATION OF 20 S PROTEASOMES

Solutions

1. *Buffer A:* 25 mM Tris–HCl (pH 7.5) containing 1 mM DTT and 20% glycerol.

2. *Buffer B:* 10 m*M* phosphate buffer (pH 6.8) containing 1 m*M* DTT and 20% glycerol.

Steps

1. Homogenize 200- to 400-g samples of animal tissue in 3 vol of 25 m*M* Tris–HCl buffer (pH 7.5) containing 1 mM DTT and 0.25 *M* sucrose in a Potter–Elvehjem homogenizer. Centrifuge the homogenate for 1 hr at 105,000 *g*, and use the resulting supernatant as the crude extract.

2. Add glycerol at a final concentration of 20% to the crude extract. Then mix the extract with 500 g of Q-Sepharose that has been equilibrated with buffer A. Wash the Q-Sepharose with the same buffer on a Büchner funnel and transfer to a column (5 × 60 cm). Wash the column with buffer A and elute the material with 2 liters of a linear gradient of 0–0.8 *M* NaCl in the same buffer. Collect fractions of 10 ml, and measure the activity of proteasomes as described in Section IV.

3. Pool fractions containing 20 S proteasomes from the Q-Sepharose column and add 50% polyethylene glycol 6000 (adjust to pH 7.4) at a final concentration of 15% with gentle stirring. After 15 min, centrifuge the mixture at 10,000 *g* for 20 min, dissolve the resulting precipitate in a minimum volume (approximately 50 ml) of buffer A, and centrifuge at 20,000 *g* for 10 min to remove insoluble material.

4. Fractionate the material precipitated with polyethylene glycol on a Bio-Gel A-1.5m column (5 × 100 cm) in buffer A. Collect fractions of 10 ml and assay their proteasome activity. Pool fractions of 20 S proteasomes.

5. Apply the active fraction from the Bio-Gel A-1.5 m column directly to a column of hydroxyapatite equilibrated with buffer B. Wash the column with the same buffer and elute the material with 400 ml of a linear gradient of 10–300 m*M* phosphate. Collect fractions of 4 ml. Elute the 20 S proteasomes with about 150 m*M* phosphate.

6. Combine the active fractions from the hydroxyapatite, dialyzed against buffer A, and apply to a column of heparin–Sepharose CL-6B equilibrated with buffer A. Wash the column with the same buffer until the absorbance of the eluate at 280 nm returns to baseline. Then elute with 200 ml of a linear gradient of 0–0.4 *M* NaCl in the same buffer, and collect fractions of 2 ml. Elute the 20 S proteasomes with approximately 75 m*M* NaCl.

7. Pool the fractions with high proteasomal activity, dialyze against buffer A, and concentrate to about 5 mg/ml protein by ultrafiltration in an Amicon cell with a PM-10 membrane. The enzyme can be stored at −80°C for at least 2 to 3 years.

B. PREPARATION OF 26 S PROTEASOMES

Solutions

1. *Buffer C:* Buffer A containing 0.5 m*M* ATP.
2. *Buffer D:* Buffer B containing 5 m*M* ATP.

Steps

1. Homogenize 200- to 400-g samples of animal tissue in 3 vol of 25 m*M* Tris–HCl buffer (pH 7.5) containing 1 m*M* DTT, 2 m*M* ATP, and 0.25 *M*

sucrose in a Potter–Elvehjem homogenizer. Centrifuge the homogenate for 1 hr at 70,100 g, and use the resulting supernatant as the starting material.

2. Recentrifugation of the crude supernatant for 5 hr at 70,100 g precipitates 26 S proteasomes almost completely. Dissolve the precipitate in a suitable volume (40–50 ml) of buffer A, and centrifuge at 20,000 g for 30 min to remove insoluble material.

3. Apply samples of the preparation from step 2 to a Bio-Gel A-1.5m column (5 × 100 cm) in buffer C. Collect fractions of 10 ml, and assay the 26 S proteasomal activity in the fractions. Pool fractions of 26 S proteasomes.

4. Add ATP at a final concentration of 5 mM to the pooled fractions of 26 S proteasomes from the Bio-Gel A-5m column. Apply a sample directly to a hydroxyapatite column with a 50-ml bed volume that has been equilibrated with buffer D. Recover the 26 S proteasomes in the flow-through fraction, because they do not associate with this column in the presence of 5 mM ATP. Approximately 70% of the proteins, including free 20 S proteasomes, bind to the hydroxyapatite resin.

5. Apply the flow-through fraction from the hydroxyapatite column to a Q-Sepharose column that has been equilibrated with buffer C without ATP, and washed with 1 bed volume of buffer C. Wash the column with 5 bed volumes of buffer C, and elute the adsorbed materials with 300 ml of a linear gradient of 0–0.8 M NaCl in the same buffer. Collect fractions of 3.0 ml of eluate. Proteins with the ability to degrade Suc-LLVY-MCA with or without 0.05% SDS are eluted with about 0.4 M NaCl as a single symmetric peak. ATPase activity and the ATP-dependent activity to degrade ^{125}I-lysozyme–Ub conjugates are observed at the same position as peptidase activity and are eluted as superimposable symmetric peaks, suggesting a specific association of ATPase with the 26 S proteasome complex. Collect protein in the fractions exhibiting high activity.

6. Concentrate the 26 S proteasome fraction obtained by Q-Sepharose chromatography to 2.0 mg/ml by ultrafiltration with an Amicon PM-10 membrane, and subject samples of 2.0 mg of protein to 10–40% glycerol density gradient centrifugation (30 ml in buffer C containing 2 mM ATP). Collect fractions of 1 ml from the bottom of the centrifuge tube. A single major peak of peptidase activity in the absence of SDS is eluted around fraction 15, but when the activity is assayed with 0.05% SDS, another small peak is observed around fraction 20. The latter peak corresponds to the elution position of 20 S proteasomes. ATPase activity is observed at the same position as peptidase activity. Activity for ATP-dependent degradation of ^{125}I-lysozyme–Ub conjugates is also observed as a single symmetric peak, coinciding in position with the ATPase and peptidase activities in the absence of SDS. No significant ^{125}I-lysozyme–Ub conjugate-degrading activity is detected in fractions of 20 S proteasomes. Pool fractions 12–16 and store at −80°C.

C. PROPERTIES OF ISOLATED PROTEASOMES

The physicochemical properties of 20 S and 26 S proteasomes in rat liver are summarized in Table I. The molecular weights of 20 S and 26 S proteasomes have been determined to be approximately 750 and 2000 kDa, respectively, by various physical techniques (Tanaka *et al.*, 1992; Yoshimura *et al.*, 1993). Although the sedimentation coefficient of the latter enzyme has been estimated to be "26 S" by glycerol density gradient centrifugation, it was recently determined to be about 30 S by analytical ultracentrifugation (Yoshimura *et al.*, 1993). On electron microscopy, the rat liver 20 S proteasome appears to be a symmetric, ring-shaped or cylindrical

TABLE I   Physicochemical Properties of 20 S and 26 S Proteasomes from Rat Liver

Parameter	Method	20 S Proteasomes[a]	26 S Proteasomes[b]
Molecular weight	Sedimentation equilibrium	743,000	
	Sedimentation velocity and diffusion	722,000	2,020,000
	Low-angle laser light scattering	760,000	
	Small-angle X-ray scattering	750,000	
	Static light scattering		1,910,000
Sedimentation coefficient	Sedimentation velocity	20 S	30 S
Diffusion coefficient	Dynamic light scattering	$2.50 \times 10^{-7} \cdot cm^2 \cdot s^{-1}$	$1.38 \times 10^{-7} \cdot cm^2 \cdot s^{-1}$
Stokes radius	Dynamic light scattering	85.0 Å	155.0 Å
	Small-angle X-ray scattering	75.6 Å	
Radius of gyration	Small-angle X-ray scattering	65.9 Å	
	Static light scattering		168.0 Å
Isoelectric point	Isoelectric focusing	5.0	
Extinction coefficient[c]	Differential refractometry	9.61	
Molar ellipticity[d]	Circular dichroism	$-12,000$ (deg·cm²·dmol⁻¹)	

[a] Tanaka *et al.* (1986b, 1988b).
[b] Yoshimura *et al.* (1993).
[c] $E_{1cm}^{1\%}$ at 280 nm.
[d] $[\theta]_{220nm}$, based on residue molarity.

particle composed of four disks (Fig. 1A). The 26 S proteasome purified from rat liver appears dumbell-shaped, consisting of two rectangular domains attached to a thinner central structure with four protein layers that we assume is the 20 S proteasome (Fig. 1C, top, Ikai *et al.*, 1991). Figure 1C (bottom) is a structural model of

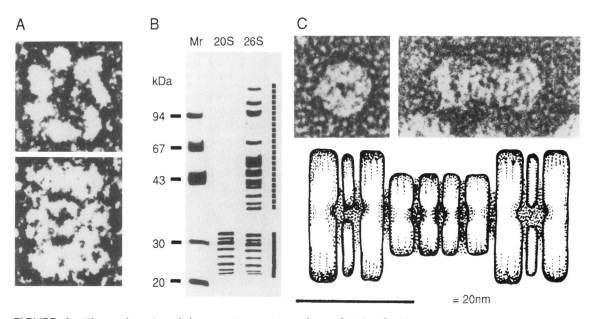

FIGURE 1   Electrophoretic and electron microscopic analyses of 20 S and 26 S proteasomes from rat liver. (A) Electron micrographs of the 20 S proteasome. Top, view from above; bottom, side view. (B) SDS–PAGE profiles of 20 S and 26 S proteasomes. Straight and dotted lines show the regions of 20 S proteasome components and associated components, respectively. (C) Electron micrographs of the 26 S proteasome. Top left, view from above; top right, side view. Bottom, proposed model of the 26 S proteasome. For details, see text.

the 26 S proteasome complex. Figure 1B shows the electrophoretic patterns of 20 S and 26 S proteasomes from rat liver. The 20 S proteasome consists of multiple components of 21–31 kDa. Structural analyses of cDNA clones have indicated that the proteasome subunits from various eukaryotes differ from any proteins known so far and are encoded by a family of homologous genes that may have evolved from a common ancestral gene (Tanaka *et al.*, 1992). The purified 26 S proteasome is composed of components of both 21–31 and 35–110 kDa, the former components being similar in size to those of the 20 S proteasome, suggesting that the 26 S proteasome complex contains a 20 S proteasome. The 20 S and 26 S proteasomes from other eukaryotic cells have essentially the same molecular properties, suggesting that their gross sizes and shapes have been highly conserved during evolution.

IV. Comments

To measure 20 S proteasomal activity, various fluorogenic peptides are useful, because proteasomes show broad substrate specificity; however, Suc-LLVY-MCA is recommended as a sensitive substrate. For proteinase assay, [³H]casein is a very good protein substrate. Latent 20 S proteasomes can be activated in various ways, such as by heat treatment or addition of SDS or polylysine, which induce their conformational change. The optimal conditions for activation differ, depending on the source of the 20 S proteasomes. We recommend use of SDS at low concentrations of 0.02 to 0.08% for activation of Suc-LLVY-MCA breakdown, the optimal concentration depending on the enzyme source and the protein concentration used. Approximately 0.05 mg/ml polylysine (10–30 kDa) is effective for activation of [³H]casein degradation (Tanaka *et al.*, 1988a).

The 26 S proteasomes are active without any treatment, unlike 20 S proteasomes, and the fluorogenic peptide Suc-LLVY-MCA can be used for their assay. For specific assay, ATP-dependent degradation of ubiquitinated ¹²⁵I-lysozyme should be measured, although this assay is not easy, because it involves purifications of multiple Ub-ligated enzymes. As 26 S proteasomes have intrinsic ATPase activity, their purification can be monitored by measuring ATPase activity (Kanayama *et al.*, 1992; Ugai *et al.*, 1993).

The 20 S proteasomes have been purified from a variety of eukaryotic cells by many investigators (Rivett, 1993). Many purification methods have been reported, but special techniques are not necessary, because 20 S proteasomes are very stable and abundant in cells, constituting 0.5–1.0% of total cellular proteins. Thus, other procedures such as cellulose–phosphate gel and phenyl-Sepharose chromatography are also useful for their purification. Procedures for purification of 20 S proteasomes differ depending on whether they are small or large operations. For their isolation from small amounts of starting materials, such as cultured cells, 10–40% glycerol density gradient centrifugation analysis is very effective. The 20 S proteasomes are present in a latent form in cells and can be isolated in this form in the presence of 20% glycerol. For their isolation in high yield, a key point is to keep them in their latent form, because their activation results in autolytic loss of a certain subunit(s) and marked reduction of enzymatic activities, particularly their hydrolyses of various proteins. Accordingly, all buffers used should contain 20% glycerol as a stabilizer. A reducing agent is also required, because 20 S proteasomes precipitate in its absence. All purification procedures are performed at 4°C, but operations in an HPLC apparatus can be carried out within a few hours at room temperature.

For purification of the 26 S proteasome, ATP (0.5 or 2 mM) together with 20% glycerol and 1 mM DTT should be added to all solutions used, because they stabilize the 26 S proteasome complex: the purified enzyme is stable during storage at −80°C for at least 6 months in the presence of 2 mM ATP, 20% glycerol, and 1 mM DTT.

Various drastic chromatographies should be avoided, because these operations may result in dissociation of the 26 S complex into its constituents.

REFERENCES

Goldberg, A., and Rock, K. L. (1992) Proteolysis, proteasomes and antigen presentation. *Nature* **357**, 375–379.

Ikai, A., Nishigai, M., Tanaka, K., and Ichihara, A. (1991) Electron micrographs of 26 S complex containing 20 S proteasome. *FEBS Lett.* **292**, 21–24.

Kanayama, H., Tamura, T., Ugai, S., Kagawa, S., Orino, E., Yoshimura, T., Tanaka, K., and Ichihara, A. (1992) Demonstration that a human 26 S proteolytic complex consists of a proteasome and multiple associated protein components and hydrolyzes ATP and ubiquitin-ligated proteins by a closely linked mechanism. *Eur. J. Biochem.* **206**, 567–578.

Murakami, Y., Matsufuji, S., Kameji, T., Hayashi, S., Igarashi, T., Tamura, K., Tanaka, K., and Ichihara, A. (1992) Ornithine decarboxylase is degraded by the 26 S proteasome without ubiquitination. *Nature* **360**, 597–599.

Rivett, A. J. (1993) Proteasomes: Multicatalytic proteinase complexes. *Biochem. J.* **291**, 1–10.

Tanaka, K., Yoshimura, T., Kumatori, A., Ichihara, A., Ikai, A., Nishigai, M., Kameyama, K., and Takagi, T. (1988a) Proteasomes (multi-protease complexes) as 20 S ring-shaped particles in a variety of eukaryotic cells. *J. Biol. Chem.* **263**, 16209–16217.

Tanaka, K., Yoshimura, T., Ichihara, A., Ikai, A., Nishigai, M., Morimoto, M., Sato, M., Tanaka, N., Katsube, Y., Kameyama, K., and Takagi, T. (1988b) Molecular organization of a high molecular weight multi-protease complex from rat liver. *J. Mol. Biol.* **203**, 985–996.

Tanaka, K., Tamura, T., Yoshimura, T., and Ichihara, A. (1992) Proteasomes: Protein and gene structures. *New Biol.* **4**, 173–187.

Ugai, S., Tamura, T., Tanahashi, N., Takai, S., Komi, N., Chung, C. H., Tanaka, K., and Ichihara, A. (1993) Purification and characterization of the 26 S proteasome complex catalyzing ATP-dependent breakdown of ubiquitin-ligated proteins from rat liver. *J. Biochem (Tokyo)* **113**, 754–768.

Yoshimura, T., Kameyama, K., Takagi, T., Ikai, A., Tokunaga, F., Koide, T., Tannahasi, N., Tamura, T., Cejka, Z., Baumeister, W., Tanaka, K., and Ichihara, A. (1993) Molecular characterization of the '26 S' proteasome complex from rat liver. *J. Struct. Biol.* **111**, 200–211.

Small-Scale Preparation of Nuclear Extracts from Mammalian Cells

Kevin A. W. Lee, Kenn Zerivitz, and Göran Akusjärvi

I. Introduction

The use of crude extracts from mammalian cells has been critical in biochemical studies of RNA processing, transcription, and DNA replication. Methods for preparation of whole cell extracts (Manley *et al.*, 1983) and nuclear extracts (Dignam *et al.*, 1983) have been established for a long time; however, preparation of nuclear extracts by the conventional procedure (Dignam *et al.*, 1983) requires relatively large numbers of cells and imposes practical difficulties in varying parameters of extract preparation. Different methods have now been described that are suited to preparation of extracts from small amounts of cells (Lee *et al.*, 1988; Lee and Green, 1990; Zerivitz and Akusjarvi, 1989). These methods are advantageous in situations demanding the economic use of scarce or expensive materials, including (1) preparation of extracts from cells that cannot be grown in large amounts in suspension, (2) preparation of biologically active extracts radioactively labeled to high specific activity, and (3) preparation of extracts from virally infected cells using mutant viruses or different cell extraction conditions. Here we describe in detail two procedures for small-scale nuclear extract preparation. Both procedures can be performed with as few as 3×10^7 cells and employ only standard laboratory supplies.

II. Materials and Instrumentation

Bovine serum albumin (Cat. No. A-7030), phenylmethylsulfonyl fluoride (Cat. No. P-7626) lysolecithin (L-α-lysophosphatidylcholine, type I, Cat. No. L-4129), DTT (Cat. No. D-9779), and Hepes (Cat. No. H-3375) are purchased form Sigma Chemical Company. Also used are 1-ml single-use hypodermic syringes, 25-gauge $\frac{5}{8}$-in. (15.9-mm) hypodermic needles, and a small magnetic stirring bar to stir 0.2 ml efficiently in a microcentrifuge tube.

III. Procedures

A. PREPARATION OF NUCLEAR EXTRACTS USING MECHANICAL DISRUPTION OF CELLS

Solutions

1. *1 M Hepes:* To make 500 ml, dissolve 119.2 g of Hepes in distilled water, adjust to the desired pH using concentrated NaOH, and then adjust volume to 500 ml. Sterile-filter through 0.22-μm filter.

2. *1 M MgCl₂:* To make 500 ml, dissolve 101.5 g of MgCl$_2$·6H$_2$O in distilled water and adjust volume to 500 ml. Sterile-filter through 0.22-μm filter.

3. *3 M KCl:* To make 1 liter, dissolve 223.6 g in distilled water and adjust volume to 1 liter. Sterile-filter through 0.22-μm filter.

4. *1 M DTT 154.3:* To make 50 ml, dissolve 7.7 g in 50 ml of distilled water. Store in aliquots at −20°C.

5. *100 mM PMSF 174:* To make 5 ml, dissolve 87 mg in 5 ml of ethanol. Store in aliquots at −20°C.

6. *4 M NaCl:* To make 1 liter, dissolve 233.76 g in distilled water and adjust volume to 1 liter. Sterile-filter through 0.22-μm filter.

7. *0.5 M EDTA:* To make 500 ml, dissolve 93 g of disodium EDTA dihydrate in distilled water and adjust the pH to 8.0 with sodium hydroxide pellets (∼10 g NaOH is required). The EDTA will not dissolve until the pH is adjusted. Sterile-filter through 0.22-μm filter.

All buffers are made from the above stock solutions stored at room temperature unless otherwise indicated.

8. *Buffer A:* 10 mM Hepes (pH 8.0), 1.5 mM MgCl$_2$, 10 mM KCl, 1 mM DTT, 0.5 mM PMSF.

9. *Buffer C:* 20 mM Hepes (pH 8.0), 1.5 mM MgCl$_2$, 25% (v/v) glycerol, 420 mM NaCl, 0.2 mM EDTA (pH 8.0), 1 mM DTT, 0.5 mM PMSF.

10. *Buffer D:* 20 mM Hepes (pH 8.0), 20% glycerol, 100 mM KCl, 0.2 mM EDTA, 1 mM DTT, 0.5 mM PMSF.

Buffers A, C, and D can be stored in the cold room for 1 week or so without the addition of DTT and PMSF. DTT and PMSF should be added fresh at the time of extract preparation. The 100 mM stock solution of PMSF should be added dropwise to buffers with vigorous stirring.

Steps

1. Perform all steps on ice unless otherwise indicated.

2. Harvest cells from three 100-mm-diameter tissue culture dishes at 80% confluence. Determine the packed cell volume (PCV) after centrifuging for 20 sec in a microcentrifuge (12,000 g). Wash cells once by resuspending in 30 vol of PBS.

3. Resuspend cell pellet in 1 PCV of buffer A and allow to swell on ice for 15 min.

4. Lyse cells by rapidly pushing them through a narrow-gauge hypodermic needle as follows: (a) Fill a 1-ml hypodermic syringe (with needle attached) with buffer A and use the syringe plunger to displace the buffer as fully as possible. This removes all of the air from the syringe and prevents excess air from being "pumped" into the cell suspension during lysis. Needles of 23- to 26-gauge diameter are suitable for breaking open cells. We routinely use a 25-gauge $\frac{5}{8}$-in. (15.9-mm) single-use Yale hypodermic needle. (b) Draw the cell suspension slowly into the syringe from a 1.5-ml microcentrifuge tube (this minimizes the amount of air drawn into the syringe) and then eject with a single rapid stroke. Five rapid strokes are usually sufficient to achieve approximately 80% cell lysis, which can be monitored using a light microscope and is sufficient to produce active extracts.

5. Centrifuge the cell homogenate for 20 sec in a microcentrifuge (12,000 *g*) to produce a crude nuclear pellet and postnuclear supernatant. This step is most easily performed at room temperature.

6. Resuspend the crude nuclear pellet in $\frac{2}{3}$ PCV (determined at the time of cell harvest) of buffer C and incubate on ice with stirring for 30 min.

7. Pellet the nuclear debris by centrifuging for 5 min in a microcentrifuge (12,000 *g*).

8. Dialyze the supernatant (nuclear extract) against buffer D for 2 hr. The dialyzed extract can be directly used or aliquoted and quick-frozen in liquid nitrogen and stored at −70°C. To an approximation, three plates (100-mm diameter) of cells at 80% confluence yield 120 μl of nuclear extract with a protein concentration of 8 mg/ml.

B. PREPARATION OF EXTRACTS FROM RADIOACTIVELY LABELED CELLS

Steps

1. Depending on the amount and specific activity of labeled protein that is required, labeled cells can be diluted with unlabeled cells to provide sufficient material for extract preparation. This minimizes the number of cells required during the hazardous labeling process.

2. Starve cells of endogenous unlabeled precursors by growth in phosphate-free or methionine-free medium containing 2% dialyzed fetal bovine serum (dialyzed against 100 vol of 150 m*M* NaCl, 20 m*M* Hepes (pH 7.2).

3. Add radioactive label, 2 mCi/ml [^{32}P]phosphate or 0.5 mCi/ml [^{35}S]methionine, in 2 ml of medium per 100-mm plate. Plates should be placed on a rocker platform in a well-humidified incubator with CO_2 adjusted to less than 5% to prevent the medium from becoming acidic. Labeling times should be empirically determined for particular experiments.

4. Prepare nuclear extract as described.

C. LYSOLECITHIN METHOD FOR SMALL-SCALE PREPARATION OF NUCLEAR EXTRACTS

Solutions

1. *1 M Sucrose:* To make 500 ml, dissolve 171 g of sucrose in distilled water and adjust the volume. Sterile-filter through 0.22-μm filter.

2. *Buffer A:* 0.25 *M* sucrose, 20 m*M* Hepes (pH 7.9), 10 m*M* KCl, 1.5 m*M* $MgCl_2$, 0.5 m*M* DTT, 0.5 m*M* spermidine, 0.15 m*M* spermine.

3. *Buffer B:* Buffer A supplemented with 3% bovine serum albumin.

4. *Buffer C:* 20 m*M* Hepes (pH 7.9), 25% (v/v) glycerol, 600 m*M* KCl, 1.5 m*M* $MgCl_2$, 0.2 m*M* EDTA, 0.5 m*M* DTT, 0.5 m*M* PMSF.

5. *Buffer D:* 20 m*M* Hepes (pH 7.9), 20% (v/v) glycerol, 100 m*M* KCl, 0.2 m*M* EDTA, 0.5 m*M* DTT 0.5 m*M* PMSF.

6. *Lysolecithin:* From a 10 mg/ml stock solution in water. Store in aliquots at −20°C.

Steps

1. Wash cells twice with at least 10 vol of ice-cold PBS. Collect cells by centrifugation for 20 sec in a microcentrifuge (12,000 g).

2. Resuspend in 10 packed cell pellet volumes of buffer A at room temperature and collect by centrifugation for 20 sec in a microcentrifuge (12,000 g).

3. Resuspend cell pellet in buffer A at a concentration of 1×10^8 cells/ml and allow to swell at room temperature for 5 min.

4. Add lysolecithin from a 10 mg/ml stock solution to a final concentration of 400 μg/ml. Note that the optimal lysolecithin concentration for different cell types should be empirically determined. It is important that the cell suspension and lysolecithin be kept at room temperature (20°C) prior to use, as lysolecithin precipitates in cold solutions. Mix the cell suspension and lysolecithin by gentle swirling or inversion for 90 sec. Longer times will adversely affect the activity of the extract.

5. Stop lysis by adding 2 vol of ice-cold buffer B. All subsequent steps are performed at 4°C.

6. Collect nuclei by centrifugation for 20 sec in a microcentrifuge (12,000 g). Remove the supernatant.

7. Resuspend the nuclear pellet with buffer C at a proportion of 20 μl of buffer C per 10^7 cells by pipetting up and down 20 times using a Gilson pipetman and pipette tip. Leave to extract by standing on ice for 30 min.

8. Pellet the nuclear debris by centrifuging for 10 min in a microcentrifuge (12,000 g). Save the supernatant, which is the crude nuclear extract.

9. Dialyze the nuclear extract at 4°C against 100 vol of buffer D with three changes in 2 hr or overnight. Clear the nuclear extract by centrifugation for 2 min in a microcentrifuge (12,000 g) and quick-freeze in aliquots in liquid nitrogen. Store at −70°C.

IV. Comments

A. PREPARATION OF EXTRACTS FROM RADIOACTIVELY LABELED CELLS

Using the procedure described in Section IIIB (Lee *et al.*, 1988; Lee and Green, 1990) nuclear extracts can be prepared for *in vitro* assays in as little as 4 hr (including dialysis) and from as few as 3×10^7 cells. The major steps in the protocol are essentially the same as for the conventional procedure (Dignam *et al.*, 1983). Time is saved because most of the centrifugation steps are performed in a microcentrifuge with reduced times compared with the conventional procedure or even complete omission of steps.

Miniextracts are fully active in pre-mRNA splicing and also efficiently transcribe class II promoters (Lee *et al.*, 1988). Moreover, the extent of leakage of nuclear-localized components into the cytoplasmic fraction is similar to that observed with the conventional procedure (Lee *et al.*, 1988). These properties suggest that known characteristics of conventionally prepared extracts apply to miniextracts. The procedure can be used for entirely different cell types, indicating that it will be generally applicable to mammalian cells (Lee *et al.*, 1988).

B. LYSOLECITHIN METHOD FOR SMALL-SCALE PREPARATION OF NUCLEAR EXTRACTS

It is very important that the lysolecithin concentration used to disrupt cells be empirically determined for a given application. Lysolecithin is highly toxic and cells lyse within 90 seconds as determined by trypan blue staining of nuclei. Effective cell lysis, however, is not a useful criterion for determining the optimal amount of lysolethicin for a given cell type or cell density. The assay of interest (e.g., pre-mRNA splicing) should be used as a functional test for the optimal lysolecithin concentration in a given situation. Lysolecithin lyses more than 99% of cells at a density of 10^6/ml at concentrations between 10 and 100 μg/ml (Zerivitz and Akusjarvi, 1989). Increasing the concentration of lysolecithin results in a decrease in observable cytoplasmic residues associated with the nuclei as well as less "aggregation" of nuclei. The concentration of lysolecithin necessary for lysis varies with cell density (Zerivitz and Akusjarvi, 1989): 300 μg/ml lysolecithin lyses 99% of Hela cells at 1.25×10^8/ml but lyses only 50% at 2.5×10^8/ml. The conventional procedure for nuclear extracts (Dignam *et al.*, 1983) uses buffer C containing 420 mM NaCl for extraction of nuclei; however, we find that buffer C containing 600 mM KCl yields much more active extracts (Zerivitz *et al.*, 1992).

The lysis capacity of lysolecithin is very high and probably more uniform than mechanical disruption. Thus, once conditions for a given situation have been optimized, preparation of extracts is highly reproducible. Furthermore, the elapsed time between cell lysis and salt extraction of nuclei is very short and may help to reduce loss of important nuclear factors due to leakage. In certain cases extracts prepared using lysolecithin may have distinct advantages over extracts made by the conventional procedure (Zerivitz *et al.*, 1992). For example, lysolecithin-based extracts are significantly more active than conventional extracts in SV40 DNA replication (Zerivitz and Akusjarvi, 1989).

V. Pitfalls

A. PREPARATION OF EXTRACTS FROM RADIOACTIVELY LABELED CELLS

The ease with which crude nuclear pellets can be resuspended for extraction varies for different cell lines. Pellets from some cell lines (e.g., JEG3) resuspend very easily, whereas for others (e.g., F9 cells) it is not possible to achieve a uniform resuspension. Our experience to date, however, is that this variability is not reflected by variations in extract activity.

B. LYSOLECITHIN METHOD FOR SMALL-SCALE PREPARATION OF NUCLEAR EXTRACTS

The majority of lysolecithin is removed during the subsequent centrifugation and dialysis steps; however, there may be a correlation between the lysolecithin concentration used for cell lysis and the amount of cytoplasm associated with the nuclei. Low lysolecithin concentrations produce contaminated nuclei, whereas too much lysolecithin yields inactive extracts due to leakage of factors from damaged nuclei. Marginal effects of these variables are not yet clear but could lead to problems in particular circumstances.

REFERENCES

Dignam, J. D., Lebovitz, R. M., and Roeder, R. G. (1983) Accurate transcription initiation by RNA polymerase II in a soluble extract from isolated mammalian nuclei. *Nucleic Acids Res.* **11**, 1475–1489.

Lee, K. A., Bindereif, A., and Green, M. R. (1988) A small-scale procedure for preparation of nuclear extracts that support efficient transcription and pre-mRNA splicing. *Gene Anal. Tech.* **5**, 22–31.

Lee, K. A. W., and Green, M. R. (1990) Small-scale preparation of extracts from radiolabeled cells efficient in Pre-mRNA splicing. *In* "Methods in Enzymology" (J. E. Dahlberg and J. N. Abelson, eds.), Vol. 181, pp. 20–30. Academic Press, San Diego.

Manley, J. L., Fire, A., Samuels, M., and Sharp, P. A. (1983) In vitro transcription: Whole-cell extract. *In* "Methods in Enzymology" (R. Wu, L. Grossman, and K. Moldave, eds.), Vol. 101, pp. 568–582. Academic Press, San Diego.

Zerivitz, K., and Akusjarvi, G. (1989) An improved nuclear extract preparation method. *Gene Anal. Tech.* **6**, 101–109.

Zerivitz, K., Kreivi, J-P., and Akusjarvi, G. (1992) Evidence for a HeLa cell splicing activity that is necessary for activation of a regulated adenovirus 3′ splice site. *Nucleic Acids Res.* **20**, 3955–3961.

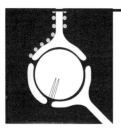

Purification of DNA Using Guanidine Thiocyanate and Isobutyl Alcohol Fractionation

James E. Nelson, Mohamed Khidhir,
and Stephen A. Krawetz

I. Introduction

Pure preparations of DNA provide one of the essential components necessary to address many of the questions modern cell biology poses. Numerous protocols have become available to purify DNA. These include phenol/chloroform extraction (Maniatis *et al.*, 1982), CsCl gradient centrifugation (Garger *et al.*, 1983), and polyethylene glycol precipitation (Lis, 1980); however, these protocols are often inefficient, time consuming, or both. To circumvent these limitations we developed a simple method to purify biologically active DNA following cell lysis (Nelson and Krawetz, 1992). This method relies on the denaturing capacity of guanidine thiocyanate to effectively dissociate DNA from other contaminants. The DNA is then separated and recovered with the addition of isobutyl alcohol. This method can be applied to effectively purify cloned and high-molecular-weight eukaryotic genomic DNA from a host of cellular sources.

II. Materials and Instrumentation

Ultrapure guanidine thiocyanate (Cat. No. 32815), Tris base (Cat. No. 22643), Tris–hydrochloride (Cat. No. 22676), and SDS (Cat. No. 21651) were purchased from U.S. Biochemicals. Analytical-grade EDTA (disodium salt, Cat. No. 15699), tryptone (Cat. No. 20046), and yeast extract (Cat. No. 23547) and molecular biology-grade ribonuclease A (Cat. No. 21199) were also purchased from U.S. Biochemicals. A 20 mg/ml solution of molecular biology-grade proteinase K (Cat. No. 1413783) was purchased from Boehringer-Mannheim. ACS-grade isobutyl alcohol (Cat. No. A397-4), potassium acetate (Cat. No. BP364-500), potassium chloride (Cat. No. P217-500), monobasic potassium phosphate (Cat. No. P285-500), sodium chloride (Cat. No. BP358-212), dibasic sodium phosphate (Cat. No. BP332-500), monobasic sodium phosphate (Cat. No. BP329-500), ethanol (Cat. No. A995-4), hydrochloric acid (Cat. No. A144-500), glacial acetic acid (Cat. No. A38-500), and 10 N solution of sodium hydroxide (Cat. No. SS255-1) were purchased from Fisher Scientific. Microcentrifuge tubes (1.5 ml, Cat. No. 05-407-10, and 2.2 ml, Cat. No. 05-407-25A); sterile, graduated, polypropylene conical tubes (15 ml, Cat. No. 05-539-5, and 50 ml, Cat. No. 05-539-6); and 10-ml polypropylene snap-cap tubes (Cat. No. 14-959-11b) were also purchased from Fisher Scientific. Additional 30-

ml round-base polypropylene tubes (Cat. No. 55.517) and caps (Cat. No. 65.791) were purchased from Sarstedt. Vacutainer EDTA blood collection tubes (Cat. No. 6528) were purchased from Becton Dickinson.

III. Procedures

A. PURIFICATION OF CLONED DNA USING GUANIDINE THIOCYANATE AND ISOBUTYL ALCOHOL FRACTIONATION FOLLOWING ALKALINE LYSIS

This procedure is adapted from those of Nelson and Krawetz (1992) and Birnboim and Doly (1979).

Solutions

1. *2× YT culture medium:* 1.6% (w/v) tryptone, 1.0% (w/v) yeast extract plus 85 mM NaCl. To make 1 liter of 2× YT medium, add 16 g of tryptone, 10 g of yeast extract, and 5 g of NaCl, and complete to 1 liter with distilled water. Mix, and then sterilize by autoclaving the solution at 15 psi for 20 min using the liquid cycle. Cool the solution to room temperature. The solution may then be stored at room temperature for at least 1 month. Prior to use, supplement the medium with the appropriate antibiotic.

2. *TE buffer:* 10 mM Tris–HCl buffer, pH 8.0 at 25°C, containing 1 mM EDTA, pH 8.0. To prepare 500 ml of the solution, add 5 ml of a 1 M stock solution of Tris–HCl buffer, pH 8.0 at 25°C, and 1 ml of a 0.5 M stock solution of EDTA, pH 8.0. Complete to 500 ml with distilled water and store at 4°C.

3. *Lysis solution:* 0.2 N NaOH with 1% SDS. To prepare 50 ml of the solution, add 1 ml of 10 N NaOH to a 50-ml graduated conical tube. Adjust to 45 ml with distilled water. Complete with 5 ml of 10% sodium dodecyl sulfate. Mix and use fresh.

4. *Neutralization solution:* 3 M potassium acetate solution, pH 4.5. To prepare 50 ml of the solution, add 30 ml of 5 M potassium acetate to a 50-ml graduated conical tube. Adjust the pH to 4.5 with glacial acetic acid (~6 ml) and complete the solution to 50 ml with distilled water. Store at 4°C.

5. *Guanidine thiocyanate:* 6 M guanidine thiocyanate. To prepare 50 ml of the solution, weigh 35.4 g of guanidine thiocyanate and place in a 50-ml graduated conical tube. Complete to 50 ml with distilled water. The solution may be warmed to facilitate dissolving. Store at room temperature.

Steps

1. Place 10 ml of 2× YT medium in a snap-cap polypropylene tube and inoculate with a single bacterial colony transformed with either the plasmid or cosmid DNA of interest. Grow the culture overnight at 37°C in a shaking incubator at 250 rpm.

2. Collect the bacteria by centrifugation at 1600 g for 10 min at 4°C. Decant the supernatant, then gently pad the tube onto a paper towel to remove any residual medium.

3. To the cell pellet, add 100 μl (0.1 vol with respect to the original culture volume) of TE buffer. Vortex the sample until the cells resuspend uniformly, then transfer the cell resuspension into a 1.5-ml microcentrifuge tube.

4. Lyse the cells by adding 200 µl of lysis solution (2 vol with respect to the TE buffer) and gently mix by inversion. Let stand on ice for 5 min.

5. Neutralize the lysate, and precipitate the SDS-complexed cellular proteins by adding 150 µl (1.5 vol with respect to the TE buffer) of chilled neutralization solution. Briefly vortex the sample and let stand on ice for 10 min.

6. Pellet the cellular debris and proteins by centrifugation at 10,000 g for 10 min at 4°C. Transfer the supernatant into a 2.2-ml microcentrifuge tube, then add 675 µl (1.5 vol with respect to the supernatant) of 6 M guanidine thiocyanate.

7. Precipitate the DNA from solution by adding 1 ml (approximately an equal volume with respect to that of the cell lysate and guanidine thiocyanate) of isobutyl alcohol. Vortex the solution for 5 sec and let stand at room temperature for 10 min.

8. Collect the DNA by centrifugation at 14,000 g for 15 min. The DNA will appear as a white or sometimes clear pellet. Carefully remove the supernatant, including any of the solution remaining in the cap or on the rim of the tube, by aspiration.

9. Wash the pellet of DNA with 2 ml of 70% ethanol, mix briefly, and then centrifuge at 14,000 g for 5 min. Carefully remove the supernatant by aspiration, then wash the DNA pellet in 70% ethanol as described above.

10. Aspirate the remaining ethanol. Remove residual ethanol from the pellet by evacuation. The vacuum should be applied for *no longer than 2–3 min.*

11. Resuspend the DNA in 100 µl of TE buffer. This may be facilitated by vortexing the tube. Residual RNA may be removed with the addition of 20 units of RNase A followed by incubation for at least 30 min at 37°C.

B. PREPARATION OF DNA FROM BLOOD

Solutions

1. *1× SSPE:* 20 mM sodium phosphate buffer, pH 7.4, containing 150 mM NaCl and 1 mM EDTA. To prepare 1 liter of the solution, dissolve 8.76 g of NaCl, 1.38 g of NaH_2PO_4, 1.09 g of Na_2HPO_4, and 0.37 g of EDTA in 800 ml of distilled water. Adjust to pH 7.4 with 10 N NaOH (~6.5 ml). Complete to 1 liter with distilled water. Sterilize by autoclaving at 15 psi using the liquid cycle. Store the solution at room temperature.

2. *10% SDS:* To prepare 1 liter of the solution, add 100 g of sodium dodecyl sulfate to 900 ml of distilled water. Place the solution on a stir plate, then add a magnetic stir bar and stir on high until dissolved. Complete to 1 liter with distilled water and store at room temperature.

3. *Guanidine thiocyanate:* 6 M guanidine thiocyanate. To prepare 50 ml of the solution, weigh 35.4 g of guanidine thiocyanate and place in a graduated conical tube. Complete to 50 ml with distilled water. The solution may be warmed to facilitate dissolving. Store at room temperature.

Steps

1. Transfer 5 ml of EDTA vacutainer-collected blood to a 30-ml polypropylene disposable tube. Rinse the collection tube with 1× SSPE, then add the rinse to the 30-ml tube. Complete to 15 ml with 1× SSPE. Mix gently by inversion.

2. Collect the lymphocytes by centrifugation at 10,000 g for 5 min at 4°C.

3. Carefully remove the red supernatant and transfer into a beaker containing household bleach. Discard as biohazardous waste.

4. To the cell pellet add 15 ml of 1× SSPE, then mix by inversion. It is not necessary to completely resuspend the pellet. Collect the lymphocytes by centrifugation at 10,000 g for 5 min at 4°C.

5. Carefully remove the supernatant, leaving just enough to cover the pellet (~0.5 ml). This will maximize the recovery of cells. Discard the supernatant as biohazardous waste as above. Resuspend the pellet in the remaining supernatant, by vortexing.

6. Lyse the cells by adding 0.4 ml of 10% SDS, then mix gently by inversion for 30 sec.

7. To the lysate add 6 ml of 6 M guanidine thiocyanate and mix by inversion. The tube will immediately become cloudy.

8. Precipitate the DNA from the solution with the addition of 12 ml of isobutyl alcohol. Place the tube on a rotary mixer at 4°C until the solution becomes clear and the thin strands of DNA float to the top of the tube. This requires approximately 15 min. Collect the DNA using a wide-bore pipette tip, then transfer to a microcentrifuge tube.

9. Wash the DNA with 1 ml of 70% ethanol and mix several times by inversion. Aspirate the remaining ethanol. Remove residual ethanol from the pellet by evacuation. The vacuum should be applied for *no longer than 2–3 min.* Gently resuspend the DNA in 0.5 ml of TE buffer at 4°C using a rotating mixer.

C. PURIFICATION OF GENOMIC DNA FROM CULTURED CELLS

Solutions

1. *PBS:* 5.7 mM phosphate buffer, pH 7.4, containing 137 mM NaCl and 2.7 mM KCl. To make 1 liter of the solution, dissolve 8 g of NaCl, 0.2 g of KCl, 1.44 g of Na_2HPO_4, and 0.24 g of KH_2PO_4 in 800 ml of distilled water. Adjust the pH to 7.4 with HCl and complete to 1 liter with distilled water. Sterilize by autoclaving the solution at 15 psi for 20 min on liquid cycle. Store at 4°C.

2. *Extraction buffer:* 10 mM Tris–HCl buffer, pH 8.0 at 25°C, containing 100 mM NaCl, 1 mM EDTA, pH 8.0, and 1% SDS. To prepare 50 ml of the solution, add 0.292 g of NaCl, 0.5 ml of a 1 M stock solution of Tris–HCl buffer, pH 8.0 at 25°C, and 0.1 ml of a 0.5 M stock solution of EDTA, pH 8.0. Add distilled water to 45 ml and mix to dissolve the NaCl. Complete with 5 ml of 10% SDS. Mix and use fresh.

3. *Guanidine thiocyanate:* 6 M guanidine thiocyanate. To make 50 ml of the solution, weigh 35.4 g of guanidine thiocyanate and place in a 50-ml graduated conical tube. Complete to 50 ml with distilled water. The solution may be warmed to facilitate dissolving. Store at room temperature.

4. *TE buffer:* 10 mM Tris–HCl buffer, pH 8.0 at 25°C containing 1 mM EDTA, pH 8.0. To prepare 500 ml of the solution, add 5 ml of a 1 M stock solution of Tris–HCl buffer, pH 8.0 at 25°C, and 1 ml of a 0.5 M stock solution of EDTA, pH 8.0. Complete to 500 ml with distilled water. Sterilize by autoclaving the solution for 20 min at 15 psi using the liquid cycle. Store the solution at 4°C.

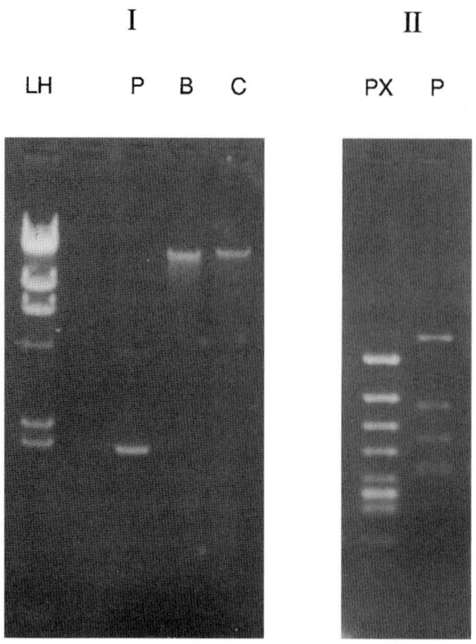

FIGURE 1 Electrophoretic analysis of representative DNAs purified using guanidine thio-cyanate and isobutyl alcohol fractionation. (I) Approximately 50 ng of plasmid (P) and human genomic DNA purified from blood (B) and cultured cells (C) was resolved by electrophoresis in a 1% agarose gel containing ethidium bromide. DNA was visualized by ultraviolet fluorescence. Relative mobilities of the λ HindIII standard (LH) are, from top to bottom, 23.1, 9.4, 6.5, 4.3, 2.3, 2.0, and 0.5 kb. (II) Approximately 250 ng of purified pTZ18R plasmid containing an 800-bp insert was digested with 5 units of DdeI for 3 hr, then electrophoretically resolved on a 2% agarose gel containing ethidium bromide. Relative mobilities of the φX174 HincII (PX) standard are, from top to bottom, 1057, 770, 612, 495, 392, 345, 341, 335, 297, 291, and 210 bp.

Steps

1. Remove cells from culture flasks by scraping or trypsinization. Transfer the cell-containing medium to a 15-ml conical tube. Collect the cells by centrifugation at 1,000 g for 10 min at 4°C.

2. Decant the medium into a beaker of household bleach and discard as biohazardous waste. To the cell pellet add 10 ml of chilled PBS. Mix by inversion. It is not necessary to completely resuspend the cells. Centrifuge at 1000 g for 10 min at 4°C.

3. Remove the supernatant by aspiration, then add 10 ml of extraction buffer to the cell pellet. Uniformly resuspend the cells by swirling the tube, then transfer the cell suspension to a 50-ml conical polypropylene tube.

4. To the cell suspension add 100 μl of a 20 mg/ml stock solution of proteinase K and swirl. Place the mixture at 50°C for 3 hr. Periodically swirl the cells to ensure uniform lysis.

5. To the lysate add 6 ml of 6 M guanidine thiocyanate, then mix by inversion. The tube will immediately become cloudy.

6. Precipitate the DNA from the solution with the addition of 12 ml of isobutyl alcohol. Place the tube on a rotary mixer at 4°C until the solution becomes clear and the thin strands of DNA float to the top of the tube. This requires approximately 15 min. Collect the DNA using a wide-bore pipette tip and transfer to a microcentrifuge tube.

7. Wash the DNA with 1 ml of 70% ethanol and mix several times by

inversion. Aspirate the remaining ethanol. Remove residual ethanol from the pellet by evacuation. The vacuum should be applied for *no longer than 2–3 min.* Gently resuspend the DNA in 0.5 ml of TE buffer at 4°C using a rotating mixer.

IV. Comments

These methods provide DNA, which serves as a good substrate for restriction endonuclease digestion, DNA polymerization, ligation, or other modifications. Representative plasmid and human genomic DNAs purified from blood and tissue cultured cells using the protocols outlined above are shown in Fig. 1.

V. Pitfalls

1. It is important to remove any of the residual guanidine thiocyanate/isobutyl alcohol solution by washing the DNA with 70% ethanol. If this step is omitted subsequent enzymatic reactions may be unsuccessful.

2. DNA that has been dried under vacuum for longer than 2–3 min is difficult to resuspend.

3. Blood samples should be collected in EDTA-containing vacutainer tubes and may be stored frozen until use. These samples must be treated as a biohazard. Proper safety precautions should be implemented.

4. Bacterial culture medium may become contaminated after prolonged storage. If the solution turns cloudy, it is contaminated and must be discarded.

ACKNOWLEDGMENTS

This work was supported by Grant 1RO1 HD-28504-O1A1 from the NICHD to S.A.K. and NIAAA Grant P50-AA-07606. J.E.N. is supported by a Graduate Research Assistantship from the Wayne State University School of Medicine.

REFERENCES

Birnboim, H. C., and Doly, J. (1979) A rapid alkaline extraction procedure for screening recombinant plasmid DNA. *Nucleic Acids Res.* **7**, 1513–1523.
Garger, S. J., Griffith, O. M., and Grill, L. K. (1983) Rapid purification of plasmid DNA by a single centrifugation in a two-step cesium chloride–ethidium bromide gradient. *Biochem. Biophys. Res. Commun.* **117**, 835–842.
Lis, J. T. (1980) Fractionation of DNA fragments by polyethylene glycol induced precipitation. *In* "Methods in Enzymology" (L. Grossman and K. Moldave, eds.), Vol. 65, pp. 347–353. Academic Press, New York.
Maniatis, T., Fritsch, E. F., and Sambrook, J. (1982) "Molecular Cloning: A Laboratory Manual." Cold Spring Harbor Laboratory, Cold Spring Harbor, NY.
Nelson, J. E., and Krawetz, S. A. (1992) Purification of cloned and genomic DNA by guanidine thiocyanate/isobutyl alcohol fractionation. *Anal. Biochem.* **207**, 197–201.

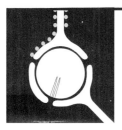

Single-Step Method of Total RNA Isolation by Acid Guanidine–Phenol Extraction

Piotr Chomczynski

I. Introduction

The single-step method (Chomczynski and Sacchi, 1987) has increasingly become the method of choice for isolation of total RNA from a variety of sources. As compared with other RNA isolation methods (Chomczynski and Sacchi, 1990; Sambrook *et al.*, 1989), it substantially reduces the amount of time required to isolate RNA, without sacrificing its quality. The single-step method performs well with small and large quantities of tissues or cells and allows simultaneous isolation of a large number of samples. A biological sample is homogenized in 4 M guanidine thiocyanate solution and mixed with phenol to form a monophase solution. After addition of chloroform and phase separation, RNA remains exclusively in the aqueous phase, whereas DNA and proteins are allocated to the interphase and organic phase. RNA is precipitated from the aqueous phase with isopropanol, reprecipitated, and washed with 75% ethanol. The entire procedure can be completed in less than 4 hr.

The use of a single-step method for commercial purposes is restricted by U.S. Patent 4,843,155.

II. Materials and Instrumentation

Guanidine thiocyanate was obtained from Fluka Chemie AG (Cat. No. 50990) and from Amresco, Inc. (Cat. No. 380). Phenol was obtained from Life Technologies, Inc. (Cat. No. 5509). Stabilized formamide was from Molecular Research Center, Inc. (Cat. No. FM 121). All other reagents were obtained from Fisher Scientific: ethanol (Cat. No. A407), chloroform (Cat. No. C297), glacial acetic acid (Cat. No. A35), isoamyl alcohol (Cat. No. A393), isopropanol (Cat. No. A416), lithium chloride (Cat. No. L119), 2-mercaptoethanol (Cat. No. 034461), sarcosyl (Cat. No. BP234), sodium acetate (Cat. No. S210), and sodium citrate (Cat. No. S279).

Centrifugation was performed in a Sorvall RC-5B centrifuge (Du Pont Instruments) in an SS 34 rotor with rubber adapters.

III. Procedures

A. HOMOGENIZATION

Solutions

1. *Denaturing solution:* 4 M guanidine thiocyanate, 25 mM sodium citrate, pH 7.0, 0.5% sarcosyl, 0.1 M 2-mercaptoethanol. Prepare a stock solution by

dissolving in 319 ml of water (at 50–60°C) the following ingredients: 250 g guanidine thiocyanate, 2.6 g sarcosyl, and 17.6 ml 0.75 M sodium citrate, pH 7.0. The stock solution can be stored at least 3 months at room temperature. The denaturing solution is prepared by adding 0.36 ml of 2-mercaptoethanol per 50 ml of stock solution. The denaturing solution can be stored 1 month at room temperature.

2. *2 M sodium acetate, pH 4:* The solution is 2 M with respect to the sodium ions. Dissolve 16.42 g of sodium acetate (anhydrous) in 40 ml water and 35 ml glacial acetic acid. Adjust the solution to pH 4.0 with glacial acetic acid and the final volume to 100 ml with water.

3. *Water-saturated phenol:* Dissolve 100 g of phenol by incubating with 100 ml of water at 50–60°C. Aspirate the upper aqueous phase and store the liquified phenol at 4°C for up to 1 month. Use distilled water without buffer or other additives.

NOTE

Caution: Phenol is a poisonous reagent. When working with phenol solutions, use gloves and eye protection (shield, safety goggles). In case of contact, immediately flush eyes or skin with a large amount of water for at least 15 min and seek immediate medical attention.

Steps

1. Immediately after removal from the animal, mince the tissue on ice and homogenize with 1 ml of denaturing solution per 100 mg of tissue. Perform homogenization at room temperature using a glass–Teflon or Polytron homogenizer. Tissues with a very high RNase content such as pancreas should be frozen and powderized in liquid nitrogen before mixing with the denaturing solution.

2. Lyse cells grown in a monolayer directly in a culture dish by adding 1 ml of denaturing solution per 10 cm^2 of dish area. For cells grown in suspension, sediment first and then lyse by adding denaturing solution (1 ml per 10^7 cells). Pass the cell lysate several times through a pipet.

B. PHASE SEPARATION

Solution

Chloroform–isoamyl alcohol (49:1, v/v).

Steps

1. Transfer the homogenate (or lysate) into a polypropylene or glass tube and add sequentially, per 1 ml of denaturing solution used for the homogenization, 0.1 ml of 2 M sodium acetate, pH 4, 1 ml of water-saturated phenol, and 0.2 ml of chloroform–isoamyl alcohol mixture.

2. Thoroughly shake the suspension for 10–20 sec and incubate it at 0–4°C for 15 min. During this incubation, the suspension separates into the top aqueous phase and the bottom organic phase.

3. Complete the phase separation by centrifuging the suspension for 20 min at 10,000 g at 4°C. Following centrifugation, total RNA remains exclusively in the

top aqueous phase, and DNA and proteins in the interphase and organic phase. The volume of the aqueous phase is approximately equal to the initial volume of denaturing solution.

C. PRECIPITATION AND WASH

Solutions

1. *Isopropanol (100%).*
2. *75% ethanol:* Prepare 75% ethanol by mixing ethanol (100%) with diethyl pyrocarbonate (DEPC)-treated water (Sambrook *et al.*, 1989).

Steps

1. Transfer the aqueous phase to a fresh tube and precipitate RNA by mixing with an equal volume of isopropanol. Place the mixture at −20°C for 30 min.
2. Sediment the RNA precipitate by centrifugation at 10,000 g for 20 min at 4°C.
3. Dissolve the RNA pellet in 0.3–0.5 ml of denaturing solution.
4. Reprecipitate RNA by mixing with 1 vol of isopropanol, storing the mixture at −20°C for 30 min, and centrifuging at 10,000 g for 10 min at 4°C.
5. Remove supernatant and suspend the RNA pellet in 75% ethanol by vortexing.
6. Centrifuge the suspension at 10,000 g for 10 min at 4°C.

D. SOLUBILIZATION

Solutions

1. *Water:* Water used for RNA solubilization should be made RNase free by DEPC treatment.
2. *Formamide:* Prepare freshly deionized formamide by stirring with ion-exchange resin (10 ml/g Bio-Rad AG 501-X8 resin, Cat. No. 143-7425) for 30 min and filtering at room temperature. Alternatively, use a commercially available, stabilized formamide (Molecular Research Center, Inc., Cat. No. FM-122).

Steps

1. Dry the RNA pellet briefly under vacuum for 5 min.
2. Dissolve the RNA pellet in water or formamide by passing the solution through a pipette tip a few times and incubate for 10–15 minutes at 55–60°C.

IV. Comments

Formamide is a more convenient solubilization agent for RNA than water. RNA solubilized in formamide is protected from degradation by RNase and can be stored at −20°C for at least 11 months (Chomczynski, 1992).

An additional step can be employed for isolation of RNA from tissues with a high glycogen content such as liver (Puissant and Houdebine, 1990). Following precipitation of RNA with isopropanol (step 3), suspend the RNA pellet with 4 *M* LiCl by vortexing and sediment the insoluble RNA at 5000 *g* for 10 min. Dissolve the pellet in denaturing solution and proceed with the RNA precipitation step as described above.

The single-step method isolates a whole spectrum of RNA molecules. Ethidium bromide staining of the RNA isolated from mammalian cells and separated in agarose gel visualizes two predominant bands of small (about 2 kb) and large (4–5 kb) ribosomal RNA, low-molecular-weight RNA (0.1–0.3 kb), and discrete bands of high-molecular-weight (7–15 kb) RNA.

V. Pitfalls

1. At the end of the procedure, do not let the RNA pellet dry completely as this greatly decreases its solubility. Avoid drying the pellet by centrifugation under vacuum.

2. When working with RNA use gloves, as hands are a likely source of ribonuclease contamination.

3. Always store tissue or cell samples and aqueous RNA solutions at −70°C. Even an overnight storage at −20°C may result in RNA degradation.

REFERENCES

Chomczynski, P. (1992) Solubilization in formamide protects RNA from degradation. *Nucleic Acids Res.* **20**, 3791–3792.
Chomczynski, P., and Sacchi, N. (1987) Single-step method of RNA isolation by acid guanidinium thiocyanate–phenol–chloroform extraction. *Anal. Biochem.* **162**, 156–159.
Chomczynski, P., and Sacchi, N. (1990) Single-step RNA isolation from cultured cells and tissues. *In* "Current Protocols in Molecular Biology" (F. M. Ausbel *et al.*, eds.), Vol. 1, pp. 4.2.4–4.2.8. Greene Publ. Assoc. and Wiley–Interscience, New York.
Puissant, C., and Houdebine, L. M. (1990) An improvement of the single-step method of RNA isolation by acid guanidinium thiocyanate–phenol–chloroform extraction. *BioTechniques* **8**, 148–149.
Sambrook, J., Fritsch, E. F., and Maniatis, T. (1989) Extraction and purification of RNA. *In* "Molecular Cloning," Vol. 1, pp. 7.3–7.23. Cold Spring Harbor Laboratory Press, Cold Spring Harbor, NY.